OPTIMUM SIGNAL PROCESSING

OPTIMUM SIGNAL PROCESSING: An Introduction

Second Edition

SOPHOCLES J. ORFANIDIS
Rutgers University

McGRAW-HILL PUBLISHING COMPANY

New York St. Louis San Francisco Auckland
Bogotá Hamburg London Madrid Milan Mexico
Montreal New Delhi Panama Paris São Paulo
Singapore Sydney Tokyo Toronto

To my parents

John and Clio Orfanidis

ISBN 0-07-047794-9

For more information about other McGraw-Hill materials, call 1-800-2-McGraw in the United States. In other countries, call your nearest McGraw-Hill office.

Library of Congress Cataloging-in-Publication Data

Orfanidis, Sophocles J.
Optimum signal processing.

Includes bibliographies and index.
1. Signal processing. I. Title.
TK5102.0246 1988 621.38′043 88-9548
ISBN 0-07-047794-9

234567890 HDHD 8921098

Preface

Digital signal processing is currently in a period of rapid growth caused by recent advances in VLSI technology. This is especially true of three areas of optimum signal processing; namely, real-time adaptive signal processing, eigenvector methods of spectrum estimation, and parallel processor implementations of optimum filtering and prediction algorithms.

In this edition the book has been brought up to date by increasing the emphasis on the above areas and including several new developments. The major additions are: a unified presentation of the fast recursive least-squares algorithms for adaptive processing; the discussion of several eigenvector methods of spectrum estimation such as MUSIC, minimum-norm, ESPRIT, spatial smoothing for coherent signals, and others; and discussion of the Schur algorithm for linear prediction admitting efficient parallel implementations, and the more efficient split Schur and split Levinson algorithms. Moreover, older but basic material has been added such as an expanded discussion of Kalman filtering and discussion of classical statistical estimation concepts such as maximum likelihood, Cramér-Rao bound, and asymptotic statistical properties applied to linear prediction and eigenstructure methods.

Two new sections have been added to Chapter 1 with the aim of strengthening the discussion of statistical concepts while at the same time emphasizing the unity of ideas of optimum signal processing. The first section, dealing with forward and backward prediction, develops further the geometrical point of view of random variables and linear estimation and provides a preliminary introduction to a large number of methods that have become important tools in signal processing; namely, Levinson's and Schur's algorithms, fast matrix factorizations, Gram-Schmidt orthogonalizations, lattice realizations of linear predictors and Wiener filters, and fast RLS algorithms. The second section discusses the properties of maximum likelihood estimators and gives a derivation of the Cramér-Rao bound using correlation canceling methods. The results of this section are used later to derive the asymptotic statistical properties of linear predictors and eigenstructure methods.

Chapter 2 has been revised to include a preliminary introduction to the Schur algorithm using a gapped function approach. Chapter 3 remains unchanged. A new section on Kalman filtering has been added to Chapter 4 that includes a derivation of the Kalman filter, a geometrical interpretation of it, and discussion of its asymptotic convergence properties.

Three new sections have been added to Chapter 5. The first deals with the problem of autocorrelation sequence extensions, such as the maximum entropy or autoregressive extensions, and discusses the case of singular autocorrelation matrices, their sinusoidal representations, and their connection to Pisarenko's harmonic retrieval method. The second section contains a discussion of the recently developed split or immitance-domain Levinson algorithm which is fifty percent more efficient than the conventional Levinson algorithm. The third section presents the Schur algorithm for linear prediction which has received a lot of attention recently because of its efficient parallel implementations, and discusses its application to fast matrix factorizations. The split or immitance-domain version of the Schur algorithm is also discussed.

The material on autoregressive spectrum estimation, spectral analysis of sinusoids in noise, and superresolution array processing, has been separated from Chapter 5 to form a new Chapter 6. This chapter also includes new sections on several eigenstructure methods and a section on the asymptotic statistical properties of such methods. The following methods are discussed: MUSIC, minimum-norm, reduced-order, maximum likelihood, ESPRIT, and spatial smoothing for coherent signals.

The chapter on adaptive filtering, now Chapter 7, has been expanded considerably. It contains a revised discussion of the adaptive gradient lattice Wiener filter and its spatial processing counterpart—the adaptive Gram-Schmidt array preprocessor based on the modified Gram-Schmidt procedure. The last four sections are devoted to a unified derivation of the exact recursive least-squares adaptation algorithms including the conventional RLS, fast Kalman and FAEST/FTF direct form versions, and RLS lattice versions. We show first that the algebraic steps and computational reductions that make all the fast versions possible are a direct consequence of the rank-one updating properties of covariance matrices, and then apply the shift-invariance property to complete the derivation of the various RLS algorithms.

A new appendix has been added containing a discussion of uniform and gaussian random number generators and ways to improve them such as shuffling. The number of subroutines discussed in the text has been tripled and the routines have been written both in FORTRAN and C. Several new problems and computer experiments have been added, and a solutions manual is available through the publisher. The material in this expanded edition is now adequate for a two-semester graduate course on the subject.

I have tried in this edition to preserve the basic style and objectives of the book and would like to thank the many colleagues and students who have given me their feedback on the first edition. Working on the revision was a great deal of fun and it was made even more so by my three-year old son, John.

Sophocles J. Orfanidis

Preface to the First Edition

THE PURPOSE OF THIS BOOK is to provide an introduction to signal processing methods that are based on optimum Wiener filtering and least-squares estimation concepts. Such methods have a remarkably broad range of applications, ranging from the analysis and synthesis of speech, data compression, image processing and modeling, channel equalization and echo cancellation in digital data transmission, geophysical signal processing in oil exploration, linear predictive analysis of EEG signals, modern methods of high-resolution spectrum estimation, and superresolution array processing, to adaptive signal processing for sonar, radar, system identification, and adaptive control applications. The structure of the book is to present the Wiener filtering concept as the basic unifying theme that ties together the various signal processing algorithms and techniques currently used in the above applications.

The book is based on lecture notes for a second-semester graduate-level course on advanced topics in digital signal processing I have taught at Rutgers University since 1979. The book is primarily addressed to beginning graduate students in electrical engineering, but it may also be used as a reference by practicing engineers who want a conscise introduction to the subject. The prerequisites for using the book are an introductory course on digital signal processing, such as on the level of Oppenheim and Schafer's book, and some familiarity with probability and random signal concepts, such as on the level of Papoulis' book.

Chapter 1 sets many of the objectives of the book and serves both as a review of probability and random signals and as an introduction to some of the basic concepts upon which the rest of the text is built. These are the concept of correlation canceling and its connection to linear mean-squared estimation, and the concept of Gram-Schmidt orthogonalization of random variables and its connection to linear prediction and signal modeling. After a brief review of some pertinent material on random signals, such as autocorrelations, power spectra, and the periodogram and its improvements, we discuss parametric signal models in which the random signal is modeled as the output of a linear system driven by white noise and present an overview of the uses of such models in signal analysis and synthesis, spectrum estimation, signal classification, and data compression applications. A first-order autoregressive model is used to illustrate many of these ideas and to motivate some practical methods of extracting the model parameters from actual data.

Chapter 2 is also introductory, and its purpose is to present a number of straightforward applications and simulation examples that illustrate the practical usage of random signal concepts. The selected topics include simple designs for signal enhancement filters, quantization noise in digital filters, and an introduction to linear prediction based on the finite past. The last two topics are then merged into an introductory discussion of data compression by DPCM methods.

Chapter 3 introduces the concept of minimal phase signals and filters and its role in the making of parametric signal models via spectral factorization. These methods are used in Chapter 4 for the solution of the Wiener filtering problem.

The basic concept of the Wiener filter as an optimum filter for estimating one signal from another is developed in Chapter 4. The Wiener filter is also viewed as a correlation canceler and as an optimal signal separator. We consider both the stationary and nonstationary Wiener filters, as well as the more practical FIR Wiener filter. While discussing a simple first-order Wiener filter example, we take the opportunity to introduce some elementary Kalman filter concepts. We demonstrate how the steady-state Kalman filter is equivalent to the Wiener filter and how its solution may be obtained from the steady-state algebraic Riccati equation which effects the spectral factorization required in the Wiener case. We also show how the Kalman filter may be thought of as the whitening filter of the observation signal and discuss its connection to the Gram-Schmidt orthogonalization and parametric signal models of Chapter 1. This chapter is mainly theoretical in character. Practical implementations and applications of Wiener filters are discussed in Chapter 5 using block-processing methods and in Chapter 6 using real-time adaptive processing techniques.

Chapter 5 begins with a discussion of the full linear prediction problem and its connection to signal modeling and continues with the problem of linear prediction based on the finite past and its efficient solution via the Levinson recursion. We discuss the analysis and synthesis lattice filters of linear prediction, as well as the lattice realizations of more general Wiener filters that are based on the orthogonality property of the backward prediction errors. The autocorrelation, covariance, and Burg's methods of linear predictive analysis are presented, and their application to speech analysis and synthesis and to spectrum estimation is discussed. The problem of estimating the frequencies of multiple sinusoids in noise and the problem of resolving the directions of point-source emitters by spatial array processing are discussed. Four approaches to these problems are presented, namely, the classical method based on the windowed autocorrelation, the maximum entropy method based on linear prediction, Capon's maximum likelihood method, and eigenvector-based methods. We also discuss the problem of wave propagation in layered media and its connection to linear prediction, and present the dynamic predictive deconvolution procedure for deconvolving the multiple reverberation effects of a layered structure from the knowledge of its reflection or transmission response. The chapter ends with a discussion of a least-squares reformulation of the Wiener filtering problem that can be used in the design of waveshaping and spiking filters for deconvolution applications.

Real-time adaptive implementations of Wiener filters are discussed in Chapter 6. The basic operation of an adaptive filter is explained by means of the simplest possible filter, namely, the correlation canceler loop, which forms the elementary building block of higher order adaptive filters. The Widrow-Hoff LMS adaptation algorithm and its convergence properties are discussed next. Several applications of adaptive filters are presented, such as adaptive noise canceling, adaptive channel equalization and echo cancellation, adaptive signal separation and the adaptive line enhancer, adaptive spectrum estimation based on linear prediction, and adaptive array processing. We also discuss some recent developments, such as the adaptive implementation of Pisarenko's method of harmonic retrieval, and two alternative adaptation algorithms that offer very fast speed of convergence, namely, recursive least-squares, and gradient lattice adaptive filters.

The subject of Wiener filtering and linear estimation is vast. The selection of material in this book reflects my preferences and views on what should be included in an introductory course on this subject. The emphasis throughout the book is on the signal processing procedures that grow out of the fundamental concept of Wiener filtering. An important ingredient of the book is the inclusion of several computer experiments and assignments that demonstrate the successes and limitations of the various signal processing algorithms that are discussed. A set of FORTRAN 77 subroutines, designed to be used as a library, has been included in an appendix.

I would like to thank my colleagues Professors T. G. Marshall and P. Sannuti for their support. I am greatly indebted to Professor R. Peskin for making available his graphics system on which many of the simulation examples were run and to my graduate student Ms. L. M. Vail for her invaluable help in producing most of the computer graphs. Most of all, I would like to thank my wife Monica, without whose love and affection this book could not have been written.

SOPHOCLES J. ORFANIDIS

Contents

OPTIMUM SIGNAL PROCESSING

1

Random Signals

1.1 *Probability Density, Mean, Variance*

In this section, we present a short review of probability concepts. It is assumed that the student has had a course on the subject on the level of Papoulis' book [1].

Let x be a *random variable* having *probability density* $p(x)$. Its *mean, variance,* and *second moment* are defined by the expectation values

$$m = E[x] = \int_{-\infty}^{\infty} x\, p(x)\, dx = \text{mean}$$

$$\sigma^2 = \text{var}(x) = E[(x-m)^2] = \int_{-\infty}^{\infty} (x-m)^2\, p(x)\, dx = \text{variance}$$

$$E[x^2] = \int_{-\infty}^{\infty} x^2\, p(x)\, dx = \text{second moment}$$

These quantities are known as *second-order statistics* of the random variable x. Their importance is linked with the fact that most optimal filter design criteria require knowledge only of the second-order statistics and do not require more detailed knowledge, such as of probability densities. It is of primary importance, then, to be able to extract such quantities from the actual measured data.

The probability that the random variable x will assume a value within an interval of values $[a,b]$ is given by

$$\text{Prob}[a \leq x \leq b] = \int_a^b p(x)\,dx = \text{shaded area}$$

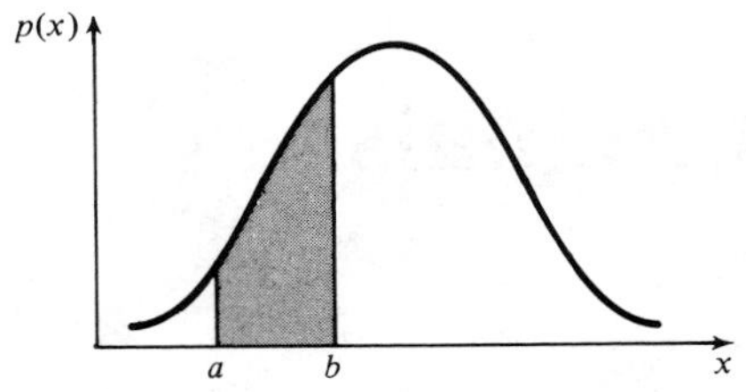

The probability density is always normalized to unity by

$$\int_{-\infty}^{\infty} p(x)\,dx = 1$$

which states that the probability of x taking a value somewhere within its range of variation is unity; that is, certainty. This property also implies

$$\sigma^2 = E[(x - m)^2] = E[x^2] - (E[x])^2 = E[x^2] - m^2$$

Example 1.1.1: Gaussian, or normal, distribution

$$p(x) = \frac{1}{\sqrt{2\pi}\,\sigma} \exp[-(x - m)^2/2\sigma^2]$$

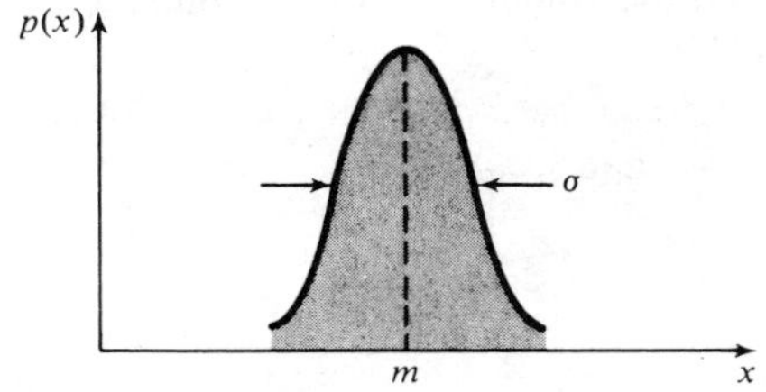

Example 1.1.2: Uniform distribution

$$p(x) = \begin{cases} 1/Q, & \text{for } -Q/2 \leq x \leq Q/2 \\ 0\ , & \text{otherwise} \end{cases}$$

Its variance is $\sigma^2 = Q^2/12$.

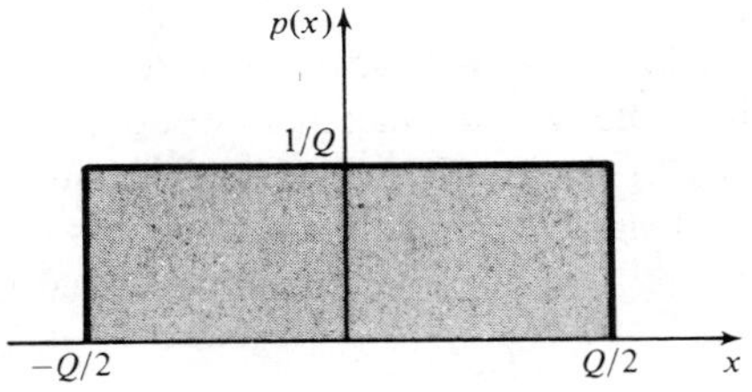

Both the gaussian and the uniform distributions will prove to be important examples. In typical signal processing problems of designing filters to remove or separate noise from signal, it is often assumed that the noise interference is gaussian. This assumption is justified on the grounds of the *central limit theorem,* provided that the noise arises from many different noise sources acting independently of each other.

The uniform distribution is also important. In digital signal processing applications, the quantization error arising from the signal quantization in the A/D converters, or the roundoff error arising from the finite accuracy of the internal arithmetic operations in digital filters, can often be assumed to be uniformly distributed.

Every computer provides system routines for the generation of random numbers. For example, the routines RANDU and GAUSS of the IBM Scientific Subroutine Package generate uniformly distributed random numbers over the interval [0,1], and gaussian-distributed numbers, respectively. GAUSS calls RANDU twelve times, thus generating twelve independent uniformly distributed random numbers $x_1, x_2, \ldots, x_{12}$. Then, their sum $x = x_1 + x_2 + \cdots + x_{12}$ will be approximately gaussian, as guaranteed by the central limit theorem. It is interesting to note that the variance of x is unity, as it follows from the fact that the variance of each x_i is 1/12:

$$\sigma_x^2 = \sigma_{x_1}^2 + \sigma_{x_2}^2 + \cdots + \sigma_{x_{12}}^2 = \frac{1}{12} + \frac{1}{12} + \cdots + \frac{1}{12} = 1$$

The mean of x is $12/2 = 6$. By shifting and scaling x, one can obtain a gaussian-distributed random number of any desired mean and variance. Appendix A contains a discussion of random number generators and methods to improve them, such as shuffling or using several generators in combination. A number of FORTRAN and C routines for generating uniform and gaussian-random numbers are included.

1.2 *Chebyshev's Inequality*

The variance σ^2 of a random variable x is a measure of the spread of the x-values about their mean. This intuitive interpretation of the variance is a direct consequence of Chebyshev's inequality, which states that the x-values tend to cluster about their mean in the sense that the probability of a value not occurring

$$\text{Prob}[|x - m| \geq \Delta] \leq \frac{\sigma^2}{\Delta^2}$$

(Chebyshev's inequality)

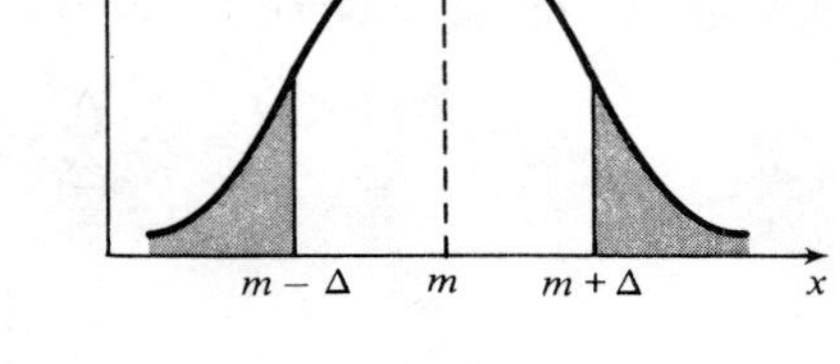

in the near vicinity of the mean is small; and it is smaller the smaller the variance. More precisely, for any probability density $p(x)$ and any $\Delta > 0$, the probability that x will fall outside the interval of values $[m - \Delta, m + \Delta]$ is bounded by σ^2/Δ^2. Thus, for fixed Δ, as the variance σ^2 becomes smaller, the x-values tend to cluster more narrowly about the mean. In the extreme limiting case of a deterministic variable $x = m$, the density becomes infinitely narrow, $p(x) = \delta(x - m)$, and has zero variance.

Chebyshev's inequality is especially important in proving asymptotic convergence results for sample estimates of parameters. For example, consider N independent samples $\{x_1, x_2, \ldots, x_N\}$ drawn from a gaussian probability distribution of mean m and variance σ^2. The sample estimate of the mean is

$$\hat{m} = \frac{1}{N}(x_1 + x_2 + \cdots + x_N) \tag{1.2.1}$$

Being a sum of N gaussian random variables, $\hat{m}$ will itself be a gaussian-random variable. Its probability density is completely specified by the corresponding mean and variance. These are found as follows.

$$E[\hat{m}] = \frac{1}{N}(E[x_1] + E[x_2] + \cdots + E[x_N]) = \frac{1}{N}(m + m + \cdots + m) = m$$

Therefore, $\hat{m}$ is an *unbiased* estimator of m. However, the goodness of $\hat{m}$ as an estimator must be judged by how small its variance is—the smaller the better, by Chebyshev's inequality. By the assumption of independence, we have

$$\text{var}(\hat{m}) = E[(\hat{m} - m)^2] = \frac{1}{N^2}(\sigma_{x_1}^2 + \cdots + \sigma_{x_N}^2) = \frac{1}{N^2}(N\sigma^2) = \frac{\sigma^2}{N} \tag{1.2.2}$$

Thus, $\hat{m}$ is also a *consistent* estimator of m in the sense that its variance tends to zero as the number of samples N increases. The values of $\hat{m}$ will tend to cluster more and more closely about the true value of m as N becomes larger. Chebyshev's inequality implies that the probability of $\hat{m}$ falling outside any fixed neighborhood of m will tend to zero for large N. Equivalently, $\hat{m}$ will converge to m with probability one. This can also be seen from the probability density of $\hat{m}$, which is the gaussian

$$p(\hat{m}) = \frac{N^{1/2}}{(2\pi)^{1/2}\sigma} \exp[-\frac{N}{2\sigma^2}(\hat{m} - m)^2]$$

In the limit of large N, this density tends to the infinitely narrow delta function density $p(\hat{m}) = \delta(\hat{m} - m)$. In addition to the sample mean, we may also compute sample estimates of the variance σ^2 by

$$\hat{\sigma}^2 = \frac{1}{N}\sum_{i=1}^{N}(x_i - \hat{m})^2 \tag{1.2.3}$$

It is easily shown [2,3] that this estimator is slightly biased. But for large N, it is *asymptotically unbiased* and *consistent* as can be seen from its mean and variance:

$$E[\hat{\sigma}^2] = \frac{N-1}{N}\sigma^2\,, \qquad \mathrm{var}(\hat{\sigma}^2) = \frac{N-1}{N^2}2\sigma^4 \tag{1.2.4}$$

An unbiased and consistent estimator of σ^2 is the *standard deviation* defined by

$$s^2 = \frac{1}{N-1}\sum_{i=1}^{N}(x_i - \hat{m})^2 \tag{1.2.5}$$

It has $E[s^2] = \sigma^2$ and $\mathrm{var}(s^2) = 2\sigma^4/(N-1)$. In addition to the requirements of asymptotic unbiasedness and consistency, a good estimator of a parameter must also be judged in terms of its *efficiency* [2,3], which determines how closely the estimator meets its Cramér-Rao bound. This is discussed in Section 1.17. We will see there that the estimators (1.2.1) and (1.2.3)—being maximum likelihood estimators—are asymptotically efficient.

1.3 *Joint and Conditional Densities, and Bayes' Rule*

Next, we discuss random vectors. A pair of two different random variables $\mathbf{x} = (x_1,x_2)$ may be thought of as a vector-valued random variable. Its statistical description is more complicated than that of a single variable and requires knowledge of the joint probability density $p(x_1,x_2)$. The two random variables may or may not have any dependence on each other. It is possible, for example, that if x_2 assumes a particular value, then this fact may influence, or restrict, the possible values that x_1 can then assume.

A quantity that provides a measure for the degree of dependence of the two variables on each other is the *conditional density* $p(x_1/x_2)$ of x_1 given x_2; and $p(x_2/x_1)$ of x_2 given x_1. These are related by *Bayes' rule*

$$p(x_1,x_2) = p(x_1/x_2)\,p(x_2) = p(x_2/x_1)\,p(x_1)$$

More generally, Bayes' rule for two events A and B is

$$p(A,B) = p(A/B)\,p(B) = p(B/A)\,p(A)$$

The two random variables x_1 and x_2 are *independent* of each other if they do not condition each other in any way; that is, if

$$p(x_1/x_2) = p(x_1) \qquad \text{or} \qquad p(x_2/x_1) = p(x_2)$$

In other words, the occurrence of x_2 does not in any way influence the variable x_1. When two random variables are independent, their joint density factors into the product of single (marginal) densities:

$$p(x_1,x_2) = p(x_1)\,p(x_2)$$

The converse is also true. The correlation between x_1 and x_2 is defined by the expectation value

$$E[x_1 x_2] = \int\int x_1 x_2\, p(x_1,x_2)\, dx_1 dx_2$$

When x_1 and x_2 are independent, the correlation also factors as $E[x_1 x_2] = E[x_1]\,E[x_2]$.

Example 1.3.1: Suppose x_1 is related to x_2 by

$$x_1 = 5x_2 + v$$

where v is a zero-mean, unit-variance, gaussian-random variable assumed to be independent of x_2. Determine the conditional density and conditional mean of x_1 given x_2.

Solution: The randomness of x_1 arises both from the randomness of x_2 and the randomness of v. But if x_2 takes on a particular value, then the randomness of x_1 will arise only from v. Identifying elemental probabilities we have

$$p(x_1/x_2)\,dx_1 = p(v)\,dv = (2\pi)^{-1/2} \exp(-\frac{1}{2}v^2)\,dv$$

But, $dx_1 = dv$ and $v = x_1 - 5x_2$. Therefore,

$$p(x_1/x_2) = (2\pi)^{-1/2} \exp[-\frac{1}{2}(x_1 - 5x_2)^2]$$

The conditional mean is the mean of x_1 with respect to the density $p(x_1/x_2)$. It is evident from the above gaussian expression that the conditional mean is $E[x_1/x_2] = 5x_2$. This can also be found directly as follows.

$$E[x_1/x_2] = E[(5x_2 + v)/x_2] = 5x_2 + E[v/x_2] = 5x_2$$

where we used the independence of v and x_2 to replace the conditional mean of v with its unconditional mean, which was given to be zero; that is,

$$E[v/x_2] = E[v] = 0.$$

The concept of a *random vector* generalizes to any dimension. A vector of N random variables

$$\mathbf{x} = \begin{bmatrix} x_1 \\ x_2 \\ \vdots \\ x_N \end{bmatrix}$$

requires knowledge of the joint density

$$p(\mathbf{x}) = p(x_1, x_2, \ldots, x_N) \tag{1.3.1}$$

for its complete statistical description. The second-order statistics of $\mathbf{x}$ are its mean, its *correlation matrix*, and its *covariance matrix*, defined by

$$\mathbf{m} = E[\mathbf{x}],\ R = E[\mathbf{x}\mathbf{x}^T],\ \Sigma = E[(\mathbf{x} - \mathbf{m})\,(\mathbf{x} - \mathbf{m})^T] \tag{1.3.2}$$

where the superscript T denotes transposition, and the expectation operations are defined in terms of the joint density Eq. (1.3.1); for example,

$$E[\mathbf{x}] = \int \mathbf{x}p(\mathbf{x})d^N\mathbf{x}$$

where $d^N\mathbf{x} = dx_1\,dx_2 \ldots dx_N$ denotes the corresponding N-dimensional volume element. The ijth element of the correlation matrix R is the correlation between the ith random variable x_i with the jth random variable x_j; that is, $R_{ij} = E[x_i x_j]$. It is easily shown that the covariance and correlation matrices are related by

$$\Sigma = R - \mathbf{m}\mathbf{m}^T$$

When the mean is zero, R and Σ coincide. Both R and Σ are *symmetric positive semi-definite* matrices.

Example 1.3.2: The probability density of a gaussian random vector $\mathbf{x} = (x_1, x_2, \ldots, x_N)^T$ is completely specified by its mean $\mathbf{m}$ and covariance matrix Σ; that is,

$$p(\mathbf{x}) = \frac{1}{(2\pi)^{N/2}\,(\det\Sigma)^{1/2}} \exp\left[-\frac{1}{2}(\mathbf{x} - \mathbf{m})^T\,\Sigma^{-1}\,(\mathbf{x} - \mathbf{m})\right]$$

Example 1.3.3: Under a *linear* transformation, a gaussian random vector remains gaussian. Let $\mathbf{x}$ be a gaussian random vector of dimension N, mean $\mathbf{m}_x$, and covariance Σ_x. Show that the linearly transformed vector

$$\boldsymbol{\xi} = B\mathbf{x} \qquad \text{where } B \text{ is a nonsingular } N \times N \text{ matrix,}$$

is gaussian-distributed with mean and covariance given by

$$\mathbf{m}_\xi = B\mathbf{m}_x,\ \Sigma_\xi = B\,\Sigma_x B^T \tag{1.3.3}$$

The relationships (1.3.3) are valid also for non-gaussian random vectors. They are easily derived as follows:

$$E[\boldsymbol{\xi}] = E[B\mathbf{x}] = BE[\mathbf{x}]$$

$$E[\boldsymbol{\xi}\boldsymbol{\xi}^T] = E[B\mathbf{x}(B\mathbf{x})^T] = BE[\mathbf{x}\mathbf{x}^T]\,B^T$$

The probability density $p_\xi(\boldsymbol{\xi})$ is related to the probability density $p_x(\mathbf{x})$ by the requirement that, under the above change of variables, they both yield the same elemental probabilities; that is,

$$p_\xi(\boldsymbol{\xi})\, d^N\boldsymbol{\xi} = p_x(\mathbf{x})\, d^N\mathbf{x} \tag{1.3.4}$$

Since the Jacobian of the transformation from $\mathbf{x}$ to $\boldsymbol{\xi}$ is $d^N\boldsymbol{\xi} = |\det B| d^N\mathbf{x}$, we obtain $p_\xi(\boldsymbol{\xi}) = p_x(\mathbf{x})/|\det B|$. Noting the invariance of the quadratic form

$$\begin{aligned}(\boldsymbol{\xi} - \mathbf{m}_\xi)^T \Sigma_\xi^{-1} (\boldsymbol{\xi} - \mathbf{m}_\xi) &= (\mathbf{x} - \mathbf{m}_x)^T B^T (B\, \Sigma_x B^T)^{-1} B\, (\mathbf{x} - \mathbf{m}_x) \\ &= (\mathbf{x} - \mathbf{m}_x)^T \Sigma_x^{-1} (\mathbf{x} - \mathbf{m}_x)\end{aligned}$$

and that $\det \Sigma_\xi = \det(B\, \Sigma_x B^T) = (\det B)^2 \det \Sigma_x$, we obtain

$$p_\xi(\boldsymbol{\xi}) = \frac{1}{(2\pi)^{N/2}(\det \Sigma_\xi)^{1/2}} \exp\left[-\frac{1}{2}(\boldsymbol{\xi} - \mathbf{m}_\xi)^T\Sigma_\xi^{-1}(\boldsymbol{\xi} - \mathbf{m}_\xi)\right]$$

Example 1.3.4: Consider two zero-mean random vectors $\mathbf{x}$ and $\mathbf{y}$ of dimensions N and M, respectively. Show that if they are *uncorrelated* and *jointly gaussian*, then they are also *independent* of each other. That $\mathbf{x}$ and $\mathbf{y}$ are jointly gaussian means that the $(N + M)$-dimensional joint vector $\mathbf{z} = \begin{pmatrix}\mathbf{x}\\ \mathbf{y}\end{pmatrix}$ is zero-mean and gaussian; that is,

$$p(\mathbf{z}) = \frac{1}{(2\pi)^{(N+M)/2}(\det R_{zz})^{1/2}} \exp\left[-\frac{1}{2}\mathbf{z}^T R_{zz}^{-1}\, \mathbf{z}\right]$$

where the correlation (covariance) matrix R_{zz} is

$$R_{zz} = E[\mathbf{z}\mathbf{z}^T] = E\left[\begin{pmatrix}\mathbf{x}\\ \mathbf{y}\end{pmatrix}(\mathbf{x}^T, \mathbf{y}^T)\right] = \begin{bmatrix} E[\mathbf{x}\mathbf{x}^T] & E[\mathbf{x}\mathbf{y}^T] \\ E[\mathbf{y}\mathbf{x}^T] & E[\mathbf{y}\mathbf{y}^T]\end{bmatrix} = \begin{bmatrix} R_{xx} & R_{xy} \\ R_{yx} & R_{yy}\end{bmatrix}$$

If $\mathbf{x}$ and $\mathbf{y}$ are uncorrelated; that is, $R_{xy} = E[\mathbf{x}\mathbf{y}^T] = 0$, then the matrix R_{zz} becomes block diagonal and the quadratic form of the joint vector becomes the sum of the individual quadratic forms:

$$\mathbf{z}^T R_{zz}^{-1}\, \mathbf{z} = [\mathbf{x}^T, \mathbf{y}^T] \begin{bmatrix} R_{xx}^{-1} & 0 \\ 0 & R_{yy}^{-1}\end{bmatrix} \begin{bmatrix}\mathbf{x}\\ \mathbf{y}\end{bmatrix} = \mathbf{x}^T R_{xx}^{-1}\, \mathbf{x} + \mathbf{y}^T R_{yy}^{-1}\, \mathbf{y}$$

Since $R_{xy} = 0$ also implies that $\det R_{zz} = (\det R_{xx})(\det R_{yy})$, it follows that the joint density $p(\mathbf{x},\mathbf{y}) = p(\mathbf{z})$ factors into the marginal densities:

$$p(\mathbf{x},\mathbf{y}) = p(\mathbf{z}) = p(\mathbf{x})\, p(\mathbf{y})$$

which shows the independence of $\mathbf{x}$ and $\mathbf{y}$.

Example 1.3.5: Given a random vector **x** with mean **m** and covariance Σ, show that the best choice of a *deterministic* vector $\hat{\mathbf{x}}$ which minimizes the quantity

$$R_{ee} = E[\mathbf{e}\mathbf{e}^T] = \text{minimum}, \qquad \text{where } \mathbf{e} = \mathbf{x} - \hat{\mathbf{x}}$$

is the mean **m** itself. That is, $\hat{\mathbf{x}} = \mathbf{m}$. Also show that for this optimal choice of $\hat{\mathbf{x}}$, the actual minimum value of the quantity R_{ee} is the covariance Σ.

This property is easily shown by working with the deviation of $\hat{\mathbf{x}}$ from the mean **m**; that is, let

$$\hat{\mathbf{x}} = \mathbf{m} + \mathbf{\Delta}$$

Then, the quantity R_{ee} becomes

$$\begin{aligned} R_{ee} &= E[\mathbf{e}\mathbf{e}^T] = E[(\mathbf{x} - \mathbf{m} - \mathbf{\Delta})\,(\mathbf{x} - \mathbf{m} - \mathbf{\Delta})^T] \\ &= E[(\mathbf{x} - \mathbf{m})\,(\mathbf{x} - \mathbf{m})^T] - \mathbf{\Delta}\, E[(\mathbf{x} - \mathbf{m})^T] \\ &\qquad - E[(\mathbf{x} - \mathbf{m})]\,\mathbf{\Delta}^T + \mathbf{\Delta}\mathbf{\Delta}^T \\ &= \Sigma + \mathbf{\Delta}\mathbf{\Delta}^T \end{aligned}$$

Where we used the fact that $E[(\mathbf{x} - \mathbf{m})] = E[\mathbf{x}] - \mathbf{m} = 0$. Since the matrix $\mathbf{\Delta}\mathbf{\Delta}^T$ is nonnegative-definite, it follows that R_{ee} will be minimized when $\mathbf{\Delta} = 0$, and in this case the minimum value will be Σ.

1.4 *Correlation Canceling*

The concept of correlation canceling plays a central role in the development of many optimum signal processing algorithms, because a correlation canceler is also the *best* linear processor for estimating one signal from another.

Consider two zero-mean random vectors **x** and **y** of dimensions N and M, respectively. If **x** and **y** are correlated with each other in the sense that $R_{xy} = E[\mathbf{x}\mathbf{y}^T] \neq 0$, then we would like to remove such correlations by means of a linear transformation of the form

$$\mathbf{e} = \mathbf{x} - H\mathbf{y} \tag{1.4.1}$$

where the $N \times M$ matrix H must be suitably chosen such that the new pair of vectors $(\mathbf{e},\mathbf{y})$ are no longer correlated with each other; that is, we require

$$R_{ey} = E[\mathbf{e}\mathbf{y}^T] = 0 \tag{1.4.2}$$

Using Eq. (1.4.1), we obtain

$$R_{ey} = E[\mathbf{e}\mathbf{y}^T] = E[(\mathbf{x} - H\mathbf{y})\mathbf{y}^T] = E[\mathbf{x}\mathbf{y}^T] - HE[\mathbf{y}\mathbf{y}^T] = R_{xy} - HR_{yy}$$

Then, the condition $R_{ey} = 0$ immediately implies that

$$H = R_{xy}\, R_{yy}^{-1} = E[\mathbf{x}\mathbf{y}^T]\, E[\mathbf{y}\mathbf{y}^T]^{-1} \tag{1.4.3}$$

Using $R_{ey} = 0$, the covariance matrix of the resulting vector **e** is easily found to be

$$R_{ee} = E[\mathbf{e}\mathbf{e}^T] = E[\mathbf{e}(\mathbf{x}^T - \mathbf{y}^T H^T)] = R_{ex} - R_{ey} H^T = R_{ex} = E[(\mathbf{x} - H\mathbf{y})\mathbf{x}^T]$$

or

$$R_{ee} = R_{xx} - H R_{yx} = R_{xx} - R_{xy} R_{yy}^{-1} R_{yx} \tag{1.4.4}$$

The vector

$$\hat{\mathbf{x}} = H\mathbf{y} = R_{xy} R_{yy}^{-1} \mathbf{y} = E[\mathbf{x}\mathbf{y}^T]\, E[\mathbf{y}\mathbf{y}^T]^{-1}\, \mathbf{y} \tag{1.4.5}$$

obtained by linearly processing the vector **y** by the matrix H is called the *linear regression*, or *orthogonal projection*, of **x** on the vector **y**. In a sense to be made precise later, $\hat{\mathbf{x}}$ also represents the best "copy", or *estimate*, of **x** that can be made on the basis of the vector **y**. Thus, the vector $\mathbf{e} = \mathbf{x} - H\mathbf{y} = \mathbf{x} - \hat{\mathbf{x}}$ may be thought of as the *estimation error*.

Actually, it is better to think of $\hat{\mathbf{x}} = H\mathbf{y}$ not as an estimate of **x** but rather as an estimate of *that part* of **x** which is correlated with **y**. Indeed, suppose that **x** consists of two parts

$$\mathbf{x} = \mathbf{x}_1 + \mathbf{x}_2$$

such that $\mathbf{x}_1$ is correlated with **y**, but $\mathbf{x}_2$ is not; that is, $R_{x_2y} = E[\mathbf{x}_2\mathbf{y}^T] = 0$. Then,

$$R_{xy} = E[\mathbf{x}\mathbf{y}^T] = E[(\mathbf{x}_1 + \mathbf{x}_2)\,\mathbf{y}^T] = R_{x_1y} + R_{x_2y} = R_{x_1y}$$

and therefore,

$$\hat{\mathbf{x}} = R_{xy} R_{yy}^{-1} \mathbf{y} = R_{x_1y} R_{yy}^{-1} \mathbf{y} = \hat{\mathbf{x}}_1$$

The vector $\mathbf{e} = \mathbf{x} - \hat{\mathbf{x}} = \mathbf{x}_1 + \mathbf{x}_2 - \hat{\mathbf{x}}_1 = (\mathbf{x}_1 - \hat{\mathbf{x}}_1) + \mathbf{x}_2$ consists of the estimation error $\mathbf{x}_1 - \hat{\mathbf{x}}_1$ of the x_1-part plus the x_2-part. Both of these terms are separately uncorrelated from **y**. These operations are summarized in block diagram form in Fig. 1.1. The most important feature of this arrangement is the *correlation cancellation* property which may be summarized as follows: If **x** has a part $\mathbf{x}_1$ which is correlated with **y**, then this part will tend to be canceled as much as possible from the output **e**. The linear processor H accomplishes this by converting **y** into the *best possible copy* $\hat{\mathbf{x}}_1$ of $\mathbf{x}_1$ and then proceeding to cancel it from the output. The output vector **e** is no longer correlated with **y**. The part

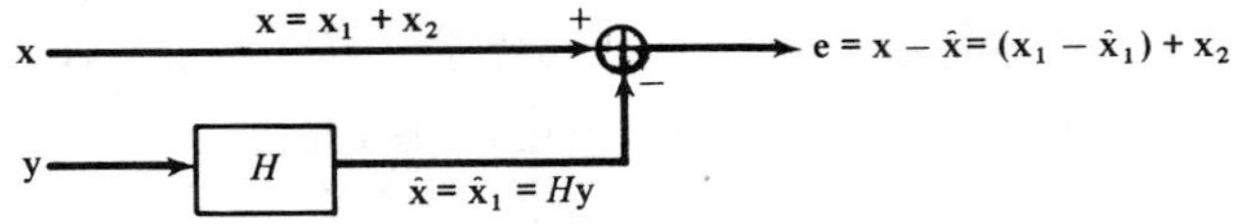

Figure 1.1 Correlation Canceler

$\mathbf{x}_2$ of $\mathbf{x}$ which is uncorrelated with $\mathbf{y}$ remains entirely unaffected. It cannot be estimated in terms of $\mathbf{y}$. The correlation canceler may also be thought of as an *optimal signal separator*. Indeed, the output of the processor H is essentially the $\mathbf{x}_1$ component of $\mathbf{x}$, whereas the output $\mathbf{e}$ is essentially the $\mathbf{x}_2$ component. The separation of $\mathbf{x}$ into $\mathbf{x}_1$ and $\mathbf{x}_2$ is optimal, in the sense that the $\mathbf{x}_1$ component of $\mathbf{x}$ is removed as much as possible from $\mathbf{e}$.

Next, we discuss the *best linear estimator property* of the correlation canceler. The choice $H = R_{xy}R_{yy}^{-1}$, which guarantees correlation cancellation, is also the choice that gives the *best estimate* of $\mathbf{x}$ as a *linear* function of $\mathbf{y}$ in the form $\hat{\mathbf{x}} = H\mathbf{y}$. It is the best estimate in the sense that it produces the lowest *mean-squared* estimation error. To see this, express the covariance matrix of the estimation error in terms of H, as follows:

$$
\begin{aligned}
R_{ee} &= E[\mathbf{e}\mathbf{e}^T] = E[(\mathbf{x} - H\mathbf{y})(\mathbf{x}^T - \mathbf{y}^T H^T)] \\
&= R_{xx} - HR_{yx} - R_{xy}H^T + HR_{yy}H^T
\end{aligned}
\tag{1.4.6}
$$

Minimizing this expression with respect to H yields the optimal choice of H:

$$H_{\text{opt}} = R_{xy}R_{yy}^{-1}$$

with the minimum value for R_{ee} given by

$$R_{ee}^{\min} = R_{xx} - R_{xy}R_{yy}^{-1}R_{yx}$$

Any other choice of H will result in a larger value for R_{ee}. An alternative way to see this is to consider a deviation ΔH of H from its optimal value; that is, in Eq. (1.4.6) replace H by

$$H = H_{\text{opt}} + \Delta H = R_{xy}R_{yy}^{-1} + \Delta H$$

Then Eq. (1.4.6) may be expressed in terms of ΔH as follows:

$$R_{ee} = R_{ee}^{\min} + \Delta H R_{yy} \Delta H^T$$

Since R_{yy} is positive definite, the second term always represents a nonnegative contribution above the minimum value $R_{ee}^{\min}$.

In summary, there are three useful ways to think of the correlation canceler:

1. Optimal estimator of $\mathbf{x}$ from $\mathbf{y}$
2. Optimal canceler of that part of $\mathbf{x}$ which is correlated with $\mathbf{y}$
3. Optimal signal separator

The point of view is determined by the application. The first view is typified by Kalman filtering, channel equalization, and linear prediction applications. The second view is taken in echo canceling, noise canceling, and sidelobe canceling applications. The third view is useful in the adaptive line enhancer, which is a method of adaptively separating a signal into its broadband and narrowband components. All of these applications are considered later on.

Example 1.4.1 If $\mathbf{x}$ and $\mathbf{y}$ are *jointly gaussian*, show that the linear estimate $\hat{\mathbf{x}} = H\mathbf{y}$ is also the *conditional mean* $E[\mathbf{x}/\mathbf{y}]$ of the vector $\mathbf{x}$ given the vector $\mathbf{y}$. The conditional mean is defined in terms of the conditional density $p(\mathbf{x}/\mathbf{y})$ of $\mathbf{x}$ given $\mathbf{y}$ as follows:

$$E[\mathbf{x}/\mathbf{y}] = \int \mathbf{x}\, p(\mathbf{x}/\mathbf{y})\, d^N\mathbf{x}$$

Instead of computing this integral, we will use the results of Examples 1.3.3 and 1.3.4. The transformation from the jointly gaussian pair $(\mathbf{x},\mathbf{y})$ to the uncorrelated pair $(\mathbf{e},\mathbf{y})$ is linear:

$$\begin{bmatrix} \mathbf{e} \\ \mathbf{y} \end{bmatrix} = \begin{bmatrix} I_N & -H \\ O & I_M \end{bmatrix} \begin{bmatrix} \mathbf{x} \\ \mathbf{y} \end{bmatrix}$$

where I_N and I_M are the unit matrices of dimensions N and M, respectively. Therefore, Example 1.3.3 implies that the transformed pair $(\mathbf{e},\mathbf{y})$ is also jointly gaussian. Furthermore, since $\mathbf{e}$ and $\mathbf{y}$ are uncorrelated, it follows from Example 1.3.4 that they must be independent of each other. The required conditional mean of $\mathbf{x}$ can be computed by writing $\mathbf{x}$ as

$$\mathbf{x} = H\mathbf{y} + \mathbf{e}$$

and noting that if $\mathbf{y}$ is given, then $H\mathbf{y}$ is no longer random. Therefore,

$$E[\mathbf{x}/\mathbf{y}] = E[(H\mathbf{y} + \mathbf{e})/\mathbf{y}] = H\mathbf{y} + E[\mathbf{e}/\mathbf{y}]$$

Since $\mathbf{e}$ and $\mathbf{y}$ are independent, the conditional mean $E[\mathbf{e}/\mathbf{y}]$ is the same as the unconditional mean $E[\mathbf{e}]$ which is zero by the zero-mean assumption. Thus,

$$E[\mathbf{x}/\mathbf{y}] = H\mathbf{y} = R_{xy}R_{yy}^{-1}\,\mathbf{y} \qquad \text{(gaussian } \mathbf{x} \text{ and } \mathbf{y}) \qquad (1.4.7)$$

Example 1.4.2: Show that the conditional mean $E[\mathbf{x}/\mathbf{y}]$ is the best *unrestricted* (i.e., not necessarily linear) estimate of $\mathbf{x}$ in the *mean-squared* sense. The best linear estimate was obtained by seeking the best linear function of $\mathbf{y}$ that minimized the error criterion (1.4.6); that is, we required a priori that the estimate was to be of the form $\hat{\mathbf{x}} = H\mathbf{y}$. Here, our task is more general: Find the most general function of $\mathbf{y}$, $\hat{\mathbf{x}} = \hat{\mathbf{x}}(\mathbf{y})$, which gives the best estimate of $\mathbf{x}$, in the sense of producing the lowest mean-squared estimation error $\mathbf{e} = \mathbf{x} - \hat{\mathbf{x}}(\mathbf{y})$

$$R_{ee} = E[\mathbf{e}\mathbf{e}^T] = E[(\mathbf{x} - \hat{\mathbf{x}}(\mathbf{y}))\,(\mathbf{x} - \hat{\mathbf{x}}(\mathbf{y}))^T] = \min$$

The functional dependence of $\hat{\mathbf{x}}(\mathbf{y})$ on $\mathbf{y}$ is not required to be linear a priori. Using $p(\mathbf{x},\mathbf{y}) = p(\mathbf{x}/\mathbf{y})p(\mathbf{y})$, the above expectation may be written as

$$R_{ee} = \int (\mathbf{x} - \hat{\mathbf{x}}(\mathbf{y}))\,(\mathbf{x} - \hat{\mathbf{x}}(\mathbf{y}))^T\, p(\mathbf{x},\mathbf{y})\, d^N\mathbf{x}\, d^M\mathbf{y}$$

$$= \int p(\mathbf{y})\, d^M\mathbf{y} \left\{ \int (\mathbf{x} - \hat{\mathbf{x}}(\mathbf{y}))\,(\mathbf{x} - \hat{\mathbf{x}}(\mathbf{y}))^T\, p(\mathbf{x}/\mathbf{y})\, d^N\mathbf{x} \right\}$$

Since $p(\mathbf{y})$ is nonnegative for all $\mathbf{y}$, it follows that R_{ee} will be minimized when the quantity

$$\int (\mathbf{x} - \hat{\mathbf{x}}(\mathbf{y}))\,(\mathbf{x} - \hat{\mathbf{x}}(\mathbf{y}))^T\, p(\mathbf{x}/\mathbf{y})\, d^N\mathbf{x}$$

is minimized with respect to $\hat{\mathbf{x}}$. But we know from Example 1.3.5 that this quantity is minimized when $\hat{\mathbf{x}}$ is chosen to be the corresponding mean; here, this is the mean with respect to the density $p(\mathbf{x}/\mathbf{y})$. Thus,

$$\hat{\mathbf{x}}(\mathbf{y}) = E[\mathbf{x}/\mathbf{y}] \tag{1.4.8}$$

To summarize, we have seen that

$$\hat{\mathbf{x}} = H\mathbf{y} = R_{xy}\, R_{yy}^{-1}\, \mathbf{y} = \text{best } \textit{linear} \text{ mean-squared estimate of } \mathbf{x}$$

$$\hat{\mathbf{x}} = E[\mathbf{x}/\mathbf{y}] = \text{best } \textit{unrestricted} \text{ mean-squared estimate of } \mathbf{x}$$

and Example 1.4.1 shows that the two are *equal* in the case of jointly gaussian vectors $\mathbf{x}$ and $\mathbf{y}$.

The concept of correlation canceling and its application to signal estimation problems will be discussed in more detail in Chapter 4. The adaptive implementation of the correlation canceler will be discussed in Chapter 7. In a typical signal processing application, the processor H would represent a *linear filtering* operation and the vectors $\mathbf{x}$ and $\mathbf{y}$ would be *blocks of signal samples*. The design of such processors requires knowledge of the quantities $R_{xy} = E[\mathbf{x}\mathbf{y}^T]$ and $R_{yy} = E[\mathbf{y}\mathbf{y}^T]$. How does one determine these?

Basically, applications fall into two classes:

1. Both $\mathbf{x}$ and $\mathbf{y}$ are available for processing, and the objective is to *cancel* the correlations that may exist between them.
2. Only the signal $\mathbf{y}$ is available for processing, and the objective is to *estimate* the signal $\mathbf{x}$ on the basis of $\mathbf{y}$.

In the first class of applications, there exist two basic design approaches:

a. *Block processing* (off-line) methods. The required correlations R_{xy} and R_{yy} are computed on the basis of two actual blocks of signal samples $\mathbf{x}$ and $\mathbf{y}$ by replacing statistical averages by *time* averages.

b. *Adaptive processing* (on-line) methods. The quantities R_{xy} and R_{yy} are "learned" gradually as the data $\mathbf{x}$ and $\mathbf{y}$ become available in real time. The processor

H is continually updated in response to the incoming data, until it reaches its optimal value.

Both methods are *data adaptive.* The first is adaptive on a *block-by-block* basis, whereas the second on a *sample-by-sample* basis. Both methods depend heavily on the assumption of *stationarity.* In block processing methods, the replacement of ensemble averages by time averages is justified by the assumption of ergodicity, which requires stationarity. The requirement of stationarity can place serious limitations on the allowed length of the signal blocks **x** and **y**. Similarly, in adaptive processing methods, convergence to the optimal value of the processor H again requires stationarity. Adaptive methods offer, however, the possibility of *tracking* nonstationary changes of the environment, as long as such changes occur slowly enough to allow convergence between changes. Thus, the issue of the *speed* of convergence of adaptation algorithms is an important one.

In the second class of applications where **x** is not available for processing, one must have a specific *model* of the relationship between **x** and **y** from which R_{xy} and R_{yy} may be calculated. This is, for example, what is done in Kalman filtering.

Example 1.4.3: As an example of the relationship that might exist between **x** and **y**, let

$$y_n = xc_n + v_n; \qquad n = 1,2, \ldots, M$$

where x and v_n are zero-mean, unit-variance, random variables, and c_n are known coefficients. It is further assumed that v_n are mutually uncorrelated, and also uncorrelated with x, so that $E[v_n v_m] = \delta_{nm}$, $E[xv_n] = 0$. We would like to determine the optimal linear estimate (1.4.5) of x, and the corresponding estimation error (1.4.4). In obvious matrix notation we have $\mathbf{y} = x\mathbf{c} + \mathbf{v}$, with $E[x\mathbf{v}] = 0$, and $E[\mathbf{v}\mathbf{v}^T] = I$, where I is the $M \times M$ unit matrix. We find

$$E[x\mathbf{y}^T] = E[x(x\mathbf{c} + \mathbf{v})^T] = \mathbf{c}^T E[x^2] + E[x\mathbf{v}^T] = \mathbf{c}^T$$

$$E[\mathbf{y}\mathbf{y}^T] = E[(x\mathbf{c} + \mathbf{v})(x\mathbf{c}^T + \mathbf{v}^T)] = \mathbf{c}\mathbf{c}^T E[x^2] + E[\mathbf{v}\mathbf{v}^T] = \mathbf{c}\mathbf{c}^T + I$$

and therefore, $H = E[x\mathbf{y}^T]\, E[\mathbf{y}\mathbf{y}^T]^{-1} = \mathbf{c}^T(I + \mathbf{c}\mathbf{c}^T)^{-1}$. Using the matrix inversion lemma we may write $(I + \mathbf{c}\mathbf{c}^T)^{-1} = I - \mathbf{c}(1 + \mathbf{c}^T\mathbf{c})^{-1}\,\mathbf{c}^T$, so that

$$H = \mathbf{c}^T\,[I - \mathbf{c}(1 + \mathbf{c}^T\mathbf{c})^{-1}\,\mathbf{c}^T] = (1 + \mathbf{c}^T\mathbf{c})^{-1}\,\mathbf{c}^T$$

The optimal estimate of x is then

$$\hat{x} = H\mathbf{y} = (1 + \mathbf{c}^T\mathbf{c})^{-1}\,\mathbf{c}^T\mathbf{y} \qquad (1.4.9)$$

The corresponding estimation error is computed by

$$E[e^2] = R_{ee} = R_{xx} - HR_{yx} = 1 - (1 + \mathbf{c}^T\mathbf{c})^{-1}\,\mathbf{c}^T\mathbf{c} = (1 + \mathbf{c}^T\mathbf{c})^{-1}$$

1.5 *Gram-Schmidt Orthogonalization*

In the previous section, we saw that any random vector $\mathbf{x}$ may be decomposed relative to another vector $\mathbf{y}$ into two parts, $\mathbf{x} = \hat{\mathbf{x}} + \mathbf{e}$, one part which is correlated with $\mathbf{y}$, and one which is not. These two parts are uncorrelated with each other since $R_{e\hat{x}} = E[\mathbf{e}\hat{\mathbf{x}}^T] = E[\mathbf{e}\mathbf{y}^T H^T] = R_{ey} H^T = 0$. In a sense, they are orthogonal to each other. In this section, we will briefly develop such a geometrical interpretation. The usefulness of the geometrical approach is threefold: First, it provides a very simple and intuitive framework in which to formulate and understand signal estimation problems. Second, through the Gram-Schmidt orthogonalization process, it provides the basis for making *signal models*, which find themselves in a variety of signal processing applications, such as speech synthesis, data compression, and modern methods of spectrum estimation. Third, again through the Gram-Schmidt construction, by decorrelating the given set of observations it provides the most convenient basis to work with, containing no redundancies. Linear estimates expressed in the decorrelated basis become computationally efficient.

Geometrical ideas may be introduced by thinking of the space of random variables under consideration as a *linear vector space* [7]. For example, in the previous section we dealt with the multicomponent random variables $\mathbf{x}$ and $\mathbf{y}$ consisting, say, of the random variables $(x_1, x_2, \ldots, x_N)$ and $(y_1, y_2, \ldots, y_M)$, respectively. In this case, the space of random variables under consideration is the set

$$\{x_1, x_2, \ldots, x_N, y_1, y_2, \ldots, y_M\} \tag{1.5.1}$$

Since any linear combination of random variables from this set is itself a random variable, the above set may be enlarged by adjoining to it all such possible linear combinations. This is the linear vector space *generated* by the given set of random variables. The next step is to convert this vector space into an *inner-product space* (a Hilbert space) by defining an inner product between two random variables u and v as follows:

$$(u, v) = E[uv] \tag{1.5.2}$$

With this definition of an inner product, "orthogonal" means "uncorrelated." The *distance* between u and v is defined by the norm $\|u - v\|$ induced by the above inner product:

$$\|u - v\|^2 = E[(u - v)^2] \tag{1.5.3}$$

Mutually orthogonal (i.e., uncorrelated) random variables may be used to define *orthogonal bases*. Consider, for example, M mutually orthogonal random variables $\epsilon_1, \epsilon_2, \ldots, \epsilon_M$; such that

$$(\epsilon_i, \epsilon_j) = E[\epsilon_i \epsilon_j] = 0; \qquad \text{if } i \neq j \tag{1.5.4}$$

and let $Y = \{\epsilon_1, \epsilon_2, \ldots, \epsilon_M\}$ be the linear subspace *spanned* by these M random variables. Without loss of generality, we may assume that the ϵ_is are linearly independent; therefore, they form a linearly independent and orthogonal basis for the subspace Y.

One of the standard results on linear vector spaces is the *orthogonal decomposition* theorem [8], which in our context may be stated as follows: Any random variable x may be decomposed *uniquely, with respect to* a subspace Y, into two mutually orthogonal parts. One part is *parallel* to the subspace Y (i.e., it lies in it), and the other is *perpendicular* to it. That is,

$$x = \hat{x} + e \qquad \text{with } \hat{x} \text{ in } Y, \text{ and } e \perp Y \tag{1.5.5}$$

The component $\hat{x}$ is called the *orthogonal projection* of x onto the subspace Y. This decomposition is depicted in Fig. 1.2. The orthogonality condition $e \perp Y$ means that e must be orthogonal to every vector in Y; or equivalently, to every basis vector ϵ_i; that is,

$$(e, \epsilon_i) = E[e\epsilon_i] = 0, \qquad \text{for } i = 1, 2, \ldots, M \tag{1.5.6}$$

Since the component $\hat{x}$ lies in Y, it may be expanded in terms of the orthogonal basis in the form

$$\hat{x} = \sum_{i=1}^{M} a_i \epsilon_i$$

The coefficients a_i can be determined using the orthogonality equations (1.5.6), as follows,

$$(x, \epsilon_i) = (\hat{x} + e, \epsilon_i) = (\hat{x}, \epsilon_i) + (e, \epsilon_i) = (\hat{x}, \epsilon_i)$$

$$= \left(\sum_{j=1}^{M} a_j \epsilon_j, \epsilon_i \right) = \sum_{j=1}^{M} a_j \, (\epsilon_j, \epsilon_i) = a_i \, (\epsilon_i, \epsilon_i)$$

where in the last equality we used Eq. (1.5.4). Thus, $a_i = (x, \epsilon_i)\,(\epsilon_i, \epsilon_i)^{-1}$, or $a_i = E[x\epsilon_i]E[\epsilon_i\epsilon_i]^{-1}$, and we can write Eq. (1.5.5) as

$$x = \hat{x} + e = \sum_{i=1}^{M} E[x\epsilon_i]E[\epsilon_i\epsilon_i]^{-1}\epsilon_i + e \tag{1.5.7}$$

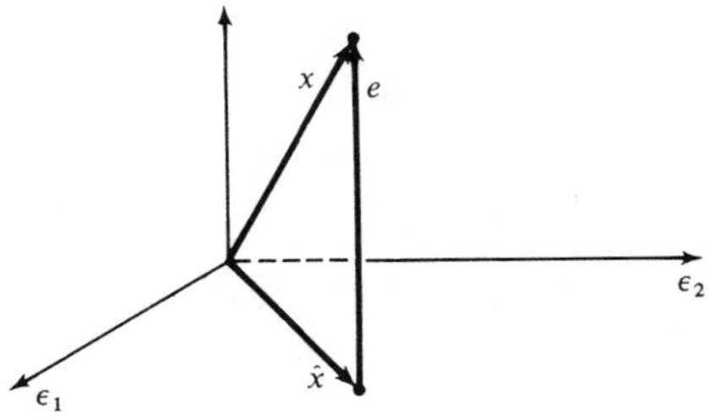

Figure 1.2 Orthogonal Decomposition with Respect to $Y = \{\epsilon_1, \epsilon_2\}$

Equation (1.5.7) may also be written in a compact matrix form by introducing the M-vector

$$\boldsymbol{\epsilon} = \begin{bmatrix} \epsilon_1 \\ \epsilon_2 \\ \vdots \\ \epsilon_M \end{bmatrix}$$

the corresponding cross-correlation M-vector

$$E[x\boldsymbol{\epsilon}] = \begin{bmatrix} E[x\epsilon_1] \\ E[x\epsilon_2] \\ \vdots \\ E[x\epsilon_M] \end{bmatrix}$$

and the correlation matrix $R_{\epsilon\epsilon} = E[\boldsymbol{\epsilon}\boldsymbol{\epsilon}^T]$, which is *diagonal* because of the conditions (1.5.4):

$$R_{\epsilon\epsilon} = E[\boldsymbol{\epsilon}\boldsymbol{\epsilon}^T] = \text{diag}\{E[\epsilon_1^2], E[\epsilon_2^2], \ldots, E[\epsilon_M^2]\}$$

Then, Eq. (1.5.7) may be written as

$$x = \hat{x} + e = E[x\boldsymbol{\epsilon}^T]\, E[\boldsymbol{\epsilon}\boldsymbol{\epsilon}^T\,]^{-1}\boldsymbol{\epsilon} + e \tag{1.5.8}$$

The orthogonality equations (1.5.6) can be written as

$$R_{e\epsilon} = E[e\boldsymbol{\epsilon}^T] = 0 \tag{1.5.9}$$

Equations (1.5.8) and (1.5.9) represent the unique orthogonal decomposition of any random variable x relative to a linear subspace Y of random variables. If one has a collection of N random variables $x_1, x_2, \ldots, x_N$, then each one may be orthogonally decomposed with respect to the same subspace Y, giving $x_i = \hat{x}_i + e_i$, $i = 1,2, \ldots, N$. All these may be grouped together into a compact matrix form as

$$\mathbf{x} = \hat{\mathbf{x}} + \mathbf{e} = E[\mathbf{x}\boldsymbol{\epsilon}^T]\, E[\boldsymbol{\epsilon}\boldsymbol{\epsilon}^T]^{-1}\boldsymbol{\epsilon} + \mathbf{e} \tag{1.5.10}$$

with

$$R_{e\epsilon} = E[\mathbf{e}\boldsymbol{\epsilon}^T] = 0$$

where $\mathbf{x}$ stands for the column N-vector $\mathbf{x} = [x_1, x_2, \ldots, x_N]^T$, and so on. This is identical to the correlation canceler decomposition of the previous section.

Next, we briefly discuss the orthogonal projection theorem. In Section 1.4, we noted the best linear estimator property of the correlation canceler decomposition. The same result may be understood geometrically by means of the orthogonal projection theorem, which states: The orthogonal projection $\hat{x}$ of a vector x onto a linear subspace Y is that vector in Y which lies *closest* to x with respect to the distance induced by the inner product of the vector space.

The theorem is a simple consequence of the orthogonal decomposition theorem and the Pythagorean theorem. Indeed, let $x = \hat{x} + e$ be the unique orthogonal decomposition of x with respect to Y, so that $\hat{x} \in Y$ and $e \perp Y$, and let y be an arbitrary vector in Y; noting that $(\hat{x} - y) \in Y$ and therefore $e \perp (\hat{x} - y)$, we have

$$\|x - y\|^2 = \|(\hat{x} - y) + e\|^2 = \|\hat{x} - y\|^2 + \|e\|^2$$

or, in terms of Eq. (1.5.3),

$$E[(x - y)^2] = E[(\hat{x} - y)^2] + E[e^2]$$

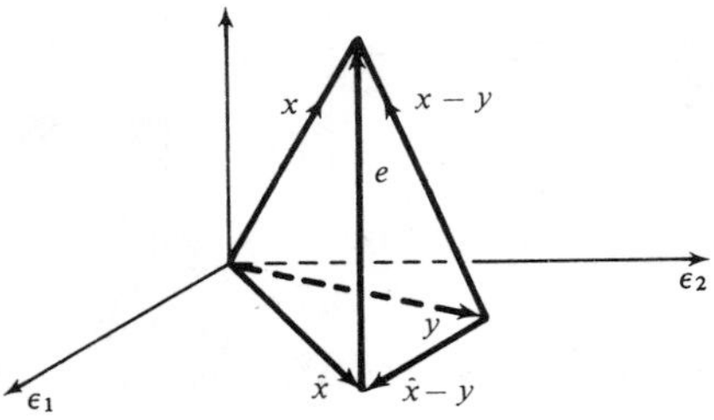

Since the vector y varies over the subspace Y, it follows that the above quantity will be minimized when $y = \hat{x}$. In summary, $\hat{x}$ represents the *best approximation* of x that can be made as a *linear* function of the random variables in Y in the minimum mean-squared sense.

Above, we developed the orthogonal decomposition of a random variable relative to a linear subspace Y which was generated by means of an orthogonal basis $\epsilon_1, \epsilon_2, \ldots, \epsilon_M$. In practice, the subspace Y is almost always defined by means of a nonorthogonal basis, such as a collection of random variables

$$Y = \{y_1, y_2, \ldots, y_M\}$$

which may be mutually correlated. The subspace Y is defined again as the *linear span* of this basis. The *Gram-Schmidt* orthogonalization process is a recursive procedure of generating an orthogonal basis $\epsilon_1, \epsilon_2, \ldots, \epsilon_M$ from $y_1, y_2, \ldots, y_M$. The basic idea of the method is this: Initialize the procedure by selecting $\epsilon_1 = y_1$. Next, consider y_2 and decompose it relative to ϵ_1. Then, the component of y_2 which is perpendicular to ϵ_1 is selected as ϵ_2; so that $(\epsilon_1, \epsilon_2) = 0$. Next, take y_3 and decompose it relative to the subspace spanned by $\{\epsilon_1, \epsilon_2\}$ and take the corresponding perpendicular component to be ϵ_3, and so on. For example, the first three steps of the procedure are

$$\epsilon_1 = y_1$$

$$\epsilon_2 = y_2 - E[y_2\epsilon_1]\, E[\epsilon_1\epsilon_1]^{-1}\epsilon_1$$

$$\epsilon_3 = y_3 - E[y_3\epsilon_1]\, E[\epsilon_1\epsilon_1]^{-1}\epsilon_1 - E[y_3\epsilon_2]\, E[\epsilon_2\epsilon_2]^{-1}\epsilon_2$$

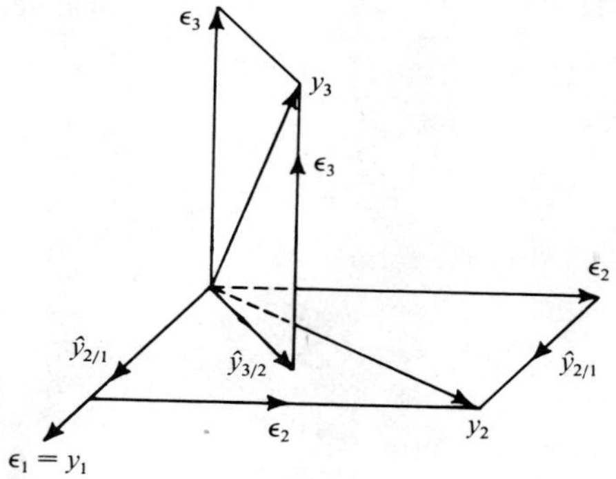

At the *n*th iteration step

$$\epsilon_n = y_n - \sum_{i=1}^{n-1} E[y_n\epsilon_i]\, E[\epsilon_i\epsilon_i]^{-1}\epsilon_i, \qquad 2 \leq n \leq M \tag{1.5.11}$$

The basis $\{\epsilon_1,\epsilon_2, \ldots ,\epsilon_M\}$ generated in this way is orthogonal by construction. The Gram-Schmidt process may be understood in terms of a hierarchy of subspaces defined by

$$Y_1 = \{\epsilon_1\} = \{y_1\}$$

$$Y_2 = \{\epsilon_1,\epsilon_2\} = \{y_1,y_2\}$$

$$Y_3 = \{\epsilon_1,\epsilon_2,\epsilon_3\} = \{y_1,y_2,y_3\}$$

$$\vdots$$

$$Y_n = \{\epsilon_1,\epsilon_2, \ldots ,\epsilon_n\} = \{y_1,y_2, \ldots ,y_n\}$$

for $n = 1,2, \ldots ,M$, where each is a subspace of the next one and differs from the next by the addition of one more basis vector. The second term in Eq. (1.5.11) may be recognized now as the component of y_n parallel to the subspace Y_{n-1}. We may denote this as

$$\hat{y}_{n/n-1} = \sum_{i=1}^{n-1} E[y_n\epsilon_i]\, E[\epsilon_i\epsilon_i]^{-1}\epsilon_i \tag{1.5.12}$$

Then Eq. (1.5.11) may be written as

$$\epsilon_n = y_n - \hat{y}_{n/n-1} \qquad \text{or} \qquad y_n = \hat{y}_{n/n-1} + \epsilon_n \tag{1.5.13}$$

which represents the *orthogonal decomposition* of y_n relative to the subspace Y_{n-1}. Since, the term $\hat{y}_{n/n-1}$ already lies in Y_{n-1}, we have the direct sum decomposition

$$Y_n = Y_{n-1} \oplus \{y_n\} = Y_{n-1} \oplus \{\epsilon_n\}$$

Introducing the notation

$$b_{ni} = E[y_n \epsilon_i]\, E[\epsilon_i \epsilon_i]^{-1} \qquad \text{for } 1 \leq i \leq n-1 \tag{1.5.14}$$

and

$$b_{nn} = 1$$

we may write Eq. (1.5.13) in the form

$$y_n = \sum_{i=1}^{n} b_{ni}\epsilon_i = \epsilon_n + \sum_{i=1}^{n-1} b_{ni}\epsilon_i = \epsilon_n + \hat{y}_{n/n-1} \tag{1.5.15}$$

for $1 \leq n \leq M$. And in matrix form,

$$\mathbf{y} = B\boldsymbol{\epsilon} \qquad \text{where } \mathbf{y} = \begin{bmatrix} y_1 \\ y_2 \\ \vdots \\ y_M \end{bmatrix} \text{ and } \boldsymbol{\epsilon} = \begin{bmatrix} \epsilon_1 \\ \epsilon_2 \\ \vdots \\ \epsilon_M \end{bmatrix} \tag{1.5.16}$$

and B is a *lower-triangular* matrix with matrix elements given by (1.5.14). Its main diagonal is *unity*. For example, for $M = 4$ we have

$$\begin{bmatrix} y_1 \\ y_2 \\ y_3 \\ y_4 \end{bmatrix} = \begin{bmatrix} 1 & 0 & 0 & 0 \\ b_{21} & 1 & 0 & 0 \\ b_{31} & b_{32} & 1 & 0 \\ b_{41} & b_{42} & b_{43} & 1 \end{bmatrix} \begin{bmatrix} \epsilon_1 \\ \epsilon_2 \\ \epsilon_3 \\ \epsilon_4 \end{bmatrix}$$

Both the matrix B and its inverse B^{-1} are unit lower-triangular matrices. The information contained in the two bases $\mathbf{y}$ and $\boldsymbol{\epsilon}$ is the *same*. Going from the basis $\mathbf{y}$ to the basis $\boldsymbol{\epsilon}$ removes all the *redundant correlations* that may exist in $\mathbf{y}$ and "distills" the essential information contained in $\mathbf{y}$ to its most basic form. Because the basis $\boldsymbol{\epsilon}$ is uncorrelated, every basis vector ϵ_i; $i = 1, \ldots, M$ will represent something different, or new. Therefore, the random variables ϵ_i are sometimes called the *innovations*, and the representation (1.5.16) of $\mathbf{y}$ in terms of $\boldsymbol{\epsilon}$, is called the *innovations representation* of $\mathbf{y}$.

Since the correlation matrix $R_{\epsilon\epsilon} = E[\boldsymbol{\epsilon}\boldsymbol{\epsilon}^T]$ is diagonal, the transformation (1.5.16) corresponds to a *LU (lower-upper)-Cholesky factorization* of the correlation matrix of $\mathbf{y}$; that is,

$$R_{yy} = E[\mathbf{y}\mathbf{y}^T] = BE[\boldsymbol{\epsilon}\boldsymbol{\epsilon}^T]\, B^T = BR_{\epsilon\epsilon}B^T \tag{1.5.17}$$

We note also the *invariance* of the projected vector $\hat{\mathbf{x}}$ of Eq. (1.5.10) under such *change of basis*:

$$\hat{\mathbf{x}} = E[\mathbf{x}\boldsymbol{\epsilon}^T]\, E[\boldsymbol{\epsilon}\boldsymbol{\epsilon}^T]^{-1}\boldsymbol{\epsilon} = E[\mathbf{x}\mathbf{y}^T]\, E[\mathbf{y}\mathbf{y}^T]^{-1}\mathbf{y} \tag{1.5.18}$$

This shows the *equivalence* of the orthogonal decompositions (1.5.10) to the correlation canceler decompositions (1.4.1). The computational efficiency of the $\boldsymbol{\epsilon}$ basis over the $\mathbf{y}$ basis is evident from the fact that the covariance matrix $E[\boldsymbol{\epsilon}\boldsymbol{\epsilon}^T]$ is diagonal, and therefore, its inverse is trivially computed.

We may also apply the property (1.5.18) to y_n itself. Defining the vectors

$$\boldsymbol{\epsilon}_{n-1} = \begin{bmatrix} \epsilon_1 \\ \epsilon_2 \\ \vdots \\ \epsilon_{n-1} \end{bmatrix} \qquad \mathbf{y}_{n-1} = \begin{bmatrix} y_1 \\ y_2 \\ \vdots \\ y_{n-1} \end{bmatrix}$$

we may write the projection $\hat{y}_{n/n-1}$ of y_n on the subspace Y_{n-1} given by Eq. (1.5.12) as follows:

$$\hat{y}_{n/n-1} = E[y_n\boldsymbol{\epsilon}_{n-1}^T]\,E[\boldsymbol{\epsilon}_{n-1}\boldsymbol{\epsilon}_{n-1}^T]^{-1}\boldsymbol{\epsilon}_{n-1}$$

$$= E[y_n\,\mathbf{y}_{n-1}^T]\,E[\mathbf{y}_{n-1}\mathbf{y}_{n-1}^T]^{-1}\mathbf{y}_{n-1} \qquad (1.5.19)$$

Equation (1.5.13) is then written as

$$\epsilon_n = y_n - \hat{y}_{n/n-1} = y_n - E[y_n\mathbf{y}_{n-1}^T]\,E[\mathbf{y}_{n-1}\mathbf{y}_{n-1}^T]^{-1}\mathbf{y}_{n-1} \qquad (1.5.20)$$

which provides a construction of ϵ_n directly in terms of the y_ns. We note that the quantity $\hat{y}_{n/n-1}$ is also the *best linear estimate* of y_n that can be made on the basis of the *previous* y_ns, $Y_{n-1} = \{y_1, y_2, \ldots, y_{n-1}\}$. If the index n represents the time index, as it does for random signals, then $\hat{y}_{n/n-1}$ is the best linear *prediction* of y_n on the basis of *its past*; and ϵ_n is the corresponding *prediction error*.

The Gram-Schmidt process, started with the first element y_1 of $\mathbf{y}$, proceeded forward to y_M. The process can just as well be started with y_M and proceed backward to y_1 (see Problem 1.16). It may be interpreted as *backward* prediction, or postdiction, and leads to the UL (rather than LU) factorization of the covariance matrix R_{yy}. In Section 1.7, we study the properties of such forward and backward orthogonalization procedures in some detail.

Example 1.5.1: Consider the three random variables $\{y_1, y_2, y_3\}$, and let $R_{ij} = E[y_i\, y_j]$ for $i,j = 1,2,3$, denote their correlation matrix. Then, the explicit construction indicated in Eq. (1.5.20) can be carried out as follows: The required vectors $\mathbf{y}_{n-1}$ are

$$\mathbf{y}_1 = [y_1], \qquad \mathbf{y}_2 = \begin{bmatrix} y_1 \\ y_2 \end{bmatrix}$$

and hence

$$E[y_2\,\mathbf{y}_1^T] = E[y_2\,y_1] = R_{21}$$

$$E[\mathbf{y}_1\,\mathbf{y}_1^T] = E[y_1\,y_1] = R_{11}$$

$$E[y_3\,\mathbf{y}_2^T] = E[y_3\,\widehat{y_1,y_2}] = [R_{31},R_{32}]$$

$$E[\mathbf{y}_2\,\mathbf{y}_2^T] = E\left[\begin{pmatrix} y_1 \\ y_2 \end{pmatrix} \widehat{y_1,y_2}\right] = \begin{bmatrix} R_{11} & R_{12} \\ R_{21} & R_{22} \end{bmatrix}$$

Therefore, Eq. (1.5.20) becomes

$$\epsilon_1 = y_1$$

$$\epsilon_2 = y_2 - R_{21}\,R_{11}^{-1}\,y_1$$

$$\epsilon_3 = y_3 - [R_{31},R_{32}] \begin{bmatrix} R_{11} & R_{12} \\ R_{21} & R_{22} \end{bmatrix}^{-1} \begin{bmatrix} y_1 \\ y_2 \end{bmatrix}$$

Example 1.5.2: The random vector $\mathbf{y} = [y_1, y_2, y_3]^T$ has covariance matrix

$$R_{yy} = \begin{bmatrix} 1 & -1 & 1 \\ -1 & 3 & 3 \\ 1 & 3 & 12 \end{bmatrix}$$

Determine the innovations representation of $\mathbf{y}$ in two ways: using the Gram-Schmidt construction and using the results of Example 1.5.1.

Solution: Starting with $\epsilon_1 = y_1$, we find $E[y_2\epsilon_1] = R_{21} = -1$ and $E[\epsilon_1^2] = R_{11} = 1$. Therefore,

$$\epsilon_2 = y_2 - E[y_2\epsilon_1]E[\epsilon_1^2]^{-1}\,\epsilon_1 = y_2 + \epsilon_1 = y_2 + y_1$$

with a mean square value $E[\epsilon_2^2] = E[y_2^2] + 2E[y_2y_1] + E[y_1^2] = 3 - 2 + 1 = 2$. Similarly, we find $E[y_3\epsilon_1] = R_{31} = 1$ and

$$E[y_3\epsilon_2] = E[y_3(y_2 + y_1)] = R_{32} + R_{31} = 3 + 1 = 4$$

Thus,

$$\epsilon_3 = y_3 - E[y_3\epsilon_1]E[\epsilon_1^2]^{-1}\,\epsilon_1 - E[y_3\epsilon_2]E[\epsilon_2^2]^{-1}\,\epsilon_2 = y_3 - \epsilon_1 - 2\epsilon_2$$

or,

$$\epsilon_3 = y_3 - y_1 - 2(y_2 + y_1) = y_3 - 2y_2 - 3y_1$$

Solving for the ys and writing the answer in matrix form we have

$$\mathbf{y} = \begin{bmatrix} y_1 \\ y_2 \\ y_3 \end{bmatrix} = \begin{bmatrix} 1 & 0 & 0 \\ -1 & 1 & 0 \\ 1 & 2 & 1 \end{bmatrix} \begin{bmatrix} \epsilon_1 \\ \epsilon_2 \\ \epsilon_3 \end{bmatrix} = B\boldsymbol{\epsilon}$$

The last row determines $E[\epsilon_3^2]$. Using the mutual orthogonality of the ϵ_is, we have

$$E[y_3^2] = E[(\epsilon_3 + 2\epsilon_2 + \epsilon_1)^2] = E[\epsilon_3^2] + 4E[\epsilon_2^2] + E[\epsilon_1^2]$$

or, $12 = E[\epsilon_3^2] + 8 + 1$, which gives $E[\epsilon_3^2] = 3$. Using the results of Example 1.5.1, we have

$$\epsilon_3 = y_3 - [R_{31}, R_{32}] \begin{bmatrix} R_{11} & R_{12} \\ R_{21} & R_{22} \end{bmatrix}^{-1} \begin{bmatrix} y_1 \\ y_2 \end{bmatrix} = y_3 - [1, 3] \begin{bmatrix} 1 & -1 \\ -1 & 3 \end{bmatrix}^{-1} \begin{bmatrix} y_1 \\ y_2 \end{bmatrix}$$

The indicated matrix operations are computed easily and lead to the same expression for ϵ_3 found above.

The innovations representation Eq. (1.5.16) and the Cholesky factorization (1.5.17) are also very useful for the purpose of *simulating* a random vector having a prescribed covariance matrix. The procedure is as follows: given $R = E[\mathbf{y}\mathbf{y}^T]$, find its Cholesky factor B and the diagonal matrix $R_{\epsilon\epsilon}$; then, using any standard random number generator, generate M independent random numbers $\boldsymbol{\epsilon} = [\epsilon_1, \ldots, \epsilon_M]^T$ of mean zero and variances equal to the diagonal entries of $R_{\epsilon\epsilon}$, and perform the matrix operation $\mathbf{y} = B\boldsymbol{\epsilon}$ to obtain a realization of the random vector $\mathbf{y}$. Conversely, if a number of independent realizations of $\mathbf{y}$ are available, say, $\{\mathbf{y}_1, \mathbf{y}_2, \ldots, \mathbf{y}_N\}$, we may form an estimate of the covariance matrix by the following expression, referred to as the *sample covariance matrix*

$$\hat{R} = \frac{1}{N} \sum_{n=1}^{N} \mathbf{y}_n \mathbf{y}_n^T \tag{1.5.21}$$

Example 1.5.3: In typical array processing applications, a linear array of, say, M equally spaced sensors measures the incident radiation field. This field may consist of a number of plane waves incident from different angles on the array plus background noise. The objective is to determine the number, angles of arrival, and strengths of the incident plane waves from measurements of the field at the sensor elements. At each time instant, the M measurements at the M sensors may be assembled into the M-dimensional random vector $\mathbf{y}$, called an instantaneous *snapshot.* Thus, the correlation matrix $R = E[\mathbf{y}\mathbf{y}^T]$ measures the correlations that exist between sensors; that is, spatial correlations. In Chapter 6, we will consider methods of extracting the angle-of-arrival information from the covariance matrix R. Most of these methods require an estimate of the covariance matrix, which is typically given by Eq. (1.5.21) on the basis of N snapshots.

How good an estimate of R is $\hat{R}$? First, note that it is an *unbiased* estimate:

$$E[\hat{R}] = \frac{1}{N} \sum_{n=1}^{N} E[\mathbf{y}_n \mathbf{y}_n^T] = \frac{1}{N}(NR) = R$$

Second, we show that it is *consistent.* The correlation between the various matrix elements of $\hat{R}$ is obtained as follows:

$$E[\hat{R}_{ij}\hat{R}_{kl}] = \frac{1}{N^2}\sum_{n=1}^{N}\sum_{m=1}^{N} E[y_{ni}y_{nj}y_{mk}y_{ml}]$$

where y_{ni} is the ith component of the nth vector $\mathbf{y}_n$. To get a simple expression for the covariance of $\hat{R}$, we will assume that $\mathbf{y}_n$, $n = 1, 2, \ldots, N$ are independent zero-mean gaussian random vectors of covariance matrix R. This implies that [4,5]

$$E[y_{ni}y_{nj}y_{mk}y_{ml}] = R_{ij}R_{kl} + \delta_{nm}(R_{ik}R_{jl} + R_{il}R_{jk})$$

It follows that

$$E[\hat{R}_{ij}\hat{R}_{kl}] = R_{ij}R_{kl} + \frac{1}{N}(R_{ik}R_{jl} + R_{il}R_{jk}) \tag{1.5.22}$$

Writing $\Delta R = \hat{R} - E[\hat{R}] = \hat{R} - R$, we obtain for the covariance

$$E[\Delta R_{ij}\Delta R_{kl}] = \frac{1}{N}(R_{ik}R_{jl} + R_{il}R_{jk}) \tag{1.5.23}$$

Thus, $\hat{R}$ is a consistent estimator. The result, Eq. (1.5.23), is typical of the asymptotic results that are available in the statistical literature [4,5]. It will be used in Chapter 6 to obtain asymptotic results for linear prediction parameters and for the eigenstructure methods of spectrum estimation.

The sample covariance matrix Eq. (1.5.21) may also be written in an *adaptive,* or recursive form,

$$\hat{R}_N = \frac{1}{N}\sum_{n=1}^{N}\mathbf{y}_n\mathbf{y}_n^T = \frac{1}{N}\left[\sum_{n=1}^{N-1}\mathbf{y}_n\mathbf{y}_n^T + \mathbf{y}_N\mathbf{y}_N^T\right] = \frac{1}{N}\left[(N-1)\hat{R}_{N-1} + \mathbf{y}_N\mathbf{y}_N^T\right]$$

where we wrote $\hat{R}_N$ to explicitly indicate the dependence on N. A more intuitive way of writing this recursion is in the "predictor/corrector" form

$$\hat{R}_N = \hat{R}_{N-1} + \frac{1}{N}(\mathbf{y}_N\mathbf{y}_N^T - \hat{R}_{N-1}) \tag{1.5.24}$$

The term $\hat{R}_{N-1}$ may be thought of as a prediction of R based on $N-1$ observations, the Nth observation $\mathbf{y}_N\mathbf{y}_N^T$ may be thought of as an instantaneous estimate of R, and the term in the parenthesis as the prediction error that is used to correct the prediction. The routine **sampcov** (see Appendix B) takes as input the old matrix R_{N-1} and the new observation $\mathbf{y}_N$, and outputs the updated matrix R_N, overwriting the old one.

Example 1.5.4: Consider the 3×3 random vector $\mathbf{y}$ defined in Example 1.5.2. Using the innovations representation of $\mathbf{y}$, generate $N = 200$ independent vectors $\mathbf{y}_n$, $n = 1,2, \ldots, N$ and then compute the estimated sample covariance matrix Eq. (1.5.21) and compare it with the theoretical R. Compute the sample covariance matrix $\hat{R}$ recursively and plot its matrix elements as functions of the iteration number N.

Solution: Generate N independent 3-vectors $\boldsymbol{\epsilon}_n$, and compute $\mathbf{y}_n = B\boldsymbol{\epsilon}_n$. The estimated and theoretical covariance matrices are

$$\hat{R} = \begin{bmatrix} 0.995 & -1.090 & 0.880 \\ -1.090 & 3.102 & 2.858 \\ 0.880 & 2.858 & 11.457 \end{bmatrix}, \quad R = \begin{bmatrix} 1 & -1 & 1 \\ -1 & 3 & 3 \\ 1 & 3 & 12 \end{bmatrix}$$

Can we claim that this is a good estimate of R? Yes, because the deviations from R are consistent with the expected deviations given by Eq. (1.5.23). The standard deviation of the ijth matrix element is

$$\delta R_{ij} = \sqrt{E[\Delta R_{ij}^2]} = \sqrt{(R_{ii}R_{jj} + R_{ij}^2)/N}$$

The estimated values $\hat{R}_{ij}$ fall within the intervals $R_{ij} - \delta R_{ij} \le \hat{R}_{ij} \le R_{ij} + \delta R_{ij}$, as can be verified by inspecting the matrices

$$R - \delta R = \begin{bmatrix} 0.901 & -1.146 & 0.754 \\ -1.146 & 2.691 & 2.534 \\ 0.754 & 2.534 & 10.857 \end{bmatrix}, \quad R + \delta R = \begin{bmatrix} 1.099 & -0.854 & 1.246 \\ -0.854 & 3.309 & 3.466 \\ 1.246 & 3.466 & 13.143 \end{bmatrix}$$

The recursive computation Eq. (1.5.24), implemented by successive calls to the routine **sampcov,** is shown in Figure 1.3, where only the matrix elements R_{11}, R_{12}, and R_{22} are plotted versus N. Such graphs give us a better idea of how fast the sample estimate $\hat{R}_N$ converges to the theoretical R.

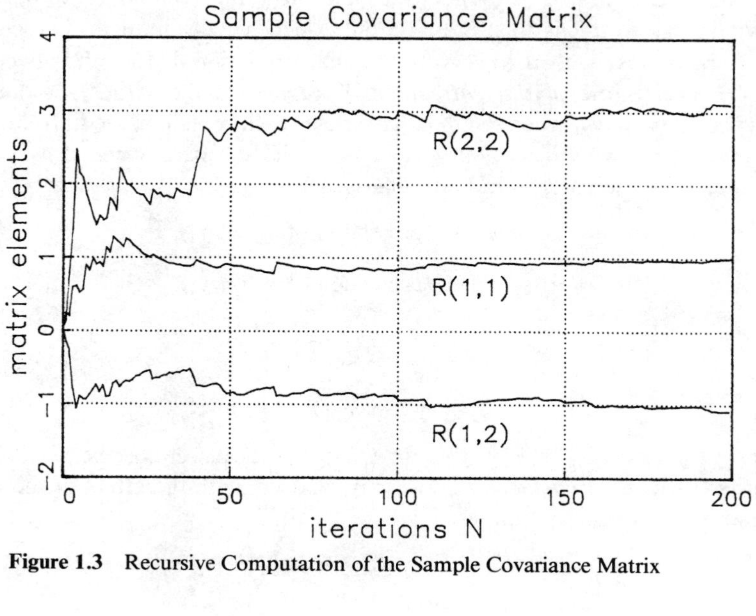

Figure 1.3 Recursive Computation of the Sample Covariance Matrix

1.6 *Partial Correlations*

A concept intimately connected to the Gram-Schmidt orthogonalization is that of the partial correlation. It plays a central role in linear prediction applications.

Consider the Gram-Schmidt orthogonalization of a random vector $\mathbf{y}$ in the form $\mathbf{y}=B\boldsymbol{\epsilon}$, where B is a unit lower-triangular matrix, and $\boldsymbol{\epsilon}$ is a vector of mutually uncorrelated components. Inverting, we have

$$\boldsymbol{\epsilon} = A\mathbf{y} \tag{1.6.1}$$

where $A = B^{-1}$. Now, suppose the vector $\mathbf{y}$ is arbitrarily subdivided into three subvectors as follows:

$$\mathbf{y} = \begin{bmatrix} \mathbf{y}_0 \\ \mathbf{y}_1 \\ \mathbf{y}_2 \end{bmatrix}$$

where $\mathbf{y}_0$, $\mathbf{y}_1$, $\mathbf{y}_2$ do not necessarily have the same dimension. Then, the matrix Eq. (1.6.1) may also be decomposed in a block-compatible form:

$$\begin{bmatrix} \boldsymbol{\epsilon}_0 \\ \boldsymbol{\epsilon}_1 \\ \boldsymbol{\epsilon}_2 \end{bmatrix} = \begin{bmatrix} A_{00} & 0 & 0 \\ A_{11} & A_{10} & 0 \\ A_{22} & A_{21} & A_{20} \end{bmatrix} \begin{bmatrix} \mathbf{y}_0 \\ \mathbf{y}_1 \\ \mathbf{y}_2 \end{bmatrix} \tag{1.6.2}$$

where A_{00}, A_{10}, A_{20} are *unit lower-triangular* matrices. Since $\mathbf{y}$ has components which are generally correlated with each other, it follows that $\mathbf{y}_0$ will be correlated with $\mathbf{y}_1$, and $\mathbf{y}_1$ will be correlated with $\mathbf{y}_2$. Thus, through the intermediate action of $\mathbf{y}_1$, the vector $\mathbf{y}_0$ will be indirectly coupled with the vector $\mathbf{y}_2$. The question we would like to ask is this: Suppose the effect of the intermediate vector $\mathbf{y}_1$ were to be removed, then what would be the correlation that is left between $\mathbf{y}_0$ and $\mathbf{y}_2$? This is the *partial correlation.* It represents the "true," or "direct" influence of $\mathbf{y}_0$ on $\mathbf{y}_2$, when the indirect influence via $\mathbf{y}_1$ is removed. To remove the effect of $\mathbf{y}_1$, we project both $\mathbf{y}_0$ and $\mathbf{y}_2$ on the subspace spanned by $\mathbf{y}_1$ and then subtract these parts from both; that is, let

$$\mathbf{e}_0 = \mathbf{y}_0 - (\text{projection of } \mathbf{y}_0 \text{ on } \mathbf{y}_1)$$

$$\mathbf{e}_2 = \mathbf{y}_2 - (\text{projection of } \mathbf{y}_2 \text{ on } \mathbf{y}_1)$$

or

$$\begin{aligned} \mathbf{e}_0 &= \mathbf{y}_0 - R_{01} R_{11}^{-1} \mathbf{y}_1 \\ \mathbf{e}_2 &= \mathbf{y}_2 - R_{21} R_{11}^{-1} \mathbf{y}_1 \end{aligned} \tag{1.6.3}$$

where we defined $R_{ij} = E[\mathbf{y}_i \mathbf{y}_j^T]$; for $i,j = 0,1,2$. We define the *partial correlation* (PARCOR) *coefficient* between $\mathbf{y}_0$ and $\mathbf{y}_2$, with the effect of the intermediate $\mathbf{y}_1$ removed, as follows:

$$\Gamma = E[\mathbf{e}_2 \mathbf{e}_0^T]\, E[\mathbf{e}_0 \mathbf{e}_0^T]^{-1} \tag{1.6.4}$$

Then, Γ may be expressed in terms of the entries of the matrix A as follows:

$$\Gamma = -A_{20}^{-1} A_{22} \tag{1.6.5}$$

To prove this result, we consider the last equation of (1.6.2):

$$\boldsymbol{\epsilon}_2 = A_{22}\,\mathbf{y}_0 + A_{21}\,\mathbf{y}_1 + A_{20}\,\mathbf{y}_2 \tag{1.6.6}$$

By construction, $\boldsymbol{\epsilon}_2$ is orthogonal to $\mathbf{y}_1$, so that $E[\boldsymbol{\epsilon}_2\,\mathbf{y}_1^T] = 0$. Thus we obtain the relationship:

$$\begin{aligned} E[\boldsymbol{\epsilon}_2\,\mathbf{y}_1^T] &= A_{22}\,E[\mathbf{y}_0\,\mathbf{y}_1^T] + A_{21}\,E[\mathbf{y}_1\,\mathbf{y}_1^T] + A_{20}\,E[\mathbf{y}_2\,\mathbf{y}_1^T] \\ &= A_{22}\,R_{01} + A_{21}\,R_{11} + A_{20}\,R_{21} = 0 \end{aligned} \tag{1.6.7}$$

Using Eqs. (1.6.3) and (1.6.7), we may express $\boldsymbol{\epsilon}_2$ in terms of $\mathbf{e}_0$ and $\mathbf{e}_2$, as follows:

$$\begin{aligned} \boldsymbol{\epsilon}_2 &= A_{22}\,(\mathbf{e}_0 + R_{01}\,R_{11}^{-1}\,\mathbf{y}_1) + A_{21}\,\mathbf{y}_1 + A_{20}\,(\mathbf{e}_2 + R_{21}\,R_{11}^{-1}\,\mathbf{y}_1) \\ &= A_{22}\,\mathbf{e}_0 + A_{20}\,\mathbf{e}_2 + (A_{22}\,R_{01} + A_{21}\,R_{11} + A_{20}\,R_{21})\,R_{11}^{-1}\,\mathbf{y}_1 \\ &= A_{22}\,\mathbf{e}_0 + A_{20}\,\mathbf{e}_2 \end{aligned} \tag{1.6.8}$$

Now, by construction, $\boldsymbol{\epsilon}_2$ is orthogonal to both $\mathbf{y}_0$ and $\mathbf{y}_1$, and hence also to $\mathbf{e}_0$; that is, $E[\boldsymbol{\epsilon}_2\,\mathbf{e}_0^T] = 0$. Using Eq. (1.6.8) we obtain

$$E[\boldsymbol{\epsilon}_2\,\mathbf{e}_0^T] = A_{22}\,E[\mathbf{e}_0\,\mathbf{e}_0^T] + A_{20}\,E[\mathbf{e}_2\,\mathbf{e}_0^T] = 0$$

from which Eq. (1.6.5) follows. It is interesting also to note that Eq. (1.6.8) may be written as

$$\boldsymbol{\epsilon}_2 = A_{20}\,\mathbf{e}$$

where $\mathbf{e} = \mathbf{e}_2 - \Gamma\,\mathbf{e}_0$ is the orthogonal complement of $\mathbf{e}_2$ relative to $\mathbf{e}_0$.

Example 1.6.1: An important special case of Eq. (1.6.5) is when $\mathbf{y}_0$ and $\mathbf{y}_2$ are selected as the first and last components of $\mathbf{y}$, and therefore $\mathbf{y}_1$ consists of *all the intermediate* components. For example, suppose $\mathbf{y} = [y_0, y_1, y_2, y_3, y_4]^T$. Then, the decomposition (1.6.2) can be written as follows:

$$\begin{bmatrix} \epsilon_0 \\ \hline \epsilon_1 \\ \epsilon_2 \\ \epsilon_3 \\ \hline \epsilon_4 \end{bmatrix} = \left[\begin{array}{c|ccc|c} 1 & 0 & 0 & 0 & 0 \\ \hline a_{11} & 1 & 0 & 0 & 0 \\ a_{22} & a_{21} & 1 & 0 & 0 \\ a_{33} & a_{32} & a_{31} & 1 & 0 \\ \hline a_{44} & a_{43} & a_{42} & a_{41} & 1 \end{array}\right] \begin{bmatrix} y_0 \\ \hline y_1 \\ y_2 \\ y_3 \\ \hline y_4 \end{bmatrix} \tag{1.6.9}$$

where $\mathbf{y}_0$, $\mathbf{y}_1$, and $\mathbf{y}_2$ are chosen as the vectors

$$\mathbf{y}_0 = [y_0], \qquad \mathbf{y}_1 = \begin{bmatrix} y_1 \\ y_2 \\ y_3 \end{bmatrix}, \qquad \mathbf{y}_2 = [y_4]$$

The matrices A_{20} and A_{22} are in this case the scalars $A_{20} = [1]$ and $A_{22} = [a_{44}]$. Therefore, the corresponding PARCOR coefficient (1.6.5) is

$$\Gamma = -a_{44}$$

Clearly, the first column $[1,a_{11},a_{22},a_{33},a_{44}]^T$ of A contains all the *lower order* PARCOR coefficients; that is, the quantity

$$\gamma_p = -a_{pp} \qquad p = 1,2,3, \ldots$$

represents the partial correlation coefficient between y_0 and y_p, with the effect of all the intermediate variables $y_1, y_2, \ldots, y_{p-1}$ removed.

We note the *backward* indexing of the entries of the matrix A in Eqs. (1.6.2) and (1.6.9). It corresponds to writing ϵ_n in a convolutional form

$$\begin{aligned}\epsilon_n &= \sum_{i=0}^{n} a_{ni} y_{n-i} = \sum_{i=0}^{n} a_{n,n-i} y_i \\ &= y_n + a_{n1} y_{n-1} + a_{n2} y_{n-2} + \cdots + a_{nn} y_0\end{aligned} \tag{1.6.10}$$

and conforms to standard notation in linear prediction applications. Comparing Eq. (1.6.10) with Eq. (1.5.13), we note that the projection of y_n onto the subspace Y_{n-1} may also be expressed directly in terms of the correlated basis $Y_{n-1} = \{y_0, y_1, \ldots, y_{n-1}\}$ as follows:

$$\hat{y}_{n/n-1} = -[a_{n1} y_{n-1} + a_{n2} y_{n-2} + \cdots + a_{nn} y_0] \tag{1.6.11}$$

An alternative expression was given in Eq. (1.5.19). Writing Eq. (1.6.10) in vector form, we have

$$\epsilon_n = [a_{nn}, \ldots, a_{n1}, 1]\begin{bmatrix} y_0 \\ \vdots \\ y_{n-1} \\ y_n \end{bmatrix} = [1, a_{n1}, \ldots, a_{nn}]\begin{bmatrix} y_n \\ y_{n-1} \\ \vdots \\ y_0 \end{bmatrix} \tag{1.6.12}$$

Thus, there are two possible definitions for the data vector **y** and corresponding weight vector **a**. According to the first definition—which is what we used in Eqs. (1.6.1) and (1.6.9)—the vector **y** is indexed from the lowest to the highest index and the vector **a** is indexed in the reverse way. According to the second definition, **y** and **a** are exactly the *reverse,* or upside-down, versions of the first definition; namely, **y** is indexed backward from high to low, whereas **a** is indexed forward. If we use the second definition and write Eq. (1.6.12) in matrix form, we obtain the *reverse* of Eq. (1.6.9); that is,

$$\boldsymbol{\epsilon}_{\text{rev}} \equiv \begin{bmatrix} \epsilon_4 \\ \epsilon_3 \\ \epsilon_2 \\ \epsilon_1 \\ \epsilon_0 \end{bmatrix} = \begin{bmatrix} 1 & a_{41} & a_{42} & a_{43} & a_{44} \\ 0 & 1 & a_{31} & a_{32} & a_{33} \\ 0 & 0 & 1 & a_{21} & a_{22} \\ 0 & 0 & 0 & 1 & a_{11} \\ 0 & 0 & 0 & 0 & 1 \end{bmatrix} \begin{bmatrix} y_4 \\ y_3 \\ y_2 \\ y_1 \\ y_0 \end{bmatrix} \equiv U\mathbf{y}_{\text{rev}} \quad (1.6.13)$$

Thus, the transformation between the correlated and decorrelated bases is now by means of a unit *upper* triangular matrix U. It corresponds to the UL (rather than LU) factorization of the covariance matrix of the reversed vector $\mathbf{y}_{\text{rev}}$. Writing $R_{\text{rev}} = E[\mathbf{y}_{\text{rev}}\mathbf{y}_{\text{rev}}^T]$ and $D_{\text{rev}} = E[\boldsymbol{\epsilon}_{\text{rev}}\boldsymbol{\epsilon}_{\text{rev}}^T]$, it follows from Eq. (1.6.13) that

$$D_{\text{rev}} = UR_{\text{rev}}U^T \quad (1.6.14)$$

The precise connection between the original basis and its reverse, and between their respective Cholesky factorizations, can be seen as follows. The operation of reversing a vector is equivalent to a linear transformation by the so-called *reversing* matrix J, consisting of ones along its antidiagonal and zeros everywhere else; for example, in the 5×5 case of Example 1.6.1,

$$J = \begin{bmatrix} 0 & 0 & 0 & 0 & 1 \\ 0 & 0 & 0 & 1 & 0 \\ 0 & 0 & 1 & 0 & 0 \\ 0 & 1 & 0 & 0 & 0 \\ 1 & 0 & 0 & 0 & 0 \end{bmatrix}$$

The reversed vectors will be $\mathbf{y}_{\text{rev}} = J\mathbf{y}$ and $\boldsymbol{\epsilon}_{\text{rev}} = J\boldsymbol{\epsilon}$. Using the property $J = J^T$, it follows that $R_{\text{rev}} = JR_{yy}J$ and $D_{\text{rev}} = JR_{\epsilon\epsilon}J$. Comparing Eq. (1.6.9) and Eq. (1.6.13) and using the property $J^2 = I$, we find,

$$\boldsymbol{\epsilon}_{\text{rev}} = J\boldsymbol{\epsilon} = JA\mathbf{y} = (JAJ)(J\mathbf{y}) = (JAJ)\mathbf{y}_{\text{rev}}$$

or,

$$U = JAJ \quad (1.6.15)$$

Note that J acting on a matrix from the left reverses each column, whereas acting from the right reverses each row. Thus, U is obtained from A by reversing all its columns and then all its rows. Regardless of the choice of the vector $\mathbf{y}$, the Gram-Schmidt construction proceeds from the lowest to the highest index of $\mathbf{y}$, and therefore, it can be interpreted as predicting the present from the past. But whether this process leads to LU or UL factorization depends on whether $\mathbf{y}$ or its reverse is used as the basis. Of course, the choice of basis does not affect the computation of linear estimates. As we saw in Eq. (1.5.18), linear estimates are invariant under *any* linear change of basis; in particular,

$$\hat{x} = E[x\mathbf{y}^T]E[\mathbf{y}\mathbf{y}^T]^{-1}\mathbf{y} = E[x\mathbf{y}_{\text{rev}}^T]E[\mathbf{y}_{\text{rev}}\mathbf{y}_{\text{rev}}^T]^{-1}\mathbf{y}_{\text{rev}}$$

In this book, we use both representations $\mathbf{y}$ and $\mathbf{y}_{\text{rev}}$, whichever is the most convenient depending on the context and the application. For example, in discussing the classical Wiener filtering problem and Kalman filtering in Chapter 4, we find the basis $\mathbf{y}$ more natural. On the other hand, the basis $\mathbf{y}_{\text{rev}}$ is more appropriate for discussing the lattice and direct-form realizations of FIR Wiener filters.

The ideas discussed in the last three sections are basic in the development of optimum signal processing algorithms, and will be pursued further in subsequent chapters. However, taking a brief look ahead, we point out how some of these concepts fit into the signal processing context:

1. The correlation canceling/orthogonal decompositions of Eqs. (1.4.1) and (1.5.10) form the basis of optimum Wiener and Kalman filtering.
2. The Gram-Schmidt process expressed by Eqs. (1.5.13) and (1.5.20) forms the basis of linear prediction and is also used in the development of the Kalman filter.
3. The representation $\mathbf{y} = B\boldsymbol{\epsilon}$ may be thought of as a signal model for synthesizing $\mathbf{y}$ by processing the uncorrelated (white noise) vector $\boldsymbol{\epsilon}$ through the linear filter B. The lower-triangular nature of B is equivalent to causality. Such signal models have a very broad range of applications, among which are speech synthesis and modern methods of spectrum estimation.
4. The inverse representation $\boldsymbol{\epsilon} = A\mathbf{y}$ of Eqs. (1.6.1) and (1.6.10) corresponds to the analysis filters of linear prediction. The PARCOR coefficients will turn out to be the reflection coefficients of the lattice filter realizations of linear prediction.
5. The Cholesky factorization (1.5.17) is the matrix analog of the spectral factorization theorem. It not only facilitates the solution of optimum Wiener filtering problems, but also the making of signal models of the type of Eq. (1.5.16).

1.7 *Forward/Backward Prediction and LU/UL Factorization*

The Gram-Schmidt orthogonalization procedure discussed in the previous sections was a *forward* procedure in the sense that the successive orthogonalization of the components of a random vector $\mathbf{y}$ proceeded forward from the first component to the last. It was given a linear prediction interpretation; that is, at each orthogonalization step, a prediction of the present component of $\mathbf{y}$ is made in terms of all the past ones.

The procedure was seen to be mathematically equivalent to the LU Cholesky factorization of the covariance matrix $R = [\mathbf{y}\mathbf{y}^T]$ (or, the UL factorization with respect to the reversed basis). We remarked in Section 1.5 (see also Problem 1.16) that if the Gram-Schmidt construction is started at the *other end* of the random vector $\mathbf{y}$ then the UL factorization of R is obtained (equivalently, the LU factorization in the reversed basis). In this section, we discuss in detail such *forward* and *backward* Gram-Schmidt constructions and their relationship to *forward* and *backward* linear prediction and to LU and UL Cholesky factorizations, and show how to realize linear estimators in the forward and backward orthogonal bases.

Our main objective is to gain further insight into the properties of the basis of observations $\mathbf{y}$ and to provide a preliminary introduction to a large number of concepts and methods that have become standard tools in modern signal processing practice; namely, Levinson's and Schur's algorithms; fast Cholesky factorizations; lattice filters for linear prediction; lattice realizations of FIR Wiener filters; and fast recursive least squares adaptive algorithms. Although these concepts are fully developed in Chapters 5 and 7, we would like to show, in this preliminary discussion, how far one can go toward these goals *without* making any assumptions about any structural properties of the covariance matrix R, such as Toeplitz and stationarity properties, or the so-called *shift-invariance* property of adaptive least squares problems.

Forward/Backward Normal Equations

Let $\mathbf{y} = [y_a, \ldots, y_b]^T$ be a random vector whose first and last components are y_a and y_b. Let $\hat{y}_b$ be the best linear estimate of y_b based on the *rest* of the vector $\mathbf{y}$; that is,

$$\hat{y}_b = E[y_b \bar{\mathbf{y}}^T] E[\bar{\mathbf{y}}\bar{\mathbf{y}}^T]^{-1} \bar{\mathbf{y}} \tag{1.7.1}$$

where $\bar{\mathbf{y}}$ is the upper part of $\mathbf{y}$; namely,

$$\mathbf{y} = \begin{bmatrix} y_a \\ \vdots \\ y_b \end{bmatrix} = \begin{bmatrix} \bar{\mathbf{y}} \\ y_b \end{bmatrix} \tag{1.7.2}$$

Similarly, let $\hat{y}_a$ be the best estimate of y_a based on the rest of $\mathbf{y}$; namely,

$$\hat{y}_a = E[y_a \tilde{\mathbf{y}}^T] E[\tilde{\mathbf{y}}\tilde{\mathbf{y}}^T]^{-1} \tilde{\mathbf{y}} \tag{1.7.3}$$

where $\tilde{\mathbf{y}}$ is the lower part of $\mathbf{y}$; that is,

$$\mathbf{y} = \begin{bmatrix} y_a \\ \vdots \\ y_b \end{bmatrix} = \begin{bmatrix} y_a \\ \tilde{\mathbf{y}} \end{bmatrix} \tag{1.7.4}$$

The decompositions (1.7.2) and (1.7.4) imply analogous decompositions of the covariance matrix $R = E[\mathbf{y}\mathbf{y}^T]$, as follows

$$R = \begin{bmatrix} \bar{R} & \mathbf{r}_b \\ \mathbf{r}_b^T & \rho_b \end{bmatrix} = \begin{bmatrix} \rho_a & \mathbf{r}_a^T \\ \mathbf{r}_a & \tilde{R} \end{bmatrix} \tag{1.7.5}$$

where

$$\begin{aligned} \tilde{R} &= E[\tilde{\mathbf{y}}\tilde{\mathbf{y}}^T], \quad \mathbf{r}_a = E[y_a \tilde{\mathbf{y}}], \quad \rho_a = E[y_a^2] \\ \bar{R} &= E[\bar{\mathbf{y}}\bar{\mathbf{y}}^T], \quad \mathbf{r}_b = E[y_b \bar{\mathbf{y}}], \quad \rho_b = E[y_b^2] \end{aligned} \tag{1.7.6}$$

We will refer to $\hat{y}_a$ and $\hat{y}_b$ as the *forward* and *backward* predictors, respectively. Since we have not yet introduced any notion of time in our discussion of random vectors, we will employ the terms forward and backward as convenient ways of referring to the above two estimates. In the present section, the basis **y** will be chosen according to the *reversed-basis* convention. As discussed in Section 1.6, LU becomes UL factorization in the reversed basis. By the same token, UL becomes LU factorization. Therefore, the term forward will be associated with UL and the term backward with LU factorization. The motivation for this choice of basis arises from the time series case, where the consistent usage of these two terms requires that **y** be *reverse-indexed* from high to low indices. For example, a typical choice of **y**, relevant in the context of Mth order FIR Wiener filtering problems, is

$$\mathbf{y} = \begin{bmatrix} y_n \\ y_{n-1} \\ \vdots \\ y_{n-M} \end{bmatrix}$$

where n represents the time index. Therefore, estimating the first element, y_n, from the rest of **y** will be equivalent to prediction, and estimating the last element, y_{n-M}, from the rest of **y** will be equivalent to postdiction.

Next, we introduce the forward and backward prediction coefficients by

$$\mathbf{a} = \begin{bmatrix} 1 \\ \boldsymbol{\alpha} \end{bmatrix}, \quad \mathbf{b} = \begin{bmatrix} \boldsymbol{\beta} \\ 1 \end{bmatrix}, \quad \text{where} \quad \boldsymbol{\alpha} = -\tilde{R}^{-1}\mathbf{r}_a, \quad \boldsymbol{\beta} = -\bar{R}^{-1}\mathbf{r}_b \tag{1.7.7}$$

In this notation, the predictors Eqs. (1.7.1) and (1.7.3) are written as

$$\hat{y}_a = -\boldsymbol{\alpha}^T\tilde{\mathbf{y}}, \quad \hat{y}_b = -\boldsymbol{\beta}^T\bar{\mathbf{y}} \tag{1.7.8}$$

The corresponding prediction errors are

$$e_a = y_a - \hat{y}_a = y_a + \boldsymbol{\alpha}^T\tilde{\mathbf{y}} = \mathbf{a}^T\mathbf{y}, \qquad e_b = y_b - \hat{y}_b = y_b + \boldsymbol{\beta}^T\bar{\mathbf{y}} = \mathbf{b}^T\mathbf{y} \tag{1.7.9}$$

with mean square values

$$E_a = E[e_a^2] = E[(\mathbf{a}^T\mathbf{y})(\mathbf{y}^T\mathbf{a})] = \mathbf{a}^T R\mathbf{a}$$
$$E_b = E[e_b^2] = E[(\mathbf{b}^T\mathbf{y})(\mathbf{y}^T\mathbf{b})] = \mathbf{b}^T R\mathbf{b} \tag{1.7.10}$$

Because the estimation errors are orthogonal to the observations that make up the estimates; that is, $E[e_b\bar{\mathbf{y}}] = 0$ and $E[e_a\tilde{\mathbf{y}}] = 0$, it follows that $E[\hat{y}_a e_a] = 0$ and $E[\hat{y}_b e_b] = 0$. Therefore, we can write $E[e_a^2] = E[y_a e_a]$ and $E[e_b^2] = E[y_b e_b]$. Thus, the *minimized* values of the prediction errors (1.7.10) can be written as

$$E_a = E[y_a e_a] = E[y_a(y_a + \boldsymbol{\alpha}^T\tilde{\mathbf{y}})] = \rho_a + \boldsymbol{\alpha}^T\mathbf{r}_a = \rho_a - \mathbf{r}_a^T\tilde{R}^{-1}\mathbf{r}_a$$
$$E_b = E[y_b e_b] = E[y_b(y_b + \boldsymbol{\beta}^T\bar{\mathbf{y}})] = \rho_b + \boldsymbol{\beta}^T\mathbf{r}_b = \rho_b - \mathbf{r}_b^T\bar{R}^{-1}\mathbf{r}_b \tag{1.7.11}$$

By construction, the mean square estimation errors are positive quantities. This also follows from the positivity of the covariance matrix R. With respect to the block decompositions (1.7.5), it is easily shown that a *necessary and sufficient* condition for R to be positive definite is that $\bar{R}$ be positive definite and $\rho_b - \mathbf{r}_b^T\bar{R}^{-1}\mathbf{r}_b > 0$; alternatively, that $\tilde{R}$ be positive definite and $\rho_a - \mathbf{r}_a^T\tilde{R}^{-1}\mathbf{r}_a > 0$.

Equations (1.7.7) and (1.7.11) may be combined now into the more compact forms, referred to as the forward and backward *normal equations* of linear prediction,

$$R\mathbf{a} = E_a\mathbf{u}, \quad R\mathbf{b} = E_b\mathbf{v}, \quad \text{where} \quad \mathbf{u} = \begin{bmatrix} 1 \\ \mathbf{0} \end{bmatrix}, \quad \mathbf{v} = \begin{bmatrix} \mathbf{0} \\ 1 \end{bmatrix} \tag{1.7.12}$$

For example,

$$R\mathbf{b} = \begin{bmatrix} \bar{R} & \mathbf{r}_b \\ \mathbf{r}_b^T & \rho_b \end{bmatrix} \begin{bmatrix} \boldsymbol{\beta} \\ 1 \end{bmatrix} = \begin{bmatrix} \bar{R}\boldsymbol{\beta} + \mathbf{r}_b \\ \mathbf{r}_b^T\boldsymbol{\beta} + \rho_b \end{bmatrix} = \begin{bmatrix} \mathbf{0} \\ E_b \end{bmatrix} = E_b\mathbf{v}$$

and similarly,

$$R\mathbf{a} = \begin{bmatrix} \rho_a & \mathbf{r}_a^T \\ \mathbf{r}_a & \tilde{R} \end{bmatrix} \begin{bmatrix} 1 \\ \boldsymbol{\alpha} \end{bmatrix} = \begin{bmatrix} \rho_a + \mathbf{r}_a^T\boldsymbol{\alpha} \\ \mathbf{r}_a + \tilde{R}\boldsymbol{\alpha} \end{bmatrix} = \begin{bmatrix} E_a \\ \mathbf{0} \end{bmatrix} = E_a\mathbf{u}.$$

Backward Prediction and LU Factorization

Next, we discuss the connection of the forward and backward predictors to the Gram-Schmidt procedure and to the Cholesky factorizations of the covariance matrix R. Consider an *arbitrary* unit lower triangular matrix $\bar{L}$ of the same dimension as $\bar{R}$ and form the larger unit lower triangular matrix whose bottom row is $\mathbf{b}^T = [\boldsymbol{\beta}^T, 1]$

$$L = \begin{bmatrix} \bar{L} & \mathbf{0} \\ \boldsymbol{\beta}^T & 1 \end{bmatrix} \tag{1.7.13}$$

Then, it follows from Eq. (1.7.12) that

$$LRL^T = \begin{bmatrix} \bar{L}\bar{R}\bar{L}^T & \mathbf{0} \\ \mathbf{0}^T & E_b \end{bmatrix} \tag{1.7.14}$$

Indeed, we have

$$LRL^T = \begin{bmatrix} \bar{L} & \mathbf{0} \\ \boldsymbol{\beta}^T & 1 \end{bmatrix} \begin{bmatrix} \bar{R} & \mathbf{r}_b \\ \mathbf{r}_b^T & \rho_b \end{bmatrix} L^T = \begin{bmatrix} \bar{L}\bar{R} & \bar{L}\mathbf{r}_b \\ \boldsymbol{\beta}^T\bar{R} + \mathbf{r}_b^T & \boldsymbol{\beta}^T\mathbf{r}_b + \rho_b \end{bmatrix} L^T = \begin{bmatrix} \bar{L}\bar{R} & \bar{L}\mathbf{r}_b \\ \mathbf{0}^T & E_b \end{bmatrix} L^T$$

$$= \begin{bmatrix} \bar{L}\bar{R}\bar{L}^T & \bar{L}\mathbf{r}_b + \bar{L}\bar{R}\boldsymbol{\beta} \\ \mathbf{0}^T & E_b \end{bmatrix} = \begin{bmatrix} \bar{L}\bar{R}\bar{L}^T & \mathbf{0} \\ \mathbf{0}^T & E_b \end{bmatrix}$$

Defining the transformed random vector $\mathbf{e}_b = L\mathbf{y}$ we have

$$\mathbf{e}_b = L\mathbf{y} = \begin{bmatrix} \bar{L} & \mathbf{0} \\ \boldsymbol{\beta}^T & 1 \end{bmatrix} \begin{bmatrix} \bar{\mathbf{y}} \\ y_b \end{bmatrix} = \begin{bmatrix} \bar{L}\bar{\mathbf{y}} \\ \boldsymbol{\beta}^T\bar{\mathbf{y}} + y_b \end{bmatrix} = \begin{bmatrix} \bar{\mathbf{e}}_b \\ e_b \end{bmatrix} \tag{1.7.15}$$

where $\bar{\mathbf{e}}_b = \bar{L}\bar{\mathbf{y}}$. It follows that LRL^T is the covariance matrix of the transformed vector $\mathbf{e}_b$; $E[\mathbf{e}_b\mathbf{e}_b^T] = E[L\mathbf{y}\mathbf{y}^TL^T] = LRL^T$. The significance of Eq. (1.7.14) is that by replacing the $\mathbf{y}$ basis by $\mathbf{e}_b$ we have achieved partial decorrelation of the random vector $\mathbf{y}$. The new basis $\mathbf{e}_b$ is better to work with because it contains less redundancy than $\mathbf{y}$. For example, choosing $\bar{L}$ to be the identity matrix, $\bar{L} = \bar{I}$, Eqs. (1.7.14) and (1.7.15) become

$$LRL^T = \begin{bmatrix} \bar{R} & \mathbf{0} \\ \mathbf{0}^T & E_b \end{bmatrix}, \quad \mathbf{e}_b = \begin{bmatrix} \bar{\mathbf{y}} \\ e_b \end{bmatrix} \tag{1.7.16}$$

This represents the direct sum decomposition of the subspace spanned by $\mathbf{y}$ into the subspace spanned by $\bar{\mathbf{y}}$ and an orthogonal part spanned by e_b; that is,

$$\{\mathbf{y}\} = \{\bar{\mathbf{y}}, y_b\} = \{\bar{\mathbf{y}}\} \oplus \{e_b\}$$

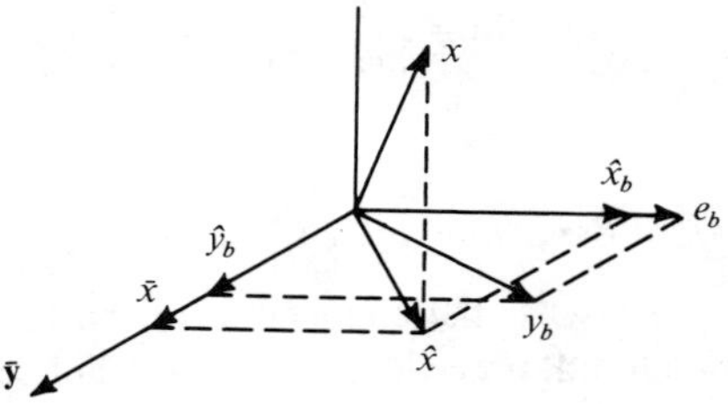

The advantage of the new basis may be appreciated by considering the estimation of a random variable x in terms of $\mathbf{y}$. The estimate $\hat{x}$ may be expressed either in the $\mathbf{y}$ basis, or in the new basis $\mathbf{e}_b$ by

$$\hat{x} = E[x\mathbf{y}^T]E[\mathbf{y}\mathbf{y}^T]^{-1}\mathbf{y} = E[x\mathbf{e}_b^T]E[\mathbf{e}_b\mathbf{e}_b^T]^{-1}\mathbf{e}_b$$

Using the orthogonality between $\bar{\mathbf{y}}$ and e_b, or the block-diagonal property of the covariance matrix of $\mathbf{e}_b$ given by Eq. (1.7.16), we find

$$\hat{x} = E[x(\bar{\mathbf{y}}^T, e_b)]\begin{bmatrix} \bar{R}^{-1} & \mathbf{0} \\ \mathbf{0}^T & E_b^{-1} \end{bmatrix}\begin{bmatrix} \bar{\mathbf{y}} \\ e_b \end{bmatrix} = E[x\bar{\mathbf{y}}^T]E[\bar{\mathbf{y}}\bar{\mathbf{y}}^T]^{-1}\bar{\mathbf{y}} + E[xe_b]E[e_b^2]^{-1}e_b$$

The two terms in $\hat{x}$ are recognized as the estimates of x based on the two orthogonal parts of the $\mathbf{y}$ basis. The first term still requires the computation of a matrix inverse; namely, $\bar{R}^{-1} = E[\bar{\mathbf{y}}\bar{\mathbf{y}}^T]^{-1}$, but the order of the matrix is *reduced* by one as compared with the original covariance matrix R. The same order-reduction procedure can now be applied to $\bar{R}$ itself, thereby reducing *its* order by one. And so on, by repeating the order-reduction procedure the original matrix R can be completely diagonalized. This process is equivalent to performing Gram-Schmidt orthogonalization on $\mathbf{y}$, starting with y_a and ending with y_b. It is also equivalent to choosing $\bar{L}$ to correspond to the LU Cholesky factorization of $\bar{R}$. Then, the matrix L will correspond to the LU factorization of R. Indeed, if $\bar{L}$ is such that $\bar{L}\bar{R}\bar{L}^T = \bar{D}_b$; that is, a diagonal matrix, then

$$LRL^T = \begin{bmatrix} \bar{L}\bar{R}\bar{L}^T & \mathbf{0} \\ \mathbf{0}^T & E_b \end{bmatrix} = \begin{bmatrix} \bar{D}_b & \mathbf{0} \\ \mathbf{0}^T & E_b \end{bmatrix} = D_b \tag{1.7.17}$$

will itself be diagonal. The basis $\mathbf{e}_b = L\mathbf{y}$ will be completely decorrelated, having diagonal covariance matrix $E[\mathbf{e}_b\mathbf{e}_b^T] = D_b$. Thus, by successively solving backward prediction problems of lower and lower order we eventually orthogonalize the original basis $\mathbf{y}$ and obtain the LU factorization of its covariance matrix. By construction, the bottom row of L is the backward predictor $\mathbf{b}^T$. Similarly, the bottom row of $\bar{L}$ will be the backward predictor of order one less, and so on. In other words, the *rows* of L are simply the *backward predictors* of successive orders. The overall construction of L is illustrated by the following example.

Example 1.7.1: The random vector $\mathbf{y} = \begin{bmatrix} y_a \\ y_c \\ y_b \end{bmatrix}$ has covariance matrix $R = \begin{bmatrix} 1 & 1 & 0 \\ 1 & 3 & 2 \\ 0 & 2 & 3 \end{bmatrix}$. By successively solving backward prediction problems of lower and lower order construct the LU factorization of R.

Solution: The backward prediction coefficients for predicting y_b are given by Eq. (1.7.7):

$$\boldsymbol{\beta} = -\bar{R}^{-1}\mathbf{r}_b = -\begin{bmatrix} 1 & 1 \\ 1 & 3 \end{bmatrix}^{-1}\begin{bmatrix} 0 \\ 2 \end{bmatrix} = -\frac{1}{2}\begin{bmatrix} 3 & -1 \\ -1 & 1 \end{bmatrix}\begin{bmatrix} 0 \\ 2 \end{bmatrix} = \begin{bmatrix} 1 \\ -1 \end{bmatrix}$$

Thus, $\mathbf{b}^T = [\boldsymbol{\beta}^T, 1] = [1, -1, 1]$. The estimation error is given by Eq. (1.7.11):

$$E_b = \rho_b + \boldsymbol{\beta}^T \mathbf{r}_b = 3 + [1, -1]\begin{bmatrix} 0 \\ 2 \end{bmatrix} = 1$$

Repeating the procedure on $\bar{R} = \begin{bmatrix} 1 & 1 \\ 1 & 3 \end{bmatrix}$, we find for the corresponding backward prediction coefficients, satisfying $\bar{R}\bar{\mathbf{b}} = \bar{E}_b \bar{\mathbf{v}}$, $\bar{\mathbf{v}} = \begin{bmatrix} 0 \\ 1 \end{bmatrix}$

$$\bar{\boldsymbol{\beta}} = -[1]^{-1}[1] = [-1], \quad \bar{\mathbf{b}}^T = [\bar{\boldsymbol{\beta}}^T, 1] = [-1, 1]$$

and $\bar{E}_b = \bar{\rho}_b + \bar{\boldsymbol{\beta}}^T \bar{\mathbf{r}}_b = 3 - 1 \times 1 = 2$. The rows of L are the backward predictor coefficients, and the diagonal entries of D_b are the E_bs. Thus,

$$L = \begin{bmatrix} 1 & 0 & 0 \\ -1 & 1 & 0 \\ 1 & -1 & 1 \end{bmatrix}, \quad D_b = \begin{bmatrix} 1 & 0 & 0 \\ 0 & 2 & 0 \\ 0 & 0 & 1 \end{bmatrix}$$

It is easily verified that $LRL^T = D_b$. Note that the first entry of D_b is always equal to ρ_a. Next, we obtain the same results by carrying out the Gram-Schmidt construction starting at y_a and ending with y_b. Starting with $\epsilon_1 = y_a$ and $E[\epsilon_1^2] = 1$, define

$$\epsilon_2 = y_c - E[y_c \epsilon_1] E[\epsilon_1^2]^{-1} \epsilon_1 = y_c - y_a$$

having $E[\epsilon_2^2] = E[y_a^2] + E[y_c^2] - 2E[y_a y_c] = 2$. Thus, the $\bar{\mathbf{e}}_b$ portion of the Gram-Schmidt construction will be

$$\bar{\mathbf{e}}_b = \begin{bmatrix} \epsilon_1 \\ \epsilon_2 \end{bmatrix} = \begin{bmatrix} 1 & 0 \\ -1 & 1 \end{bmatrix} \begin{bmatrix} y_a \\ y_c \end{bmatrix} = \bar{L}\bar{\mathbf{y}}$$

The last step of the Gram-Schmidt construction is

$$e_b = y_b - E[y_b \epsilon_1] E[\epsilon_1^2]^{-1} \epsilon_1 - E[y_b \epsilon_2] E[\epsilon_2^2]^{-1} \epsilon_2 = y_b - (y_c - y_a) = y_a - y_c + y_b$$

giving for the last row of L, $\mathbf{b}^T = [1, -1, 1]$. In the above step, we used

$$E[y_b \epsilon_2] = E[y_b(y_c - y_a)] = E[y_b y_c] - E[y_b y_a] = 2 - 0 = 2.$$

Linear Estimation in the Backward Basis

Equation (1.7.17) may be written in the form

$$R = L^{-1} D_b L^{-T} \tag{1.7.18}$$

where L^{-T} is the inverse of the transpose of L. Thus, L^{-1} and L^{-T} correspond to the conventional LU Cholesky factors of R. The computational advantage of this form becomes immediately obvious when we consider the inverse of R,

$$R^{-1} = L^T D_b^{-1} L \tag{1.7.19}$$

which shows that R^{-1} can be computed *without* any matrix inversion (the inverse of the diagonal matrix D_b is trivial). The design of linear estimators is simplified considerably in the $\mathbf{e}_b$ basis. The estimate of x is

$$\hat{x} = \mathbf{h}^T\mathbf{y} \tag{1.7.20}$$

where $\mathbf{h} = E[\mathbf{y}\mathbf{y}^T]^{-1}E[x\mathbf{y}] \equiv R^{-1}\mathbf{r}$. Writing $\mathbf{y} = L^{-1}\mathbf{e}_b$ and defining a new vector of estimation weights by $\mathbf{g} = L^{-T}\mathbf{h}$, we can rewrite Eq. (1.7.20) as

$$\hat{x} = \mathbf{h}^T\mathbf{y} = \mathbf{h}^T L^{-1}\mathbf{e}_b = \mathbf{g}^T\mathbf{e}_b \tag{1.7.21}$$

The block diagram representations of the two realizations are shown below:

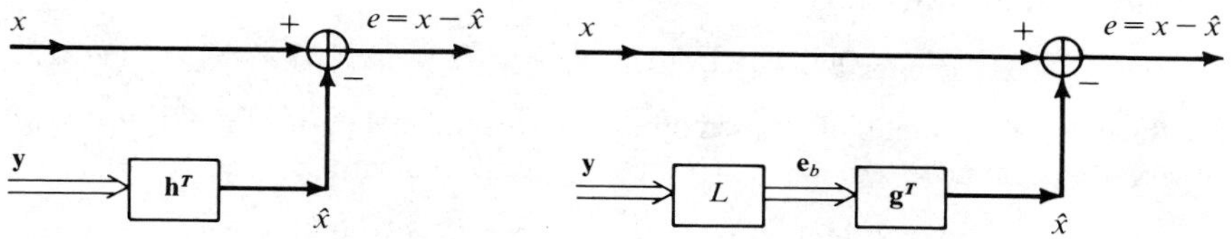

There are three major advantages of the representation of Eq. (1.7.21) over Eq. (1.7.20). First, to get the estimate $\hat{x}$ using Eq. (1.7.20), the processor has to linearly combine a lot of *redundant* information because the $\mathbf{y}$ basis is correlated, whereas the processor Eq. (1.7.21) linearly combines only the *nonredundant* part of the same information. This has important implications for the adaptive implementations of such processors. An adaptive processor that uses the representation Eq. (1.7.20) will tend to be slow in *learning* the statistics of the data vector $\mathbf{y}$ because it has to process all the redundancies in the data. Moreover, the more the redundancies, or equivalently, the higher the correlations in the data $\mathbf{y}$, the slower the speed of adaptation. On the other hand, an adaptive processor based on Eq. (1.7.21) should adapt very quickly. The preprocessing operation, $\mathbf{e}_b = L\mathbf{y}$, that decorrelates the data vector $\mathbf{y}$ can also be implemented adaptively. In time series applications, it is conveniently realized by means of a *lattice structure.* In adaptive array applications, it gives rise to the so-called *Gram-Schmidt preprocessor* implementations.

Second, the computation of $\mathbf{g}$ can be done efficiently without any matrix inversion. Given the LU factors of R as in Eq. (1.7.19) and the cross correlation vector $\mathbf{r}$, we may compute $\mathbf{g}$ by

$$\mathbf{g} = L^{-T}\mathbf{h} = L^{-T}R^{-1}\mathbf{r} = L^{-T}(L^T D_b^{-1} L)\mathbf{r} = D_b^{-1}L\mathbf{r} \tag{1.7.22}$$

If so desired, the original weights $\mathbf{h}$ may be recovered from $\mathbf{g}$ by

$$\mathbf{h} = L^T\mathbf{g} \tag{1.7.23}$$

The third advantage of the form Eq. (1.7.21) is that any lower-order portion of the weight vector $\mathbf{g}$ is already *optimal* for that order. Thus, the order of the estimator can be increased without having to redesign the lower-order portions of it. Recognizing that $L\mathbf{r} = LE[x\mathbf{y}] = E[x\mathbf{e}_b]$, we write Eq. (1.7.22) as

$$\mathbf{g} = D_b^{-1} E[x\mathbf{e}_b] = \begin{bmatrix} \bar{D}_b^{-1} E[x\bar{\mathbf{e}}_b] \\ E_b^{-1} E[xe_b] \end{bmatrix} \equiv \begin{bmatrix} \bar{\mathbf{g}} \\ g \end{bmatrix}$$

where we used the diagonal nature of D_b given in Eq. (1.7.17) and the decomposition Eq. (1.7.15). The estimate Eq. (1.7.21) can be written as

$$\hat{x} = \mathbf{g}^T\mathbf{e}_b = [\bar{\mathbf{g}}^T, g]\begin{bmatrix} \bar{\mathbf{e}}_b \\ e_b \end{bmatrix} = \bar{\mathbf{g}}^T\bar{\mathbf{e}}_b + ge_b \equiv \bar{x} + \hat{x}_b \tag{1.7.24}$$

It is clear that the two terms

$$\bar{x} = \bar{\mathbf{g}}^T\bar{\mathbf{e}}_b = E[x\bar{\mathbf{e}}_b^T]\bar{D}_b^{-1}\bar{\mathbf{e}}_b\,, \quad \hat{x}_b = ge_b = E[xe_b]E_b^{-1}e_b \tag{1.7.25}$$

are the optimal estimates of x based on the two orthogonal parts of the subspace of observations; namely,

$$\{\mathbf{y}\} = \{\bar{\mathbf{y}}\} \oplus \{e_b\}\,, \quad \text{or,} \quad \{\mathbf{e}_b\} = \{\bar{\mathbf{e}}_b\} \oplus \{e_b\}$$

The first term, $\bar{x}$, is the same estimate of x based on $\bar{\mathbf{y}}$ that we considered earlier but now it is expressed in the diagonal basis $\bar{\mathbf{e}}_b = \bar{L}\bar{\mathbf{y}}$. The second term, $\hat{x}_b$, represents the *improvement* in the estimate that arises by taking into account one more observation; namely, y_b. It represents that part of x that cannot be estimated from $\bar{\mathbf{y}}$. And, it is computable only from that part of the new observation y_b that *cannot* be predicted from $\bar{\mathbf{y}}$; that is, e_b. The degree of improvement of $\hat{x}$ over $\bar{x}$, as measured by the mean square estimation errors, can be computed explicitly in this basis. To see this, denote the estimation errors based on $\mathbf{y}$ and $\bar{\mathbf{y}}$ by

$$e = x - \hat{x} = x - \mathbf{g}^T\mathbf{e}_b\,, \quad \bar{e} = x - \bar{x} = x - \bar{\mathbf{g}}^T\bar{\mathbf{e}}_b$$

Then, Eq. (1.7.24) implies $e = x - \hat{x} = (x - \bar{x}) - \hat{x}_b$, or

$$e = \bar{e} - ge_b \tag{1.7.26}$$

Because e and $\mathbf{y}$, or $\mathbf{e}_b$, are orthogonal, we have $E[\hat{x}e] = 0$, which implies that

$$\mathcal{E} = E[e^2] = E[xe] = E[x(x - \mathbf{g}^T\mathbf{e}_b)] = E[x^2] - \mathbf{g}^T E[x\mathbf{e}_b]$$

Similarly, $\bar{\mathcal{E}} = E[\bar{e}^2] = E[x^2] - \bar{\mathbf{g}}^T E[x\bar{\mathbf{e}}_b]$. It follows that

$$\mathcal{E} = \bar{\mathcal{E}} - gE[xe_b] = \bar{\mathcal{E}} - g^2E_b \tag{1.7.27}$$

where we used $g = E[xe_b]E_b^{-1}$. The subtracted term represents the improvement obtained by including one more observation in the estimate. It follows from the above discussion that the lower-order portion $\bar{\mathbf{g}}$ of $\mathbf{g}$ is already optimal. This is not so in the $\mathbf{y}$ basis; that is, the lower-order portion of $\mathbf{h}$ is not equal to the lower-order optimal weights $\bar{\mathbf{h}} = \bar{R}^{-1}\bar{\mathbf{r}}$, where $\bar{\mathbf{r}} = E[x\bar{\mathbf{y}}]$. The explicit relationship between the two may be found as follows. Inserting the block decomposition Eq. (1.7.13) of L into

Eq. (1.7.19) and using the lower-order result $\bar{R}^{-1} = \bar{L}^T\bar{D}_b^{-1}\bar{L}$, we may derive the following order-updating expression for R^{-1}

$$R^{-1} = \begin{bmatrix} \bar{R}^{-1} & \mathbf{0} \\ \mathbf{0}^T & 0 \end{bmatrix} + \frac{1}{E_b}\mathbf{b}\mathbf{b}^T \tag{1.7.28}$$

Noting that $\bar{\mathbf{r}}$ is the lower-order part of $\mathbf{r}$; $\mathbf{r} = [\bar{\mathbf{r}}^T, r_b]^T$, where $r_b = E[xy_b]$, we obtain the following order-updating equation for the optimal $\mathbf{h}$

$$\mathbf{h} = R^{-1}\mathbf{r} = \begin{bmatrix} \bar{R}^{-1} & \mathbf{0} \\ \mathbf{0}^T & 0 \end{bmatrix}\begin{bmatrix} \bar{\mathbf{r}} \\ r_b \end{bmatrix} + \frac{1}{E_b}(\mathbf{b}^T\mathbf{r})\mathbf{b} = \begin{bmatrix} \bar{\mathbf{h}} \\ 0 \end{bmatrix} + c_b\mathbf{b} \tag{1.7.29}$$

where $c_b = (\mathbf{b}^T\mathbf{r})/E_b = (\boldsymbol{\beta}^T\bar{\mathbf{r}} + r_b)/E_b$. A block diagram realization that takes into account the order-recursive construction of the estimate Eq. (1.7.24) and estimation error Eq. (1.7.26) is shown below.

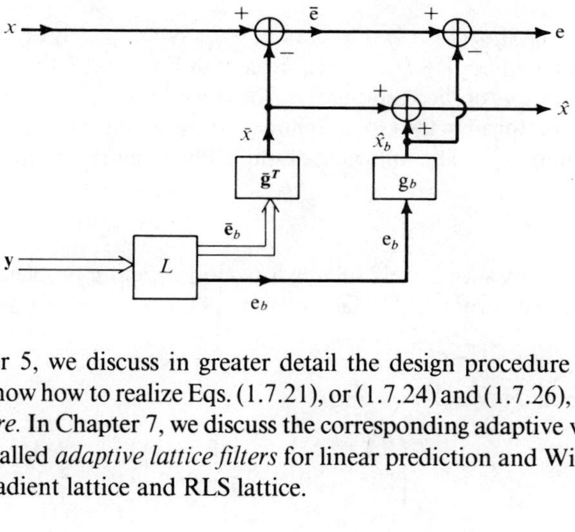

In Chapter 5, we discuss in greater detail the design procedure given by Eq. (1.7.22) and show how to realize Eqs. (1.7.21), or (1.7.24) and (1.7.26), by means of a *lattice structure.* In Chapter 7, we discuss the corresponding adaptive versions, leading to the so-called *adaptive lattice filters* for linear prediction and Wiener filtering, such as the gradient lattice and RLS lattice.

Forward Prediction and UL Factorization

Next, we turn our attention to the forward predictors defined in Eq. (1.7.12). They lead to UL (rather than LU) factorization of the covariance matrix. Considering an arbitrary unit upper triangular matrix $\tilde{U}$ of the same dimension as $\tilde{R}$, we may form the larger unit upper triangular matrix whose top row is the forward predictor $\mathbf{a}^T = [1, \boldsymbol{\alpha}^T]$

$$U = \begin{bmatrix} 1 & \boldsymbol{\alpha}^T \\ \mathbf{0} & \tilde{U} \end{bmatrix} \tag{1.7.30}$$

Then, it follows from Eq. (1.7.12) that

$$URU^T = \begin{bmatrix} E_a & \mathbf{0}^T \\ \mathbf{0} & \tilde{U}\tilde{R}\tilde{U}^T \end{bmatrix} \tag{1.7.31}$$

It follows that URU^T is the covariance matrix of the transformed vector

$$\mathbf{e}_a = U\mathbf{y} = \begin{bmatrix} 1 & \boldsymbol{\alpha}^T \\ \mathbf{0} & \tilde{U} \end{bmatrix} \begin{bmatrix} y_a \\ \tilde{\mathbf{y}} \end{bmatrix} = \begin{bmatrix} y_a + \boldsymbol{\alpha}^T\tilde{\mathbf{y}} \\ \tilde{U}\tilde{\mathbf{y}} \end{bmatrix} = \begin{bmatrix} e_a \\ \tilde{\mathbf{e}}_a \end{bmatrix} \tag{1.7.32}$$

Choosing $\tilde{U}$ to correspond to the UL factor of $\tilde{R}$: that is, $\tilde{U}\tilde{R}\tilde{U}^T = \tilde{D}_a$, where $\tilde{D}_a$ is diagonal, then Eq. (1.7.31) implies that U will correspond to the UL factor of R:

$$URU^T = \begin{bmatrix} E_a & \mathbf{0}^T \\ \mathbf{0} & \tilde{D}_a \end{bmatrix} = D_a \tag{1.7.33}$$

This is equivalent to Eq. (1.6.14). The basis $\mathbf{e}_a = U\mathbf{y}$ is completely decorrelated, with covariance matrix $E[\mathbf{e}_a\mathbf{e}_a^T] = D_a$. It is equivalent to Eq. (1.6.13). The *rows* of U are the forward predictors of successive orders. And therefore, the UL factorization of R is equivalent to performing the Gram-Schmidt construction starting at the endpoint y_b and proceeding to y_a. The following example illustrates the method.

Example 1.7.2: By successively solving forward prediction problems of lower and lower order, construct the UL factorization of the covariance matrix R of Example 1.7.1.

Solution: Using Eq. (1.7.7) we find

$$\boldsymbol{\alpha} = -\tilde{R}^{-1}\mathbf{r}_a = -\begin{bmatrix} 3 & 2 \\ 2 & 3 \end{bmatrix}^{-1} \begin{bmatrix} 1 \\ 0 \end{bmatrix} = -\frac{1}{5}\begin{bmatrix} 3 & -2 \\ -2 & 3 \end{bmatrix}\begin{bmatrix} 1 \\ 0 \end{bmatrix} = \begin{bmatrix} -3/5 \\ 2/5 \end{bmatrix}$$

Thus, $\mathbf{a}^T = [1, \boldsymbol{\alpha}^T] = [1, -3/5, 2/5]$. The estimation error is

$$E_a = \rho_a + \boldsymbol{\alpha}^T\mathbf{r}_a = 1 + [-3/5,\ 2/5]\begin{bmatrix} 1 \\ 0 \end{bmatrix} = 2/5$$

Repeating the procedure on $\tilde{R} = \begin{bmatrix} 3 & 2 \\ 2 & 3 \end{bmatrix}$, we find the corresponding forward prediction coefficients, satisfying $\tilde{R}\tilde{\mathbf{a}} = \tilde{E}_a\tilde{\mathbf{u}}$, $\tilde{\mathbf{u}} = \begin{bmatrix} 1 \\ 0 \end{bmatrix}$,

$$\tilde{\boldsymbol{\alpha}} = -[3]^{-1}[2] = [-2/3]\,, \quad \tilde{\mathbf{a}}^T = [1,\ \tilde{\boldsymbol{\alpha}}^T] = [1,\ -2/3]$$

and $\tilde{E}_a = \tilde{\rho}_a + \tilde{\boldsymbol{\alpha}}^T \tilde{\mathbf{r}}_a = 3 - (2/3) \times 2 = 5/3$. The rows of U are the forward predictor coefficients and the diagonal entries of D_a are the E_as:

$$U = \begin{bmatrix} 1 & -3/5 & 2/5 \\ 0 & 1 & -2/3 \\ 0 & 0 & 1 \end{bmatrix}, \quad D_a = \begin{bmatrix} 2/5 & 0 & 0 \\ 0 & 5/3 & 0 \\ 0 & 0 & 3 \end{bmatrix}$$

It is easily verified that $URU^T = D_a$. Note that the last entry of D_a is always equal to ρ_b.

Equation (1.7.33) can be used to compute the inverse of R:

$$R^{-1} = U^T D_a^{-1} U \tag{1.7.34}$$

Using the lower-order result $\tilde{R}^{-1} = \tilde{U}^T \tilde{D}_a^{-1} \tilde{U}$ and the decomposition Eq. (1.7.30), we find the following order-updating equation for R^{-1}, analogous to Eq. (1.7.28)

$$R^{-1} = \begin{bmatrix} 0 & \mathbf{0}^T \\ \mathbf{0} & \tilde{R}^{-1} \end{bmatrix} + \frac{1}{E_a} \mathbf{a}\mathbf{a}^T \tag{1.7.35}$$

Denoting $\tilde{\mathbf{r}} = E[x\tilde{\mathbf{y}}]$ and $r_a = E[xy_a]$, we obtain the alternative order-update equation for $\mathbf{h}$, analogous to Eq. (1.7.29)

$$\mathbf{h} = R^{-1}\mathbf{r} = \begin{bmatrix} 0 & \mathbf{0}^T \\ \mathbf{0} & \tilde{R}^{-1} \end{bmatrix} \begin{bmatrix} r_a \\ \tilde{\mathbf{r}} \end{bmatrix} + \frac{1}{E_a}(\mathbf{a}^T\mathbf{r})\mathbf{a} = \begin{bmatrix} 0 \\ \tilde{\mathbf{h}} \end{bmatrix} + c_a \mathbf{a} \tag{1.7.36}$$

where $c_a = (\mathbf{a}^T\mathbf{r})/E_a = (r_a + \boldsymbol{\alpha}^T \tilde{\mathbf{r}})/E_a$, and $\tilde{\mathbf{h}} = \tilde{R}^{-1}\tilde{\mathbf{r}}$ is the lower-order *optimal* estimator for estimating x from $\tilde{\mathbf{y}}$. By analogy to Eq. (1.7.21), we could also choose to express the estimates in the $\mathbf{e}_a$ basis

$$\hat{x} = \mathbf{h}^T \mathbf{y} = \mathbf{h}^T U^{-1} \mathbf{e}_a = \mathbf{g}_u^T \mathbf{e}_a \tag{1.7.37}$$

where $\mathbf{g}_u = U^{-T}\mathbf{h}$. A realization is shown below.

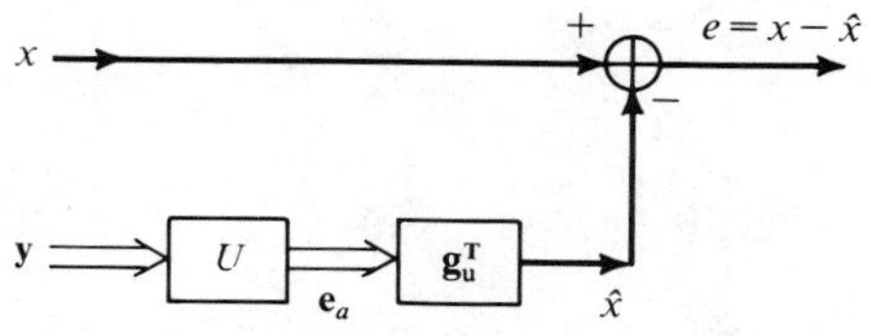

The most important part of the realizations based on the diagonal bases $\mathbf{e}_b$ or $\mathbf{e}_a$ is the preprocessing part that decorrelates the $\mathbf{y}$ basis; namely, $\mathbf{e}_b = L\mathbf{y}$, or $\mathbf{e}_a = U\mathbf{y}$. We will see in Chapters 5 and 7 that this part can be done efficiently using the Levinson recursion and the *lattice structures* of linear prediction. The LU representation, based on the backward predictors $\mathbf{e}_b = L\mathbf{y}$, is preferred because it is somewhat more conveniently realized in terms of the lattice structure than the UL representation $\mathbf{e}_a = U\mathbf{y}$.

Order Updates

So far, we studied the problems of forward and backward prediction separately from each other. Next, we would like to consider the two problems together and show how to construct the solution of the *pair* of equations (1.7.12) from the solution of a similar pair of *lower* order. This construction is the essence behind Levinson's algorithm for solving the linear prediction problem, both in the stationary and in the adaptive least squares cases. Consider the following pair of lower-order forward and backward predictors, defined in terms of the block decompositions Eq. (1.7.5) of R

$$\bar{R}\bar{\mathbf{a}} = \bar{E}_a\bar{\mathbf{u}}, \quad \tilde{R}\tilde{\mathbf{b}} = \tilde{E}_b\tilde{\mathbf{v}} \tag{1.7.38}$$

where $\bar{\mathbf{u}}$ and $\tilde{\mathbf{v}}$ are unit vectors of dimension one less than those of Eq. (1.7.12). They are related to $\mathbf{u}$ and $\mathbf{v}$ through the decompositions

$$\mathbf{u} = \begin{bmatrix} \bar{\mathbf{u}} \\ 0 \end{bmatrix}, \quad \mathbf{v} = \begin{bmatrix} 0 \\ \tilde{\mathbf{v}} \end{bmatrix} \tag{1.7.39}$$

The basic result we would like to show is that the solution of the pair (1.7.12) may be constructed from the solution of the pair (1.7.38) by

$$\mathbf{a} = \begin{bmatrix} \bar{\mathbf{a}} \\ 0 \end{bmatrix} - \gamma_b \begin{bmatrix} 0 \\ \tilde{\mathbf{b}} \end{bmatrix}, \quad \mathbf{b} = \begin{bmatrix} 0 \\ \tilde{\mathbf{b}} \end{bmatrix} - \gamma_a \begin{bmatrix} \bar{\mathbf{a}} \\ 0 \end{bmatrix} \tag{1.7.40}$$

This result is motivated by Eq. (1.7.39), which shows that the right-hand sides of Eqs. (1.7.38) are already part of the right-hand sides of Eq. (1.7.12), and therefore, the solutions of Eq. (1.7.38) may appear as part of the solutions of Eq. (1.7.12). The prediction errors are updated by

$$E_a = (1 - \gamma_a\gamma_b)\bar{E}_a, \quad E_b = (1 - \gamma_a\gamma_b)\tilde{E}_b \tag{1.7.41}$$

where

$$\gamma_b = \frac{\Delta_a}{\tilde{E}_b}, \quad \gamma_a = \frac{\Delta_b}{\bar{E}_a} \tag{1.7.42}$$

The γs are known as the *reflection* or *PARCOR* coefficients. The quantities Δ_a and Δ_b are defined by

$$\Delta_a = \bar{\mathbf{a}}^T\mathbf{r}_b, \quad \Delta_b = \tilde{\mathbf{b}}^T\mathbf{r}_a \tag{1.7.43}$$

The two Δs are equal as seen by the following considerations. Using the decompositions Eq. (1.7.5), we find

$$R\begin{bmatrix}\bar{\mathbf{a}}\\0\end{bmatrix}=\begin{bmatrix}\bar{R} & \mathbf{r}_b\\ \mathbf{r}_b^T & \rho_b\end{bmatrix}\begin{bmatrix}\bar{\mathbf{a}}\\0\end{bmatrix}=\begin{bmatrix}\bar{R}\bar{\mathbf{a}}\\ \mathbf{r}_b^T\bar{\mathbf{a}}\end{bmatrix}=\begin{bmatrix}\bar{E}_a\bar{\mathbf{u}}\\ \Delta_a\end{bmatrix}$$

$$R\begin{bmatrix}0\\ \tilde{\mathbf{b}}\end{bmatrix}=\begin{bmatrix}\rho_a & \mathbf{r}_a^T\\ \mathbf{r}_a & \tilde{R}\end{bmatrix}\begin{bmatrix}0\\ \tilde{\mathbf{b}}\end{bmatrix}=\begin{bmatrix}\mathbf{r}_a^T\tilde{\mathbf{b}}\\ \tilde{R}\tilde{\mathbf{b}}\end{bmatrix}=\begin{bmatrix}\Delta_b\\ \tilde{E}_b\tilde{\mathbf{v}}\end{bmatrix}$$

They may be written more conveniently as

$$R\begin{bmatrix}\bar{\mathbf{a}}\\0\end{bmatrix}=\begin{bmatrix}\bar{E}_a\bar{\mathbf{u}}\\ \Delta_a\end{bmatrix}=\bar{E}_a\begin{bmatrix}\bar{\mathbf{u}}\\0\end{bmatrix}+\Delta_a\begin{bmatrix}\mathbf{0}\\1\end{bmatrix}=\bar{E}_a\mathbf{u}+\Delta_a\mathbf{v} \tag{1.7.44a}$$

$$R\begin{bmatrix}0\\ \tilde{\mathbf{b}}\end{bmatrix}=\begin{bmatrix}\Delta_b\\ \tilde{E}_b\tilde{\mathbf{v}}\end{bmatrix}=\Delta_b\begin{bmatrix}1\\ \mathbf{0}\end{bmatrix}+\tilde{E}_b\begin{bmatrix}0\\ \tilde{\mathbf{v}}\end{bmatrix}=\Delta_b\mathbf{u}+\tilde{E}_b\mathbf{v} \tag{1.7.44b}$$

Noting that $\mathbf{d}^T\mathbf{u}$ and $\mathbf{d}^T\mathbf{v}$ are equal to the first and last components of a vector $\mathbf{d}$, we have $[0,\tilde{\mathbf{b}}^T]\mathbf{u}=0$ and $[0,\tilde{\mathbf{b}}^T]\mathbf{v}=1$ because the first and last components of $[0,\tilde{\mathbf{b}}^T]$ are zero and one, respectively. Similarly, $[\bar{\mathbf{a}}^T,0]\mathbf{u}=1$ and $[\bar{\mathbf{a}}^T,0]\mathbf{v}=0$. Thus, multiplying Eq. (1.7.44a) from the left by $[0,\tilde{\mathbf{b}}^T]$ and Eq. (1.7.44b) by $[\bar{\mathbf{a}}^T,0]$, we find

$$[0,\tilde{\mathbf{b}}^T]R\begin{bmatrix}\bar{\mathbf{a}}\\0\end{bmatrix}=\Delta_a\,,\qquad [\bar{\mathbf{a}}^T,0]R\begin{bmatrix}0\\ \tilde{\mathbf{b}}\end{bmatrix}=\Delta_b \tag{1.7.45}$$

The equality of the Δs follows now from the fact that R is a symmetric matrix. Thus,

$$\Delta_a=\Delta_b\equiv\Delta \tag{1.7.46}$$

An alternative proof, based on partial correlations, will be given later. Equations (1.7.40) and (1.7.41) follow now in a straightforward fashion from Eq. (1.7.44). Multiplying the first part of Eq. (1.7.40) by R and using Eqs. (1.7.12) and (1.7.44), we find

$$R\mathbf{a}=R\begin{bmatrix}\bar{\mathbf{a}}\\0\end{bmatrix}-\gamma_b R\begin{bmatrix}0\\ \tilde{\mathbf{b}}\end{bmatrix}$$

or,

$$E_a\mathbf{u}=(\bar{E}_a\mathbf{u}+\Delta_a\mathbf{v})-\gamma_b(\Delta_b\mathbf{u}+\tilde{E}_b\mathbf{v})=(\bar{E}_a-\gamma_b\Delta_b)\mathbf{u}+(\Delta_a-\gamma_b\tilde{E}_b)\mathbf{v}$$

which implies the conditions

$$E_a=\bar{E}_a-\gamma_b\Delta_b\,,\qquad \Delta_a-\gamma_b\tilde{E}_b=0 \tag{1.7.47}$$

Similarly, multiplying the second part of Eq. (1.7.40) by R, we obtain

$$E_b\mathbf{v}=(\Delta_b\mathbf{u}+\tilde{E}_b\mathbf{v})-\gamma_a(\bar{E}_a\mathbf{u}+\Delta_a\mathbf{v})=(\Delta_b-\gamma_a\bar{E}_a)\mathbf{u}+(\tilde{E}_b-\gamma_a\Delta_a)\mathbf{v}$$

which implies

$$E_b = \tilde{E}_b - \gamma_a \Delta_a\,, \qquad \Delta_b - \gamma_a \bar{E}_a = 0 \tag{1.7.48}$$

Equations (1.7.41) and (1.7.42) follow now from Eqs. (1.7.47) and (1.7.48). By analogy with Eq. (1.7.9), we may now define the prediction errors corresponding to the lower-order predictors $\bar{\mathbf{a}}$ and $\tilde{\mathbf{b}}$ by

$$\bar{e}_a = \bar{\mathbf{a}}^T \bar{\mathbf{y}}\,, \qquad \tilde{e}_b = \tilde{\mathbf{b}}^T \tilde{\mathbf{y}} \tag{1.7.49}$$

Using Eqs. (1.7.9) and (1.7.40) we find the following updating equations for the prediction errors

$$\mathbf{a}^T \mathbf{y} = [\bar{\mathbf{a}}^T, 0] \begin{bmatrix} \bar{\mathbf{y}} \\ y_b \end{bmatrix} - \gamma_b\, [0, \tilde{\mathbf{b}}^T] \begin{bmatrix} y_a \\ \tilde{\mathbf{y}} \end{bmatrix} = \bar{\mathbf{a}}^T \bar{\mathbf{y}} - \gamma_b\, \tilde{\mathbf{b}}^T \tilde{\mathbf{y}}$$

$$\mathbf{b}^T \mathbf{y} = [0, \tilde{\mathbf{b}}^T] \begin{bmatrix} y_a \\ \tilde{\mathbf{y}} \end{bmatrix} - \gamma_a\, [\bar{\mathbf{a}}^T, 0] \begin{bmatrix} \bar{\mathbf{y}} \\ y_b \end{bmatrix} = \tilde{\mathbf{b}}^T \tilde{\mathbf{y}} - \gamma_a\, \bar{\mathbf{a}}^T \bar{\mathbf{y}}$$

or,

$$e_a = \bar{e}_a - \gamma_b \tilde{e}_b\,, \qquad e_b = \tilde{e}_b - \gamma_a \bar{e}_a \tag{1.7.50}$$

A *lattice* type realization of Eq. (1.7.50) is shown below. It forms the basis of the lattice structures of linear prediction discussed in Chapters 5.

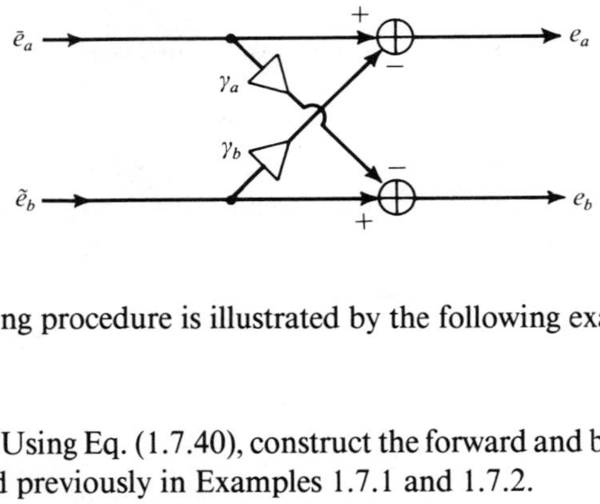

The order-updating procedure is illustrated by the following example.

Example 1.7.3: Using Eq. (1.7.40), construct the forward and backward predictors **a** and **b** found previously in Examples 1.7.1 and 1.7.2.

Solution: The first part of Eq. (1.7.38), $\bar{R}\bar{\mathbf{a}} = \bar{E}_a \bar{\mathbf{u}}$, is solved as follows:

$$\begin{bmatrix} 1 & 1 \\ 1 & 3 \end{bmatrix} \begin{bmatrix} 1 \\ \bar{\alpha} \end{bmatrix} = \bar{E}_a \begin{bmatrix} 1 \\ 0 \end{bmatrix} \quad \Longrightarrow \quad \bar{\alpha} = -1/3$$

Therefore, $\bar{\mathbf{a}} = \begin{bmatrix} 1 \\ -1/3 \end{bmatrix}$ and $\bar{E}_a = 2/3$. Similarly, $\tilde{R}\tilde{\mathbf{b}} = \tilde{E}_b\tilde{\mathbf{v}}$, is solved by

$$\begin{bmatrix} 3 & 2 \\ 2 & 3 \end{bmatrix} \begin{bmatrix} \tilde{\beta} \\ 1 \end{bmatrix} = \tilde{E}_b \begin{bmatrix} 0 \\ 1 \end{bmatrix} \quad \Rightarrow \quad \tilde{\beta} = -2/3$$

Hence, $\tilde{\mathbf{b}} = \begin{bmatrix} -2/3 \\ 1 \end{bmatrix}$ and $\tilde{E}_b = 5/3$. Next, we determine

$$\Delta = \bar{\mathbf{a}}^T \mathbf{r}_b = [1, -\frac{1}{3}] \begin{bmatrix} 0 \\ 2 \end{bmatrix} = -\frac{2}{3}, \quad \gamma_b = \frac{\Delta}{\tilde{E}_b} = -\frac{2}{5}, \quad \gamma_a = \frac{\Delta}{\bar{E}_a} = -1$$

It follows from Eq. (1.7.40) that

$$\mathbf{a} = \begin{bmatrix} \bar{\mathbf{a}} \\ 0 \end{bmatrix} - \gamma_b \begin{bmatrix} 0 \\ \tilde{\mathbf{b}} \end{bmatrix} = \begin{bmatrix} 1 \\ -1/3 \\ 0 \end{bmatrix} - (-\frac{2}{5}) \begin{bmatrix} 0 \\ -2/3 \\ 1 \end{bmatrix} = \begin{bmatrix} 1 \\ -3/5 \\ 2/5 \end{bmatrix}$$

$$\mathbf{b} = \begin{bmatrix} 0 \\ \tilde{\mathbf{b}} \end{bmatrix} - \gamma_a \begin{bmatrix} \bar{\mathbf{a}} \\ 0 \end{bmatrix} = \begin{bmatrix} 0 \\ -2/3 \\ 1 \end{bmatrix} - (-1) \begin{bmatrix} 1 \\ -1/3 \\ 0 \end{bmatrix} = \begin{bmatrix} 1 \\ -1 \\ 1 \end{bmatrix}$$

and the prediction errors are found from Eq. (1.7.41)

$$E_a = \bar{E}_a(1 - \gamma_a\gamma_b) = \frac{2}{3}(1 - \frac{2}{5}) = \frac{2}{5}, \quad E_b = \tilde{E}_b(1 - \gamma_a\gamma_b) = \frac{5}{3}(1 - \frac{2}{5}) = 1.$$

Partial Correlation Interpretation

Next, we show that γ_a and γ_b are partial correlation coefficients in the sense of Section 1.6. Let $\mathbf{y}_c$ denote all the components of $\mathbf{y}$ that lie between y_a and y_b, so that

$$\mathbf{y} = \begin{bmatrix} y_a \\ \mathbf{y}_c \\ y_b \end{bmatrix}, \quad \bar{\mathbf{y}} = \begin{bmatrix} y_a \\ \mathbf{y}_c \end{bmatrix}, \quad \tilde{\mathbf{y}} = \begin{bmatrix} \mathbf{y}_c \\ y_b \end{bmatrix} \tag{1.7.51}$$

The forward predictor $\mathbf{a}$ was defined as the best estimator of y_a based on the rest of the vector $\mathbf{y}$. By the same token, $\bar{\mathbf{a}}$ is the best estimator of y_a based on the rest of $\bar{\mathbf{y}}$; that is, $\mathbf{y}_c$. Similarly, the backward predictor $\tilde{\mathbf{b}}$ defines the best estimator of y_b based on the rest of the vector $\tilde{\mathbf{y}}$; again, $\mathbf{y}_c$. Decomposing $\bar{\mathbf{a}}$ and $\tilde{\mathbf{b}}$ as

$$\bar{\mathbf{a}} = \begin{bmatrix} 1 \\ \bar{\alpha} \end{bmatrix}, \quad \tilde{\mathbf{b}} = \begin{bmatrix} \tilde{\beta} \\ 1 \end{bmatrix}$$

we may write the best estimates of y_a and y_b based on $\mathbf{y}_c$ as

$$\hat{y}_{a/c} = E[y_a \mathbf{y}_c^T] E[\mathbf{y}_c \mathbf{y}_c^T]^{-1} \mathbf{y}_c = -\bar{\alpha}^T \mathbf{y}_c \,, \qquad \hat{y}_{b/c} = E[y_b \mathbf{y}_c^T] E[\mathbf{y}_c \mathbf{y}_c^T]^{-1} \mathbf{y}_c = -\bar{\beta}^T \mathbf{y}_c$$

and the estimation errors

$$\bar{e}_a = \bar{\mathbf{a}}^T \bar{\mathbf{y}} = y_a - \hat{y}_{a/c} \,, \qquad \tilde{e}_b = \bar{\mathbf{b}}^T \bar{\mathbf{y}} = y_b - \hat{y}_{b/c} \tag{1.7.52}$$

Thus, $\bar{e}_a$ and $\tilde{e}_b$ represent what is left of y_a and y_b after we project out their dependence on the intermediate vector $\mathbf{y}_c$. The direct influence of y_a on y_b, with the effect of $\mathbf{y}_c$ removed, is measured by the correlation $E[\bar{e}_a \tilde{e}_b]$. This correlation is equal to the quantity Δ defined in Eq. (1.7.46). This follows from Eq. (1.7.43)

$$\Delta_a = \bar{\mathbf{a}}^T \mathbf{r}_b = \bar{\mathbf{a}}^T E[y_b \bar{\mathbf{y}}] = E[y_b(\bar{\mathbf{a}}^T \bar{\mathbf{y}})] = E[y_b \bar{e}_a]$$

similarly,

$$\Delta_b = \bar{\mathbf{b}}^T \mathbf{r}_a = \bar{\mathbf{b}}^T E[y_a \bar{\mathbf{y}}] = E[y_a(\bar{\mathbf{b}}^T \bar{\mathbf{y}})] = E[y_a \tilde{e}_b]$$

Now, because $\bar{e}_a$ is orthogonal to $\mathbf{y}_c$ and $\hat{y}_{b/c}$ is a linear combination of $\mathbf{y}_c$, it follows that $E[\hat{y}_{b/c}\bar{e}_a] = 0$. Similarly, because $\tilde{e}_b$ is orthogonal to $\mathbf{y}_c$ and $\hat{y}_{a/c}$ is linearly related to $\mathbf{y}_c$, it follows that $E[\hat{y}_{a/c}\tilde{e}_b] = 0$. Thus,

$$\Delta_a = E[y_b \bar{e}_a] = E[(y_b - \hat{y}_{b/c})\bar{e}_a] = E[\tilde{e}_b \bar{e}_a]$$

$$\Delta_b = E[y_a \tilde{e}_b] = E[(y_a - \hat{y}_{a/c})\tilde{e}_b] = E[\bar{e}_a \tilde{e}_b]$$

Therefore, Δ_a and Δ_b are equal

$$\Delta_a = \Delta_b = E[\bar{e}_a \tilde{e}_b] \tag{1.7.53}$$

This is an alternative proof of Eq. (1.7.46). It follows that γ_a and γ_b are normalized PARCOR coefficients in the sense of Section 1.6:

$$\gamma_b = \frac{E[\bar{e}_a \tilde{e}_b]}{E[\tilde{e}_b^2]} \,, \qquad \gamma_a = \frac{E[\tilde{e}_b \bar{e}_a]}{E[\bar{e}_a^2]} \tag{1.7.54}$$

Using the Schwarz inequality for the inner product between two random variables; namely, $(E[uv])^2 \le E[u^2]E[v^2]$, we find the inequality

$$0 \le \gamma_a \gamma_b = \frac{E[\bar{e}_a \tilde{e}_b]^2}{E[\bar{e}_a^2] E[\tilde{e}_b^2]} \le 1 \tag{1.7.55}$$

This inequality also follows from Eq. (1.7.41) and the fact that E_a and $\bar{E}_a$ are positive quantities, both being mean square errors.

Example 1.7.4: For Example 1.7.1, compute the estimates $\hat{y}_{a/c}$ and $\hat{y}_{b/c}$ directly and compare them with the results of Example 1.7.3.

Solution: From the matrix elements of R we have $E[y_a y_c] = 1$, $E[y_b y_c] = 2$, and $E[y_c^2] = 3$. Thus,

$$\hat{y}_{a/c} = E[y_a y_c]E[y_c^2]^{-1}y_c = \frac{1}{3}y_c\,, \quad \hat{y}_{b/c} = E[y_b y_c]E[y_c^2]^{-1}y_c = \frac{2}{3}y_c$$

The corresponding errors will be

$$\bar{e}_a = y_a - \frac{1}{3}y_c = [1, -\frac{1}{3}]\bar{\mathbf{y}}\,, \quad \bar{e}_b = y_b - \frac{2}{3}y_c = [-\frac{2}{3}, 1]\bar{\mathbf{y}}$$

The results are identical to those of Exercise 1.7.3.

Conventional Cholesky Factorizations

Equation (1.7.18) shows that the *conventional* Cholesky factor of R is given by the inverse matrix L^{-1}. A direct construction of the conventional Cholesky factor that avoids the computation of this inverse is as follows. Define

$$G_b = E[\mathbf{y}\mathbf{e}_b^T] \tag{1.7.56}$$

If we use $\mathbf{e}_b = L\mathbf{y}$ and $E[\mathbf{e}_b\mathbf{e}_b^T] = D_b$, it follows that

$$LG_b = LE[\mathbf{y}\mathbf{e}_b^T] = E[\mathbf{e}_b\mathbf{e}_b^T] = D_b$$

or,

$$G_b = L^{-1}D_b \tag{1.7.57}$$

Thus, G_b is a *lower* triangular matrix. Its main diagonal consists of the diagonal entries of D_b. Solving for $L^{-1} = G_b D_b^{-1}$ and inserting in Eq. (1.7.18), we find the conventional LU factorization of R:

$$R = (G_b D_b^{-1})D_b(D_b^{-1}G_b^T) = G_b D_b^{-1} G_b^T \tag{1.7.58}$$

Similarly, the conventional UL factorization of R is obtained from Eq. (1.7.33) by defining the *upper* triangular matrix

$$G_a = E[\mathbf{y}\mathbf{e}_a^T] \tag{1.7.59}$$

Using $\mathbf{e}_a = U\mathbf{y}$ and $E[\mathbf{e}_a\mathbf{e}_a^T] = D_a$, we find

$$UG_a = D_a \quad \text{or,} \quad G_a = U^{-1}D_a \tag{1.7.60}$$

which yields the conventional UL factorization of R:

$$R = U^{-1}D_a U^{-T} = G_a D_a^{-1} G_a^T$$

The columns of the matrices G_a and G_b will be referred to as the forward and backward *gapped* functions. This terminology will be justified in Chapters 2 and 5. The decomposition of G_b into its columns can be done order-recursively using the decomposition (1.7.15). We have

$$G_b = E[\mathbf{y}(\bar{\mathbf{e}}_b^T, e_b)] \equiv [\bar{G}_b, \mathbf{g}_b] \tag{1.7.61}$$

where $\bar{G}_b = E[\mathbf{y}\bar{\mathbf{e}}_b^T]$ and $\mathbf{g}_b = E[\mathbf{y}e_b]$. Similarly, using Eq. (1.7.23) we find

$$G_a = E[\mathbf{y}(e_a, \tilde{\mathbf{e}}_a{}^T)] = [\mathbf{g}_a, \tilde{G}_a] \tag{1.7.62}$$

where $\tilde{G}_a = E[\mathbf{y}\tilde{\mathbf{e}}_a^T]$ and $\mathbf{g}_a = E[\mathbf{y}e_a]$. Motivated by the lattice recursions (1.7.50), we are led to define the lower-order gapped functions

$$\tilde{\mathbf{g}}_b = E[\mathbf{y}\tilde{e}_b] \quad \text{and} \quad \bar{\mathbf{g}}_a = E[\mathbf{y}\bar{e}_a]$$

It follows that the gapped functions $\mathbf{g}_a = E[\mathbf{y}e_a]$ and $\mathbf{g}_b = E[\mathbf{y}e_b]$ can be constructed order-recursively by the lattice-type equations

$$\mathbf{g}_a = \bar{\mathbf{g}}_a - \gamma_b \tilde{\mathbf{g}}_b \,, \qquad \mathbf{g}_b = \tilde{\mathbf{g}}_b - \gamma_a \bar{\mathbf{g}}_a \tag{1.7.63}$$

The proof is straightforward. For example, $E[\mathbf{y}e_a] = E[\mathbf{y}(\bar{e}_a - \gamma_b\tilde{e}_b)]$. In Chapter 5 we will see that these equations are equivalent to the celebrated *Schur algorithm* for solving the linear prediction problem. In recent years, the Schur algorithm has emerged as an important signal processing tool because it admits efficient fixed-point and parallel processor implementations. Equations (1.7.63) are mathematically equivalent to the Levinson-type recursions (1.7.40). In fact, Eq. (1.7.40) can be derived from Eq. (1.7.63) as follows. Using $e_a = \mathbf{a}^T\mathbf{y}$ and $e_b = \mathbf{b}^T\mathbf{y}$, it follows that

$$\mathbf{g}_a = E[\mathbf{y}e_a] = E[\mathbf{y}(\mathbf{y}^T\mathbf{a})] = R\mathbf{a} \,, \qquad \mathbf{g}_b = E[\mathbf{y}e_b] = E[\mathbf{y}(\mathbf{y}^T\mathbf{b})] = R\mathbf{b}$$

Similarly, we have

$$\bar{\mathbf{g}}_a = R\begin{bmatrix}\bar{\mathbf{a}}\\0\end{bmatrix}, \qquad \tilde{\mathbf{g}}_b = R\begin{bmatrix}0\\\tilde{\mathbf{b}}\end{bmatrix} \tag{1.7.64}$$

These are easily shown. For example,

$$R\begin{bmatrix}\bar{\mathbf{a}}\\0\end{bmatrix} = E[\mathbf{y}(\bar{\mathbf{y}}^T, y_b)]\begin{bmatrix}\bar{\mathbf{a}}\\0\end{bmatrix} = E[\mathbf{y}\bar{\mathbf{y}}^T]\bar{\mathbf{a}} = E[\mathbf{y}\bar{e}_a] = \bar{\mathbf{g}}_a$$

Therefore, the first part of Eq. (1.7.63) is equivalent to

$$R\mathbf{a} = R\begin{bmatrix}\bar{\mathbf{a}}\\0\end{bmatrix} - \gamma_b R\begin{bmatrix}0\\\tilde{\mathbf{b}}\end{bmatrix}$$

Equation (1.7.40) follows now by canceling out the matrix factor R. One of the essential features of the Schur algorithm is that the reflection coefficients can also be computed from the knowledge of the lower-order gapped functions $\bar{\mathbf{g}}_a$ and $\tilde{\mathbf{g}}_b$, as follows. Using Eq. (1.7.64) and dotting Eq. (1.7.44) with the unit vectors $\mathbf{u}$ and $\mathbf{v}$, we easily find

$$\bar{E}_a = \mathbf{u}^T\bar{\mathbf{g}}_a \,, \quad \tilde{E}_b = \mathbf{v}^T\tilde{\mathbf{g}}_b \,, \quad \Delta = \mathbf{u}^T\tilde{\mathbf{g}}_b = \mathbf{v}^T\bar{\mathbf{g}}_a \tag{1.7.65}$$

Thus, Eq. (1.7.42) may be written as

$$\gamma_b = \frac{\mathbf{v}^T\bar{\mathbf{g}}_a}{\mathbf{v}^T\tilde{\mathbf{g}}_b}, \qquad \gamma_a = \frac{\mathbf{u}^T\tilde{\mathbf{g}}_b}{\mathbf{u}^T\bar{\mathbf{g}}_a} \tag{1.7.66}$$

Summary

We have argued that the solution of the general linear estimation problem can be made more efficient by working with the decorrelated bases $\mathbf{e}_a$ or $\mathbf{e}_b$, which contain no redundancies. Linear prediction ideas come into play in this context because the linear transformations U and L that decorrelate the data vector $\mathbf{y}$ are constructible from the forward and backward linear prediction coefficients $\mathbf{a}$ and $\mathbf{b}$. Moreover, linear prediction was seen to be equivalent to the Gram-Schmidt construction and to the Cholesky factorization of the covariance matrix R. The order-recursive solutions of the linear prediction problem and the linear estimation problem, Eqs. (1.7.24) through (1.7.26), give rise to efficient lattice implementations with many desirable properties, such as robustness under coefficient quantization and modularity of structure admitting parallel VLSI implementations.

In this section, we intentionally did not make any additional assumptions about any structural properties of the covariance matrix R. To *close the loop* and obtain the efficient computational algorithms mentioned previously, we need to make additional assumptions on R. The simplest case is to assume that R has a Toeplitz structure. This case arises when $\mathbf{y}$ is a block of successive signal samples from a stationary time series. The Toeplitz property means that the matrix elements along each diagonal of R are the same. Equivalently, the matrix element R_{ij} depends only on the difference of the indices, that is, $R_{ij} = R(i-j)$. With respect to the subblock decomposition (1.7.5), it is easily verified that a necessary and sufficient condition for R to be Toeplitz is that

$$\tilde{R} = \bar{R}$$

This condition implies that linear prediction solutions for $\bar{R}$ and $\tilde{R}$ must be the same; that is,

$$\tilde{\mathbf{b}} = \bar{\mathbf{b}}, \qquad \tilde{\mathbf{a}} = \bar{\mathbf{a}}$$

Thus, from the forward and backward linear prediction solutions $\bar{\mathbf{a}}$ and $\bar{\mathbf{b}}$ of the lower-order Toeplitz submatrix $\bar{R}$, we first obtain $\tilde{\mathbf{b}} = \bar{\mathbf{b}}$ and then use Eq. (1.7.40) to get the linear prediction solution of the higher order matrix R. This is the essence behind Levinson's algorithm. It will be discussed further in Chapters 2 and 5.

In the nonstationary time series case, the matrix R is not Toeplitz. Even then one can obtain some useful results by means of the so-called shift invariance property. In this case, the data vector $\mathbf{y}$ consists of successive signal samples starting at some arbitrary sampling instant n

$$\mathbf{y}(n) = \begin{bmatrix} y_n \\ y_{n-1} \\ \vdots \\ y_{n-M+1} \\ y_{n-M} \end{bmatrix} = \begin{bmatrix} \bar{\mathbf{y}}(n) \\ y_{n-M} \end{bmatrix} = \begin{bmatrix} y_n \\ \tilde{\mathbf{y}}(n) \end{bmatrix}$$

It follows that

$$\bar{\mathbf{y}}(n) = \begin{bmatrix} y_n \\ \vdots \\ y_{n-M+1} \end{bmatrix}, \quad \tilde{\mathbf{y}}(n) = \begin{bmatrix} y_{n-1} \\ \vdots \\ y_{n-M} \end{bmatrix}, \quad \text{or,} \quad \tilde{\mathbf{y}}(n) = \bar{\mathbf{y}}(n-1)$$

This implies that $\tilde{R}(n) = \bar{R}(n-1)$, and therefore

$$\tilde{\mathbf{a}}(n) = \bar{\mathbf{a}}(n-1)\,, \qquad \tilde{\mathbf{b}}(n) = \bar{\mathbf{b}}(n-1)$$

Thus, order updating is coupled with time updating. These results are used in the development of the fast recursive least-squares adaptive filters, to be discussed in Chapter 7.

1.8 *Random Signals*

A random signal (random process, or stochastic process) is defined as a sequence of random variables $\{x_0, x_1, x_2, \ldots, x_n, \ldots\}$ where the index n is taken to be the time. The statistical description of so many random variables is very complicated since it requires knowledge of all the joint densities

$$p(x_0, x_1, \ldots, x_n)$$

for each $n = 0, 1, 2, \ldots$.

If the mean $E[x_n]$ of the random signal is not zero, it can be removed by redefining a new signal $x_n - E[x_n]$. From now on, we will assume that this has been done, and shall work with *zero-mean* random signals. The *autocorrelation function* is defined as

$$R_{xx}(n,m) = E[x_n x_m]; \qquad n,m = 0,1,2, \ldots$$

Sometimes it will be convenient to think of the random signal as a (possibly infinite) random vector $\mathbf{x} = [x_0, x_1, \ldots, x_n, \ldots]^T$, and of the autocorrelation function as a (possibly infinite) matrix $R_{xx} = E[\mathbf{x}\mathbf{x}^T]$. R_{xx} is positive semi-definite and symmetric. The autocorrelation function may also be written as

$$R_{xx}(n + k,n) = E[x_{n+k}\, x_n] \tag{1.8.1}$$

It provides a *measure* of the influence of the sample x_n on the sample x_{n+k}, which lies in the future (if $k > 0$) by k units of time. The relative time separation k of the two samples is called *the lag*.

If the signal x_n is *stationary* (or wide-sense stationary), then the above average is *independent* of the absolute time n, and is a function only of the *relative lag* k; abusing somewhat the above notation, we may write in this case:

$$R_{xx}(k) = E[x_{n+k}\, x_n] = E[x_{n'+k}\, x_{n'}] \qquad \text{(autocorrelation)} \tag{1.8.2}$$

In other words, the self-correlation properties of a stationary signal x_n are the same on the average, regardless of when this average is computed. In a way, the stationary random signal x_n looks the same for all times. In this sense, if we take two different blocks of data of length N, as shown in Fig. 1.4, we should expect the *average properties*, such as means and autocorrelations, extracted from these blocks of data to be roughly the same. The relative time separation of the two blocks as a whole should not matter.

A direct consequence of stationarity is the *reflection-invariance* of the autocorrelation function $R_{xx}(k)$ of Eq. (1.8.2):

$$R_{xx}(k) = E[x_{n+k}\, x_n] = R_{xx}(-k) \tag{1.8.3}$$

One way to introduce a systematization of the various types of random signals is the Markov classification into zeroth order Markov, first order Markov, and so on. The simplest possible random signal is the zeroth order Markov, or *purely random signal*, defined by the requirement that all the (zero-mean) random variables $x_0, x_1, \ldots, x_n, \ldots$ be independent of each other and arise from a common density $p(x)$; this implies

$$p(x_0, x_1, \ldots, x_n, \ldots) = p(x_0)\, p(x_1) \ldots p(x_n) \ldots$$
$$R_{xx}(n,m) = E[x_n\, x_m] = 0; \qquad \text{for } n \neq m$$

Such a random signal is stationary. The quantity $R_{xx}(n,n)$ is independent of n, and represents the variance of each sample:

$$R_{xx}(0) = E[x_n^2] = \sigma_x^2$$

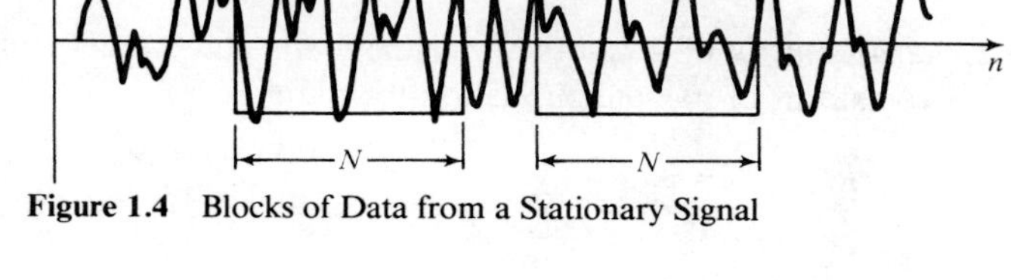

Figure 1.4 Blocks of Data from a Stationary Signal

In this case, the autocorrelation function $R_{xx}(k)$ may be expressed compactly as

$$R_{xx}(k) = E[x_{n+k}\, x_n] = \sigma_x^2\, \delta(k) \tag{1.8.4}$$

A purely random signal has no memory, as can be seen from the property

$$p(x_n, x_{n-1}) = p(x_n)\, p(x_{n-1}) \qquad \text{or} \qquad p(x_n/x_{n-1}) = p(x_n)$$

That is, the occurrence of x_{n-1} at time instant $n-1$ does not in any way affect, or restrict, the values of x_n at the next time instant. Successive signal values are entirely independent of each other. Past values do not influence future values. No memory is retained from sample to sample; the next sample will take a value regardless of the value that the previous sample has already taken. Since successive samples are random, such a signal will exhibit very rapid time variations. But it will also exhibit slow time variations. Such time variations are best discussed in the frequency domain. This will lead directly to frequency concepts, power spectra, periodograms, and the like. It is expected that a purely random signal will contain all frequencies, from the very low to the very high, in equal proportions (white noise).

The next least complicated signal is the first order Markov signal, which has memory only of one sampling instant. Such a signal ''remembers'' only the previous sample. It is defined by the requirement that

$$p(x_n/x_{n-1}, x_{n-2}, \ldots, x_1, x_0) = p(x_n/x_{n-1})$$

which states that x_n may be influenced directly only by the previous sample value x_{n-1}, and not by the samples $x_{n-2}, \ldots, x_0$ that are further in the past. The complete statistical description of such random signal is considerably simplified. It is sufficient to know only the marginal densities $p(x_n)$ and the conditional densities $p(x_n/x_{n-1})$. Any other joint density may be constructed in terms of these. For instance,

$$\begin{aligned} p(x_3, x_2, x_1, x_0) &= p(x_3/x_2, x_1, x_0)\, p(x_2, x_1, x_0) \qquad \text{(by Bayes' rule)} \\ &= p(x_3/x_2)\, p(x_2, x_1, x_0) \qquad \text{(by the Markov property)} \\ &= p(x_3/x_2)\, p(x_2/x_1, x_0)\, p(x_1, x_0) \\ &= p(x_3/x_2)\, p(x_2/x_1)\, p(x_1, x_0) \\ &= p(x_3/x_2)\, p(x_2/x_1)\, p(x_1/x_0)\, p(x_0) \end{aligned}$$

1.9 *Power Spectrum and Its Interpretation*

The *power spectral density* of a *stationary* random signal x_n is defined as the double-sided z-transform of its autocorrelation function

$$S_{xx}(z) = \sum_{k=-\infty}^{\infty} R_{xx}(k)\, z^{-k} \tag{1.9.1}$$

where $R_{xx}(k)$ is given by Eq. (1.8.2). If $R_{xx}(k)$ is strictly stable, the region of convergence of $S_{xx}(z)$ will include the unit circle in the complex z-plane. This allows us to define the *power spectrum* $S_{xx}(\omega)$ of the random signal x_n by setting $z = \exp(j\omega)$ in Eq. (1.9.1); abusing the notation somewhat, we have in this case

$$S_{xx}(\omega) = \sum_{k=-\infty}^{\infty} R_{xx}(k)\, e^{-j\omega k} \qquad \text{(power spectrum)} \tag{1.9.2}$$

This quantity conveys very useful information. It is a measure of the frequency content of the signal x_n and of the distribution of the power of x_n over frequency. To see this, consider the inverse z-transform

$$R_{xx}(k) = \oint_{u.c.} S_{xx}(z)\, z^k \frac{dz}{2\pi jz} \tag{1.9.3}$$

where, since $R_{xx}(k)$ is stable, the integration contour may be taken to be the unit circle. Using $z = \exp(j\omega)$, we find for the integration measure

$$\frac{dz}{2\pi jz} = \frac{d\omega}{2\pi}$$

Thus, Eq. (1.9.3) may also be written as an inverse Fourier transform

$$R_{xx}(k) = \int_{-\pi}^{\pi} S_{xx}(\omega)\, e^{j\omega k} \frac{d\omega}{2\pi} \tag{1.9.4}$$

In particular, the variance of x_n can be written as

$$R_{xx}(0) = \sigma_x^2 = E[x_n^2] = \int_{-\pi}^{\pi} S_{xx}(\omega) \frac{d\omega}{2\pi} \tag{1.9.5}$$

Since the quantity $E[x_n^2]$ represents the average *total power* contained in x_n, it follows that $S_{xx}(\omega)$ will represent the *power per unit frequency interval*. A typical power spectrum is depicted in Fig. 1.5. As suggested by this figure, it is possible for the power to be mostly concentrated about some frequencies and not about others. The area under the curve represents the total power of the signal x_n.

If x_n is an uncorrelated (white-noise) random signal with a delta-function

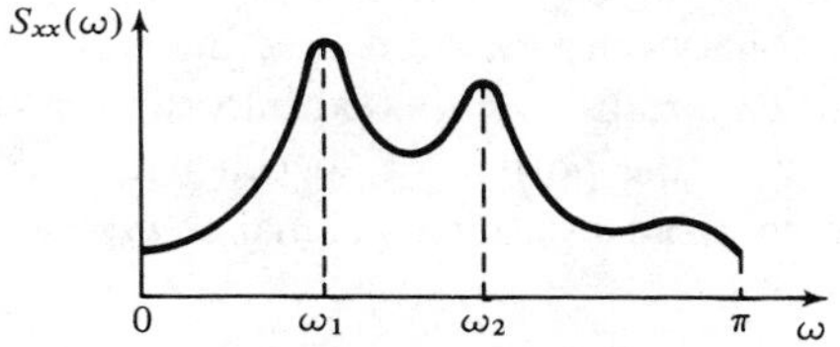

Figure 1.5 Typical Power Spectrum

autocorrelation, given by Eq. (1.8.4), it will have a *flat* power spectrum with power level equal to the variance σ_x^2:

$$S_{xx}(\omega) = \sigma_x^2 \qquad (1.9.6)$$

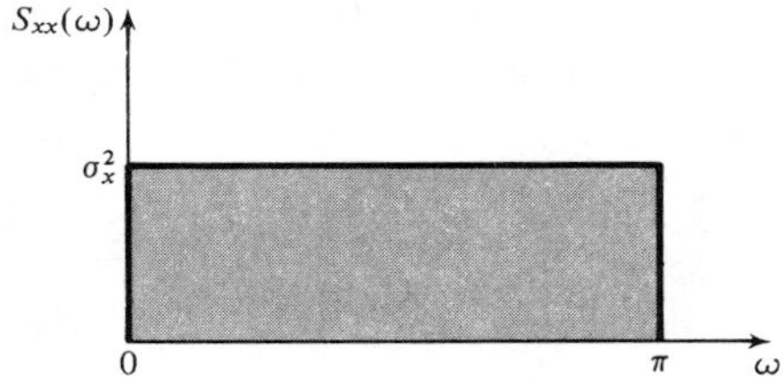

Another useful concept is that of the *cross-correlation* and *cross-spectrum* between two stationary random sequences x_n and y_n. These are defined by

$$R_{yx}(k) = E[y_{n+k}\, x_n] \qquad S_{yx}(z) = \sum_{k=-\infty}^{\infty} R_{yx}(k)\, z^{-k} \qquad (1.9.7)$$

Using stationarity, it is easy to show the reflection symmetry property

$$R_{yx}(k) = R_{xy}(-k) \qquad (1.9.8)$$

that is analogous to Eq. (1.8.3). In the z-domain, the reflection symmetry properties (1.8.3) and (1.9.8) are translated into:

$$S_{xx}(z) = S_{xx}(z^{-1}) \qquad S_{yx}(z) = S_{xy}(z^{-1}) \qquad (1.9.9)$$

respectively; and also

$$S_{xx}(\omega) = S_{xx}(-\omega) \qquad S_{yx}(\omega) = S_{xy}(-\omega) \qquad (1.9.10)$$

1.10 *Sample Autocorrelation and the Periodogram*

From now on we will work mostly with stationary random signals. If a block of N signal samples is available, we will assume that it is a segment from a stationary signal. The length N of the available data segment is an important consideration. For example, in computing frequency spectra, we know that high resolution in frequency requires a long record of data. However, if the record is too long the assumption of stationarity may no longer be justified. This is the case in many applications, as for example in speech and EEG signal processing. The speech waveform does not remain stationary for long time intervals. It may be assumed to be stationary only for short time intervals. Such a signal may be called *piece-wise stationary*. If it is divided into short segments of duration of 20–30 milliseconds, then the portion of speech within each segment may be assumed to be a segment from a stationary signal. A typical piece-wise stationary signal is depicted in Fig. 1.6.

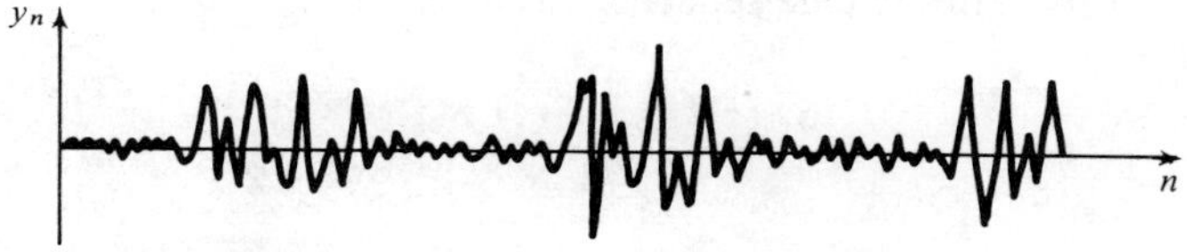

Figure 1.6 Piece-Wise Stationary Signal

The main reason for assuming stationarity, or piece-wise stationarity, is that most of our methods of handling random signals depend heavily on this assumption. For example, the statistical autocorrelations based on the ensemble averages (1.8.2) may be replaced in practice by *time averages.* This can be justified only if the signals are stationary (actually, they must be ergodic). If the underlying signal processes are not stationary (and therefore definitely not ergodic) we cannot use time averages. If a signal is piece-wise stationary and divided into stationary blocks, then for each such block, ensemble averages may be replaced by time averages. The time average approximation of an autocorrelation function is called the *sample autocorrelation* and is defined as follows: Given a block of length N of measured signal samples

$$\boxed{y_0, y_1, y_2, \cdots, y_{N-1}}$$

define

$$\hat{R}_{yy}(k) = \frac{1}{N} \sum_{n=0}^{N-1-k} y_{n+k}\, y_n \qquad \text{for } 0 \le k \le (N - 1) \tag{1.10.1}$$

and

$$\hat{R}_{yy}(k) = \hat{R}_{yy}(-k) \qquad \text{for } -(N - 1) \le k \le -1$$

The subroutine **corr** (see Appendix B) takes as inputs two length-N signal blocks $y_n, x_n, n = 0, 1, \ldots, N-1$, and computes their sample *cross-correlation* defined as

$$\hat{R}_{yx}(k) = \frac{1}{N} \sum_{n=0}^{N\text{-}1\text{-}k} y_{n+k}x_n\,, \qquad k = 0, 1, \cdots, N\text{-}1$$

This routine may be used to compute either autocorrelations or cross-correlations.

The *periodogram* is defined as the (double-sided) z-transform of the sample autocorrelation

$$\hat{S}_{yy}(z) = \sum_{k=-(N-1)}^{N-1} \hat{R}_{yy}(k)\, z^{-k} \tag{1.10.2}$$

It may be thought of as an approximation (estimate) of the true power spectral density $S_{yy}(z)$. It is easily shown that the periodogram may be expressed in terms of the z-transform of the data sequence itself, as

$$\hat{S}_{yy}(z) = \frac{1}{N} Y(z)\, Y(z^{-1}) \tag{1.10.3}$$

where

$$Y(z) = \sum_{n=0}^{N-1} y_n\, z^{-n} \tag{1.10.4}$$

As a concrete example, consider a length-3 signal $\mathbf{y} = (y_0, y_1, y_2)$. Then,

$$\begin{aligned} Y(z)\, Y(z^{-1}) &= (y_0 + y_1 z^{-1} + y_2 z^{-2})(y_0 + y_1 z + y_2 z^2) \\ &= (y_0^2 + y_1^2 + y_2^2) + (y_0 y_1 + y_1 y_2) z^{-1} \\ &\quad + (y_0 y_1 + y_1 y_2) z + (y_0 y_2) z^{-2} + (y_0 y_2) z^2 \end{aligned}$$

from which we extract the inverse z-transform

$$\begin{aligned} \hat{R}_{yy}(0) &= [y_0^2 + y_1^2 + y_2^2]/3 \\ \hat{R}_{yy}(-1) = \hat{R}_{yy}(1) &= [y_0 y_1 + y_1 y_2]/3 \\ \hat{R}_{yy}(-2) = \hat{R}_{yy}(2) &= [y_0 y_2]/3 \end{aligned}$$

These equations may also be written in a nice matrix form, as follows

$$\underbrace{\begin{bmatrix} \hat{R}_{yy}(0) & \hat{R}_{yy}(1) & \hat{R}_{yy}(2) \\ \hat{R}_{yy}(1) & \hat{R}_{yy}(0) & \hat{R}_{yy}(1) \\ \hat{R}_{yy}(2) & \hat{R}_{yy}(1) & \hat{R}_{yy}(0) \end{bmatrix}}_{\hat{R}_{yy}}$$

$$= \frac{1}{3} \underbrace{\begin{bmatrix} y_0 & y_1 & y_2 & 0 & 0 \\ 0 & y_0 & y_1 & y_2 & 0 \\ 0 & 0 & y_0 & y_1 & y_2 \end{bmatrix}}_{Y^T} \underbrace{\begin{bmatrix} y_0 & 0 & 0 \\ y_1 & y_0 & 0 \\ y_2 & y_1 & y_0 \\ 0 & y_2 & y_1 \\ 0 & 0 & y_2 \end{bmatrix}}_{Y}; \quad \hat{R}_{yy} = \frac{1}{3} Y^T Y$$

The matrix $\hat{R}_{yy}$ on the left is called the sample autocorrelation matrix. It is a *Toeplitz matrix*; that is, it has the same entry in each diagonal. The right hand side also shows that the autocorrelation matrix is positive definite. In the general case of a length-N sequence y_n, the matrix Y has N columns, each a down-shifted (delayed) version of the previous one, corresponding to a total of $N - 1$ delays. This requires the length of each column to be $N + (N - 1)$; that is, there are $2N - 1$ rows. We will encounter again this matrix factorization of the covariance matrix $\hat{R}_{yy}$ in the least-squares design of waveshaping filters.

The sample autocorrelation may also be thought of as *ordinary convolution*. Note that $Y(z^{-1})$ represents the z-transform of a signal which is the original signal $\mathbf{y} = (y_0, y_1, \ldots, y_{N-1})$ *reflected* about the time origin. The reflected signal may be made causal by a *delay* of $N - 1$ units of time. The reflected-delayed signal has some significance, and is known as the *reversed signal*. Its z-transform is the *reverse polynomial* of $Y(z)$

$$Y^R(z) = z^{-(N-1)}Y(z^{-1})$$

$$\begin{array}{llllll}
(0 \ldots 0 & 0 \;\; y_0 & y_1 \ldots & y_{N-2} y_{N-1}) & \rightarrow Y(z) & = \text{original} \\
(y_{N-1}\, y_{N-2} \ldots y_1\, y_0 & 0 \ldots & 0 & 0) & \rightarrow Y(z^{-1}) & = \text{reflected} \\
(0 \ldots 0 & 0 \;\; y_{N-1}\, y_{N-2} \ldots & y_1 & y_0) & \rightarrow z^{-(N-1)}Y(z^{-1}) & = \text{reversed}
\end{array}$$

The periodogram is expressed then in the form

$$\hat{S}_{yy}(z) = \frac{1}{N} Y(z)Y(z^{-1}) = \frac{1}{N} Y(z)Y^R(z)\, z^{(N-1)}$$

which implies that $\hat{R}_{yy}(k)$ may be obtained by convolving the original data sequence with the reversed sequence and then advancing the result in time by $N-1$ time units. This is seen by the following convolution table.

	y_0	y_1	y_2
y_2	y_2y_0	y_2y_1	y_2^2
y_1	y_1y_0	y_1^2	y_1y_2
y_0	y_0^2	y_0y_1	y_0y_2

The *periodogram spectrum* is obtained by substituting $z = e^{j\omega}$

$$\hat{S}_{yy}(\omega) = \frac{1}{N} \mid Y(\omega) \mid^2 = \frac{1}{N} \left| \sum_{n=0}^{N-1} y_n\, e^{-j\omega n} \right|^2 \tag{1.10.5}$$

The periodogram spectrum (1.10.5) may be computed efficiently using FFT methods. The digital frequency ω [in radians/sample] is related to the physical frequency f [in Hz] by

$$\omega = 2\pi f T = \frac{2\pi f}{f_s}$$

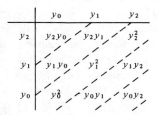

where f_s is the sampling rate, and $T = 1/f_s$ the time interval between samples. The frequency resolution afforded by a length-N sequence is

$$\Delta\omega = \frac{2\pi}{N} \quad \text{or} \quad \Delta f = \frac{f_s}{N} = \frac{1}{NT} = \frac{1}{T_R} \text{ [in Hz]}$$

where $T_R = NT$ is the *duration* of the data record. The periodogram spectrum suffers from two major drawbacks. First, the rectangular windowing of the data segment introduces significant *sidelobe leakage*. This can cause misinterpretation of sidelobe spectral peaks as being part of the true spectrum. And second, it is well-known that the periodogram spectrum is *not* a good (consistent) estimator of the true power spectrum $S_{yy}(\omega)$. The development of methods to *improve* on the periodogram is the subject of *classical spectral analysis* [9–19]. We just mention, in passing, one of the most popular of such methods; namely, *Welch's method* [20]. The given data record of length N is subdivided into K shorter segments which may be overlapping or nonoverlapping. If they are nonoverlapping then each will have length $M = N/K$; if they are 50% overlapping then $M = 2N/(K + 1)$. Each such segment is then windowed by a length-M data window, such as a Hamming window. The window reduces the sidelobe frequency leakage at the expense of resolution. The window $w(n)$ is typically normalized to have unit average energy; that is, $(1/M)\sum_{n=0}^{M-1} w(n)^2 = 1$. The periodogram of each windowed segment is then computed by FFT methods and the K periodograms are averaged together to obtain the spectrum estimate

$$S(\omega) = \frac{1}{K}\sum_{i=1}^{K} S_i(\omega)$$

where $S_i(\omega)$ is the periodogram of the ith segment. The above subdivision into segments imitates ensemble averaging, and therefore, it results in a spectrum estimate of improved statistical stability. However, since each periodogram is computed from a length-M sequence, the frequency resolution is reduced from $\Delta\omega = 2\pi/N$ to roughly $\Delta\omega = 2\pi/M$ (for a well-designed window). Therefore, to maintain high frequency resolution (large M), as well as improved statistical stability of the spectrum estimate (large K), a long data record N is required; a condition that can easily come into conflict with stationarity. The so-called "modern methods" of spectrum estimation, which are based on *parametric signal models*, can provide high resolution spectrum estimates from *short* data records N.

1.11 *Random Signal Models and Their Uses*

Models that provide a characterization of the properties and nature of random signals are of primary importance in the design of optimum signal processing systems. This section offers an overview of such models and outlines their major applications. Many of the ideas presented here will be developed in greater detail in later chapters.

One of the most useful ways to model a random signal [21] is to consider it as being the *output* of a *causal and stable* linear filter $B(z)$ which is driven by a *stationary uncorrelated* (white-noise) sequence $\{\epsilon_0, \epsilon_1, \ldots, \epsilon_n, \ldots\}$:

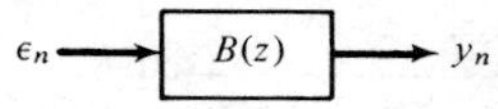

$$B(z) = \sum_{n=0}^{\infty} b_n z^{-n}$$

where $R_{\epsilon\epsilon}(k) = E[\epsilon_{n+k}\epsilon_n] = \sigma_\epsilon^2 \delta(k)$. The output random signal y_n is obtained by convolving the input sequence ϵ_n with the filter's impulse response b_n:

$$y_n = \sum_{i=0}^{n} b_{n-i}\epsilon_i \qquad n = 0,1,2, \ldots \tag{1.11.1}$$

The stability of the filter $B(z)$ is essential as it guarantees the stationarity of the sequence y_n. This point will be discussed later on. By readjusting, if necessary, the value of σ_ϵ^2, we may assume that $b_0 = 1$. Then Eq. (1.11.1) corresponds exactly to the Gram-Schmidt form of Eqs. (1.5.15) and (1.5.16), where the matrix elements b_{ni} are given in terms of the impulse response of the filter $B(z)$:

$$b_{ni} = b_{n-i} \tag{1.11.2}$$

In this case, the structure of the matrix B is considerably simplified. Writing the convolutional equation (1.11.1) in matrix form

$$\begin{bmatrix} y_0 \\ y_1 \\ y_2 \\ y_3 \\ y_4 \end{bmatrix} = \begin{bmatrix} 1 & 0 & 0 & 0 & 0 \\ b_1 & 1 & 0 & 0 & 0 \\ b_2 & b_1 & 1 & 0 & 0 \\ b_3 & b_2 & b_1 & 1 & 0 \\ b_4 & b_3 & b_2 & b_1 & 1 \end{bmatrix} \begin{bmatrix} \epsilon_0 \\ \epsilon_1 \\ \epsilon_2 \\ \epsilon_3 \\ \epsilon_4 \end{bmatrix} \tag{1.11.3}$$

we observe that the first column of B is the impulse response b_n of the filter. Each subsequent column is a down-shifted (delayed) version of the previous one, and each diagonal has the same entry (i.e., B is a Toeplitz matrix). The lower-triangular nature of B is equivalent to the assumed *causality* of the filter $B(z)$.

Such signal models are quite general. In fact, there is a general theorem by Wold that essentially guarantees the *existence* of such models for any stationary signal y_n [22,23]. Wold's construction of $B(z)$ is none other than the Gram-Schmidt construction of the orthogonalized basis ϵ_n. However, the practical usage of such models requires further that the transfer function $B(z)$ be *rational*; that is, the ratio of two polynomials in z. In this case, the I/O equation (1.11.1) is most conveniently expressed as a *difference equation.*

Example 1.11.1: Suppose

$$B(z) = \frac{1 + c_1 z^{-1} + c_2 z^{-2}}{1 + d_1 z^{-1} + d_2 z^{-2}} \tag{1.11.4}$$

Then Eq. (1.11.1) is equivalent to the difference equation

$$y_n = -d_1 y_{n-1} - d_2 y_{n-2} + \epsilon_n + c_1 \epsilon_{n-1} + c_2 \epsilon_{n-2} \tag{1.11.5}$$

which may be realized as follows.

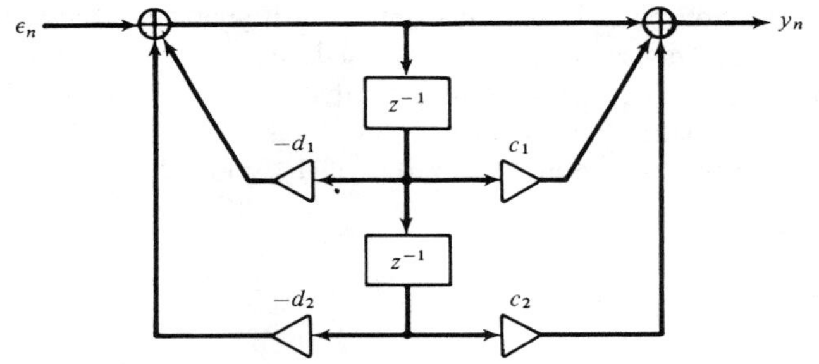

The filter $B(z)$ is called a *synthesis filter* and may be thought of as a random signal generator, or a signal model for the random signal y_n. The numerator and denominator coefficients of the filter $B(z)$, and the variance σ_ϵ^2 of the input white noise, are referred to as the *model parameters.* For instance, in Example 1.11.1 the model parameters are $\{c_1, c_2, d_1, d_2; \sigma_\epsilon^2\}$. Such parametric models have received a lot of attention in recent years. They are very common in speech and geophysical signal processing, image processing, EEG signal processing, spectrum estimation, data compression, and other time series analysis applications. How are such models used? One of the main objectives in such applications has been to develop appropriate *analysis procedures* for extracting the model parameters (filter coefficients and σ_ϵ^2) on the basis of a given set of actual signal samples y_n. This is a *system identification* problem. The analysis procedures are designed to provide effectively the *best fit* of the data samples to a particular model. The procedures typically begin with a measured block of signal samples $\{y_0, y_1, \ldots, y_{N-1}\}$—also referred to as an *analysis frame*—and through an appropriate analysis algorithm extract *estimates* of the model parameters. This is depicted in Fig. 1.7.

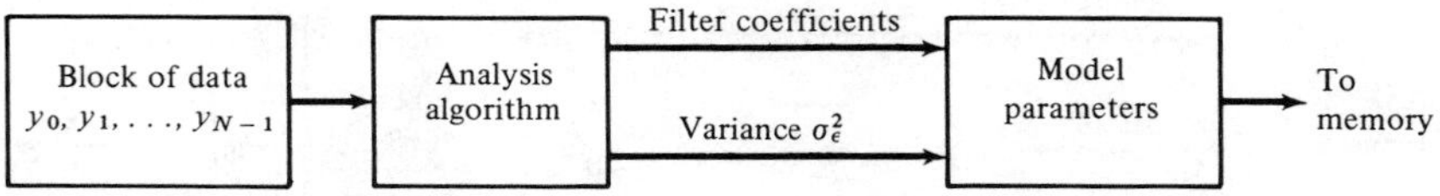

Figure 1.7 Analysis Procedure

The given frame of samples $\{y_0, y_1, \ldots, y_{N-1}\}$ is *represented* now by the set of model parameters extracted from it. Following the analysis procedure, the resulting model may be used in a variety of ways. The four major uses of such models are in:

1. Signal synthesis
2. Spectrum estimation
3. Signal classification
4. Data compression

We will discuss each of these briefly. To synthesize a particular realization of the random signal y_n, it is only necessary to recall from memory the appropriate model parameters, to generate a random uncorrelated sequence ϵ_n having variance σ_ϵ^2, and send it through the filter $B(z)$. Such uncorrelated sequence may be *computer-generated* using a standard random number generator routine. The synthetic signal will appear at the output of the filter. This is shown in Fig. 1.8. This is the basic principle behind most speech synthesis systems. In speech, the synthesis filter $B(z)$ represents a model of the transfer characteristics of the *vocal tract* considered as an acoustic tube. A typical analysis frame of speech has duration of 20 msec. If sampled at a 10-kHz sampling rate, it will consist of $N = 200$ samples. To synthesize a particular frame of 200 samples, the model parameters representing that frame are recalled from memory, and the synthesis filter is run for 200 sampling instances generating 200 output speech samples, which may be sent to a D/A converter. The next frame of 200 samples can be synthesized by recalling from memory *its* model parameters, and so on. Entire words or sentences can be synthesized in such a piece-wise, or frame-wise, manner. A realistic representation of each speech frame requires the specification of two additional parameters besides the filter coefficients and σ_ϵ^2; namely, the *pitch* period and a *voiced/unvoiced* (V/UV) decision. Unvoiced sounds, such as the "sh" in the word "should," have a white-noise sounding nature, and are

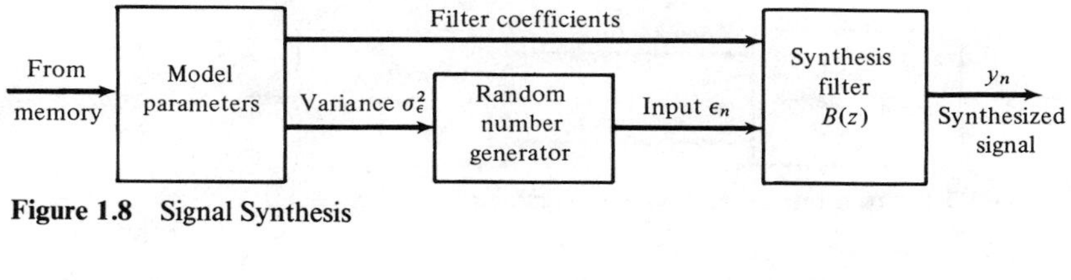

Figure 1.8 Signal Synthesis

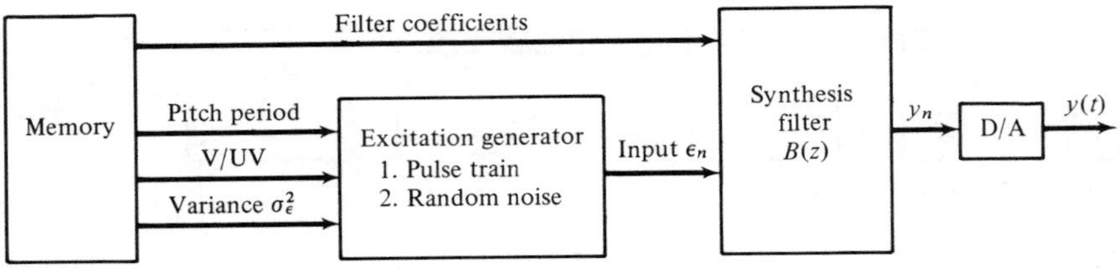

Figure 1.9 Typical Speech Synthesis System

generated by the turbulent flow of air through constrictions of the vocal tract. Such sounds may be represented adequately by the above random signal models. On the other hand, voiced sounds, such as vowels, are pitched sounds, and have a pitch period associated with them. They may be assumed to be generated by the periodic excitation of the vocal tract by a train of impulses separated by the pitch period. The vocal tract responds to each of these impulses by producing its impulse response, resulting therefore in a quasi-periodic output which is characteristic of such sounds. Thus, depending on the type of sound, the nature of the generator of the excitation input to the synthesis filter will be different; namely, it will be a *random noise generator* for unvoiced sounds, and a *pulse train generator* for voiced sounds. A typical speech synthesis system that incorporates the above features is shown in Fig. 1.9.

Another major application of parametric models is to *spectrum estimation*. This is based on the property that

$$S_{yy}(\omega) = \sigma_\epsilon^2 \, |B(\omega)|^2 \tag{1.11.6}$$

which will be proved later. It states that the spectral shape of the power spectrum $S_{yy}(\omega)$ of the signal y_n arises only from the spectral shape of the model filter $B(\omega)$. For example, the signal y_n generated by the model of Example 1.11.1 will have

$$S_{yy}(\omega) = \sigma_\epsilon^2 \left| \frac{1 + c_1 e^{-j\omega} + c_2 e^{-2j\omega}}{1 + d_1 e^{-j\omega} + d_2 e^{-2j\omega}} \right|^2$$

This approach to spectrum estimation is depicted in Fig. 1.10. The parametric approach to spectrum estimation must be contrasted with the classical approach which is based on *direct computation* of the Fourier transform of the available data record; that is, the periodogram spectrum, or its improvements. The classical

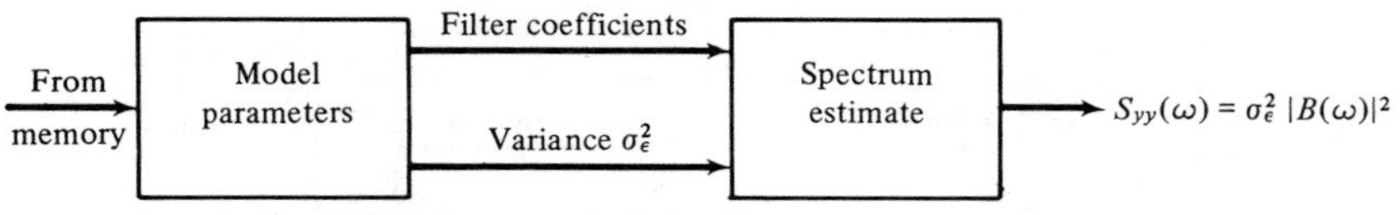

Figure 1.10 Spectrum Estimation with Parametric Models

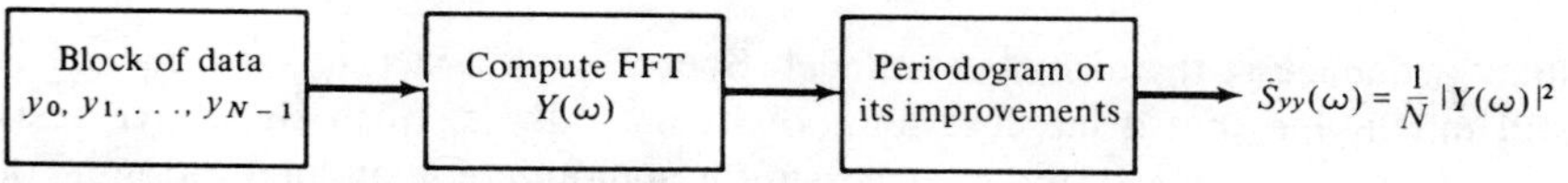

Figure 1.11 Classical Spectrum Estimation

periodogram method is shown in Fig. 1.11. As we mentioned in the previous section, spectrum estimates based on such parametric models tend to have much better frequency resolution properties than the classical methods, especially when the length N of the available data record is short.

In *signal classification* applications, such as speech recognition, speaker verification, or EEG pattern classification, the basic problem is to compare two available blocks of data samples and decide whether they belong to the same class or not. One of the two blocks might be a prestored and preanalyzed *reference template* against which the other block is to be compared. Instead of comparing the data records sample by sample, what are compared are the corresponding model parameters extracted from these blocks. In pattern recognition nomenclature, the vector of model parameters is the "feature vector." The closeness of the two sets of model parameters to each other is decided on the basis of an appropriate *distance measure*. We will discuss examples of distance measures for speech and EEG signals in Chapter 5. This approach to signal classification is depicted in Fig. 1.12.

Next, we discuss the application of such models to *data compression*. The signal synthesis method described above is a form of data compression because instead of saving the N data samples y_n as such, what are saved are the corresponding model parameters which are typically much *fewer* in number than N. For example, in speech synthesis systems a savings of about a factor of 20 in memory may be achieved with this approach. Indeed, as we discussed above, a typical frame of speech consists of 200 samples, whereas the number of model parameters typically needed to represent this frame is about 10 to 15. The main limitation of this approach is that the reproduction of the original signal segment is not exact but depends on the particular realization of the computer-generated

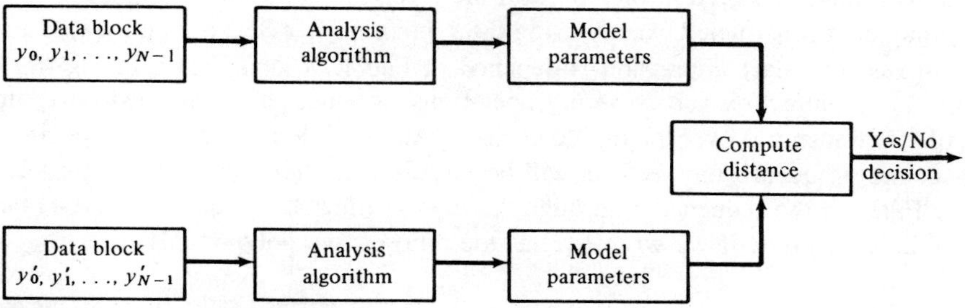

Figure 1.12 Signal Classification

input sequence ϵ_n that drives the model. Speech synthesized in such manner is still intelligible, but it has lost some of its naturalness. Such signal synthesis methods are not necessarily as successful or appropriate in all applications. For example, in image processing, if one makes a parametric model of an image and attempts to "synthesize" it by driving the model with a computer-generated uncorrelated sequence, the reproduced image will bear no resemblance to the original image; not even vaguely so.

For *exact* reproduction, both the model parameters and the entire sequence ϵ_n must be stored. This would still provide some form of data compression, as will be explained below. Such an approach to data compression is widely used in digital data transmission or digital data storage applications for all types of data, including speech and image data. The method may be described as follows: the given data record $\{y_0, y_1, \ldots, y_{N-1}\}$ is subjected to the appropriate analysis algorithm to extract the model parameters, and then the segment is filtered through the *inverse filter*

$$A(z) = \frac{1}{B(z)} \qquad (1.11.7)$$

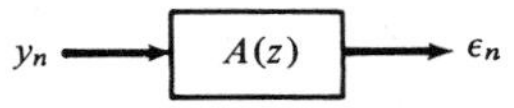

to provide the sequence ϵ_n. The inverse filter $A(z)$ is also known as the *whitening filter*, the *prediction-error filter*, or the *analysis filter*. The resulting sequence ϵ_n has a compressed dynamic range relative to y_n and therefore it requires fewer number of bits for the representation of each sample ϵ_n. A quantitative measure for the *data compression gain* is given by the ratio $G = \sigma_y^2/\sigma_\epsilon^2$ which is always greater than one. This can be seen easily using Eqs. (1.11.6) and (1.9.5)

$$\sigma_y^2 = \int_{-\pi}^{\pi} S_{yy}(\omega)\frac{d\omega}{2\pi} = \sigma_\epsilon^2 \int_{-\pi}^{\pi} |B(\omega)|^2 \frac{d\omega}{2\pi} = \sigma_\epsilon^2 \sum_{n=0}^{\infty} b_n^2$$

Since $b_0 = 1$, we find

$$G = \frac{\sigma_y^2}{\sigma_\epsilon^2} = \sum_{n=0}^{\infty} b_n^2 = 1 + b_1^2 + b_2^2 + \cdots \qquad (1.11.8)$$

The entire sequence ϵ_n and the model parameters are then transmitted over the data link, or stored in memory. At the receiving end, the original sequence y_n may be reconstructed exactly using the synthesis filter $B(z)$ driven by ϵ_n. This approach to data compression is depicted in Fig. 1.13. Not shown in Fig. 1.13 are the *quantization* and *encoding* operations that must be performed on ϵ_n in order to transmit it over the digital channel. An example that properly takes into account the quantization effects will be discussed in more detail in Chapter 2.

Filtering the sequence y_n through the inverse filter $A(z)$ requires that $A(z)$ be stable and causal. If we write $B(z)$ as the ratio of two polynomials

$$B(z) = \frac{N(z)}{D(z)} \qquad (1.11.9)$$

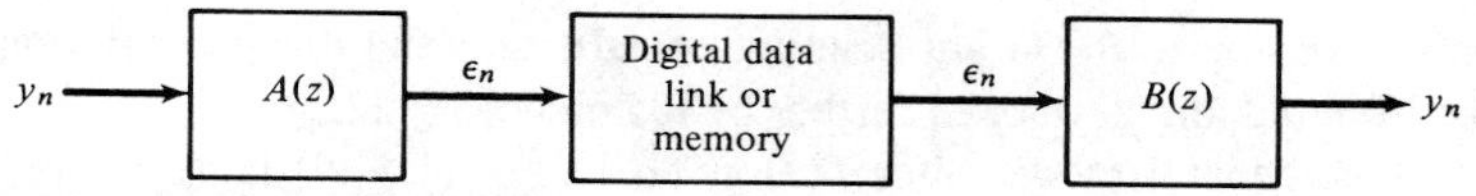

Figure 1.13 Data Compression

then the stability and causality of $B(z)$ requires that the zeros of the polynomial $D(z)$ lie inside the unit circle in the complex z-plane; whereas the stability and causality of the inverse $A(z) = D(z)/N(z)$ requires the zeros of $N(z)$ to be inside the unit circle. Thus, both the poles and the zeros of $B(z)$ must be inside the unit circle. Such filters are called *minimal phase* filters and will be discussed further in Chapter 3. When $A(z)$ is stable and causal it may be expanded in the form

$$A(z) = \sum_{n=0}^{\infty} a_n z^{-n} = 1 + a_1 z^{-1} + a_2 z^{-2} + \cdots \qquad (1.11.10)$$

and the I/O equation of Eq. (1.11.7) becomes

$$\epsilon_n = \sum_{i=0}^{n} a_i y_{n-i} = y_n + a_1 y_{n-1} + a_2 y_{n-2} + \cdots + a_n y_0 \qquad (1.11.11)$$

for $n = 0,1,2, \ldots$ It may be written in matrix form $\boldsymbol{\epsilon} = A\mathbf{y}$ as

$$\begin{bmatrix} \epsilon_0 \\ \epsilon_1 \\ \epsilon_2 \\ \epsilon_3 \\ \epsilon_4 \end{bmatrix} = \begin{bmatrix} 1 & 0 & 0 & 0 & 0 \\ a_1 & 1 & 0 & 0 & 0 \\ a_2 & a_1 & 1 & 0 & 0 \\ a_3 & a_2 & a_1 & 1 & 0 \\ a_4 & a_3 & a_2 & a_1 & 1 \end{bmatrix} \begin{bmatrix} y_0 \\ y_1 \\ y_2 \\ y_3 \\ y_4 \end{bmatrix}$$

Both this matrix form and Eq. (1.11.11) are recognized as special cases of Eqs. (1.6.1) and (1.6.10). According to Eq. (1.6.11), the quantity

$$\hat{y}_{n/n-1} = -[a_1 y_{n-1} + a_2 y_{n-2} + \cdots a_n y_0] \qquad (1.11.12)$$

is the projection of y_n on the subspace spanned by $Y_{n-1} = \{y_{n-1}, y_{n-2}, \ldots, y_0\}$. Therefore, it represents the best linear estimate of y_n on the basis of (all) its past values Y_{n-1}; that is, $\hat{y}_{n/n-1}$ is the *best prediction* of y_n from its (entire) past. Equation (1.11.11) gives the corresponding prediction error $\epsilon_n = y_n - \hat{y}_{n/n-1}$. We note here an interesting connection between linear prediction concepts and signal modeling concepts [21–25]; namely, that the best linear predictor (1.11.12) determines the whitening filter $A(z)$ which, in turn, determines the generator model $B(z) = 1/A(z)$ of y_n. In other words, solving the prediction problem also solves the modeling problem.

The above modeling approach to the representation of stationary time series, and its relationship to the Gram-Schmidt construction and linear prediction was initiated by Wold and developed further by Kolmogorov [22,24].

The most general model filter $B(z)$ given in Eq. (1.11.9) is called an *autoregressive moving average* (ARMA), or a pole-zero model. Two special cases of interest are the *moving average* (MA), or all-zero models, and the *autoregressive* (AR), or all-pole models. The MA model has a nontrivial numerator only, $B(z) = N(z)$, so that $B(z)$ is a finite polynomial:

$$B(z) = 1 + b_1 z^{-1} + b_2 z^{-2} + \cdots + b_M z^{-M} \qquad \text{(MA model)}$$

The AR model has a nontrivial denominator only, $B(z) = 1/D(z)$, so that its inverse $A(z) = D(z)$ is a polynomial:

$$B(z) = \frac{1}{1 + a_1 z^{-1} + a_2 z^{-2} + \cdots + a_M z^{-M}} \qquad \text{(AR model)}$$

$$A(z) = 1 + a_1 z^{-1} + a_2 z^{-2} + \cdots + a_M z^{-M}$$

Autoregressive models are the most widely used models, because the analysis algorithms for extracting the model parameters $\{a_1, a_2, \ldots, a_M; \sigma_\epsilon^2\}$ are fairly simple. In the sequel, we will concentrate mainly on such models.

1.12 *Filter Model of First Order Markov Process*

To gain some understanding of filter models of the above type, we consider now a very simple example of a first order recursive filter $B(z)$ driven by a purely random sequence of variance σ_ϵ^2:

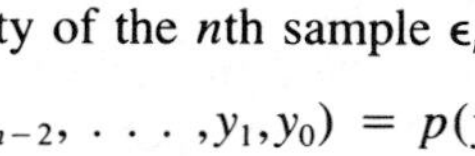

$$B(z) = \frac{1}{1 - az^{-1}}$$

This serves also as a simple model for generating a first order Markov signal. The signal y_n is generated by the difference equation of the filter:

$$y_n = ay_{n-1} + \epsilon_n \tag{1.12.1}$$

Let the probability of the nth sample ϵ_n be $f(\epsilon_n)$. We would like to show that

$$p(y_n/y_{n-1}, y_{n-2}, \ldots, y_1, y_0) = p(y_n/y_{n-1}) = f(\epsilon_n) = f(y_n - ay_{n-1})$$

which not only shows the Markov property of y_n, but also how to compute the related conditional density. Perhaps the best way to see this is to start at $n = 0$:

$$y_0 = \epsilon_0 \qquad \text{(assuming zero initial conditions)}$$

$$y_1 = ay_0 + \epsilon_1$$

$$y_2 = ay_1 + \epsilon_2, \qquad \text{etc.}$$

To compute $p(y_2/y_1,y_0)$, suppose that y_1 and y_0 are both given. Since y_1 is given, the third equation above shows that the randomness left in y_2 arises from ϵ_2 only. Thus, $p(y_2/y_1) = f(\epsilon_2)$. From the first two equations it follows that specifying y_0 and y_1 is equivalent to specifying ϵ_0 and ϵ_1. Therefore, $p(y_2/y_1,y_0) = f(\epsilon_2/\epsilon_1,\epsilon_0) = f(\epsilon_2)$, the last equation following from the purely random nature of the sequence ϵ_n. We have shown that

$$p(y_2/y_1,y_0) = p(y_2/y_1) = f(\epsilon_2) = f(y_2 - ay_1)$$

Using the results of Section 1.8, we also note

$$\begin{aligned} p(y_2,y_1,y_0) &= p(y_2/y_1)\,p(y_1/y_0)\,p(y_0) \\ &= f(\epsilon_2)\,f(\epsilon_1)\,f(\epsilon_0) \\ &= f(y_2 - ay_1)\,f(y_1 - ay_0)\,f(y_0) \end{aligned}$$

The solution of the difference equation (1.12.1) is obtained by convolving the impulse response of the filter $B(z)$

$$b_n = a^n u(n) \qquad u(n) = \text{unit step}$$

with the input sequence ϵ_n as follows:

$$y_n = \sum_{i=0}^{n} b_i\,\epsilon_{n-i} = \sum_{i=0}^{n} a^i\,\epsilon_{n-i} \tag{1.12.2}$$

for $n = 0,1,2,\ldots$ This is the innovations representation of y_n given by Eqs. (1.5.15), (1.5.16), and (1.11.1). In matrix form it reads:

$$\begin{bmatrix} y_0 \\ y_1 \\ y_2 \\ y_3 \end{bmatrix} = \begin{bmatrix} 1 & 0 & 0 & 0 \\ a & 1 & 0 & 0 \\ a^2 & a & 1 & 0 \\ a^3 & a^2 & a & 1 \end{bmatrix} \begin{bmatrix} \epsilon_0 \\ \epsilon_1 \\ \epsilon_2 \\ \epsilon_3 \end{bmatrix} \tag{1.12.3}$$

The inverse equation $\boldsymbol{\epsilon} = B^{-1}\mathbf{y} = A\mathbf{y}$, is obtained by writing Eq. (1.12.1) as $\epsilon_n = y_n - ay_{n-1}$. In matrix form, this reads

$$\begin{bmatrix} \epsilon_0 \\ \epsilon_1 \\ \epsilon_2 \\ \epsilon_3 \end{bmatrix} = \begin{bmatrix} 1 & 0 & 0 & 0 \\ -a & 1 & 0 & 0 \\ 0 & -a & 1 & 0 \\ 0 & 0 & -a & 1 \end{bmatrix} \begin{bmatrix} y_0 \\ y_1 \\ y_2 \\ y_3 \end{bmatrix} \tag{1.12.4}$$

According to the discussion of Example 1.6.1, the partial correlation coefficients can be read off from the *first column* of this matrix. We conclude, therefore, that all partial correlation coefficients of order greater than two are zero. This property is in accordance with our intuition about first order Markov processes; due to the recursive nature of Eq. (1.12.1) a given sample, say y_n, will have an indirect influence on all future samples. However, the *only direct* influence is to the next sample.

Higher order Markov random signals can be generated by sending white noise through higher order filters. For example, the second order difference equation

$$y_n = a_1 y_{n-1} + a_2 y_{n-2} + \epsilon_n \tag{1.12.5}$$

will generate a second order Markov signal. In this case, the difference equation directly couples two successive samples, but not more than two. Therefore, all the partial correlations of order greater than three will be zero. This may be seen also by writing Eq. (1.12.5) in matrix form and inspecting the first column of the matrix A:

$$\begin{bmatrix} \epsilon_0 \\ \epsilon_1 \\ \epsilon_2 \\ \epsilon_3 \\ \epsilon_4 \end{bmatrix} = \begin{bmatrix} 1 & 0 & 0 & 0 & 0 \\ -a_1 & 1 & 0 & 0 & 0 \\ -a_2 & -a_1 & 1 & 0 & 0 \\ 0 & -a_2 & -a_1 & 1 & 0 \\ 0 & 0 & -a_2 & -a_1 & 1 \end{bmatrix} \begin{bmatrix} y_0 \\ y_1 \\ y_2 \\ y_3 \\ y_4 \end{bmatrix}$$

1.13 *Stability and Stationarity*

In this section we discuss the importance of stability of the signal generator filter $B(z)$. We demonstrate that the generated signal y_n will be stationary *only* if the generating filter is stable. And in this case, the sequence y_n will become stationary only after the *transient effects* introduced by the filter have died out.

To demonstrate these ideas, consider the lag $= 0$ autocorrelation of our first order Markov signal

$$\begin{aligned} R_{yy}(n,n) &= E[y_n^2] = E[(ay_{n-1} + \epsilon_n)^2] \\ &= a^2 E[y_{n-1}^2] + 2aE[y_{n-1}\epsilon_n] + E[\epsilon_n^2] \\ &= a^2 R_{yy}(n-1, n-1) + \sigma_\epsilon^2 \end{aligned} \tag{1.13.1}$$

where we set $\sigma_\epsilon^2 = E[\epsilon_n^2]$, and $E[y_{n-1}\epsilon_n] = 0$, which follows by using Eq. (1.12.2) to get

$$y_{n-1} = \epsilon_{n-1} + a\epsilon_{n-2} + a^2\epsilon_{n-3} + \cdots + a^{n-1}\epsilon_0$$

and noting that ϵ_n is uncorrelated with all these terms, due to its white-noise nature. The above difference equation for $R_{yy}(n,n)$ can now be solved to get

$$R_{yy}(n,n) = E[y_n^2] = \frac{\sigma_\epsilon^2}{1-a^2} + \sigma_\epsilon^2\left(1 - \frac{1}{1-a^2}\right)a^{2n} \tag{1.13.2}$$

where the initial condition was taken to be $E[y_0^2] = E[\epsilon_0^2] = \sigma_\epsilon^2$.

If the filter is stable; that is, $|a| < 1$, then the second term above tends to zero exponentially, and $R_{yy}(n,n)$ eventually "loses" its dependence on the absolute time n. For large n, it tends to the steady-state value

$$R_{yy}(0) = E[y_n^2] = \sigma_y^2 = \frac{\sigma_\epsilon^2}{1 - a^2} \tag{1.13.3}$$

The same result is obtained, of course, by assuming stationarity from the start. The difference equation (1.13.1) can be written as

$$E[y_n^2] = a^2 E[y_{n-1}^2] + \sigma_\epsilon^2$$

If y_n is assumed to be already stationary, then $E[y_{n-1}^2] = E[y_n^2]$. This implies the same steady-state solution as Eq. (1.13.3).

If the filter is unstable; that is, $|a| > 1$, then the second term of Eq. (1.13.2) blows up exponentially. The marginal case $a = 1$ is also unacceptable, but is of historical interest being the famous Wiener process, or random walk. In this case, the signal model is

$$y_n = y_{n-1} + \epsilon_n$$

and the difference equation for the variance becomes

$$R_{yy}(n,n) = R_{yy}(n - 1, n - 1) + \sigma_\epsilon^2$$

with solution

$$R_{yy}(n,n) = E[y_n^2] = (n + 1)\,\sigma_\epsilon^2$$

In summary, for true stationarity to set in, the signal generator filter $B(z)$ must be *strictly* stable (all its poles must be strictly inside the unit circle).

1.14 *Parameter Identification by the Maximum Likelihood Method*

One of the most important practical questions is how to extract the model parameters, such as the above filter parameter a, from the actual data values. As an introduction to the analysis methods used to answer this question, let us suppose that the white noise input sequence ϵ_n is gaussian

$$f(\epsilon_n) = \frac{1}{\sqrt{2\pi}\,\sigma_\epsilon} \exp(-\epsilon_n^2/2\sigma_\epsilon^2)$$

and assume that a block of N measured values of the signal y_n is available

$$y_0, y_1, y_2, \ldots, y_{N-1}$$

Can we extract the filter parameter a from this block of data? Can we also extract the variance σ_ϵ^2 of the driving white noise ϵ_n? If so, then instead of saving the

N measured values $y_0, y_1, \ldots, y_{N-1}$, we can save the extracted filter parameter a and the variance σ_ϵ^2. Whenever we want to "synthesize" our original sequence y_n, we will simply generate a white-noise input sequence ϵ_n of variance σ_ϵ^2, using a pseudorandom number generator routine, and then drive with it the signal model whose parameter a was previously extracted from the original data. Somehow, all the significant information contained in the original samples, has now been packed or compressed into the two numbers a and σ_ϵ^2.

One possible criterion for extracting the filter parameter a is the maximum likelihood (ML) criterion: The parameter a is selected so as to *maximize* the joint density

$$p(y_{N-1}, \ldots, y_1, y_0) = f(\epsilon_{N-1}) \ldots f(\epsilon_1)\, f(\epsilon_0)$$

$$= \left(\frac{1}{\sqrt{2\pi}\,\sigma_\epsilon}\right)^N \exp\left[-\sum_{n=1}^{N-1} (y_n - a y_{n-1})^2/2\sigma_\epsilon^2\right] \exp[-y_0^2/2\sigma_\epsilon^2]$$

that is, the parameter a is selected so as to render the actual measured values $y_0, y_1, \ldots, y_{N-1}$ most likely. The criterion is equivalent to minimizing the exponent with respect to a:

$$\mathcal{E}(a) = \sum_{n=1}^{N-1} (y_n - a y_{n-1})^2 + y_0^2 = \sum_{n=0}^{N-1} e_n^2 = \min \tag{1.14.1}$$

where we set $e_n = y_n - a y_{n-1}$, and $e_0 = y_0$. The minimization of Eq. (1.14.1) gives

$$\frac{\partial \mathcal{E}(a)}{\partial a} = -2 \sum_{n=1}^{N-1} (y_n - a y_{n-1}) y_{n-1} = 0$$

or

$$a = \frac{\displaystyle\sum_{n=1}^{N-1} y_n\, y_{n-1}}{\displaystyle\sum_{n=1}^{N-1} y_{n-1}\, y_{n-1}} = \frac{y_0 y_1 + y_1 y_2 + \cdots + y_{N-2} y_{N-1}}{y_0^2 + y_1^2 + \cdots + y_{N-2}^2} \tag{1.14.2}$$

There is a potential problem with the above ML criterion for extracting the filter parameter a; namely, the parameter may turn out to have magnitude greater than one, which will correspond to an unstable filter generating the sequence y_n. This is easily seen from Eq. (1.14.2). Whereas the numerator has dependence on the last sample y_{N-1}, the denominator does not. Therefore it is possible, for sufficiently large values of y_{N-1}, for the parameter a to be greater than one. There are other criteria for extracting the Markov model parameters that guarantee the stability of the resulting synthesis filters, such as the so-called autocorrelation method, or Burg's method. These will be discussed later on.

1.15 *Parameter Identification by the Yule-Walker Method*

In this section, we introduce the *autocorrelation* or *Yule-Walker method* of extracting the model parameters from a block of data. We begin by expressing the model parameters in terms of output statistical quantities and then replace ensemble averages by time averages. Assuming stationarity has set in, we find

$$\begin{aligned} R_{yy}(1) &= E[y_n\, y_{n-1}] = E[(ay_{n-1} + \epsilon_n)y_{n-1}] = aE[y_{n-1}^2] + E[\epsilon_n\, y_{n-1}] \\ &= a\, R_{yy}(0) \end{aligned}$$

from which

$$a = \frac{R_{yy}(1)}{R_{yy}(0)}$$

The input parameter σ_ϵ^2 can be expressed as

$$\sigma_\epsilon^2 = (1 - a^2)\, \sigma_y^2 = (1 - a^2)\, R_{yy}(0)$$

These two equations may be written in matrix form as

$$\begin{bmatrix} R_{yy}(0) & R_{yy}(1) \\ R_{yy}(1) & R_{yy}(0) \end{bmatrix} \begin{bmatrix} 1 \\ -a \end{bmatrix} \begin{bmatrix} \sigma_\epsilon^2 \\ 0 \end{bmatrix}$$

These are called the *normal equations* of linear prediction. Their generalization will be considered later on. These results are important because they allow the extraction of the signal model parameters directly in terms of *output* quantities; that is, from experimentally accessible quantities.

We may obtain estimates of the model parameters by replacing the theoretical autocorrelations by the corresponding *sample autocorrelations*, defined by Eq. (1.10.1):

$$\hat{a} = \frac{\hat{R}_{yy}(1)}{\hat{R}_{yy}(0)} = \frac{\dfrac{1}{N}\displaystyle\sum_{n=0}^{N-1-1} y_{n+1}\, y_n}{\dfrac{1}{N}\displaystyle\sum_{n=0}^{N-1} y_n\, y_n} = \frac{y_0 y_1 + y_1 y_2 + \cdots + y_{N-2} y_{N-1}}{y_0^2 + y_1^2 + \cdots + y_{N-2}^2 + y_{N-1}^2}$$

$$\hat{\sigma}_\epsilon^2 = (1 - \hat{a}^2)\, \hat{R}_{yy}(0)$$

It is easily checked that the parameter $\hat{a}$, defined as above, is always of magnitude less than one; thus, the stability of the synthesis filter is guaranteed. Note the difference with the ML expression. The numerators are the same, but the denominators differ by an extra term. It is also interesting to note that the above expressions may be obtained by a *minimization criterion;* known as the autocorrelation method, or the Yule-Walker method:

$$\mathcal{E}(a) = \sum_{n=0}^{N} e_n^2 = \sum_{n=0}^{N} (y_n - ay_{n-1})^2 = \min \qquad (1.15.1)$$

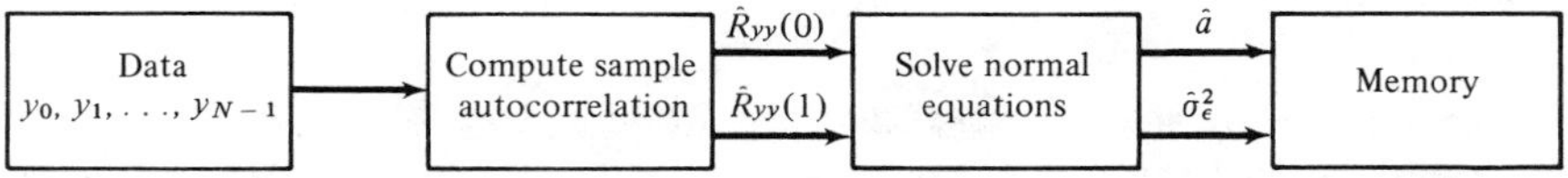

Figure 1.14 Yule-Walker Analysis Method

This differs from the ML criterion (1.14.1) only in the range of summation for n. Whereas in the ML criterion the summation index n does not run off the ends of the data block, it does so in the Yule-Walker case. We may think of the block of data as having been extended to both directions by padding it with zeros

$$0, \ldots, 0, y_0, y_1, \ldots, y_{N-1}, 0, 0, \ldots 0, \ldots$$

The difference between this and the ML criterion arises from the last term in the sum

$$\mathcal{E}(a) = \sum_{n=0}^{N} e_n^2 = \sum_{n=0}^{N-1} e_n^2 + e_N^2 = \sum_{n=0}^{N-1} (y_n - ay_{n-1})^2 + (0 - ay_{N-1})^2$$

The Yule-Walker analysis algorithm for this first order example is summarized in Fig. 1.14.

How good are $\hat{a}$ and $\hat{\sigma}_\epsilon^2$ as estimates of the model parameters a and σ_ϵ^2? It can be shown that they, and the maximum likelihood estimates of the previous section, are asymptotically unbiased and consistent. The corresponding variances are given for large N by [4–6]

$$E[\Delta a^2] = \frac{1 - a^2}{N}, \quad E[(\Delta \sigma_\epsilon^2)^2] = \frac{2\sigma_\epsilon^4}{N} \tag{1.15.2}$$

where $\Delta a = \hat{a} - a$ and $\Delta\sigma_\epsilon^2 = \hat{\sigma}_\epsilon^2 - \sigma_\epsilon^2$. Such asymptotic properties are discussed in greater detail in Chapter 6. Here, we present some simulation examples showing that (1.15.2) are adequate even for fairly small N.

Example 1.15.1: The following $N = 30$ signal samples of y_n have been generated by passing zero-mean white noise through the difference equation $y_n = ay_{n-1} + \epsilon_n$, with $a = 0.8$ and $\sigma_\epsilon^2 = 1$:

$$y_n = \{2.583, 2.617, 2.289, 2.783, 2.862, 3.345, 2.704, 1.527, 2.096, 2.050, 2.314, 0.438, 1.276, 0.524, -0.449, -1.736, -2.599, -1.633, 1.096, 0.348, 0.745, 0.797, 1.123, 1.031, -0.219, 0.593, 2.855, 0.890, 0.970, 0.924\}.$$

Using the Yule-Walker method, we obtain the following estimates of the model parameters

$$\hat{a} = 0.806, \qquad \hat{\sigma}_\epsilon^2 = 1.170$$

Both estimates are consistent with the theoretically expected fluctuations about their means given by Eq. (1.15.2), falling within the one-standard deviation

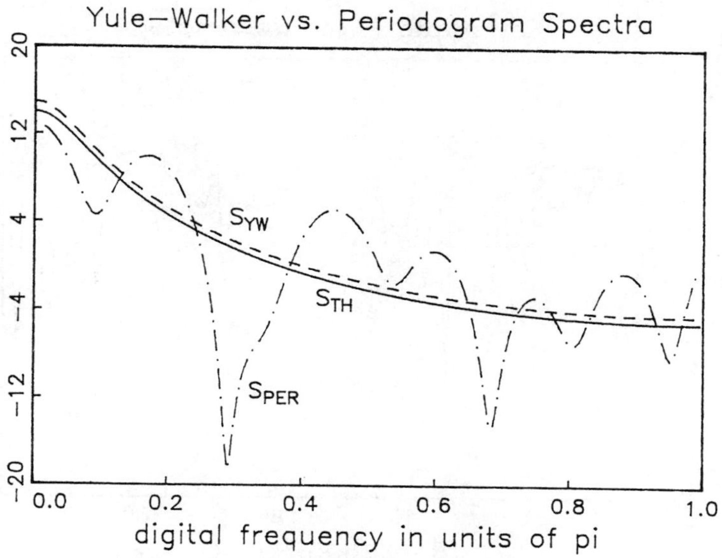

Figure 1.15 Comparison of Yule-Walker and Periodogram Spectrum Estimates

intervals $a \pm \delta a$ and $\sigma_\epsilon^2 \pm \delta\sigma_\epsilon^2$, where δa and $\delta\sigma_\epsilon^2$ are the square roots of (1.15.2). For $N = 30$, the numerical values of these intervals are: $0.690 \le \hat{a} \le 0.910$ and $0.742 \le \hat{\sigma}_\epsilon^2 \le 1.258$. Given the theoretical and estimated model parameters, we can obtain the theoretical and estimated power spectral densities of y_n by

$$S_{\mathrm{TH}}(\omega) = \frac{\sigma_\varepsilon^2}{|1 - a e^{-j\omega}|^2}, \qquad S_{\mathrm{YW}}(\omega) = \frac{\hat{\sigma}_\varepsilon^2}{|1 - \hat{a} e^{-j\omega}|^2}$$

The periodogram spectrum based on the given length-N data block is

$$S_{\mathrm{PER}}(\omega) = \frac{1}{N}\left|\sum_{n=0}^{N-1} y_n e^{-jn\omega}\right|^2$$

These three spectra are plotted in Figure 1.15, in units of decibels; that is, $10 \log_{10} S$, over the right half of the Nyquist interval $0 \le \omega \le \pi$. Note the excellent agreement of the Yule-Walker spectrum with the theoretical spectrum and the several sidelobes of the periodogram spectrum caused by the windowing of y_n.

Example 1.15.2: The purpose of this example is to demonstrate the reasonableness of the asymptotic variances, Eq. (1.15.2). For the first order model defined in the previous example, we generated 100 different realizations of the length-30 signal block y_n. From each realization, we extracted the Yule-Walker estimates of the model parameters $\hat{a}$ and $\hat{\sigma}_\epsilon^2$. They are shown in Figures 1.16 and 1.17 versus realization, together with the corresponding asymptotic one-standard deviation intervals that were computed in the previous example.

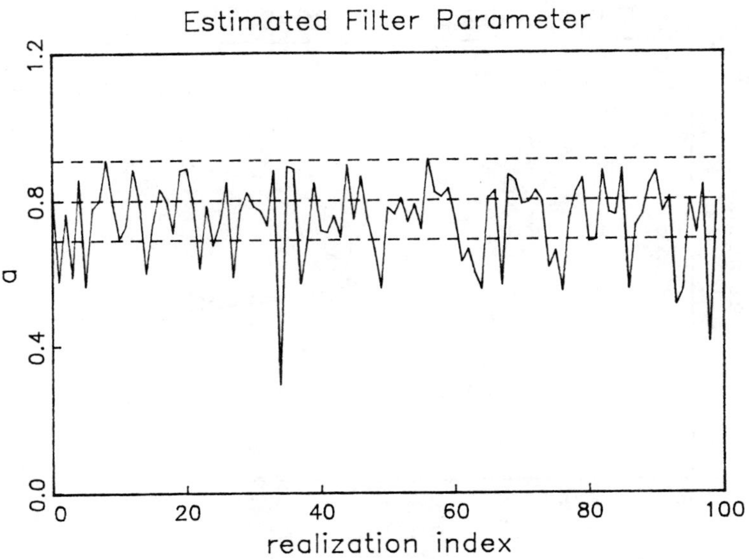

Figure 1.16 Filter Parameter a Estimated from 100 Realizations of the Length-30 Data Block y_n

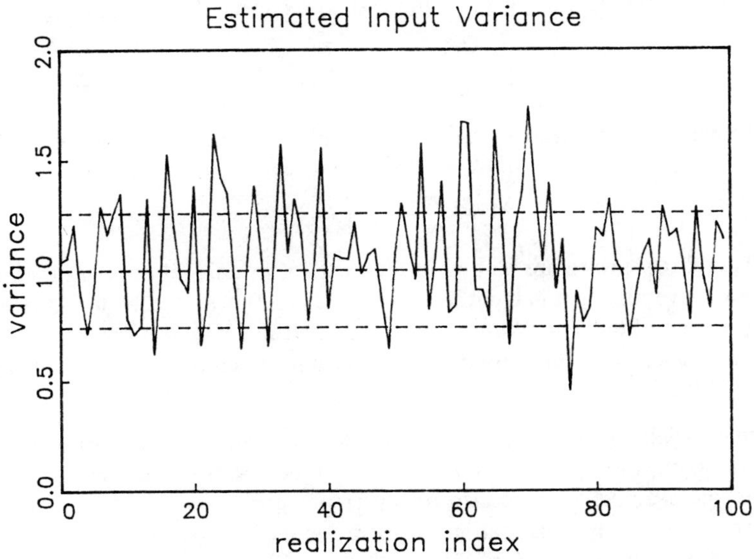

Figure 1.17 Input Variance σ_ϵ^2 Estimated from 100 Realizations of the Length-30 Data Block y_n

1.16 *Linear Prediction and Signal Modeling*

Linear prediction ideas are introduced in the context of our simple example by noting that the least-squares minimization criteria (1.14.1) and (1.15.1)

$$\mathcal{E}(a) = \sum_n e_n^2 = \text{minimum} \tag{1.16.1}$$

essentially force each e_n to be small. Thus, if we reinterpret

$$\hat{y}_n = ay_{n-1}$$

as the linear prediction of the sample y_n made on the basis of just the previous sample y_{n-1}, then $e_n = y_n - ay_{n-1} = y_n - \hat{y}_n$ may be thought of as the prediction error. The minimization criterion (1.16.1) essentially minimizes the prediction error in an average least-squares sense, thus attempting to make the best prediction possible.

As we mentioned in Section 1.11, the solution of the linear prediction problem provides the corresponding random signal generator model for y_n, which can be used, in turn, in a number of ways as outlined in Section 1.11. This is the main reason for our interest in linear prediction.

A more intuitive way to understand the connection between linear prediction and signal models is as follows: Suppose we have a predictor $\hat{y}_n$ of y_n which is not necessarily the best predictor. The predictor $\hat{y}_n$ is given as a linear combination of the past values $\{y_{n-1}, y_{n-2}, \ldots\}$:

$$\hat{y}_n = -[a_1 y_{n-1} + a_2 y_{n-2} + \cdots] \tag{1.16.2}$$

The corresponding prediction error will be

$$e_n = y_n - \hat{y}_n = y_n + a_1 y_{n-1} + a_2 y_{n-2} + \cdots \tag{1.16.3}$$

and it may be considered as the output of the prediction-error filter $A(z)$ (which is assumed to be stable and causal):

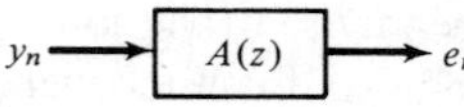

$$A(z) = 1 + a_1 z^{-1} + a_2 z^{-2} + \cdots$$

Suppose further that $A(z)$ has a stable and causal inverse filter

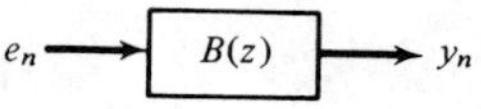

$$B(z) = \frac{1}{A(z)} = 1 + b_1 z^{-1} + b_2 z^{-2} + \cdots$$

so that y_n may be expressed *causally* in terms of e_n; that is,

$$y_n = e_n + b_1 e_{n-1} + b_2 e_{n-2} + \cdots \tag{1.16.4}$$

Then, Eqs. (1.16.3) and (1.16.4) imply that the linear spaces generated by the random variables

$$\{y_{n-1}, y_{n-2}, \ldots\} \quad \text{and} \quad \{e_{n-1}, e_{n-2}, \ldots\}$$

are the same space. One can pass from one set to the other by a causal and causally invertible linear filtering operation.

Now, if the prediction $\hat{y}_n$ of y_n is the best possible prediction, then what remains after the prediction is made—namely, the error signal e_n—should be entirely *unpredictable* on the basis of the past values $\{y_{n-1}, y_{n-2}, \ldots\}$. That is, e_n must be uncorrelated with all of these. But this implies that e_n must be uncorrelated with all $\{e_{n-1}, e_{n-2}, \ldots\}$, and therefore e_n must be a white-noise sequence. It follows that $A(z)$ and $B(z)$ are the analysis and synthesis filters for the sequence y_n.

The *least-squares* minimization criteria of the type (1.16.1) that are based on time averages, provide a *practical* way to solve the *linear prediction problem* and hence also the *modeling problem*. Their generalization to higher order predictors will be discussed in Chapter 5.

1.17 *Cramér-Rao Bound and Maximum Likelihood*

The Cramér-Rao inequality [2–5,26] provides a *lower* bound for the variance of *unbiased* estimators of parameters. Thus, the best any parameter estimator can do is to meet its Cramér-Rao bound. Such estimators are called *efficient*. Parameter estimators based on the principle of *maximum likelihood*, such as the one presented in Section 1.14, have several nice properties; namely, as the number of observations becomes large, they are asymptotically unbiased, consistent, efficient, and are asymptotically normally distributed about the theoretical value of the parameter with covariance given by the Cramér-Rao bound.

In this section, we present a derivation of the Cramér-Rao inequality using correlation canceling methods and discuss its connection to maximum likelihood. Consider N observations $Y = \{\mathbf{y}_1, \mathbf{y}_2, \ldots, \mathbf{y}_N\}$, where each observation is assumed to be an M-dimensional random vector. Based on these observations, we would like to estimate a number of (deterministic) parameters, assembled into a parameter vector $\boldsymbol{\lambda}$. We will write $p(Y, \boldsymbol{\lambda})$ to indicate the dependence of the joint probability density on $\boldsymbol{\lambda}$. As a concrete example, consider the case of N independent scalar observations drawn from a normal distribution with mean m and variance σ^2. The joint density is

$$p(Y, \lambda) = (2\pi\sigma^2)^{-N/2} \exp\left[-\frac{1}{2\sigma^2} \sum_{n=1}^{N} (y_n - m)^2\right] \tag{1.17.1}$$

For the parameter vector we may choose $\boldsymbol{\lambda} = [m, \sigma^2]^T$, if we want to estimate both the mean and variance.

The dependence of $p(Y, \boldsymbol{\lambda})$ on $\boldsymbol{\lambda}$ may be expressed in terms of the gradient with respect to $\boldsymbol{\lambda}$ of the log-likelihood function

$$\psi(Y, \lambda) \equiv \frac{\partial}{\partial \lambda} \ln p(Y, \lambda) = \frac{1}{p} \frac{\partial p}{\partial \lambda} \tag{1.17.2}$$

Expectation values with respect to the joint density will, in general, depend on the parameter $\boldsymbol{\lambda}$. We have the following result for the expectation value of an arbitrary function $F(Y,\boldsymbol{\lambda})$:

$$\frac{\partial}{\partial\lambda}E[F] = E[\frac{\partial F}{\partial\lambda}] + E[F\psi] \tag{1.17.3}$$

Writing $dY = d^M\mathbf{y}_1 d^M\mathbf{y}_2 \cdots d^M\mathbf{y}_N$ for the volume element over the space of observations, the proof of Eq. (1.17.3) follows from

$$\frac{\partial}{\partial\lambda}\int pF\,dY = \int\frac{\partial}{\partial\lambda}(pF)\,dY = \int p\frac{\partial F}{\partial\lambda}dY + \int pF\,\frac{\partial \ln p}{\partial\lambda}dY$$

Applying this property to $F = 1$, we find $E[\psi] = 0$. Applying it to ψ itself; that is, $F = \psi$, we find

$$J \equiv E[\psi\psi^T] = E[\Psi], \tag{1.17.4}$$

where

$$\Psi \equiv -\frac{\partial\psi}{\partial\lambda}$$

This is known as the *Fisher information matrix* based on Y. Component-wise, we have

$$J_{ij} = E[\psi_i\psi_j] = E[\Psi_{ij}]$$

where

$$\psi_i = \frac{\partial \ln p}{\partial\lambda_i}, \qquad \Psi_{ij} = -\frac{\partial\psi_i}{\partial\lambda_j} = -\frac{\partial^2 \ln p}{\partial\lambda_i\partial\lambda_j}$$

Next, we derive the Cramér-Rao bound. Let $\hat{\boldsymbol{\lambda}}(Y)$ be any estimator of $\boldsymbol{\lambda}$ based on Y. Because both $\hat{\boldsymbol{\lambda}}(Y)$ and $\psi(Y)$ depend on Y, they will be correlated with each other. Using the correlation canceling methods of Section 1.4, we can remove these correlations by writing

$$\mathbf{e} = \hat{\lambda} - E[\hat{\lambda}\psi^T]E[\psi\psi^T]^{-1}\psi$$

Then, $\mathbf{e}$ will not be correlated with ψ. Because ψ has mean zero, it follows that $E[\hat{\boldsymbol{\lambda}}] = E[\mathbf{e}]$. Working with the deviations about the corresponding means, namely, $\Delta\boldsymbol{\lambda} = \hat{\boldsymbol{\lambda}} - E[\hat{\boldsymbol{\lambda}}]$ and $\Delta\mathbf{e} = \mathbf{e} - E[\mathbf{e}]$, we have

$$\Delta\mathbf{e} = \Delta\lambda - MJ^{-1}\psi \tag{1.17.5}$$

where we denoted $M = E[\hat{\boldsymbol{\lambda}}\psi^T]$. Following Eq. (1.4.4), we obtain for the covariance of $\Delta\mathbf{e}$

$$E[\Delta\mathbf{e}\,\Delta\mathbf{e}^T] = E[\Delta\lambda\,\Delta\lambda^T] - MJ^{-1}M^T \tag{1.17.6}$$

Thus, the difference of terms in the right-hand side is a positive semidefinite matrix. This may be expressed symbolically as $E[\Delta\mathbf{e}\Delta\mathbf{e}^T] \geq 0$, or, $E[\Delta\boldsymbol{\lambda}\Delta\boldsymbol{\lambda}^T] \geq MJ^{-1}M^T$. The quantity M depends on the *bias* of the estimator. For an *unbiased* estimator, M is the identity matrix, $M = I$, and we obtain the Cramér-Rao inequality

$$\mathrm{cov}(\hat{\boldsymbol{\lambda}}) \equiv E[\Delta\boldsymbol{\lambda}\Delta\boldsymbol{\lambda}^T] \geq J^{-1} \qquad \text{(Cramér-Rao)} \tag{1.17.7}$$

The dependence of M on the bias can be seen as follows. Because $\hat{\boldsymbol{\lambda}}(Y)$ has no explicit dependence on $\boldsymbol{\lambda}$, it follows from property (1.17.3) that

$$M = E[\hat{\boldsymbol{\lambda}}\boldsymbol{\psi}^T] = \frac{\partial}{\partial\boldsymbol{\lambda}} E[\hat{\boldsymbol{\lambda}}]$$

Define the bias of the estimator as the deviation of the mean from the true value of the parameter; i.e., $E[\hat{\boldsymbol{\lambda}}] = \boldsymbol{\lambda} + \mathbf{b}(\boldsymbol{\lambda})$, $\mathbf{b}(\boldsymbol{\lambda}) =$ bias. Then, $M = I + \dfrac{\partial\mathbf{b}}{\partial\boldsymbol{\lambda}} \equiv I + B$. For an unbiased estimator, $B = 0$ and $M = I$. It follows from Eq. (1.17.6) that for the Cramér-Rao inequality to be satisfied as an equality, it is necessary that $\Delta\mathbf{e} = 0$ in Eq. (1.17.5), i.e., $\Delta\boldsymbol{\lambda} = MJ^{-1}\boldsymbol{\psi}$, and in the unbiased case, we obtain the condition

$$\frac{\partial}{\partial\boldsymbol{\lambda}} \ln p(Y, \boldsymbol{\lambda}) = J[\hat{\boldsymbol{\lambda}}(Y) - \boldsymbol{\lambda}] \tag{1.17.8}$$

Estimators that satisfy this condition and thus, meet their Cramér-Rao bound, are called *efficient*.

Example 1.17.1: The log-likelihood function of Eq. (1.17.1) is

$$\ln p = -\frac{N}{2}\ln(2\pi) - \frac{N}{2}\ln\sigma^2 - \frac{1}{2\sigma^2}\sum_{n=1}^{N}(y_n - m)^2$$

The gradient with respect to the parameters m and σ^2 is

$$\begin{aligned} \frac{\partial \ln p}{\partial m} &= \frac{1}{\sigma^2}\sum_{n=1}^{N}(y_n - m) \\ \frac{\partial \ln p}{\partial \sigma^2} &= -\frac{N}{2\sigma^2} + \frac{1}{2\sigma^4}\sum_{n=1}^{N}(y_n - m)^2 \end{aligned} \tag{1.17.9}$$

The second derivatives are the matrix elements of the matrix Ψ:

$$\Psi_{mm} = -\frac{\partial^2 \ln p}{\partial m\,\partial m} = \frac{N}{\sigma^2}, \qquad \Psi_{m\sigma^2} = -\frac{\partial^2 \ln p}{\partial m\,\partial\sigma^2} = \frac{1}{\sigma^4}\sum_{n=1}^{N}(y_n - m), \quad \text{and}$$

$$\Psi_{\sigma^2\sigma^2} = -\frac{\partial^2 \ln p}{\partial\sigma^2\partial\sigma^2} = -\frac{N}{2\sigma^4} + \frac{1}{\sigma^6}\sum_{n=1}^{N}(y_n - m)^2$$

Taking expectation values, we find the matrix elements of J

$$J_{mm} = \frac{N}{\sigma^2}, \quad J_{m\sigma^2} = 0, \quad J_{\sigma^2\sigma^2} = \frac{N}{2\sigma^4}$$

Therefore, the Cramér-Rao bound of any unbiased estimator of m and σ^2 will be

$$\begin{bmatrix} E[\Delta m \Delta m] & E[\Delta m \Delta\sigma^2] \\ E[\Delta\sigma^2 \Delta m] & E[\Delta\sigma^2\Delta\sigma^2] \end{bmatrix} \geq \begin{bmatrix} \sigma^2/N & 0 \\ 0 & 2\sigma^4/N \end{bmatrix}$$

Example 1.17.2: We note that the sample mean $\hat{m}$ defined by Eq. (1.2.1) has variance equal to its Cramér-Rao bound, and therefore, it is an efficient estimator. It also satisfies condition (1.17.8). Writing $\sum_{n=1}^{N} y_n = N\hat{m}$, we obtain from Eq. (1.17.9)

$$\frac{\partial \ln p}{\partial m} = \frac{1}{\sigma^2}\sum_{n=1}^{N}(y_n - m) = \frac{1}{\sigma^2}\left[\sum_{n=1}^{N} y_n - Nm\right] = J_{mm}[\hat{m} - m]$$

We also note that the sample variance s^2 having variance $2\sigma^4/(N-1)$ meets its Cramér-Rao bound only asymptotically. The biased definition of the sample variance, Eq. (1.2.3), has variance given by Eq. (1.2.4). It is easily verified that it is *smaller* than its Cramér-Rao bound (1.17.7). But this is no contradiction because Eq. (1.17.7) is valid only for unbiased estimators. For a biased estimator, the lower bound $MJ^{-1}M^T$ must be used. Equation (1.2.4) does satisfy this bound.

Next, we discuss the principle of maximum likelihood. The *maximum likelihood estimator* of a parameter λ is the value $\hat{\lambda}$ that maximizes the joint density $p(Y,\lambda)$; i.e.,

$$p(Y,\lambda)\,|_{\lambda=\hat{\lambda}} = \text{maximum} \tag{1.17.10}$$

Equivalently,

$$\psi(\hat{\lambda}) = \frac{\partial}{\partial\lambda}\ln p(Y,\lambda)\,|_{\lambda=\hat{\lambda}} = 0 \tag{1.17.11}$$

In general, this equation is difficult to solve. However, the asymptotic properties of the solution for large N are simple enough to obtain. Assuming $\hat{\lambda}$ is near the true value of the parameter λ we may expand the gradient ψ about the true value:

$$\psi(\hat{\lambda}) \approx \psi(\lambda) + \frac{\partial\psi(\lambda)}{\partial\lambda}(\hat{\lambda} - \lambda) = \psi - \Psi(\hat{\lambda} - \lambda)$$

where we used the matrix Ψ defined in Eq. (1.17.4). For the maximum likelihood solution, the left-hand side is zero. Thus, solving for $\Delta\lambda = \hat{\lambda} - \lambda$, we obtain

$$\Delta\lambda = \Psi^{-1}\psi \tag{1.17.12}$$

Assuming the N observations are independent of each other, the joint density $p(Y,\lambda)$ factors into the marginal densities $\prod_{n=1}^{N} p(\mathbf{y}_n,\lambda)$. Therefore, the gradient ψ will be a sum of gradients

$$\psi = \frac{\partial}{\partial \lambda} \ln p(Y, \lambda) = \sum_{n=1}^{N} \frac{\partial}{\partial \lambda} \ln p(\mathbf{y}_n, \lambda) = \sum_{n=1}^{N} \psi_n$$

Similarly,

$$\Psi = -\frac{\partial \psi}{\partial \lambda} = -\sum_{n=1}^{N} \frac{\partial \psi_n}{\partial \lambda} = \sum_{n=1}^{N} \Psi_n$$

Individual terms in these sums are mutually independent. Thus, from the law of large numbers, we can replace Ψ by its mean $\Psi \approx E[\Psi] = J$, and Eq. (1.17.12) becomes

$$\Delta\lambda \approx J^{-1}\psi \tag{1.17.13}$$

This asymptotic equation contains essentially all the nice properties of the maximum likelihood estimator. First, from $E[\psi] = 0$, it follows that $E[\Delta\lambda] = 0$, or that $\hat{\lambda}$ is *asymptotically unbiased.* Second, its asymptotic covariance agrees with the Cramér-Rao bound

$$E[\Delta\lambda\Delta\lambda^T] = J^{-1}E[\psi\psi^T]J^{-1} = J^{-1}JJ^{-1} = J^{-1}$$

Thus, $\hat{\lambda}$ is *asymptotically efficient.* The same conclusion can be reached by noting that Eq. (1.17.13) is the same as condition (1.17.8). Third, $\hat{\lambda}$ is *asymptotically consistent,* in the sense that its covariance tends to zero for large N. This follows from the fact that the information matrix for N independent observations is equal to N times the information matrix for one observation:

$$J = E[\Psi] = \sum_{n=1}^{N} E[\Psi_n] = NE[\Psi_1] = NJ_1$$

Therefore, $J^{-1} = N^{-1}J_1^{-1}$ tends to zero for large N. Fourth, because ψ is the sum of N independent terms, it follows from the vector version of the central limit theorem that ψ will be *asymptotically normally distributed.* Thus, so will be $\hat{\lambda}$, with mean λ and covariance J^{-1}.

Example 1.17.3: Setting the gradients (1.17.9) to zero, we obtain the maximum likelihood estimates of the parameters m and σ^2. It is easily verified that they coincide with the sample mean and sample variance defined by Eqs. (1.2.1) and (1.2.3).

Example 1.17.4: In many applications, the mean is known to be zero and only the variance needs to be estimated. For example, setting $m = 0$ in Eq. (1.17.1) we obtain the log-likelihood

$$\ln p = -\frac{N}{2}\ln(2\pi) - \frac{N}{2}\ln\sigma^2 - \frac{1}{2\sigma^2}\sum_{n=1}^{N} y_n^2$$

The maximum likelihood estimate of σ^2 is obtained from

$$\frac{\partial \ln p}{\partial \sigma^2} = -\frac{N}{2\sigma^2} + \frac{1}{2\sigma^4}\sum_{n=1}^{N} y_n^2 = 0$$

with solution

$$\hat{\sigma}^2 = \frac{1}{N}\sum_{n=1}^{N} y_n^2$$

It is easily verified that this is an *unbiased* estimate. It is the scalar version of Eq. (1.5.21). Using $E[y_n^2 y_m^2] = \sigma^4 + 2\delta_{nm}\sigma^4$, which is valid for independent zero mean gaussian y_ns, we find for the variance of σ^2

$$E[\Delta\sigma^2\,\Delta\sigma^2] = \frac{2\sigma^4}{N}\,, \qquad \text{where} \qquad \Delta\sigma^2 = \hat{\sigma}^2 - \sigma^2 \tag{1.17.14}$$

This agrees with the corresponding Cramér-Rao bound. Thus, $\hat{\sigma}^2$ is efficient. Equation (1.17.14) is the scalar version of Eq. (1.5.23).

Example 1.17.5: Show that the multivariate sample covariance matrix, $\hat{R}$, given by Eq. (1.5.21) is the maximum likelihood estimate of R, assuming the mean is zero.

Solution: The log-likelihood function is, up to a constant

$$\ln p(\mathbf{y}_1, \mathbf{y}_2, \cdots, \mathbf{y}_N) = -\frac{N}{2}\ln(\det R) - \frac{1}{2}\sum_{n=1}^{N}\mathbf{y}_n^T R^{-1}\mathbf{y}_n$$

The second term may be written as the trace:

$$\sum_{n=1}^{N}\mathbf{y}_n^T R^{-1}\mathbf{y}_n = \mathrm{tr}[R^{-1}\sum_{n=1}^{N}\mathbf{y}_n\mathbf{y}_n^T] = N\,\mathrm{tr}[R^{-1}\hat{R}]$$

where we used $\sum_{n=1}^{N}\mathbf{y}_n\mathbf{y}_n^T = N\hat{R}$. Using the matrix property $\ln(\det R) = \mathrm{tr}(\ln R)$, we may write the log-likelihood in the form

$$\ln p = -\frac{N}{2}\,\mathrm{tr}[\ln R + R^{-1}\hat{R}]$$

The maximum likelihood solution for R satisfies $\partial \ln p/\partial R = 0$. To solve it, we find it more convenient to work with differentials. Using the two matrix properties

$$d\,\mathrm{tr}(\ln R) = \mathrm{tr}(R^{-1}dR)\,, \qquad dR^{-1} = -R^{-1}dRR^{-1} \tag{1.17.15}$$

we obtain;

$$d\ln p = -\frac{N}{2}\,\mathrm{tr}[R^{-1}dR - R^{-1}dRR^{-1}\hat{R}\,] = -\frac{N}{2}\,\mathrm{tr}[R^{-1}dRR^{-1}(R-\hat{R})] \tag{1.17.16}$$

Because dR is arbitrary, the vanishing of $d\ln p$ implies $R = \hat{R}$. An alternative proof is to show that $f(R) \geq f(\hat{R})$, where $f(R) \equiv \mathrm{tr}(\ln R + R^{-1}\hat{R})$. This is shown easily using the inequality $x - 1 - \ln x \geq 0$, for $x \geq 0$, with equality reached at $x = 1$.

In many applications, the desired parameter $\boldsymbol{\lambda}$ to be estimated appears only *through* the covariance matrix R of the observations $\mathbf{y}$; that is, $R = R(\boldsymbol{\lambda})$. For example, we will see in Chapter 6 that the covariance matrix of a plane wave incident on an array of two sensors in the presence of noise is given by

$$R = \begin{bmatrix} P + \sigma^2 & Pe^{jk} \\ Pe^{-jk} & P + \sigma^2 \end{bmatrix}$$

where possible parameters to be estimated are the power P and wavenumber k of the wave, and the variance σ^2 of the background noise. Thus, $\boldsymbol{\lambda} = [P,k,\sigma^2]^T$.

In such cases, we have the following general expression for the Fisher information matrix J, valid for independent zero-mean gaussian observations:

$$J_{ij} = \frac{N}{2}\,\mathrm{tr}[R^{-1}\frac{\partial R}{\partial \lambda_i}R^{-1}\frac{\partial R}{\partial \lambda_j}] \tag{1.17.17}$$

Writing $\partial_i = \partial/\partial\lambda_i$ for brevity, we have from Eq. (1.17.16)

$$\partial_i \ln p = -\frac{N}{2}\,\mathrm{tr}[R^{-1}\,\partial_i R\,R^{-1}\,(R-\hat{R})]$$

Differentiating once more, we find

$$\Psi_{ij} = -\partial_i\partial_j \ln p = \frac{N}{2}\,\mathrm{tr}[\partial_j(R^{-1}\partial_i R\,R^{-1})(R-\hat{R}) + R^{-1}\partial_i R\,R^{-1}\partial_j R\,]$$

Equation (1.17.17) follows now by taking expectation values $J_{ij} = E[\Psi_{ij}]$ and noting that the expectation value of the first term vanishes. This follows from the fact that $\hat{R}$ is an unbiased estimator of R and therefore, $E[\mathrm{tr}(F(R - \hat{R}))] = 0$, for any matrix F.

Problems

Problem 1.1:

Two dice are available for throwing. One is fair, but the other bears only sixes. One die is selected as follows: A coin is tossed. If the outcome is tails then the fair die is selected, but if the outcome is heads, the biased die is selected. The coin itself is not fair, and the probability of bearing heads or tails is 1/3 or 2/3, respectively. A die is now selected according to this procedure and tossed twice and the number of sixes is noted.

Let x be a random variable that takes on the value 0 when the fair die is selected or 1 if the biased die is selected. Let y be a random variable denoting the number of sixes obtained in the two tosses; thus, the possible values of y are 0,1,2.

(a) For all possible values of x and y, compute $p(y/x)$; that is, the probability that the number of sixes will be y, given that the x die was selected.

(b) For each y, compute $p(y)$; that is, the probability that the number of sixes will be y, regardless of which die was selected.

(c) Compute the mean number of sixes $E[y]$.

(d) For all values of x and y, compute $p(x/y)$; that is, the probability that we selected die x, given that we already observed a y number of sixes.

Problem 1.2: Inversion Method
Let $F(x)$ be the cumulative distribution of a probability density $p(x)$. Suppose u is a uniform random number in the interval [0,1). Show that the solution of the equation $F(x) = u$, or equivalently, $x = F^{-1}(u)$, generates a random number x distributed according to $p(x)$. This is the inversion method of generating random numbers from uniform random numbers (see Appendix A).

Problem 1.3: Computer Experiment
Let x be a random variable with the exponential probability density

$$p(x) = \frac{1}{\mu} e^{-x/\mu}, \quad \text{for } x \geq 0$$

Show that x has mean μ and variance μ^2. Determine the cumulative distribution function $F(x)$ of x. Determine the inverse formula $x = F^{-1}(u)$ for generating x from a uniform u. Take $\mu = 2$. Using the inversion formula and a uniform random number generator routine, such as **ran** of Appendix A, generate a block of 200 random numbers x distributed according to $p(x)$. Compute their sample mean and sample variance, Eqs. (1.2.1) and (1.2.3), and compare them with their theoretical values. Do the estimated values fall within the standard deviation intervals defined by Eqs. (1.2.2) and (1.2.4)?

Problem 1.4:
The Rayleigh probability density finds application in fading communication channels

$$p(r) = \frac{r}{\sigma^2} e^{-r^2/2\sigma^2}, \; r \geq 0$$

Using the inversion method, $r = F^{-1}(u)$, show how to generate a Rayleigh-distributed random variable r from a uniform u.

Problem 1.5: Computer Experiment
To see the effects of using a poor random number generator, replace the routine **ran** of Appendix A by a poor version defined by means of the following linear congruential generator parameters: $a = 111$, $c = 11$, and $m = 151$. Use this version of **ran** in the gaussian generator **gran**.

(a) Generate 100 zero-mean unit-variance random numbers $x_n, n = 0, 1, \ldots, 99$ using the routine **gran** and plot them versus n. Do you observe any periodicities arising from the poor choice of **ran**?
(b) Repeat part (a) using the shuffled versions **gran2** and **ran2**. Do you still observe periodicities?

Problem 1.6:
(a) Following the notation of Section 1.4, show the matrix identity

$$\begin{bmatrix} I_N & -H \\ 0 & I_M \end{bmatrix} \begin{bmatrix} R_{xx} & R_{xy} \\ R_{yx} & R_{yy} \end{bmatrix} \begin{bmatrix} I_N & -H \\ 0 & I_M \end{bmatrix}^T = \begin{bmatrix} R_{xx} - R_{xy}R_{yy}^{-1}R_{yx} & 0 \\ 0 & R_{yy} \end{bmatrix}$$

where $H = R_{xy}R_{yy}^{-1}$.
(b) Rederive the correlation canceling results (1.4.3) and (1.4.4) using this identity.

Problem1.7:
Using the matrix identity of Problem 1.6, derive directly the result of Example 1.4.1; that is, $E[\mathbf{x}/\mathbf{y}] = R_{xy}R_{yy}^{-1}\mathbf{y}$. Work directly with probability densities; do not use the results of Examples 1.3.3 and 1.3.4.

Problem 1.8:
Show that the orthogonal projection $\hat{\mathbf{x}}$ of a vector $\mathbf{x}$ onto another vector $\mathbf{y}$, defined by Eq. (1.4.5) or Eq. (1.5.18), is a linear function of $\mathbf{x}$; that is, show

$$\widehat{A_1\mathbf{x}_1 + A_2\mathbf{x}_2} = A_1\hat{\mathbf{x}}_1 + A_2\hat{\mathbf{x}}_2$$

Problem 1.9: Noise Canceling
Suppose x consists of two components $x = s + n_1$, a desired component s, and a noise component n_1. Suppose that y is a related noise component n_2 to which we have access, $y = n_2$. The relationship between n_1 and n_2 is assumed to be linear, $n_1 = Fn_2$. For example, s might represent an electrocardiogram signal which is contaminated by 60 Hz power frequency pick-up noise n_1; then, a reference 60 Hz noise $y = n_2$ can be obtained from the wall outlet. (a) Show that the correlation canceler is $H = F$, and that complete cancellation of n_1 takes place. (b) If $n_1 = Fn_2 + v$, where v is uncorrelated with n_2 and s, show that $H = F$ still, and n_1 is canceled completely. The part v remains unaffected.

Problem 1.10: Signal Cancellation Effects
In the previous problem, we assumed that the reference signal y did not contain any part related to the desired component s. There are applications, however, where both the signal and the noise components contribute to both x and y, as for example in antenna sidelobe cancellation. Since the reference signal y contains part of s, the correlation canceler will act also to cancel part of the useful signal s from the output. To see this effect, consider a simple one-dimensional example

$$x = s + n_1$$

$$y = n_2 + \epsilon s$$

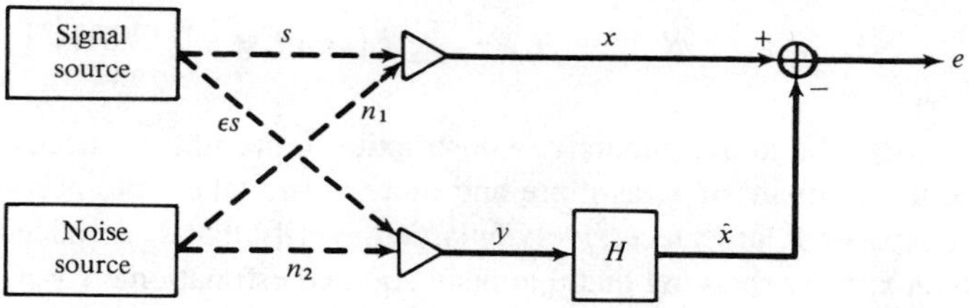

with $n_1 = Fn_2$, where we assume that y contains a small part proportional to the desired signal s. Assume that n_2 and s are uncorrelated. Show that the output e of the correlation canceler will contain a reduced noise component n_1 as well as a partially canceled signal s, as follows:

$$e = as + bn_1 \qquad \text{where} \qquad a = 1 - \frac{F\epsilon(1 + F\epsilon G)}{1 + F^2\epsilon^2 G}, \quad b = -\epsilon FGa$$

and G is a signal to noise ratio $G = E[s^2]/E[n_1^2]$. Note that when $\epsilon = 0$, then $a = 1$, and $b = 0$, as it should.

Problem 1.11:
Consider a special case of Example 1.4.3 defined by $c_n = 1$, so that $y_n = x + v_n$, $n = 1,2, \ldots ,M$. This represents the noisy measurement of a constant x. By comparing the corresponding mean-squared estimation errors $E[e^2]$, show that the optimal estimate of x given in Eq. (1.4.9) is indeed better than the straight average estimate

$$\hat{x}_{av} = \frac{1}{M}(y_1 + y_2 + \cdots + y_M)$$

Problem 1.12: Recursive Estimation
Consider the subspaces $Y_n = \{y_1, y_2, \ldots, y_n\}$ for $n = 1,2, \ldots ,M$, as defined in Section 1.5. Equation (1.5.18) defines the estimate $\hat{\mathbf{x}}$ of a random vector $\mathbf{x}$ based on the largest one of these subspaces; namely, Y_M.

(a) Show that this estimate can also be generated recursively as follows

$$\hat{\mathbf{x}}_n = \hat{\mathbf{x}}_{n-1} + \mathbf{G}_n(y_n - \hat{y}_{n/n-1})$$

for $n = 1,2, \ldots ,M$; and initialized by $\hat{\mathbf{x}}_0 = 0$, and $\hat{y}_{1/0} = 0$, where $\hat{\mathbf{x}}_n$ denotes the best estimate of $\mathbf{x}$ based on the subspace Y_n and $\mathbf{G}_n$ is a gain coefficient given by $\mathbf{G}_n = E[\mathbf{x}\epsilon_n]\, E[\epsilon_n\epsilon_n]^{-1}$. (*Hint:* Note $\hat{\mathbf{x}}_n = \sum_{i=1}^{n} E[\mathbf{x}\epsilon_i]\, E[\epsilon_i\epsilon_i]^{-1}\epsilon_i$.)

(b) Show that the innovations $\epsilon_n = y_n - \hat{y}_{n/n-1}$ is orthogonal to $\hat{\mathbf{x}}_{n-1}$; that is, show that $E[\hat{\mathbf{x}}_{n-1}\epsilon_n] = 0$ for $n = 1,2, \ldots M$.

(c) Let $\mathbf{e}_n = \mathbf{x} - \hat{\mathbf{x}}_n$ be the corresponding estimation error of $\mathbf{x}$ with respect to the subspace Y_n. Using Eq. (1.4.4), show that its covariance matrix can be expressed in the ϵ-basis as

$$R_{e_ne_n} = R_{xx} - \sum_{i=1}^{n} E[\mathbf{x}\epsilon_i]\, E[\epsilon_i\epsilon_i]^{-1}\, E[\epsilon_i\mathbf{x}^T]$$

(d) The above recursive construction represents a successive improvement of the estimate of $\mathbf{x}$, as more and more ys are taken into account; that is, as the subspaces Y_n are successively enlarged. Verify that $\hat{\mathbf{x}}_n$ is indeed a better estimate than $\hat{\mathbf{x}}_{n-1}$ by showing that the mean-squared estimation error $R_{e_ne_n}$ of $\hat{\mathbf{x}}_n$ is smaller than the mean-squared error $R_{e_{n-1}e_{n-1}}$ of $\hat{\mathbf{x}}_{n-1}$. This is a very intuitive result; the more information we use the better the estimate.

Such recursive updating schemes are the essence of Kalman filtering. In that context, $\mathbf{G}_n$ is referred to as the "Kalman gain."

Problem 1.13:

The recursive updating procedure given in Problem 1.12 is useful only if the gain coefficient $\mathbf{G}_n$ can be computed at each iteration n. For that, a knowledge of the relationship between $\mathbf{x}$ and y_n is required. Consider the case of Example 1.4.3 where $y_n = c_n x + v_n$; define the vectors

$$\mathbf{c}_n = [c_1, c_2, \ldots, c_n]^T \quad \text{and} \quad \mathbf{y}_n = [y_1, y_2, \ldots, y_n]^T \qquad \text{for } n = 1,2, \ldots, M$$

and let $\hat{x}_n$ and $e_n = x - \hat{x}_n$ denote the estimate of x on the basis of Y_n and the corresponding estimation error.

(a) Using Eq. (1.4.9), show that

$$\hat{x}_n = (1 + \mathbf{c}_n^T\mathbf{c}_n)^{-1}\, \mathbf{c}_n^T\mathbf{y}_n \quad \text{and} \quad E[e_n^2] = E[xe_n] = (1 + \mathbf{c}_n^T\mathbf{c}_n)^{-1}$$

(b) Using Eq. (1.5.19), compute $\hat{y}_{n/n-1}$ and show that it may be expressed in the form

$$\hat{y}_{n/n-1} = c_n\hat{x}_{n-1} = c_n\,(1 + \mathbf{c}_{n-1}^T\,\mathbf{c}_{n-1})^{-1}\,\mathbf{c}_{n-1}^T\,\mathbf{y}_{n-1}$$

(c) Let $e_{n-1} = x - \hat{x}_{n-1}$ be the estimation error based on Y_{n-1}. Writing

$$\epsilon_n = y_n - \hat{y}_{n/n-1} = (c_n\,x + v_n) - c_n\,\hat{x}_{n-1} = c_n\,e_{n-1} + v_n$$

show that

$$E[\epsilon_n\,\epsilon_n] = (1 + \mathbf{c}_n^T\,\mathbf{c}_n)\,(1 + \mathbf{c}_{n-1}^T\,\mathbf{c}_{n-1})^{-1}$$

$$E[x\,\epsilon_n] = c_n(1 + \mathbf{c}_{n-1}^T\,\mathbf{c}_{n-1})^{-1}$$

(d) Show that the estimate $\hat{x}_n$ of x can be computed recursively by

$$\hat{x}_n = \hat{x}_{n-1} + G_n(y_n - c_n\hat{x}_{n-1}), \qquad \text{where} \qquad G_n = c_n\,(1 + \mathbf{c}_n^T\mathbf{c}_n)^{-1}$$

Problem 1.14:
Rederive the recursive updating equation given in Problem 1.13 (d), without any reference to innovations or projections, by simply manipulating Eq. (1.4.9) algebraically, and writing it in recursive form.

Problem 1.15: Computer Experiment
A three-component random vector $\mathbf{y}$ has autocorrelation matrix

$$R = \begin{bmatrix} 1 & 2 & 3 \\ 2 & 6 & 14 \\ 3 & 14 & 42 \end{bmatrix}, \qquad \mathbf{y} = \begin{bmatrix} y_1 \\ y_2 \\ y_3 \end{bmatrix}$$

Carry out the Gram-Schmidt orthogonalization procedure to determine the innovations representation $\mathbf{y} = B\boldsymbol{\epsilon}$, where $\boldsymbol{\epsilon} = [\epsilon_1, \epsilon_2, \epsilon_3]^T$ is a vector of uncorrelated components. The vector $\mathbf{y}$ can be simulated by generating a zero-mean gaussian vector of uncorrelated components $\boldsymbol{\epsilon}$ of the appropriate variances and constructing $\mathbf{y} = B\boldsymbol{\epsilon}$. Generate $N = 50$ such vectors $\mathbf{y}_n, n = 1, 2, \ldots, N$ and compute the corresponding sample covariance matrix $\hat{R}$ given by Eq. (1.5.21). Compare it with the theoretical R. Is $\hat{R}$ consistent with the standard deviation intervals (1.5.23)? Repeat for $N = 100$.

Problem 1.16:
The Gram-Schmidt orthogonalization procedure for a subspace $Y = \{y_1, y_2, \ldots, y_M\}$ is initialized at the leftmost random variable y_1, $\epsilon_1 = y_1$, and progresses to the right by successively orthogonalizing y_2, y_3, and so on. It results in the lower triangular representation $\mathbf{y} = B\boldsymbol{\epsilon}$. The procedure can just as well be started at the rightmost variable y_M and proceed backwards as follows:

$$\eta_M = y_M$$

$$\eta_{M-1} = y_{M-1} - (\text{projection of } y_{M-1} \text{ on } \eta_M)$$

$$\eta_{M-2} = y_{M-2} - (\text{projection of } y_{M-2} \text{ on } \{\eta_M, \eta_{M-1}\})$$

and so on. Show that the resulting uncorrelated vector $\boldsymbol{\eta} = [\eta_1, \eta_2, \ldots, \eta_M]^T$ is related to $\mathbf{y} = [y_1, y_2, \ldots, y_M]^T$ by a linear transformation

$$\mathbf{y} = U\boldsymbol{\eta}$$

where U is a unit *upper-triangular* matrix. Show also that this corresponds to a *UL* (rather than *LU*) Cholesky factorization of the covariance matrix R_{yy}.

Problem 1.17:
Since "orthogonal" means "uncorrelated," the Gram-Schmidt orthogonalization procedure can also be understood as a correlation canceling operation. Explain how Eq. (1.5.20) may be thought of as a special case of the correlation canceler defined by Eqs. (1.4.1) and (1.4.2). What are **x**, **y**, **e**, and H, in this case? Draw the correlation canceler diagram of Fig. 1.1 as it applies here, showing explicitly the components of all the vectors.

Problem 1.18:
Using Eq. (1.6.11), show that the vector of coefficients $[a_{n1}, a_{n2}, \ldots, a_{nn}]^T$ can be expressed explicitly in terms of the **y**-basis as follows:

$$\begin{bmatrix} a_{n1} \\ a_{n2} \\ \vdots \\ a_{nn} \end{bmatrix} = -E[\mathbf{y}_{n-1}\mathbf{y}_{n-1}^T]^{-1} E[y_n \mathbf{y}_{n-1}], \qquad \text{where} \qquad \mathbf{y}_{n-1} = \begin{bmatrix} y_{n-1} \\ y_{n-2} \\ \vdots \\ y_0 \end{bmatrix}$$

Problem 1.19:
Show that the mean-squared estimation error of y_n on the basis of Y_{n-1}—that is, $E[\epsilon_n^2]$, where $\epsilon_n = y_n - \hat{y}_{n/n-1}$—can be expressed as

$$E[\epsilon_n^2] = E[\epsilon_n y_n] = E[y_n^2] - E[y_n \mathbf{y}_{n-1}^T]\, E[\mathbf{y}_{n-1}\mathbf{y}_{n-1}^T]^{-1} E[y_n \mathbf{y}_{n-1}]$$

Problem 1.20:
Let $\mathbf{a}_n = [1, a_{n1}, a_{n2}, \ldots, a_{nn}]^T$ for $n = 1, 2, \ldots, M$. Show that the results of the last two problems can be combined into one enlarged matrix equation

$$E[\mathbf{y}_n \mathbf{y}_n^T]\, \mathbf{a}_n = E[\epsilon_n^2]\, \mathbf{u}_n$$

where $\mathbf{u}_n$ is the unit-vector $\mathbf{u}_n = [1, 0, 0, \ldots, 0]^T$ consisting of one followed by n zeros, and $\mathbf{y}_n = [y_n, y_{n-1}, \ldots, y_1, y_0]^T = [y_n, \mathbf{y}_{n-1}^T]^T$.

Problem 1.21:
The quantity $\hat{y}_{n/n-1}$ of Eq. (1.5.19) is the best estimate of y_n based on all the previous ys; namely, $Y_{n-1} = \{y_0, y_1, \ldots, y_{n-1}\}$. This can be understood in three ways: First, in terms of the orthogonal projection theorem as we demonstrated in the text. Second, in terms of the correlation canceler interpretation as suggested in Problem 1.17. And third, it may be proved directly as follows: Let $\hat{y}_{n/n-1}$ be given as a linear combination of the previous ys as in Eq. (1.6.11); the coefficients $[a_{n1}, a_{n2}, \ldots, a_{nn}]^T$ are to be chosen optimally to minimize the estimation error ϵ_n given by Eq. (1.6.10) in the mean-squared sense. In terms of the notation of Problem 1.20, Eq. (1.6.10) and $E[\epsilon_n^2]$ can be written in the compact vectorial form

$$\epsilon_n = \mathbf{a}_n^T \mathbf{y}_n \qquad \text{and} \qquad \mathcal{E}(\mathbf{a}_n) = E[\epsilon_n^2] = \mathbf{a}_n^T E[\mathbf{y}_n \mathbf{y}_n^T]\, \mathbf{a}_n$$

The quantity $\mathcal{E}(\mathbf{a}_n)$ is to be minimized with respect to $\mathbf{a}_n$. The minimization must be subject to the constraint that the first entry of the vector $\mathbf{a}_n$ be unity. This constraint can be expressed in vector form as

$$\mathbf{a}_n^T\mathbf{u}_n = 1$$

where $\mathbf{u}_n$ is the unit vector defined in Problem 1.20. Incorporate this constraint with a Lagrange multiplier and minimize the performance index

$$\mathcal{E}(\mathbf{a}_n) = \mathbf{a}_n^T\, E[\mathbf{y}_n\mathbf{y}_n^T]\, \mathbf{a}_n + \lambda\,(1 - \mathbf{a}_n^T\mathbf{u}_n)$$

with respect to $\mathbf{a}_n$, then fix λ by enforcing the constraint, and finally show that the resulting solution of the minimization problem is identical to that given in Problem 1.20.

Problem 1.22:
Show that the normal Equations (1.7.12) can also be obtained by minimizing the performance indices (1.7.10) with respect to **a** and **b**, subject to the constraints that the first element of **a** and the last element of **b** be unity. (*Hint:* These constraints are expressible in the form $\mathbf{u}^T\mathbf{a} = 1$ and $\mathbf{v}^T\mathbf{b} = 1$.)

Problem 1.23:
Using Eq. (1.7.16), show that E_b can be expressed as the ratio of the two determinants $E_b = \det R/\det\bar{R}$.

Problem 1.24:
Show Eqs. (1.7.28) and (1.7.35).

Problem 1.25:
A random signal $x(n)$ is defined as a linear function of time by

$$x(n) = a + bn$$

where a and b are independent zero-mean gaussian random variables of variances σ_a^2 and σ_b^2, respectively.

(a) Compute $E[x(n)^2]$.

(b) Is $x(n)$ a stationary process? Is it ergodic? Explain.

(c) For each fixed n, compute the probability density $p(x(n))$.

(d) For each fixed n and m $(n \neq m)$, compute the conditional probability density $p(x(n)/x(m))$ of $x(n)$ given $x(m)$.
(*Hint:* $x(n) - x(m) = b(n - m)$.)

Problem 1.26:
Compute the sample autocorrelation of the sequences

(a) $y_n = 1$, for $0 \leq n \leq 10$

(b) $y_n = (-1)^n$, for $0 \leq n \leq 10$

in two ways: First in the time domain, using Eq. (1.10.1), and then in the z-domain, using Eq. (1.10.3) and computing its inverse z-transform.

Problem 1.27: FFT Computation of Autocorrelations
In many applications, a fast computation of sample autocorrelations or cross-correlations is required, as in the matched filtering operations in radar data processors. A fast way to compute the sample autocorrelation $\hat{R}_{yy}(k)$ of a length-N data segment $\mathbf{y} = [y_0, y_1, \ldots, y_{N-1}]^T$ is based on Eq. (1.10.5) which can be computed using FFTs. Performing an inverse FFT on Eq. (1.10.5), we find the computationally efficient formula

$$\hat{R}_{yy}(k) = \frac{1}{N}\,\mathrm{IFFT}[|\mathrm{FFT}(\mathbf{y})|^2] \qquad \text{(P.1)}$$

To avoid wrap-around errors introduced by the FFT, the length N' of the FFT must be selected to be greater than the length of the function $\hat{R}_{yy}(k)$. Since $\hat{R}_{yy}(k)$ is double-sided with an extent $-(N-1) \leq k \leq (N-1)$, it will have length equal to $2N-1$. Thus, we must select $N' \geq 2N-1$. To see the wrap-around effects, consider a length-4 signal $\mathbf{y} = [1,2,2,1]^T$.

(a) Compute $\hat{R}_{yy}(k)$ using the time-domain definition.
(b) Compute $\hat{R}_{yy}(k)$ according to Eq. (P.1) using 4-point FFTs.
(c) Repeat using 8-point FFTs.

Problem 1.28: Computer Experiment

(a) Generate 1000 samples $x(n)$, $n = 0,1, \ldots, 999$, of a zero-mean, unit-variance, white gaussian noise sequence.

(b) Compute and plot the first 100 lags of its sample autocorrelation; that is, $\hat{R}_{yy}(k)$, for $k = 0,1, \ldots, 99$. Does $\hat{R}_{xx}(k)$ look like a delta function, $\delta(k)$?

(c) Generate 10 different realizations of the length-1000 sequence $x(n)$, and compute 100 lags of the corresponding sample autocorrelations. Define an average autocorrelation by

$$\hat{R}(k) = \frac{1}{10}\sum_{i=1}^{10} \hat{R}_i(k), \qquad k = 0,1, \ldots, 99,$$

where $\hat{R}_i(k)$ is the sample autocorrelation of the ith realization of $x(n)$. Plot $\hat{R}(k)$ versus k. Do you notice any improvement?

Problem 1.29:
A 500-millisecond record of a stationary random signal is sampled at a rate of 2 kHz and the resulting N samples are recorded for further processing. What is N? The record of N samples is then divided into K contiguous segments, each of length M, so that $M = N/K$. The periodograms from each segment are computed and averaged together to obtain an estimate of the power spectrum of the signal. A frequency resolution of $\Delta f = 20$ Hz is required. What is the

shortest length M that will guarantee such resolution? (Larger Ms will have better resolution than required but will result in a poorer power spectrum estimate because K will be smaller.) What is K in this case?

Problem 1.30:

A random signal y_n is generated by sending unit-variance zero-mean white noise ϵ_n through the filters defined by the following difference equations:

1. $y_n = -0.9\, y_{n-1} + \epsilon_n$
2. $y_n = 0.9\, y_{n-1} + \epsilon_n + \epsilon_{n-1}$
3. $y_n = \epsilon_n + 2\, \epsilon_{n-1} + \epsilon_{n-2}$
4. $y_n = -0.81\, y_{n-2} + \epsilon_n$
5. $y_n = 0.1\, y_{n-1} + 0.72\, y_{n-2} + \epsilon_n - 2\, \epsilon_{n-1} + \epsilon_{n-2}$

(a) For each case, determine the transfer function $B(z)$ of the filter and draw its canonical implementation form, identify the set of model parameters, and decide whether the model is ARMA, MA, or AR.

(b) Write explicitly the power spectrum $S_{yy}(\omega)$ using Eq. (1.11.6).

(c) Based on the pole/zero pattern of the filter $B(z)$, draw a rough sketch of the power spectrum $S_{yy}(\omega)$ for each case.

Problem 1.31: Computer Experiment

Two different realizations of a stationary random signal $y(n)$, $n = 0, 1, \ldots, 19$ are given. It is known that this signal has been generated by a model of the form

$$y(n) = ay(n-1) + \epsilon(n)$$

where $\epsilon(n)$ is gaussian zero-mean white noise of variance σ_ϵ^2.

(a) Estimate the model parameters a and σ_ϵ^2, using the maximum likelihood criterion for both realizations. (The exact, simulated, values were $a = 0.95$ and $\sigma_\epsilon^2 = 1$.)

(b) Repeat, using the Yule-Walker method.

This situation might, for example, arise in speech analysis where $y(n)$ might represent a short segment of sampled unvoiced speech from which the filter parameters (model parameters) are to be extracted and stored for future regeneration of that segment. A realistic speech model would of course require a higher-order filter; typically, order 10 to 15.

n	$y(n)$	$y(n)$
0	3.848	5.431
1	3.025	5.550
2	5.055	4.873
3	4.976	5.122
4	6.599	5.722
5	6.217	5.860
6	6.572	6.133
7	6.388	5.628
8	6.500	6.479
9	5.564	4.321
10	5.683	5.181
11	5.255	4.279
12	4.523	5.469
13	3.952	5.087
14	3.668	3.819
15	3.668	2.968
16	3.602	2.751
17	1.945	3.306
18	2.420	3.103
19	2.104	3.694

Problem 1.32: Computer Experiment

(a) Using the Yule-Walker estimates $\{\hat{a};\ \hat{\sigma}_\epsilon^2\}$ of the model parameters extracted from the first realization of y_n given in Problem 1.31, make a plot of the estimate of the power spectrum following Eq. (1.11.6); that is,

$$\hat{S}_{yy}(\omega) = \frac{\hat{\sigma}_\epsilon^2}{|1 - \hat{a}\, e^{-j\omega}|^2}$$

versus frequency ω in the interval $0 \leqslant \omega \leqslant \pi$.

(b) Also, plot the true power spectrum

$$S_{yy}(\omega) = \frac{\sigma_\epsilon^2}{|1 - a\, e^{-j\omega}|^2}$$

defined by the true model parameters $\{a;\ \sigma_\epsilon^2\} = \{0.95;\ 1.0\}$.

(c) Using the given data values y_n for the first realization, compute and plot the corresponding periodogram spectrum of Eq. (1.10.5). Preferably, plot all three spectra on the same graph. Compute the spectra at 100 or 200 equally spaced frequency points in the interval $[0, \pi]$. Plot all spectra in decibels.

(d) Repeat parts (a) through (c) using the second realization of y_n.

Better agreement between estimated and true spectra can be obtained using Burg's analysis procedure instead of the Yule-Walker method. Burg's method performs remarkably well on the basis of very short data records. The Yule-Walker method also performs well but it requires somewhat longer records. These methods will be compared in Chapter 6.

Problem 1.33:

In addition to the asymptotic results (1.15.2) for the model parameters, we will show in Chapter 6 that the estimates of filter parameter and the input variance are asymptotically uncorrelated, $E[\Delta a \Delta\sigma_\epsilon^2] = 0$. Using this result and Eq. (1.15.2), show that the variance of the spectrum estimate is given asymptotically by

$$E\,[\Delta S\,(\omega)\Delta S\,(\omega)] = \frac{2S\,(\omega)^2}{N}\left[1 + \frac{2(1 - a^2)(\cos\omega - a)^2}{(1 - 2a\cos\omega + a^2)^2}\right]$$

where $\Delta S(\omega) = \hat{S}(\omega) - S(\omega)$, with the theoretical and estimated spectra given in terms of the theoretical and estimated model parameters by

$$S\,(\omega) = \frac{\sigma_\varepsilon^2}{|1\ \ a e^{-j\omega}\,|^2}\,, \qquad \hat{S}\,(\omega) = \frac{\hat{\sigma}_\varepsilon^2}{|1 - \hat{a}\, e^{-j\omega}\,|^2}$$

Problem 1.34:

For any positive semi-definite matrix B show the inequality $\mathrm{tr}(B - I - \ln B) \geq 0$ with equality achieved for $B = I$. Using this property, show the inequality $f(R) \geq f(\hat{R})$ where $f(R) = \mathrm{tr}(\ln R + R^{-1}\hat{R})$. This implies the maximum likelihood property of $\hat{R}$, discussed in Section 1.17.

Problem 1.35:

Show the following three matrix properties, used in Section 1.17:

$$\ln(\det R) = \mathrm{tr}(\ln R)\,, \qquad d\,\mathrm{tr}(\ln R) = \mathrm{tr}(R^{-1}dR)\,, \qquad dR^{-1} = -R^{-1}dR\,R^{-1}$$

(*Hints:* for the first two, use the eigenvalue decomposition of R; for the third, start with $R^{-1}R = I$.)

References

1. A. Papoulis, *Probability, Random Variables, and Stochastic Processes,* (2nd ed.), New York, McGraw-Hill, 1984.
2. M. G. Kendall and A. Stuart, *The Advanced Theory of Statistics,* vol. 2, (4th ed.), London, Griffin, 1979.
3. H. W. Sorenson, *Parameter Estimation,* New York, Marcel Dekker, 1980.
4. T. W. Anderson, *An Introduction to Multivariate Statistical Analysis,* (2nd ed.), New York, Wiley, 1984.
5. M. G. Kendall and A. Stuart, *The Advanced Theory of Statistics,* vol. 3, (3d ed.), New York, Hafner Press, 1976.
6. J. Cryer, *Times Series Analysis,* Boston, Duxbury Press, 1986.
7. J. L. Doob, *Stochastic Processes*, New York, Wiley, 1953.
8. P. R. Halmos, *Finite-Dimensional Vector Spaces*, New York, Van Nostrand, 1958.
9. R. B. Blackman and J. W. Tukey, *The Measurement of Power Spectra*, New York, Dover, 1958.
10. C. Bingham, M. D. Godfrey, and J. W. Tukey, Modern Techniques of Power Spectrum Estimation, *IEEE Trans. Audio Electroacoust.*, **AU-15,** 56–66 (1967).
11. G. M. Jenkins and D. G. Watts, *Spectral Analysis and Its Applications,* San Francisco, Holden-Day, 1968.
12. A. V. Oppenheim and R. W. Schafer, *Digital Signal Processing,* Englewood Cliffs, NJ, Prentice-Hall, 1975.
13. R. K. Otnes and L. Enochson, *Digital Time Series Analysis*, New York, Wiley, 1972.
14. W. Davenport and W. Root, *Introduction to the Theory of Random Signals and Noise*, New York, McGraw-Hill, 1958.
15. D. Childers, Ed., *Modern Spectrum Analysis,* New York, Wiley, 1978.
16. F. J. Harris, On the Use of Windows for Harmonic Analysis with the Discrete Fourier Transform, *Proc. IEEE*, **66,** 51–83 (1978).
17. A. H. Nuttal and G. C. Carter, A Generalized Framework for Power Spectral Estimation, *IEEE Trans. Acoust., Speech, Signal Process.*, **ASSP-28,** 334–335 (1980).
18. S. M. Kay, *Modern Spectral Estimation,* Englewood Cliffs, NJ, Prentice-Hall, 1988.
19. S. L. Marple, *Digital Spectral Analysis with Applications,* Englewood Cliffs, NJ, Prentice-Hall, 1987.

20. P. D. Welch, The Use of Fast Fourier Transform for the Estimation of Power Spectra: A Method Based on Time Averaging over Short, Modified Periodograms, *IEEE Trans. Audio Electroacoust.,* **AU-15,** 70–73 (1967).

21. G. P. Box and G. M. Jenkins, *Time Series Analysis Forecasting and Control*, New York, Holden-Day, 1970.

22. H. Wold, *A Study in the Analysis of Time Series*, Uppsala, Sweden, Almqvist and Wiksell, 1931 and 1954.

23. A. Papoulis, Predictable Processes and Wold's Decomposition: A Review, *IEEE Trans. Acoust., Speech, Signal Processing,* **ASSP-33,** 933 (1985).

24. A. N. Kolmogorov, Sur l'Interpolation et Extrapolation des Suites Stationnaires, *C. R. Acad. Sci.*, **208,** 2043–2045 (1939). See also Interpolation and Extrapolation of Stationary Random Sequences, and Stationary Sequences in Hilbert Space, reprinted in T. Kailath, Ed., *Linear Least-Squares Estimation*, Stroudsburg, PA, Dowden, Hutchinson, and Ross, 1977.

25. E. A. Robinson, *Time Series Analysis and Applications*, Houston, TX, Goose Pond Press, 1981.

26. C. R. Rao, *Linear Statistical Inference and Its Applications,* (2nd ed.), New York, Wiley, 1973.

2

Some Signal Processing Applications

IN THE NEXT FEW SECTIONS, we shall present some applications of the random signal concepts that we introduced in the previous chapter. We shall discuss system identification by cross-correlation techniques, design simple filters to remove noise from noisy measurements, apply these concepts to the problem of quantization effects in digital filter structures, introduce the problem of linear prediction and its iterative solution through Levinson's algorithm, and discuss a data compression example.

2.1 *Filtering of Stationary Random Signals*

In this section, we discuss the effect of linear filtering on random signals. The results are very basic and of importance in suggesting guidelines for the design of signal processing systems for many applications of random signals [1–3].

Suppose a stationary random signal x_n is sent into a linear filter defined by a transfer function $H(z)$. Let y_n be the output random signal. Our objective is to derive relationships between the autocorrelation functions of the input and output signals, and also between the corresponding power spectra.

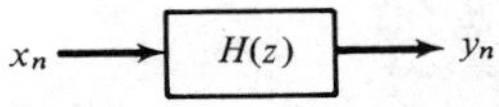

$$H(z) = \sum_{n=0}^{\infty} h_n z^{-n}$$

Using the input/output filtering equation in the z-domain

$$Y(z) = H(z)\,X(z) \tag{2.1.1}$$

we determine first a relationship between the periodograms of the input and output signals. Using the factorization (1.10.3) and dropping the factor $1/N$ for convenience, we find

$$\begin{aligned}\hat{S}_{yy}(z) &= Y(z)\,Y(z^{-1}) \\ &= H(z)\,X(z)\,H(z^{-1})\,X(z^{-1}) = H(z)\,H(z^{-1})\,X(z)\,X(z^{-1}) \qquad (2.1.2)\\ &= H(z)\,H(z^{-1})\,\hat{S}_{xx}(z) = S_{hh}(z)\,\hat{S}_{xx}(z)\end{aligned}$$

where we used the notation $S_{hh}(z) = H(z)H(z^{-1})$. This quantity is the z-transform of the sample autocorrelation of the filter; that is,

$$S_{hh}(z) = H(z)\,H(z^{-1}) = \sum_{k=-\infty}^{\infty} R_{hh}(k)\,z^{-k} \qquad (2.1.3)$$

where $R_{hh}(k)$ is the filter's autocorrelation function

$$R_{hh}(k) = \sum_{n} h_{n+k}\,h_n \qquad (2.1.4)$$

Equation (2.1.3) is easily verified by writing

$$R_{hh}(k) = \sum_{i,j=0}^{\infty} h_i h_j\,\delta(k - (i - j))$$

Taking inverse z-transforms of Eq. (2.1.2), we find the time-domain equivalent relationships between input and output sample autocorrelations

$$\hat{R}_{yy}(k) = \sum_{m=-\infty}^{\infty} R_{hh}(m)\,\hat{R}_{xx}(k - m) = \text{convolution of } R_{hh} \text{ with } \hat{R}_{xx} \qquad (2.1.5)$$

Similarly, we find for the cross-periodograms

$$\hat{S}_{yx}(z) = Y(z)\,X(z^{-1}) = H(z)\,X(z)\,X(z^{-1}) = H(z)\,\hat{S}_{xx}(z) \qquad (2.1.6)$$

and also, replacing z by z^{-1},

$$\hat{S}_{xy}(z) = \hat{S}_{xx}(z)\,H(z^{-1}) \qquad (2.1.7)$$

The same relationships hold for the statistical autocorrelations and power spectra. We summarize these as follows: In the z-domain the power spectral densities are related by

$$\begin{aligned}S_{yy}(z) &= H(z)\,H(z^{-1})\,S_{xx}(z)\\ S_{yx}(z) &= H(z)\,S_{xx}(z) \qquad (2.1.8)\\ S_{xy}(z) &= S_{xx}(z)\,H(z^{-1})\end{aligned}$$

Setting $z = \exp(j\omega)$, we may also write Eq. (2.1.8) in terms of the corresponding power spectra, as follows

$$
\begin{aligned}
S_{yy}(\omega) &= |H(\omega)|^2 \, S_{xx}(\omega) \\
S_{yx}(\omega) &= H(\omega) \, S_{xx}(\omega) \\
S_{xy}(\omega) &= S_{xx}(\omega) \, H(\omega)^*
\end{aligned}
\tag{2.1.9}
$$

In the time domain, the correlation functions are related by

$$
\begin{aligned}
R_{yy}(k) &= \sum_{m=-\infty}^{\infty} R_{hh}(m) \, R_{xx}(k - m) \\
R_{yx}(k) &= \sum_{m=0}^{\infty} h_m R_{xx}(k - m)
\end{aligned}
\tag{2.1.10}
$$

The proof of these is straightforward; for example, to prove Eq. (2.1.10), use stationarity and the I/O convolutional equation

$$
y_n = \sum_{m=0}^{\infty} h_m x_{n-m}
$$

to find

$$
\begin{aligned}
R_{yy}(k) &= E[y_{n+k} \, y_n] = E\left[\sum_{i=0}^{\infty} h_i x_{n+k-i} \sum_{j=0}^{\infty} h_j x_{n-j}\right] \\
&= \sum_{i,j=0}^{\infty} h_i h_j \, E[x_{n+k-i} \, x_{n-j}] = \sum_{i,j=0}^{\infty} h_i h_j R_{xx}(k - (i - j)) \\
&= \sum_{i,j,m} h_i h_j \, \delta(m - (i - j)) \, R_{xx}(k - m) = \sum_{m} R_{hh}(m) \, R_{xx}(k - m)
\end{aligned}
$$

An important special case is when the input signal is white with variance σ_x^2:

$$
R_{xx}(k) = E[x_{n+k} \, x_n] = \sigma_x^2 \, \delta(k) \qquad S_{xx}(z) = \sigma_x^2 \tag{2.1.11}
$$

Then, Eqs. (2.1.8) through (2.1.10) simplify to

$$
\begin{aligned}
S_{yy}(z) &= H(z) \, H(z^{-1}) \, \sigma_x^2 \\
S_{yx}(z) &= H(z) \, \sigma_x^2
\end{aligned}
\tag{2.1.12}
$$

and

$$
\begin{aligned}
S_{yy}(\omega) &= |H(\omega)|^2 \, \sigma_x^2 \\
S_{yx}(\omega) &= H(\omega) \, \sigma_x^2
\end{aligned}
\tag{2.1.13}
$$

and

$$
\begin{aligned}
R_{yy}(k) &= \sigma_x^2 \sum_{n=0}^{\infty} h_{n+k} \, h_n \\
R_{yx}(k) &= \sigma_x^2 \, h_k
\end{aligned}
\tag{2.1.14}
$$

These results show how the filtering operation reshapes the flat white-noise spectrum of the input signal into a shape defined by the magnitude response $|H(\omega)|^2$ of the filter, and how the filtering operation introduces self-correlations in the output signal. Equation (2.1.13) is also the proof of the previously stated result (1.11.6).

As an example, consider the first order Markov signal y_n defined previously as the output of the filter

$$y_n = ay_{n-1} + \epsilon_n \qquad H(z) = \frac{1}{1 - az^{-1}}$$

driven by white noise ϵ_n of variance σ_ϵ^2. The impulse response of the filter is

$$h_n = a^n u(n), \qquad u(n) = \text{unit step}$$

The output autocorrelation $R_{yy}(k)$ may be computed in two ways. In the time-domain (assuming first that $k \geqslant 0$):

$$R_{yy}(k) = \sigma_\epsilon^2 \sum_{n=0}^{\infty} h_{n+k}\, h_n = \sigma_\epsilon^2 \sum_{n=0}^{\infty} a^{n+k}\, a^n = \sigma_\epsilon^2\, a^k \sum_{n=0}^{\infty} a^{2n} = \frac{\sigma_\epsilon^2\, a^k}{1 - a^2}$$

And second, in the z-domain using power spectral densities and inverse z-transforms (again take $k \geqslant 0$):

$$S_{yy}(z) = H(z)\, H(z^{-1})\, \sigma_\epsilon^2 = \frac{\sigma_\epsilon^2}{(1 - az^{-1})(1 - az)}$$

$$R_{yy}(k) = \oint_{u.c.} S_{yy}(z)\, z^k \frac{dz}{2\pi jz} = \oint_{u.c.} \frac{\sigma_\epsilon^2 z^k}{(z - a)(1 - az)} \frac{dz}{2\pi j}$$

$$= (\text{Residue at } z = a) = \frac{\sigma_\epsilon^2 a^k}{1 - a^2}$$

In particular, we verify the results of Section 1.14:

$$R_{yy}(0) = \frac{\sigma_\epsilon^2}{1 - a^2} \qquad R_{yy}(1) = \frac{\sigma_\epsilon^2\, a}{1 - a^2}$$

$$a = \frac{R_{yy}(1)}{R_{yy}(0)} \qquad \sigma_\epsilon^2 = (1 - a^2)\, R_{yy}(0)$$

It is interesting to note the exponentially decaying nature of $R_{yy}(k)$ with increasing lag k, as shown in Fig. 2.1. We noted earlier that direct correlations exist only between samples separated by lag one; and that indirect correlations also exist due to the indirect influence of a given sample y_n on all future samples, as propagated by the difference equation. In going from one sampling instant to the next, the difference equation scales y_n by a factor a; therefore, we expect these indirect correlations to decrease fast (exponentially) with increasing lag.

Whenever the autocorrelation drops off very fast with increasing lag, this

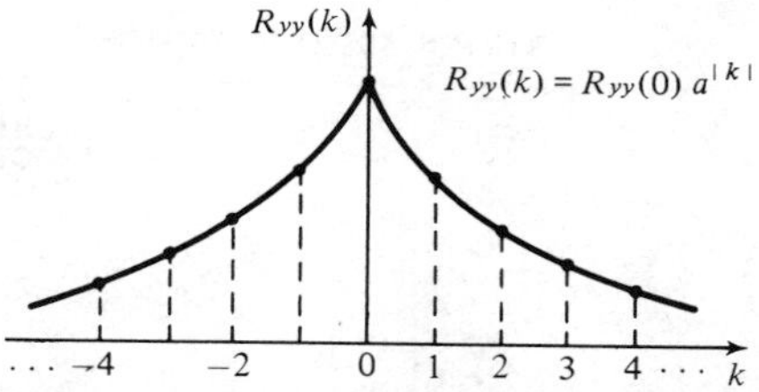

Figure 2.1 Exponentially Decaying Autocorrelation

can be taken as an indication that there exists a stable difference equation model for the random signal.

However, not all random signals have exponentially decaying autocorrelations. For example, a pure sinusoid with random phase

$$y_n = A\cos(\omega_0 n + \phi)$$

where ϕ is a uniformly distributed random phase, has autocorrelation

$$R_{yy}(k) = \frac{1}{2} A^2 \cos(\omega_0 k)$$

which never dies out. A particular realization of the random variable ϕ defines the entire realization of the time series y_n. Thus, as soon as ϕ is fixed, the entire y_n is fixed. Such random signals are called *deterministic*, since a few past values—e.g., a complete cycle—of y_n are sufficient to determine all future values of y_n.

2.2 *System Identification by Cross-Correlation Methods*

The filtering results derived in Section 2.1 suggest a system identification procedure to identify an unknown system $H(z)$ on the basis of input/output measurements: Generate pseudorandom white noise x_n, send it through the unknown linear system, and compute the cross-correlation of the resulting output sequence y_n with the known sequence x_n. According to Eq. (2.1.14), this cross-correlation is proportional to the impulse response of the unknown system. This identification scheme is shown in Fig. 2.2. A simulated example is shown in Fig. 2.3. The

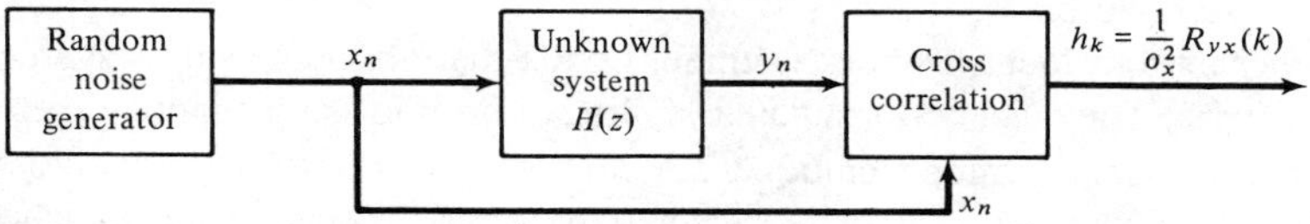

Figure 2.2 System Identification

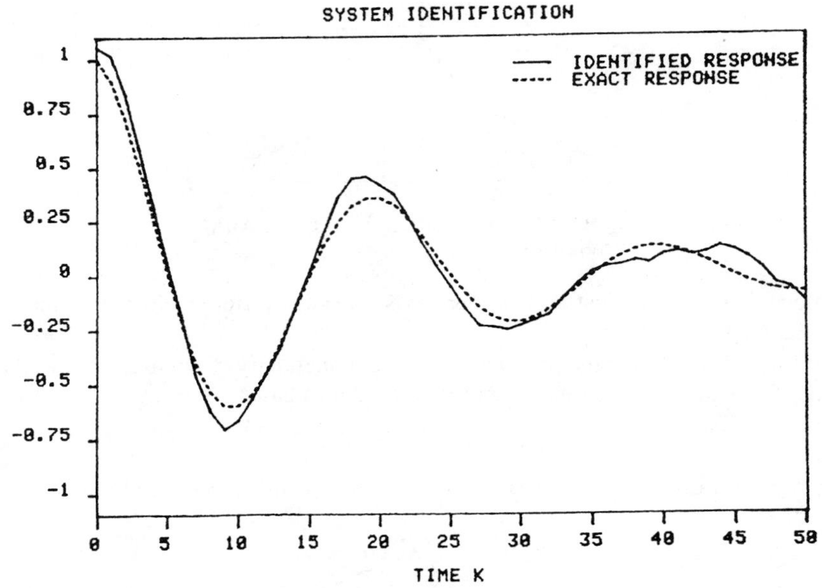

Figure 2.3 System Identification by Cross-Correlation

system $H(z)$ was defined by a sinusoidally damped impulse response of length 50, given by

$$h_k = (0.95)^k \cos(0.1\pi k) \qquad \text{for } 0 \leqslant k \leqslant 50 \tag{2.2.1}$$

Using a random number generator routine, 1500 samples of a unit-variance zero-mean white-noise sequence x_n were generated and filtered through the filter H to obtain the output sequence y_n. Then, the first 50 lags of the sample cross-correlation were computed according to

$$\hat{R}_{yx}(k) = \frac{1}{N} \sum_{n=0}^{N-1-k} y_{n+k}\, x_n$$

with $N = 1500$ and $k = 0, 1, \ldots, 50$. Figure 2.3 shows the impulse response identified according to $h_k = \hat{R}_{yx}(k)/\sigma_x^2 = \hat{R}_{yx}(k)$, plotted together with the exact response defined by Eq. (2.2.1).

Other system identification techniques exist that are based on least-squares error criteria. They can be formulated off-line or on-line using adaptive methods [4–10]. Such identification techniques are intimately connected to the analysis procedures of extracting the model parameters of signal models, as we discussed in Section 1.11.

2.3 *Noise Reduction and Signal Enhancement Filters*

In signal processing applications for noise removal, or signal enhancement, the ratio σ_y^2/σ_x^2 plays an important role. We have

$$\sigma_y^2 = \int_{-\pi}^{\pi} S_{yy}(\omega)\, d\omega/2\pi = \int_{-\pi}^{\pi} |H(\omega)|^2 S_{xx}(\omega)\, d\omega/2\pi = \sigma_x^2 \int_{-\pi}^{\pi} |H(\omega)|^2 \frac{d\omega}{2\pi}$$

provided x_n is white noise. The ratio σ_y^2/σ_x^2 determines whether the input noise is amplified or attenuated as it is filtered through $H(z)$. It will be referred to as the *noise reduction ratio*. Using Parseval's identity, we find the alternative expressions for it

$$\begin{aligned}\frac{\sigma_y^2}{\sigma_x^2} &= \int_{-\pi}^{\pi} |H(\omega)|^2 \frac{d\omega}{2\pi} \\ &= \sum_{n=0}^{\infty} h_n^2 \qquad (2.3.1) \\ &= \oint_{u.c.} H(z)\, H(z^{-1}) \frac{dz}{2\pi j z}\end{aligned}$$

We may denote any one of these as $\|H\|^2$; that is, the quadratic norm of H. Computationally, the most recommended procedure is by the contour integral, and the least recommended is by the frequency integral. Use the contour formula for IIR filters and the sum of impulse responses squared for FIR filters.

Example 2.3.1: Compute the noise reduction ratio of white noise sent through the first order recursive filter

$$H(z) = \frac{1}{1 - az^{-1}} \qquad \sigma_y^2/\sigma_x^2 = \sum_{n=0}^{\infty} h_n^2 = \sum_{n=0}^{\infty} a^{2n} = \frac{1}{1 - a^2}$$

The alternative derivation using contour integration has already been done.

Consider now the problem of extracting a signal x_n from noisy measurements y_n of the form

$$y_n = x_n + v_n$$

where the measurement noise v_n is typically white noise. We wish to design a filter $H(z)$ to process the available measurements y_n to remove the noise component without affecting the signal component. (Our notation throughout uses the symbol y_n to denote the available noisy measurements, and x_n to denote the desired signal to be extracted.) These two requirements are illustrated in Fig. 2.4.

Often, the separation of signal from noise can be done on the basis of

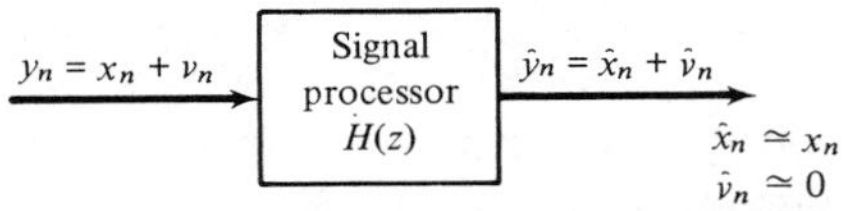

Figure 2.4 Signal Processor Requirements

bandwidth. If the power spectra of the signal and noise components occupy separate frequency bands, then their separation is easy: Simply design a filter whose frequency response is zero over the entire band over which there is significant noise power, and equal to unity over the band of the signal. An example of this situation arises in Doppler radar, which is designed to detect moving objects; the returned echo signal includes a considerable amount of clutter noise arising from the radar pulses bouncing off stationary objects such as trees, buildings, and the like. The frequency spectrum of the clutter noise is mainly concentrated near DC, whereas the spectrum of the desired signal from moving targets occupies a higher frequency band, not overlapping with the clutter.

On the other hand, if the noise is white, its power spectrum will extend over all frequencies, and therefore it will overlap with the signal band. For example, suppose the signal and noise have power spectra as shown in Fig. 2.5. If we design an ideal bandpass filter $H(\omega)$ whose passband includes the signal band, then after filtering, the output power spectra will look as in Fig. 2.6. A lot of noise energy is removed by the filter, thus tending to reduce the overall output noise variance

$$\sigma_{\hat{v}}^2 = \int_{-\pi}^{\pi} S_{\hat{v}\hat{v}}(\omega)\, d\omega / 2\pi$$

At the same time, the signal spectrum is left undistorted.

Some knowledge of the frequency spectra for the desired signal and the interfering noise was required in order to design the filter. The basic idea was to design a filter whose passband coincided with the spectral band of the desired signal, and whose stopband coincided with the spectral band of the noise. Clearly, if noise and signal have highly overlapping spectra, such simple signal processing design techniques will not be successful. Thus, an important question arises: For a given signal spectrum and noise spectrum, what is the best linear filter to separate noise from signal? The answer will lead to the methods of Wiener or optimal filtering to be discussed later on. In the remainder of this section, we present four examples illustrating the above ideas.

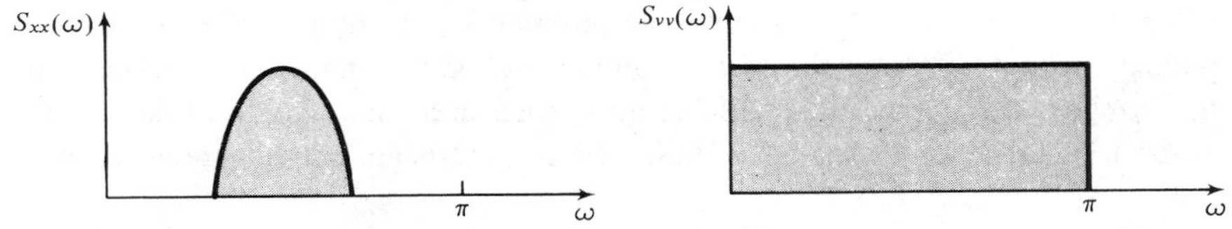

Figure 2.5 Signal and Noise Spectra before Processing

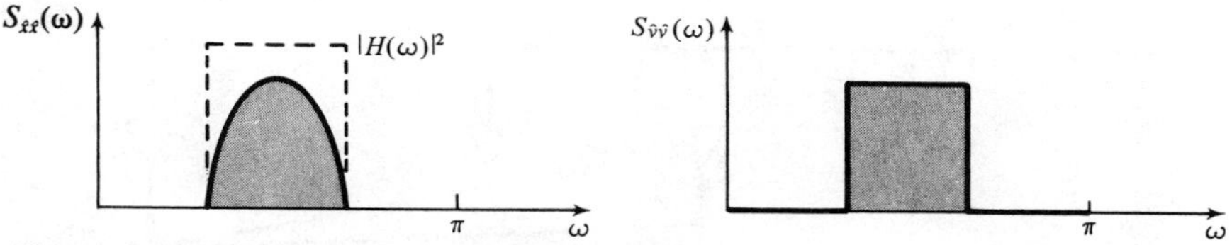

Figure 2.6 Signal and Noise Spectra after Processing

Example 2.3.2 Clutter Rejection Filters in Coherent MTI Radar

By taking advantage of the Doppler effect, moving target indicator (MTI) radar systems [11] can distinguish between weak echo returns from small moving objects and strong echo returns from stationary objects (clutter), such as trees, buildings, the sea, the weather, and so on. An MTI radar sends out short-duration sinusoidal pulses of some carrier frequency, say f_0. The pulses are sent out every T seconds (the pulse repetition interval). A pulse reflected from a target moving with velocity v will suffer a Doppler frequency shift to $f_0 + f$, where f is the Doppler shift given by

$$f = \frac{2v}{\lambda_0} = \frac{2v}{c} f_0$$

The receiver maintains a phase-coherent reference carrier signal, so that the target echo signal and the reference signal can be heterodyned to leave only the relative frequency shift; that is, the Doppler shift. Thus, after the removal of the carrier, the returned echo pulses will have a basic sinusoidal dependence

$$\exp(j2\pi f t)$$

Clutter returns from truly stationary objects ($v = 0$) will correspond to the DC component ($f = 0$) of the returned signal. But, clutter returns from slightly nonstationary objects such as trees or the weather, will not be exactly DC and will be characterized by a small frequency spread about DC. Thus, a typical clutter spectrum will occupy a narrow frequency band about DC as shown:

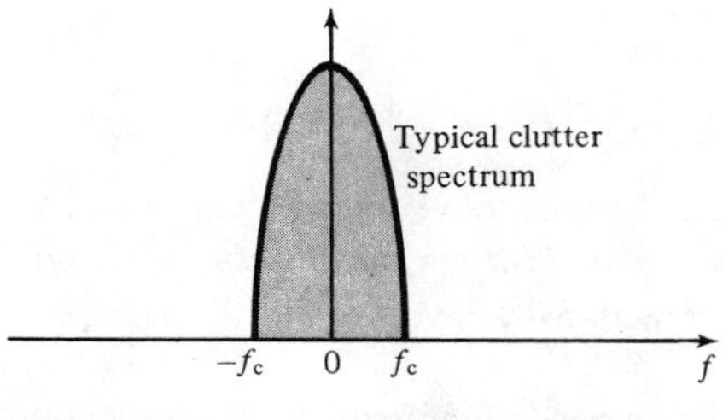

Subsequent processing with a clutter rejection filter can remove the clutter frequency components. According to the previous discussion, such a filter must essentially be an ideal high pass filter with a low frequency stopband

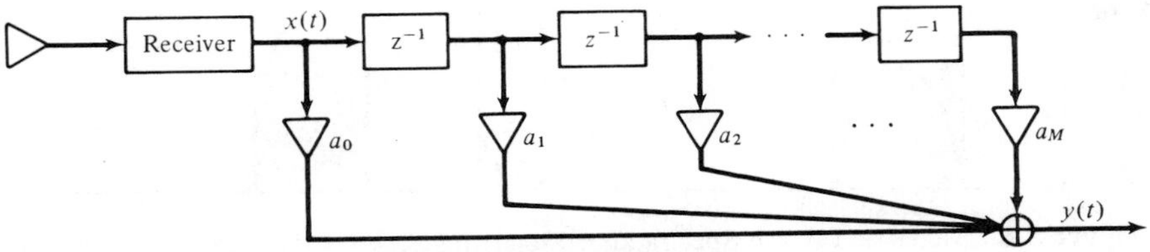

Figure 2.7 Tapped Delay Line Clutter Rejection Filter

that coincides with the clutter spectral band. Since the MTI system is a pulsed system with period T, such a filter can be designed as simple tapped delay line using delays of T seconds, as shown in Fig. 2.7, where z^{-1} represents a delay by T seconds. The I/O equation of this filter is

$$y(t) = \sum_{m=0}^{M} a_m\, x(t - mT)$$

with transfer function

$$H(z) = a_0 + a_1 z^{-1} + a_2 z^{-2} + \cdots + a_M z^{-M}$$

Its frequency response is obtained by setting $z = \exp(j\omega) = \exp(j2\pi fT)$. Due to the sampled-data nature of this problem, the frequency response of the filter is periodic in f with period $f_s = 1/T$; that is, the pulse repetition frequency. An ideally designed clutter filter would vanish over the clutter passband, as shown in Fig. 2.8. Because of the periodic nature of the frequency response, the filter will also reject the frequency bands around multiples of the sampling frequency f_s. If a target is moving at speeds that correspond to such frequencies, that is,

$$n\, f_s = \frac{2v}{c} f_0 \qquad n = 1,2, \ldots$$

then such a target cannot be seen; it also gets canceled by the filter. Such speeds are known as "blind speeds." In practice, the single and double delay high-pass filters

$$H(z) = 1 - z^{-1}$$

$$H(z) = (1 - z^{-1})^2 = 1 - 2\,z^{-1} + z^{-2}$$

are commonly used. Nonrecursive tapped delay-line filters are preferred over recursive ones, since the former have short transient response; e.g., MT seconds for a filter with M delays.

Example 2.3.3: Radar measurements of the Earth-Moon distance D are taken of the form

$$y_n = D + v_n$$

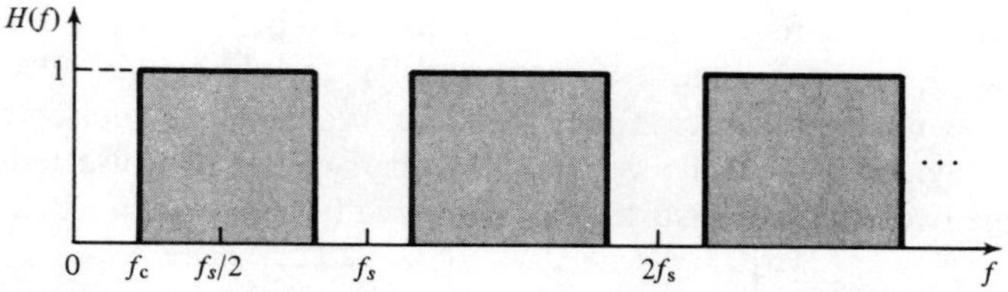

Figure 2.8 Ideal Frequency Response of Clutter Rejection Filter

where v_n is zero-mean white noise of variance σ_v^2, representing measurement errors. Two signal processing schemes are to be compared as to their noise reduction and signal enhancing capability:

a recursive filter	and	a nonrecursive filter
$\hat{y}_n = a\hat{y}_{n-1} + by_n$		$\hat{y}_n = ay_n + by_{n-1}$

Discuss the selection of the filter parameters so that on the one hand they do not distort the desired signal, and on the other they tend to reduce the noise. Discuss any tradeoffs. Compare the two cases.

The transfer functions of the two filters are

$$H(z) = \frac{b}{1 - az^{-1}} \qquad \text{and} \qquad H(z) = a + b\,z^{-1}$$

The desired signal $x_n = D$ must be able to go through these filters entirely undistorted. Since it is a DC signal, we require the frequency response $H(\omega)$ to be unity at zero frequency $\omega = 0$, or equivalently, at $z = \exp(j\omega) = 1$

$$H(1) = \frac{b}{1 - a} = 1 \qquad \text{and} \qquad H(1) = a + b = 1$$

In both cases, we find the constraint $b = 1 - a$, so that

$$H(z) = \frac{1 - a}{1 - az^{-1}} \qquad \text{and} \qquad H(z) = a + (1 - a)\,z^{-1}$$

Both of these filters will allow the DC constant signal $x_n = D$ to pass through undistorted. There is still freedom in selecting the parameter a. The effectiveness of the filter in reducing the noise is decided on the basis of the noise reduction ratio

$$\frac{\sigma_y^2}{\sigma_x^2} = \frac{(1 - a)^2}{1 - a^2} = \frac{1 - a}{1 + a} \qquad \text{and} \qquad \frac{\sigma_y^2}{\sigma_x^2} = a^2 + b^2 = a^2 + (1 - a)^2$$

These are easily derived using either the contour integral formula, or the sum of the impulse responses squared.

Effective noise reduction will be achieved if these ratios are made as small as possible. For the recursive case, stability of the filter requires a to be $-1 < a < 1$. The requirement that the noise ratio be less than one further implies that $0 < a < 1$. And it becomes smaller the closer a is selected to one. For the nonrecursive case, the minimum value of the noise ratio is obtained when $a = 0.5$. The graphical comparison of the noise reduction ratios in the two cases suggests that the recursive filter will do a much better

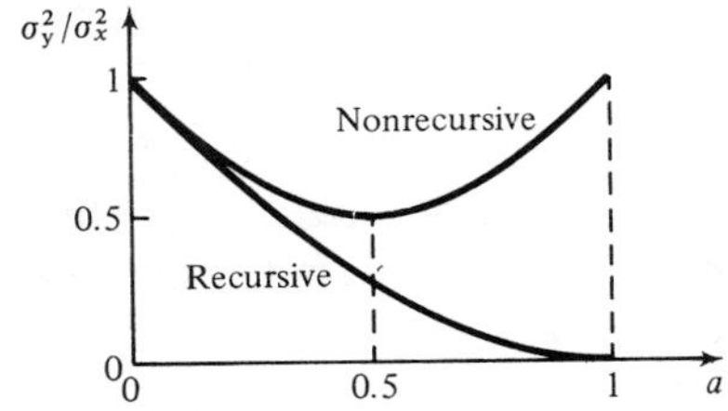

job than the nonrecursive one. But there is a price to be paid for that. The closer a is to unity—that is, the closer the pole is moved to the unit circle—the slower the response of the filter will be, as can be seen by inspecting the impulse response of the filter

$$h_n = ba^n$$

The effectiveness of the recursive filter may also be seen by plotting its magnitude response versus frequency for various values of a, as in Fig. 2.9. As the parameter a tends to one, the filter's response becomes more and more narrow around the frequency $\omega = 0$ (this is the signal band in this case). Therefore, the filter is able to remove more power from the noise.

Finally, we should not leave the impression that nonrecursive filters are always bad. For example, if we allow a filter with, say, M taps

$$\hat{y}_n = \frac{1}{M}(y_n + y_{n-1} + \cdots + y_{n-M})$$

the noise ratio is easily found to be

$$\frac{\sigma_y^2}{\sigma_x^2} = \sum_{n=0}^{M} h_n^2 = \frac{1}{M^2}(1 + 1 + \cdots + 1) = \frac{M}{M^2} = \frac{1}{M}$$

which can be made as small as desired by increasing the number of taps M.

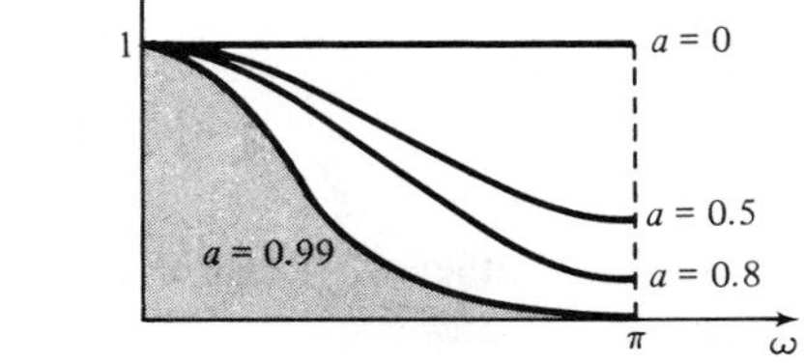

Figure 2.9 Magnitude Response for Various Values of a

Figures 2.10 through 2.16 demonstrate the various ideas behind this example. Figure 2.10 shows 100 samples of a zero-mean white gaussian noise v_n of variance $\sigma_v^2 = 100$, generated by means of a standard gaussian random number generator subroutine. Next, these samples were filtered by the first order recursive filter $\hat{v}_n = a\hat{v}_{n-1} + (1-a)v_n$, with the parameter a chosen as $a = 0.95$. Figure 2.11 shows the lowpass filtering effect as well as the noise-reducing property of this filter. The output signal $\hat{v}_n$ has been plotted together with the white noise input v_n. Figures 2.12 and 2.13 show a comparison of the theoretically expected autocorrelations and the experimentally computed sample autocorrelations from the actual sample values, both for the input and the output signals. The theoretical autocorrelations are

$$R_{vv}(k) = \sigma_v^2\,\delta(k) \qquad \text{and} \qquad R_{\hat{v}\hat{v}}(k) = R_{\hat{v}\hat{v}}(0)\,a^{|k|}$$

Figures 2.14 through 2.16 show the interplay between noise reduction and speed of response of the filter as the filter parameter a is gradually selected closer and closer to unity. The values $a = 0.8$, 0.9, and 0.95 were tried. The input to the filter was the noisy measurement signal y_n and the output $\hat{y}_n$ was computed by iterating the difference equation of the filter starting with zero initial conditions.

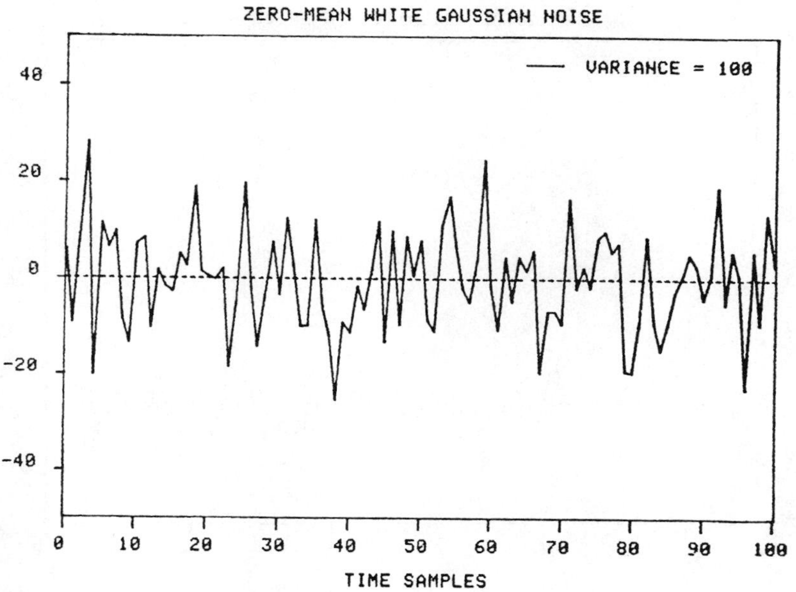

Figure 2.10 Zero-Mean White Noise

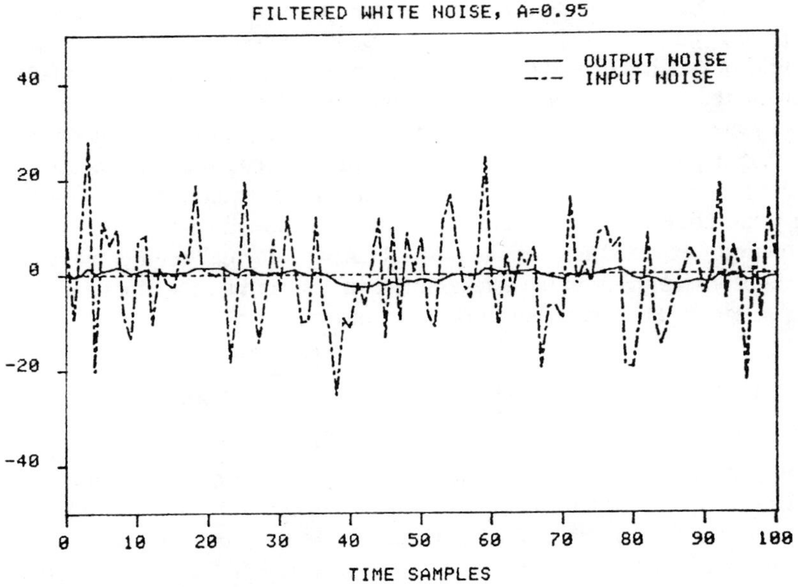

Figure 2.11 Filtered White Noise

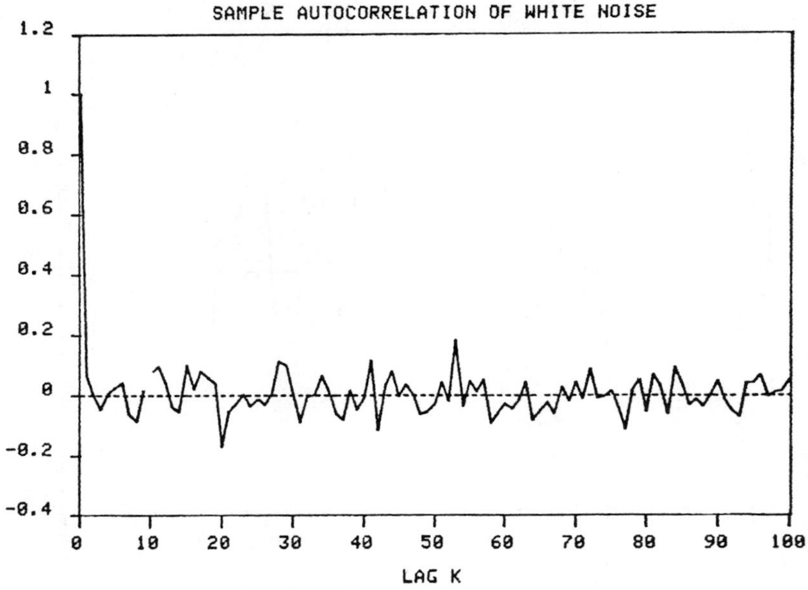

Figure 2.12 Sample Autocorrelation of White Noise

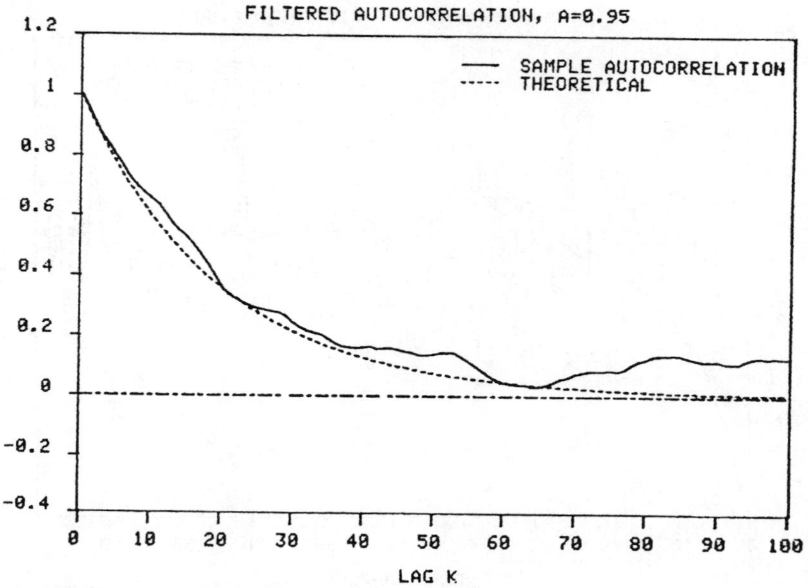

Figure 2.13 Sample Autocorrelation of Filtered Noise

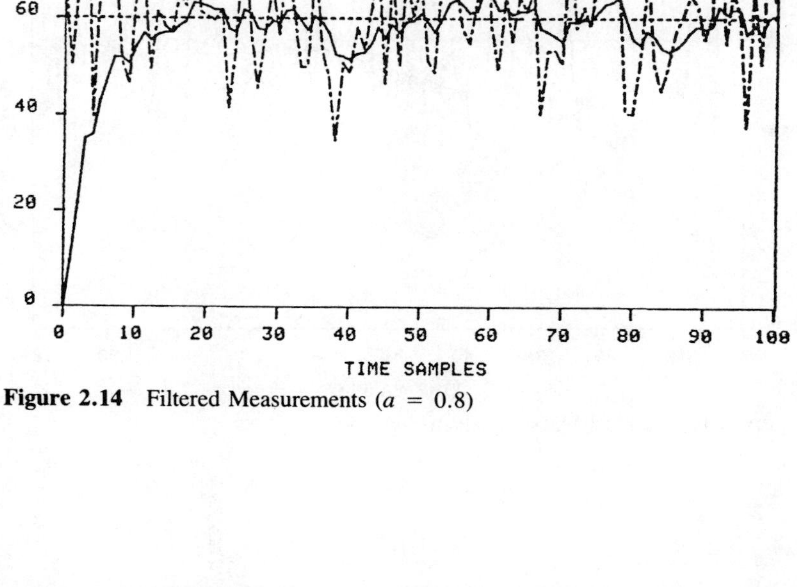

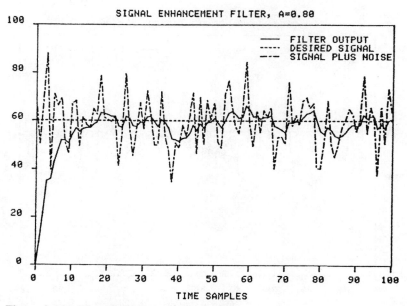

Figure 2.14 Filtered Measurements ($a = 0.8$)

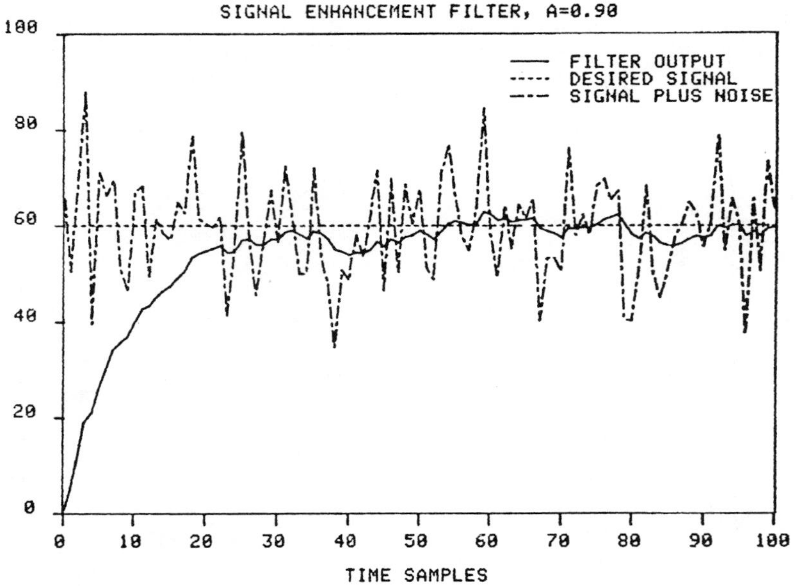

Figure 2.15 Filtered Measurements ($a = 0.9$)

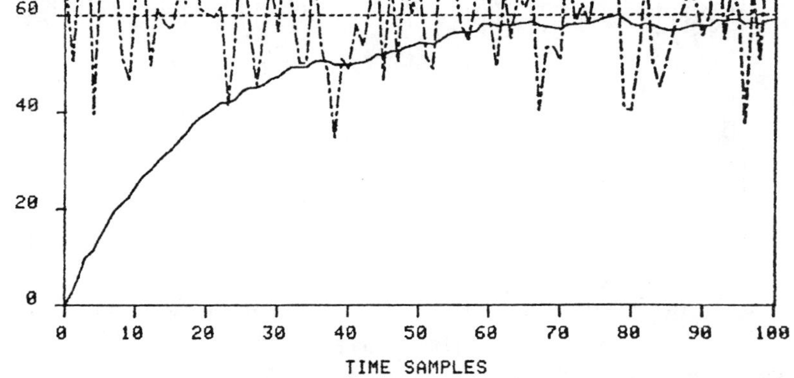

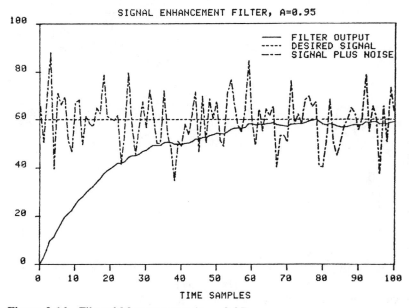

Figure 2.16 Filtered Measurements ($a = 0.95$)

Example 2.3.4: A digital AM receiver is to lock onto a carrier signal of frequency of 10 kHz. The available signal consists of the carrier signal plus white noise. If the available signal is sampled at a rate of 40 kHz, show that its samples will be of the form

$$y_n = x_n + v_n = \cos(\pi n/2) + v_n$$

where the first term represents the sampled carrier and the second the noise. To separate the signal from the noise, a 2nd order filter is used of the form

$$\hat{y}_n = -a^2\hat{y}_{n-2} + (1 - a^2)\, y_n \qquad (|a|<1)$$

Discuss the noise reduction properties of this filter.

Again, this filter has been chosen so that the desired signal which is a sinusoid of frequency $\omega_0 = \pi/2$ will pass through unchanged. That is, at $z = \exp(j\omega_0) = \exp(j\pi/2) = j$, the frequency response must be unity

$$H(z) = \frac{1 - a^2}{1 + a^2 z^{-2}} \qquad \text{with} \qquad H(z)\Big|_{z=j} = \frac{1 - a^2}{1 - a^2} = 1$$

The noise reduction ratio is most easily computed by the contour integral

$$\frac{\sigma_y^2}{\sigma_x^2} = \oint_{u.c.} H(z)\, H(z^{-1}) \frac{dz}{2\pi jz} = \oint_{u.c.} \frac{(1 - a^2)^2 z}{(z - aj)(z + aj)(1 + a^2z^2)} \frac{dz}{2\pi j}$$

$$= (\text{residues at z} = \pm ja) = \frac{(1 - a^2)^2}{1 - a^4} = \frac{1 - a^2}{1 + a^2}$$

Selecting the poles $\pm ja$ to be near the unit circle (from inside) will result in a slow but efficient filter in reducing the noise component.

Example 2.3.5: *Signal Enhancement by Digital Averaging.*

Signal averaging computers are routinely used to improve the signal to noise ratio of signals that are corrupted by noise and can be measured repeatedly—for example, in measuring evoked action potentials using scalp electrodes, or in integrating successive returns in pulsed radar. A similar concept is also used in the so-called "beamforming" operation in sonar and radar arrays. The objective is to measure a signal $x(n)$ of duration of N samples, $n = 0,1, \ldots ,N - 1$. The measurement can be performed (evoked) repeatedly. A total of M such measurements are performed and the results are averaged by the signal averaging computer. Let the results of the mth measurement, for $m = 1,2, \ldots ,M$, be the samples

$$y_m(n) = x(n) + v_m(n), \qquad \text{for } n = 0,1, \ldots ,N - 1$$

A signal averaging computer averages (integrates) the results of the M measurements

$$\hat{x}(n) = \frac{1}{M}\sum_{m=1}^{M} y_m(n) \qquad \text{for } n = 0,1, \ldots, N-1$$

by accumulating (integrating) the results of the M measurements, as shown in following diagram

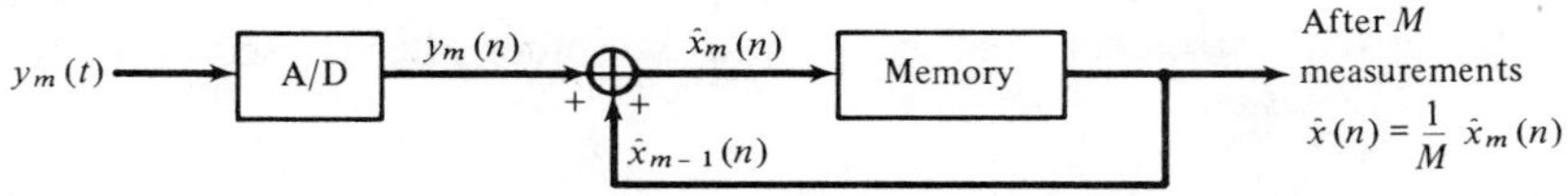

The result of the averaging operation may be expressed as

$$\hat{x}(n) = \frac{1}{M}\sum_{m=1}^{M} y_m(n) = \frac{1}{M}\sum_{m=1}^{M} [x(n) + v_m(n)] = x(n) + \hat{v}(n)$$

where

$$\hat{v}(n) = \frac{1}{M}\sum_{m=1}^{M} v_m(n)$$

Assuming $v_m(n)$ to be mutually uncorrelated; that is, $E[v_m(n)v_l(n)] = \sigma_v^2\, \delta_{ml}$, we compute the variance of the averaged noise $\hat{v}(n)$:

$$\sigma_{\hat{v}}^2 = E[\hat{v}(n)^2] = \frac{1}{M^2}\sum_{m,l=0}^{M} E[v_m(n)v_l(n)] = \frac{1}{M^2}\sum_{m,l=0}^{M} \sigma_v^2\, \delta_{ml}$$

$$= \frac{1}{M^2}(\sigma_v^2 + \sigma_v^2 + \cdots + \sigma_v^2) = \frac{1}{M^2} M\sigma_v^2 = \frac{1}{M}\sigma_v^2$$

Therefore, the signal to noise ratio (SNR) is improved by a factor of M.

The routine **sigav** (Appendix B) performs signal averaging. Its inputs are the file containing the data points to be averaged, the period N, and the number M of periods to be averaged. Its output is the averaged signal $\hat{x}(n)$, $n = 0, 1, \ldots, N - 1$.

2.4 *Quantization Noise*

In digital filtering operations, such as shown in the following diagram, one must deal with the following types of quantization errors [2,3,12]:

1. Quantization of the input samples x_n due to the A/D conversion
2. Quantization of the filter coefficients a_i, b_i
3. Roundoff errors from the internal multiplications

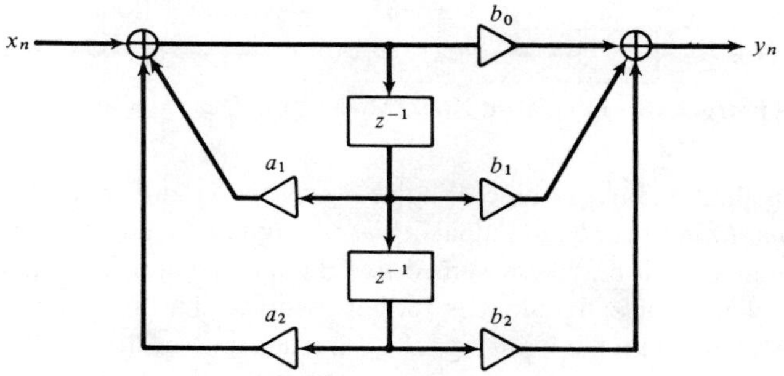

A typical uniform quantization operation of a sampled signal is shown in Fig. 2.17. The spacing between levels is denoted by Q and the overall range of variation of the signal by R. If b bits are assigned to represent each sample value, then the total number of representable signal values is 2^b, and therefore the number of levels that can fit within the range R is

$$2^b = \frac{R}{Q}$$

which also leads to the so-called ''6 dB per bit'' rule for the dynamic range of the quantizer

$$\text{dB} = 10 \log_{10} \left(\frac{R}{Q}\right)^2 = b\, 20 \log_{10}(2) = 6b \text{ decibels}$$

The quantization operation may be represented as

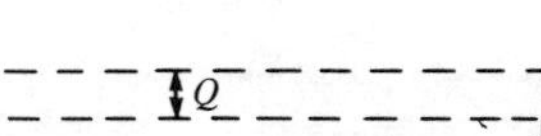

where $[x_n]$ denotes the quantized value of x_n; that is, the nearest level. The quantization error is $\delta_n = [x_n] - x_n$. The quantization operation may be replaced

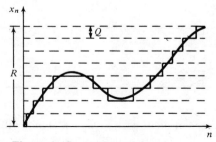

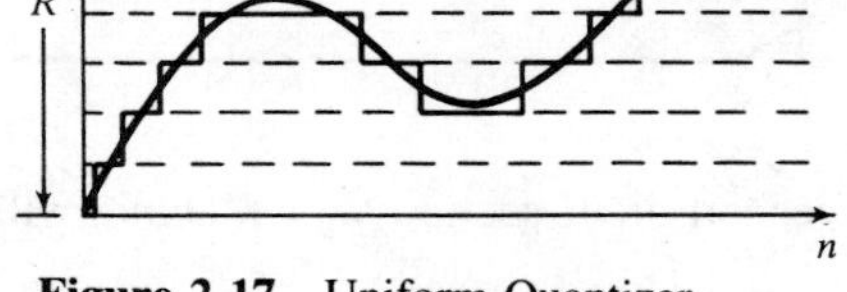

Figure 2.17 Uniform Quantizer

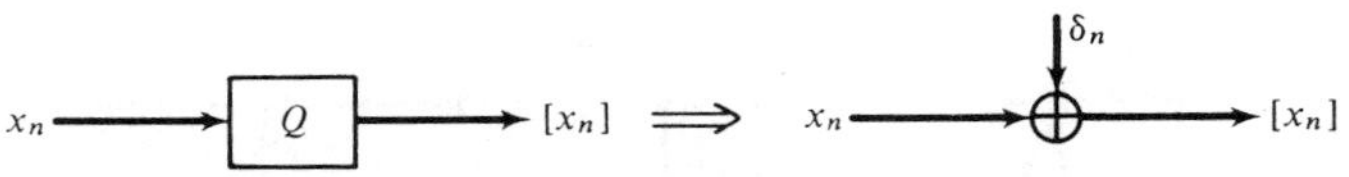

Figure 2.18 Equivalent Noise Model for a Quantizer

by an equivalent additive source of noise δ_n, as shown in Fig. 2.18. In the case of *large-amplitude wideband* signals; that is, signals that vary rapidly through the entire range R, it may be assumed that the quantization error is a *uniformly* distributed *white-noise* signal. It is further assumed that the quantization noise δ_n is uncorrelated with the input signal x_n. In such a case, the quantization noise lends itself to simple statistical treatment. Namely, the quantization operation may be replaced by an equivalent additive white-noise source, acting where the quantization operation is occurring. Since δ_n is assumed to be uniformly distributed in the range $-Q/2 \leq \delta_n \leq Q/2$, it follows that it has zero mean and variance

$$\sigma_\delta^2 = \frac{Q^2}{12} \tag{2.4.1}$$

2.5 *Statistical Treatment of Multiplier Roundoff Error*

Here, we would like to use the results of the previous section in the computation of the roundoff noise arising from the internal multiplications in digital filters. Consider a typical multiplier in a digital filter

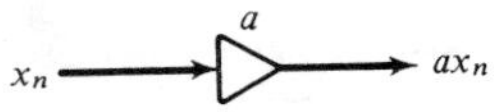

The result of the multiplication requires double precision to be represented fully. If this result is subsequently rounded to single precision, then the overall operation, and its noise-equivalent model, will be of the form

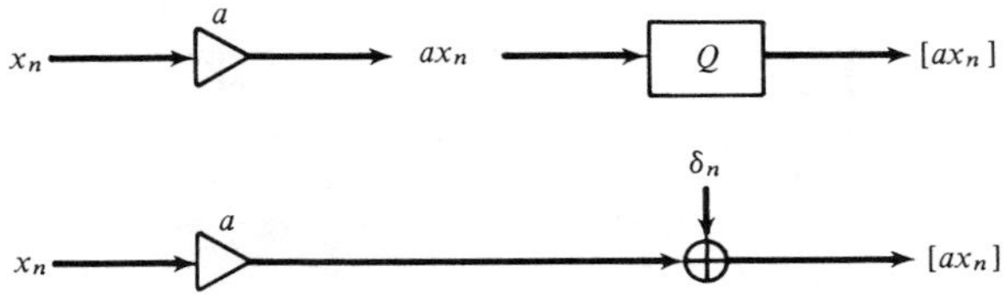

For example, the second order section shown above will be replaced by

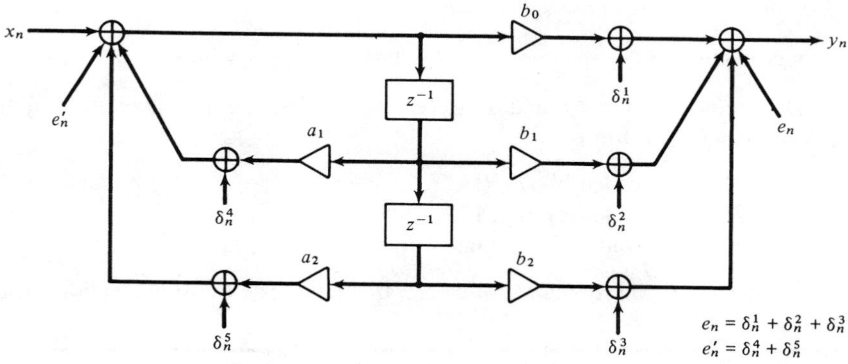

with five elementary noise sources acting independently of each other at the locations shown. In placing these noise sources at those locations, we are implicitly assuming that a quantization operation is being performed immediately after each multiplication. This may not always be true, especially in the newer hardware configurations which employ special purpose chips, such as the TMS320, or the TRW multiplier-accumulators. Such chips perform the multiplication operation with full double precision. Depending on the specific digital filter implementation, it is possible for such full precision products to accumulate somewhat before the result is finally rounded back to single precision. The methods presented here can easily be extended to such a situation. For illustrative purposes, we shall assume that the quantizing operations occur just after each multiplication.

To find the output noise power resulting from each noise source we must identify the transfer function from each noise source to the output of the filter. For example, the three elementary noises at the forward multipliers may be combined into one acting at the output adder and having combined variance

$$\sigma_e^2 = 3\,\sigma_\delta^2 = 3\,Q^2/12$$

and the two noises at the two feedback multipliers may be replaced by one acting at the input adder and having variance

$$\sigma_{e'}^2 = 2\,\sigma_\delta^2 = 2\,Q^2/12$$

The transfer function from e'_n to the output is $H(z)$ itself, and from e_n to the output it is unity. Adding the output noise variances due to e'_n and e_n, we find the total output roundoff noise power

$$\sigma_\epsilon^2 = \sigma_{e'}^2\,\|H\|^2 + \sigma_e^2$$

Example 2.5.1: Suppose $H(z) = H_1(z)H_2(z)$,

where $H_1(z) = \dfrac{1}{1 - az^{-1}}$, and $H_2(z) = \dfrac{1}{1 - bz^{-1}}$ with $a > b$.

Determine the output roundoff noise powers when the filter is realized in the following three forms:

1. $H_1(z)$ cascaded by $H_2(z)$
2. $H_2(z)$ cascaded by $H_1(z)$
3. $H(z)$ realized in its canonical form

In case 1, the roundoff noises are as shown. The transfer functions of e_n

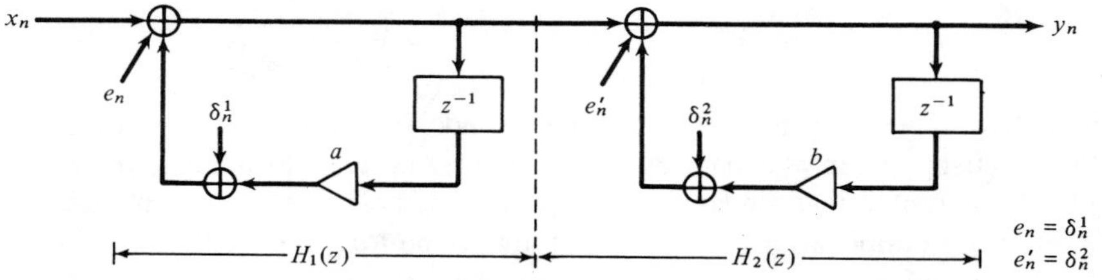

and e_n' to the output are $H(z)$ and $H_2(z)$, respectively. Adding the output noise power from each we find

$$\sigma_\epsilon^2 = \sigma_\delta^2 \|H\|^2 + \sigma_\delta^2 \|H_2\|^2$$

$$= \frac{Q^2}{12} \frac{1 + ab}{(1 - ab)(1 - a^2)(1 - b^2)} + \frac{Q^2}{12} \frac{1}{1 - b^2}$$

Interchanging the role of H_1 and H_2 we find, for case 2,

$$\sigma_\epsilon^2 = \frac{Q^2}{12} \frac{1 + ab}{(1 - ab)(1 - a^2)(1 - b^2)} + \frac{Q^2}{12} \frac{1}{1 - a^2}$$

And finally in case 3, the canonical realization has two elementary noise

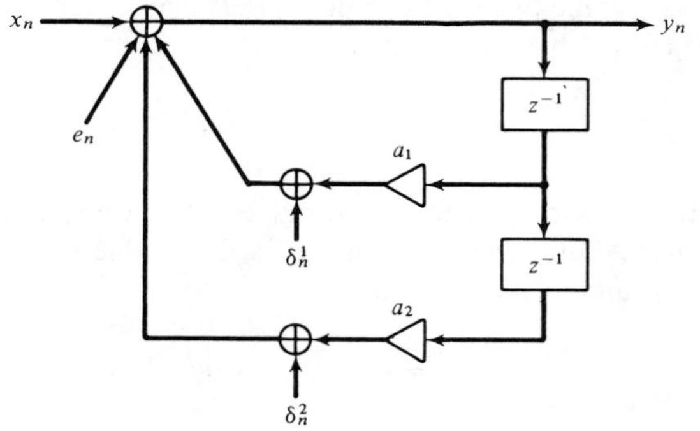

sources as shown. They may be combined into one acting at the input adder. Its variance will be $\sigma_e^2 = 2\,Q^2/12$. The transfer function to the output is $H(z)$ itself; thus,

$$\sigma_\epsilon^2 = \sigma_e^2\,\|H\|^2 = 2\,\frac{Q^2}{12}\,\frac{1 + ab}{(1 - ab)(1 - a^2)(1 - b^2)}$$

It can be seen from the above example that the output roundoff power depends on the particular *realization* of the digital filter. A great deal of research has gone into developing realization structures that minimize the roundoff noise [13–21].

2.6 *Introduction to Linear Prediction*

In this section, we present a preliminary introduction to the concepts and methods of linear prediction based on the finite past. We have already mentioned how prediction ideas come into play by reinterpreting

$$\hat{y}_n = ay_{n-1} = \text{prediction of } y_n \text{ based on one past sample}$$

$$e_n = y_n - \hat{y}_n = y_n - ay_{n-1} = \text{prediction error}$$

and have indicated how to determine the prediction coefficient a by a least squares minimization criterion. Here, we would like to replace that criterion, based on time averages, with a least squares criterion based on statistical averages:

$$\mathcal{E}(a) = E[e_n^2] = E[(y_n - ay_{n-1})^2] = \min$$

We will no longer assume that y_n is a first order autoregressive Markov process; thus, the prediction error e_n will not quite be white noise. The problem we are posing is to find the best linear predictor based on the previous sample alone, regardless of whether y_n is a first order autoregressive process or not. That is, we seek the projection of y_n on the subspace $Y_{n-1} = \{y_{n-1}\}$ spanned only by the previous sample y_{n-1}; this projection is the best linear estimate of y_n based on y_{n-1} only. If, accidentally, the signal y_n happened to be first order autoregressive, then e_n would turn out to be white and our methods would determine the proper value for the Markov model parameter a.

The best value for the prediction coefficient a is obtained by differentiating $\mathcal{E}$ with respect to a, and setting the derivative to zero

$$\frac{\partial \mathcal{E}}{\partial a} = 2\,E\left[e_n\,\frac{\partial e_n}{\partial a}\right] = -2\,E[e_n\,y_{n-1}] = 0$$

Thus, we obtain the orthogonality equation

$$E[e_n\,y_{n-1}] = 0$$

which states that the prediction error e_n is decorrelated from y_{n-1}. An equivalent way of writing this condition is the normal equation

$$E[e_n\, y_{n-1}] = E[(y_n - ay_{n-1})y_{n-1}] = E[y_n\, y_{n-1}] - a\, E[y_{n-1}^2] = 0$$

or, in terms of the autocorrelations $R_{yy}(k) = E[y_{n+k}y_n]$,

$$R_{yy}(1) = a\, R_{yy}(0) \qquad \text{or} \qquad a = \frac{R_{yy}(1)}{R_{yy}(0)}$$

The minimum value of the prediction error $\mathcal{E}(a)$ for the above optimal value of a, may be written as

$$\begin{aligned} \min \mathcal{E} = E[e_n^2] &= E[e_n(y_n - ay_{n-1})] = E[e_n\, y_n] - a\, E[e_n\, y_{n-1}] \\ &= E[e_n\, y_n] = E[(y_n - ay_{n-1})y_n] = E[y_n^2] - a\, E[y_{n-1}\, y_n] \\ &= R_{yy}(0) - a\, R_{yy}(1) = R_{yy}(0) - [R_{yy}(1)^2/R_{yy}(0)] \\ &= (1 - a^2)\, R_{yy}(0) \end{aligned}$$

The resulting prediction-error filter has transfer function

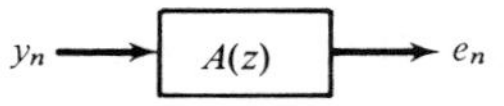

$$e_n = y_n - ay_{n-1};\ A(z) = 1 - az^{-1}$$

A realization of the prediction filter is drawn in Fig. 2.19. The upper output is the prediction error, whose average power has been minimized, and the lower output is the predicted waveform. The original signal may be written as a sum of two terms:

$$y_n = \hat{y}_n + e_n$$

The first term $\hat{y}_n = ay_{n-1}$ is highly correlated with the secondary signal y_{n-1}, which in turn is input to the multiplier. The second term e_n, by virtue of the orthogonality relations, is completely uncorrelated with y_{n-1}. In Fig. 2.19 we have indicated a dividing line between the input part and the correlation canceler part. The latter may be recognized as a special case of the correlation canceler configuration of Fig. 1.1. The input part simply provides the two inputs to the correlation canceler. Since these two inputs are y_n and y_{n-1}, the canceler tries

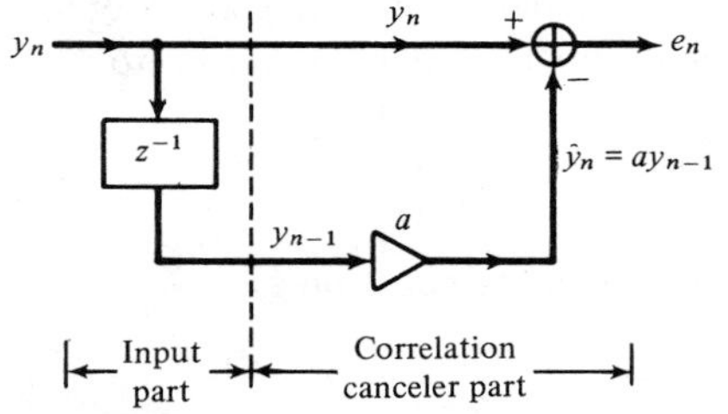

Figure 2.19 First Order Linear Predictor

to cancel any correlations that may exist between these two signals; in other words, it tries to remove any serial correlations that might be present in y_n.

Next, we discuss higher order predictors and find their connection to lower order predictors. First, we change to a more standard notation by replacing the parameter a by $a_1 = -a$. That is, we take

$$\hat{y}_n = -a_1 y_{n-1} = \text{prediction of } y_n \text{ based on } one \text{ past sample}$$

$$e_n = y_n - \hat{y}_n = y_n + a_1 y_{n-1} = \text{prediction error} \tag{2.6.1}$$

$$\mathcal{E}(a_1) = E[e_n^2] = E[(y_n + a_1 y_{n-1})^2] = \text{minimum}$$

It will prove instructive to discuss, in parallel, the second order case of predicting y_n on the basis of two past samples y_{n-1} and y_{n-2}

$$\hat{y}'_n = -[a'_1 y_{n-1} + a'_2 y_{n-2}]$$
$$= \text{prediction of } y_n \text{ based on } two \text{ past samples}$$

$$e'_n = y_n - \hat{y}'_n = y_n + a'_1 y_{n-1} + a'_2 y_{n-2} = \text{prediction error}$$

$$\mathcal{E}(a'_1, a'_2) = E[e'^2_n] = E[(y_n + a'_1 y_{n-1} + a'_2 y_{n-2})^2] = \text{minimum}$$

The second order predictor $\hat{y}'_n$ of y_n is the orthogonal projection of y_n onto the subspace spanned by the past two samples $Y'_{n-1} = \{y_{n-1}, y_{n-2}\}$. A realization of the second order predictor is shown in Fig. 2.20. Again, it may be recognized as a special case of the correlation canceler. The input part provides the necessary inputs to the canceler. The main input to the canceler is y_n and the secondary input is the 2-vector $\begin{bmatrix} y_{n-1} \\ y_{n-2} \end{bmatrix}$. The canceler tries to remove any correlations between y_n and y_{n-1} as well as y_{n-2}. That is, it tries to remove even more sequential correlations than the first order predictor did.

The corresponding prediction-error filters are for the two cases

$$A(z) = 1 + a_1 z^{-1} \qquad \text{and} \qquad A'(z) = 1 + a'_1 z^{-1} + a'_2 z^{-2}$$

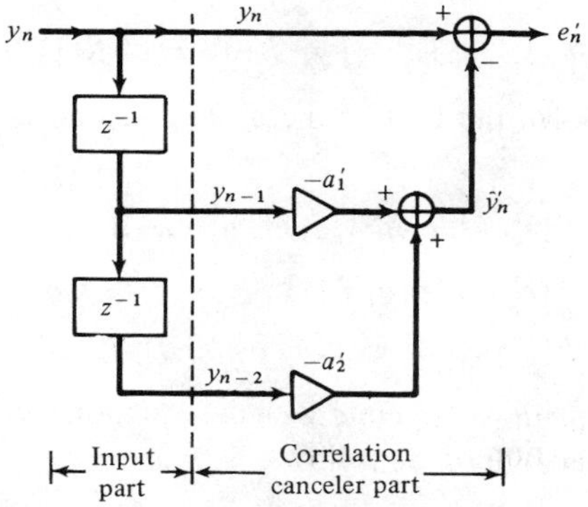

Figure 2.20 Second Order Linear Predictor

Our objective is to determine the best choice of the prediction-error filters $(1,a_1)$ and $(1,a_1',a_2')$ such that the corresponding mean-squared prediction errors are minimized. The minimization conditions in the two cases become

$$\frac{\partial \mathcal{E}}{\partial a_1} = 2E\left[e_n \frac{\partial e_n}{\partial a_1}\right] = 2E[e_n\, y_{n-1}] = 0$$

$$\frac{\partial \mathcal{E}'}{\partial a_1'} = 2E\left[e_n' \frac{\partial e_n'}{\partial a_1'}\right] = 2E[e_n'\, y_{n-1}] = 0,$$

$$\frac{\partial \mathcal{E}'}{\partial a_2'} = 2E[e_n'\, y_{n-2}] = 0$$

Inserting

$$e_n = \sum_{m=0}^{1} a_m\, y_{n-m} \qquad \text{(we set } a_0 = 1\text{)}$$

$$e_n' = \sum_{m=0}^{2} a_m'\, y_{n-m} \qquad \text{(again, } a_0' = 1\text{)}$$

into these orthogonality equations, we obtain the two sets of normal equations

$$R(1) + a_1\, R(0) = 0 \qquad \text{(first order predictor)} \tag{2.6.2}$$

$$R(1) + a_1'\, R(0) + a_2'\, R(1) = 0 \tag{2.6.3}$$

$$R(2) + a_1'\, R(1) + a_2'\, R(0) = 0 \qquad \text{(second order predictor)}$$

which determine the best prediction coefficients. We have also simplified our previous notation and set $R(k) = E[y_{n+k}\, y_n]$. The corresponding minimal values for the mean-squared errors are expressed as

$$\mathcal{E} = E[e_n^2] = E[e_n\, y_n] = R(0) + a_1\, R(1) \tag{2.6.4}$$

$$\mathcal{E}' = E[e_n'^2] = E[e_n'\, y_n] = R(0) + a_1'\, R(1) + a_2'\, R(2) \tag{2.6.5}$$

We have already shown the first of these. The second is derived by a similar procedure

$$\begin{aligned}\mathcal{E}' = E[e_n'^2] &= E[e_n'(y_n + a_1'\, y_{n-1} + a_2'\, y_{n-2})] \\ &= E[e_n'\, y_n] + a_1'\, E[e_n'\, y_{n-1}] + a_2'\, E[e_n'\, y_{n-2}] = E[e_n'\, y_n] \\ &= E[(y_n + a_1'\, y_{n-1} + a_2'\, y_{n-2})y_n], \text{ etc.}\end{aligned}$$

The orthogonality equations, together with the equations for the prediction errors, can be put into a matrix form as follows

$$\begin{bmatrix} R(0) & R(1) \\ R(1) & R(0) \end{bmatrix} \begin{bmatrix} 1 \\ a_1 \end{bmatrix} = \begin{bmatrix} \mathcal{E} \\ 0 \end{bmatrix}$$

$$\begin{bmatrix} R(0) & R(1) & R(2) \\ R(1) & R(0) & R(1) \\ R(2) & R(1) & R(0) \end{bmatrix} \begin{bmatrix} 1 \\ a'_1 \\ a'_2 \end{bmatrix} = \begin{bmatrix} \mathcal{E}' \\ 0 \\ 0 \end{bmatrix} \tag{2.6.6}$$

Example 2.6.1: Rederive the results (2.6.3) and (2.6.5) for the second order predictor using the correlation canceler formulation of Section 1.4. In the notation of Section 1.4, the primary input to the canceler is the 1-vector $\mathbf{x} = [y_n]$ and the secondary input is the 2-vector $\mathbf{y} = \begin{bmatrix} y_{n-1} \\ y_{n-2} \end{bmatrix}$. Then,

$$R_{xy} = E[y_n \widehat{y_{n-1}, y_{n-2}}] = [E[y_n\, y_{n-1}],\, E[y_n\, y_{n-2}]] = [R(1),\, R(2)]$$

$$R_{yy} = E\left[\begin{pmatrix} y_{n-1} \\ y_{n-2} \end{pmatrix} \widehat{y_{n-1}, y_{n-2}}\right] = \begin{bmatrix} R(0) & R(1) \\ R(1) & R(0) \end{bmatrix}$$

Therefore,

$$H = R_{xy}\, R_{yy}^{-1} = [R(1), R(2)] \begin{bmatrix} R(0) & R(1) \\ R(1) & R(0) \end{bmatrix}^{-1}$$

If we denote this row vector by $H = -[a'_1, a'_2]$, we find

$$-[a'_1, a'_2] = [R(1),\, R(2)] \begin{bmatrix} R(0) & R(1) \\ R(1) & R(0) \end{bmatrix}^{-1}$$

which is the solution of Eq. (2.6.3). The corresponding estimate $\hat{\mathbf{x}} = H\mathbf{y}$ is then

$$\hat{y}'_n = -[a'_1, a'_2] \begin{bmatrix} y_{n-1} \\ y_{n-2} \end{bmatrix} = -[a'_1\, y_{n-1} + a'_2\, y_{n-2}]$$

and the minimum value of the mean-squared estimation error is

$$\mathcal{E}' = E[e'^2_n] = R_{xx} - H\, R_{yx} = E[y_n^2] + [a'_1, a'_2] \begin{bmatrix} R(1) \\ R(2) \end{bmatrix}$$

$$= R(0) + a'_1\, R(1) + a'_2\, R(2)$$

which agrees with Eq. (2.6.5).

Example 2.6.2: Using the results of Section 1.7, determine the forward and backward predictors of first and second orders. In the notation of Section 1.7, the data vector $\mathbf{y}$ and the subvectors $\bar{\mathbf{y}}$ and $\tilde{\mathbf{y}}$ are

$$\mathbf{y} = \begin{bmatrix} y_n \\ y_{n-1} \\ y_{n-2} \end{bmatrix}, \quad \bar{\mathbf{y}} = \begin{bmatrix} y_n \\ y_{n-1} \end{bmatrix}, \quad \tilde{\mathbf{y}} = \begin{bmatrix} y_{n-1} \\ y_{n-2} \end{bmatrix}$$

The corresponding covariance matrix $R = E[\mathbf{y}\mathbf{y}^T]$ and its subblocks are

$$R = \begin{bmatrix} R(0) & R(1) & R(2) \\ R(1) & R(0) & R(1) \\ R(2) & R(1) & R(0) \end{bmatrix}, \quad \tilde{R} = \bar{R} = \begin{bmatrix} R(0) & R(1) \\ R(1) & R(0) \end{bmatrix}$$

Similarly,

$$\mathbf{r}_a = \begin{bmatrix} R(1) \\ R(2) \end{bmatrix}, \quad \mathbf{r}_b = \begin{bmatrix} R(2) \\ R(1) \end{bmatrix}, \quad \rho_a = \rho_b = R(0)$$

We note that $\mathbf{r}_a$ and $\mathbf{r}_b$ are the reverse of each other. Formally, $\mathbf{r}_a = \bar{J}\mathbf{r}_b$, where $\bar{J}$ is the order-2 reversing matrix $\bar{J} = \begin{bmatrix} 0 & 1 \\ 1 & 0 \end{bmatrix}$. The first and second order forward predictors will be

$$\tilde{\mathbf{a}} = \bar{\mathbf{a}} = \begin{bmatrix} 1 \\ a_1 \end{bmatrix}, \quad \mathbf{a} = \begin{bmatrix} 1 \\ a_1' \\ a_2' \end{bmatrix}$$

Noting the $\bar{R}$ and hence $\bar{R}^{-1}$ both commute with the reversing matrix $\bar{J}$, we obtain for the backward prediction vector, given by (1.7.7)

$$\boldsymbol{\beta} = -\bar{R}^{-1}\mathbf{r}_b = -\bar{R}^{-1}\bar{J}\mathbf{r}_a = -\bar{J}\bar{R}^{-1}\mathbf{r}_a = \bar{J}\boldsymbol{\alpha}$$

It follows that the backward predictors are the *reverse* of the forward ones:

$$\tilde{\mathbf{b}} = \bar{\mathbf{b}} = \begin{bmatrix} a_1 \\ 1 \end{bmatrix}, \quad \mathbf{b} = \begin{bmatrix} a_2' \\ a_1' \\ 1 \end{bmatrix}$$

The corresponding matrices L and U whose rows are the backward and forward predictors, Eqs. (1.7.14) and (1.7.30), are

$$L = \begin{bmatrix} 1 & 0 & 0 \\ a_1 & 1 & 0 \\ a_2' & a_1' & 1 \end{bmatrix}, \quad U = \begin{bmatrix} 1 & a_1' & a_2' \\ 0 & 1 & a_1 \\ 0 & 0 & 1 \end{bmatrix}$$

It follows from the reversing symmetry of R that they are reverses of each other, i.e., $U = JLJ$, where J is the order-3 reversing matrix. Similarly, the diagonal matrices D_a and D_b are reverses of each other; namely,

$$D_b = \text{diag}\{R(0),\mathcal{E},\mathcal{E}'\}, \qquad D_a = \text{diag}\{\mathcal{E}',\mathcal{E},R(0)\}$$

2.7 *Gapped Functions, Levinson and Schur Recursions*

Instead of solving the matrix equations (2.6.6) directly, or independently, of each other, we would like to develop an iterative procedure for constructing the solution $(1,a_1',a_2')$ in terms of the solution $(1,a_1)$. The procedure is known as Levinson's algorithm. To this end, it proves convenient to work with the elegant concept of the "gapped" functions, first introduced into this context by Robinson and Treitel [22]. Gapped functions are also used in the development of the Schur algorithm [23]. The gapped functions for the first and second order predictors are defined by

$$g(k) = E[e_n\, y_{n-k}] \qquad \text{(for first order predictor)}$$

$$g'(k) = E[e_n'\, y_{n-k}] \qquad \text{(for second order predictor)}$$

They are the cross-correlations between the prediction-error sequences and the sequence y_n. These definitions are motivated by the orthogonality equations, which are the determining equations for the prediction coefficients. That is, if the best coefficients $(1,a_1)$ and $(1,a_1',a_2')$ are used, then the gapped functions must vanish at lags $k = 1$ for the first order case, and $k = 1,2$ for the second order case; that is,

$$g(1) = E[e_n\, y_{n-1}] = 0$$

$$g'(1) = E[e_n'\, y_{n-1}] = 0, \qquad g'(2) = E[e_n'\, y_{n-2}] = 0$$

Thus, the functions $g(k)$ and $g'(k)$ develop gaps of lengths one and two, respectively, as seen in Fig. 2.21. A special role is played by the value of the

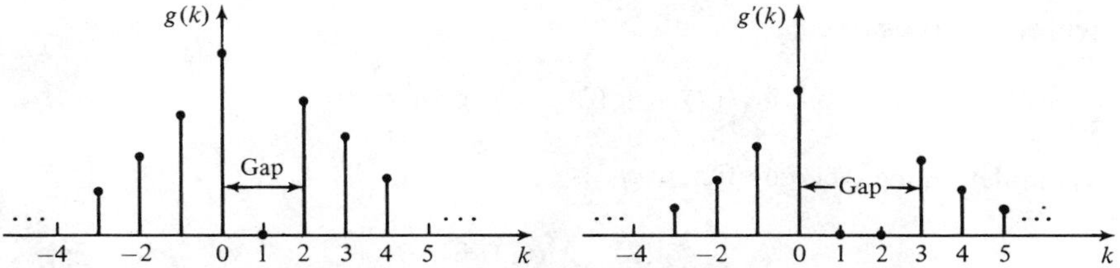

Figure 2.21 Gapped Functions of Orders One and Two

gapped functions at $k = 0$. It follows from the expressions (2.6.4) for the minimized prediction errors that

$$\mathcal{E} = g(0) = E[e_n\, y_n] \qquad \text{and} \qquad \mathcal{E}' = g'(0) = E[e'_n\, y_n] \tag{2.7.1}$$

The gapped functions may also be expressed as the *convolution* of the prediction-error filters $(1,a_1)$ and $(1,a'_1,a'_2)$ with the autocorrelation function $R(k) = E[y_{n+k}\, y_n]$, as can be seen from the definition

$$\begin{aligned} g(k) &= E[e_n\, y_{n-k}] = E\left[\left(\sum_{m=0}^{1} a_m\, y_{n-m}\right) y_{n-k}\right] \\ &= \sum_{m=0}^{1} a_m E[y_{n-m}\, y_{n-k}] = \sum_{m=0}^{1} a_m\, R(k-m) \end{aligned} \tag{2.7.2}$$

and similarly

$$g'(k) = E[e'_n\, y_{n-k}] = \sum_{m=0}^{2} a'_m\, R(k-m) \tag{2.7.3}$$

Thus, they are the outputs of the prediction-error filters, when the input is the autocorrelation function $R(k)$.

The *Levinson recursion*, which iteratively constructs the best linear predictor of order two from the best predictor of order one, can be derived with the help of the gapped functions. The basic idea is to use the gapped function of order one, which already has a gap of length one, and construct from it a new gapped function with gap of length two.

Starting with $g(k)$, first *reflect* it about the origin, then *delay* it sufficiently until the gap of the reflected function is aligned with the gap of $g(k)$. In the present case, the required delay is only two units, as can be seen from Fig. 2.22. Any linear combination of the two gapped functions $g(k)$ and $g(2-k)$ will have gap of at least length one. Now, select the coefficients in the linear combination so that the gap becomes of length two

$$g'(k) = g(k) - \gamma_2\, g(2-k) \tag{2.7.4}$$

with the extra gap condition $g'(2) = 0$

$$g'(2) = g(2) - \gamma_2\, g(0) = 0$$

which determines the coefficient γ_2 as

$$\gamma_2 = \frac{g(2)}{g(0)} = \frac{R(2) + a_1 R(1)}{R(0) + a_1 R(1)} \tag{2.7.5}$$

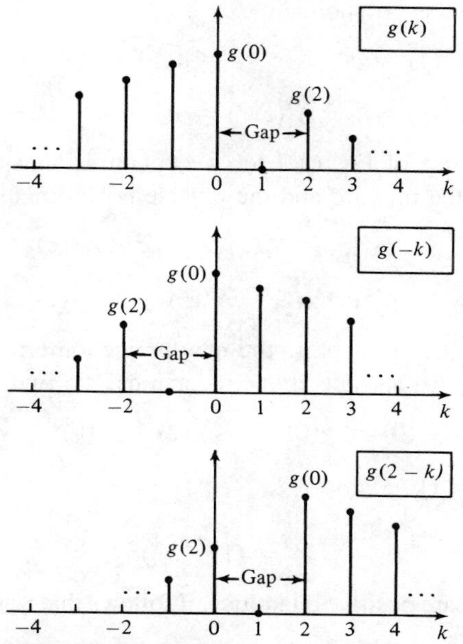

Figure 2.22 Reflected and Delayed Gapped Function

The coefficient γ_2 is called the *reflection coefficient* or PARCOR coefficient and if selected as above, it will ensure that the new gapped function $g'(k)$ has a gap of length two. To find the new prediction-error filter, we write Eq. (2.7.4) in the z-domain, noting that the z-transform of $g(-k)$ is $G(z^{-1})$, and that of $g(2 - k)$ is $z^{-2}G(z^{-1})$

$$G'(z) = G(z) - \gamma_2 z^{-2} G(z^{-1})$$

Using the convolutional equations (2.7.2) and (2.7.3), expressed in the z-domain, we find

$$A'(z) S_{yy}(z) = A(z) S_{yy}(z) - \gamma_2 z^{-2} A(z^{-1}) S_{yy}(z^{-1})$$

Since $S_{yy}(z^{-1}) = S_{yy}(z)$, it can be canceled from both sides, giving the desired relationship between the new and the old prediction-error filters

$$A'(z) = A(z) - \gamma_2 z^{-2} A(z^{-1}) \qquad \text{(Levinson recursion)} \qquad (2.7.6)$$

and equating coefficients

$$\begin{bmatrix} 1 \\ a_1' \\ a_2' \end{bmatrix} = \begin{bmatrix} 1 \\ a_1 \\ 0 \end{bmatrix} - \gamma_2 \begin{bmatrix} 0 \\ a_1 \\ 1 \end{bmatrix} \qquad \begin{aligned} a_1' &= a_1 - \gamma_2 a_1 \\ a_2' &= -\gamma_2 \end{aligned}$$

Introducing the reverse polynomials

$$A^R(z) = z^{-1} A(z^{-1}) = a_1 + z^{-1}$$

$$A'^R(z) = z^{-2} A'(z^{-1}) = a_2' + a_1' z^{-1} + z^{-2}$$

and taking the reverse of Eq. (2.7.6), we obtain a more convenient recursion that involves both the forward and the reverse polynomials:

$$\begin{aligned} A'(z) &= A(z) - \gamma_2 z^{-1} A^R(z) \\ A'^R(z) &= z^{-1} A^R(z) - \gamma_2 A(z) \end{aligned} \tag{2.7.7}$$

It is of interest also to express the new prediction error in terms of the old one. Using $\mathcal{E}' = g'(0)$ and the above recursions, we find

$$\begin{aligned} \mathcal{E}' &= g'(0) = g(0) - \gamma_2 g(2) = g(0) - \gamma_2^2 g(0) \\ &= (1 - \gamma_2^2)\mathcal{E} \end{aligned}$$

or

$$\mathcal{E}' = (1 - \gamma_2^2)\mathcal{E} \tag{2.7.8}$$

Since both $\mathcal{E}$ and $\mathcal{E}'$ are positive quantities, it follows that γ_2 must have magnitude less than one.

Using Eq. (2.6.4), we also obtain

$$\begin{aligned} \mathcal{E} &= E[e_n^2] = g(0) = R(0) + a_1 R(1) \\ &= (1 - \gamma_1^2)\, R(0) = (1 - \gamma_1^2)\, \sigma_y^2 \end{aligned} \tag{2.7.9}$$

where, by convention, the reflection coefficient γ_1 for the first order predictor was defined as $\gamma_1 = -a_1$. Equation (2.7.9) implies that γ_1 also has magnitude less than one. Combining Eqs. (2.7.8) and (2.7.9), we find

$$\mathcal{E}' = (1 - \gamma_2^2)\mathcal{E} = (1 - \gamma_2^2)(1 - \gamma_1^2)\, \sigma_y^2 \tag{2.7.10}$$

The Levinson recursion (2.7.7) leads directly to the so-called *lattice filters* of linear prediction. Instead of realizing just the filter $A'(z)$, the lattice realizations *simultaneously* realize both $A'(z)$ and its reverse $A'^R(z)$. The input to both filters is the sequence y_n being predicted. Since $A'(z)$ is related to $A(z)$, first a lattice realization of $A(z)$ will be constructed. Writing $A(z) = 1 + a_1 z^{-1} = 1 - \gamma_1 z^{-1}$ and $A^R(z) = -\gamma_1 + z^{-1}$, a simultaneous realization of both, with a common input y_n, is shown in Fig. 2.23, where a common multiplier γ_1 is indicated for

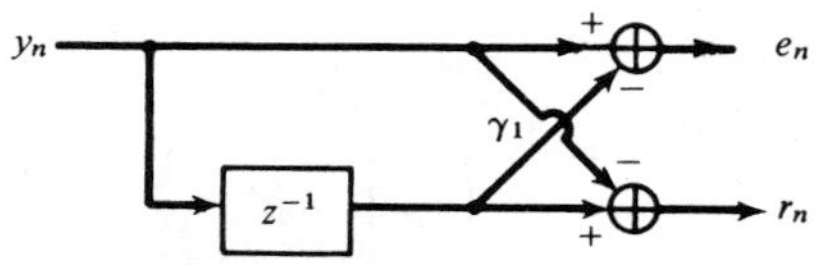

Figure 2.23 Lattice Realization of First Order Prediction-Error Filter

both branches. The transfer functions from y_n to e_n and r_n are $A(z)$ and $A^R(z)$, respectively. Using Eq. (2.7.7), it should be evident that a simultaneous realization of both $A'(z)$ and $A'^R(z)$ can be obtained by simply adding one more lattice section involving the coefficient γ_2, as shown in Fig. 2.24. Again, the transfer functions from the common input y_n to e_n' and r_n' are $A'(z)$ and $A'^R(z)$, respectively.

The I/O equations for the lattice filter, Fig. 2.24, with overall input y_n are

$$\begin{aligned} e_n &= y_n - \gamma_1 y_{n-1}\,, \qquad r_n = y_{n-1} - \gamma_1 y_n \\ e_n' &= e_n - \gamma_2 r_{n-1}\,, \qquad r_n' = r_{n-1} - \gamma_2 e_n \end{aligned} \tag{2.7.11}$$

We observe that the Levinson recursion (2.7.6) is identical to the order updating Eq. (1.7.40). Because **b** is the reverse of **a**, the second of Eqs. (1.7.40) is simply the upside down version of the first. The lattice recursions (1.7.50) are identical to Eq. (2.7.11). Indeed,

$$e_a = \mathbf{a}^T\mathbf{y} = [1, a_1', a_2']\begin{bmatrix} y_n \\ y_{n-1} \\ y_{n-2}\end{bmatrix} = e_n'\,, \qquad e_b = \mathbf{b}^T\mathbf{y} = [a_2', a_1', 1]\begin{bmatrix} y_n \\ y_{n-1} \\ y_{n-2}\end{bmatrix} = r_n'$$

and using the definitions (1.7.49), we find

$$\bar{e}_a = \bar{\mathbf{a}}^T\bar{\mathbf{y}} = [1, a_1]\begin{bmatrix} y_n \\ y_{n-1}\end{bmatrix} = e_n\,, \qquad \bar{e}_b = \bar{\mathbf{b}}^T\bar{\mathbf{y}} = [a_1, 1]\begin{bmatrix} y_{n-1} \\ y_{n-2}\end{bmatrix} = r_{n-1}$$

Next, we develop the Schur algorithm for first and second order predictors. Motivated by the appearance of the reversed polynomials in the Levinson recursion (2.7.7), we are led to define the *backward* gapped functions of orders one and two by their z-transforms

$$G_-(z) \equiv z^{-1}G(z^{-1}) = A^R(z)S_{yy}(z)\,, \quad G_-'(z) \equiv z^{-2}G'(z^{-1}) = A'^R(z)S_{yy}(z) \tag{2.7.12}$$

In the time domain,

$$g_-(k) = g(1-k)\,, \quad g_-'(k) = g'(2-k) \tag{2.7.13}$$

Thus, they are reflected and appropriately delayed versions of the forward gapped functions (the delay being one less than required to align the gaps). They satisfy the following gap conditions: Because $g(k)$ and $g'(k)$ vanish at $k = 1$ and $k = 1, 2$, it

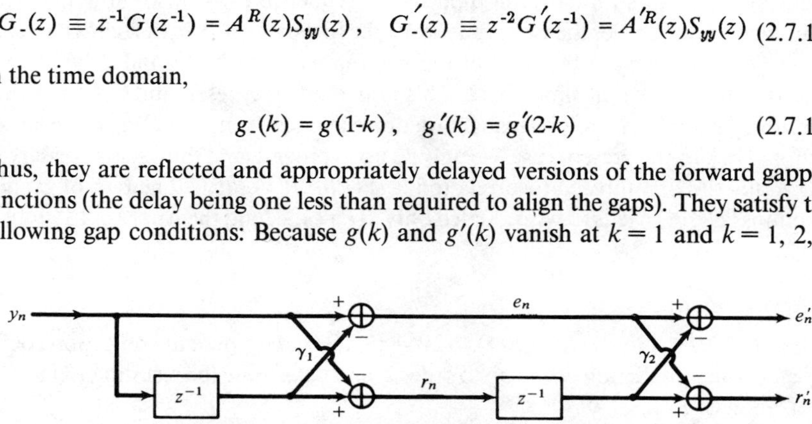

Figure 2.24 Lattice Realization of Second Order Prediction-Error Filter

follows from Eq. (2.7.13) that $g_-(k)$ and $g'_-(k)$ will vanish at $k=0$ and $k=0$, 1, respectively. The lattice recursions satisfied by the forward and backward gapped functions are obtained as follows. For the first order case, we write

$$G(z) = A(z)S_{yy}(z) = (1 - \gamma_1 z^{-1})S_{yy}(z), \qquad G_-(z) = A^R(z)S_{yy}(z) = (-\gamma_1 + z^{-1})S_{yy}(z)$$

Multiplying Eq. (2.7.7) by $S_{yy}(z)$ and using the definition (2.7.12), we have for the second-order case,

$$G'(z) = G(z) - \gamma_2 z^{-1} G_-(z), \qquad G'_-(z) = z^{-1} G_-(z) - \gamma_2 G(z)$$

Writing the above equations in the time domain we obtain the *Schur algorithm:*

1. Compute $\gamma_1 = \dfrac{R(1)}{R(0)}$
2. Compute the first-order gapped functions:
$$g(k) = R(k) - \gamma_1 R(k-1), \qquad g_-(k) = R(k-1) - \gamma_1 R(k) \quad (2.7.14)$$
3. Compute the first-order prediction error $\mathcal{E} = g_-(1) = g(0)$
4. Compute $\gamma_2 = \dfrac{g(2)}{g_-(1)} = \dfrac{g(2)}{g(0)}$
5. Compute the second-order gapped functions:
$$g'(k) = g(k) - \gamma_2 g_-(k-1), \qquad g'_-(k) = g_-(k-1) - \gamma_2 g(k) \quad (2.7.15)$$
6. Compute the second-order prediction error $\mathcal{E}' = g'_-(2) = g'(0)$

The Schur algorithm is an alternative to Levinson's algorithm for computing the reflection coefficients γ_1 and γ_2. The difference between the two is that although Levinson's algorithm works with the polynomial recursions (2.7.6), Schur's algorithm works with the gapped functions themselves. Note that Eqs. (2.7.14) and (2.7.15) generate the *output* signals from the first and second segments of the lattice filter, Fig. 2.24, when the overall input is the sequence $R(k)$. Also, note that γ_1 is computed as the *ratio* of the two inputs (past the first delay) to the first lattice section at time $k=1$, and γ_2 as the ratio of the two inputs (past the second delay) to the second lattice section at time $k=2$. This lattice filter representation of the Schur algorithm generalizes easily to higher order predictors by simply adding more lattice sections [23]. In the present case, we only go up to order 2, and thus, it is necessary to know only the first three autocorrelation lags $\{R(0), R(1), R(2)\}$. The pair of gapped functions (2.7.14) needs to be evaluated only at $k = 1, 2$, and the pair (2.7.15) only at $k=2$.

Example 2.7.1: Given $\{R(0), R(1), R(2)\} = \{8, 4, -1\}$, compute the reflection coefficients and prediction errors up to order 2, and determine the resulting LU factorization of R.

Solution: We will use the Schur algorithm. First, we compute $\gamma_1 = 4/8 = 0.5$. Then, evaluate (2.7.14) at $k = 1$ and $k = 2$:

$$g(1) = R(1) - \gamma_1 R(0) = 4 - 0.5\times 8 = 0 \quad \text{(the first gap)}$$

$$g_-(1) = R(0) - \gamma_1 R(1) = 8 - 0.5\times 4 = 6 = \mathcal{E}$$

$$g(2) = R(2) - \gamma_1 R(1) = -1 - 0.5\times 4 = -3$$

$$g_-(2) = R(1) - \gamma_1 R(2) = 4 - 0.5\times(-1) = 4.5$$

Then, compute $\gamma_2 = g(2)/g_-(1) = -3/6 = -0.5$, and evaluate (2.7.15) at $k = 2$:

$$g'(2) = g(2) - \gamma_2 g_-(1) = (-3) - (-0.5)\times 6 = 0 \quad \text{(the second gap)}$$

$$g'_-(2) = g_-(1) - \gamma_2 g(2) = 6 - (-0.5)\times(-3) = 4.5 = \mathcal{E}'$$

It is evident from the above computations that, because of the gap conditions, we did not need to compute $g(k)$ at $k = 1$ and $g'(k)$ at $k = 2$. We did so, however, to maintain the symmetry of the forward/backward pair of gapped function equations. The predictor polynomials are obtained from the γs by Eq. (2.7.6)

$$\begin{bmatrix} 1 \\ a_1 \end{bmatrix} = \begin{bmatrix} 1 \\ -\gamma_1 \end{bmatrix} = \begin{bmatrix} 1 \\ -0.5 \end{bmatrix}, \quad \begin{bmatrix} 1 \\ a'_1 \\ a'_2 \end{bmatrix} = \begin{bmatrix} 1 \\ -0.5 \\ 0 \end{bmatrix} - (-0.5) \begin{bmatrix} 0 \\ -0.5 \\ 1 \end{bmatrix} = \begin{bmatrix} 1 \\ -0.75 \\ 0.5 \end{bmatrix}$$

Next, we construct the LU factorization of R according to Eqs. (1.7.18) and (1.7.58). The matrix L was constructed in Example 2.6.2:

$$L = \begin{bmatrix} 1 & 0 & 0 \\ a_1 & 1 & 0 \\ a'_2 & a'_1 & 1 \end{bmatrix} = \begin{bmatrix} 1 & 0 & 0 \\ -0.5 & 1 & 0 \\ 0.5 & -0.75 & 1 \end{bmatrix}$$

It is easily verified that $LRL^T = D_b = \text{diag}\{8,6,4.5\}$. The matrix G_b has as columns the backward gapped functions of successive orders. The first column is the order-0 backward gapped function, namely, the given autocorrelation function $R(k)$. Thus,

$$G_b = \begin{bmatrix} R(0) & g_-(0) & g'_-(0) \\ R(1) & g_-(1) & g'_-(1) \\ R(2) & g_-(2) & g'_-(2) \end{bmatrix} = \begin{bmatrix} 8 & 0 & 0 \\ 4 & 6 & 0 \\ -1 & 4.5 & 4.5 \end{bmatrix}$$

It is lower triangular because of the gap conditions for the backward gapped functions, namely, $g_-(0) = 0$ and $g'_-(0) = 0$, $g'_-(1) = 0$. Equations $LG_b = D_b$ and $R = G_b D_b^{-1} G_b^T$ are easily verified.

Example 2.7.2: For the above example, compute the inverse of the matrices R and $\bar{R}$ using the order recursive constructions (1.7.28) and (1.7.35).

Solution: First we apply Eq. (1.7.28) to $\bar{R}$. Noting that the backward predictors **b** are the reverse of the forward ones, **a**, we find

$$\bar{R}^{-1} = \begin{bmatrix} R(0) & R(1) \\ R(1) & R(0) \end{bmatrix}^{-1} = \begin{bmatrix} R(0)^{-1} & 0 \\ 0 & 0 \end{bmatrix} + (1/\mathcal{E}) \begin{bmatrix} a_1 \\ 1 \end{bmatrix} [a_1, 1]$$

$$= \begin{bmatrix} 1/8 & 0 \\ 0 & 0 \end{bmatrix} + \frac{1}{6} \begin{bmatrix} -0.5 \\ 1 \end{bmatrix} [-0.5, 1] = \frac{1}{6} \begin{bmatrix} 1 & -0.5 \\ -0.5 & 1 \end{bmatrix}$$

Then, apply Eq. (1.7.28) to R, using $\mathbf{b} = [0.5, -0.75, 1]^T$

$$R^{-1} = \begin{bmatrix} \bar{R}^{-1} & \mathbf{0} \\ \mathbf{0}^T & 0 \end{bmatrix} + (1/\mathcal{E}')\mathbf{b}\mathbf{b}^T$$

$$= \begin{bmatrix} 1/6 & -0.5/6 & 0 \\ -0.5/6 & 1/6 & 0 \\ 0 & 0 & 0 \end{bmatrix} + \frac{1}{4.5} \begin{bmatrix} 0.5 \\ -0.75 \\ 1 \end{bmatrix} [0.5, -0.75, 1] = \frac{1}{9} \begin{bmatrix} 2 & -1.5 & 1 \\ -1.5 & 2.625 & -1.5 \\ 1 & -1.5 & 2 \end{bmatrix}$$

Note that the inverse of the Toeplitz matrix R is not Toeplitz. It still satisfies, however, the symmetry property of commuting with the reversing matrix J, $JR^{-1}J = R^{-1}$, which implies that R^{-1} remains invariant under reversal of its rows and then its columns. The application of Eq. (1.7.35) can be done directly, or, it can be derived from the above result by noting that Eq. (1.7.28) gets mapped into Eq. (1.7.35) under the reversal operation, that is, by multiplying both sides of Eq. (1.7.28) by the reversing matrix J.

Lattice realizations are alternatives to the direct form realizations given in Figs. 2.19 and 2.20. One of the nicest properties of lattice realizations is that higher order predictors can be easily obtained by simply *adding* more lattice sections. Another important property is that lattice filters are better behaved (less sensitive) under quantization of the multiplier coefficients than the direct form realizations.

The linear prediction problem solved here was to find the best predictor based on just *one* or *two* past samples. It must be contrasted with the full linear prediction problem mentioned in Sections 1.11 and 1.16, which was based on the *entire* past of y_n. It is, of course, the latter that whitens the error e_n and provides the signal model of y_n. However, in practice, the full prediction problem is difficult to solve because it requires the determination of an infinite number of prediction coefficients $\{a_1, a_2, \ldots\}$. Thus, the problem of linear prediction based on the finite past is of more practical interest. A more complete discussion of linear prediction, Levinson's and Schur's algorithms, and lattice filters, will be presented in Chapter 5.

2.8 *Introduction to Data Compression and DPCM*

In this section, we discuss the application of linear prediction ideas to the problem of data compression by *differential PCM* (DPCM) methods. For illustrative purposes, we work with a second order predictor. The predictor is to be used to compress the dynamic range of a signal y_n so that it may be transmitted more efficiently. Suppose we have already found the best predictor coefficients $(1,a_1,a_2)$ that minimize the prediction error by solving Eq. (2.6.3) (for simplicity, the primes have been dropped):

$$\mathcal{E} = E[e_n^2] = \min$$

$$e_n = y_n - \hat{y}_n = y_n + a_1\, y_{n-1} + a_2\, y_{n-2}$$

The basic idea in data compression is that if the predictor is good, then the prediction error e_n will be small, or rather it will have a compressed dynamic range compared to the original signal. If we were to code and transmit e_n rather than y_n, we would need fewer bits to represent each sample e_n than we would need for y_n. At the receiving end, the original waveform y_n can be reconstructed by processing e_n through the inverse of the prediction error filter. The overall system is represented as follows

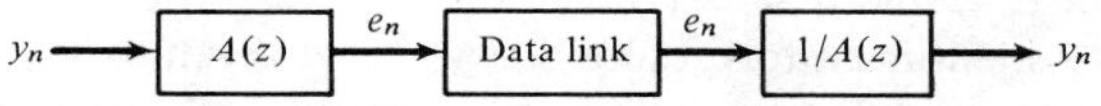

For meaningful reconstruction, it is necessary that the inverse filter $1/A(z)$ be stable (and causal). This requires that the zeros of the prediction-error filter $A(z)$ lie inside the unit circle in the z-plane. Two proofs of this fact will be presented later on, in Sections 3.7 and 5.8. The gain in the dynamic ratio that we expect to achieve with this method of data compression is given by the ratio

$$G = \frac{\sigma_y^2}{\sigma_e^2} = \frac{\sigma_y^2}{\mathcal{E}} = \frac{1}{(1 - \gamma_2^2)(1 - \gamma_1^2)}$$

where we used Eq. (2.7.10). This is always greater than one, since both γ_1 and γ_2 have magnitude less than one. Even without this result, we could have concluded that the above ratio is greater than one. Indeed, the quantity $\sigma_y^2 = R_{yy}(0)$ is the prediction error for the trivial choice of the prediction-error coefficients $\mathbf{a} = (1,a_1,a_2) = (1,0,0)$, whereas $\mathcal{E} = \sigma_e^2$ corresponds to the choice that minimizes the prediction error; therefore, $\sigma_y^2 > \sigma_e^2$.

Next, we discuss the question of *quantizing* the prediction-error sequence e_n for the purpose of transmission or storage. First, we note that *any* prediction-error filter $A(z)$ may be realized as

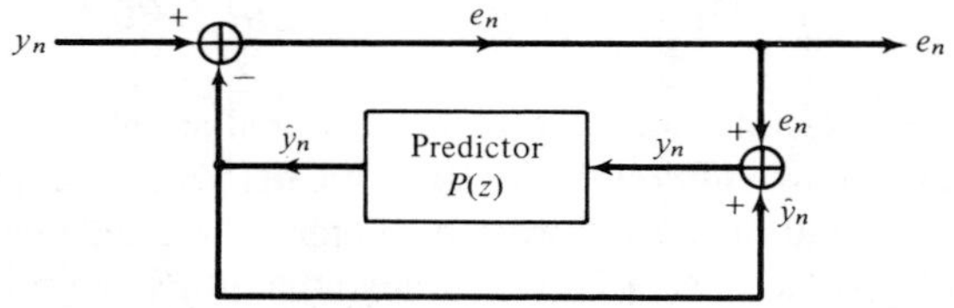

where $P(z) = 1 - A(z)$ is the corresponding predictor filter; for example, $P(z) = -[a_1z^{-1} + a_2z^{-2}]$ for the second order case. The conventional differential PCM encoder is a predictor realized in this manner with a quantizer inserted as shown in Fig. 2.25. The presence of the quantizer introduces a quantization error δ_n such that

$$\tilde{e}_n = e_n + \delta_n \tag{2.8.1}$$

where δ_n may be assumed to be zero-mean uniform white noise of variance $\sigma_\delta^2 = Q^2/12$, where Q is the step size of the quantizer. This particular realization ensures that, at the reconstructing end, the quantization errors *do not accumulate*. This follows from the property that

$$\tilde{y}_n - y_n = (\tilde{e}_n + \hat{y}_n) - y_n = \tilde{e}_n - e_n = \delta_n \tag{2.8.2}$$

which states that $\tilde{y}_n$ differs from y_n only by the quantization error δ_n suffered by the current input e_n to the quantizer. The complete DPCM system is shown in Fig. 2.26. It is evident from this figure that $\tilde{y}_n - y_n$ given by Eq. (2.8.2) is the *reconstruction error*, resulting only from the (irreversible) quantization error δ_n. The data compression gain afforded by such a system is conveniently expressed in terms of the following SNRs:

$$\text{SNR(DPCM)} = \frac{\sigma_e^2}{\sigma_\delta^2} = \text{signal-to-quantization noise of the DPCM signal } e_n$$

$$\text{SNR(PCM)} = \frac{\sigma_y^2}{\sigma_\delta^2} = \text{signal-to-quantization noise of the PCM signal } y_n$$

$$G = \frac{\sigma_y^2}{\sigma_e^2} = \text{gain of the predictor system}$$

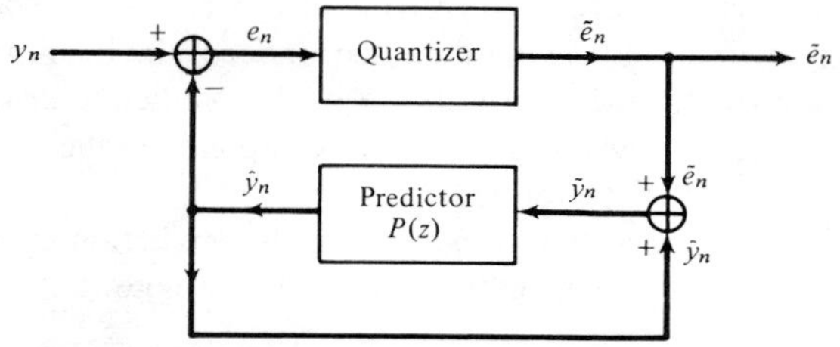

Figure 2.25 DPCM Encoder

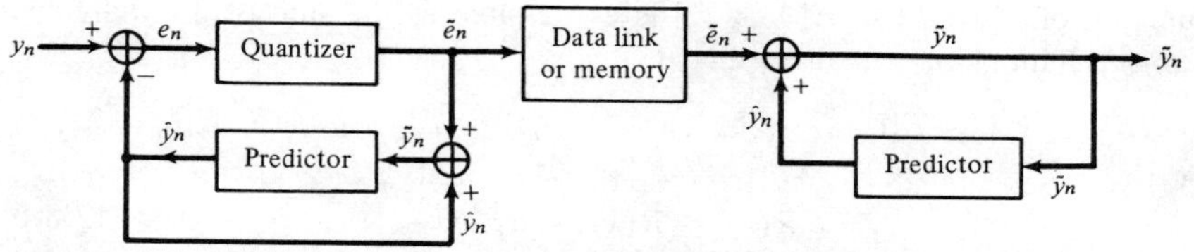

Figure 2.26 DPCM System for Digital Data Transmission, or Storage

These three quantities are related by

$$\text{SNR(DPCM)} = \text{SNR(PCM)}/G$$

or, expressed in dB,

$$10 \log_{10} \text{SNR(DPCM)} = 10 \log_{10} \text{SNR(PCM)} - 10 \log_{10} G \qquad (2.8.3)$$

Therefore, the quantity $10 \log_{10} G$ is the data compression gain afforded by the DPCM system *over* PCM. The best DPCM coder is thus the one maximizing the predictor gain G, or equivalently, minimizing the mean-squared prediction error

$$\mathcal{E} = \sigma_e^2 = E[e_n^2] = \min \qquad (2.8.4)$$

The presence of the quantizer makes this minimization problem somewhat different from the ordinary prediction problem. However, it can be handled easily using the standard assumptions regarding the quantization noise δ_n; namely, that δ_n is white noise and that it is uncorrelated with the input sequence y_n. First, we note that minimizing $\mathcal{E}$ is equivalent to minimizing

$$\tilde{\mathcal{E}} = E[\tilde{e}_n^2] = E[(e_n + \delta_n)^2] = E[e_n^2] + E[\delta_n^2] = \mathcal{E} + \sigma_\delta^2,$$

or

$$\tilde{\mathcal{E}} = E[\tilde{e}_n^2] = \min \qquad (2.8.5)$$

Replacing the quantizer by the equivalent noise source (2.8.1), we may redraw the DPCM coder with δ_n acting at the input adder:

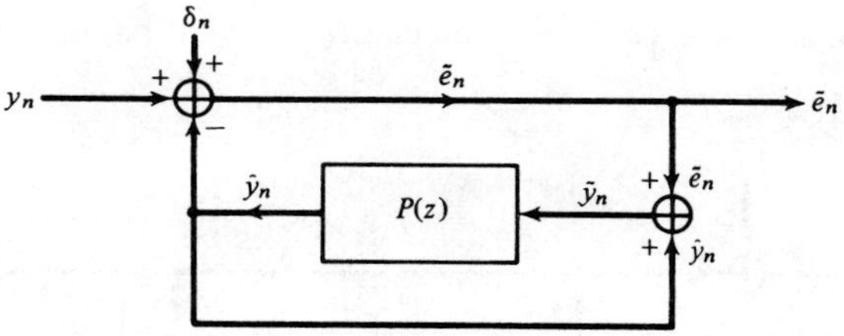

It is evident from this figure that the minimization problem (2.8.5) is equivalent to an effective linear prediction problem of predicting the noisy sequence $\tilde{y}_n = y_n + \delta_n$. Since y_n and δ_n are mutually uncorrelated, the autocorrelation function of $\tilde{y}_n$; $\tilde{R}(k) = E[\tilde{y}_{n+k}\,\tilde{y}_n]$ is expressible as the sum of the individual autocorrelations of y_n and δ_n; that is,

$$E[\tilde{y}_{n+k}\,\tilde{y}_n] = E[(y_{n+k} + \delta_{n+k})(y_n + \delta_n)] = E[y_{n+k}\,y_n] + E[\delta_{n+k}\,\delta_n]$$

or

$$\tilde{R}(k) = R(k) + \sigma_\delta^2\,\delta(k) \tag{2.8.6}$$

where we used $E[\delta_{n+k}\,\delta_n] = \sigma_\delta^2\,\delta(k)$. Only the diagonal entries of the autocorrelation matrix $\tilde{R}$ are different from those of R, and are shifted by an amount

$$\tilde{R}(0) = R(0) + \sigma_\delta^2 = R(0)\,[1 + \epsilon] \tag{2.8.7}$$

where $\epsilon = \sigma_\delta^2/\sigma_y^2 = 1/\mathrm{SNR(PCM)}$. The optimal prediction coefficients are obtained by solving the corresponding normal equations (2.6.3) or (2.6.6), but with $R(0)$ replaced by $\tilde{R}(0)$. Typically, SNR(PCM) is fairly large, and therefore ϵ is only a small correction which may be ignored without degrading much the performance of the system.

We also point out that a similar change in the autocorrelation matrix, given by (2.8.7), occurs in a different context in the least-squares design of wave-shaping filters from noisy data. In that context, ϵ is referred to as the Backus-Gilbert parameter. This will be discussed in Chapter 5.

DPCM encoding methods have been applied successfully to speech and image data compression [24–26]. In speech, a compression gain of 4 to 12 dB over PCM can be obtained. The gain can be increased even further using adaptive quantizers and/or adaptive predictors. For images, using 3d order predictors, the gain is typically 20 dB over PCM.

Finally, we remark that DPCM transmission systems are susceptible to channel errors. Unlike quantization errors which do not accumulate at the reconstructing end, channel errors do accumulate and get amplified. This may be seen as follows: Let the received sequence $\tilde{e}_n$ be corrupted by white gaussian channel noise v_n, as shown in Fig. 2.27. Then, both $\tilde{e}_n$ and the channel noise v_n get filtered through the reconstructing inverse filter $B(z) = 1/A(z)$. This filter is designed to decompress $\tilde{e}_n$ back to $\tilde{y}_n$ and thus, it has a gain which is greater than one. This will also cause the channel noise v_n to be amplified as it goes

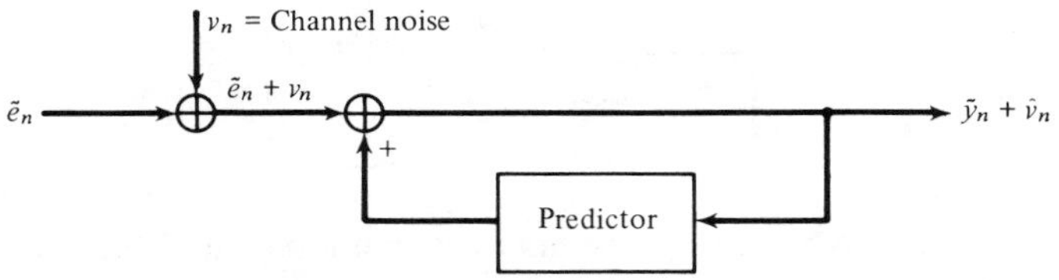

Figure 2.27 Channel Noise in a DPCM Receiver

through $B(z)$. The output to input noise power is given by the quadratic norm $\|B\|^2$:

$$\frac{\sigma_{\tilde{v}}^2}{\sigma_v^2} = \|B\|^2 = \left\|\frac{1}{A}\right\|^2 = \oint_{u.c.} \frac{1}{A(z)A(z^{-1})}\frac{dz}{2\pi jz}$$

which is always greater than one. For example, for the second order predictor it can be shown that

$$\|B\|^2 = \left\|\frac{1}{A}\right\|^2 = \frac{1}{(1-\gamma_1^2)(1-\gamma_2^2)}$$

where γ_1 and γ_2 are the reflection coefficients of the prediction problem (2.8.5).

To combat against channel errors, some channel encoding with error-protection must be done prior to transmission [27,28].

Problems

Problem 2.1:

Let $x(n)$ be a zero-mean white-noise sequence of unit variance. For each of the following filters compute the output autocorrelation $R_{yy}(k)$ for all k, using z-transforms:

1. $y(n) = x(n) - x(n-1)$
2. $y(n) = x(n) - 2\,x(n-1) + x(n-2)$
3. $y(n) = -0.5\,y(n-1) + x(n)$
4. $y(n) = 0.25\,y(n-2) + x(n)$

Also, sketch the output power spectrum $S_{yy}(\omega)$ versus frequency ω.

Problem 2.2:

Let y_n be the output of a (stable and causal) filter $H(z)$ driven by the signal x_n, and let w_n be another unrelated signal. Assume all signals are stationary random signals. Show the following relationships between power spectral densities:

(a) $S_{yw}(z) = H(z)\,S_{xw}(z)$

(b) $S_{wy}(z) = S_{wx}(z)\,H(z^{-1})$

Problem 2.3:

A stationary random signal y_n is sent through a finite filter $A(z) = a_0 + a_1z^{-1} + \cdots + a_Mz^{-M}$ to obtain the output signal e_n:

$$e_n = \sum_{m=0}^{M} a_m\, y_{n-m}$$

Show that the average power of the output signal e_n can be expressed in the two alternative forms:

$$E[e_n^2] = \int_{-\pi}^{\pi} S_{yy}(\omega)\,|A(\omega)|^2 \frac{d\omega}{2\pi} = \mathbf{a}^T R_{yy}\,\mathbf{a}$$

where $\mathbf{a} = [a_0, a_1, \ldots, a_M]^T$ and R_{yy} is the $(M+1) \times (M+1)$ autocorrelation matrix of y_n having matrix elements $R_{yy}(i,j) = E[y_i\, y_j] = R_{yy}(i-j)$.

Problems 2.4:
Consider two autoregressive random signals y_n and y'_n generated by the signal models:

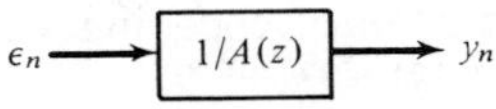

and

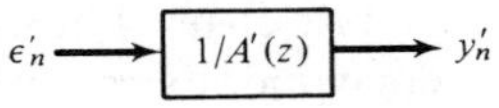

$$A(z) = 1 + a_1 z^{-1} + \cdots + a_M z^{-M}$$

and

$$A'(z) = 1 + a'_1 z^{-1} + \cdots + a'_M z^{-M}$$

(a) Suppose y_n is filtered through the analysis filter $A'(z)$ of y'_n producing the output signal e_n; that is,

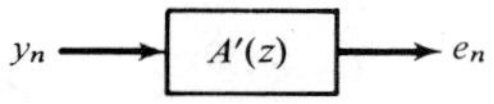

$$e_n = \sum_{m=0}^{M} a'_m\, y_{n-m}$$

If y_n were to be filtered through its own analysis filter $A(z)$, it would produce the innovations sequence ϵ_n. Show that the average power of e_n, compared to the average power of ϵ_n, is given by

$$\frac{\sigma_e^2}{\sigma_\epsilon^2} = \frac{\mathbf{a}'^T R_{yy}\,\mathbf{a}'}{\mathbf{a}^T R_{yy}\,\mathbf{a}} = \int_{-\pi}^{\pi} \left|\frac{A'(\omega)}{A(\omega)}\right|^2 \frac{d\omega}{2\pi} = \left\|\frac{A'}{A}\right\|^2$$

where $\mathbf{a}$, $\mathbf{a}'$, and R_{yy} have the same meaning as in Problem 2.3. This ratio can be taken as a measure of *similarity* between the two signal models. The log of this ratio is Itakura's *LPC distance measure* used in speech recognition.

(b) Alternatively, show that if y'_n were to be filtered through y_n's analysis filter $A(z)$ resulting in $e'_n = \Sigma_{m=0}^{M} a_m\, y'_{n-m}$, then

$$\frac{\sigma_{e'}^2}{\sigma_{\epsilon'}^2} = \frac{\mathbf{a}^T R'_{yy}\,\mathbf{a}}{\mathbf{a}'^T R'_{yy}\,\mathbf{a}'} = \int_{-\pi}^{\pi} \left|\frac{A(\omega)}{A'(\omega)}\right|^2 \frac{d\omega}{2\pi} = \left\|\frac{A}{A'}\right\|^2$$

Problem 2.5:
The autocorrelation function of complex-valued signals is defined by

$$R_{yy}(k) = E[y_{n+k}\, y_n^*]$$

(a) Show that stationarity implies $R_{yy}(-k) = R_{yy}(k)^*$.

(b) If y_n is filtered through a (possibly complex-valued) filter $A(z) = a_0 + a_1 z^{-1} + \cdots + a_M z^{-M}$, show that the average power of the output signal e_n can be expressed as

$$\mathcal{E} = E[e_n^* e_n] = \mathbf{a}^{\dagger} R_{yy} \mathbf{a}$$

where $\mathbf{a}^{\dagger}$ denotes the hermitian conjugate of $\mathbf{a}$, and R_{yy} has matrix elements

$$R_{yy}(i,j) = R_{yy}(i - j).$$

Problem 2.6:

(a) Let $y_n = A_1 \exp[j(\omega_1 n + \phi_1)]$ be a complex sinusoid of amplitude A_1 and frequency ω_1. The randomness of y_n arises only from the phase ϕ_1 which is assumed to be a random variable uniformly distributed over the interval $0 \leqslant \phi_1 \leqslant 2\pi$. Show that the autocorrelation function of y_n is

$$R_{yy}(k) = |A_1|^2 \exp(j\omega_1 k)$$

(b) Let y_n be the sum of two complex sinusoids

$$y_n = A_1 \exp[j(\omega_1 n + \phi_1)] + A_2 \exp[j(\omega_2 n + \phi_2)]$$

with uniformly distributed random phases ϕ_1 and ϕ_2 which are also assumed to be independent of each other. Show that the autocorrelation of y_n is

$$R_{yy}(k) = |A_1|^2 \exp(j\omega_1 k) + |A_2|^2 \exp(j\omega_2 k)$$

Problem 2.7: Sinusoids in Noise

Suppose y_n is the sum of L complex sinusoids with random phases, in the presence of uncorrelated noise:

$$y_n = v_n + \sum_{i=1}^{L} A_i \exp[j(\omega_i n + \phi_i)]$$

where ϕ_i; $i = 1,2, \ldots L$, are uniformly distributed random phases which are assumed to be mutually independent, and v_n is zero-mean white noise of variance σ_v^2. Also, assume that v_n is independent of ϕ_i.

(a) Show that $E[e^{j\phi_i} e^{-j\phi_k}] = \delta_{ik}$; $i,k = 1,2, \ldots ,L$

(b) Show that the autocorrelation of y_n is

$$R_{yy}(k) = \sigma_v^2 \, \delta(k) + \sum_{i=1}^{L} |A_i|^2 \exp(j\omega_i k)$$

(c) Suppose y_n is filtered through a filter $A(z) = a_0 + a_1 z^{-1} + \cdots + a_M z^{-M}$ of order M, producing the output signal e_n. Show that the average output power is expressible as

$$\mathcal{E} = E[e_n^* e_n] = \mathbf{a}^\dagger R_{yy} \mathbf{a} = \sigma_v^2 \, \mathbf{a}^\dagger \mathbf{a} + \sum_{i=1}^{L} |A_i|^2 |A(\omega_i)|^2$$

where $\mathbf{a}$, $\mathbf{a}^\dagger$, R_{yy} have the same meaning as Problem 2.5, and $A(\omega_i)$ is the frequency response of the filter evaluated at the sinusoid frequencies ω_i; $i = 1,2, \ldots, L$; that is,

$$A(\omega_i) = \sum_{m=0}^{M} a_m \, e^{-j\omega_i m}$$

(d) If the noise v_n is correlated with autocorrelation $Q(k)$, so that $E[v_{n+k} v_n^*] = Q(k)$, show that in this case

$$\mathcal{E} = E[e_n^* e_n] = \mathbf{a}^\dagger R_{yy} \mathbf{a} = \mathbf{a}^\dagger Q \mathbf{a} + \sum_{i=1}^{L} |A_i|^2 |A(\omega_i)|^2$$

where Q is the noise covariance matrix, $Q(i,j) = Q(i - j)$.

Problem 2.8: Computer Experiment
Consider the linear system defined by Eq. (2.2.1). Generate 1500 samples of a unit-variance, zero-mean, white-noise sequence x_n; $n = 0,1, \ldots, 1499$ and filter them through the filter H to obtain the output sequence y_n. Compute the sample cross-correlation $\hat{R}_{yx}(k)$ for $k = 0,1, \ldots, 50$ to obtain estimates of the impulse response h_k. Plot the estimated impulse response versus time together with the simulated response (2.2.1) on the same graph. Repeat, using a different realization of x_n.

Problem 2.9:
A filter is defined by $y(n) = -0.64\, y(n - 2) + 0.36\, x(n)$.

(a) Suppose the input is zero-mean, unit-variance, white noise. Compute the output spectral density $S_{yy}(z)$ and power spectrum $S_{yy}(\omega)$ and plot it roughly versus frequency.

(b) Compute the output autocorrelation $R_{yy}(k)$ for all lags k.

(c) Compute the noise reduction ratio of this filter.

(d) What signal $s(n)$ can pass through this filter and remain entirely unaffected (at least in the steady-state regime)?

(e) How can the filter coefficients be changed so that (i) the noise reduction capability of the filter is improved, while at the same time (ii) the above signal $s(n)$ still goes through unchanged. Explain any tradeoffs.

Problem 2.10: Computer Experiment

(a) Generate 1000 samples of a zero-mean, unit-variance, white gaussian noise sequence $x(n)$; $n = 0,1, \ldots ,999$, and filter them through the filter defined by the difference equation

$$y(n) = a\, y(n - 1) + (1 - a)\, x(n)$$

with $a = 0.95$. To avoid the transient effects introduced by the filter, discard the first 900 output samples and save the last 100 samples of $y(n)$. Compute the sample autocorrelation of $y(n)$ from this length-100 block of samples.

(b) Determine the theoretical autocorrelation $R_{yy}(k)$, and on the same graph plot the theoretical and sample autocorrelations versus k. Do they agree?

Problem 2.11:

Following the procedure of Example (2.6.1), rederive the results of Eqs. (2.6.2) and (2.6.4) for the first order predictor using the correlation canceling formulation of Section 1.4.

Problem 2.12:

Let $y(n) = (1,1,1,1)$ for $n = 0,1,2,3$. We want to "predict" the fifth sample in this sequence.

(a) Compute the sample autocorrelation of this sequence.

(b) Using the Yule-Walker method, determine the best first order predictor of the form

$$\hat{y}(n) = -a_1\, y(n - 1)$$

What is the predicted value of the fifth sample? What is the mean squared prediction error?

(c) Since we only have sample autocorrelations to work with, let us define the gapped function $g(k)$ as the *convolution* of the prediction-error filter $(1,a_1)$ with the sample autocorrelation $\hat{R}_{yy}(k)$, in accordance with Eq. (2.7.2). Verify that $g(k)$ has a gap of length one.

(d) It is desired next, to determine the best second order predictor

$$\hat{y}'(n) = -[a_1'\, y(n - 1) + a_2'\, y(n - 2)]$$

Using the gapped function $g(k)$, construct a new gapped function $g'(k)$ having a gap of length two. Determine the prediction-error filter $(1,a_1'a_2')$.

(e) Compute the predicted value of the fifth sample in this case, and the mean-squared prediction error. Is the predicted fifth value what you expected?

Is the value predicted by the second order predictor "better" than that predicted by the first order predictor?

(f) Determine the zeros of the prediction filter $(1,a_1',a_2')$ and verify that they lie inside the unit circle in the z-plane.

Problem 2.13:

(a) Repeat parts (a) and (b) of Problem 2.12 for the sequence $y_n = (-1, 1, -1, 1)$.

(b) Repeat for $y_n = (1,2,3,4)$.

Problem 2.14:

Show that the inverse lattice filter of Fig. 2.23 is realized as

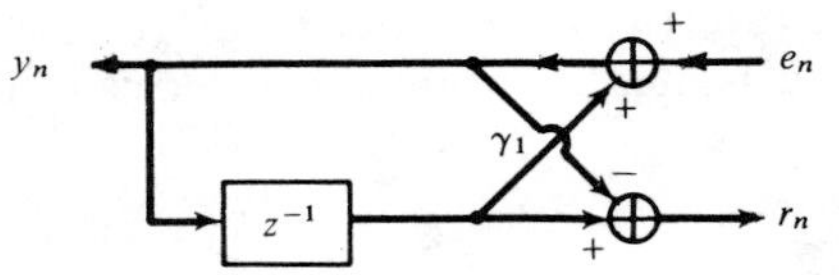

Show that the transfer function from e_n to y_n is the synthesis filter $1/A(z)$. (Note the different sign conventions at the upper adder.)

Problem 2.15:

The second order synthesis lattice filter is realized as follows:

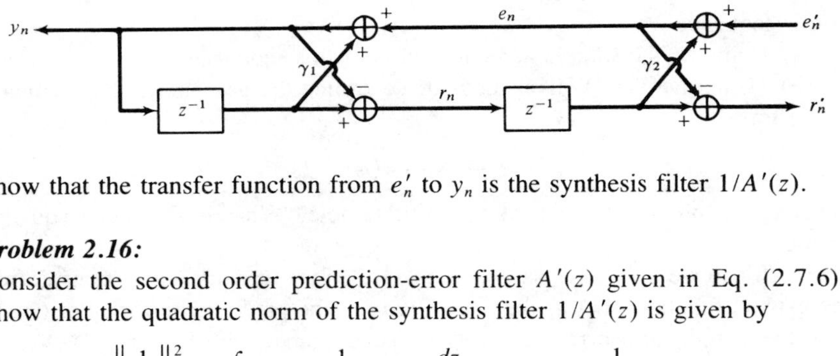

Show that the transfer function from e_n' to y_n is the synthesis filter $1/A'(z)$.

Problem 2.16:

Consider the second order prediction-error filter $A'(z)$ given in Eq. (2.7.6). Show that the quadratic norm of the synthesis filter $1/A'(z)$ is given by

$$\left\|\frac{1}{A'}\right\|^2 = \oint_{\text{u.c.}} \frac{1}{A'(z)A'(z^{-1})}\frac{dz}{2\pi jz} = \frac{1}{(1-\gamma_1^2)(1-\gamma_2^2)}$$

where γ_1 and γ_2 are the corresponding reflection coefficients. (*Hint:* factor $A'(z)$ into its zeros, which are both inside the unit circle, perform the indicated contour integration, and rewrite the result in terms of γ_1 and γ_2.)

The above result was used in Section 2.8 in the discussion of the channel errors in DPCM systems.

References

1. A. Papoulis, *Probability, Random Variables, and Stochastic Processes*, New York, McGraw-Hill, 1965.
2. A. V. Oppenheim and R. W. Schafer, *Digital Signal Processing,* Englewood Cliffs, NJ, Prentice-Hall, 1975
3. S. Tretter, *Introduction to Discrete-Time Signal Processing,* New York, Wiley, 1974.
4. K. J. Aström and P. Eykhoff, System Identification—A Survey, *Automatica,* **7,** 123–162 (1971).
5. P. Eykhoff, *System Identification: Parameter and State Estimation,* New York, Wiley, 1974.
6. G. C. Goodwin and R. L. Payne, *Dynamic System Identification, Experimental Design and Data Analysis,* New York, Academic, 1977.
7. L. Ljung and T. Söderström, *Theory and Practice of Recursive Identification,* Cambridge, MA, MIT Press, 1983.
8. L. Ljung, *System Identification: Theory for the User,* Englewood Cliffs, NJ, Prentice-Hall, 1987.
9. T. Söderström and P. Stoica, *System Identification,* Englewood Cliffs, NJ, Prentice-Hall, 1987.
10. G. C. Goodwin and K. S. Sin, *Adaptive Filtering, Prediction, and Control,* Englewood Cliffs, NJ, Prentice-Hall, 1984.
11. M. I. Skolnik, *Introduction to Radar Systems,* New York, McGraw-Hill, 1980.
12. L. Rabiner and B. Gold, *Theory and Application of Digital Signal Processing,* Englewood-Cliffs, NJ, Prentice-Hall, 1975.
13. L. B. Jackson, Roundoff Noise Analysis for Fixed-Point Digital Filters Realized in Cascade or Parallel Form, *IEEE Trans. Audio Electroacoust.,* **AU-18,** 107–122 (1970).
14. B. Liu, Effect of Finite Word Length on the Accuracy of Digital Filters—A Review, *IEEE Trans. Circuit Th.,* **CT-18,** 670–677 (1971).
15. C. T. Mullis and R. A. Roberts, Synthesis of Minimum Roundoff Noise Fixed Point Digital Filters, *IEEE Trans. Circuits Syst.,* **CAS-23,** 551–562 (1976).
16. S. Y. Hwang, Roundoff Noise in State-Space Digital Filtering: A General Analysis, *IEEE Trans. Acoust., Speech, Signal Process.,* **ASSP-24,** 256–262 (1976).
17. A. B. Sripad and D. L. Snyder, A Necessary and Sufficient Condition for Quantization Errors to Be Uniform and White, *IEEE Trans. Acoust., Speech, Signal Process.,* **ASSP-25,** 442–448 (1977).
18. T. L. Chang and S. A. White, An Error Cancellation Digital Filter Structure and its Distributed Arithmetic Implementation, *IEEE Trans. Circuits Syst.,* **CAS-28,** 339–342 (1981).
19. W. E. Higgins and D. C. Munson, Jr., Noise Reduction Strategies for Digital Filters: Error Spectrum Shaping versus the Optimal Linear State-Space Formulation, *IEEE Trans. Acoust., Speech, Signal Process.,* **ASSP-30,** 963–973 (1982).
20. C. T. Mullis and R. A. Roberts, An Interpretation of Error Spectrum Shaping in

Digital Filters, *IEEE Trans. Acoust., Speech, Signal Process.*, **ASSP-30,** 1013–1015 (1982).

21. R. A. Roberts and C. T. Mullis, *Digital Signal Processing,* Reading, MA, Addison-Wesley, 1987.
22. E. Robinson and S. Treitel, Maximum Entropy and the Relationship of the Partial Autocorrelation to the Reflection Coefficients of a Layered System, *IEEE Trans. Acoust., Speech, Signal Process.,* **ASSP-28,** 22 (1980).
23. T. Kailath, A Theorem of I. Schur and Its Impact on Modern Signal Processing, in I. Gohberg, Ed., *I. Schur Methods in Operator Theory and Signal Processing, Operator Theory: Advances and Applications,* vol. 18, Boston, Birkhäuser, 1986.
24. J. L. Flanagan, et al., Speech Coding, *IEEE Trans. Commun.,* **COM-27,** 710–736, (1979).
25. N. S. Jayant and P. Noll, *Digital Coding of Waveforms,* Englewood Cliffs, NJ, Prentice-Hall, 1984.
26. A. K. Jain, Image Data Compression: A Review, *Proc. IEEE,* **69,** 349–389 (1981).
27. J. W. Modestino and D. G. Daut, Combined Source-Channel Coding of Images, *IEEE Trans. Commun.,* **COM-27,** 1644–1659 (1979).
28. D. G. Daut and J. W. Modestino, Two-Dimensional DPCM Image Transmission over Fading Channels, *IEEE Trans. Commun.,* **COM-31,** 315–328 (1983).

3

Spectral Factorization

IN THIS CHAPTER, we discuss the concept of minimal-phase signals and filters, state the spectral factorization theorem and demonstrate its importance in making signal models, and present a proof of the minimal-phase property of the prediction-error filter of linear prediction.

3.1 *Minimal-Phase Signals and Filters* [1–4]

A *minimal-phase* sequence $\mathbf{a} = (a_0, a_1, \ldots, a_M)$ has a z-transform with all its zeros inside the unit circle in the complex z-plane

$$\begin{aligned} A(z) &= a_0 + a_1 z^{-1} + \cdots + a_M z^{-M} \\ &= a_0 (1 - z_1 z^{-1})(1 - z_2 z^{-1}) \cdots (1 - z_M z^{-1}) \end{aligned} \tag{3.1.1}$$

with $|z_i| < 1$; $i = 1, 2, \ldots, M$. Such a polynomial is also called a *minimal-delay* polynomial. Define the following related polynomials

$$A^*(z) = a_0^* + a_1^* z^{-1} + \cdots + a_M^* z^{-M} = \text{complex-conjugated coefficients}$$

$$\bar{A}(z) = a_0^* + a_1^* z + \cdots + a_M^* z^M = \text{conjugated and reflected}$$

$$A^R(z) = a_M^* + a_{M-1}^* z^{-1} + \cdots + a_0^* z^{-M} = \text{reversed and conjugated}$$

We note the relationships

$$\bar{A}(z) = A^*(z^{-1}) \qquad \text{and} \qquad A^R(z) = z^{-M}\bar{A}(z) = z^{-M}A^*(z^{-1}) \tag{3.1.2}$$

We also note that when we set $z = \exp(j\omega)$ to obtain the corresponding frequency responses, $\bar{A}(\omega)$ becomes the complex conjugate of $A(\omega)$

$$\bar{A}(\omega) = A(\omega)^* \tag{3.1.3}$$

It is easily verified that all these polynomials have the *same* magnitude spectrum. That is,

$$|A(\omega)|^2 = |\bar{A}(\omega)|^2 = |A^*(\omega)|^2 = |A^R(\omega)|^2 \tag{3.1.4}$$

For example, in the case of a doublet $\mathbf{a} = (a_0, a_1)$ and its reverse $\mathbf{a}^R = (a_1^*, a_0^*)$ we verify explicitly

$$\begin{aligned} |A(\omega)|^2 = A(\omega)\, A(\omega)^* &= (a_0 + a_1 e^{-j\omega})\,(a_0^* + a_1^* e^{j\omega}) \\ &= a_0^* a_0 + a_1^* a_1 + 2\, Re(a_0^* a_1 e^{-j\omega}) \\ &= (a_1^* + a_0^* e^{-j\omega})\,(a_1 + a_0 e^{j\omega}) \\ &= A^R(\omega)\, (A^R(\omega))^* = |A^R(\omega)|^2 \end{aligned}$$

Thus, on the basis of the magnitude spectrum, one cannot distinguish the doublet $\mathbf{a} = (a_0, a_1)$ from its reverse $\mathbf{a}^R = (a_1^*, a_0^*)$.

In the more general case of a polynomial of degree M, factored into doublets as in Eq. (3.1.1), we note that each doublet can be replaced by its reverse

$$(1, -z_i) \rightarrow (-z_i^*, 1), \qquad \text{or} \qquad (1 - z_i z^{-1}) \rightarrow (-z_i^* + z^{-1})$$

without affecting the overall magnitude spectrum $|A(\omega)|^2$. Since there are M such factors, there will be a total of 2^M different Mth degree polynomials, or equivalently 2^M different length-$(M + 1)$ sequences, all having the *same magnitude spectrum*. Every time a factor $(1 - z_i z^{-1})$ is reversed to become $(-z_i^* + z^{-1})$, the corresponding zero changes from $z = z_i$ to $z = 1/z_i^*$. If z_i is inside the unit circle, then $1/z_i^*$ is outside, as shown

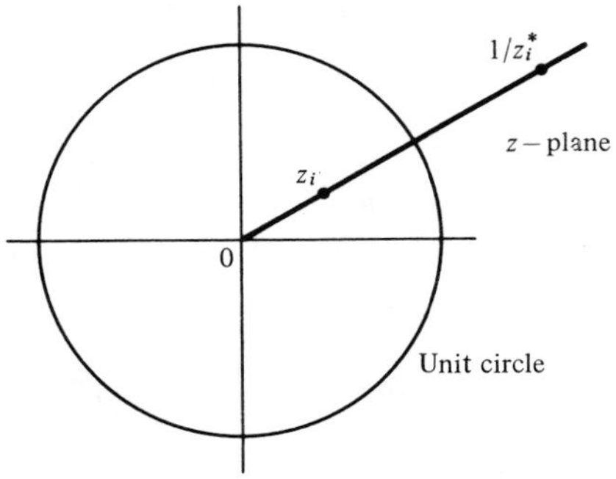

To enumerate all these sequences, start by taking all zeros z_i to be inside the unit circle and successively keep reversing each factor until all 2^M possibilities have been exhausted. At the last step, all the factors will have been flipped, corresponding to all the zeros being outside the unit circle. The resulting polynomial and sequence are referred to as *maximal-phase*, or *maximal-delay*.

As an example consider the two doublets

$$\mathbf{a} = (2,1) \qquad \text{and} \qquad \mathbf{b} = (3,2)$$

and form the four different sequences, where * denotes convolution

$$\mathbf{c}_0 = \mathbf{a} * \mathbf{b} = (2,1) * (3,2) = (6,7,2), \qquad C_0(z) = A(z)\,B(z)$$

$$\mathbf{c}_1 = \mathbf{a}^R * \mathbf{b} = (1,2) * (3,2) = (3,8,4), \qquad C_1(z) = A^R(z)\,B(z)$$

$$\mathbf{c}_2 = \mathbf{a} * \mathbf{b}^R = (2,1) * (2,3) = (4,8,3), \qquad C_2(z) = A(z)\,B^R(z)$$

$$\mathbf{c}_3 = \mathbf{a}^R * \mathbf{b}^R = (1,2) * (2,3) = (2,7,6), \qquad C_3(z) = A^R(z)\,B^R(z)$$

All four sequences have the same magnitude spectrum.

3.2 *Partial Energy and Minimal Delay*

Since the total energy of a sequence $\mathbf{a} = (a_0, a_1, \ldots, a_M)$ is given by Parseval's equality as

$$\sum_{m=0}^{M} |a_m|^2 = \int_{-\pi}^{\pi} |A(\omega)|^2 \frac{d\omega}{2\pi}$$

it follows that all of the above 2^M sequences, having the same magnitude spectrum, will also have the same *total energy*. However, the *distribution* of the total energy over time may be different. And this will allow an alternative characterization of the minimal phase sequences, first given by Robinson.

Define the *partial* energy by

$$P_a(n) = \sum_{m=0}^{n} |a_m|^2 = |a_0|^2 + |a_1|^2 + \cdots + |a_n|^2; \qquad n = 0,1, \ldots ,M$$

then, for the above example, the partial energies for the four different sequences are given in the table

	$\mathbf{c}_0$	$\mathbf{c}_1$	$\mathbf{c}_2$	$\mathbf{c}_3$
$P(0)$	36	9	16	4
$P(1)$	85	73	80	53
$P(2)$	89	89	89	89

We note that $\mathbf{c}_0$ which has both its zeros inside the unit circle (i.e., minimal phase) is also the sequence that has most of its energy concentrated at the *earlier* times; that is, it makes its impact as early as possible, *with minimal delay*. In contrast, the maximal-phase sequence $\mathbf{c}_3$ has most of its energy concentrated at its tail; thus, making most of its impact at the end, *with maximal delay*.

3.3 *Invariance of the Autocorrelation Function*

This section will present yet another characterization of the above class of sequences. It will be important in proving the minimal-phase property of the linear prediction filters.

The *sample autocorrelation* of a (possibly complex-valued) sequence $\mathbf{a} = (a_0, a_1, \ldots, a_M)$ is defined by

$$\begin{aligned} R_{aa}(k) &= \sum_{n=0}^{M-k} a_{n+k}\, a_n^*, \qquad \text{for } 0 \leqslant k \leqslant M \\ R_{aa}(k) &= R_{aa}(-k)^*, \qquad \text{for } -M \leqslant k \leqslant -1 \end{aligned} \tag{3.3.1}$$

It is easily verified that the corresponding power spectral density is factored as

$$S_{aa}(z) = \sum_{k=-M}^{M} R_{aa}(k)\, z^{-k} = A(z)\, \bar{A}(z) \tag{3.3.2}$$

The magnitude spectrum is obtained by setting $z = e^{j\omega}$

$$S_{aa}(\omega) = |A(\omega)|^2 \tag{3.3.3}$$

with an inversion formula

$$R_{aa}(k) = \int_{-\pi}^{\pi} |A(\omega)|^2 e^{j\omega k}\, \frac{d\omega}{2\pi} \tag{3.3.4}$$

It follows from Eq. (3.3.4) that the above 2^M different sequences having the same magnitude spectrum, also have the *same* sample autocorrelation. They cannot be distinguished on the basis of their autocorrelation.

Therefore, there are 2^M different spectral factorizations of $S_{aa}(z)$ of the form

$$S_{aa}(z) = A(z)\, \bar{A}(z) \tag{3.3.5}$$

but there is only one with minimal-phase factors. The procedure for obtaining it is straightforward: Find the zeros of $S_{aa}(z)$, which come in pairs z_i and $1/z_i^*$. Thus there are $2M$ such zeros. Group those that lie inside the unit circle into a common factor. This defines $A(z)$ as a minimal-phase polynomial.

3.4 *Minimal-Delay Property*

Here, we discuss the effect of flipping a zero from the inside to the outside of the unit circle, on the minimal-delay and the minimal-phase properties of the signal. Suppose $A(z)$ is of degree M and has a zero z_1 inside the unit circle. Let

$B(z)$ be the polynomial that results by flipping this zero to the outside; that is, $z_1 \to 1/z_1^*$

$$A(z) = (1 - z_1 z^{-1})\, F(z)$$
$$B(z) = (-z_1^* + z^{-1})\, F(z) \tag{3.4.1}$$

where $F(z)$ is a polynomial of degree $M - 1$. Both $A(z)$ and $B(z)$ have the same magnitude spectrum. We may think of this operation as sending $A(z)$ through an *all-pass* filter

$$B(z) = \frac{-z_1^* + z^{-1}}{1 - z_1 z^{-1}} A(z)$$

In terms of the polynomial coefficients, Eq. (3.4.1) becomes

$$a_n = f_n - z_1 f_{n-1}$$
$$b_n = -z_1^* f_n + f_{n-1} \tag{3.4.2}$$

for $n = 0, 1, \ldots, M$, from which we obtain

$$|a_n|^2 - |b_n|^2 = (1 - |z_1|^2)(|f_n|^2 - |f_{n-1}|^2) \tag{3.4.3}$$

Summing to get the partial energies $P_a(n) = \sum_{m=0}^{n} |a_m|^2$, we find

$$P_a(n) - P_b(n) = (1 - |z_1|^2)\,|f_n|^2 \tag{3.4.4}$$

for $0 \leq n \leq M$. Thus, the partial energy of the sequence **a** remains greater than that of **b**, for *all* times n; that is, $A(z)$ is of earlier delay than $B(z)$. The total energy is, of course, the same as follows from the fact that $F(z)$ is of degree $M - 1$, thus, missing the Mth term or $f_M = 0$. We have then

$$P_a(n) \geq P_b(n)$$

for $0 \leq n \leq M$, and in particular, we have

$$P_a(M) = P_b(M) \quad \text{and} \quad P_a(0) \geq P_b(0)$$

The last inequality can also be stated as $|a_0| \geq |b_0|$, and will be important in our proof of the minimal-phase property of the prediction-error filter of linear prediction.

3.5 *Minimal-Phase Property*

The effect of reversing the zero z_1 on the phase responses of $A(z)$ and $B(z)$ of Eq. (3.4.1), can be seen as follows. For $z = \exp(j\omega)$, define the *phase lag* as the negative of the *phase response*

$$A(\omega) = |A(\omega)|\, e^{j\mathrm{Arg}A(\omega)}$$

$$\theta_A(\omega) = -\mathrm{Arg}A(\omega) = \text{phase-lag response}$$

and similarly for $B(z)$. Since $A(\omega)$ and $B(\omega)$ have the same magnitude, they will differ only by a phase

$$\frac{A(\omega)}{B(\omega)} = \exp[j(\theta_B - \theta_A)] = \frac{1 - z_1 e^{-j\omega}}{-z_1^* + e^{-j\omega}} = \frac{e^{j\omega} - z_1}{e^{-j\omega} - z_1^*} e^{-j\omega} = e^{2j\psi} e^{-j\omega}$$

With reference to the figure below, let $\psi = \mathrm{Arg}(e^{j\omega} - z_1)$; then we easily find

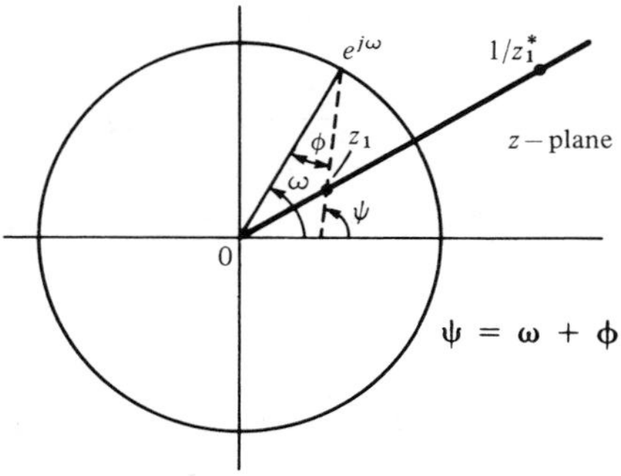

the angle relationships

$$\theta_B(\omega) - \theta_A(\omega) = 2\psi - \omega = 2(\omega + \phi) - \omega = \omega + 2\phi \geqslant 0$$

which show that $\theta_B(\omega) \geqslant \theta_A(\omega)$ for all ω in $[0,\pi]$. Thus, the phase lag of $A(z)$ remains *smaller* than that of $B(z)$. The phase-lag curve for the case when $A(z)$ has all its zeros inside the unit circle will remain below all the other phase-lag curves. The term *minimal-phase* strictly speaking means *minimal phase-lag*.

3.6 *Spectral Factorization Theorem*

We finish our digression on minimal-phase sequences by quoting the spectral factorization theorem [5]:

> Any *rational* power spectral density $S_{yy}(z)$ of a stationary signal y_n, can be factored in a minimal-phase form
>
> $$S_{yy}(z) = \sigma_\epsilon^2 B(z) B(z^{-1}) \tag{3.6.1}$$
>
> where
>
> $$B(z) = \frac{N(z)}{D(z)} \tag{3.6.2}$$
>
> with *both* $D(z)$ and $N(z)$ minimal-phase polynomials; that is, both having all their zeros inside the unit circle. By adjusting the overall constant σ_ϵ^2, both $D(z)$ and $N(z)$ may be taken to be *monic* polynomials. Then, they are *unique*.

This theorem guarantees the existence of a *causal and stable* random signal generator filter for the signal y_n of the type discussed in Section 1.11:

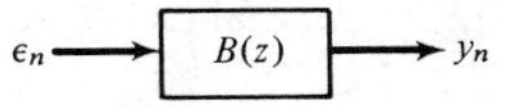

(signal model for y_n)

with ϵ_n white noise of variance σ_ϵ^2. The minimal-phase property of $B(z)$ also guarantees the *stability* of the (causal) inverse filter $1/B(z)$; that is, the whitening filter

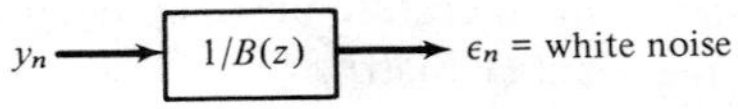

The proof of the spectral factorization theorem is straightforward. Since $S_{yy}(z)$ is the power spectral density of a (real-valued) stationary process y_n, it will satisfy the symmetry conditions $S_{yy}(z) = S_{yy}(z^{-1})$. Therefore, if z_i is zero then $1/z_i$ is also a zero, and if z_i is truly complex then the reality of $R_{yy}(k)$ implies that z_i^* will also be a zero. Thus, both z_i and $1/z_i^*$ are zeros. Therefore, the numerator polynomial of $S_{yy}(z)$ is of the type of Eq. (3.3.5) and can be factored into its minimal phase polynomials $N(z)N(z^{-1})$. This is also true of the denominator of $S_{yy}(z)$.

All sequential correlations in the original signal y_n arise from the *filtering* action of $B(z)$ on the white noise input ϵ_n. This follows from Eq. (2.1.14):

$$R_{yy}(k) = \sigma_\epsilon^2 \sum_n b_{n+k}\, b_n \qquad B(z) = \sum_{n=0}^{\infty} b_n\, z^{-n} \tag{3.6.3}$$

Effectively, we have modeled the statistical autocorrelation $R_{yy}(k)$ by the sample autocorrelation of the impulse response of the synthesis filter $B(z)$. Since $B(z)$ is causal, such factorization, corresponds to a LU, or Cholesky, factorization of the autocorrelation matrix.

This matrix representation can be seen as follows: Let B be the lower triangular Toeplitz matrix defined exactly as in Eq. (1.11.2)

$$b_{ni} = b_{n-i}$$

and let the autocorrelation matrix of y_n be

$$R_{yy}(i,j) = R_{yy}(i-j)$$

Then, the transpose matrix B^T will have matrix elements

$$(B^T)_{ni} = b_{i-n}$$

and Eq. (3.6.3) can be written in the form

$$R_{yy}(i,j) = R_{yy}(i-j) = \sigma_\epsilon^2 \sum_n b_{n+i-j}\, b_n$$

$$= \sigma_\epsilon^2 \sum_k b_{i-k}\, b_{j-k} = \sigma_\epsilon^2 \sum_k (B)_{ik}\, (B^T)_{kj} = \sigma_\epsilon^2\, (B\, B^T)_{ij}$$

Thus, in matrix notation

$$R_{yy} = \sigma_\epsilon^2 BB^T \tag{3.6.4}$$

This equation is a special case of the more general LU factorization of the Gram-Schmidt construction given by Eq. (1.5.17). Indeed, the assumption of stationarity implies that the quantity

$$\sigma_\epsilon^2 = E[\epsilon_n^2]$$

is independent of the time n, and therefore the diagonal matrix $R_{\epsilon\epsilon}$ of Eq. (1.5.17) becomes a multiple of the identity matrix.

3.7 *Minimal-Phase Property of the Prediction-Error Filter*

As mentioned in Section 2.8, the minimal-phase property of the prediction-error filter $A(z)$ of linear prediction is an important property because it guarantees the stability of the causal inverse synthesis filter $1/A(z)$. There are many proofs of this property in the literature [6–10]. Here, we would like to present a simple proof [11] which is based directly on the fact that the optimal prediction coefficients minimize the mean-squared prediction error. Although we have only discussed first and second order linear predictors, for the purposes of this proof we will work with the more general case of an Mth order predictor defined by

$$\hat{y}_n = -[a_1 y_{n-1} + a_2 y_{n-2} + \cdots + a_M y_{n-M}]$$

which is taken to represent the best prediction of y_n based on the *past* M samples $Y_n = \{y_{n-1}, y_{n-2}, \ldots, y_{n-M}\}$. The corresponding prediction error is

$$e_n = y_n + a_1 y_{n-1} + a_2 y_{n-2} + \cdots + a_M y_{n-M}$$

The best set of prediction coefficients $\{a_1, a_2, \ldots, a_M\}$ is found by minimizing the mean-squared prediction error

$$\begin{aligned} \mathcal{E}(a_1, a_2, \ldots, a_M) &= E[e_n^* e_n] = \sum_{m,k=0}^{M} a_m^* E[y_{n-m} y_{n-k}]\, a_k \\ &= \sum_{m,k=0}^{M} a_m^* R_{yy}(m-k)\, a_k \end{aligned} \tag{3.7.1}$$

where we set $a_0 = 1$. For the proof of the minimal phase property, we do not need the explicit solution of this minimization problem; we only use the fact that the optimal coefficients minimize Eq. (3.7.1). The key to the proof is based on the observation that Eq. (3.7.1) can be written in the alternative form

$$\mathcal{E}(\mathbf{a}) = \sum_{k=-M}^{M} R_{yy}(k)\, R_{aa}(k) \tag{3.7.2}$$

where $R_{aa}(k)$ is the sample autocorrelation of the prediction-error filter sequence $\mathbf{a} = [1,a_1,a_2, \ldots ,a_M]^T$, as defined in Eq. (3.3.1). The equivalence of Eqs. (3.7.1) and (3.7.2) can be seen easily, either by rearranging the summation indices of Eq. (3.7.1), or by using the results of Problems 2.3 and 2.5.

Example 3.7.1: We demonstrate this explicitly for the $M = 2$ case. Using the definition (3.3.1) we have

$$R_{aa}(0) = |a_0|^2 + |a_1|^2 + |a_2|^2 = 1 + |a_1|^2 + |a_2|^2$$

$$R_{aa}(1) = R_{aa}(-1)^* = a_1 a_0^* + a_2 a_1^* = a_1 + a_2 a_1^*$$

$$R_{aa}(2) = R_{aa}(-2)^* = a_2 a_0^* = a_2$$

Since y_n is real-valued stationary, we have $R_{yy}(k) = R_{yy}(-k)$. Then, Eq. (3.7.1) becomes explicitly

$$\mathcal{E}(\mathbf{a}) = \sum_{m,k=0}^{M} a_m^* R_{yy}(m-k)\, a_k = [1,a_1^*,a_2^*] \begin{bmatrix} R_{yy}(0) & R_{yy}(1) & R_{yy}(2) \\ R_{yy}(1) & R_{yy}(0) & R_{yy}(1) \\ R_{yy}(2) & R_{yy}(1) & R_{yy}(0) \end{bmatrix} \begin{bmatrix} 1 \\ a_1 \\ a_2 \end{bmatrix}$$

$$\begin{aligned} &= R_{yy}(0)\,[1 + a_1^* a_1 + a_2^* a_2] + R_{yy}(1)\,[(a_1 + a_2 a_1^*) + (a_1^* + a_2^* a_1)] \\ &\quad + R_{yy}(2)\,[a_2 + a_2^*] = R_{yy}(0) R_{aa}(0) + R_{yy}(1)\,[R_{aa}(1) + R_{aa}(-1)] \\ &\quad + R_{yy}(2)\,[R_{aa}(2) + R_{aa}(-2)] \end{aligned}$$

Let $\mathbf{a} = [1,a_1,a_2, \ldots ,a_M]^T$ be the optimal set of coefficients which minimize $\mathcal{E}(\mathbf{a})$, and let z_i; $i = 1,2, \ldots ,M$ be the zeros of the corresponding prediction-error filter; that is,

$$1 + a_1 z^{-1} + a_2 z^{-2} + \cdots + a_M z^{-M} = (1 - z_1 z^{-1})(1 - z_2 z^{-1}) \cdots (1 - z_M z^{-1}) \qquad (3.7.3)$$

Reversing any one of the zero factors in this equation; that is, replacing $(1 - z_i z^{-1})$ by its reverse $(-z_i^* + z^{-1})$, results in a sequence that has the same sample autocorrelation as $\mathbf{a}$. As we have seen, there are 2^M such sequences, all with the same sample autocorrelation. We would like to show that among these, $\mathbf{a}$ is the one having the minimal phase property.

To this end, let $\mathbf{b} = [b_0,b_1, \ldots ,b_M]^T$ be any one of the above 2^M sequences, and define the normalized sequence

$$\mathbf{c} = \mathbf{b}/b_0 = [1,b_1/b_0,b_2/b_0, \ldots ,b_M/b_0]^T \qquad (3.7.4)$$

Using the fact that $\mathbf{b}$ has the same sample autocorrelation as $\mathbf{a}$, we find for the sample autocorrelation of $\mathbf{c}$:

$$R_{cc}(k) = R_{bb}(k)/|b_0|^2 = R_{aa}(k)/|b_0|^2 \qquad (3.7.5)$$

The performance index (3.7.2) evaluated at **c** is then

$$\mathcal{E}(\mathbf{c}) = \sum_{k=-M}^{M} R_{yy}(k)\, R_{cc}(k) = \sum_{k=-M}^{M} R_{yy}(k)\, R_{aa}(k)/|b_0|^2 \tag{3.7.6}$$

or

$$\mathcal{E}(\mathbf{c}) = \mathcal{E}(\mathbf{a})/|b_0|^2 \tag{3.7.7}$$

Since **a** minimizes $\mathcal{E}$, it follows that $\mathcal{E}(\mathbf{c}) \geqslant \mathcal{E}(\mathbf{a})$. Therefore, Eq. (3.7.7) implies that

$$|b_0| \leqslant 1 \tag{3.7.8}$$

This must be true of all **b**s in the above class. Eq. (3.7.8) then, immediately implies the minimal-phase property of **a**. Indeed, choosing **b** to be that sequence which is obtained from Eq. (3.7.3) by reversing only the ith zero factor $(1 - z_i z^{-1})$ and not the other zero factors, it follows that in this case

$$b_0 = -z_i^*$$

and therefore Eq. (3.7.8) implies that

$$|z_i| \leqslant 1 \tag{3.7.9}$$

which shows that all the zeros of $A(z)$ are inside the unit circle and thus, $A(z)$ is minimal-phase. An alternative proof based on the Levinson recursion and Rouche's theorem of complex analysis will be presented in Chapter 5.

Problems

Problem 3.1:
Prove Eq. (3.3.2).

Problem 3.2:
Using Eq. (3.4.1), show Eqs. (3.4.3) and (3.4.4)

Problem 3.3:
A random signal y_n has autocorrelation function

$$R_{yy}(k) = (0.5)^{|k|} \qquad \text{for all } k$$

Find a random signal generator model for y_n.

Problem 3.4:
Repeat Problem 3.3 when

$$R_{yy}(k) = (0.5)^{|k|} + (-0.5)^{|k|} \qquad \text{for all } k$$

Problem 3.5:
The autocorrelation of a stationary random signal $y(n)$ is

$$R_{yy}(k) = \frac{1 - R^2}{1 + R^2} R^{|k|} \cos(\pi k/2) \qquad \text{for all } k$$

where R is a parameter such that $0 < R < 1$.

(a) Compute the power spectrum of $y(n)$, and sketch it roughly versus frequency for various values of R. What happens as R tends to 1?

(b) Find the signal generator filter for $y(n)$ and determine its difference equation and its poles and zeros.

Problem 3.6:
A stationary random signal y_n has a rational spectral density given by

$$S_{yy}(z) = \frac{2.18 - 0.6\,(z + z^{-1})}{1.25 - 0.5\,(z + z^{-1})}$$

Determine the signal model filter $B(z)$ and the parameter σ_ϵ^2. Write the difference equation generating y_n.

Problem 3.7:
Let $y_n = c\,x_n + v_n$. It is given that

$$S_{xx}(z) = \frac{Q}{(1 - az^{-1})(1 - az)}, \qquad S_{vv}(z) = R, \qquad S_{xv}(z) = 0$$

where a,c,Q,R are given constants (assume $|a| < 1$ for stability of x_n).

(a) Show that the filter model for y_n is of the form

$$B(z) = \frac{1 - fz^{-1}}{1 - az^{-1}}$$

where f has magnitude *less* than one and is the solution of the algebraic quadratic equation

$$a\,R\,(1 + f^2) = [c^2\,Q + R\,(1 + a^2)]\,f$$

and show that the other solution has magnitude greater than one.

(b) Show that f can alternatively be expressed as

$$f = \frac{Ra}{R + c^2 P}$$

where P is the *positive* solution of the quadratic equation

$$Q = P - \frac{PRa^2}{R + c^2 P}$$

known as the *algebraic Riccati* equation. Show that the other solution is negative.

Show that positivity of P is essential to guarantee that f has magnitude less than one.

(c) Show that the scale factor σ_ϵ^2 that appears in the spectral factorization (3.6.1) can also be expressed in terms of P as

$$\sigma_\epsilon^2 = R + c^2 P$$

This method of solution of the spectral factorization problem by reducing it to the solution of an algebraic Riccati equation is quite general, and can be extended to the multichannel case.

Problem 3.8:

Consider a stable (but not necessarily causal) sequence $\{b_n;\ -\infty < n < \infty\}$ with a z-transform $B(z)$

$$B(z) = \sum_{n=-\infty}^{\infty} b_n z^{-n}$$

Define an infinite Toeplitz matrix B by

$$B_{ni} = b_{n-i}, \qquad \text{for } -\infty < n,i < \infty$$

This establishes a correspondence between stable z-transforms or stable sequences and infinite Toeplitz matrices.

(a) Show that if the sequence b_n is causal, then B is lower triangular, as shown here:

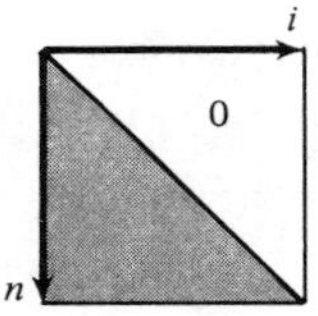

In the literature of integral operators and kernels, such matrices are rotated by 90 degrees as shown:

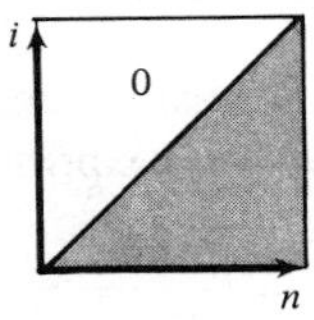

so that the n-axis is the horizontal-axis. For this reason, in that context they are called "right Volterra kernels," or "causal kernels."

(b) Show that the transpose B^T corresponds to the reflected (about the origin) sequence b_{-n} and to the z-transform $B(z^{-1})$.

(c) Show that the convolution of two sequences a_n and b_n

$$c_n = a_n * b_n \qquad \text{or} \qquad C(z) = A(z)\,B(z)$$

corresponds to the commutative matrix product

$$C = A\,B = B\,A$$

Problem 3.9:
Prove Eq. (3.7.2) for any M.

References

1. E. Robinson and S. Treitel, *Geophysical Signal Analysis,* Englewood Cliffs, NJ, Prentice-Hall, 1980.
2. E. A. Robinson, *Statistical Communication and Detection,* New York, Hafner, 1967.
3. E. A. Robinson, *Multichannel Time-Series Analysis with Digital Computer Programs,* (2nd ed.), Houston, TX, Goose Pond Press, 1983.
4. A. V. Oppenheim and R. W. Schafer, *Digital Signal Processing,* Englewood Cliffs, NJ, Prentice-Hall, 1975.
5. P. Whittle, *Prediction and Regulation*, New York, Van Nostrand Reinhold, 1963.
6. J. D. Markel and A. H. Gray, Jr., *Linear Prediction and Speech*, New York, Springer-Verlag, 1976.
7. E. A. Robinson and S. Treitel, Digital Signal Processing in Geophysics, in A. V. Oppenheim, Ed., *Applications of Digital Signal Processing,* Englewood Cliffs, NJ, Prentice-Hall, 1978.
8. S. Lang and J. McClellan, A Simple Proof of Stability for All-Pole Linear Prediction Models, *Proc. IEEE*, **67,** 860–861 (1979).
9. S. Kay and L. Pakula, Simple Proofs of the Minimum Phase Property of the Prediction Error Filter, *IEEE Trans. Acoust., Speech, Signal Process.*, **ASSP-31,** 501 (1983).
10. P. Stoica and A. Nehorai, On Stability and Root Location of Linear Prediction Models, *IEEE Trans. Acoust., Speech, Signal Process.,* **ASSP-35,** 582 (1987).
11. S. J. Orfanidis, A Proof of the Minimal Phase Property of the Prediction Error Filter, *Proc. IEEE,* **71,** 905 (1983).

4

Linear Estimation of Signals

THE PROBLEM OF ESTIMATING one signal from another is one of the most important in signal processing. In many applications, the desired signal is not available or observable directly. Instead, the observable signal is a degraded or distorted version of the original signal. The signal estimation problem is to recover, in the best way possible, the desired signal from its degraded replica. We mention some typical examples: (1) The desired signal may be corrupted by strong additive noise, such as weak evoked brain potentials measured against the strong background of ongoing EEGs; or weak radar returns from a target in the presence of strong clutter. (2) An antenna array designed to be sensitive towards a particular "look" direction may be vulnerable to strong jammers from other directions due to sidelobe leakage; the signal processing task here is to null the jammers while at the same time maintaining the sensitivity of the array towards the desired look direction. (3) A signal transmitted over a communications channel can suffer phase and amplitude distortions and can be subject to additive channel noise; the problem is to recover the transmitted signal from the distorted received signal. (4) A Doppler radar processor tracking a moving target must take into account dynamical noise—such as small purely random accelerations—affecting the dynamics of the target, as well as measurement errors. (5) An image recorded by an imaging system is subject to distortions such as blurring due to motion or to the finite aperture of the system, or other geometric distortions; the problem here is to undo the distortions introduced by the imaging system and restore the original image. A related problem, of interest in medical image processing, is that of reconstructing an image from its projections. (6) In remote sensing and inverse scattering applications, the basic problem is, again, to infer one signal from another; for example, to infer the temperature profile of the atmosphere from measurements of the spectral distribution of infrared energy; or to deduce the structure of a dielectric medium, such as the ionosphere, by studying its response to electromagnetic wave scattering; or, in oil exploration, to infer the layered structure of the earth by measuring its response to an impulsive input near its surface.

In this chapter, we pose the signal estimation problem and discuss some of the criteria used in the design of signal estimation algorithms.

We do not present a complete discussion of all methods of signal recovery and estimation that have been invented for applications as diverse as those mentioned above. Our emphasis is on traditional linear least-squares estimation methods, not only because they are widely used, but also because they have served as the motivating force for the development of other estimation techniques and as the yardstick for evaluating them. We develop the theoretical solution of the Wiener filter both in the stationary and nonstationary cases, and discuss its connection to the orthogonal projection, Gram-Schmidt constructions, and correlation canceling ideas of Chapter 1. By means of an example, we introduce Kalman filter concepts and discuss their connection to Wiener filtering and to signal modeling. Practical implementations of the Wiener filter are discussed in Chapters 5 and 6. Other signal recovery methods for deconvolution applications that are based on alternative design criteria are briefly discussed in Chapter 5, where we also discuss some interesting connections between Wiener filtering/linear prediction methods and inverse scattering methods.

4.1 *Linear and Nonlinear Estimation of Signals*

The signal estimation problem can be stated as follows: We wish to estimate a random signal x_n on the basis of available observations of a related signal y_n. The available signal y_n is to be processed by an optimal processor that produces the best possible estimate of x_n:

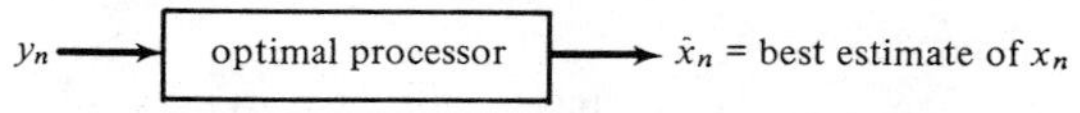

The resulting estimate $\hat{x}_n$ will be a functional of the observations y_n. If the optimal processor is linear, such as a linear filter, then the estimate $\hat{x}_n$ will be a linear function of the observations. We are going to concentrate mainly on linear processors. However, we would like to point out that, depending on the estimation criterion, there are cases where the estimate $\hat{x}_n$ may turn out to be a nonlinear function of the y_ns.

We discuss briefly four major estimation criteria for designing such optimal processors. They are:

(1) The maximum a posteriori (MAP) criterion
(2) The maximum likelihood (ML) criterion
(3) The mean squared (MS) criterion
(4) The linear mean squared (LMS) criterion

The LMS criterion is a special case of the MS criterion. It requires, *a priori*, that the estimate $\hat{x}_n$ be a *linear* function of the y_ns. Note that the acronym LMS is also used, especially in the context of adaptive filtering, for *least mean squared*. The main advantage of the LMS processor is that it requires only knowledge of second order statistics for its design, whereas the other, nonlinear, processors require more detailed knowledge of probability densities.

To explain the various estimation criteria, let us assume that the desired signal x_n is to be estimated over a finite time interval $n_a \leqslant n \leqslant n_b$. Without loss of generality, we may assume that the observed signal y_n is also available over the same interval. Define the vectors

$$\mathbf{x} = \begin{bmatrix} x_{n_a} \\ x_{n_a+1} \\ \vdots \\ x_{n_b} \end{bmatrix} \qquad \mathbf{y} = \begin{bmatrix} y_{n_a} \\ y_{n_a+1} \\ \vdots \\ y_{n_b} \end{bmatrix}$$

For each value of n, we seek the functional dependence

$$\hat{x}_n = \hat{x}_n(\mathbf{y})$$

of $\hat{x}_n$ on the given observation vector $\mathbf{y}$ that provides the *best estimate* of the nth sample x_n.

1. The criterion for the MAP estimate is to maximize the a posteriori conditional density of x_n given that $\mathbf{y}$ already occurred; namely,

$$p(x_n/\mathbf{y}) = \text{maximum} \tag{4.1.1}$$

in other words, the optimal estimate $\hat{x}_n$ is that x_n which maximizes this quantity for the given vector $\mathbf{y}$; $\hat{x}_n$ is therefore the most probable choice resulting from the given set of observations $\mathbf{y}$.

2. The ML criterion, on the other hand, selects $\hat{x}_n$ to maximize the conditional density of $\mathbf{y}$ given x_n; that is,

$$p(\mathbf{y}/x_n) = \text{maximum} \tag{4.1.2}$$

This criterion selects $\hat{x}_n$ as though the already collected observations $\mathbf{y}$ were the most likely ones to occur.

3. The MS criterion minimizes the mean-squared estimation error

$$\mathcal{E}_n = E[e_n^2] = \min, \qquad \text{where } e_n = x_n - \hat{x}_n(\mathbf{y}) \tag{4.1.3}$$

That is, the best choice of functional dependence $\hat{x}_n = \hat{x}_n(\mathbf{y})$ is sought that minimizes this expression. We know from our results in Section 1.4 that the required choice is the corresponding *conditional mean*

$$\hat{x}_n(\mathbf{y}) = E[x_n/\mathbf{y}] = \text{MS estimate} \tag{4.1.4}$$

computed with respect to the conditional density $p(x_n/\mathbf{y})$.

4. Finally, the LMS criterion requires the estimate to be a linear function of the observations

$$\hat{x}_n = \sum_{i=n_a}^{n_b} h(n,i)y_i \tag{4.1.5}$$

For each n, the weights $h(n,i)$, $n_a \leq i \leq n_b$ are selected so as to *minimize* the mean-squared estimation error

$$\mathcal{E}_n = E[e_n^2] = E[(x_n - \hat{x}_n)^2] = \text{minimum} \tag{4.1.6}$$

With the exception of the LMS estimate, all the other estimates $\hat{x}_n(\mathbf{y})$ are, in general, nonlinear in $\mathbf{y}$.

Example 4.1.1: If both x_n and $\mathbf{y}$ are zero-mean and jointly gaussian, then Examples 1.4.1 and 1.4.2 imply that the MS and the LMS estimates of x_n are the *same*. Furthermore, since $p(x_n/\mathbf{y})$ is gaussian it will be a curve symmetric about its maximum which occurs at its mean; that is, at $E[x_n/\mathbf{y}]$. Therefore, the MAP estimate of x_n is equal to the MS estimate. In conclusion, for *zero-mean jointly gaussian* x_n and $\mathbf{y}$, the three estimates MAP, MS, and LMS *coincide*.

Example 4.1.2: To see the nonlinear character and the differences among the various estimates, consider the following example: A discrete-amplitude, constant-in-time signal x can take on the three values

$$x = -1 \qquad x = 0 \qquad x = +1$$

each with probability of 1/3. This signal is placed on a known carrier waveform c_n and transmitted over a noisy channel. The received samples are of the form

$$y_n = c_n x + v_n$$

$n = 1,2, \ldots, M$, where v_n are zero-mean white gaussian noise samples of variance σ_v^2, assumed to be independent of x. The above set of measurements can be written in an obvious vector notation

$$\mathbf{y} = \mathbf{c}x + \mathbf{v}$$

(a) Determine the conditional densities $p(\mathbf{y}/x)$ and $p(x/\mathbf{y})$.

(b) Determine and compare the four alternative estimates MAP, ML, MS, and LMS of x.

To compute $p(\mathbf{y}/x)$, note that if x is given, then the only randomness left in $\mathbf{y}$ arises from the noise term $\mathbf{v}$. Since v_n are uncorrelated and gaussian, they will be independent; therefore,

$$p(\mathbf{y}/x) = p(\mathbf{v}) = \prod_{n=1}^{M} p(v_n)$$

$$= (2\pi\sigma_v^2)^{-M/2} \exp\left[-\frac{1}{2\sigma_v^2}\sum_{n=1}^{M} v_n^2\right]$$

$$= (2\pi\sigma_v^2)^{-M/2} \exp\left[-\frac{1}{2\sigma_v^2}\mathbf{v}^2\right]$$

$$= (2\pi\sigma_v^2)^{-M/2} \exp\left[-\frac{1}{2\sigma_v^2}(\mathbf{y} - \mathbf{c}x)^2\right]$$

Using Bayes' rule we find $p(x/\mathbf{y}) = p(\mathbf{y}/x)p(x)/p(\mathbf{y})$. Since

$$p(x) = [\delta(x - 1) + \delta(x) + \delta(x + 1)]/3$$

we find

$$p(x/\mathbf{y}) = [p(\mathbf{y}/1)\delta(x - 1) + p(\mathbf{y}/0)\delta(x) + p(\mathbf{y}/-1)\delta(x + 1)]/A$$

where the constant A is

$$A = 3p(\mathbf{y}) = 3\int p(\mathbf{y}/x)p(x)\,dx = p(\mathbf{y}/1) + p(\mathbf{y}/0) + p(\mathbf{y}/-1)$$

To find the MAP estimate of x, the quantity $p(x/\mathbf{y})$ must be maximized with respect to x. Since the expression for $p(x/\mathbf{y})$ forces x to be one of the three values $+1, 0, -1$, it follows that the maximum among the three coefficients $p(\mathbf{y}/1)$, $p(\mathbf{y}/0)$, $p(\mathbf{y}/-1)$ determines the value of x. Thus, for a given $\mathbf{y}$ we select that x such that

$$p(\mathbf{y}/x) = \text{maximum of } \{p(\mathbf{y}/1), p(\mathbf{y}/0), p(\mathbf{y}/-1)\}$$

Using the gaussian nature of $p(\mathbf{y}/x)$, we find equivalently

$$(\mathbf{y} - \mathbf{c}x)^2 = \text{minimum of } \{(\mathbf{y} - \mathbf{c})^2, \mathbf{y}^2, (\mathbf{y} + \mathbf{c})^2\}$$

Subtracting $\mathbf{y}^2$ from both sides, dividing by $\mathbf{c}^T\mathbf{c}$, and denoting

$$\bar{y} = \frac{\mathbf{c}^T\mathbf{y}}{\mathbf{c}^T\mathbf{c}}$$

we find the equivalent equation

$$x^2 - 2x\bar{y} = \min\{1 - 2\bar{y}, 0, 1 + 2\bar{y}\}$$

and in particular, applying these for $x = +1, 0, -1$, we find

$$\hat{x}_{\text{MAP}} = \begin{cases} 1 \text{ if } \bar{y} > \dfrac{1}{2} \\[2ex] 0 \text{ if } -\dfrac{1}{2} < \bar{y} < \dfrac{1}{2} \\[2ex] -1 \text{ if } \bar{y} < -\dfrac{1}{2} \end{cases}$$

To determine the ML estimate, we must maximize $p(\mathbf{y}/x)$ with respect to x. The ML estimate does not require knowledge of the probability density $p(x)$ of x. Therefore, differentiating $p(\mathbf{y}/x)$ with respect to x and setting the derivative to zero gives

$$\frac{\partial}{\partial x} p(\mathbf{y}/x) = 0 \qquad \text{or} \qquad \frac{\partial}{\partial x} \ln p(\mathbf{y}/x) = 0 \qquad \text{or} \qquad \frac{\partial}{\partial x} (\mathbf{y} - \mathbf{c}x)^2 = 0$$

which gives

$$\hat{x}_{\text{ML}} = \frac{\mathbf{c}^T\mathbf{y}}{\mathbf{c}^T\mathbf{c}} = \bar{y}$$

The MS estimate is obtained by computing the conditional mean

$$\begin{aligned} E[x/\mathbf{y}] &= \int x p(x/\mathbf{y})\, dx \\ &= \int x[p(\mathbf{y}/1)\delta(x - 1) + p(\mathbf{y}/0)\delta(x) + p(\mathbf{y}/-1)\delta(x + 1)]\, dx/A \\ &= [p(\mathbf{y}/1) - p(\mathbf{y}/-1)]/A \end{aligned}$$

or

$$\hat{x}_{\text{MS}} = \frac{p(\mathbf{y}/+1) - p(\mathbf{y}/-1)}{p(\mathbf{y}/+1) + p(\mathbf{y}/0) + p(\mathbf{y}/-1)}$$

Canceling some common factors from numerator and denominator, we find a simpler expression

$$\hat{x}_{\text{MS}} = \frac{2\text{sh}(2a\bar{y})}{e^a + 2\text{ch}(2a\bar{y})} \qquad \text{where} \qquad a = \frac{\mathbf{c}^T\mathbf{c}}{2\sigma_v^2}$$

Finally, the LMS estimate can be computed as in Example 1.4.3. We find

$$\hat{x}_{\text{LMS}} = \frac{1}{\dfrac{\sigma_v^2}{\sigma_x^2} + \mathbf{c}^T\mathbf{c}} \mathbf{c}^T\mathbf{y} = \frac{\mathbf{c}^T\mathbf{c}}{\dfrac{\sigma_v^2}{\sigma_x^2} + \mathbf{c}^T\mathbf{c}} \bar{y}$$

All four estimates have been expressed in terms of $\bar{y}$. Note that the ML estimate is linear but has a different slope than the LMS estimate. The nonlinearity of the various estimates is best seen in the following figure:

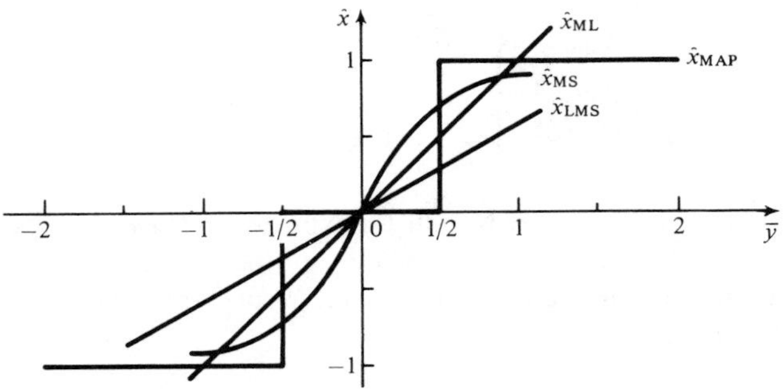

4.2 *Orthogonality and Normal Equations*

From now on, we will concentrate on the optimal linear estimate defined by Eqs. (4.1.5) and (4.1.6). For each time instant n, at which an estimate $\hat{x}_n$ is sought, the optimal weights $h(n,i)$; $n_a \leq i \leq n_b$ must be determined that minimize the error criterion (4.1.6). In general, a new set of optimal weights must be computed for each time instant n. In the special case when the processes x_n and y_n are stationary and the observations are available for a long time; that is, $n_a = -\infty$, the weights become time-invariant in the sense that $h(n,i) = h(n - i)$, and the linear processor becomes an ordinary *time-invariant linear filter*. We will discuss the solution for $h(n,i)$ both for the time-invariant and the more general cases. The problem of determining the optimal weights $h(n,i)$ according to the mean-squared minimization criterion (4.1.6) is in general referred to as the *Wiener filtering problem* [1–11]. An interesting historical account of the development of this problem and its ramifications is given in the review article by Kailath [12].

Wiener filtering problems are conventionally divided into three types:

(1) The optimal *smoothing* problem
(2) The optimal *filtering* problem, and
(3) The optimal *prediction* problem.

In all cases, the optimal estimate of x_n at a given time instant n is given by an expression of the form (4.1.5), as a linear combination of the available observations y_n in the interval $n_a \leq n \leq n_b$. The division into three types of problems depends on *which* of the available observations in that interval are taken into account *in making up* the linear combination (4.1.5).

1. In the smoothing problem, *all* the observations in the interval $[n_a, n_b]$ are taken into account. The shaded part in the following figure denotes the range of observations that are used in the summation of Eq. (4.1.5):

$$\hat{x}_n = \sum_{i=n_a}^{n_b} h(n,i) y_i$$

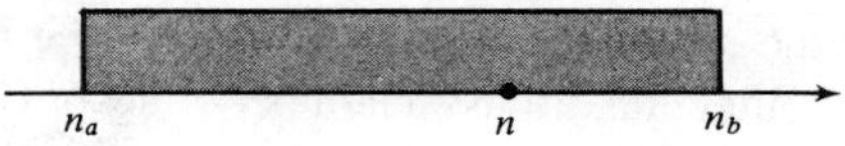

Since some of the observations are to the future of x_n, the linear operation is not causal. This does not present a problem if the sequence y_n is already available and stored in memory.

2. The optimal filtering problem, on the other hand, requires the linear operation (4.1.5) to be *causal*; that is, only those observations that are in the *present* and *past* of the current sample x_n must be used in making up the estimate $\hat{x}_n$. This requires that the matrix of optimal weights $h(n,i)$ be *lower* triangular; that is,

$$h(n,i) = 0, \qquad \text{for } n < i$$

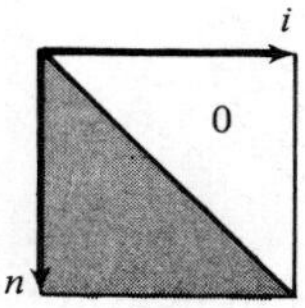

Thus, in reference to the figure below, only the shaded portion of the observation interval is used at the current time instant:

$$\hat{x}_n = \sum_{i=n_a}^{n} h(n,i) y_i$$

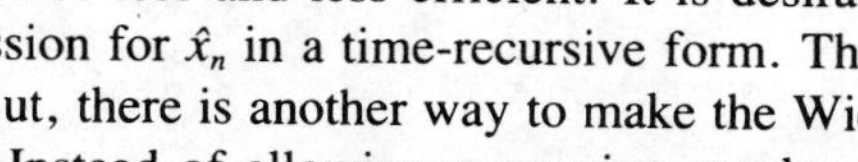

The estimate $\hat{x}_n$ depends on the present and all the past observations, from the fixed starting point n_a to the current time instant n. As n increases, more and more observations are taken into account in making up the estimate $\hat{x}_n$, and the actual computation of $\hat{x}_n$ becomes less and less efficient. It is desirable, then, to be able to recast the expression for $\hat{x}_n$ in a time-recursive form. This is what is done in Kalman filtering. But, there is another way to make the Wiener filter computationally manageable. Instead of allowing a growing number of observations, only the current and the *past M* observations y_i; $i = n, n-1, \ldots, n-M$ are taken into account. In this case, only $(M+1)$ filter weights are to be computed at each time instant n. This is depicted below:

$$\hat{x}_n = \sum_{i=n-M}^{n} h(n,i) y_i = \sum_{m=0}^{M} h(n, n-m) y_{n-m}$$

This is referred to as the *finite impulse response* (FIR) Wiener filter. Because of its simple implementation, the FIR Wiener filter has enjoyed widespread popularity. Depending on the particular application, the practical implementation of the filter may vary. In Section 4.3 we present the theoretical formulation that applies to the stationary case; in Chapter 5 we reconsider it as a waveshaping and spiking filter and discuss a number of deconvolution applications. In Chapter 7 we consider its adaptive implementation using the Widrow-Hoff LMS algorithm and discuss a number of applications such as channel equalization and echo cancellation; we also discuss two alternative adaptive implementations—the so-called "gradient lattice," and the "recursive least-squares".

3. Finally, the linear prediction problem is a special case of the optimal filtering problem with the additional stipulation that observations only up to time instant $n - D$ must be used in obtaining the current estimate $\hat{x}_n$; this is equivalent to the problem of predicting D units of time into the future. The range of observations used in this case is shown below:

$$\hat{x}_n = \sum_{i=n_a}^{n-D} h(n,i)y_i$$

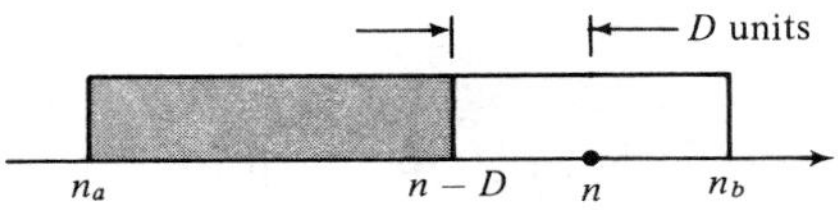

Of special interest to us will be the case of *one-step* prediction, corresponding to the choice $D = 1$. This is depicted below:

$$\hat{x}_n = \sum_{i=n_a}^{n-1} h(n,i)y_i$$

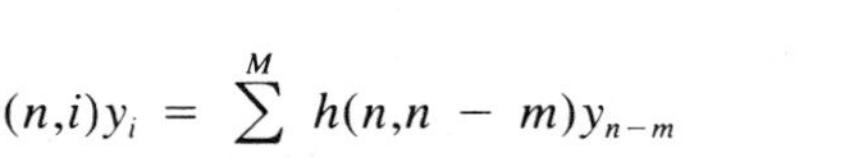

If we demand that the prediction be based only on the past M samples (from the current sample), we obtain the FIR version of the prediction problem, referred to as *linear prediction based on the past M samples*, which is depicted below:

$$\hat{x}_n = \sum_{i=n-M}^{n-1} h(n,i)y_i = \sum_{m=1}^{M} h(n,n - m)y_{n-m}$$

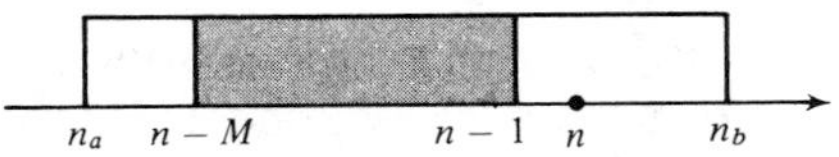

Next, we set up the orthogonality and normal equations for the optimal weights. We begin with the smoothing problem. The estimation error is in this case

$$e_n = x_n - \hat{x}_n = x_n - \sum_{i=n_a}^{n_b} h(n,i)y_i \tag{4.2.1}$$

Differentiating the mean-squared estimation error (4.1.6) with respect to *each* weight $h(n,i)$, $n_a \leq i \leq n_b$, and setting the derivative to zero, we obtain the *orthogonality equations* that are enough to determine the weights:

$$\frac{\partial \mathcal{E}_n}{\partial h(n,i)} = 2E\left[e_n \frac{\partial e_n}{\partial h(n,i)}\right] = -2E[e_n y_i] = 0, \qquad \text{for } n_a \leq i \leq n_b$$

or

$$R_{ey}(n,i) = E[e_n y_i] = 0 \qquad \text{(orthogonality equations)} \tag{4.2.2}$$

for $n_a \leq i \leq n_b$. Thus, the estimation error e_n is orthogonal (uncorrelated) to *each* observation y_i used in *making up* the estimate $\hat{x}_n$. The orthogonality equations provide exactly as many equations as there are unknown weights.

Inserting Eq. (4.2.1) for e_n, the orthogonality equations may be written in an equivalent form, known as the *normal equations*

$$E\left[\left(x_n - \sum_{k=n_a}^{n_b} h(n,k)y_k\right) y_i\right] = 0$$

or

$$E[x_n y_i] = \sum_{k=n_a}^{n_b} h(n,k)E[y_k y_i] \qquad \text{(normal equations)} \tag{4.2.3}$$

for $n_a \leq i \leq n_b$. These determine the optimal weights at the current time instant n. In the vector notation of Section 4.1, we write Eq. (4.2.3) as

$$E[\mathbf{x}\mathbf{y}^T] = HE[\mathbf{y}\mathbf{y}^T]$$

where H is the *matrix of weights* $h(n,i)$. The optimal H and the estimate are then

$$\hat{\mathbf{x}} = H\mathbf{y} = E[\mathbf{x}\mathbf{y}^T]E[\mathbf{y}\mathbf{y}^T]^{-1}\mathbf{y}$$

This is identical to the correlation canceler of Section 1.4. The orthogonality equations (4.2.2) are precisely the correlation cancellation conditions. Extracting the nth row of this matrix equation, we find an explicit expression for the nth estimate $\hat{x}_n$

$$\hat{x}_n = E[x_n\mathbf{y}^T]E[\mathbf{y}\mathbf{y}^T]^{-1}\mathbf{y}$$

which is recognized as the projection of the random variable x_n onto the subspace spanned by the *available* observations; namely, $Y = \{y_{n_a}, y_{n_a+1}, \ldots, y_{n_b}\}$. This is a general result: The minimum mean-squared linear estimate $\hat{x}_n$ is the projection of x_n onto the subspace spanned by *all* the observations that are used *to make up* that estimate. This result is a direct consequence of the quadratic minimization criterion (4.1.6) and the orthogonal projection theorem discussed in Section 1.5.

Using the methods of Section 1.4, the minimized estimation error at time instant n is easily computed by

$$\mathcal{E}_n = E[e_n e_n] = E[e_n x_n] = E\left[\left(x_n - \sum_{i=n_a}^{n_b} h(n,i) y_i\right) x_n\right]$$

$$= E[x_n^2] - \sum_{i=n_a}^{n_b} h(n,i) E[y_i x_n]$$

$$= E[x_n^2] - E[x_n \mathbf{y}^T] E[\mathbf{y}\mathbf{y}^T]^{-1} E[\mathbf{y} x_n]$$

which corresponds to the diagonal entries of the covariance matrix of the estimation error $\mathbf{e}$:

$$R_{ee} = E[\mathbf{e}\mathbf{e}^T] = E[\mathbf{x}\mathbf{x}^T] - E[\mathbf{x}\mathbf{y}^T] E[\mathbf{y}\mathbf{y}^T]^{-1} E[\mathbf{y}\mathbf{x}^T]$$

The optimal filtering problem is somewhat more complicated because of the causality condition. In this case, the estimate at time n is given by

$$\hat{x}_n = \sum_{i=n_a}^{n} h(n,i) y_i \tag{4.2.4}$$

Inserting this into the minimization criterion (4.1.6) and differentiating with respect to $h(n,i)$ for $n_a \leqslant i \leqslant n$, we find again the orthogonality conditions

$$R_{ey}(n,i) = E[e_n y_i] = 0 \qquad \text{for } n_a \leqslant i \leqslant n \tag{4.2.5}$$

where the most important difference from Eq. (4.2.2) is the restriction on the *range* of i's; that is, e_n is decorrelated only from the present and past values of y_i. Again, the estimation error e_n is orthogonal to each observation y_i that is being used in making up the estimate. The orthogonality equations can be converted into the normal equations as follows:

$$E[e_n y_i] = E\left[\left(x_n - \sum_{k=n_a}^{n} h(n,k) y_k\right) y_i\right] = 0$$

or

$$E[x_n y_i] = \sum_{k=n_a}^{n} h(n,k) E[y_k y_i] \qquad \text{for } n_a \leqslant i \leqslant n \tag{4.2.6}$$

or

$$R_{xy}(n,i) = \sum_{k=n_a}^{n} h(n,k) R_{yy}(k,i) \qquad \text{for } n_a \leqslant i \leqslant n \tag{4.2.7}$$

Such equations are generally known as *Wiener-Hopf equations*. Introducing the vector of observations *up to* the current time n; namely,

$$\mathbf{y}_n = [y_{n_a}, y_{n_a+1}, \ldots, y_n]^T$$

we may write Eq. (4.2.6) in vector form as

$$E[x_n \mathbf{y}_n^T] = [h(n,n_a), h(n,n_a + 1), \ldots, h(n,n)]E[\mathbf{y}_n \mathbf{y}_n^T]$$

which can be solved for the vector of weights

$$[h(n,n_a), h(n,n_a + 1), \ldots, h(n,n)] = E[x_n \mathbf{y}_n^T]E[\mathbf{y}_n \mathbf{y}_n^T]^{-1}$$

and for the estimate $\hat{x}_n$:

$$\hat{x}_n = E[x_n \mathbf{y}_n^T]E[\mathbf{y}_n \mathbf{y}_n^T]^{-1}\mathbf{y}_n \tag{4.2.8}$$

Again, $\hat{x}_n$ is recognized as the *projection* of x_n onto the space spanned by the observations that are used in making up the estimate; namely, $Y_n = \{y_{n_a}, y_{n_a+1}, \ldots, y_n\}$. This solution of Eqs. (4.2.5) and (4.2.7) will be discussed in more detail in Section 4.8, using covariance factorization methods.

4.3 *Stationary Wiener Filter*

In this section, we make two assumptions that simplify the structure of Eqs. (4.2.6) and (4.2.7). The first is to assume *stationarity* for all signals so that the cross-correlation and autocorrelation appearing in Eq. (4.2.7) become functions of the *differences* of their arguments. The second assumption is to take the initial time n_a to be the *infinite past*; $n_a = -\infty$, that is, the observation interval is $Y_n = \{y_i; -\infty < i \leqslant n\}$.

The assumption of stationarity can be used as follows: Suppose we have the solution of $h(n,i)$ of Eq. (4.2.7) for the best weights to estimate x_n, and wish to determine the best weights $h(n + \Delta,i)$, $n_a \leqslant i \leqslant n + \Delta$ for estimating the sample $x_{n+\Delta}$ at the future time $n + \Delta$. Then, the new weights will satisfy the same equations as (4.2.7) with the changes

$$R_{xy}(n + \Delta,i) = \sum_{k=n_a}^{n+\Delta} h(n + \Delta,k)R_{yy}(k,i) \qquad \text{for } n_a \leqslant i \leqslant n + \Delta \tag{4.3.1}$$

Making a change of variables $i \to i + \Delta$ and $k \to k + \Delta$, we rewrite Eq. (4.3.1) as

$$R_{xy}(n + \Delta,i + \Delta) = \sum_{k=n_a-\Delta}^{n} h(n + \Delta,k + \Delta)R_{yy}(k + \Delta,i + \Delta)$$

$$\text{for } n_a - \Delta \leqslant i \leqslant n \tag{4.3.2}$$

Now, if we assume stationarity, Eqs. (4.2.7) and (4.3.2) become

$$\begin{aligned} R_{xy}(n - i) &= \sum_{k=n_a}^{n} h(n,k)R_{yy}(k - i) \quad \text{for } n_a \leqslant i \leqslant n \\ R_{xy}(n - i) &= \sum_{k=n_a-\Delta}^{n} h(n + \Delta,k + \Delta)R_{yy}(k - i) \\ &\qquad\qquad \text{for } n_a - \Delta \leqslant i \leqslant n \end{aligned} \tag{4.3.3}$$

If it were not for the differences in the ranges of i and k, these two equations would be the same. But this is exactly what happens when we make the second assumption that $n_a = -\infty$. Therefore, by uniqueness of the solution, we find in this case

$$h(n + \Delta,k + \Delta) = h(n,k)$$

and since Δ is arbitrary, it follows that $h(n,k)$ must be a function of the difference of its arguments, that is,

$$h(n,k) = h(n - k) \tag{4.3.4}$$

Thus, the optimal linear processor becomes a *shift-invariant causal linear filter*; the estimate is given by

$$\hat{x}_n = \sum_{i=-\infty}^{n} h(n - i)y_i = \sum_{i=0}^{\infty} h(i)y_{n-i} \tag{4.3.5}$$

and Eq. (4.3.3) becomes in this case

$$R_{xy}(n - i) = \sum_{k=-\infty}^{n} h(n - k)R_{yy}(k - i) \qquad \text{for } -\infty < i \leqslant n$$

With the change of variables $n - i \rightarrow n$, and $n - k \rightarrow k$, we find

$$R_{xy}(n) = \sum_{k=0}^{\infty} R_{yy}(n - k)h(k) \qquad \text{for } n \geqslant 0 \tag{4.3.6}$$

and written in matrix form

$$\begin{bmatrix} R_{yy}(0) & R_{yy}(1) & R_{yy}(2) & R_{yy}(3) & \cdots \\ R_{yy}(1) & R_{yy}(0) & R_{yy}(1) & R_{yy}(2) & \cdots \\ R_{yy}(2) & R_{yy}(1) & R_{yy}(0) & R_{yy}(1) & \cdots \\ R_{yy}(3) & R_{yy}(2) & R_{yy}(1) & R_{yy}(0) & \cdots \\ \vdots & \vdots & \vdots & \vdots & \end{bmatrix} \begin{bmatrix} h(0) \\ h(1) \\ h(2) \\ h(3) \\ \vdots \end{bmatrix} = \begin{bmatrix} R_{xy}(0) \\ R_{xy}(1) \\ R_{xy}(2) \\ R_{xy}(3) \\ \vdots \end{bmatrix} \tag{4.3.7}$$

These are the *discrete-time Wiener-Hopf equations*. Were it not for the restriction $n \geqslant 0$ (which reflects the requirement of causality), they could be solved easily by z-transform methods. As written above, they require methods of *spectral factorization* for their solution.

Before we discuss such methods, we mention in passing the continuous-time version of the Wiener-Hopf equation:

$$R_{xy}(t) = \int_0^\infty R_{yy}(t - t')h(t')\,dt' \qquad \text{for } t \geqslant 0$$

We also consider the FIR Wiener filtering problem in the stationary case. The observation interval in this case is $Y_n = \{y_i;\ n - M \leqslant i \leqslant n\}$. Using the same arguments as above we have $h(n,i) = h(n - i)$, and the estimate $\hat{x}_n$ is obtained by an ordinary FIR linear filter

$$\hat{x}_n = \sum_{i=n-M}^{n} h(n - i)y_i = h(0)y_n + h(1)y_{n-1} + \cdots + h(M)y_{n-M} \tag{4.3.8}$$

where the $M + 1$ optimal filter weights $h(0), h(1), \ldots, h(M)$ are obtained by the $(M + 1) \times (M + 1)$ matrix version of the Wiener-Hopf, normal, equations

$$\begin{bmatrix} R_{yy}(0) & R_{yy}(1) & R_{yy}(2) & \cdots & R_{yy}(M) \\ R_{yy}(1) & R_{yy}(0) & R_{yy}(1) & \cdots & R_{yy}(M-1) \\ R_{yy}(2) & R_{yy}(1) & R_{yy}(0) & \cdots & R_{yy}(M-2) \\ \vdots & \vdots & \vdots & & \vdots \\ R_{yy}(M) & R_{yy}(M-1) & R_{yy}(M-2) & \cdots & R_{yy}(0) \end{bmatrix} \begin{bmatrix} h(0) \\ h(1) \\ h(2) \\ \vdots \\ h(M) \end{bmatrix} = \begin{bmatrix} R_{xy}(0) \\ R_{xy}(1) \\ R_{xy}(2) \\ \vdots \\ R_{xy}(M) \end{bmatrix} \tag{4.3.9}$$

Exploiting the Toeplitz property of the matrix R_{yy}, the above matrix equation can be solved efficiently using Levinson's algorithm. This will be discussed in Chapter 5. In Chapter 6, we will consider adaptive implementations of the FIR Wiener filter which produce the optimal filter weights *adaptively* without requiring prior knowledge of the autocorrelation and cross-correlation matrices R_{yy} and R_{xy} and without requiring any matrix inversion.

We summarize our results on the stationary Wiener filter in Fig. 4.1. The optimal filter weights $h(n)$; $n = 0,1,2, \ldots,$ are computed from Eq. (4.3.7)

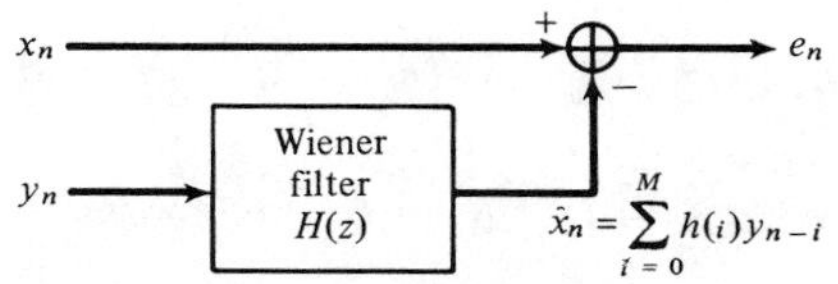

Figure 4.1 Time-Invariant Wiener Filter.

or Eq. (4.3.9). The action of the filter is precisely that of the *correlation canceler*: The filter processes the observation signal y_n *causally* to produce the *best possible estimate* $\hat{x}_n$ of x_n, and then it proceeds to cancel it from the output e_n. As a result, the output e_n is no longer correlated with any of the present and past values of y_n; that is, $E[e_n y_{n-i}] = 0$, for all $i = 0,1,2, \ldots$. As we remarked in Section 1.4, it is better to think of $\hat{x}_n$ as the optimal estimate of *that part* of the primary signal x_n which happens to be correlated with the secondary signal y_n; this follows from the property that if $x_n = x_1(n) + x_2(n)$ with $R_{x_2 y} = 0$, then $R_{xy} = R_{x_1 y}$. Therefore, the solution of Eq. (4.3.7) for the best weights to estimate x_n is also the solution for the best weights to estimate $x_1(n)$. The filter may also be thought of as the *optimal signal separator* of the two signal components $x_1(n)$ and $x_2(n)$.

4.4 *Construction of the Wiener Filter by Prewhitening*

The normal equations (4.3.6) would have a trivial solution if the sequence y_n were a white-noise sequence with delta-function autocorrelation. Thus, the solution procedure is first to whiten the sequence y_n and then solve the normal equations. To this end, let y_n have a signal model, as guaranteed by the spectral factorization theorem

$$S_{yy}(z) = \sigma_\epsilon^2 B(z)B(z^{-1}) \tag{4.4.1}$$

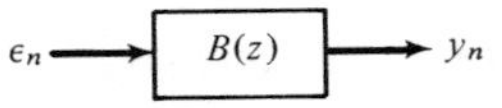

where ϵ_n is the driving white noise, and $B(z)$ a minimal-phase filter.

The problem of estimating x_n in terms of the sequence y_n becomes equivalent to the problem of estimating x_n in terms of the white-noise sequence ϵ_n:

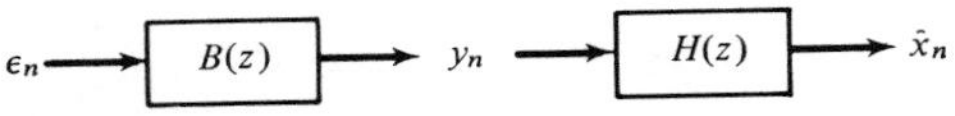

If we could determine the combined filter

$$F(z) = B(z)H(z)$$

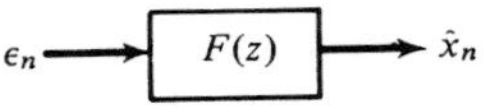

we would then solve for the desired Wiener filter $H(z)$

$$H(z) = \frac{F(z)}{B(z)} \tag{4.4.2}$$

Since $B(z)$ is minimal-phase, the indicated inverse $1/B(z)$ is guaranteed to be *stable and causal*. Let f_n be the impulse response of $F(z)$. Then, it satisfies the normal equations of the type of Eq. (4.3.6):

$$R_{x\epsilon}(n) = \sum_{i=0}^{\infty} f_i R_{\epsilon\epsilon}(n-i), \qquad n \geq 0 \tag{4.4.3}$$

Since $R_{\epsilon\epsilon}(n-i) = \sigma_\epsilon^2\,\delta(n-i)$, Eq. (4.4.3) collapses to

$$R_{x\epsilon}(n) = \sigma_\epsilon^2 f_n$$

or

$$f_n = R_{x\epsilon}(n)/\sigma_\epsilon^2, \qquad \text{for } n \geq 0 \tag{4.4.4}$$

Next, compute the corresponding z-transform $F(z)$

$$F(z) = \sum_{n=0}^{\infty} f_n z^{-n} = \sum_{n=0}^{\infty} R_{x\epsilon}(n) z^{-n}/\sigma_\epsilon^2 = [S_{x\epsilon}(z)]_+/\sigma_\epsilon^2 \tag{4.4.5}$$

where $[S_{x\epsilon}(z)]_+$ denotes the *causal part* of the double-sided z-transform $S_{x\epsilon}(z)$. Generally, the causal part of a z-transform

$$G(z) = \sum_{n=-\infty}^{\infty} g_n z^{-n}$$

is defined as

$$[G(z)]_+ = \sum_{n=0}^{\infty} g_n z^{-n}$$

The causal instruction in Eq. (4.4.5) was necessary since the above solution for f_n was valid only for $n \geq 0$. Since y_n is the output of the filter $B(z)$ driven by ϵ_n, it follows that

$$S_{xy}(z) = S_{x\epsilon}(z)B(z^{-1}) \qquad \text{or} \qquad S_{x\epsilon}(z) = S_{xy}(z)/B(z^{-1})$$

Combining Eqs. (4.4.2) and (4.4.5), we finally find

$$H(z) = \frac{1}{\sigma_\epsilon^2 B(z)} \left[\frac{S_{xy}(z)}{B(z^{-1})} \right]_+ \qquad \text{(Wiener filter)} \tag{4.4.6}$$

Thus, the construction of the optimal filter first requires spectral factorization of $S_{yy}(z)$ to obtain $B(z)$, and then use of the above formula. This is the optimal *realizable* Wiener filter based on the *infinite past*. If the causal instruction is ignored, one obtains the optimal *unrealizable* Wiener filter

$$H_{\text{unreal}}(z) = \frac{S_{xy}(z)}{\sigma_\epsilon^2 B(z) B(z^{-1})} = \frac{S_{xy}(z)}{S_{yy}(z)} \tag{4.4.7}$$

The *minimum value* of the *mean-squared estimation error* can be conveniently expressed by a contour integral, as follows

$$\begin{aligned} \mathcal{E} = E[e_n^2] &= E[e_n(x_n - \hat{x}_n)] = E[e_n x_n] - E[e_n \hat{x}_n] = E[e_n x_n] = R_{ex}(0) \\ &= \oint_{\text{u.c.}} S_{ex}(z)\, dz/2\pi jz = \oint_{\text{u.c.}} [S_{xx}(z) - S_{\hat{x}x}(z)]\, dz/2\pi jz \end{aligned}$$

or

$$\mathcal{E} = \oint_{\text{u.c.}} [S_{xx}(z) - H(z)S_{yx}(z)] \frac{dz}{2\pi jz} \tag{4.4.8}$$

4.5 *Wiener Filter Example*

This example, in addition to illustrating the above ideas, will also serve as a short introduction to *Kalman filtering*. It is desired to estimate the signal x_n on the basis of noisy observations

$$y_n = x_n + v_n,$$

where v_n is white noise of unit variance, $\sigma_v^2 = 1$, uncorrelated with x_n. The signal x_n is a first order Markov process, having a signal model

$$x_{n+1} = 0.6\, x_n + w_n$$

where w_n is white noise of variance $\sigma_w^2 = 0.82$.

Enough information is given above to compute the required power spectral densities $S_{xy}(z)$ and $S_{yy}(z)$. First we note that the signal generator transfer function for x_n is

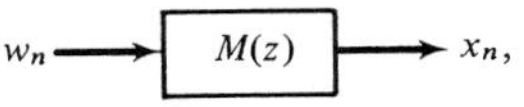

$$M(z) = \frac{1}{z - 0.6}$$

so that

$$S_{xx}(z) = \sigma_w^2 M(z) M(z^{-1}) = \frac{0.82}{(z - 0.6)(z^{-1} - 0.6)} = \frac{0.82}{(1 - 0.6z^{-1})(1 - 0.6z)}$$

Then we find

$$S_{xy}(z) = S_{x(x+v)} = S_{xx} + S_{xv} = S_{xx}(z) = \frac{0.82}{(1 - 0.6z^{-1})(1 - 0.6z)}$$

$$S_{yy}(z) = S_{(x+v)(x+v)} = S_{xx} + S_{xv} + S_{vx} + S_{vv} = S_{xx} + S_{vv}$$

$$= \frac{0.82}{(1 - 0.6z^{-1})(1 - 0.6z)} + 1 = \frac{0.82 + (1 - 0.6z^{-1})(1 - 0.6z)}{(1 - 0.6z^{-1})(1 - 0.6z)}$$

$$= \frac{2(1 - 0.3z^{-1})(1 - 0.3z)}{(1 - 0.6z^{-1})(1 - 0.6z)} = 2 \cdot \frac{1 - 0.3z^{-1}}{1 - 0.6z^{-1}} \cdot \frac{1 - 0.3z}{1 - 0.6z}$$

$$= \sigma_\epsilon^2 B(z) B(z^{-1})$$

Then according to Eq. (4.4.6), we must compute the causal part of

$$G(z) = \frac{S_{xy}(z)}{B(z^{-1})} = \frac{\dfrac{0.82}{(1 - 0.6z^{-1})(1 - 0.6z)}}{\dfrac{(1 - 0.3z)}{(1 - 0.6z)}} = \frac{0.82}{(1 - 0.6z^{-1})(1 - 0.3z)}$$

This may be done by partial fraction expansion, but the fastest way is to use the contour inversion formula to compute g_k, for $k \geqslant 0$, and then resum this series:

$$g_k = \oint_{\text{u.c.}} G(z)z^k \, dz/2\pi jz = \oint_{\text{u.c.}} \frac{0.82z^k}{(1 - 0.3z)(z - 0.6)} \frac{dz}{2\pi j}$$

$$= (\text{residue at } z = 0.6) = \frac{0.82(0.6)^k}{(1 - 0.3 \times 0.6)} = (0.6)^k, \qquad k \geqslant 0$$

Resumming, we find the required causal part

$$[G(z)]_+ = \frac{1}{1 - 0.6z^{-1}}$$

Finally, the optimal Wiener estimation filter is

$$H(z) = \frac{1}{\sigma_\epsilon^2 B(z)} \left[\frac{S_{xy}(z)}{B(z^{-1})} \right]_+ = \frac{[G(z)]_+}{\sigma_\epsilon^2 B(z)} = \frac{0.5}{1 - 0.3z^{-1}} \tag{4.5.1}$$

which can be realized as the difference equation

$$\hat{x}_n = 0.3\hat{x}_{n-1} + 0.5y_n, \tag{4.5.2}$$

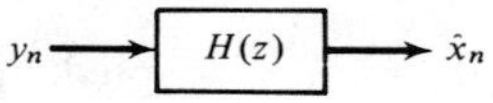

The estimation error is also easily computed using the contour formula of Eq. (4.4.8):

$$\mathcal{E} = E[e_n^2] = \oint_{\text{u.c.}} [S_{xx}(z) - H(z)S_{yx}(z)] \, dz/2\pi jz = 0.5$$

To appreciate the improvement afforded by filtering, this error must be compared with the error in case no processing is made and y_n is itself taken to represent a noisy estimate of x_n. The estimation error in the latter case is $y_n - x_n = v_n$, so that $\sigma_v^2 = 1$. Thus, the gain afforded by processing is

$$\frac{\sigma_e^2}{\sigma_v^2} = 0.5, \qquad \text{or} \qquad 3 \text{ dB}$$

4.6 *Wiener Filter as Kalman Filter*

We would like to cast this example in a Kalman filter form. The difference equation (4.5.2) for the Wiener filter seems to have the "wrong" state transition matrix; namely, 0.3 instead of 0.6, which is the state matrix for the state model of x_n. However, it is not accidental that the Wiener filter difference equation may be rewritten in the alternative form

$$\hat{x}_n = 0.6\hat{x}_{n-1} + 0.5(y_n - 0.6\hat{x}_{n-1})$$

The quantity $\hat{x}_n$ is the best estimate of x_n, at time n, based on all the observations up to that time; that is, $Y_n = \{y_i;\ -\infty < i \leq n\}$. To simplify the subsequent notation, we denote it by $\hat{x}_{n/n}$. It is the projection of x_n on the space Y_n. Similarly, $\hat{x}_{n-1}$ denotes the best estimate of x_{n-1} based on the observations up to time $n - 1$; that is, $Y_{n-1} = \{y_i;\ i \leq n - 1\}$. The above filtering equation is written in this notation as

$$\hat{x}_{n/n} = 0.6\hat{x}_{n-1/n-1} + 0.5(y_n - 0.6\hat{x}_{n-1/n-1}) \tag{4.6.1}$$

It allows the computation of the *current best* estimate $\hat{x}_{n/n}$ in terms of the *previous best* estimate $\hat{x}_{n-1/n-1}$ and the new observation y_n that becomes available at the current time instant n.

The various terms of Eq. (4.6.1) have nice interpretations: Suppose that the best estimate $\hat{x}_{n-1/n-1}$ of the previous sample x_{n-1} is available. Even before the next observation y_n comes in, we may use this estimate to make a reasonable prediction as to what the next best estimate ought to be. Since we know the system dynamics of x_n, we may try to "boost" $\hat{x}_{n-1/n-1}$ to the next time instant n according to the system dynamics; that is, we take

$$\hat{x}_{n/n-1} = 0.6\hat{x}_{n-1/n-1} = \text{prediction of } x_n \text{ on the basis of } Y_{n-1} \tag{4.6.2}$$

Since $y_n = x_n + v_n$, we may use this prediction of x_n to make a prediction of the next measurement y_n; that is, we take

$$\hat{y}_{n/n-1} = \hat{x}_{n/n-1} = \text{prediction of } y_n \text{ on the basis of } Y_{n-1} \tag{4.6.3}$$

If this prediction were perfect, and if the next observation y_n were noise free, then this would be the value that we would observe. Since we actually observe y_n, the observation or innovations residual will be

$$\alpha_n = y_n - \hat{y}_{n/n-1} = \text{innovations residual} \tag{4.6.4}$$

This quantity represents that part of y_n that *cannot* be predicted on the basis of the previous observations Y_{n-1}. It represents the truly new information contained in the observation y_n. Actually, if we are making the best prediction possible, then the most we can expect of our prediction is to make the innovations residual a white-noise (uncorrelated) signal; that is, if we make the best possible prediction, then what remains should be unpredictable. According to the general discussion of the relationship between signal models and linear prediction given in Section 1.16, it follows that if $\hat{y}_{n/n-1}$ is the best predictor of y_n then α_n must be the whitening sequence that drives the signal model of y_n. We shall verify this fact shortly. This establishes an intimate connection between the *Wiener/Kalman filtering* problem and the *signal modeling* problem. If we overestimate the observation y_n, the innovation residual will be negative; and if we underestimate it, the residual will be positive. In either case, we would like to correct our tentative estimate in the right direction. This may be accomplished by

$$\begin{aligned} \hat{x}_{n/n} &= \hat{x}_{n/n-1} + G(y_n - \hat{y}_{n/n-1}) \\ &= 0.6\hat{x}_{n-1/n-1} + G(y_n - 0.6\hat{x}_{n-1/n-1}) \end{aligned} \tag{4.6.5}$$

where the gain G, known as the *Kalman gain*, should be a positive quantity. The *prediction/correction* procedure defined by Eqs. (4.6.2) through (4.6.5) is known as the *Kalman filter*. It should be clear that any value for the gain G will provide an estimate, even if suboptimal, of x_n. Our solution for the Wiener filter has precisely the above structure of a Kalman filter; but it has a gain $G = 0.5$. This value for the gain is the "best" possible, or optimal, value. It is a very instructive exercise to show this in two ways: First, with G arbitrary, the estimation filter of Eq. (4.6.5) has transfer function

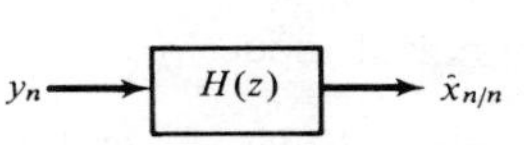

$$H(z) = \frac{G}{1 - 0.6(1 - G)z^{-1}}$$

Insert this expression into the mean-squared estimation error $\mathcal{E} = E[e_n^2]$, where $e_n = x_n - \hat{x}_{n/n}$, and minimize it with respect to the parameter G. This should give $G = 0.5$.

Alternatively, G should be such that to *render* the innovations residual (4.6.4) a white noise signal. In requiring this, it is useful to use the spectral factorization model for y_n; that is, the fact that y_n is the output of $B(z)$ when driven by the white noise signal ϵ_n. Let us work with z-transforms

$$\begin{aligned} \alpha(z) &= Y(z) - 0.6z^{-1}\hat{X}(z) = Y(z) - 0.6z^{-1}H(z)Y(z) \\ &= \left[1 - 0.6z^{-1}\frac{G}{1 - 0.6(1 - G)z^{-1}}\right]Y(z) \\ &= \left[\frac{1 - 0.6z^{-1}}{1 - 0.6(1 - G)z^{-1}}\right]Y(z) \\ &= \left[\frac{1 - 0.6z^{-1}}{1 - 0.6(1 - G)z^{-1}}\right]\left[\frac{1 - 0.3z^{-1}}{1 - 0.6z^{-1}}\right]\epsilon(z) \\ &= \frac{1 - 0.3z^{-1}}{1 - 0.6(1 - G)z^{-1}}\epsilon(z) \end{aligned}$$

Since ϵ_n is white, it follows that the transfer function relationship between α_n and ϵ_n must be trivial; otherwise, there will be sequential correlations present in α_n. Thus, we must have $0.6(1 - G) = 0.3$, or $G = 0.5$; and in this case, $\alpha_n = \epsilon_n$. It is also possible to set $0.6(1 - G) = 1/0.3$, but this would correspond to an unstable filter.

We have obtained a most interesting result; namely, that when the Wiener filtering problem is recast into its Kalman filter form given by Eq. (4.6.1), then the innovations residual α_n, which is computable on line with the estimate $\hat{x}_{n/n}$, is *identical* to the whitening sequence ϵ_n of the signal model of y_n. In other words, the Kalman filter can be thought of as *the whitening filter* for the *observation signal* y_n.

To appreciate further the connection between Wiener and Kalman filters and between Kalman filters and the whitening filters of signal models, we consider a generalized version of the above example and cast it in standard Kalman filter notation.

It is desired to estimate x_n from y_n. The signal model for x_n is taken to be first-order Markov model

$$x_{n+1} = ax_n + w_n \qquad \text{(state model)} \tag{4.6.6}$$

with $|a| < 1$. The observation signal y_n is related to x_n by

$$y_n = cx_n + v_n \qquad \text{(measurement model)} \tag{4.6.7}$$

It is further assumed that the state and measurement noises, w_n and v_n, are zero-mean, mutually uncorrelated, white noises of variances Q and R, respectively; that is,

$$E[w_n w_i] = Q\delta_{ni}, \qquad E[v_n v_i] = R\delta_{ni}, \qquad E[w_n v_i] = 0 \tag{4.6.8}$$

We also assume that v_n is uncorrelated with x_n. The parameters a,c,Q,R are assumed to be known. Let $x_1(n)$ be the signal defined by

$$x_1(n) = x_{n+1}$$

and consider the two related Wiener filtering problems of estimating x_n and $x_1(n)$ on the basis of $Y_n = \{y_i;\ -\infty < i \leq n\}$, depicted below

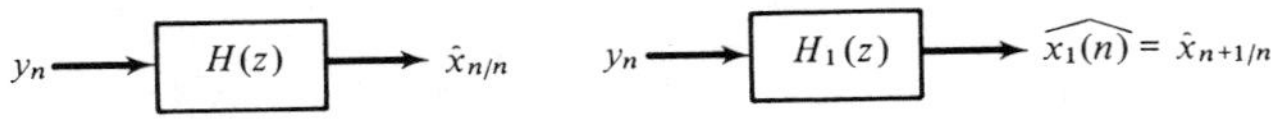

The problem of estimating $x_1(n) = x_{n+1}$ is equivalent to the problem of *one-step prediction* into the future on the basis of the past and present. Therefore, we will denote this estimate by $\widehat{x_1(n)} = \hat{x}_{n+1/n}$. The state equation (4.6.6) determines the spectral density of x_n:

$$S_{xx}(z) = S_{ww}(z)\frac{1}{(z-a)(z^{-1}-a)} = \frac{Q}{(1-az^{-1})(1-az)}$$

The observation equation (4.6.7) determines the cross-densities

$$S_{xy}(z) = cS_{xx}(z) + S_{xv}(z) = cS_{xx}(z)$$

$$S_{x_1y}(z) = zS_{xy}(z) = zcS_{xx}(z)$$

where we used the filtering equation $X_1(z) = zX(z)$. The spectral density of y_n can be factored as follows:

$$S_{yy}(z) = c^2 S_{xx}(z) + S_{vv}(z) = \frac{c^2 Q}{(1 - az^{-1})(1 - az)} + R$$

$$= \frac{c^2 Q + R(1 - az^{-1})(1 - az)}{(1 - az^{-1})(1 - az)} = \sigma_\epsilon^2 \left(\frac{1 - fz^{-1}}{1 - az^{-1}}\right)\left(\frac{1 - fz}{1 - az}\right)$$

where f and σ_ϵ^2 satisfy the equations

$$\sigma_\epsilon^2 f = Ra \tag{4.6.9}$$

$$\sigma_\epsilon^2(1 + f^2) = c^2 Q + R(1 + a^2) \tag{4.6.10}$$

and f has magnitude less than one. Thus, the corresponding signal model for y_n is the filter

$$B(z) = \frac{1 - fz^{-1}}{1 - az^{-1}} \tag{4.6.11}$$

Next, we compute the causal parts as required by Eq. (4.4.6):

$$[S_{xy}(z)/B(z^{-1})]_+ = \left[\frac{cQ}{(1 - az^{-1})(1 - fz)}\right]_+ = \frac{cQ}{1 - fa}\,\frac{1}{1 - az^{-1}}$$

$$[S_{x_1y}(z)/B(z^{-1})]_+ = \left[\frac{cQz}{(1 - az^{-1})(1 - fz)}\right]_+ = \frac{cQa}{1 - fa}\,\frac{1}{1 - az^{-1}}$$

Using Eq. (4.4.6), we determine the optimal Wiener filters $H(z)$ and $H_1(z)$ as follows:

$$H(z) = \frac{1}{\sigma_\epsilon^2 B(z)}\left[\frac{S_{xy}(z)}{B(z^{-1})}\right]_+ = \frac{\dfrac{cQ/(1 - fa)}{(1 - az^{-1})}}{\sigma_\epsilon^2\left(\dfrac{1 - fz^{-1}}{1 - az^{-1}}\right)} = \frac{\left(\dfrac{cQ}{\sigma_\epsilon^2(1 - fa)}\right)}{1 - fz^{-1}}$$

Or, defining the gain G by

$$G = \frac{cQ}{\sigma_\epsilon^2(1 - fa)} \tag{4.6.12}$$

we finally find

$$H(z) = \frac{G}{1 - fz^{-1}} \tag{4.6.13}$$

$$H_1(z) = aH(z) = \frac{K}{1 - fz^{-1}} \tag{4.6.14}$$

where in Eq. (4.6.14) we defined a related gain, also called the Kalman gain, as follows:

$$K = aG = \frac{acQ}{\sigma_\epsilon^2(1 - fa)} \tag{4.6.15}$$

Eq. (4.6.14) immediately implies that

$$\hat{x}_{n+1/n} = a\hat{x}_{n/n} \tag{4.6.16}$$

which is the precise justification of Eq. (4.6.2). The difference equations of the two filters are

$$\begin{aligned} \hat{x}_{n+1/n} &= f\hat{x}_{n/n-1} + Ky_n \\ \hat{x}_{n/n} &= f\hat{x}_{n-1/n-1} + Gy_n \end{aligned} \tag{4.6.17}$$

Using the results of Problem 3.7, we may express all the quantities f, σ_ϵ^2, K, and G in terms of a single positive quantity P which satisfies the *algebraic Riccati* equation:

$$Q = P - \frac{PRa^2}{R + c^2P} \tag{4.6.18}$$

Then, we find the interrelationships

$$K = aG = \frac{acP}{R + c^2P}, \qquad \sigma_\epsilon^2 = R + c^2P,$$

$$f = a - cK = \frac{Ra}{R + c^2P} \tag{4.6.19}$$

It is left as an exercise to show that the minimized mean-squared estimation errors are given in terms of P by

$$E[e_{n/n-1}^2] = P, \qquad E[e_{n/n}^2] = \frac{PR}{R + c^2P}$$

where

$$e_{n/n-1} = x_n - \hat{x}_{n/n-1} \qquad \text{and} \qquad e_{n/n} = x_n - \hat{x}_{n/n}$$

are the corresponding estimation errors for the optimally predicted and filtered estimates, respectively.

Using Eq. (4.6.19), we may rewrite the filtering equation (4.6.17) as

$$\hat{x}_{n+1/n} = (a - cK)\,\hat{x}_{n/n-1} + Ky_n$$

or

$$\hat{x}_{n+1/n} = a\hat{x}_{n/n-1} + K(y_n - c\hat{x}_{n/n-1}) \tag{4.6.20}$$

or

$$\hat{x}_{n+1/n} = a\hat{x}_{n/n-1} + K(y_n - \hat{y}_{n/n-1})$$

where we set

$$\hat{y}_{n/n-1} = c\hat{x}_{n/n-1} \tag{4.6.21}$$

A realization of the estimation filter based on (4.6.20) is shown below:

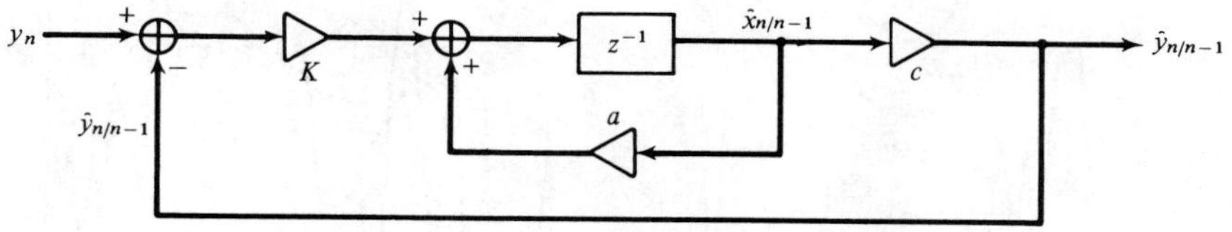

Inserting $K = aG$ and using Eq. (4.6.16) we also find

$$\hat{x}_{n/n} = \hat{x}_{n/n-1} + G(y_n - \hat{y}_{n/n-1}) \tag{4.6.22}$$

The quantity $\hat{y}_{n/n-1}$ defined in Eq. (4.6.21) is the best estimate of y_n based on its past Y_{n-1}. This can be seen in two ways: First, using the results of Problem 1.8 on the linearity of the estimates, we find

$$\hat{y}_{n/n-1} = \widehat{cx_n + v_n} = c\hat{x}_{n/n-1} + \hat{v}_{n/n-1} = c\hat{x}_{n/n-1}$$

where the term $\hat{v}_{n/n-1}$ was dropped. This term represents the estimate of v_n on the basis of the past ys; that is, Y_{n-1}. Since v_n is white and also uncorrelated with x_n, it follows that it will be uncorrelated with all past ys; therefore, $\hat{v}_{n/n-1} = 0$. The second way to show that $\hat{y}_{n/n-1}$ is the best prediction of y_n is to show that the innovations residual

$$\alpha_n = y_n - \hat{y}_{n/n-1} = y_n - c\hat{x}_{n/n-1} \tag{4.6.23}$$

is a white-noise sequence and coincides with the whitening sequence ϵ_n of y_n. Indeed, working in the z-domain and using Eq. (4.6.17) and the signal model of y_n we find

$$\begin{aligned}
\alpha(z) &= Y(z) - cz^{-1}\hat{X}_1(z) = Y(z) - cz^{-1}H_1(z)Y(z) \\
&= \left[1 - cz^{-1}\frac{K}{1 - fz^{-1}}\right]Y(z) = \left[\frac{1 - (f + cK)z^{-1}}{1 - fz^{-1}}\right]Y(z) \\
&= \left[\frac{1 - az^{-1}}{1 - fz^{-1}}\right]Y(z) = \frac{1}{B(z)}\,Y(z) = \epsilon(z)
\end{aligned}$$

which implies that

$$\alpha_n = \epsilon_n$$

Finally, we note that the recursive updating of the estimate of x_n given by Eq. (4.6.22) is identical to the result of Problem 1.12.

Our purpose in presenting this example was to tie together a number of ideas from Chapter 1 (correlation canceling, estimation, Gram-Schmidt orthogonalization, linear prediction, and signal modeling) to ideas from this chapter on

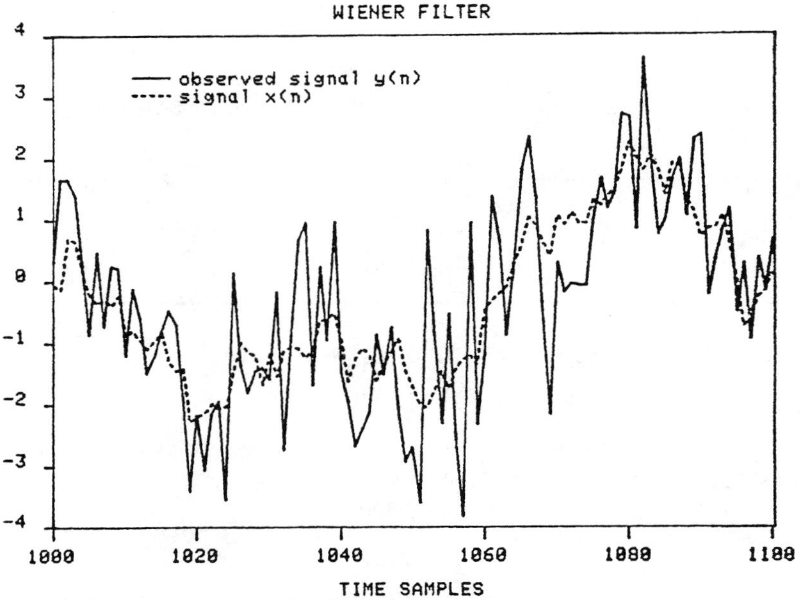

Figure 4.2 Desired Signal and Its Noisy Observation

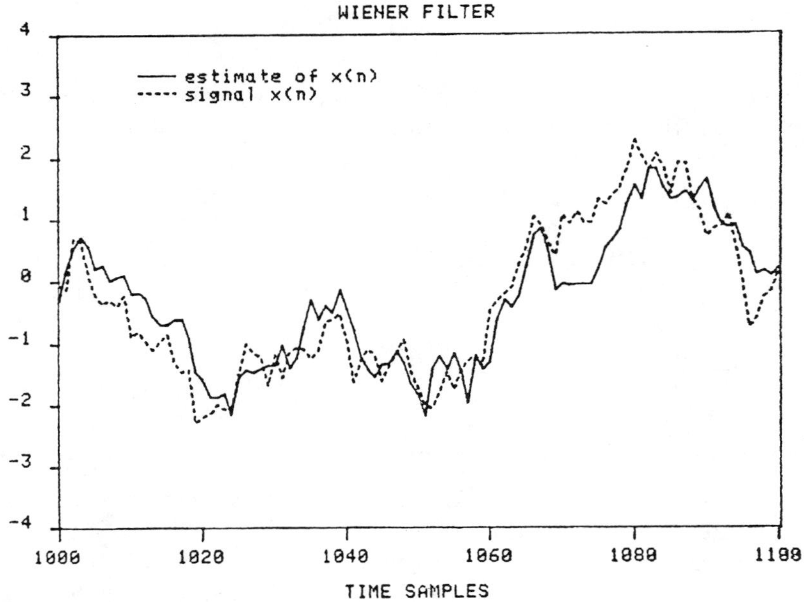

Figure 4.3 Best Estimate of Desired Signal

Wiener filtering and its recursive reformulation as a Kalman filter [8–10, 12–18].

We conclude this section by presenting a simulation of this example defined by the following choice of parameters:

$$a = 0.95, \qquad c = 1, \qquad Q = 1 - a^2, \qquad R = 1$$

the above choice for Q normalizes the variance of x_n to unity. Solving the Riccati equation (4.6.18) and using Eq. (4.6.19), we find

$$P = 0.312, \qquad K = 0.226, \qquad G = 0.238, \qquad f = a - cK = 0.724$$

Figure 4.2 shows 100 samples of the observed signal $y(n)$ together with the desired signal $x(n)$. The signal $y(n)$ processed through the Wiener filter $H(z)$ defined by the above parameters is shown in Fig. 4.3 together with $x(n)$. The tracking properties of the filter are evident from the graph. It should be emphasized that this is the best one can do by means of ordinary causal linear filtering!

4.7 *Construction of the Wiener Filter by the Gapped Function*

Next, we would like to give an alternative construction of the optimal Wiener filter based on the concept of the gapped function. The gapped function is especially useful in linear prediction. It is defined as the cross-correlation between the estimation error e_n and the observation sequence y_n as follows:

$$g(k) = R_{ey}(k) = E[e_n y_{n-k}] \qquad \text{for all } k \tag{4.7.1}$$

This definition is motivated by the orthogonality equations which state that the prediction error e_n must be orthogonal to all of the available observations; namely, $Y_n = \{y_i;\ -\infty < i \leqslant n\}$. That is, for the optimal set of filter weights we have

$$g(k) = R_{ey}(k) = E[e_n y_{n-k}] = 0, \qquad \text{for } k \geqslant 0 \tag{4.7.2}$$

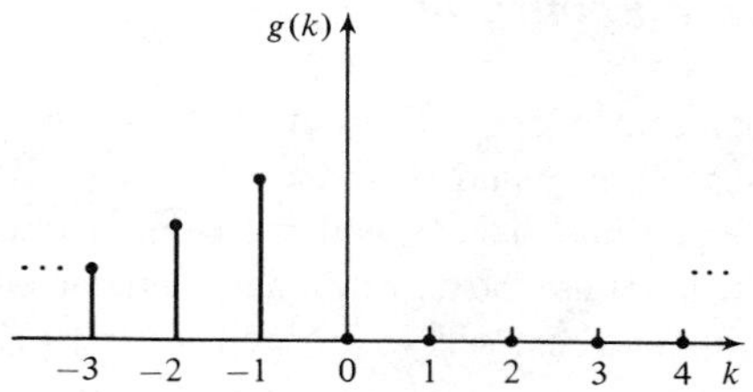

and $g(k)$ develops a right-hand gap. On the other hand, $g(k)$ may be written in the alternative form

$$g(k) = E[e_n y_{n-k}] = E\left[\left(x_n - \sum_{i=0}^{\infty} h_i y_{n-i}\right) y_{n-k}\right]$$

$$= R_{xy}(k) - \sum_{i=0}^{\infty} h_i R_{yy}(k-i)$$

or

$$g(k) = R_{ey}(k) = R_{xy}(k) - \sum_{i=0}^{\infty} h_i R_{yy}(k-i) \tag{4.7.3}$$

Taking z-transforms we find

$$G(z) = S_{xy}(z) - H(z)S_{yy}(z)$$

Due to the gap conditions, the left-hand side contains only positive powers of z, whereas the right-hand side contains both positive and negative powers of z. Thus, the nonpositive powers of z must drop out of the right side. This condition precisely determines $H(z)$. Introducing the spectral factorization of $S_{yy}(z)$ and dividing both sides by $B(z^{-1})$ we find

$$G(z) = S_{xy}(z) - H(z)S_{yy}(z) = S_{xy}(z) - H(z)B(z)B(z^{-1})\sigma_\epsilon^2$$

$$\frac{G(z)}{B(z^{-1})} = \frac{S_{xy}(z)}{B(z^{-1})} - H(z)B(z)\sigma_\epsilon^2$$

The z-transform $B(z^{-1})$ is anticausal and, because of the gap conditions, so is the ratio $G(z)/B(z^{-1})$. Therefore, taking causal parts of both sides we find

$$0 = \left[\frac{S_{xy}(z)}{B(z^{-1})}\right]_+ - H(z)B(z)\sigma_\epsilon^2$$

which can be solved for $H(z)$ to give Eq. (4.4.6).

4.8 *Construction of the Wiener Filter by Covariance Factorization*

In this section, we present a generalization of the gapped-function method to the more general nonstationary and/or finite-past Wiener filter. This is defined by the Wiener-Hopf equations (4.2.7), which are equivalent to the orthogonality equations (4.2.5). The latter are the nonstationary versions of the gapped function of the previous section. The best way to proceed is to cast Eqs. (4.2.5) in matrix form as follows: Without loss of generality we may take the starting point $n_a = 0$. The final point n_b is left arbitrary. Introduce the vectors

$$\mathbf{x} = \begin{bmatrix} x_0 \\ x_1 \\ \vdots \\ x_{n_b} \end{bmatrix} \qquad \mathbf{y} = \begin{bmatrix} y_0 \\ y_1 \\ \vdots \\ y_{n_b} \end{bmatrix}$$

and the corresponding correlation matrices

$$R_{xy} = E[\mathbf{x}\mathbf{y}^T] \qquad \text{and} \qquad R_{yy} = E[\mathbf{y}\mathbf{y}^T]$$

The filtering equation (4.2.4) may be written in vector form as

$$\hat{\mathbf{x}} = H\mathbf{y} \tag{4.8.1}$$

where H is the matrix of optimal weights $\{h(n,i)\}$. The *causality* of the filtering operation (4.8.1), requires H to be *lower-triangular*. The minimization problem becomes equivalent to the problem of minimizing the mean-squared estimation error subject to the constraint that H be lower-triangular. The minimization conditions are the normal equations (4.2.5) which, in this matrix notation, state that the matrix R_{ey} has no lower-triangular (causal) part; or, equivalently, that R_{ey} is *strictly* upper-triangular (i.e., even the main diagonal of R_{ey} is zero), therefore

$$R_{ey} = \text{strictly upper triangular} \tag{4.8.2}$$

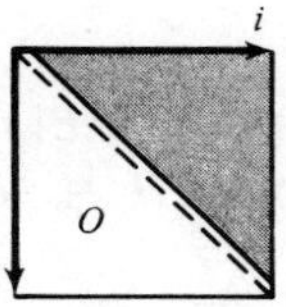

Inserting Eq. (4.8.1) into R_{ey} we find

$$R_{ey} = E[\mathbf{e}\mathbf{y}^T] = E[(\mathbf{x} - H\mathbf{y})\mathbf{y}^T]$$

or

$$R_{ey} = R_{xy} - HR_{yy} \tag{4.8.3}$$

The minimization conditions (4.8.2) require H to be that lower-triangular matrix which renders the combination (4.8.3) upper-triangular. In other words, H should be such that the lower triangular part of the right hand side must vanish. To solve Eqs. (4.8.2) and (4.8.3), we introduce the *LU Cholesky factorization* of the covariance matrix R_{yy} given by

$$R_{yy} = BR_{\epsilon\epsilon}B^T \tag{4.8.4}$$

where B is unit *lower*-triangular, and $R_{\epsilon\epsilon}$ is diagonal. This was discussed in Section 1.5. Inserting in Eq. (4.8.3) we find

$$R_{ey} = R_{xy} - HBR_{\epsilon\epsilon}B^T \tag{4.8.5}$$

Multiplying by the inverse transpose of B we obtain

$$R_{ey}B^{-T} = R_{xy}B^{-T} - HBR_{\epsilon\epsilon} \tag{4.8.6}$$

Now, the matrix B^{-T} is unit upper-triangular, but R_{ey} is *strictly* upper, therefore, the product $R_{ey}B^{-T}$ will be strictly upper. This can be verified easily for any two such matrices. Extracting the lower-triangular parts of both sides of Eq. (4.8.6) we find

$$0 = [R_{xy}B^{-T}]_+ - HBR_{\epsilon\epsilon}$$

where we used the fact that the left-hand side was strictly upper and that the term $HBR_{\epsilon\epsilon}$ was already lower-triangular. The notation $[\ ]_+$ denotes the lower-triangular part of a matrix including the diagonal. We find finally

$$H = [R_{xy}B^{-T}]_+ R_{\epsilon\epsilon}^{-1}B^{-1} \tag{4.8.7}$$

This is the most general solution of the Wiener filtering problem [18,19]. It includes the results of the stationary case, as a special case. Indeed, if all the signals are stationary, then the matrices R_{xy} and B and B^T become Toeplitz and have a z-transform associated with them as discussed in Problem 3.8. Using the results of that problem, it is easily seen that Eq. (4.8.7) is the *time domain analog* of Eq. (4.4.6).

The prewhitening approach of Section 4.4 can also be understood in the present matrix framework. Making the change of variables

$$\mathbf{y} = B\boldsymbol{\epsilon}$$

we find that $R_{xy} = E[\mathbf{x}\mathbf{y}^T] = E[\mathbf{x}\boldsymbol{\epsilon}^T]B^T = R_{x\epsilon}B^T$, and therefore $R_{xy}B^{-T} = R_{x\epsilon}$, and the filter H becomes $H = [R_{x\epsilon}]_+R_{\epsilon\epsilon}^{-1}B^{-1}$. The corresponding estimate is then

$$\hat{\mathbf{x}} = H\mathbf{y} = HB\boldsymbol{\epsilon} = F\boldsymbol{\epsilon}, \qquad \text{where} \qquad F = HB = [R_{x\epsilon}]_+R_{\epsilon\epsilon}^{-1} \tag{4.8.8}$$

This is the matrix analog of Eq. (4.4.5). The matrix F is lower-triangular by construction. Therefore, to extract the nth component $\hat{x}_n$ of Eq. (4.8.8), it is enough to consider the *nxn* submatrices as shown below:

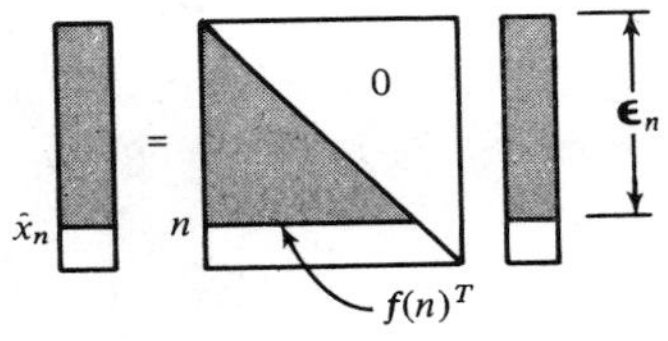

The nth row of F is $\mathbf{f}(n)^T = E[x_n\boldsymbol{\epsilon}_n^T]E[\boldsymbol{\epsilon}_n\boldsymbol{\epsilon}_n^T]^{-1}$. Therefore, the nth estimate becomes

$$\hat{x}_n = E[x_n\boldsymbol{\epsilon}_n^T]E[\boldsymbol{\epsilon}_n\boldsymbol{\epsilon}_n^T]^{-1}\boldsymbol{\epsilon}_n$$

which may also be written in the recursive form

$$\hat{x}_{n/n} = \sum_{i=0}^{n} E[x_n\epsilon_i]E[\epsilon_i\epsilon_i]^{-1}\epsilon_i = \sum_{i=0}^{n-1} E[x_n\epsilon_i]E[\epsilon_i\epsilon_i]^{-1}\epsilon_i + G_n\epsilon_n$$

or

$$\hat{x}_{n/n} = \hat{x}_{n/n-1} + G_n\epsilon_n \tag{4.8.9}$$

where we made an obvious change in notation, and $G_n = E[x_n\epsilon_n]E[\epsilon_n\epsilon_n]^{-1}$. This is identical to Eq. (4.6.22); in the stationary case, G_n is a constant independent of n. We can also recast the nth estimate in "batch" form, expressed directly in terms of the observation vector $\mathbf{y}_n = [y_0, y_1, \ldots, y_n]^T$. By considering the nxn subblock part of the Gram-Schmidt construction, we may write $\mathbf{y}_n = B_n\boldsymbol{\epsilon}_n$, where B_n is unit lower-triangular. Then, $\hat{x}_n$ can be expressed as

$$\hat{x}_n = E[x_n\boldsymbol{\epsilon}_n^T]E[\boldsymbol{\epsilon}_n\boldsymbol{\epsilon}_n^T]^{-1}\boldsymbol{\epsilon}_n = E[x_n\mathbf{y}_n^T]E[\mathbf{y}_n\mathbf{y}_n^T]^{-1}\mathbf{y}_n$$

which is identical to Eq. (4.2.8).

4.9 *The Kalman Filter*

The Kalman filter formulation of Section 4.6 and its equivalence to the Wiener filter was based on the asymptotic Kalman filter for which the observations were available from the infinite past to the present, namely, $\{y_m; -\infty < m \leq n\}$. In Section 4.7, we solved the most general Wiener filtering problem based on the *finite* past for which the observation space was

$$Y_n = \{y_0, y_1, \cdots, y_n\} \tag{4.9.1}$$

Here, we recast these results in a time-recursive form and obtain the time-varying Kalman filter for estimating x_n based on the finite observation subspace Y_n. We also discuss its asymptotic properties for large n and show that it converges to the steady-state Kalman filter of Section 4.6.

Our discussion is based on Eq. (4.8.9), which is essentially the starting point in Kalman's original derivation [13]. To make Eq. (4.8.9) truly recursive, we must have a means of recursively computing the required gain G_n from one time instant to the next. As in Section 4.8, we denote by $\hat{x}_{n/n}$ and $\hat{x}_{n/n-1}$ the optimal estimates of x_n based on the observation subspaces Y_n and Y_{n-1} defined in Eq. (4.9.1), with the initial condition $\hat{x}_{0/-1} = 0$. Iterating the state and measurement models (4.6.6) and (4.6.7) starting at $n = 0$, we obtain the following two results, previously derived for the steady-state case

$$\hat{x}_{n+1/n} = a\hat{x}_{n/n}, \quad \hat{y}_{n/n-1} = c\hat{x}_{n/n-1} \tag{4.9.2}$$

The proof of both is based on the linearity property of estimates; for example,

$$\hat{x}_{n+1/n} = \widehat{ax_n + w_n} = a\hat{x}_{n/n} + \hat{w}_{n/n} = a\hat{x}_{n/n}$$

where $\hat{w}_{n/n}$ was set to zero because w_n does not depend on any of the observations Y_n. This is seen as follows. The iteration of the state Eq. (4.6.6) leads to the expression $x_n = a^n x_0 + a^{n-1}w_0 + a^{n-2}w_1 + \cdots + aw_{n-2} + w_{n-1}$. It follows from this and Eq. (4.6.7) that the observation subspace Y_n will depend only on

$$\{x_0, w_0, w_1, \cdots, w_{n-1}, v_0, v_1, \cdots, v_n\}$$

Making the additional assumption that x_0 is uncorrelated with w_n, it follows that w_n will be uncorrelated with all random variables in the above set, and thus, with Y_n. The second part of Eq. (4.9.2) is shown by similar arguments. Next, we develop the recursions for the gain G_n. Using Eq. (4.8.9), the estimation and prediction errors may be related as follows

$$e_{n/n} = x_n - \hat{x}_{n/n} = x_n - \hat{x}_{n/n-1} - G_n\epsilon_n = e_{n/n-1} - G_n\epsilon_n$$

Taking the correlation of both sides with x_n, we find

$$E[e_{n/n}x_n] = E[e_{n/n-1}x_n] - G_nE[\epsilon_n x_n] \tag{4.9.3}$$

Using the orthogonality properties $E[e_{n/n}\hat{x}_{n/n}] = 0$ and $E[e_{n/n-1}\hat{x}_{n/n-1}] = 0$, which follow from the optimality of the two estimates $\hat{x}_{n/n}$ and $\hat{x}_{n/n-1}$, we can write the mean square estimation and prediction errors as

$$P_{n/n} = E[e^2_{n/n}] = E[e_{n/n}x_n], \qquad P_{n/n-1} = E[e^2_{n/n-1}] = E[e_{n/n-1}x_n] \tag{4.9.4}$$

We find also

$$\epsilon_n = y_n - \hat{y}_{n/n-1} = (c\,x_n + v_n) - c\,\hat{x}_{n/n-1} = ce_{n/n-1} + v_n$$

Using the fact that $e_{n/n-1}$ depends only on x_n and Y_{n-1}, it follows that the two terms in the right-hand side are uncorrelated with each other. Thus,

$$E[\epsilon_n^2] = c^2E[e^2_{n/n-1}] + E[v_n^2] = c^2P_{n/n-1} + R \tag{4.9.5}$$

also

$$E[\epsilon_n x_n] = cE[e_{n/n-1}x_n] + E[v_nx_n] = cP_{n/n-1} \tag{4.9.6}$$

Therefore, the gain G_n is computable by

$$G_n = \frac{E[\epsilon_n x_n]}{E[\epsilon_n^2]} = \frac{cP_{n/n-1}}{R + cP_{n/n-1}} \tag{4.9.7}$$

Using Eqs. (4.9.4), (4.9.6), and (4.9.7) into Eq. (4.9.3), we obtain

$$P_{n/n} = P_{n/n-1} - G_ncP_{n/n-1} = P_{n/n-1} - \frac{c^2P^2_{n/n-1}}{R + c^2P_{n/n-1}} \tag{4.9.8}$$

The subtracted term represents the *improvement* in estimating x_n using $\hat{x}_{n/n}$ over using $\hat{x}_{n/n-1}$. Equations (4.9.5), (4.9.7), and (4.9.8) admit a nice geometrical interpretation [20]. The two right-hand side terms in $\epsilon_n = ce_{n/n-1} + v_n$ are orthogonal and can be represented by the orthogonal triangle

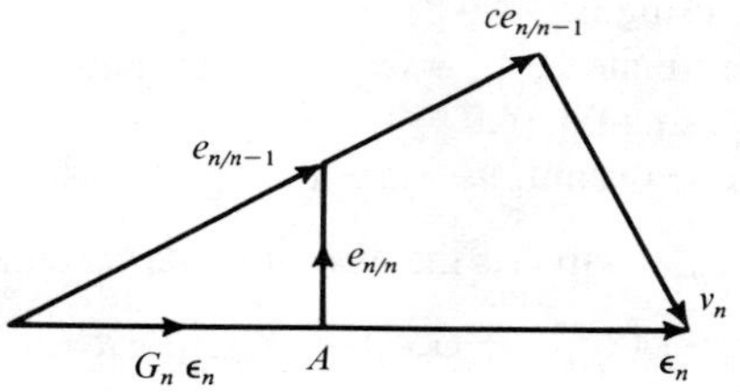

where the prediction error $e_{n/n-1}$ has been scaled up by the factor c. Thus, Eq. (4.9.5) is the statement of the Pythagorean theorem for this triangle. Next, write the equation $e_{n/n} = e_{n/n-1} - G_n\epsilon_n$ as

$$e_{n/n-1} = e_{n/n} + G_n\epsilon_n$$

Because $e_{n/n}$ is orthogonal to all the observations in Y_n and ϵ_n is a linear combination of the same observations, it follows that the two terms in the right-hand side will be orthogonal. Thus, $e_{n/n-1}$ may be resolved in two orthogonal parts, one being in the direction of ϵ_n. This is represented by the smaller orthogonal triangle in the previous diagram. Clearly, the length of the side $e_{n/n}$ is minimized at right angles at point A. It follows from the similarity of the two orthogonal triangles that

$$\frac{G_n\sqrt{E[\epsilon_n^2]}}{\sqrt{E[e_{n/n-1}^2]}} = \frac{c\sqrt{E[e_{n/n-1}^2]}}{\sqrt{E[\epsilon_n^2]}}$$

which is equivalent to Eq. (4.9.7). Finally, the Pythagorean theorem applied to the smaller triangle implies $E[e_{n/n-1}^2] = E[e_{n/n}^2] + G_n^2 E[\epsilon_n^2]$, which is equivalent to Eq. (4.9.8).

To obtain a truly recursive scheme, we need next to find a relationship between $P_{n/n}$ and the next prediction error $P_{n+1/n}$. It is found as follows. From the state model (4.6.6) and (4.9.2), we have

$$e_{n+1/n} = x_{n+1} - \hat{x}_{n+1/n} = (a x_n + w_n) - a\hat{x}_{n/n} = a\,e_{n/n} + w_n$$

Because $e_{n/n}$ depends only on x_n and Y_n, it follows that the two terms in the right-hand side will be uncorrelated. Therefore, $E[e_{n+1/n}^2] = a^2E[e_{n/n}^2] + E[w_n^2]$, or,

$$P_{n+1/n} = a^2P_{n/n} + Q \qquad (4.9.9)$$

The first term corresponds to the *propagation* of the estimate $\hat{x}_{n/n}$ forward in time according to the system dynamics; the second term represents the *worsening* of the estimate due to the presence of the dynamical noise w_n. The Kalman filter algorithm is now complete. It is summarized below:

0. Initialize by $\hat{x}_{0/-1} = 0$ and $P_{0/-1} = E[x_0^2]$
1. At time n, $\hat{x}_{n/n-1}$, $P_{n/n-1}$, and the new measurement y_n are available
2. Compute $\hat{y}_{n/n-1} = c\hat{x}_{n/n-1}$, $\epsilon_n = y_n - \hat{y}_{n/n-1}$, and the gain G_n using Eq. (4.9.7)
3. Correct the predicted estimate $\hat{x}_{n/n} = \hat{x}_{n/n-1} + G_n\epsilon_n$ and compute its mean square error $P_{n/n}$ using Eq. (4.9.8)
4. Predict the next estimate $\hat{x}_{n+1/n} = a\hat{x}_{n/n}$ and compute the mean square prediction error $P_{n+1/n}$ using Eq. (4.9.9)
5. Go to the next time instant, $n \rightarrow n+1$

The optimal predictor $\hat{x}_{n/n-1}$ satisfies the *Kalman filtering* equation

$$\hat{x}_{n+1/n} = a\hat{x}_{n/n} = a(\hat{x}_{n/n-1} + G_n\epsilon_n) = a\hat{x}_{n/n-1} + aG_n(y_n - c\hat{x}_{n/n-1})$$

or,

$$\hat{x}_{n+1/n} = f_n \hat{x}_{n/n-1} + K_n y_n \tag{4.9.10}$$

where we defined

$$K_n = aG_n\,, \qquad f_n = a - cK_n \tag{4.9.11}$$

These are the time-varying analogs of Eqs. (4.6.17) and (4.6.19). Equations (4.9.8) and (4.9.9) may be combined into one updating equation for $P_{n/n-1}$, known as the discrete Riccati *difference* equation

$$P_{n+1/n} = \frac{a^2 R P_{n/n-1}}{R + c^2 P_{n/n-1}} + Q \tag{4.9.12}$$

It is the time-varying version of Eq. (4.6.18). We note that in deriving all of the above results, we did not need to assume that the model parameters $\{a,c,Q,R\}$ were constants, independent of time. They can just as well be replaced by time-varying model parameters:

$$\{a_n, c_n, Q_n, R_n\}$$

The asymptotic properties of the Kalman filter depend, of course, on the particular time variations in the model parameters. In the time-invariant case, with $\{a,c,Q,R\}$ constant, we expect the solution of the Riccati equation (4.9.12) to converge, for large n, to some steady-state value $P_{n/n-1} \rightarrow P$. In this limit, the Riccati difference equation (4.9.12) tends to the steady-state algebraic Riccati equation (4.6.18), which determines the limiting value P. The Kalman filter parameters will converge to the limiting values $f_n \rightarrow f$, $K_n \rightarrow K$ and $G_n \rightarrow G$ given by Eq. (4.6.19).

It is possible to solve Eq. (4.9.12) in closed form and explicitly demonstrate these convergence properties. Using the techniques of [21,22], we obtain

$$P_{n/n-1} = P + \frac{f^{2n} E_0}{1 + S_n E_0}\,, \qquad \text{for } n = 0, 1, 2, \cdots \tag{4.9.13}$$

where $E_0 = P_{0/-1} - P$ and

$$S_n = B\,\frac{1 - f^{2n}}{1 - f^2}\,, \qquad B = \frac{c^2}{R + c^2 P}$$

We have already mentioned (see Problem 3.7) that the stability of the signal model and the positivity of the asymptotic solution P imply the minimum phase condition $|f| < 1$. Thus, the second term of Eq. (4.9.13) converges to zero exponentially with a time constant determined by f.

Example 4.9.1: Determine the closed form solutions of the time-varying Kalman filter for the state and measurement models:

$$x_{n+1} = x_n + w_n\,, \qquad y_n = x_n + v_n$$

with $Q = 0.5$ and $R = 1$. Thus, $a = 1$ and $c = 1$. The Riccati equations are

$$P_{n+1/n} = \frac{P_{n/n-1}}{1 + P_{n/n-1}} + 0.5\,, \qquad P = \frac{P}{1+P} + 0.5$$

The solution of the algebraic Riccati is $P = 1$. This implies $f = aR/(R + c^2P) = 0.5$. To illustrate the solution (4.9.13), we take the initial condition to be zero, $P_{0/-1} = 0$. We find $B = c^2/(R + c^2P) = 0.5$, and $S_n = \frac{2}{3}[1 - (0.5)^{2n}]$. Thus

$$P_{n/n-1} = 1 - \frac{(0.5)^{2n}}{1 - \frac{2}{3}[1 - (0.5)^{2n}]} = \frac{1 - (0.5)^{2n}}{1 + 2(0.5)^{2n}}$$

The first few values calculated from this formula are

$$P_{1/0} = \frac{1}{2}\,, \quad P_{2/1} = \frac{5}{6}\,, \quad P_{3/2} = \frac{21}{22}\,, \ldots$$

and quickly converge to $P = 1$. They may also be obtained by iterating Eq. (4.9.12).

Problems

Problem 4.1:
Let $\mathbf{x} = [x_{n_a}, \ldots, x_{n_b}]^T$ and $\mathbf{y} = [y_{n_a}, \ldots, y_{n_b}]^T$ be the desired and available signal vectors. The relationship between $\mathbf{x}$ and $\mathbf{y}$ is assumed to be linear of the form

$$\mathbf{y} = C\mathbf{x} + \mathbf{v}$$

where C represents a linear degradation and $\mathbf{v}$ is a vector of zero-mean independent gaussian samples with a common variance σ_v^2. Show that the maximum likelihood (ML) estimation criterion is in this case equivalent to the following least-squares criterion, based on the quadratic vector norm:

$$\mathcal{E} = \|\mathbf{y} - C\mathbf{x}\|^2 = \text{minimum with respect to } \mathbf{x}$$

Show that the resulting estimate is given by

$$\hat{\mathbf{x}} = (C^TC)^{-1}C^T\mathbf{y}$$

Problem 4.2:
Let $\hat{\mathbf{x}} = H\mathbf{y}$ be the optimal linear smoothing estimate of $\mathbf{x}$ given by Eq. (4.1.5). It is obtained by minimizing the mean-squared estimation error $\mathcal{E}_n = E[e_n^2]$ for each n in the interval $[n_a, n_b]$.

(a) Show that this solution for H also minimizes the error covariance matrix

$$R_{ee} = E[\mathbf{e}\mathbf{e}^T]$$

where $\mathbf{e}$ is the vector of estimation errors $\mathbf{e} = [e_{na}, \ldots, e_{nb}]^T$.

(b) Show that H also minimizes every quadratic index of the form

$$E[\mathbf{e}^T Q \mathbf{e}] = \text{minimum}$$

for any positive semi-definite matrix Q.

(c) Explain how the minimization of each $E[e_n^2]$ can be understood in terms of part (b).

Problem 4.3:
Consider the smoothing problem of estimating the signal vector $\mathbf{x}$ from the signal vector $\mathbf{y}$. Assume that $\mathbf{x}$ and $\mathbf{y}$ are linearly related by

$$\mathbf{y} = C\mathbf{x} + \mathbf{v}$$

and that $\mathbf{v}$ and $\mathbf{x}$ are uncorrelated from each other, and that the covariance matrices of $\mathbf{x}$ and $\mathbf{v}$, R_{xx} and R_{vv}, are known. Show that the smoothing estimate of $\mathbf{x}$ is in this case

$$\hat{\mathbf{x}} = R_{xx}C^T[CR_{xx}C^T + R_{vv}]^{-1}\mathbf{y}$$

Problem 4.4:
A stationary random signal has autocorrelation function $R_{xx}(k) = \sigma_x^2 a^{|k|}$, for all k. The observation signal is $y_n = x_n + v_n$, where v_n is a zero-mean, white noise sequence of variance σ_v^2, uncorrelated from x_n.

(a) Determine the optimal FIR Wiener filter of order $M = 1$ for estimating x_n in terms of y_n.

(b) Repeat for the optimal linear predictor of order $M = 2$ for predicting x_n on the basis of the past two samples y_{n-1} and y_{n-2}.

Problem 4.5:
A stationary random signal x_n has autocorrelation function $R_{xx}(k) = \sigma_x^2 a^{|k|}$, for all k. Consider a time interval $[n_a, n_b]$. The random signal x_n is known only at the end-points of that interval; that is, the only available observations are

$$y(n_a) = x(n_a), \qquad y(n_b) = x(n_b)$$

Determine the optimal estimate of $x(n)$ based on just these two samples in the form

$$\hat{x}(n) = h(n,n_a)y(n_a) + h(n,n_b)y(n_b)$$

for the following values of n: (a) $n_a \leqslant n \leqslant n_b$ (b) $n \leqslant n_a$ (c) $n \geqslant n_b$

Problem 4.6:
A stationary random signal x_n is to be estimated on the basis of the noisy observations

$$y_n = x_n + v_n$$

It is given that

$$S_{xx}(z) = \frac{1}{(1 - 0.5z^{-1})(1 - 0.5z)}, \qquad S_{vv}(z) = 5, \qquad S_{xv}(z) = 0$$

(a) Determine the optimal realizable Wiener filter for estimating the signal x_n on the basis of the observations $Y_n = \{y_i; i \leqslant n\}$. Write the difference equation of this filter. Compute the mean-squared estimation error.

(b) Determine the optimal realizable Wiener filter for predicting one step into the future; that is, estimate x_{n+1} on the basis of Y_n.

(c) Cast the results of (a) and (b) in a predictor/corrector Kalman filter form, and show explicitly that the innovations residual of the observation signal y_n is identical to the corresponding whitening sequence ϵ_n driving the signal model of y_n.

Problem 4.7:
Repeat the previous problem for the following choice of state and measurement models

$$x_{n+1} = x_n + w_n, \qquad y_n = x_n + v_n$$

where w_n and v_n have variances $Q = 0.5$ and $R = 1$, respectively.

Problem 4.8:
Consider the state and measurement equations

$$x_{n+1} = ax_n + w_n \qquad y_n = cx_n + v_n$$

as discussed in Section 4.6. For *any* value of the Kalman gain K, consider the Kalman predictor/corrector algorithm defined by the equation

$$\hat{x}_{n+1/n} = a\hat{x}_{n/n-1} + K(y_n - c\hat{x}_{n/n-1}) = f\hat{x}_{n/n-1} + Ky_n \qquad \text{(P.1)}$$

where $f = a - cK$. The stability requirement of this estimation filter requires further that K be such that $|f| < 1$.

(a) Let $e_{n/n-1} = x_n - \hat{x}_{n/n-1}$ be the corresponding estimation error. Assuming all signals are stationary, and working with z-transforms, show that the power spectral density of $e_{n/n-1}$ is given by

$$S_{ee}(z) = \frac{Q + K^2 R}{(1 - fz^{-1})(1 - fz)}$$

(b) Integrating (a) around the unit circle, show that the mean-squared value of the estimation error is given by

$$\mathcal{E} = E[e_{n/n-1}^2] = \frac{Q + K^2 R}{1 - f^2} = \frac{Q + K^2 R}{1 - (a - cK)^2} \qquad \text{(P.2)}$$

(c) To select the *optimal value* of the Kalman gain K, differentiate $\mathcal{E}$ with respect to K and set the derivative to zero. Show that the resulting equation for K can be expressed in the form

$$K = \frac{caP}{R + c^2 P}$$

where P stands for the minimized value of $\mathcal{E}$; that is,

$$P = \mathcal{E}_{\min}$$

(d) Inserting this expression for K back into the expression (P.2) for $\mathcal{E}$, show that the quantity P must satisfy the algebraic Riccati equation

$$Q = P - \frac{PRa^2}{R + c^2 P}$$

Thus, the resulting estimator filter is identical to the optimal one-step prediction filter discussed in Section 4.6.

Problem 4.9:

(a) Show that Eq. (P.2) of Problem 4.8 can be derived without using z-transforms, by using only stationarity, as suggested below: Using the state and measurement model equations and Eq. (P.1), show that the estimation error $e_{n/n-1}$ satisfies the difference equation

$$e_{n+1/n} = fe_{n/n-1} + w_n - Kv_n$$

Then, invoking stationarity, derive Eq. (P.2).

(b) Using similar methods, show that the mean-squared estimation error is given by

$$E[e_{n/n}^2] = \frac{PR}{R + c^2 P}$$

where $e_{n/n} = x_n - \hat{x}_{n/n}$ is the estimation error of the optimal filter (4.6.13).

Problem 4.10:

Consider the general example of Section 4.6. It was shown there that the innovations residual was the same as the whitening sequence ϵ_n driving the signal model of y_n

$$\epsilon_n = y_n - \hat{y}_{n/n-1} = y_n - c\hat{x}_{n/n-1}$$

Show that it can be written as

$$\epsilon_n = ce_{n/n-1} + v_n$$

where $e_{n/n-1} = x_n - \hat{x}_{n/n-1}$ is the estimation error. Then, show that

$$\sigma_\epsilon^2 = E[\epsilon_n^2] = c^2P + R$$

Problem 4.11: Computer experiment

Consider the signal and measurement model defined by Eqs. (4.6.6) through (4.6.8), with the choices $a = 0.9$, $c = 1$, $Q = 1 - a^2$, and $R = 1$. Generate 1500 samples of the random noises w_n and v_n. Generate the corresponding signals x_n and y_n according to the state and measurement equations. Determine the optimal Wiener filter of the form (4.6.13) for estimating x_n on the basis of y_n. Filter the sequence y_n through the Wiener filter to generate the sequence $\hat{x}_{n/n}$.

(a) On the same graph, plot the desired signal x_n and the available noisy version y_n for n ranging over the last 100 values (i.e., $n = 1400$–1500).

(b) On the same graph, plot the recovered signal $\hat{x}_{n/n}$ together with the original signal x_n for n ranging over the last 100 values.

(c) Repeat (a) and (b) using a different realization of w_n and v_n.

(d) Repeat (a), (b), and (c) for the choice $a = -0.9$.

Problem 4.12:

Consider the optimal Wiener filtering problem in its matrix formulation of Section 4.8. Let $\mathbf{e} = \mathbf{x} - \hat{\mathbf{x}} = \mathbf{x} - H\mathbf{y}$ be the estimation error corresponding to a particular choice of the lower-triangular matrix H. Minimize the error covariance matrix $R_{ee} = E[\mathbf{e}\mathbf{e}^T]$ with respect to H subject to the *constraint* that H be lower-triangular. These constraints are $H_{ni} = 0$ for $n < i$. To do this, introduce a set of Lagrange multipliers Λ_{ni}; $n < i$, one for each constraint equation, and incorporate them into an effective performance index

$$J = E[\mathbf{e}\mathbf{e}^T] + \Lambda H^T + H\Lambda^T$$

where the matrix Λ is strictly upper-triangular. Show that this formulation of the minimization problem yields exactly the same solution as Eq. (4.8.7).

References

1. N. Wiener, *Extrapolation, Interpolation and Smoothing of Stationary Time Series with Engineering Applications*, New York, Wiley, 1949.

2. A. N. Kolmogorov, Sur l'Interpolation et Extrapolation des Suites Stationnaires, *C. R. Acad. Sci*, **208,** 2043–2045 (1939). See also Interpolation and Extrapolation of Stationary Random Sequences, and Stationary Sequences in Hilbert Space, reprinted in T. Kailath, Ed., *Linear Least-Squares Estimation*, Stroudsburg, PA, Dowden, Hutchinson, and Ross, 1977.
3. H. W. Bode and C. E. Shannon, A Simplified Derivation of Linear Least-Squares Smoothing and Prediction Theory, *Proc. IRE*, **38,** 417–425 (1950).
4. P. Whittle, *Prediction and Regulation*, New York: Van Nostrand Reinhold, 1963.
5. A. M. Yaglom, *Theory of Stationary Random Functions,* Englewood Cliffs, NJ, Prentice-Hall, 1962.
6. E. A. Robinson, *Multichannel Time-Series Analysis with Digital Computer Programs,* (2nd ed.), Houston, TX, Goose Pond Press, 1983.
7. E. A. Robinson, *Statistical Communication and Detection*, New York, Hafner, 1967.
8. A. P. Sage and J. L. Melsa, *Estimation Theory with Applications to Communication and Control*, New York, McGraw-Hill, 1971.
9. S. Tretter, *Introduction to Discrete-Time Signal Processing*, New York, Wiley, 1976.
10. M. Srinath and P. Rajasekaran, *Introduction to Statistical Signal Processing*, New York, Wiley, 1979.
11. E. Robinson and S. Treitel, *Geophysical Signal Analysis,* Englewood Cliffs, NJ, Prentice-Hall, 1980.
12. T. Kailath, A View of Three Decades of Linear Filtering Theory, *IEEE Trans. Info. Theory,* **IT-20,** 146 (1974).
13. R. E. Kalman, A New Approach to Linear Filtering and Prediction Problems, *Trans. ASME*, Ser. D, *J. Basic Eng.*, **82,** 34–45 (1960).
14. R. E. Kalman and R. S. Bucy, New Results in Linear Filtering and Prediction Theory, *Trans. ASME*, Ser. D, *J. Basic Eng.*, **83,** 95–107 (1961).
15. B. Anderson and J. Moore, *Optimal Filtering,* Englewood Cliffs, NJ, Prentice-Hall, 1979.
16. A. Gelb, *Applied Optimal Estimation,* Cambridge, MA, MIT Press, 1974.
17. H. W. Sorenson, Least-Squares Estimation: From Gauss to Kalman, *IEEE Spectrum,* **7,** 63 (1970).
18. T. Kailath, An Innovations Approach to Least-Squares Estimation. Part I: Linear Filtering in Additive White Noise, *IEEE Trans. Autom. Control,* **AC-13,** 646–655 (1968).
19. T. Kailath, Some Topics in Linear Estimation, in M. Hazewinkel and J. C. Willems, Eds., *Stochastic Systems: The Mathematics of Filtering and Identification,* Boston, D. Reidel Publications, 1981, pp. 307–350.
20. T. R. Kronhamm, Geometric Illustration of the Kalman Filter Gain and Covariance Update Algorithms, *IEEE Control Syst. Magazine,* May 1985, p. 41.
21. S. J. Orfanidis, An Exact Solution of the Time-Invariant Discrete Kalman Filter, *IEEE Trans. Automat. Contr.,* **AC-27,** 240 (1982).
22. S. J. Orfanidis, A Group Theoretical Approach to Optimal Estimation and Control, *J. Math. Anal. Appl.,* **97,** 393 (1983).

5

Linear Prediction

5.1 *Pure Prediction and Signal Modeling*

In Sections 1.11 and 1.16, we discussed the connection between linear prediction and signal modeling. Here, we rederive the same results by considering the linear prediction problem as a special case of the Wiener filtering problem, given by Eq. (4.4.6). Our aim is to cast the results in a form that will suggest a practical way to solve the prediction problem and hence also the modeling problem. Consider a stationary signal y_n having a signal model

$$S_{yy}(z) = \sigma_\epsilon^2 B(z)B(z^{-1}) \qquad (5.1.1)$$

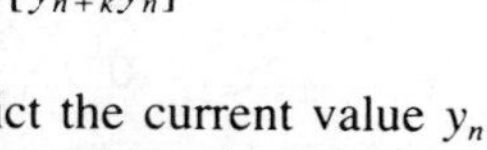

as guaranteed by the spectral factorization theorem. Let $R_{yy}(k)$ denote the autocorrelation of y_n:

$$R_{yy}(k) = E[y_{n+k}y_n]$$

The linear prediction problem is to predict the current value y_n on the basis of all the past values $Y_{n-1} = \{y_i;\ -\infty < i \leq n - 1\}$. If we define the delayed signal $y_1(n) = y_{n-1}$, then the linear prediction problem is equivalent to the optimal Wiener filtering problem of estimating y_n from the related signal $y_1(n)$. The optimal estimation filter $H(z)$ is given by Eq. (4.4.6), where we must identify

x_n and y_n with y_n and $y_1(n)$ of the present notation. Using the filtering equation $Y_1(z) = z^{-1}Y(z)$, we find that y_n and $y_1(n)$ have the same spectral factor $B(z)$

$$S_{y_1y_1}(z) = (z^{-1})(z^{-1})^{-1}S_{yy}(z) = S_{yy}(z) = \sigma_\epsilon^2 B(z)B(z^{-1})$$

and also that

$$S_{yy_1}(z) = S_{yy}(z)z = z\sigma_\epsilon^2 B(z)B(z^{-1})$$

Inserting these into Eq. (4.4.6) we find for the optimal filter $H(z)$

$$H(z) = \frac{1}{\sigma_\epsilon^2 B(z)}\left[\frac{S_{yy_1}(z)}{B(z^{-1})}\right]_+ = \frac{1}{\sigma_\epsilon^2 B(z)}\left[\frac{z\sigma_\epsilon^2 B(z)B(z^{-1})}{B(z^{-1})}\right]_+$$

or

$$H(z) = \frac{1}{B(z)}[zB(z)]_+ \tag{5.1.2}$$

The causal instruction can be removed as follows: Noting that $B(z)$ is a causal and stable filter, we may expand it in the power series

$$B(z) = 1 + b_1 z^{-1} + b_2 z^{-2} + b_3 z^{-3} + \cdots .$$

The causal part of $zB(z)$ is then

$$\begin{aligned}[zB(z)]_+ &= [z + b_1 + b_2 z^{-1} + b_3 z^{-2} + \cdots]_+ \\ &= b_1 + b_2 z^{-1} + b_3 z^{-2} + \cdots \\ &= z(b_1 z^{-1} + b_2 z^{-2} + b_3 z^{-3} + \cdots) \\ &= z[B(z) - 1]\end{aligned}$$

The prediction filter $H(z)$ then becomes

$$H(z) = \frac{1}{B(z)} z[B(z) - 1] = z\left[1 - \frac{1}{B(z)}\right] \tag{5.1.3}$$

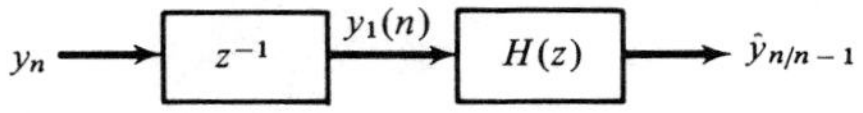

The input to this filter is $y_1(n)$ and the output is the prediction $\hat{y}_{n/n-1}$.

Example 5.1.1: Suppose y_n is generated by driving the all-pole filter

$$y_n = 0.9y_{n-1} - 0.2y_{n-2} + \epsilon_n$$

by zero-mean white noise ϵ_n. Find the best predictor $\hat{y}_{n/n-1}$. The signal model in this case is $B(z) = 1/(1 - 0.9z^{-1} + 0.2z^{-2})$ and Eq. (5.1.3) gives

$$\begin{aligned}z^{-1}H(z) &= 1 - \frac{1}{B(z)} = 1 - (1 - 0.9z^{-1} + 0.2z^{-2}) \\ &= 0.9z^{-1} - 0.2z^{-2}\end{aligned}$$

The I/O equation for the prediction filter is obtained by

$$\hat{Y}(z) = H(z)Y_1(z) = z^{-1}H(z)Y(z) = [0.9z^{-1} - 0.2z^{-2}]Y(z)$$

and in the time domain

$$\hat{y}_{n/n-1} = 0.9y_{n-1} - 0.2y_{n-2}$$

Example 5.1.2: Suppose

$$S_{yy}(z) = \frac{(1 - 0.25z^{-2})(1 - 0.25z^{2})}{(1 - 0.8z^{-1})(1 - 0.8z)}$$

Determine the best predictor $\hat{y}_{n/n-1}$. Here, the minimal-phase spectral factor is

$$B(z) = \frac{1 - 0.25z^{-2}}{1 - 0.8z^{-1}}$$

and therefore the prediction filter is

$$z^{-1}H(z) = 1 - \frac{1 - 0.8z^{-1}}{1 - 0.25z^{-2}}$$
$$= \frac{1 - 0.25z^{-2} - 1 + 0.8z^{-1}}{1 - 0.25z^{-2}} = \frac{0.8z^{-1} - 0.25z^{-2}}{1 - 0.25z^{-2}}$$

The I/O equation of this filter is conveniently given recursively by the difference equation

$$\hat{y}_{n/n-1} = 0.25\hat{y}_{n-2/n-3} + 0.8y_{n-1} - 0.25y_{n-2}$$

The prediction error

$$e_{n/n-1} = y_n - \hat{y}_{n/n-1}$$

is *identical* to the whitening sequence ϵ_n driving the signal model (5.1.1) of y_n; indeed,

$$E(z) = Y(z) - \hat{Y}(z) = Y(z) - H(z)Y_1(z) = Y(z) - H(z)z^{-1}Y(z)$$
$$= [1 - H(z)z^{-1}]Y(z) = \frac{1}{B(z)}Y(z) = \epsilon(z)$$

Thus,

$$e_{n/n-1} = y_n - \hat{y}_{n/n-1} = \epsilon_n \tag{5.1.4}$$

in accordance with the results of Sections 1.11 and 1.16. An overall realization of the linear predictor is shown in Fig. 5.1.

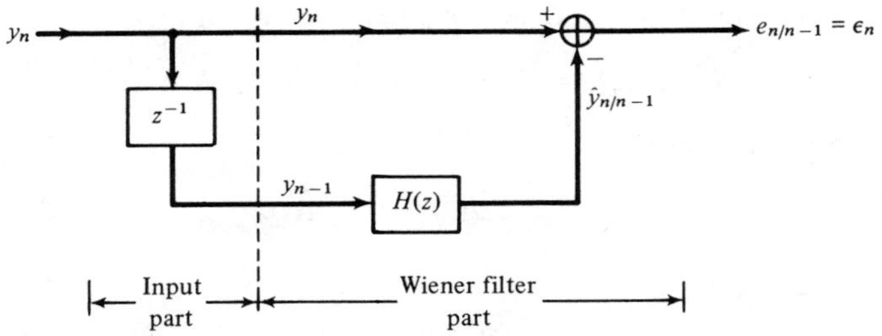

Figure 5.1 Linear Predictor

The indicated dividing line separates the linear predictor into the Wiener filtering part and the input part which provides the proper input signals to the Wiener part. The transfer function from y_n to $e_{n/n-1}$ is the *whitening inverse filter*

$$A(z) = \frac{1}{B(z)} = 1 - z^{-1}H(z)$$

which is *stable and causal* by the minimal-phase property of the spectral factorization (5.1.1). In the z-domain we have

$$E(z) = \epsilon(z) = A(z)Y(z)$$

and in the time domain

$$e_{n/n-1} = \epsilon_n = \sum_{m=0}^{\infty} a_m y_{n-m} = y_n + a_1 y_{n-1} + a_2 y_{n-2} + \cdots$$

The predicted estimate $\hat{y}_{n/n-1} = y_n - e_{n/n-1}$ is

$$\hat{y}_{n/n-1} = -[a_1 y_{n-1} + a_2 y_{n-2} + \cdots]$$

These results are identical to Eqs. (1.16.2) and (1.16.3). The relationship noted above between linear prediction and signal modeling can also be understood in terms of the gapped-function approach of Section 4.7. Rewriting Eq. (5.1.1) in terms of the prediction-error filter $A(z)$ we have

$$S_{yy}(z) = \frac{\sigma_\epsilon^2}{A(z)A(z^{-1})} \tag{5.1.5}$$

from which we obtain

$$A(z)S_{yy}(z) = \frac{\sigma_\epsilon^2}{A(z^{-1})} = \sigma_\epsilon^2 B(z^{-1}) \tag{5.1.6}$$

Since we have the filtering equation $\epsilon(z) = A(z)Y(z)$, it follows that

$$S_{\epsilon y}(z) = A(z)S_{yy}(z)$$

and in the time domain

$$R_{\epsilon y}(k) = E[\epsilon_n y_{n-k}] = \sum_{i=0}^{\infty} a_i R_{yy}(k-i) \tag{5.1.7}$$

which is recognized as the *gapped* function (4.7.1). By construction, ϵ_n is the orthogonal complement of y_n with respect to the *entire* past subspace $Y_{n-1} = \{y_{n-k};\ k = 1,2,\ldots\}$, therefore, ϵ_n will be orthogonal to each y_{n-k} for $k \geq 1$. These are precisely the gap conditions. Because the prediction is based on the entire past, the gapped function develops an infinite right-hand side gap. Thus, Eq. (5.1.7.) implies

$$R_{\epsilon y}(k) = E[\epsilon_n y_{n-k}] = \sum_{i=0}^{\infty} a_i R_{yy}(k-i) = 0 \qquad \text{for all } k = 1,2,\ldots \tag{5.1.8}$$

The same result, of course, also follows from the z-domain equation (5.1.6). Both sides of the equation are stable, but since $A(z)$ is minimal-phase, $A(z^{-1})$ will be maximum phase, and therefore it will have a stable but anticausal inverse $1/A(z^{-1})$. Thus, the right-hand side of Eq. (5.1.6) has no strictly causal part. Equating to zero all the coefficients of positive powers of z^{-1}, results in Eq. (5.1.8). The value of the gapped function at $k = 0$ is equal to σ_ϵ^2. Indeed, using Eq. (5.1.8) we find

$$\begin{aligned}\sigma_\epsilon^2 &= E[\epsilon_n^2] = E[\epsilon_n(y_n + a_1 y_{n-1} + a_2 y_{n-2} + \cdots)] \\ &= R_{\epsilon y}(0) + a_1 R_{\epsilon y}(1) + a_2 R_{\epsilon y}(2) + \cdots \\ &= R_{\epsilon y}(0) = E[\epsilon_n y_n]\end{aligned}$$

Using Eq. (5.1.7) with $k = 0$ and the symmetry property $R_{yy}(i) = R_{yy}(-i)$, we find

$$\begin{aligned}\sigma_\epsilon^2 &= E[\epsilon_n^2] = E[\epsilon_n y_n] \\ &= R_{yy}(0) + a_1 R_{yy}(1) + a_2 R_{yy}(2) + \cdots\end{aligned} \tag{5.1.9}$$

Equations (5.1.8) and (5.1.9) may be combined into one,

$$\sum_{i=0}^{\infty} a_i R_{yy}(k-i) = \sigma_\epsilon^2 \delta(k) \qquad \text{for all } k \geq 0 \tag{5.1.10}$$

which can be cast in the matrix form

$$\begin{bmatrix} R_{yy}(0) & R_{yy}(1) & R_{yy}(2) & R_{yy}(3) & \cdots \\ R_{yy}(1) & R_{yy}(0) & R_{yy}(1) & R_{yy}(2) & \cdots \\ R_{yy}(2) & R_{yy}(1) & R_{yy}(0) & R_{yy}(1) & \cdots \\ R_{yy}(3) & R_{yy}(2) & R_{yy}(1) & R_{yy}(0) & \cdots \\ \vdots & \vdots & \vdots & \vdots & \end{bmatrix} \begin{bmatrix} 1 \\ a_1 \\ a_2 \\ a_3 \\ \vdots \end{bmatrix} = \begin{bmatrix} \sigma_\epsilon^2 \\ 0 \\ 0 \\ 0 \\ \vdots \end{bmatrix} \tag{5.1.11}$$

These equations are known as the *normal equations* of linear prediction [1–12]. They provide the solution to both *signal modeling* and linear *prediction* problems. They determine the *model parameters* $\{a_1, a_2, \ldots ; \sigma_\epsilon^2\}$ of the signal y_n directly in terms of the *experimentally accessible* quantities $R_{yy}(k)$. To render them computationally manageable, the infinite matrix equation (5.1.11) must be reduced to a *finite* one, and furthermore, the quantities $R_{yy}(k)$ must be *estimated* from actual data samples of y_n. We discuss these matters next.

5.2 *Autoregressive Models*

In general, the number of prediction coefficients $\{a_1, a_2, \ldots\}$ is infinite since the predictor is based on the infinite past. However, there is an important exception to this; namely, when the process y_n is *autoregressive*. In this case, the signal model $B(z)$ is an *all-pole* filter of the type

$$B(z) = \frac{1}{A(z)} = \frac{1}{1 + a_1 z^{-1} + a_2 z^{-2} + \cdots + a_p z^{-p}} \tag{5.2.1}$$

which implies that the prediction-error filter is a polynomial

$$A(z) = 1 + a_1 z^{-1} + a_2 z^{-2} + \cdots + a_p z^{-p} \tag{5.2.2}$$

The signal generator for y_n is the following difference equation, driven by the uncorrelated sequence ϵ_n:

$$y_n + a_1 y_{n-1} + a_2 y_{n-2} + \cdots + a_p y_{n-p} = \epsilon_n \tag{5.2.3}$$

and the optimal prediction of y_n is simply given by

$$\hat{y}_{n/n-1} = -[a_1 y_{n-1} + a_2 y_{n-2} + \cdots + a_p y_{n-p}] \tag{5.2.4}$$

In this case, the best prediction of y_n depends *only* on the past p samples $\{y_{n-1}, y_{n-2}, \ldots, y_{n-p}\}$. The infinite set of equations (5.1.10) or (5.1.11) are still satisfied even though only the first $p + 1$ coefficients $1, a_1, a_2, \ldots, a_p$ are nonzero. The $(p + 1) \times (p + 1)$ portion of Eq. (5.1.11) is *sufficient* to determine the $(p + 1)$ model parameters $\{a_1, a_2, \ldots, a_p; \sigma_\epsilon^2\}$:

$$\begin{bmatrix} R_{yy}(0) & R_{yy}(1) & R_{yy}(2) & \cdots & R_{yy}(p) \\ R_{yy}(1) & R_{yy}(0) & R_{yy}(1) & \cdots & R_{yy}(p-1) \\ R_{yy}(2) & R_{yy}(1) & R_{yy}(0) & \cdots & R_{yy}(p-2) \\ \vdots & \vdots & \vdots & & \vdots \\ R_{yy}(p) & R_{yy}(p-1) & R_{yy}(p-2) & \cdots & R_{yy}(0) \end{bmatrix} \begin{bmatrix} 1 \\ a_1 \\ a_2 \\ \vdots \\ a_p \end{bmatrix} = \begin{bmatrix} \sigma_\epsilon^2 \\ 0 \\ 0 \\ \vdots \\ 0 \end{bmatrix} \tag{5.2.5}$$

Such equations may be solved efficiently by Levinson's algorithm, which requires $O(p^2)$ operations and $O(p)$ storage locations to obtain the a_is, instead of

$O(p^3)$ and $O(p^2)$, respectively, that would be required if the inverse of the autocorrelation matrix R_{yy} were to be computed. The finite set of model parameters $\{a_1, a_2, \ldots, a_p; \sigma_\epsilon^2\}$ determines the signal model of y_n completely. Setting $z = \exp(j\omega)$ into Eq. (5.1.5) we find a simple *parametric representation* of the power spectrum of the AR signal y_n:

$$
\begin{aligned}
S_{yy}(\omega) &= \frac{\sigma_\epsilon^2}{|A(\omega)|^2} \\
&= \frac{\sigma_\epsilon^2}{|1 + a_1 e^{-j\omega} + a_2 e^{-2j\omega} + \cdots + a_p e^{-j\omega p}|^2} \qquad \text{(AR spectrum)}
\end{aligned}
\tag{5.2.6}
$$

In practice, the normal equations (5.2.5) provide a means of determining approximate estimates for the model parameters $\{a_1, a_2, \ldots, a_p; \sigma_\epsilon^2\}$. Typically, a block of length N of recorded data is available

$$\boxed{y_0,\ y_1,\ y_2 \cdots y_{N-1}}$$

There are many different methods of extracting reasonable estimates of the model parameters using this block of data. We mention: (1) the *autocorrelation* or *Yule-Walker* method, (2) the *covariance* method, and (3) *Burg's* method. There are also some variations of these methods. The first method, the Yule-Walker method, is perhaps the most obvious and straightforward one. In the normal equations (5.2.5), one simply replaces the ensemble autocorrelations $R_{yy}(k)$ by the corresponding *sample* autocorrelations computed from the given block of data; that is,

$$\hat{R}_{yy}(k) = \frac{1}{N} \sum_{n=0}^{N-1-k} y_{n+k} y_n \qquad \text{for } 0 \leq k \leq p \tag{5.2.7}$$

where only the first $p + 1$ lags are needed in Eq. (5.2.5). We must have, of course, $p \leq N - 1$. As discussed in Section 1.11, the resulting *estimates* of the model parameters $\{\hat{a}_1, \hat{a}_2, \ldots, \hat{a}_p; \hat{\sigma}_\epsilon^2\}$ may be used now in a number of ways; examples include obtaining a *spectral estimate* of the power spectrum of the sequence y_n

$$\hat{S}_{yy}(\omega) = \frac{\hat{\sigma}_\epsilon^2}{|1 + \hat{a}_1 e^{-j\omega} + \hat{a}_2 e^{-2j\omega} + \cdots + \hat{a}_p e^{-j\omega p}|^2} \qquad \text{(YW spectral estimate)}$$

and *representing* the block of N samples y_n in terms of a few (i.e., $p + 1$) filter parameters. To synthesize the original samples one would generate white noise ϵ_n of variance $\hat{\sigma}_\epsilon^2$, and send it through the generator filter whose coefficients are the estimated values; that is, the filter

$$\hat{B}(z) = \frac{1}{\hat{A}(z)} = \frac{1}{1 + \hat{a}_1 z^{-1} + \hat{a}_2 z^{-2} + \cdots + \hat{a}_p z^{-p}}$$

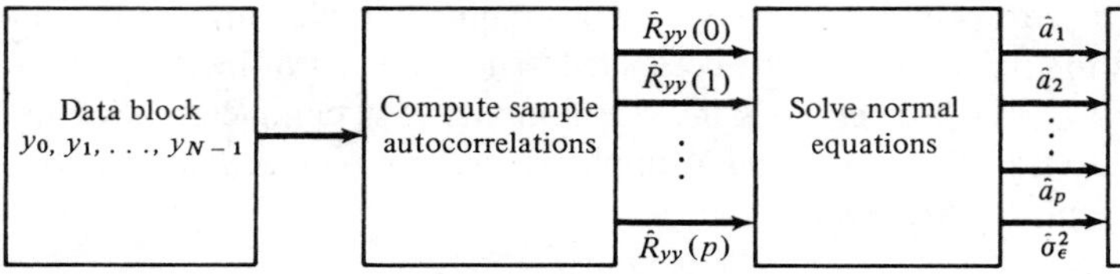

Figure 5.2 Yule-Walker Analysis Algorithm

The Yule-Walker analysis procedure, also referred to as the autocorrelation method of linear prediction [3], is summarized in Fig. 5.2.

5.3 *Linear Prediction Based on the Finite Past—Levinson Recursion*

In the last section, we saw that if the signal being predicted is autoregressive of order p, then the optimal linear predictor collapses to a pth order predictor. The infinite dimensional Wiener filtering problem collapses to a *finite* dimensional one. A geometrical way to understand this property is to say that the projection of y_n on the subspace spanned by the entire past $\{y_{n-i};\ i = 1,2, \ldots\}$ is the same as the projection of y_n onto the subspace spanned only by the past p samples; namely, $\{y_{n-i};\ i = 1,2, \ldots, p\}$. This is a consequence of the difference equation (5.2.3) generating y_n. If the process y_n is not autoregressive, these two projections will be different. For any given p, the projection of y_n onto the past p samples will still provide the *best linear prediction* of y_n that can be made on the basis of these *past p samples*. As p increases, more and more past information is taken into account, and we expect the prediction of y_n to become better and better in the sense of yielding a smaller mean-squared prediction error. In this section, we consider the finite-past prediction problem and discuss its efficient solution via the Levinson recursion [1–12]. For *sufficiently large* values of p, it may be considered an adequate *approximation* to the *full* prediction problem and hence also to the *modeling* problem.

Consider a stationary time series y_n with autocorrelation function $R(k) = E[y_{n+k}y_n]$. For any given p, we seek the best linear predictor of order p of the form

$$\hat{y}_n = -[a_1 y_{n-1} + a_2 y_{n-2} + \cdots + a_p y_{n-p}] \qquad (5.3.1)$$

The p prediction coefficients $a_1, a_2, \ldots, a_p$ are chosen to minimize the mean-squared prediction error

$$\mathcal{E} = E[e_n^2] = \min \qquad (5.3.2)$$

where e_n is the prediction error

$$e_n = y_n - \hat{y}_n = y_n + a_1 y_{n-1} + a_2 y_{n-2} + \cdots + a_p y_{n-p} \qquad (5.3.3)$$

Differentiating Eq. (5.3.2) with respect to each coefficient a_i; $i = 1,2, \ldots, p$ yields the orthogonality equations

$$E[e_n y_{n-i}] = 0, \qquad \text{for } i = 1,2, \ldots, p \tag{5.3.4}$$

which express the fact that the optimal predictor $\hat{y}_n$ is the projection onto the span of the past p samples; that is, $\{y_{n-i}; i = 1,2, \ldots, p\}$. Inserting the expression (5.3.3) for e_n into Eq. (5.3.4), we obtain p linear equations for the coefficients

$$\sum_{j=0}^{p} a_j E[y_{n-j} y_{n-i}] = \sum_{j=0}^{p} R(i-j) a_j = 0, \qquad \text{for } i = 1,2, \ldots, p \tag{5.3.5}$$

Using the conditions (5.3.4) we also find for the *minimized* value of

$$\sigma_e^2 = \mathcal{E} = E[e_n^2] = E[e_n y_n] = \sum_{i=0}^{p} R(i) a_i \tag{5.3.6}$$

Equations (5.3.5) and (5.3.6) can be combined into the $(p+1) \times (p+1)$ matrix equation

$$\begin{bmatrix} R(0) & R(1) & R(2) & \cdots & R(p) \\ R(1) & R(0) & R(1) & \cdots & R(p-1) \\ R(2) & R(1) & R(0) & \cdots & R(p-2) \\ \vdots & \vdots & \vdots & & \vdots \\ R(p) & R(p-1) & R(p-2) & \cdots & R(0) \end{bmatrix} \begin{bmatrix} 1 \\ a_1 \\ a_2 \\ \vdots \\ a_p \end{bmatrix} = \begin{bmatrix} \sigma_e^2 \\ 0 \\ 0 \\ \vdots \\ 0 \end{bmatrix} \tag{5.3.7}$$

which is identical to Eq. (5.2.5) for the autoregressive case. It is also the *truncated* version of the infinite matrix equation (5.1.11) for the full prediction problem.

Instead of solving the normal equations (5.3.7) directly, we would like to imbed this problem into a whole class of similar problems; namely, of determining the best linear predictors of orders $p = 1$, $p = 2$, $p = 3$, . . . and so on. This approach will lead to Levinson's algorithm and to the so-called lattice realizations of linear prediction filters. Pictorially this class of problems is illustrated below

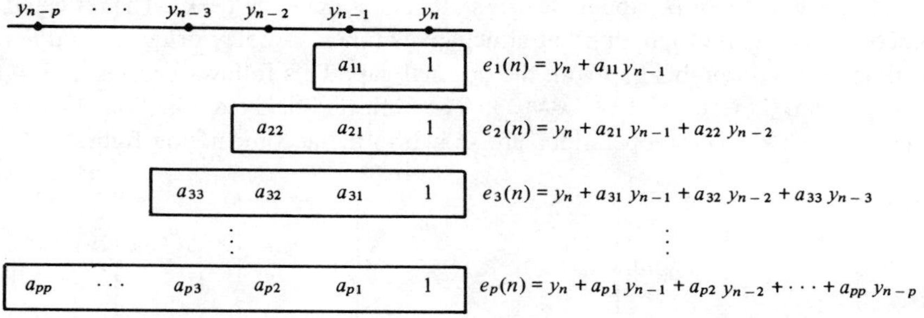

where $(1,a_{11})$, $(1,a_{21},a_{22})$, $(1,a_{31},a_{32},a_{33})$, . . . represent the best predictors of orders $p = 1,2,3, \ldots$, respectively. It was necessary to attach an extra index indicating the order of the predictor. Levinson's algorithm is an iterative procedure that constructs the *next* predictor from the *previous* one. In the process, *all* optimal predictors of lower order are also computed.

Consider the predictors of orders p and $p + 1$, below.

y_{n-p-1} ' y_{n-p} $\cdots$ y_{n-2} y_{n-1} y_n

| a_{pp} | $\cdots$ | a_{p2} | a_{p1} | 1 |

$e_p(n) = y_n + a_{p1}\, y_{n-1} + a_{p2}\, y_{n-2} + \cdots + a_{pp}\, y_{n-p}$

| $a_{p+1,p+1}$ $a_{p+1,p}$ | $\cdots$ | $a_{p+1,2}$ | $a_{p+1,1}$ | 1 |

$e_{p+1}(n) = y_n + a_{p+1,1}\, y_{n-1} + \cdots + a_{p+1,p+1}\, y_{n-p-1}$

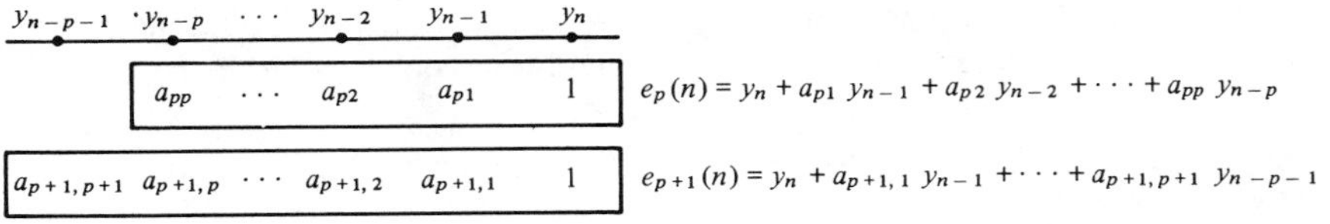

Our objective is to construct the latter in terms of the former. We will use the approach of Robinson and Treitel, based on gapped functions [9]. Suppose that the best predictor of order p, $(1, a_{p1}, a_{p2}, \ldots, a_{pp})$, has already been constructed. The corresponding gapped function is

$$g_p(k) = E[e_p(n)y_{n-k}] = E\left[\left(\sum_{i=0}^{p} a_{pi}y_{n-i}\right)y_{n-k}\right]$$

$$= \sum_{i=0}^{p} a_{pi}R(k - i) \tag{5.3.8}$$

It has a gap of length p as shown; that is,

$$g_p(k) = 0, \quad \text{for } 1 \leq k \leq p$$

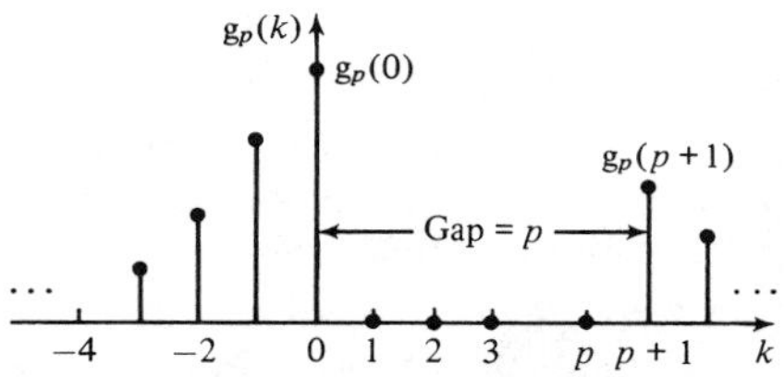

These gap conditions are the same as the orthogonality equations (5.3.4). Using $g_p(k)$ we now construct a new gapped function $g_{p+1}(k)$ of gap $p + 1$. To do this, first we reflect $g_p(k)$ about the origin; that is, $g_p(k) \rightarrow g_p(-k)$. The reflected function has a gap of length p but at negatives times. A delay of $(p + 1)$ units of time will *realign* this gap with the original gap. This follows because if $1 \leq k \leq p$, then $1 \leq p + 1 - k \leq p$. The reflected-delayed function will be $g_p(p + 1 - k)$. These operations are shown in the accompanying figure.

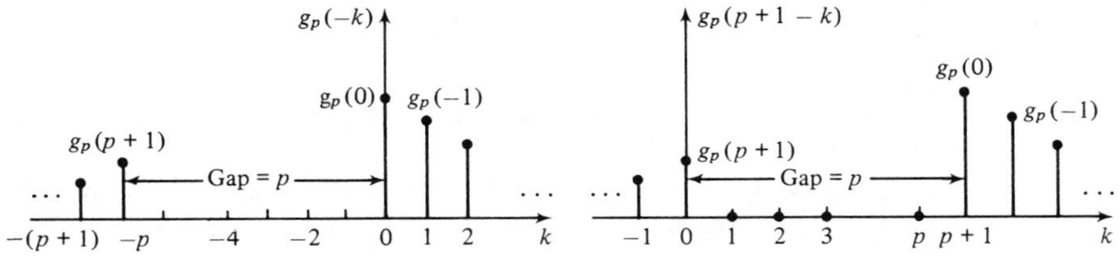

Since both $g_p(k)$ and $g_p(p+1-k)$ have exactly the same gap, it follows that so will any linear combination of them. Therefore,

$$g_{p+1}(k) = g_p(k) - \gamma_{p+1} g_p(p+1-k) \tag{5.3.9}$$

will have a gap of length at least p. We now select the parameter γ_{p+1} so that $g_{p+1}(k)$ acquires an *extra* gap point; its gap is now of length $p+1$. The extra gap condition is

$$g_{p+1}(p+1) = g_p(p+1) - \gamma_{p+1} g_p(0) = 0$$

which may be solved for

$$\gamma_{p+1} = \frac{g_p(p+1)}{g_p(0)}$$

Evaluating Eq. (5.3.8) at $k = p + 1$, and using the fact that the value of the gapped function at $k = 0$ is the *minimized* value of the mean-squared error, that is,

$$E_p = E[e_p(n)^2] = E[e_p(n)y_n] = g_p(0) \tag{5.3.10}$$

we finally find

$$\gamma_{p+1} = \frac{\Delta_p}{E_p} \tag{5.3.11}$$

Where we set $g_p(p+1) = \Delta_p$

$$\Delta_p = \sum_{i=0}^{p} a_{pi} R(p+1-i) = R(p+1) + a_{p1} R(p) + a_{p2} R(p-1) + \cdots + a_{pp} R(1) \tag{5.3.12}$$

The coefficients γ_{p+1} are called *reflection, PARCOR,* or *Schur* coefficients. This terminology will become clear later. Evaluating Eq. (5.3.9) at $k = 0$ and using $\gamma_{p+1} = g_p(p+1)/g_p(0)$, we also find a recursion for the quantity $E_{p+1} = g_{p+1}(0)$

$$E_{p+1} = g_{p+1}(0) = g_p(0) - \gamma_{p+1} g_p(p+1) = (1 - \gamma_{p+1}^2) g_p(0)$$

or

$$E_{p+1} = (1 - \gamma_{p+1}^2) E_p \tag{5.3.13}$$

This represents the minimum value of the mean-squared prediction error $E[e_{p+1}(n)^2]$ for the predictor of order $p + 1$. Since both E_p and E_{p+1} are nonnegative, it follows that the factor $(1 - \gamma_{p+1}^2)$ will be positive and less than one. It represents the *improvement* in the prediction afforded by using a predictor of order $p + 1$ instead of a predictor of order p. It also follows that γ_{p+1} has *magnitude less* than one. To find the new prediction coefficients, we use the fact that the gapped functions are equal to the convolution of the corresponding prediction-error filters with the autocorrelation function of y_n:

$$g_p(k) = \sum_{m=0}^{p} a_{pm}R(k - m) \rightarrow G_p(z) = A_p(z)S_{yy}(z)$$

$$g_{p+1}(k) = \sum_{m=0}^{p+1} a_{p+1,m}R(k - m) \rightarrow G_{p+1}(z) = A_{p+1}(z)S_{yy}(z)$$

where $S_{yy}(z)$ is the power spectral density of y_n. Taking the z-transforms of both sides of Eq. (5.3.9), we find

$$G_{p+1}(z) = G_p(z) - \gamma_{p+1}z^{-(p+1)}G_p(z^{-1})$$

or

$$A_{p+1}(z)S_{yy}(z) = A_p(z)S_{yy}(z) - \gamma_{p+1}z^{-(p+1)}A_p(z^{-1})S_{yy}(z^{-1})$$

where we used the fact that the reflected gapped function has z-transform $G_p(z^{-1})$, and therefore the delayed (by $p + 1$) as well as reflected gapped function $g_p(p + 1 - k)$ has z-transform $z^{-(p+1)}G_p(z^{-1})$. Since $S_{yy}(z) = S_{yy}(z^{-1})$ because of the symmetry relations $R(k) = R(-k)$, it follows that $S_{yy}(z)$ is a common factor in all terms. Therefore, we obtain a relationship between the new best prediction-error filter $A_{p+1}(z)$ and the old one $A_p(z)$

$$A_{p+1}(z) = A_p(z) - \gamma_{p+1}z^{-(p+1)}A_p(z^{-1}) \qquad \text{(Levinson recursion)} \qquad (5.3.14)$$

Taking inverse z-transforms, we find

$$\begin{bmatrix} 1 \\ a_{p+1,1} \\ a_{p+1,2} \\ \vdots \\ a_{p+1,p} \\ a_{p+1,p+1} \end{bmatrix} = \begin{bmatrix} 1 \\ a_{p1} \\ a_{p2} \\ \vdots \\ a_{pp} \\ 0 \end{bmatrix} - \gamma_{p+1} \begin{bmatrix} 0 \\ a_{pp} \\ a_{p,p-1} \\ \vdots \\ a_{p1} \\ 1 \end{bmatrix} \qquad (5.3.15)$$

which can also be written as

$$a_{p+1,m} = a_{pm} - \gamma_{p+1}a_{p,p+1-m} \qquad \text{for } 1 \leqslant m \leqslant p$$

$$a_{p+1,p+1} = -\gamma_{p+1}$$

Introducing the *reverse* polynomial $A_p^R(z) = z^{-p}A_p(z^{-1})$, we may write Eq. (5.3.14) as

$$A_{p+1}(z) = A_p(z) - \gamma_{p+1}z^{-1}A_p^R(z) \qquad (5.3.16)$$

Taking the reverse of both sides we find

$$A_{p+1}(z^{-1}) = A_p(z^{-1}) - \gamma_{p+1}z^{p+1}A_p(z)$$

$$A_{p+1}^R(z) = z^{-(p+1)}A_{p+1}(z^{-1}) = z^{-(p+1)}A_p(z^{-1}) - \gamma_{p+1}A_p(z)$$

or

$$A_{p+1}^R(z) = z^{-1}A_p^R(z) - \gamma_{p+1}A_p(z) \tag{5.3.17}$$

Equation (5.3.17) is, in a sense, redundant, but it will prove convenient to think of the Levinson recursion as a recursion on *both* the forward, $A_p(z)$, and the reverse, $A_p^R(z)$, polynomials. Equations (5.3.16) and Eq. (5.3.17) may be combined into a 2×2 matrix recursion equation

$$\begin{bmatrix} A_{p+1}(z) \\ A_{p+1}^R(z) \end{bmatrix} = \begin{bmatrix} 1 & -\gamma_{p+1}z^{-1} \\ -\gamma_{p+1} & z^{-1} \end{bmatrix} \begin{bmatrix} A_p(z) \\ A_p^R(z) \end{bmatrix} \quad \text{(forward recursion)} \tag{5.3.18}$$

The recursion is initialized at $p = 0$, by setting

$$A_0(z) = 1, \qquad A_0^R(z) = 1, \qquad \text{and} \qquad E_0 = R(0) = E[y_n^2] \tag{5.3.19}$$

which correspond to no prediction at all.

We summarize the computational sequence of the Levinson algorithm:

0. Initialize at $p = 0$ using Eq. (5.3.19)
1. At stage p, the filter $A_p(z)$ and error E_p are available
2. Using Eq. (5.3.11), compute γ_{p+1}
3. Using Eq. (5.3.14) or Eq. (5.3.18), determine the new polynomial $A_{p+1}(z)$
4. Using Eq. (5.3.13), update the mean-squared prediction error to E_{p+1}
5. Go to stage $p + 1$

The iteration may be continued until the final desired order is reached. The dependence on the autocorrelation $R(k)$ of the signal y_n is entered through Eq. (5.3.11) and $E_0 = R(0)$. To reach stage p, only the first $p + 1$ autocorrelation lags $R(0), R(1), \ldots, R(p)$ are required. At the pth stage, the iteration already has provided *all* the prediction filters of lower order, and all the previous reflection coefficients. Thus, an alternative parametrization of the pth order predictor is in terms of the sequence of reflection coefficients $\{\gamma_1, \gamma_2, \ldots, \gamma_p\}$ and the prediction error E_p

$$\{E_p, a_{p1}, a_{p2}, \ldots, a_{pp}\} \leftrightarrow \{E_p, \gamma_1, \gamma_2, \ldots, \gamma_p\}$$

One may pass from one parameter set to another. And both sets are equivalent to the autocorrelation set $\{R(0), R(1), \ldots, R(p)\}$. The alternative parametrization of the autocorrelation function $R(k)$ of a stationary random sequence in terms of the equivalent set of reflection coefficients is a general result [13,14], and has also been extended to the multichannel case [15]. If the process y_n is autoregressive of order p, then as soon as the Levinson recursion reaches this order, it will provide the autoregressive coefficients $a_1, a_2, \ldots, a_p$ which are also the best prediction coefficients for the full prediction problem. Further continuation of the Levinson recursion will produce nothing new; all prediction coefficients of order higher than p will be zero.

The four subroutines **lev, frwlev, bkwlev,** and **rlev** (see Appendix B) allow the passage from one parameter set to another. The subroutine **lev** is an implementation of the computational sequence outlined above. The input to the subroutine is the final desired order of the predictor, say M, and the vector of autocorrelation lags $\{R(0),R(1), \ldots ,R(M)\}$. Its output is the lower-triangular matrix L whose rows are the *reverse* of all the lower order prediction-error filters. For example, for $M = 4$ the matrix L would be

$$L = \begin{bmatrix} 1 & 0 & 0 & 0 & 0 \\ a_{11} & 1 & 0 & 0 & 0 \\ a_{22} & a_{21} & 1 & 0 & 0 \\ a_{33} & a_{32} & a_{31} & 1 & 0 \\ a_{44} & a_{43} & a_{42} & a_{41} & 1 \end{bmatrix} \qquad (5.3.20)$$

The first column of L contains the negatives of all the reflection coefficients. This follows from the Levinson recursion (5.3.14) which implies that the *negative* of the highest coefficient of the pth prediction-error filter is the pth reflection coefficient; namely,

$$\gamma_p = -a_{pp}; \qquad p = 1,2, \ldots ,M \qquad (5.3.21)$$

This choice for L is justified below and in Section 5.9. The subroutine **lev** also produces the vector of mean-squared prediction errors $\{E_0,E_1, \ldots ,E_M\}$ according to the recursion (5.3.13). The subroutine **frwlev** is an implementation of the forward Levinson recursion (5.3.18) or (5.3.15). Its input is the set of reflection coefficients $\{\gamma_1,\gamma_2, \ldots ,\gamma_M\}$ and its output is the set of all prediction-error filters up to order M; that is, $A_p(z)$; $p = 1,2, \ldots ,M$. Again, this output is arranged into the matrix L. The subroutine **bkwlev** is the inverse operation to **frwlev**. Its input is the prediction-error filter coefficients $[1,a_{M1},a_{M2}, \ldots ,a_{MM}]$ of the final order M, and its output is the matrix L containing all the lower order prediction-error filters. The set of reflection coefficients are extracted from the first column of L. This subroutine is based on the inverse of the matrix equation (5.3.18). Shifting p down by one unit, we write Eq. (5.3.18) as

$$\begin{bmatrix} A_p(z) \\ A_p^R(z) \end{bmatrix} = \begin{bmatrix} 1 & -\gamma_p z^{-1} \\ -\gamma_p & z^{-1} \end{bmatrix} \begin{bmatrix} A_{p-1}(z) \\ A_{p-1}^R(z) \end{bmatrix} \qquad (5.3.22)$$

Its inverse is

$$\begin{bmatrix} A_{p-1}(z) \\ A_{p-1}^R(z) \end{bmatrix} = \frac{1}{1-\gamma_p^2} \begin{bmatrix} 1 & \gamma_p \\ \gamma_p z & z \end{bmatrix} \begin{bmatrix} A_p(z) \\ A_p^R(z) \end{bmatrix} \quad \text{(backward recursion)} \qquad (5.3.23)$$

At each stage p, start with $A_p(z)$ and extract $\gamma_p = -a_{pp}$ from the highest coefficient of $A_p(z)$. Then, use Eq. (5.3.23) to obtain the polynomial $A_{p-1}(z)$. The iteration begins at the given order M and proceeds downwards to $p = M-1, M-2, \ldots, 1, 0$. Finally, the subroutine **rlev** generates the set of autocorrelation lags $\{R(0), R(1), \ldots, R(M)\}$ from the knowledge of the *final* prediction-error filter $A_M(z)$ and *final* prediction error E_M. It calls **bkwlev** to generate all the lower order prediction-error filters, and then it reconstructs the autocorrelation lags using the gapped function condition $g_p(p) = \sum_{i=0}^{p} a_{pi} R(p-i) = 0$, which may be solved for $R(p)$ in terms of $R(p-i)$; $i = 1, 2, \ldots, p$, as follows:

$$R(p) = -\sum_{i=1}^{p} a_{pi} R(p-i) \qquad p = 1, 2, \ldots, M \tag{5.3.24}$$

For example, the first few iterations of Eq. (5.3.24) will be

$$R(1) = -[a_{11} R(0)]$$
$$R(2) = -[a_{21} R(1) + a_{22} R(0)]$$
$$R(3) = -[a_{31} R(2) + a_{32} R(1) + a_{33} R(0)]$$

To get this recursion started, the value of $R(0)$ may be obtained from Eq. (5.3.13). Using Eq. (5.3.13) repeatedly, and $E_0 = R(0)$ we find

$$E_M = (1 - \gamma_1^2)(1 - \gamma_2^2) \cdots (1 - \gamma_M^2) R(0) \tag{5.3.25}$$

Since the reflection coefficients are already known and E_M is given, this equation provides the right value for $R(0)$.

The routine **schur,** based on the Schur algorithm and discussed in Section 5.10, is an alternative to **lev.** The logical interconnection of these routines is shown below.

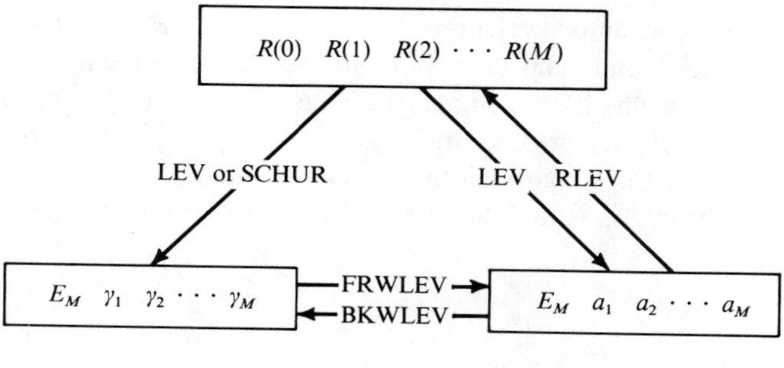

Example 5.3.1: Given the five autocorrelation lags

$$\{R(0), R(1), R(2), R(3), R(4)\} = \{128, -64, 80, -88, 89\}$$

Find all the prediction-error filters $A_p(z)$ up to order four, the four reflection coefficients, and the corresponding mean-squared prediction errors.

It is recommended that the reader go through the iteration of the Levinson algorithm by hand. Below, we simply state the results obtained using the subroutine **lev**.

$$A_1(z) = 1 + 0.5z^{-1}$$
$$A_2(z) = 1 + 0.25z^{-1} - 0.5z^{-2}$$
$$A_3(z) = 1 - 0.375z^{-2} + 0.5z^{-3}$$
$$A_4(z) = 1 - 0.25z^{-1} - 0.1875z^{-2} + 0.5z^{-3} - 0.5z^{-4}$$

The reflection coefficients are the negatives of the highest coefficients; thus,

$$\{\gamma_1,\gamma_2,\gamma_3,\gamma_4\} = \{-0.5,0.5,-0.5,0.5\}$$

The vector of mean-squared prediction errors is given by

$$\{E_0,E_1,E_2,E_3,E_4\} = \{128,96,72,54,40.5\}$$

Sending the above vector of reflection coefficients through the subroutine **frwlev** would generate the above set of polynomials. Sending the coefficients of $A_4(z)$ through **bkwlev** would generate the same set of polynomials. Sending the coefficients of $A_4(z)$ and $E_4 = 40.5$ through **rlev** would recover the original autocorrelation lags $R(k)$; $k = 0,1, \ldots ,4$.

The *Yule-Walker method* (see Section 5.2) can be used to extract the linear prediction parameters from a given set of signal samples. From a given block of data

$$\boxed{y_0, y_1, \ldots, y_{N-1}}$$

compute the sample autocorrelations $\{\hat{R}(0),\hat{R}(1), \ldots ,\hat{R}(M)\}$ using, for example, Eq. (5.2.7), and send them through the Levinson recursion. The subroutine **yw** (see Appendix B) implements the Yule-Walker method. The input to the subroutine is the data vector of samples $\{y_0,y_1, \ldots ,y_{N-1}\}$ and the desired final order M of the predictor. Its output is the set of all prediction-error filters up to order M, arranged in the matrix L, and the vector of mean-squared prediction errors up to order M, $\{E_0,E_1, \ldots ,E_M\}$.

Example 5.3.2: Given the signal samples

$$\{y_0,y_1,y_2,y_3,y_4\} = \{1,1,1,1,1\}$$

determine all the prediction-error filters up to order four. Using the fourth order predictor, predict the sixth value in the above sequence.

The sample autocorrelation of the above signal is easily computed using the methods of Chapter 1. We find (ignoring the $1/N$ normalization factor):

$$\{\hat{R}(0),\hat{R}(1),\hat{R}(2),\hat{R}(3),\hat{R}(4)\} = \{5,4,3,2,1\}$$

Sending these lags through the subroutine **lev** we find the prediction-error filters

$$A_1(z) = 1 - 0.8z^{-1}$$
$$A_2(z) = 1 - 0.889z^{-1} + 0.111z^{-2}$$
$$A_3(z) = 1 - 0.875z^{-1} + 0.125z^{-3}$$
$$A_4(z) = 1 - 0.857z^{-1} + 0.143z^{-4}$$

Therefore, the fourth order prediction of y_n given by Eq. (5.3.1) is

$$\hat{y}_n = 0.857y_{n-1} - 0.143y_{n-4}$$

which gives $\hat{y}_5 = 0.857 - 0.143 = 0.714$

The results of this section can also be derived from those of Section 1.7 by invoking stationarity and making the proper identification of the various quantities, as we did in Example 2.6.2. The data vector $\mathbf{y}$ and the subvectors $\bar{\mathbf{y}}$ and $\tilde{\mathbf{y}}$ are $\mathbf{y} = \mathbf{y}_{p+1}(n)$, $\bar{\mathbf{y}} = \mathbf{y}_p(n)$, and $\tilde{\mathbf{y}} = \mathbf{y}_p(n-1)$, where

$$\mathbf{y}_{p+1}(n) = \begin{bmatrix} y_n \\ y_{n-1} \\ \vdots \\ y_{n-p} \\ y_{n-p-1} \end{bmatrix}, \quad \mathbf{y}_p(n) = \begin{bmatrix} y_n \\ y_{n-1} \\ \vdots \\ y_{n-p} \end{bmatrix}, \quad \mathbf{y}_p(n-1) = \begin{bmatrix} y_{n-1} \\ y_{n-2} \\ \vdots \\ y_{n-1-p} \end{bmatrix} \tag{5.3.26}$$

It follows from stationarity that the autocorrelation matrices of these vectors are independent of the absolute time instant n; therefore, we write

$$R_p = E[\mathbf{y}_p(n)\mathbf{y}_p(n)^T] = E[\mathbf{y}_p(n-1)\mathbf{y}_p(n-1)^T], \qquad R_{p+1} = E[\mathbf{y}_{p+1}(n)\mathbf{y}_{p+1}(n)^T]$$

It is easily verified that R_p is the order-p autocorrelation matrix defined in Eq. (5.3.7) and that the order-$(p+1)$ autocorrelation matrix R_{p+1} admits the block decompositions

$$R_{p+1} = \left[\begin{array}{c|ccc} R(0) & R(1) & \cdots & R(p+1) \\ \hline R(1) & & & \\ \vdots & & R_p & \\ R(p+1) & & & \end{array}\right] = \left[\begin{array}{ccc|c} & & & R(p+1) \\ & R_p & & \vdots \\ & & & R(1) \\ \hline R(p+1) & \cdots & R(1) & R(0) \end{array}\right]$$

It follows that $\bar{R} = \tilde{R} = R_p$, $\rho_a = \rho_b = R(0)$, and

$$\mathbf{r}_a = \begin{bmatrix} R(1) \\ \vdots \\ R(p+1) \end{bmatrix}, \quad \mathbf{r}_b = \begin{bmatrix} R(p+1) \\ \vdots \\ R(1) \end{bmatrix}$$

Thus, $\mathbf{r}_a$ and $\mathbf{r}_b$ are the reverse of each other. As in Example 2.6.2, it follows that the backward predictors are the reverse of the forward ones. Therefore, Eq. (5.3.14) is the same as Eq. (1.7.40), with the identifications

$$\mathbf{a} = \mathbf{a}_{p+1}\,, \quad \mathbf{b} = \mathbf{b}_{p+1}\,, \quad \bar{\mathbf{a}} = \tilde{\mathbf{a}} = \mathbf{a}_p\,, \quad \bar{\mathbf{b}} = \tilde{\mathbf{b}} = \mathbf{b}_p$$

where

$$\mathbf{a}_{p+1} = \begin{bmatrix} 1 \\ a_{p+1,1} \\ \vdots \\ a_{p+1,p+1} \end{bmatrix}, \quad \mathbf{b}_{p+1} = \begin{bmatrix} a_{p+1,p+1} \\ \vdots \\ a_{p+1,1} \\ 1 \end{bmatrix}, \quad \mathbf{a}_p = \begin{bmatrix} 1 \\ a_{p1} \\ \vdots \\ a_{pp} \end{bmatrix}, \quad \mathbf{b}_p = \begin{bmatrix} a_{pp} \\ \vdots \\ a_{p1} \\ 1 \end{bmatrix}$$

Symbolically, $\mathbf{b}_p = \mathbf{a}_p^R$ and $\mathbf{b}_{p+1} = \mathbf{a}_{p+1}^R$. We have also $\bar{E}_a = \tilde{E}_b = E_p$ and $\gamma_a = \gamma_b = \gamma_{p+1}$. Thus, Eq. (5.3.11) may be written as

$$\mathbf{a}_{p+1} = \begin{bmatrix} \mathbf{a}_p \\ 0 \end{bmatrix} - \gamma_{p+1} \begin{bmatrix} 0 \\ \mathbf{b}_p \end{bmatrix} = \begin{bmatrix} \mathbf{a}_p \\ 0 \end{bmatrix} - \gamma_{p+1} \begin{bmatrix} 0 \\ \mathbf{a}_p^R \end{bmatrix} \tag{5.3.27}$$

The normal Eqs. (5.3.7) can be written for orders p and $p + 1$ in the compact form of Eqs. (1.7.38) and (1.7.12)

$$R_p \mathbf{a}_p = E_p \mathbf{u}_p\,, \quad R_{p+1}\mathbf{a}_{p+1} = E_{p+1}\mathbf{u}_{p+1}\,, \quad \mathbf{u}_p = \begin{bmatrix} 1 \\ \mathbf{0} \end{bmatrix}, \quad \mathbf{u}_{p+1} = \begin{bmatrix} \mathbf{u}_p \\ 0 \end{bmatrix} \tag{5.3.28}$$

Recognizing that Eq. (5.3.12) can be written as $\Delta_p = \mathbf{a}_p^T \mathbf{r}_b$, it follows that the reflection coefficient equation (5.3.11) is the same as (1.7.42). The rows of the matrix L defined by Eq. (5.3.20) are the reverse of the forward predictors; that is, the backward predictors of successive orders. Thus, L is the same as that defined in Eq. (1.7.13). The rows of the matrix U defined in Eq. (1.7.30) are the forward predictors, with the first row being the predictor of highest order. For example,

$$U = \begin{bmatrix} 1 & a_{41} & a_{42} & a_{43} & a_{44} \\ 0 & 1 & a_{31} & a_{32} & a_{33} \\ 0 & 0 & 1 & a_{21} & a_{22} \\ 0 & 0 & 0 & 1 & a_{11} \\ 0 & 0 & 0 & 0 & 1 \end{bmatrix}$$

Comparing L with U, we note that one is obtained from the other by reversing its rows and then its columns; formally, $U = JLJ$, where J is the corresponding reversing matrix.

5.4 *Levinson's Algorithm in Matrix Form*

In this section, we illustrate the mechanics of the Levinson recursion — cast in matrix form — by explicitly carrying out a few of the recursions given in Eq. (5.3.15). The objective of such recursions is to solve normal equations of the type

$$
\begin{bmatrix} R_0 & R_1 & R_2 & R_3 \\ R_1 & R_0 & R_1 & R_2 \\ R_2 & R_1 & R_0 & R_1 \\ R_3 & R_2 & R_1 & R_0 \end{bmatrix} \begin{bmatrix} 1 \\ a_{31} \\ a_{32} \\ a_{33} \end{bmatrix} = \begin{bmatrix} E_3 \\ 0 \\ 0 \\ 0 \end{bmatrix}
$$

for the unknowns $(1, a_{31}, a_{32}, a_{33})$ and also indirectly for E_3. The corresponding prediction-error filter will be

$$
A_3(z) = 1 + a_{31}z^{-1} + a_{32}z^{-2} + a_{33}z^{-3}
$$

and the minimum value of the prediction error will be E_3.

The solution is obtained in an iterative manner, by solving a family of similar matrix equations of lower dimensionality. Starting at the upper left corner, the

$$
\begin{array}{|c|c|c|c|}
\hline
R_0 & R_1 & R_2 & R_3 \\
\hline
R_1 & R_0 & R_1 & R_2 \\
\hline
R_2 & R_1 & R_0 & R_1 \\
\hline
R_3 & R_2 & R_1 & R_0 \\
\hline
\end{array}
$$

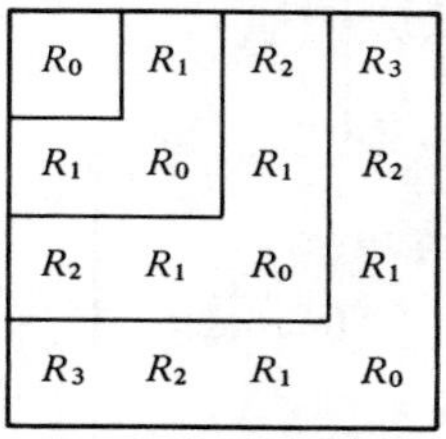

R matrices are successively enlarged until the desired dimension is reached (4×4 in this example). Therefore, one successively solves

$$
[R_0][1] = [E_0]; \qquad \begin{bmatrix} R_0 & R_1 \\ R_1 & R_0 \end{bmatrix} \begin{bmatrix} 1 \\ a_{11} \end{bmatrix} = \begin{bmatrix} E_1 \\ 0 \end{bmatrix};
$$

$$
\begin{bmatrix} R_0 & R_1 & R_2 \\ R_1 & R_0 & R_1 \\ R_2 & R_1 & R_0 \end{bmatrix} \begin{bmatrix} 1 \\ a_{21} \\ a_{22} \end{bmatrix} = \begin{bmatrix} E_2 \\ 0 \\ 0 \end{bmatrix}; \text{ etc.}
$$

The solution of each problem is obtained *in terms of* the solution of the previous one. In this manner, the final solution is gradually built up. In the process, one also finds *all* the lower order prediction-error filters.

The iteration is based on two key properties of the autocorrelation matrix:

first, the autocorrelation matrix of a given size contains as *subblocks* all the lower order autocorrelation matrices; and second, the autocorrelation matrix is *reflection invariant*. That is, it remains invariant under interchange of its columns and then its rows. This interchanging operation is equivalent to the similarity transformation by the "reversing" matrix J defined by

$$J = \begin{bmatrix} 0 & 0 & 0 & 1 \\ 0 & 0 & 1 & 0 \\ 0 & 1 & 0 & 0 \\ 1 & 0 & 0 & 0 \end{bmatrix} \tag{5.4.1}$$

The invariance property means that the autocorrelation matrix commutes with the matrix J

$$JRJ^{-1} = R \tag{5.4.2}$$

This property immediately implies that if

$$\begin{bmatrix} R_0 & R_1 & R_2 & R_3 \\ R_1 & R_0 & R_1 & R_2 \\ R_2 & R_1 & R_0 & R_1 \\ R_3 & R_2 & R_1 & R_0 \end{bmatrix} \begin{bmatrix} a_0 \\ a_1 \\ a_2 \\ a_3 \end{bmatrix} = \begin{bmatrix} b_0 \\ b_1 \\ b_2 \\ b_3 \end{bmatrix}$$

then also
$$\begin{bmatrix} R_0 & R_1 & R_2 & R_3 \\ R_1 & R_0 & R_1 & R_2 \\ R_2 & R_1 & R_0 & R_1 \\ R_3 & R_2 & R_1 & R_0 \end{bmatrix} \begin{bmatrix} a_3 \\ a_2 \\ a_1 \\ a_0 \end{bmatrix} = \begin{bmatrix} b_3 \\ b_2 \\ b_1 \\ b_0 \end{bmatrix}$$

The steps of the algorithm are explicitly as follows:

Step 0

Solve $R_0 \cdot 1 = E_0$. This defines E_0. Then, enlarge to the next size by padding a zero; that is,

$$\begin{bmatrix} R_0 & R_1 \\ R_1 & R_0 \end{bmatrix} \begin{bmatrix} 1 \\ 0 \end{bmatrix} = \begin{bmatrix} E_0 \\ \Delta_0 \end{bmatrix};$$ this defines Δ_0. Then also,

$$\begin{bmatrix} R_0 & R_1 \\ R_1 & R_0 \end{bmatrix} \begin{bmatrix} 0 \\ 1 \end{bmatrix} = \begin{bmatrix} \Delta_0 \\ E_0 \end{bmatrix};$$ by reversal invariance.

These are the preliminaries to Step 1.

Step 1

We wish to solve

$$\begin{bmatrix} R_0 & R_1 \\ R_1 & R_0 \end{bmatrix} \begin{bmatrix} 1 \\ a_{11} \end{bmatrix} = \begin{bmatrix} E_1 \\ 0 \end{bmatrix}$$

Try an expression of the form

$$\begin{bmatrix} 1 \\ a_{11} \end{bmatrix} = \begin{bmatrix} 1 \\ 0 \end{bmatrix} - \gamma_1 \begin{bmatrix} 0 \\ 1 \end{bmatrix} \qquad \text{with } \gamma_1 \text{ to be determined.}$$

Acting on both sides by

$$\begin{bmatrix} R_0 & R_1 \\ R_1 & R_0 \end{bmatrix}$$ and using the results of Step 0, we obtain

$$\begin{bmatrix} E_1 \\ 0 \end{bmatrix} = \begin{bmatrix} E_0 \\ \Delta_0 \end{bmatrix} - \gamma_1 \begin{bmatrix} \Delta_0 \\ E_0 \end{bmatrix}$$

or

$$E_0 - \gamma_1 \Delta_0 = E_1$$
$$\Delta_0 - \gamma_1 E_0 = 0$$

or

$$\gamma_1 = \frac{\Delta_0}{E_0}, \qquad E_1 = E_0 - \gamma_1 \Delta_0 = (1 - \gamma_1^2) E_0$$

These define γ_1 and E_1. As a preliminary step to Step 2, enlarge to the next size by padding a zero

$$\begin{bmatrix} R_0 & R_1 & R_2 \\ R_1 & R_0 & R_1 \\ R_2 & R_1 & R_0 \end{bmatrix} \begin{bmatrix} 1 \\ a_{11} \\ 0 \end{bmatrix} = \begin{bmatrix} E_1 \\ 0 \\ \Delta_1 \end{bmatrix}; \qquad \text{this defines } \Delta_1\text{. Then also,}$$

$$\begin{bmatrix} R_0 & R_1 & R_2 \\ R_1 & R_0 & R_1 \\ R_2 & R_1 & R_0 \end{bmatrix} \begin{bmatrix} 0 \\ a_{11} \\ 1 \end{bmatrix} = \begin{bmatrix} \Delta_1 \\ 0 \\ E_1 \end{bmatrix}; \qquad \text{by reversal invariance.}$$

Step 2

We wish to solve

$$\begin{bmatrix} R_0 & R_1 & R_2 \\ R_1 & R_0 & R_1 \\ R_2 & R_1 & R_0 \end{bmatrix} \begin{bmatrix} 1 \\ a_{21} \\ a_{22} \end{bmatrix} = \begin{bmatrix} E_2 \\ 0 \\ 0 \end{bmatrix}$$

Try expression

$$\begin{bmatrix} 1 \\ a_{21} \\ a_{22} \end{bmatrix} = \begin{bmatrix} 1 \\ a_{11} \\ 0 \end{bmatrix} = \gamma_2 \begin{bmatrix} 0 \\ a_{11} \\ 1 \end{bmatrix}; \qquad \text{with } \gamma_2 \text{ to be determined.}$$

From Step 1, we find

$$\begin{bmatrix} E_2 \\ 0 \\ 0 \end{bmatrix} = \begin{bmatrix} E_1 \\ 0 \\ \Delta_1 \end{bmatrix} - \gamma_2 \begin{bmatrix} \Delta_1 \\ 0 \\ E_1 \end{bmatrix}$$

or

$$E_1 - \gamma_2 \Delta_1 = E_2$$

$$\Delta_1 - \gamma_2 E_1 = 0$$

or

$$\gamma_2 = \frac{\Delta_1}{E_1} = \frac{R_2 + a_{11}R_1}{R_0 + a_{11}R_1}, \qquad \text{and} \qquad E_2 = (1 - \gamma_2^2)E_1$$

These define γ_2 and E_2. Enlarge to next size by padding a zero

$$\begin{bmatrix} R_0 & R_1 & R_2 & R_3 \\ R_1 & R_0 & R_1 & R_2 \\ R_2 & R_1 & R_0 & R_1 \\ R_3 & R_2 & R_1 & R_0 \end{bmatrix} \begin{bmatrix} 1 \\ a_{21} \\ a_{22} \\ 0 \end{bmatrix} = \begin{bmatrix} E_2 \\ 0 \\ 0 \\ \Delta_2 \end{bmatrix}; \qquad \text{this defines } \Delta_2\text{. Then also,}$$

$$\begin{bmatrix} R_0 & R_1 & R_2 & R_3 \\ R_1 & R_0 & R_1 & R_2 \\ R_2 & R_1 & R_0 & R_1 \\ R_3 & R_2 & R_1 & R_0 \end{bmatrix} \begin{bmatrix} 0 \\ a_{22} \\ a_{21} \\ 1 \end{bmatrix} = \begin{bmatrix} \Delta_2 \\ 0 \\ 0 \\ E_2 \end{bmatrix}; \qquad \text{by reversal invariance.}$$

Step 3

We wish to solve

$$\begin{bmatrix} R_0 & R_1 & R_2 & R_3 \\ R_1 & R_0 & R_1 & R_2 \\ R_2 & R_1 & R_0 & R_1 \\ R_3 & R_2 & R_1 & R_0 \end{bmatrix} \begin{bmatrix} 1 \\ a_{31} \\ a_{32} \\ a_{33} \end{bmatrix} = \begin{bmatrix} E_3 \\ 0 \\ 0 \\ 0 \end{bmatrix}$$

Try expression

$$\begin{bmatrix} 1 \\ a_{31} \\ a_{32} \\ a_{33} \end{bmatrix} = \begin{bmatrix} 1 \\ a_{21} \\ a_{22} \\ 0 \end{bmatrix} - \gamma_3 \begin{bmatrix} 0 \\ a_{22} \\ a_{21} \\ 1 \end{bmatrix} \quad \text{with } \gamma_3 \text{ to be determined}$$

From Step 2 we find

$$\begin{bmatrix} E_3 \\ 0 \\ 0 \\ 0 \end{bmatrix} = \begin{bmatrix} E_2 \\ 0 \\ 0 \\ \Delta_2 \end{bmatrix} - \gamma_3 \begin{bmatrix} \Delta_2 \\ 0 \\ 0 \\ E_2 \end{bmatrix}$$

or

$$E_2 - \gamma_3 \Delta_2 = E_3$$
$$\Delta_2 - \gamma_3 E_2 = 0$$

or

$$\gamma_3 = \frac{\Delta_2}{E_2} = \frac{R_3 + a_{21}R_2 + a_{22}R_1}{R_0 + a_{21}R_1 + a_{22}R_2}, \quad \text{and} \quad E_3 = (1 - \gamma_3^2)E_2$$

Clearly, the procedure can be continued to higher and higher dimensions, as required in each problem. Note that at each step, we used the order-updating Eqs. (1.7.40) in conjunction with Eq. (1.7.47).

5.5 *Autocorrelation Sequence Extensions*

In this section, we discuss the problem of extending an autocorrelation function and the related issues of singular autocorrelation matrices. The equivalence between an autocorrelation function and the set of reflection coefficients provides a convenient and systematic way to (a) *test* whether a given finite set of numbers are the autocorrelation lags of a stationary signal and (b) *extend* a given finite set of autocorrelation lags to arbitrary lengths while preserving the autocorrelation property.

For a finite set of numbers $\{R(0), R(1), \ldots, R(p)\}$ to be the lags of an autocorrelation function, it is *necessary and sufficient* that all reflection coefficients, extracted from this set via the Levinson recursion, have magnitude less than one; that is, $|\gamma_i| < 1$ for $i = 1,2, \ldots, p$, and also that $R(0) > 0$. These conditions are equivalent to the *positive definiteness* of the autocorrelation matrix R_p. The proof follows from the fact that the positivity of R_p is equivalent to the conditions on the prediction errors $E_i > 0$ for all $i = 0,1, \ldots, p$. In turn, these conditions are equivalent to $E_0 = R(0) > 0$

and, through Eq. (5.3.13), to the reflection coefficients having magnitude less than one.

The problem of extending a finite set $\{R(0), R(1), \ldots, R(p)\}$ of autocorrelation lags is to find a number $R(p+1)$ such that the extended set $\{R(0), \ldots, R(p), R(p+1)\}$ is still an autocorrelation sequence. This can be done by parametrizing $R(p+1)$ in terms of the next reflection coefficient γ_{p+1}. Solving Eq. (5.3.12) for $R(p+1)$ and using Eq. (5.3.11), we obtain

$$R(p+1) = \gamma_{p+1} E_p - [a_{p1} R(p) + \cdots + a_{pp} R(1)] \tag{5.5.1}$$

Any number γ_{p+1} in the range $-1 < \gamma_{p+1} < 1$ will give rise to an acceptable value for $R(p+1)$. The choice $\gamma_{p+1} = 0$ is special and corresponds to the so-called *autoregressive* or *maximum entropy extension* of the autocorrelation function (see Problem 5.16). If this choice is repeated to infinity, we will obtain the set of reflection coefficients

$$\{\gamma_1, \gamma_2, \cdots, \gamma_p, 0, 0, \cdots\}$$

It follows from the Levinson recursion that all prediction-error filters of order greater than p will remain equal to the pth filter, $A_p(z) = A_{p+1}(z) = A_{p+2}(z) = \cdots$. Therefore, the corresponding whitening filter will be $A(z) = A_p(z)$; that is, an autoregressive model of order p. With the exception of the above autoregressive extension that leads to an all-pole signal model, the extendibility conditions $|\gamma_{p+i}| < 1$, $i \geqslant 1$ do not necessarily guarantee that the resulting signal model will be a *rational* (pole-zero) model. See [16–20] for some recent results on this subject.

Example 5.5.1: Consider the three numbers $\{R(0), R(1), R(2)\} = \{8, 4, -1\}$. The Levinson recursion gives $\{\gamma_1, \gamma_2\} = \{0.5, -0.5\}$ and $\{E_1, E_2\} = \{6, 4.5\}$. Thus, the above numbers qualify to be autocorrelation lags. The corresponding prediction-error filters are

$$\mathbf{a}_1 = \begin{bmatrix} 1 \\ a_{11} \end{bmatrix} = \begin{bmatrix} 1 \\ -0.5 \end{bmatrix}, \quad \mathbf{a}_2 = \begin{bmatrix} 1 \\ a_{21} \\ a_{22} \end{bmatrix} = \begin{bmatrix} 1 \\ -0.75 \\ 0.5 \end{bmatrix}$$

The next lag in this sequence can be chosen according to Eq. (5.5.1)

$$R(3) = \gamma_3 E_2 - [a_{21} R(2) + a_{22} R(1)] = 4.5\gamma_3 - 2.75$$

where γ_3 is any number in the interval $-1 < \gamma_3 < 1$. The resulting possible values of $R(3)$ are plotted below versus γ_3. In particular, the autoregressive extension corresponds to $\gamma_3 = 0$, which gives $R(3) = -2.75$.

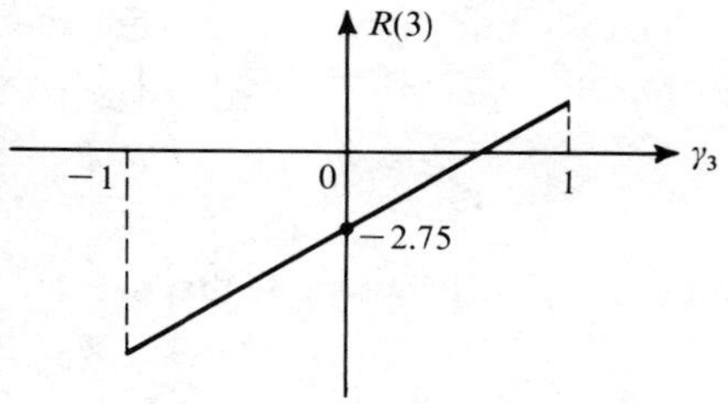

The end-points, $\gamma_{p+1} = \pm 1$, of the allowed interval $(-1,1)$ correspond to the two possible extreme values of $R(p+1)$:

$$R(p+1) = \pm E_p - [a_{p1} R(p) + \cdots + a_{pp} R(1)]$$

In this case, the corresponding prediction error vanishes $E_{p+1} = (1 - \gamma_{p+1}^2) E_p = 0$. This makes the resulting order-$(p+1)$ autocorrelation matrix R_{p+1} singular. The prediction filter becomes either the symmetric (if $\gamma_{p+1} = -1$) or antisymmetric (if $\gamma_{p+1} = 1$) combination

$$\mathbf{a}_{p+1} = \begin{bmatrix} \mathbf{a}_p \\ 0 \end{bmatrix} + \begin{bmatrix} 0 \\ \mathbf{a}_p^R \end{bmatrix}, \qquad A_{p+1}(z) = A_p(z) + z^{-1} A_p^R(z)$$

or,

$$\mathbf{a}_{p+1} = \begin{bmatrix} \mathbf{a}_p \\ 0 \end{bmatrix} - \begin{bmatrix} 0 \\ \mathbf{a}_p^R \end{bmatrix}, \qquad A_{p+1}(z) = A_p(z) - z^{-1} A_p^R(z)$$

In either case, it can be shown that the zeros of the polynomial $A_{p+1}(z)$ lie *on* the unit circle, and that the prediction filter $\mathbf{a}_{p+1}$ becomes an *eigenvector* of R_{p+1} with zero eigenvalue; namely, $R_{p+1}\mathbf{a}_{p+1} = 0$. This follows from the normal Eqs. (5.3.28) $R_{p+1}\mathbf{a}_{p+1} = E_{p+1}\mathbf{u}_{p+1}$ and $E_{p+1} = 0$.

Example 5.5.2: Consider the extended autocorrelation sequence of Example 5.5.1 defined by the singular choice $\gamma_3 = -1$. Then, $R(3) = -4.5 - 2.75 = -7.25$. The corresponding order 3 prediction-error filter is computed using the order 2 predictor and the Levinson recursion

$$\mathbf{a}_3 = \begin{bmatrix} 1 \\ a_{31} \\ a_{32} \\ a_{33} \end{bmatrix} = \begin{bmatrix} 1 \\ -0.75 \\ 0.5 \\ 0 \end{bmatrix} - \gamma_3 \begin{bmatrix} 0 \\ 0.5 \\ -0.75 \\ 1 \end{bmatrix} = \begin{bmatrix} 1 \\ -0.25 \\ -0.25 \\ 1 \end{bmatrix}$$

It is symmetric about its middle. Its zeros, computed as the solutions of $(1-0.25z^{-1}-0.25z^{-2}+z^{-3})=(1+z^{-1})(1-1.25z^{-1}+z^{-2})=0$, are

$$z = -1, \qquad z = \frac{5 \pm j\sqrt{39}}{8}$$

and lie on the unit circle. Finally, we verify that $\mathbf{a}_3$ is an eigenvector of R_3 with zero eigenvalue:

$$R_3\mathbf{a}_3 = \begin{bmatrix} 8 & 4 & -1 & -7.25 \\ 4 & 8 & 4 & -1 \\ -1 & 4 & 8 & 4 \\ -7.25 & -1 & 4 & 8 \end{bmatrix} \begin{bmatrix} 1 \\ -0.25 \\ -0.25 \\ 1 \end{bmatrix} = 0$$

Singular autocorrelation matrices, and the associated symmetric or antisymmetric prediction filters with zeros on the unit circle, find application in the method of *line spectrum pairs* (LSP) of speech analysis [21]. They are also intimately related to the eigenvector methods of spectrum estimation, such as Pisarenko's method of harmonic retrieval, discussed in Section 6.2. This connection arises from the property that singular autocorrelation matrices (with nonsingular principal minors) admit a *representation* as a sum of sinusoidal components [22], the frequencies of which are given precisely by the zeros, on the unit circle, of the corresponding prediction filter. This sinusoidal representation is equivalent to the eigen-decomposition of the matrix. The prediction filter can, alternatively, be computed as the eigenvector belonging to zero eigenvalue. The proof of these results can be derived as a limiting case; namely, the noise-free case, of the more general eigenvector methods that deal with sinusoids in noise. A direct proof is suggested in Problem 6.10.

Example 5.5.3: Consider the autocorrelation matrix $R = \begin{bmatrix} 2 & 1 & -1 \\ 1 & 2 & 1 \\ -1 & 1 & 2 \end{bmatrix}$. It is easily verified that the corresponding autocorrelation lags $R(k)$ admit the sinusoidal representation

$$R(k) = 2\cos(\omega_1 k) = e^{j\omega_1 k} + e^{-j\omega_1 k}, \quad \text{for} \quad k = 0, 1, 2$$

where $\omega_1 = \pi/3$. Sending these lags through the Levinson recursion, we find $\{\gamma_1, \gamma_2\} = \{0.5, -1\}$ and $\{E_1, E_2\} = \{1.5, 0\}$. Thus, R singular. Its eigenvalues are $\{0,3,3\}$. The corresponding prediction filters are $\mathbf{a}_1 = [1, -0.5]^T$ and $\mathbf{a}_2 = [1, -1, 1]^T$. It is easily verified that $\mathbf{a}_2$ is an eigenvector of R with zero eigenvalue, i.e., $R\mathbf{a}_2 = 0$. The corresponding eigenfilter $A_2(z) = 1 - z^{-1} + z^{-2}$ is symmetric about its middle and has zeros on the unit circle coinciding with the sinusoids present in R, namely, $z = e^{\pm j\omega_1}$. The other two eigenvectors of R are

$$\mathbf{c} = \begin{bmatrix} 1 \\ \cos\omega_1 \\ \cos 2\omega_1 \end{bmatrix} = \begin{bmatrix} 1 \\ 0.5 \\ -0.5 \end{bmatrix}, \qquad \mathbf{d} = \begin{bmatrix} 0 \\ \sin\omega_1 \\ \sin 2\omega_1 \end{bmatrix} = \sqrt{3} \begin{bmatrix} 0 \\ 0.5 \\ 0.5 \end{bmatrix}$$

both belonging to eigenvalue $\lambda = 3$. Their norm is $\|\mathbf{c}\| = \|\mathbf{d}\| = \sqrt{3/2}$. The three eigenvectors $\mathbf{a}_2$, $\mathbf{c}$, and $\mathbf{d}$ are mutually orthogonal. It is easily verified that the matrix R may be represented in the form $R = 2\mathbf{c}\mathbf{c}^T + 2\mathbf{d}\mathbf{d}^T$, which, after normalizing $\mathbf{c}$ and $\mathbf{d}$ to unit norm, is recognized as the eigen-decomposition of R, We can also express R in terms of its complex sinusoidal components in the form $R = \mathbf{s}\mathbf{s}^\dagger + \mathbf{s}^*\mathbf{s}^{*\dagger}$, where

$$\mathbf{s} = \mathbf{c} + j\mathbf{d} = \begin{bmatrix} 1 \\ e^{j\omega_1} \\ e^{2j\omega_1} \end{bmatrix}, \qquad \mathbf{s}^* = \mathbf{c} - j\mathbf{d} = \begin{bmatrix} 1 \\ e^{-j\omega_1} \\ e^{-2j\omega_1} \end{bmatrix}$$

Example 5.5.4: Similarly, one can verify that the four autocorrelation lags $\{8, 4, -1, -7.25\}$ of the singular matrix of Example 5.5.2 can be represented in the sinusoidal form

$$R(k) = P_1 e^{j\omega_1 k} + P_2 e^{j\omega_2 k} + P_3 e^{j\omega_3 k}, \quad \text{for} \quad k = 0, 1, 2, 3$$

where $P_1 = 8/13$. $P_2 = P_3 = 96/13$, and ω_i correspond to the zeros of the prediction filter $\mathbf{a}_3$; namely,

$$e^{j\omega_1} = -1, \quad e^{\pm j\omega_2} = \frac{5 \pm j\sqrt{39}}{8}$$

The matrix itself has the sinusoidal representation

$$R = P_1 \mathbf{s}_1 \mathbf{s}_1^\dagger + P_2 \mathbf{s}_2 \mathbf{s}_2^\dagger + P_3 \mathbf{s}_3 \mathbf{s}_3^\dagger, \qquad \text{where} \qquad \mathbf{s}_i = \begin{bmatrix} 1 \\ e^{j\omega_i} \\ e^{2j\omega_i} \\ e^{3j\omega_i} \end{bmatrix}$$

5.6 *Split Levinson Algorithm*

The main computational burden of Levinson's algorithm is $2p$ multiplications per stage, arising from the p multiplications in Eq. (5.3.15) and in the computation of the inner product (5.3.12). Thus, for M stages, the algorithm requires

$$2 \sum_{p=1}^{M} p = M(M+1)$$

or, $O(M^2)$ multiplications. This represents a factor of M savings over solving the normal Eq. (5.3.7) by direct matrix inversion, requiring $O(M^3)$ operations. The savings can be substantial considering that in speech processing $M = 10-15$, and in seismic processing $M = 100-200$. Progress in VLSI hardware has motivated the development of efficient *parallel* implementations of Levinson's algorithm and its variants [23–42]. With M parallel processors, the complexity of the algorithm is typically reduced by another factor of M to $O(M)$ or $O(M \log M)$ operations.

An interesting recent development is the realization that Levinson's algorithm has some inherent *redundancy,* which can be exploited to derive more efficient versions of the algorithm allowing an additional 50% reduction in computational complexity. These versions were motivated by a new stability test for linear prediction polynomials by Bistritz [43], and have been termed *Split Levinson* or *Immitance-Domain Levinson* algorithms [44–51]. They are based on efficient *three-term* recurrence relations for the *symmetrized* or antisymmetrized prediction polynomials. Following [44], we define the order-p symmetric polynomial

$$F_p(z) = A_{p-1}(z) + z^{-1}A_{p-1}^R(z), \qquad \mathbf{f}_p = \begin{bmatrix} \mathbf{a}_{p-1} \\ 0 \end{bmatrix} + \begin{bmatrix} 0 \\ \mathbf{a}_{p-1}^R \end{bmatrix} \tag{5.6.1}$$

The coefficient vector $\mathbf{f}_p$ is symmetric about its middle; that is, $f_{p0} = f_{pp} = 1$ and $f_{pi} = a_{p-1,i} + a_{p-1,p-i} = f_{p,p-i}$ for $i = 1, 2, \ldots, p-1$. Thus, only *half* of the vector $\mathbf{f}_p$ is needed to specify it completely. Using the backward recursion (5.3.22) to write $A_{p-1}(z)$ in terms of $A_p(z)$, we obtain the alternative expression

$$F_p = \frac{1}{1-\gamma_p^2}\left[(A_p + \gamma_p A_p^R) + z^{-1}(\gamma_p z A_p + z A_p^R)\right] = \frac{1}{1-\gamma_p}\left[A_p + A_p^R\right]$$

or,

$$(1-\gamma_p)F_p(z) = A_p(z) + A_p^R(z), \qquad (1-\gamma_p)\mathbf{f}_p = \mathbf{a}_p + \mathbf{a}_p^R \tag{5.6.2}$$

The polynomial $A_p(z)$ and its reverse may be recovered from the knowledge of the symmetric polynomials $F_p(z)$. Writing Eq. (5.6.1) for order $p+1$, we obtain $F_{p+1}(z) = A_p(z) + z^{-1}A_p^R(z)$. This equation, together with Eq. (5.6.2), may be solved for $A_p(z)$ and $A_p^R(z)$, yielding

$$A_p(z) = \frac{F_{p+1}(z) - (1-\gamma_p)z^{-1}F_p(z)}{1-z^{-1}}, \qquad A_p^R(z) = \frac{(1-\gamma_p)F_p(z) - F_{p+1}(z)}{1-z^{-1}} \tag{5.6.3}$$

Inserting these expressions into the forward Levinson recursion (5.3.16) and canceling the common factor $1/(1-z^{-1})$, we obtain a three-term recurrence relation for $F_p(z)$:

$$F_{p+2} - (1-\gamma_{p+1})z^{-1}F_{p+1} = \left[F_{p+1} - (1-\gamma_p)z^{-1}F_p\right] - \gamma_{p+1}z^{-1}\left[(1-\gamma_p)F_p - F_{p+1}\right]$$

or,

$$F_{p+2}(z) = (1+z^{-1})F_{p+1}(z) - \alpha_{p+1}z^{-1}F_p(z) \tag{5.6.4}$$

where $\alpha_{p+1} = (1+\gamma_{p+1})(1-\gamma_p)$. In block diagram form

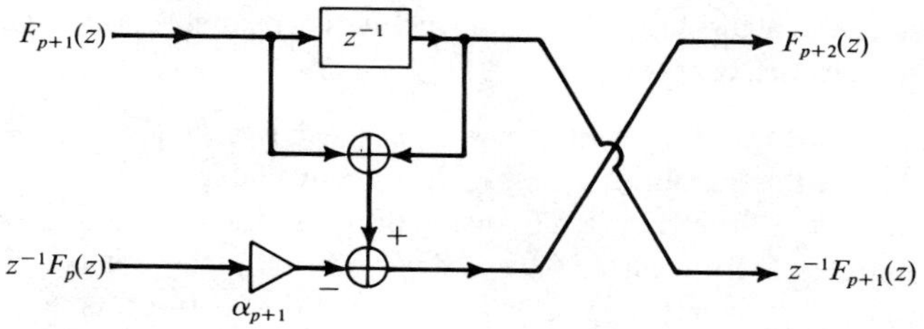

Because $F_p(z)$ has order p and is delayed by z^{-1}, the coefficient form of (5.6.4) is

$$\mathbf{f}_{p+2} = \begin{bmatrix} \mathbf{f}_{p+1} \\ 0 \end{bmatrix} + \begin{bmatrix} 0 \\ \mathbf{f}_{p+1} \end{bmatrix} - \alpha_{p+1} \begin{bmatrix} 0 \\ \mathbf{f}_p \\ 0 \end{bmatrix} \tag{5.6.5}$$

The recursion is initialized by $F_0(z) = 2$ and $F_1(z) = 1 + z^{-1}$. Because of the symmetric nature of the polynomial $F_p(z)$ only *half* of its coefficients need be updated by Eqs. (5.6.4) or (5.6.5). To complete the recursion, we need an efficient way to update the coefficients α_{p+1}. Taking the dot product of both sides of Eq. (5.6.2) with the vector $[R(0), R(1), \ldots, R(p)]^T$, we obtain

$$[R(0), \cdots, R(p)]\,\mathbf{a}_p + [R(0), \cdots, R(p)]\,\mathbf{a}_p^R = (1 - \gamma_p)\,[R(0), \cdots, R(p)]\,\mathbf{f}_p$$

The first term is recognized as the gapped function $g_p(0) = E_p$ and the second term as $g_p(p) = 0$. Dividing by $1 - \gamma_p$ and denoting $\tau_p = E_p/(1 - \gamma_p)$, we obtain

$$\tau_p = [R(0), R(1), \cdots, R(p)]\,\mathbf{f}_p = \sum_{i=0}^{p} R(i)\,f_{pi} \tag{5.6.6}$$

Because of the symmetric nature of $\mathbf{f}_p$, the quantity τ_p can be computed using only *half* of the terms in the above inner product. For example, if p is odd, the above sum may be folded to half its terms

$$\tau_p = \sum_{i=0}^{(p-1)/2} [R(i) + R(p-i)]\,f_{pi}$$

Because Eqs. (5.6.5) and (5.6.6) can be folded in half, the total number of multiplications per stage will be $2(p/2)$ or p, as compared with $2p$ for the classical Levinson algorithm. This is how the 50% reduction in computational complexity arises. The recursion is completed by noting that α_{p+1} can be computed in terms of τ_p by

$$\alpha_{p+1} = \frac{\tau_{p+1}}{\tau_p} \tag{5.6.7}$$

This follows from Eq. (5.3.13),

$$\frac{\tau_{p+1}}{\tau_p} = \frac{E_{p+1}}{1 - \gamma_{p+1}}\,\frac{1 - \gamma_p}{E_p} = \frac{1 - \gamma_{p+1}^2}{1 - \gamma_{p+1}}(1 - \gamma_p) = (1 + \gamma_{p+1})(1 - \gamma_p) = \alpha_{p+1}$$

A summary of the algorithm, which also includes a recursive computation of the reflection coefficients, is as follows:

0. Initialize with $\tau_0 = E_0 = R(0)$, $\gamma_0 = 0$, $\mathbf{f}_0 = [2]$, $\mathbf{f}_1 = [1,1]^T$
1. At stage p, the quantities τ_p, γ_p, $\mathbf{f}_p$, $\mathbf{f}_{p+1}$ are available
2. Compute τ_{p+1} from Eq. (5.6.6), using only half the terms in the sum
3. Compute α_{p+1} from Eq. (5.6.7), and solve for $\gamma_{p+1} = -1 + \alpha_{p+1}/(1 - \gamma_p)$
4. Compute $\mathbf{f}_{p+2}$ from Eq. (5.6.5), using half of the coefficients
5. Go to stage $p + 1$

After the final desired order is reached, the linear prediction polynomial can be recovered from Eq. (5.6.3). It can be written recursively as

$$a_{pi} = a_{p,i-1} + f_{p+1,i} - (1 - \gamma_p) f_{p,i-1}\,, \quad i = 1, 2, \cdots, p \tag{5.6.8}$$

with $a_{p0} = 1$, or vectorially

$$\begin{bmatrix} \mathbf{a}_p \\ 0 \end{bmatrix} = \begin{bmatrix} 0 \\ \mathbf{a}_p \end{bmatrix} + \mathbf{f}_{p+1} - (1 - \gamma_p) \begin{bmatrix} 0 \\ \mathbf{f}_p \end{bmatrix} \tag{5.6.9}$$

Using the three-term recurrence (5.6.5), we may replace $\mathbf{f}_{p+1}$ in terms of $\mathbf{f}_p$ and $\mathbf{f}_{p-1}$, and rewrite Eq. (5.6.9) as

$$\begin{bmatrix} \mathbf{a}_p \\ 0 \end{bmatrix} = \begin{bmatrix} 0 \\ \mathbf{a}_p \end{bmatrix} + \begin{bmatrix} \mathbf{f}_p \\ 0 \end{bmatrix} + \gamma_p \begin{bmatrix} 0 \\ \mathbf{f}_p \end{bmatrix} - \alpha_p \begin{bmatrix} 0 \\ \mathbf{f}_{p-1} \\ 0 \end{bmatrix} \tag{5.6.10}$$

or,

$$A_p(z) = z^{-1} A_p(z) + (1 + \gamma_p z^{-1}) F_p(z) - \alpha_p z^{-1} F_{p-1}(z) \tag{5.6.11}$$

Example 5.6.1: We rederive the results of Example 5.3.1 using this algorithm, showing explicitly the computational savings. Initialize with $\tau_0 = R(0) = 128$, $\mathbf{f}_0 = [2]$, and $\mathbf{f}_1 = [1,1]^T$. Using (5.6.6), we compute

$$\tau_1 = [R(0), R(1)]\,\mathbf{f}_1 = [R(0) + R(1)] f_{10} = 128 - 64 = 64$$

Thus, $\alpha_1 = \tau_1/\tau_0 = 64/128 = 0.5$ and $\gamma_1 = -1 + \alpha_1 = -0.5$. Using Eq. (5.6.5), we find

$$\mathbf{f}_2 = \begin{bmatrix} \mathbf{f}_1 \\ 0 \end{bmatrix} + \begin{bmatrix} 0 \\ \mathbf{f}_1 \end{bmatrix} - \alpha_1 \begin{bmatrix} 0 \\ \mathbf{f}_0 \\ 0 \end{bmatrix} = \begin{bmatrix} 1 \\ 1 \\ 0 \end{bmatrix} + \begin{bmatrix} 0 \\ 1 \\ 1 \end{bmatrix} - 0.5 \begin{bmatrix} 0 \\ 2 \\ 0 \end{bmatrix} = \begin{bmatrix} 1 \\ 1 \\ 1 \end{bmatrix}$$

and compute τ_2

$$\tau_2 = [R(0), R(1), R(2)]\,\mathbf{f}_2 = [R(0) + R(2)] f_{20} + R(1) f_{21} = 144$$

Thus, $\alpha_2 = \tau_2/\tau_1 = 144/64 = 2.25$ and $\gamma_2 = -1 + \alpha_2/(1-\gamma_1) = -1 + 2.25/1.5 = 0.5$. Next, compute $\mathbf{f}_3$ and τ_3

$$\mathbf{f}_3 = \begin{bmatrix} \mathbf{f}_2 \\ 0 \end{bmatrix} + \begin{bmatrix} 0 \\ \mathbf{f}_2 \end{bmatrix} - \alpha_2 \begin{bmatrix} 0 \\ \mathbf{f}_1 \\ 0 \end{bmatrix} = \begin{bmatrix} 1 \\ 1 \\ 1 \\ 0 \end{bmatrix} + \begin{bmatrix} 0 \\ 1 \\ 1 \\ 1 \end{bmatrix} - 2.25 \begin{bmatrix} 0 \\ 1 \\ 1 \\ 0 \end{bmatrix} = \begin{bmatrix} 1 \\ -0.25 \\ -0.25 \\ 1 \end{bmatrix}$$

$\tau_3 = [R(0), R(1), R(2), R(3)]\mathbf{f}_3 = [R(0) + R(3)]f_{30} + [R(1) + R(2)]f_{31} = 36$, which gives $\alpha_3 = \tau_3/\tau_2 = 36/144 = 0.25$ and $\gamma_3 = -1 + \alpha_3/(1-\gamma_2) = -0.5$. Next, compute $\mathbf{f}_4$ and τ_4

$$\mathbf{f}_4 = \begin{bmatrix} \mathbf{f}_3 \\ 0 \end{bmatrix} + \begin{bmatrix} 0 \\ \mathbf{f}_3 \end{bmatrix} - \alpha_3 \begin{bmatrix} 0 \\ \mathbf{f}_2 \\ 0 \end{bmatrix} = \begin{bmatrix} 1 \\ -0.25 \\ -0.25 \\ 1 \\ 0 \end{bmatrix} + \begin{bmatrix} 0 \\ 1 \\ -0.25 \\ -0.25 \\ 1 \end{bmatrix} - 0.25 \begin{bmatrix} 0 \\ 1 \\ 1 \\ 1 \\ 0 \end{bmatrix} = \begin{bmatrix} 1 \\ 0.5 \\ -0.75 \\ 0.5 \\ 1 \end{bmatrix}$$

$$\tau_3 = [R(0), R(1), R(2), R(3), R(4)]\mathbf{f}_4 =$$

$$= [R(0) + R(4)]f_{40} + [R(1) + R(3)]f_{41} + R(2)f_{42} = 81$$

which gives $\alpha_4 = \tau_4/\tau_3 = 81/36 = 2.25$ and $\gamma_4 = -1 + \alpha_4/(1-\gamma_3) = 0.5$. The final prediction filter $\mathbf{a}_4$ can be computed using Eq. (5.6.9) or (5.6.10). To avoid computing $\mathbf{f}_5$, we use Eq. (5.6.10), which gives

$$\begin{bmatrix} 1 \\ a_{41} \\ a_{42} \\ a_{43} \\ a_{44} \\ 0 \end{bmatrix} = \begin{bmatrix} 0 \\ 1 \\ a_{41} \\ a_{42} \\ a_{43} \\ a_{44} \end{bmatrix} + \begin{bmatrix} 1 \\ 0.5 \\ -0.75 \\ 0.5 \\ 1 \\ 0 \end{bmatrix} + 0.5 \begin{bmatrix} 0 \\ 1 \\ 0.5 \\ -0.75 \\ 0.5 \\ 1 \end{bmatrix} - 2.25 \begin{bmatrix} 0 \\ 1 \\ -0.25 \\ -0.25 \\ 1 \\ 0 \end{bmatrix}$$

with solution $\mathbf{a}_4 = [1, -0.25, -0.1875, 0.5, -0.5]^T$.

5.7 *Analysis and Synthesis Lattice Filters*

The Levinson recursion, expressed in the 2×2 matrix form of Eq. (5.3.18) forms the basis of the so-called *lattice*, or ladder, realizations of the prediction-error filters and their inverses [3,6]. Remembering that the prediction-error sequence $e_p(n)$ is the convolution of the prediction-error filter $(1, a_{p1}, a_{p2}, \ldots, a_{pp})$ with the original data sequence y_n; that is,

$$e_p^+(n) = y_n + a_{p1}y_{n-1} + a_{p2}y_{n-2} + \cdots + a_{pp}y_{n-p} \tag{5.7.1}$$

we find in the z-domain

$$E_p^+(z) = A_p(z)Y(z) \tag{5.7.2}$$

where we changed the notation slightly and denoted $e_p(n)$ by $e_p^+(n)$.

At this point, it proves convenient to introduce the *backward* prediction-error sequence, defined in terms of the *reverse* of the prediction-error filter, as follows:

$$E_p^-(z) = A_p^R(z)Y(z) \tag{5.7.3}$$

$$e_p^-(n) = y_{n-p} + a_{p1}y_{n-p+1} + a_{p2}y_{n-p+2} + \cdots + a_{pp}y_n \tag{5.7.4}$$

where $A_p^R(z)$ is the reverse of $A_p(z)$; namely,

$$\begin{aligned} A_p^R(z) &= z^{-p}A_p(z^{-1}) \\ &= a_{pp} + a_{p,p-1}z^{-1} + a_{p,p-2}z^{-2} + \cdots + a_{p1}z^{-(p-1)} + z^{-p} \end{aligned}$$

The signal sequence $e_p^-(n)$ may be interpreted as the *postdiction* error in postdicting the value of y_{n-p} on the basis of the *future p samples* $\{y_{n-p+1}, y_{n-p+2}, \ldots, y_n\}$, as shown below

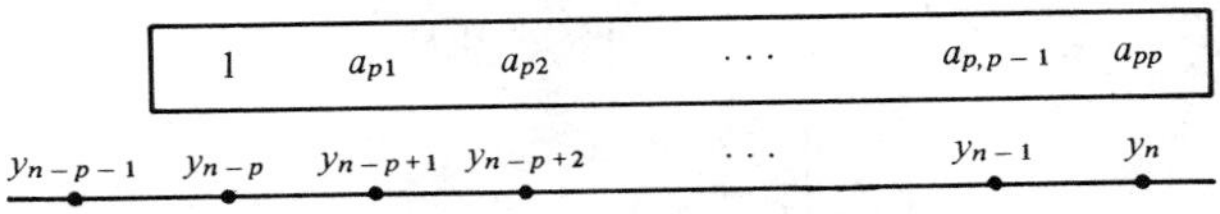

Actually, the above choice of postdiction coefficients is the *optimal* one that minimizes the *mean-squared postdiction error*

$$E[e_p^-(n)^2] = \min \tag{5.7.5}$$

This is easily shown by inserting Eq. (5.7.4) into Eq. (5.7.5) and using stationarity

$$\begin{aligned} E[e_p^-(n)^2] &= E\left[\left(\sum_{m=0}^{p} a_{pm}y_{n-p+m}\right)^2\right] = \sum_{m,k=0}^{p} a_{pm}E[y_{n-p+m}y_{n-p+k}]a_{pk} \\ &= \sum_{m,k=0}^{p} a_{pm}R(m-k)a_{pk} = E[e_p^+(n)^2] \end{aligned}$$

which shows that the forward and the backward prediction error criteria are the same, thus having the *same* solution for the optimal coefficients.

We can write Eqs. (5.7.1) and (5.7.4) vectorially

$$e_p^+(n) = [1, a_{p1}, \cdots, a_{pp}] \begin{bmatrix} y_n \\ y_{n-1} \\ \vdots \\ y_{n-p} \end{bmatrix} = \mathbf{a}_p^T \mathbf{y}_p(n) \tag{5.7.6a}$$

$$e_p^-(n) = [a_{pp}, a_{p,p-1}, \cdots, 1] \begin{bmatrix} y_n \\ y_{n-1} \\ \vdots \\ y_{n-p} \end{bmatrix} = \mathbf{a}_p^{RT} \mathbf{y}_p(n) = \mathbf{b}_p^T \mathbf{y}_p(n) \tag{5.7.6b}$$

They are recognized as the forward and backward prediction errors e_a and e_b of Eq. (1.7.9). Multiplying both sides of the Levinson recursion (5.3.18) by $Y(z)$, we cast it in the equivalent form in terms of the forward and backward prediction-error sequences:

$$\begin{bmatrix} E_{p+1}^+(z) \\ E_{p+1}^-(z) \end{bmatrix} = \begin{bmatrix} 1 & -\gamma_{p+1} z^{-1} \\ -\gamma_{p+1} & z^{-1} \end{bmatrix} \begin{bmatrix} E_p^+(z) \\ E_p^-(z) \end{bmatrix} \tag{5.7.7}$$

and in the time domain

$$\begin{aligned} e_{p+1}^+(n) &= e_p^+(n) - \gamma_{p+1} e_p^-(n-1) \\ e_{p+1}^-(n) &= e_p^-(n-1) - \gamma_{p+1} e_p^+(n) \end{aligned} \tag{5.7.8}$$

These are to be initialized at $p = 0$ by

$$E_0^{\pm}(z) = A_0(z) Y(z) = Y(z) \qquad \text{and} \qquad e_0^{\pm}(n) = y_n \tag{5.7.9}$$

These recursions are identical to Eq. (1.7.50), with the identifications $e_a \to e_{p+1}^+(n)$, $\bar{e}_a \to e_p^+(n)$, $e_b \to e_{p+1}^-(n)$, $\tilde{e}_b \to e_p^-(n-1)$, the last following from Eq. (5.3.26).

The lattice realization of the prediction-error filter is based on the recursion (5.7.8). Starting at $p = 0$ the output of the pth stage of (5.7.8) becomes the input of the $(p + 1)$th stage, up to the final desired order $p = M$. This is depicted in Fig. 5.3.

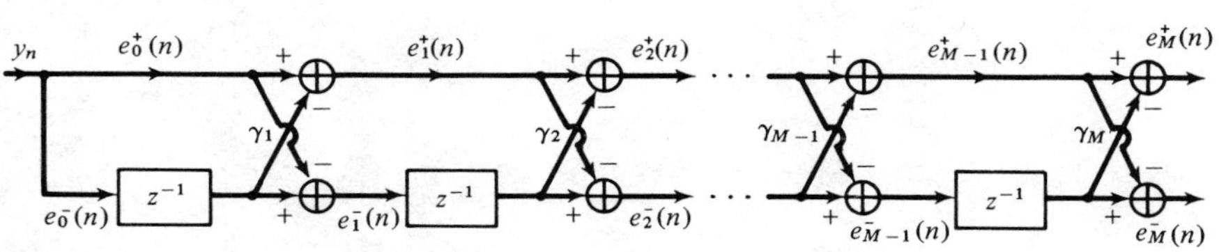

Figure 5.3 Analysis Lattice Filter

At each time instant n, the numbers held in the M delay registers of the lattice can be taken as the internal state of the lattice. The subroutine **lattice** (see Appendix B) is an implementation of Fig. 5.3. At each instant n, the routine takes two overall inputs $e_0^{\pm}(n)$, makes M calls to the routine **section** that implements the single lattice section (5.7.8), produces the two overall outputs $e_M^{\pm}(n)$, and updates the internal state of the lattice in preparation for the next call. By allowing the reflection coefficients to change between calls, the routine can also be used in adaptive lattice filters.

Equations (5.7.2) and (5.7.3) imply that the transfer function from the input y_n to the output $e_M^+(n)$ is the desired prediction-error filter $A_M(z)$, whereas the transfer function from y_n to $e_M^-(n)$ is the reversed filter $A_M^R(z)$. The lattice realization is therefore equivalent to the direct form realization

$$e_M^+(n) = y_n + a_{M1}y_{n-1} + \cdots + a_{MM}y_{n-M}$$

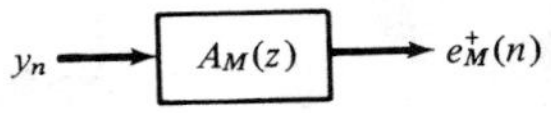

realized directly in terms of the prediction coefficients. It is depicted below

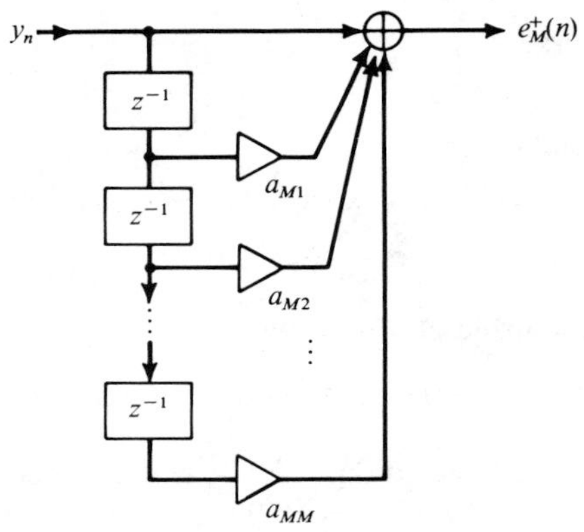

The synthesis filter $1/A_M(z)$ can also be realized in a lattice form. The input to the synthesis filter is the prediction error sequence $e_M^+(n)$ and its output is the original sequence y_n:

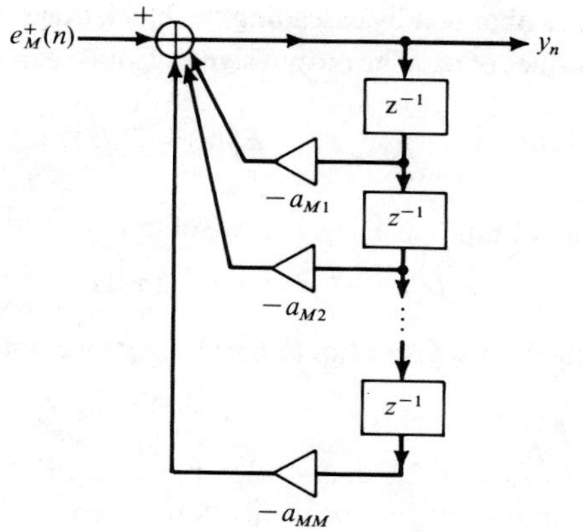

Since y_n corresponds to $e_0^+(n)$, we must write Eq. (5.7.8) in an order-decreasing form, starting at $e_M^+(n)$ and ending with $e_0^+(n) = y_n$. Rearranging the terms of the first of Eqs. (5.7.8) we have

$$\begin{aligned} e_p^+(n) &= e_{p+1}^+(n) + \gamma_{p+1} e_p^-(n-1) \\ e_{p+1}^-(n) &= e_p^-(n-1) - \gamma_{p+1} e_p^+(n) \end{aligned} \tag{5.7.10}$$

which can be realized as shown below:

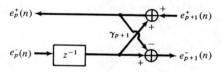

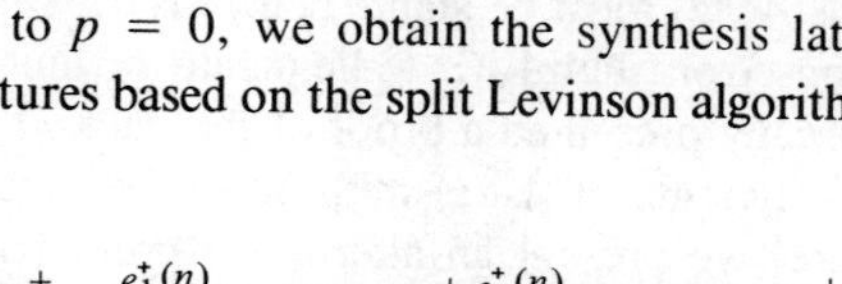

Note the difference in signs in the upper and lower adders. Putting together the stages from $p = M$ to $p = 0$, we obtain the synthesis lattice filter shown in Fig. 5.4. Lattice structures based on the split Levinson algorithm can also be devel-

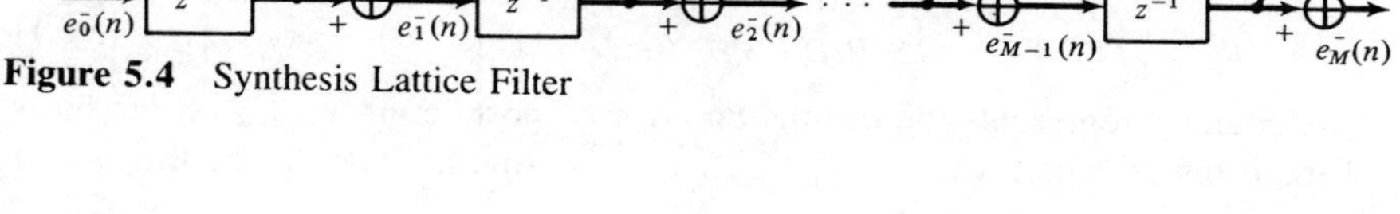

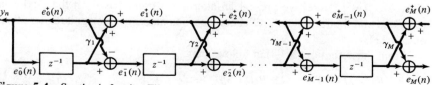

Figure 5.4 Synthesis Lattice Filter

oped [46,47]. They are obtained by cascading the block diagram realizations of Eq. (5.6.4) for different values of α_p. The output signals from each section are defined by

$$e_p(n) = \sum_{i=0}^{p} f_{pi} y_{n-i}\,, \qquad E_p(z) = F_p(z)Y(z)$$

Multiplying both sides of Eq. (5.6.1) by $Y(z)$ we obtain the time-domain expression

$$e_p(n) = e^{+}_{p-1}(n) + e^{-}_{p-1}(n-1)$$

Similarly, multiplying both sides of Eq. (5.6.4) by $Y(z)$ we obtain the recursions

$$e_{p+2}(n) = e_{p+1}(n) + e_{p+1}(n-1) - \alpha_{p+1} e_p(n-1)$$

They are initialized by $e_0(n) = 2y_n$ and $e_1(n) = y_n + y_{n-1}$. Putting together the various sections we obtain the lattice-type realization

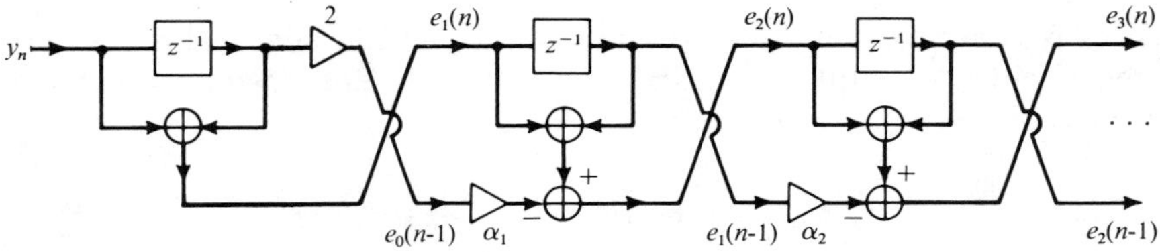

The forward prediction error may be recovered from Eq. (5.6.3) or (5.6.11) by multiplying both sides with $Y(z)$; for example, using Eq. (5.6.11) we find

$$e^{+}_p(n) = e^{+}_p(n-1) + e_p(n) + \gamma_p e_p(n-1) - \alpha_p e_{p-1}(n-1)$$

5.8 *Alternative Proof of the Minimal-Phase Property*

The synthesis filter $1/A_M(z)$ must be stable and causal, which requires all the M zeros of the prediction-error filter $A_M(z)$ to lie inside the unit circle in the complex z-plane. We have already presented a proof of this fact which was based on the property that the coefficients of $A_M(z)$ minimized the mean-squared prediction error $E[e^{+}_M(n)^2]$. Here, we present an alternative proof based on the Levinson recursion and the fact that all reflection coefficients γ_p have magnitude less than one [6,11].

From the definition (5.7.4), it follows that

$$e^{-}_p(n-1) = y_{n-p-1} + a_{p1}y_{n-p} + a_{p2}y_{n-p+1} + \cdots + a_{pp}y_{n-1} \qquad (5.8.1)$$

This quantity represents the estimation error of postdicting y_{n-p-1} on the basis of the p future samples $y_{n-p}, y_{n-p+1}, \ldots, y_{n-1}$. Another way to say this is that the linear combination of these p samples is the projection of y_{n-p-1} onto the subspace of random variables spanned by $\{y_{n-p}, y_{n-p+1}, \ldots, y_{n-1}\}$; that is,

$$e_p^-(n-1) = y_{n-p-1} - (\text{projection of } y_{n-p-1} \text{ onto } \{y_{n-p}, y_{n-p+1}, \ldots, y_{n-1}\}) \tag{5.8.2}$$

On the other hand, $e_p^+(n)$ given in Eq. (5.7.1) is the estimation error of y_n based on the *same* set of samples. Therefore,

$$e_p^+(n) = y_n - (\text{projection of } y_n \text{ onto } \{y_{n-p}, y_{n-p+1}, \ldots, y_{n-1}\}) \tag{5.8.3}$$

The samples $y_{n-p}, y_{n-p+1}, \ldots, y_{n-1}$ are the *intermediate* set of samples between y_{n-p-1} and y_n, as shown below:

Therefore, according to the discussion in Section 1.6, the PARCOR coefficient between y_{n-p-1} and y_n with the effect of intermediate samples removed is given by

$$\text{PARCOR} = \frac{E[e_p^+(n)e_p^-(n-1)]}{E[e_p^-(n-1)^2]}$$

This is precisely the reflection coefficient γ_{p+1} of Eq. (5.3.11). Indeed, using Eq. (5.8.1) and the gapped conditions we find

$$\begin{aligned} E[e_p^+(n)e_p^-(n-1)] &= E[e_p^+(n)(y_{n-p-1} + a_{p1}y_{n-p} + \cdots + a_{pp}y_{n-1})] \\ &= g_p(p+1) + a_{p1}g_p(p) + a_{p2}g_p(p-1) \\ &\qquad + \cdots + a_{pp}g_p(1) \\ &= g_p(p+1) \end{aligned}$$

Similarly, invoking stationarity and Eq. (5.7.5),

$$E[e_p^-(n-1)^2] = E[e_p^-(n)^2] = E[e_p^+(n)^2] = g_p(0)$$

Thus, the reflection coefficient γ_{p+1} is really a *PARCOR coefficient*:

$$\gamma_{p+1} = \frac{E[e_p^+(n)e_p^-(n-1)]}{E[e_p^-(n-1)^2]} = \frac{E[e_p^+(n)e_p^-(n-1)]}{E[e_p^+(n)^2]} \tag{5.8.4}$$

Using the Schwarz inequality with respect to the inner product $E[uv]$, that is,

$$(E[uv])^2 \leq E[u^2]E[v^2]$$

Eq. (5.8.4) implies that γ_{p+1} has magnitude less than one:

$$|\gamma_{p+1}| \leq 1 \qquad \text{for each } p = 0, 1, \ldots \tag{5.8.5}$$

To prove the minimal-phase property of $A_M(z)$ we must show that all of its M zeros are inside the unit circle. We will do this by induction. Let Z_p and N_p

denote the number of zeros and poles of $A_p(z)$ that lie *inside* the unit circle. Levinson's recursion, Eq. (5.3.13), expresses $A_{p+1}(z)$ as the sum of $A_p(z)$ and a correction term $F(z) = -\gamma_{p+1}z^{-1}A_p^R(z)$

$$A_{p+1}(z) = A_p(z) + F(z)$$

Using the inequality (5.6.5) and the fact that $A_p^R(z)$ has the *same* magnitude spectrum as $A_p(z)$, we find the inequality

$$|F(z)| = |-\gamma_{p+1}z^{-1}A_p^R(z)| = |\gamma_{p+1}A_p(z)| \leq |A_p(z)|$$

for $z = \exp(j\omega)$ on the unit circle. Then, the argument principle and Rouche's theorem imply that the addition of the function $F(z)$ will not affect the difference $N_p - Z_p$ of poles and zeros contained inside the unit circle. Thus,

$$N_{p+1} - Z_{p+1} = N_p - Z_p$$

Since the only pole of $A_p(z)$ is the multiple pole of order p at the origin arising from the term z^{-p}, it follows that $N_p = p$. Therefore,

$$(p + 1) - Z_{p+1} = p - Z_p$$

or

$$Z_{p+1} = Z_p + 1$$

Starting at $p = 0$ with $A_0(z) = 1$, we have $Z_0 = 0$. It follows that

$$Z_p = p$$

which states that for each p, all the p zeros of the polynomial $A_p(z)$ lie inside the unit circle.

Another way to state this result is: "A necessary and sufficient condition for a polynomial $A_M(z)$ to have all of its M zeros strictly inside the unit circle is that all reflection coefficients $\{\gamma_1, \gamma_2, \ldots, \gamma_M\}$ resulting from $A_M(z)$ via the backward recursion (5.3.21) have magnitude strictly less than one." This is essentially equivalent to the classic *Schur-Cohn* test of stability [52–56]. The subroutine **bkwlev** can be used in this regard to obtain the sequence of reflection coefficients. The Bistritz test [43], mentioned in Section 5.6, is an alternative stability test.

Example 5.8.1: Test the minimal phase property of the polynomials

(a) $A(z) = 1 - 2.60z^{-1} + 2.55z^{-2} - 2.80z^{-3} + 0.50z^{-4}$
(b) $A(z) = 1 - 1.40z^{-1} + 1.47z^{-2} - 1.30z^{-3} + 0.50z^{-4}$

Sending the coefficients of each through the subroutine **bkwlev** we find the set of reflection coefficients

(a) $\{0.4, -0.5, 2.0, -0.5\}$
(b) $\{0.4, -0.5, 0.8, -0.5\}$

Since among (a) there is one reflection coefficient of magnitude greater than one, case (a) will not be minimal phase, whereas case (b) is.

5.9 *Orthogonality of Backward Prediction Errors—Cholesky Factorization*

Another interesting structural property of the lattice realizations is that, in a certain sense, the *backward* prediction errors $e_p^-(n)$ are orthogonal to each other [3,6]. To see this, consider the case $M = 3$, and form the matrix product

$$\underbrace{\begin{bmatrix} R_0 & R_1 & R_2 & R_3 \\ R_1 & R_0 & R_1 & R_2 \\ R_2 & R_1 & R_0 & R_1 \\ R_3 & R_2 & R_1 & R_0 \end{bmatrix}}_{R} \underbrace{\begin{bmatrix} 1 & a_{11} & a_{22} & a_{33} \\ 0 & 1 & a_{21} & a_{32} \\ 0 & 0 & 1 & a_{31} \\ 0 & 0 & 0 & 1 \end{bmatrix}}_{L^T} = \underbrace{\begin{bmatrix} E_0 & 0 & 0 & 0 \\ * & E_1 & 0 & 0 \\ * & * & E_2 & 0 \\ * & * & * & E_3 \end{bmatrix}}_{L_1}$$

Because the normal equations (written upside down) are satisfied by each prediction-error filter, the right-hand side will be a lower-triangular matrix. The "don't care" entries have been denoted by *s. Multiply from the left by L to get

$$LRL^T = LL_1 = \begin{bmatrix} E_0 & 0 & 0 & 0 \\ * & E_1 & 0 & 0 \\ * & * & E_2 & 0 \\ * & * & * & E_3 \end{bmatrix}$$

Since L is by definition lower-triangular, the right-hand side will still be lower-triangular. But the left-hand side is symmetric. Thus, so is the right-hand side and as a result it must be diagonal. We have shown

$$LRL^T = D = \operatorname{diag}\{E_0, E_1, E_2, E_3\} \tag{5.9.1}$$

or, written explicitly,

$$\begin{bmatrix} 1 & 0 & 0 & 0 \\ a_{11} & 1 & 0 & 0 \\ a_{22} & a_{21} & 1 & 0 \\ a_{33} & a_{32} & a_{31} & 1 \end{bmatrix} \begin{bmatrix} R_0 & R_1 & R_2 & R_3 \\ R_1 & R_0 & R_1 & R_2 \\ R_2 & R_1 & R_0 & R_1 \\ R_3 & R_2 & R_1 & R_0 \end{bmatrix} \begin{bmatrix} 1 & a_{11} & a_{22} & a_{33} \\ 0 & 1 & a_{21} & a_{32} \\ 0 & 0 & 1 & a_{31} \\ 0 & 0 & 0 & 1 \end{bmatrix}$$

$$= \begin{bmatrix} E_0 & 0 & 0 & 0 \\ 0 & E_1 & 0 & 0 \\ 0 & 0 & E_2 & 0 \\ 0 & 0 & 0 & E_3 \end{bmatrix}$$

This is identical to Eq. (1.7.17).

The pqth element of this matrix equation is then

$$\mathbf{b}_p^T R \mathbf{b}_q = \delta_{pq} E_p \qquad 0 \leqslant p,q \leqslant 3 \tag{5.9.2}$$

where $\mathbf{b}_p$ and $\mathbf{b}_q$ denote the pth and qth columns of L^T. These are recognized as the *backward prediction-error filters* of orders p and q. Eq. (5.9.2) implies then the orthogonality of the backward prediction-error filters with respect to an inner product $\mathbf{x}^T R \mathbf{y}$.

The backward prediction errors $e_p^-(n)$ can be expressed in terms of the $\mathbf{b}_p$s and the vector of samples $\mathbf{y}(n) = [y_n, y_{n-1}, y_{n-2}, y_{n-3}]^T$, as follows:

$$\begin{aligned}
e_0^-(n) &= [1,\ 0,\ 0,\ 0]\mathbf{y}(n) = \mathbf{b}_0^T\mathbf{y}(n) = y_n \\
e_1^-(n) &= [a_{11}, 1,\ 0,\ 0]\mathbf{y}(n) = \mathbf{b}_1^T\mathbf{y}(n) = a_{11}y_n + y_{n-1} \\
e_2^-(n) &= [a_{22}, a_{21}, 1,\ 0]\mathbf{y}(n) = \mathbf{b}_2^T\mathbf{y}(n) = a_{22}y_n + a_{21}y_{n-1} + y_{n-2} \\
e_3^-(n) &= [a_{33}, a_{32}, a_{31}, 1]\mathbf{y}(n) = \mathbf{b}_3^T\mathbf{y}(n) = a_{33}y_n + a_{32}y_{n-1} + a_{31}y_{n-2} + y_{n-3}
\end{aligned} \tag{5.9.3}$$

which can be arranged into the vector form

$$\mathbf{e}^-(n) = \begin{bmatrix} e_0^-(n) \\ e_1^-(n) \\ e_2^-(n) \\ e_3^-(n) \end{bmatrix} = \begin{bmatrix} 1 & 0 & 0 & 0 \\ a_{11} & 1 & 0 & 0 \\ a_{22} & a_{21} & 1 & 0 \\ a_{33} & a_{32} & a_{31} & 1 \end{bmatrix} \begin{bmatrix} y_n \\ y_{n-1} \\ y_{n-2} \\ y_{n-3} \end{bmatrix} = L\mathbf{y}(n) \tag{5.9.4}$$

It is identical to Eq. (1.7.15). Using Eq. (5.9.1), it follows now that the covariance matrix of $\mathbf{e}^-(n)$ is *diagonal;* indeed, since $R = E[\mathbf{y}(n)\mathbf{y}(n)^T]$,

$$R_{e^-e^-} = E[\mathbf{e}^-(n)\mathbf{e}^-(n)^T] = LRL^T = D \tag{5.9.5}$$

which can also be expressed component-wise as the zero lag cross-correlation

$$R_{e_p^-e_q^-}(0) = E[e_p^-(n)e_q^-(n)] = \delta_{pq}E_p \tag{5.9.6}$$

Thus, at each time instant n, the backward prediction errors $e_p^-(n)$ are mutually uncorrelated (orthogonal) with each other. The orthogonality conditions (5.9.6) and the lower-triangular nature of L render the transformation (5.9.4) equivalent to the *Gram-Schmidt* orthogonalization of the data vector $\mathbf{y}(n) = [y_n, y_{n-1}, y_{n-2}, y_{n-3}]^T$. Equation (5.9.1), written as

$$R = L^{-1}DL^{-T}$$

corresponds to an *LU Cholesky factorization* of the covariance matrix R.

Since the backward errors $e_p^-(n)$; $p = 0,1,2, \ldots, M$, for an Mth order predictor are generated at the output of each successive lattice segment of Fig. 5.3, we may view the *analysis lattice* filter as an *implementation* of the *Gram-*

Schmidt orthogonalization of the vector $\mathbf{y}(n) = [y_n, y_{n-1}, y_{n-2}, \ldots, y_{n-M}]^T$. It is interesting to note, in this respect, that this implementation requires only knowledge of the reflection coefficients $\{\gamma_1, \gamma_2, \ldots, \gamma_M\}$.

The data vector $\mathbf{y}(n)$ can also be orthogonalized by means of the forward predictors, using the matrix U. This representation, however, is not as conveniently realized by the lattice structure because the resulting orthogonalized vector consists of forward prediction errors that are orthogonal, but *not* at the same time instant. This can be seen from the definition of the forward errors

$$U\mathbf{y}(n) = \begin{bmatrix} 1 & a_{31} & a_{32} & a_{33} \\ 0 & 1 & a_{21} & a_{22} \\ 0 & 0 & 1 & a_{11} \\ 0 & 0 & 0 & 1 \end{bmatrix} \begin{bmatrix} y_n \\ y_{n-1} \\ y_{n-2} \\ y_{n-3} \end{bmatrix} = \begin{bmatrix} e_3^+(n) \\ e_2^+(n-1) \\ e_1^+(n-2) \\ e_0^+(n-3) \end{bmatrix}$$

Thus, additional delays must be inserted at the forward outputs of the lattice structure to achieve orthogonalization. For this reason, the backward outputs, being mutually orthogonal at the *same* time instant n, are preferred. The corresponding UL factorization of R is in this basis

$$URU^T = \text{diag}\{E_3, E_2, E_1, E_0\}$$

This is the reverse of Eq. (5.9.1) obtained by acting on both sides by the reversing matrix J and using the fact that $U = JLJ$, the invariance of $R = JRJ$, and $J^2 = I$.

The above orthogonalization may also be understood in the z-domain: Since the backward prediction error $e_p^-(n)$ is the output of the reversed prediction-error filter $A_p^R(z)$ driven by the data sequence y_n, we have for the cross-density

$$S_{e_p^- e_q^-}(z) = A_p^R(z) S_{yy}(z) A_q^R(z^{-1})$$

Integrating this expression over the unit circle and using Eq. (5.9.6), we find

$$\begin{aligned} \oint_{\text{u.c.}} A_p^R(z) S_{yy}(z) A_q^R(z^{-1}) \frac{dz}{2\pi jz} &= \oint S_{e_p^- e_q^-}(z) \frac{dz}{2\pi jz} = R_{e_p^- e_q^-}(0) \\ &= E[e_p^-(n) e_q^-(n)] = \delta_{pq} E_p \end{aligned} \tag{5.9.7}$$

That is, the reverse polynomials $A_p^R(z)$ are *mutually orthogonal* with respect to the above inner product defined by the (positive-definite) weighting function $S_{yy}(z)$. Equation (5.9.7) is the z-domain expression of Eq. (5.9.2). This result establishes an intimate connection between the linear prediction problem and the theory of *orthogonal polynomials* on the unit circle developed by Szegö [57,58].

The LU factorization of R implies a UL factorization of the inverse of R; that is, solving Eq. (5.9.1) for R^{-1} we have:

$$R^{-1} = L^T D^{-1} L \tag{5.9.8}$$

Since the Levinson recursion generates all the lower order prediction-error filters, it essentially generates the inverse of R.

The computation of this inverse may also be done *recursively* in the *order*, as follows. To keep track of the order let us use an extra index

$$R_3^{-1} = L_3^T D_3^{-1} L_3 \tag{5.9.9}$$

The matrix L_3 contains as a submatrix the matrix L_2; in fact

$$L_3 = \left[\begin{array}{ccc|c} 1 & 0 & 0 & 0 \\ a_{11} & 1 & 0 & 0 \\ a_{22} & a_{21} & 1 & 0 \\ \hline a_{33} & a_{32} & a_{31} & 1 \end{array}\right] = \left[\begin{array}{c|c} L_2 & \mathbf{0} \\ \hline \boldsymbol{\alpha}_3^{RT} & 1 \end{array}\right] \tag{5.9.10}$$

where $\boldsymbol{\alpha}_3^{RT}$ denotes the transpose of the *reverse* of the vector of prediction coefficients; namely, $\boldsymbol{\alpha}_3^{RT} = [a_{33}, a_{32}, a_{31}]$. The diagonal matrix D_3^{-1} may also be block divided in the same manner:

$$D_3^{-1} = \left[\begin{array}{c|c} D_2^{-1} & \mathbf{0} \\ \hline \mathbf{0}^T & E_3^{-1} \end{array}\right]$$

Inserting these block decompositions into Eq. (5.9.9) and using the lower order result $R_2^{-1} = L_2^T D_2^{-1} L_2$, we find

$$R_3^{-1} = \left[\begin{array}{c|c} R_2^{-1} + \dfrac{1}{E_3}\boldsymbol{\alpha}_3^R \boldsymbol{\alpha}_3^{RT} & \dfrac{1}{E_3}\boldsymbol{\alpha}_3^R \\ \hline \dfrac{1}{E_3}\boldsymbol{\alpha}_3^{RT} & \dfrac{1}{E_3} \end{array}\right] = \begin{bmatrix} R_2^{-1} & \mathbf{0} \\ \mathbf{0}^T & 0 \end{bmatrix} + \frac{1}{E_3}\mathbf{b}_3\mathbf{b}_3^T \tag{5.9.11}$$

where $\mathbf{b}_3 = \mathbf{a}_3^R = [\boldsymbol{\alpha}_3^{RT}, 1]^T$. This is identical to Eq. (1.7.28).

Thus, through Levinson's algorithm, as the prediction coefficients $\boldsymbol{\alpha}_3$ and error E_3 are obtained, the inverse of R may be *updated* to the next higher order. The result (5.9.11) also suggests an efficient way of solving more general normal equations of the type

$$R_3\mathbf{h}_3 = \begin{bmatrix} R_0 & R_1 & R_2 & R_3 \\ R_1 & R_0 & R_1 & R_2 \\ R_2 & R_1 & R_0 & R_1 \\ R_3 & R_2 & R_1 & R_0 \end{bmatrix} \begin{bmatrix} h_{30} \\ h_{31} \\ h_{32} \\ h_{33} \end{bmatrix} = \begin{bmatrix} r_0 \\ r_1 \\ r_2 \\ r_3 \end{bmatrix} = \mathbf{r}_3 \tag{5.9.12}$$

for a given right-hand vector $\mathbf{r}_3$. Such normal equations arise in the design of FIR Wiener filters; for example, Eq. (4.3.9). The solution for $\mathbf{h}_3$ is obtained recursively from the solution of similar linear equations of lower order. For example, let $\mathbf{h}_2$ be the solution of the previous order

$$R_2\mathbf{h}_2 = \begin{bmatrix} R_0 & R_1 & R_2 \\ R_1 & R_0 & R_1 \\ R_2 & R_1 & R_0 \end{bmatrix} \begin{bmatrix} h_{20} \\ h_{21} \\ h_{22} \end{bmatrix} = \begin{bmatrix} r_0 \\ r_1 \\ r_2 \end{bmatrix} = \mathbf{r}_2$$

where the right-hand side vector $\mathbf{r}_2$ is *part* of $\mathbf{r}_3$. Then, Eq. (5.9.11) implies a recursive relationship between $\mathbf{h}_3$ and $\mathbf{h}_2$:

$$\mathbf{h}_3 = R_3^{-1}\mathbf{r}_3 = \left[\begin{array}{c|c} R_2^{-1} + \frac{1}{E_3}\boldsymbol{\alpha}_3^R\boldsymbol{\alpha}_3^{RT} & \frac{1}{E_3}\boldsymbol{\alpha}_3^R \\ \hline \frac{1}{E_3}\boldsymbol{\alpha}_3^{RT} & \frac{1}{E_3} \end{array}\right] \left[\begin{array}{c} \mathbf{r}_2 \\ \hline r_3 \end{array}\right]$$

$$= \left[\begin{array}{c} \mathbf{h}_2 + \frac{1}{E_3}\boldsymbol{\alpha}_3^R(r_3 + \boldsymbol{\alpha}_3^{RT}\mathbf{r}_2) \\ \hline \frac{1}{E_3}(r_3 + \boldsymbol{\alpha}_3^{RT}\mathbf{r}_2) \end{array}\right]$$

In terms of the reverse prediction-error filter $\mathbf{a}_3^{RT} = [a_{33}, a_{32}, a_{31}, 1] = [\boldsymbol{\alpha}_3^{RT}, 1]$, we may write

$$\mathbf{h}_3 = \left[\begin{array}{c} \mathbf{h}_2 \\ \hline 0 \end{array}\right] + c\mathbf{b}_3^T \qquad \text{where } c = (r_3 + \boldsymbol{\alpha}_3^{RT}\mathbf{r}_2)/E_3 = \mathbf{b}_3^T\mathbf{r}_3/E_3 \tag{5.9.13}$$

Thus, the recursive updating of the solution $\mathbf{h}$ must be done by carrying out the auxiliary updating of the prediction-error filters. The method requires $O(M^2)$ operations, compared to $O(M^3)$ if the inverse of R were to be computed directly. This recursive method of solving general normal equations, developed by Robinson and Treitel, has been reviewed elsewhere [7,8,59–61].

Some additional insight into the properties of these recursions can be gained by using the Toeplitz property of R. This property together with the symmetric nature of R imply that R commutes with the reversing matrix:

$$J_3 = \begin{bmatrix} 0 & 0 & 0 & 1 \\ 0 & 0 & 1 & 0 \\ 0 & 1 & 0 & 0 \\ 1 & 0 & 0 & 0 \end{bmatrix} = J_3^{-1} \qquad J_3R_3J_3 = R_3 \tag{5.9.14}$$

Therefore, even though the inverse R_3^{-1} is not Toeplitz, it still commutes with this reversing matrix; that is,

$$J_3 R_3^{-1} J_3 = R_3^{-1} \tag{5.9.15}$$

The effect of this symmetry property on the block decomposition (5.9.11) may be seen by decomposing J_3 also as

$$J_3 = \left[\begin{array}{c|c} \mathbf{0} & J_2 \\ \hline 1 & \mathbf{0}^T \end{array}\right] = \left[\begin{array}{c|c} \mathbf{0}^T & 1 \\ \hline J_2 & \mathbf{0} \end{array}\right]$$

where J_2 is the lower order reversing matrix. Combining Eq. (5.9.15) with Eq. (5.9.11) we find

$$R_3^{-1} = J_3 R_3^{-1} J_3 = \left[\begin{array}{c|c} \mathbf{0}^T & 1 \\ \hline J_2 & \mathbf{0} \end{array}\right] \left[\begin{array}{c|c} R_2^{-1} + \dfrac{1}{E_3}\boldsymbol{\alpha}_3^R \boldsymbol{\alpha}_3^{RT} & \dfrac{1}{E_3}\boldsymbol{\alpha}_3^R \\ \hline \dfrac{1}{E_3}\boldsymbol{\alpha}_3^{RT} & \dfrac{1}{E_3} \end{array}\right] \left[\begin{array}{c|c} \mathbf{0} & J_2 \\ \hline 1 & \mathbf{0}^T \end{array}\right]$$

or, since R_2 commutes with J_2 and $J_2 \boldsymbol{\alpha}_3^R = \boldsymbol{\alpha}_3$,

$$R_3^{-1} = \left[\begin{array}{c|c} \dfrac{1}{E_3} & \dfrac{1}{E_3}\boldsymbol{\alpha}_3^T \\ \hline \dfrac{1}{E_3}\boldsymbol{\alpha}_3 & R_2^{-1} + \dfrac{1}{E_3}\boldsymbol{\alpha}_3 \boldsymbol{\alpha}_3^T \end{array}\right] = \begin{bmatrix} 0 & \mathbf{0}^T \\ \mathbf{0} & R_2^{-1} \end{bmatrix} + \frac{1}{E_3}\mathbf{a}_3 \mathbf{a}_3^T \tag{5.9.16}$$

which is the same as Eq. (1.7.35).

Both ways of expressing R_3^{-1}, given by Eqs. (5.9.16) and (5.9.11), are useful. They may be combined as follows: Eq. (5.9.16) gives for the ijth entry

$$(R_3^{-1})_{ij} = (R_2^{-1} + \boldsymbol{\alpha}_3 \boldsymbol{\alpha}_3^T E_3^{-1})_{i-1,j-1} = (R_2^{-1})_{i-1,j-1} + \alpha_{3i}\alpha_{3j} E_3^{-1}$$

which is valid for $1 \leq i, j \leq 3$. On the other hand, from Eq. (5.9.11) we have

$$(R_3^{-1})_{i-1,j-1} = (R_2^{-1})_{i-1,j-1} + \alpha_{3i}^R \alpha_{3j}^R E_3^{-1}$$

which is valid also for $1 \leq i,j \leq 3$. Subtracting the two to cancel the common term $(R_2^{-1})_{i-1,j-1}$ we obtain the Goberg-Semencul-Trench-Zohar recursion [62–66]

$$(R_3^{-1})_{ij} = (R_3^{-1})_{i-1,j-1} + (\boldsymbol{\alpha}_3 \boldsymbol{\alpha}_3^T - \boldsymbol{\alpha}_3^R \boldsymbol{\alpha}_3^{RT})_{ij}\, E_3^{-1}, \quad 1 \leq i,j \leq 3 \tag{5.9.17}$$

which allows the building-up of R_3^{-1} along *each diagonal,* provided one knows the "boundary" values to get these recursions started. But these are:

$$(R_3^{-1})_{00} = E_3^{-1}, \qquad (R_3^{-1})_{i0} = (R_3^{-1})_{0i} = a_{3i}E_3^{-1}, \qquad 1 \leq i \leq 3 \tag{5.9.18}$$

Thus, from the prediction-error filter $\mathbf{a}_3$ and its reverse, the entire inverse of the autocorrelation matrix may be built up. Computationally, of course, the best procedure is to use Eq. (5.9.8), where L and D are obtained as byproducts of the Levinson recursion. The subroutine **lev** of the appendix starts with the $M+1$ autocorrelation lags $\{R(0), R(1), \ldots, R(M)\}$ and generates the required matrices L and D. The main reason for the existence of fast algorithms for Toeplitz matrices can be traced to the nesting property that the principal submatrices of a Toeplitz matrix are simply the lower order Toeplitz submatrices. Similar fast algorithms have been developed for other types of structured matrices, such as Hankel and Vandermonde matrices [67–69].

5.10 *Schur Algorithm*

The Schur algorithm has its roots in the original work of Schur on the theory of functions bounded in the unit disk [70,71]. It is an important signal processing tool in a variety of contexts, such as linear prediction and signal modeling, fast matrix factorizations, filter synthesis, inverse scattering, and other applications [71–92].

In linear prediction, Schur's algorithm is an efficient alternative to Levinson's algorithm and can be used to compute the set of reflection coefficients from the autocorrelation lags and also to compute the *conventional* LU Cholesky factorization of the autocorrelation matrix. The Schur algorithm is essentially the gapped function recursion (5.3.9). It proves convenient to work simultaneously with Eq. (5.3.9) and its reverse. We define the *forward and backward* gapped functions of order p

$$g_p^+(k) = E[e_p^+(n)y_{n-k}], \qquad g_p^-(k) = E[e_p^-(n)y_{n-k}] \tag{5.10.1}$$

The forward one is identical to that of Eq. (5.3.8). The backward one is the convolution of the backward filter $\mathbf{b}_p = \mathbf{a}_p^R$ with the autocorrelation function; that is,

$$g_p^+(k) = \sum_{i=0}^{p} a_{pi}R(k-i), \qquad g_p^-(k) = \sum_{i=0}^{p} b_{pi}R(k-i) \tag{5.10.2}$$

where, $b_{pi} = a_{p,p-i}$. In the z-domain, we have

$$G_p^+(z) = A_p(z)S_{yy}(z), \qquad G_p^-(z) = A_p^R(z)S_{yy}(z) \tag{5.10.3}$$

Using $S_{yy}(z) = S_{yy}(z^{-1})$, it follows that

$$G_p^-(z) = A_p^R(z)S_{yy}(z) = z^{-p}A_p(z^{-1})S_{yy}(z) = z^{-p}G_p^+(z^{-1})$$

and in the time domain

$$g_p^-(k) = g_p^+(p-k) \tag{5.10.4}$$

Thus, the backward gapped function is the reflected and delayed version of the forward one. However, the delay is only p units—one less than required to completely align the gaps. Therefore, the forward and backward gapped functions have slightly different gaps of length p; namely,

$$g_p^+(k) = 0\,, \quad k = 1,2,\cdots,p\,, \quad \text{and} \quad g_p^-(k) = 0\,, \quad k = 0,1,\cdots,p\text{-}1 \tag{5.10.5}$$

By definition Eq. (5.10.1), the gap conditions of the backward function are equivalent to the orthogonality conditions for the backward predictor; namely, that the estimation error $e_p^-(n)$ be orthogonal to the observations $\{y_{n-k}; k = 0,1, \ldots ,p - 1\}$ that make up the estimate y_{n-p}. Inserting the lattice recursions (5.7.8) into (5.10.1), or using the polynomial recursions (5.3.18) into (5.10.3), we obtain the lattice recursions for the gapped functions, known as the *Schur recursions*

$$g_{p+1}^+(k) = g_p^+(k) - \gamma_{p+1} g_p^-(k-1)\,, \quad g_{p+1}^-(k) = g_p^-(k-1) - \gamma_{p+1} g_p^+(k) \tag{5.10.6}$$

or, in matrix form

$$\begin{bmatrix} g_{p+1}^+(k) \\ g_{p+1}^-(k) \end{bmatrix} = \begin{bmatrix} 1 & -\gamma_{p+1} \\ -\gamma_{p+1} & 1 \end{bmatrix} \begin{bmatrix} g_p^+(k) \\ g_p^-(k-1) \end{bmatrix}$$

They are initialized by $g_0^\pm(k) = R(k)$. The first term of Eq. (5.10.6) is identical to Eq. (5.3.9) and the second term is the reverse of Eq. (5.3.9) obtained by the substitution $k \to p + 1 - k$. The forward gap condition $g_{p+1}^+(p + 1) = 0$ can be solved for the reflection coefficient

$$\gamma_{p+1} = \frac{g_p^+(p+1)}{g_p^-(p)} \tag{5.10.7}$$

Note that Eq. (5.10.4) implies $g_p^-(p) = g_p^+(0) = E_p$, and therefore, Eq. (5.10.7) is the same as Eq. (5.3.11). For an Mth order predictor, we only need to consider the values $g_p^\pm(k)$, for $k = 0,1 \ldots ,M$. We arrange these values (for the backward function) into the column vector

$$\mathbf{g}_p^- = \begin{bmatrix} g_p^-(0) \\ g_p^-(1) \\ \vdots \\ g_p^-(M) \end{bmatrix} \tag{5.10.8}$$

By virtue of the gap conditions (5.10.5), the first p entries, $k = 0,1, \ldots ,p - 1$, of this vector are zero. Therefore, we may construct the *lower triangular* matrix having the $\mathbf{g}_p^-$ s as columns

$$G = [\mathbf{g}_0^-, \mathbf{g}_1^-, \cdots, \mathbf{g}_M^-] \tag{5.10.9}$$

For example, if $M = 3$

$$G = \begin{bmatrix} g_0^-(0) & 0 & 0 & 0 \\ g_0^-(1) & g_1^-(1) & 0 & 0 \\ g_0^-(2) & g_1^-(2) & g_2^-(2) & 0 \\ g_0^-(3) & g_1^-(3) & g_2^-(3) & g_3^-(3) \end{bmatrix}$$

The first column of G consists simply of the M autocorrelation lags;

$$\mathbf{g}_0^- = [R(0), R(1), \cdots, R(M)]^T \qquad (5.10.10)$$

The main diagonal consists of the prediction errors of successive orders, namely, $g_p^-(p) = E_p$, $p = 0,1, \ldots, M$. Stacking the values of definition (5.10.1) into a vector, we can write compactly,

$$\mathbf{g}_p^- = E[e_p^-(n)\mathbf{y}(n)] \qquad (5.10.11)$$

where $\mathbf{y}(n) = [y_n, y_{n-1}, \ldots, y_{n-M}]^T$ is the data vector for an Mth order predictor. Thus, the matrix G can be written as in Eq. (1.7.56)

$$G = E\Big[\mathbf{y}(n)[e_0^-(n), e_1^-(n), \cdots, e_M^-(n)]\Big] = E[\mathbf{y}(n)\mathbf{e}^-(n)^T] \qquad (5.10.12)$$

where $\mathbf{e}^-(n) = [e_0^-(n), e_1^-(n), \ldots, e_M^-(n)]^T$ is the decorrelated vector of backward prediction errors. Following Eq. (1.7.57), we multiply (5.10.12) from the left by the lower triangular matrix L, and using the transformation $\mathbf{e}^-(n) = L\mathbf{y}(n)$ and Eq. (5.9.5), we obtain

$$LG = LE[\mathbf{y}(n)\mathbf{e}^-(n)^T] = E[\mathbf{e}^-(n)\mathbf{e}^-(n)^T] = D$$

Therefore, G is essentially the inverse of L

$$G = L^{-1}D \qquad (5.10.13)$$

Using Eq. (5.9.1), we obtain the *conventional* LU Cholesky factorization of the autocorrelation matrix R in the form

$$R = L^{-1}DL^{-T} = (GD^{-1})D(D^{-1}G^T) = GD^{-1}G^T \qquad (5.10.14)$$

The backward gapped functions are computed by iterating the Schur recursions (5.10.6) for $0 \leq k \leq M$ and $0 \leq p \leq M$. One computational simplification is that, because of the presence of the gap, the functions $g_p^\pm(k)$ need only be computed for $p \leq k \leq M$ (actually, $g_p^+(p) = 0$ could also be skipped). This gives rise to the *Schur algorithm:*

0. Initialize by $g_0^\pm(k) = R(k)$, $k = 0,1, \ldots, M$
1. At stage p, we have available $g_p^\pm(k)$ for $p \leq k \leq M$
2. Compute $\gamma_{p+1} = \dfrac{g_p^+(p+1)}{g_p^-(p)}$

3. For $p+1 \leq k \leq M$ compute

$$g^+_{p+1}(k) = g^+_p(k) - \gamma_{p+1} g^-_p(k-1),\ g^-_{p+1}(k) = g^-_p(k-1) - \gamma_{p+1} g^+_p(k)$$

4. Go to stage $p+1$
5. At the final order M, set $E_M = g^-_M(M)$

The subroutine **schur** (see Appendix B) is an implementation of this algorithm. The inputs to the routine are the order M and the lags $\{R(0), R(1), \ldots, R(M)\}$. The outputs are the parameters $\{E_M, \gamma_1, \gamma_2, \ldots, \gamma_M\}$. This routine is a simple alternative to **lev.** It may be used in conjunction with **frwlev, bkwlev,** and **rlev,** to pass from one linear prediction parameter set to another. The subroutine **schur1** is a small modification of **schur** that, in addition to the reflection coefficients, outputs the lower triangular Cholesky factor G. The prediction errors can be read off from the main diagonal of G; that is, $E_p = G(p,p)$, $p = 0, 1, \ldots, M$.

Example 5.10.1: Sending the five autocorrelation lags, $\{128, -64, 80, -88, 89\}$, of Example 5.3.1 through **schur1** gives the set of reflection coefficients $\{\gamma_1, \gamma_1 \gamma_2, \gamma_4\} = \{-0.5, 0.5, -0.5, 0.5\}$, and the matrix G

$$G = \begin{bmatrix} 128 & 0 & 0 & 0 & 0 \\ -64 & 96 & 0 & 0 & 0 \\ 80 & -24 & 72 & 0 & 0 \\ -88 & 36 & 0 & 54 & 0 \\ 89 & -43.5 & 13.5 & 13.5 & 40.5 \end{bmatrix}$$

Recall that the first column should be the autocorrelation lags and the main diagonal should consist of the mean square prediction errors. It is easily verified that $GD^{-1}G^T = R$.

The computational *bottleneck* of the classical Levinson recursion is the computation of the inner product (5.3.12). The Schur algorithm avoids this step by computing γ_{p+1} as the ratio of the two gapped function values (5.10.7). Moreover, at each stage p, the computations indicated in step 3 of the algorithm can be done in *parallel.* Thus, with M parallel processors, the overall computation can be reduced to $O(M)$ operations. VLSI parallel hardware implementations of the Schur algorithm already exist [82,33]. As formulated above, the Schur algorithm is essentially equivalent to the Le Roux-Gueguen fixed-point algorithm [75]. The possibility of a fixed-point implementation arises from the fact that all gapped functions have a fixed dynamic range, bounded by

$$|g^\pm_p(k)| \leq R(0) \tag{5.10.15}$$

This is easily seen by applying the Schwarz inequality to definition (5.10.1) and using $E_p \leq R(0)$

$$|g^\pm_p(k)|^2 = |E[e^\pm_p(n) y_{n-k}]|^2 \leq E[e^\pm_p(n)^2] E[y^2_{n-k}] \leq E_p R(0) \leq R(0)^2$$

The Schur algorithm admits a nice filtering interpretation in terms of the lattice structure. By definition, the gapped functions are the convolution of the forward/backward pth order prediction filters with the autocorrelation sequence $R(k)$. Therefore, $g_p^{\pm}(k)$ will be the *outputs* from the pth section of the lattice filter, Fig. 5.3, driven by the input $R(k)$. Moreover, Eq. (5.10.6) states that the $(p+1)$st reflection coefficient is obtainable as the ratio of the two *inputs* to the $(p+1)$st lattice section, at time instant $p+1$ (note, $g_p^-(p) = g_p^-(p+1-1)$ is outputted at time p from the pth section and is delayed by one time unit before it is inputted to the $(p+1)$st section at time $p+1$). The correct values of the gapped functions $g_p^{\pm}(k)$ are obtained when the input to the lattice filter is the infinite double-sided sequence $R(k)$. If we send in the finite *causal* sequence

$$x(k) = \{R(0), R(1), \cdots, R(M), 0, 0, \cdots\}$$

then, because of the initial and final transient behavior of the filter, the outputs of the pth section will agree with $g_p^{\pm}(k)$ only for $p \leq k \leq M$. To see this, let $y_p^{\pm}(k)$ denote the two outputs. Because of the causality of the input and filter and the finite length of the input, the convolutional filtering equation will be

$$y_p^{+}(k) = \sum_{i=\max\{0,k-M\}}^{\min\{p,k\}} a_{pi}\, x(k-i) = \sum_{i=\max\{0,k-M\}}^{\min\{p,k\}} a_{pi}\, R(k-i)$$

This agrees with Eq. (5.10.2) only after time p and before time M, that is,

$$y_p^{\pm}(k) = g_p^{\pm}(k)\,, \quad \text{only for} \quad p \leq k \leq M$$

The column vector $\mathbf{y}_p^- = [y_p^-(0), y_p^-(1), \ldots, y_p^-(M)]^T$, formed by the first M backward output samples of the pth section, will agree with $\mathbf{g}_p^-$ only for the entries $p \leq k \leq M$. Thus, the matrix of backward outputs $Y^- = [\mathbf{y}_0^-, \mathbf{y}_1^-, \ldots, \mathbf{y}_M^-]$ formed by the columns $\mathbf{y}_p^-$ will agree with G only in its *lower* triangular part. But, this is *enough* to determine G because its upper triangular part is zero.

Example 5.10.2: Send the autocorrelation lags of Example 5.10.1 into the lattice filter of Fig. 5.3 (with all its delay registers initialized to zero), arrange the forward/backward outputs from the pth section into the column vectors, $\mathbf{y}_p^{\pm}$, and put these columns together to form the output matrices $Y^{\pm}$. The result is

$$Y^- = \begin{bmatrix} 128 & 64 & -64 & 64 & -64 \\ -64 & 96 & 64 & -80 & 96 \\ 80 & -24 & 72 & 64 & -96 \\ -88 & 36 & 0 & 54 & 64 \\ 89 & -43.5 & 13.5 & 13.5 & 40.5 \end{bmatrix}, \qquad Y^+ = \begin{bmatrix} 128 & 128 & 128 & 128 & 128 \\ -64 & 0 & -32 & -64 & -96 \\ 80 & 48 & 0 & 32 & 72 \\ -88 & -48 & -36 & 0 & -32 \\ 89 & 45 & 27 & 27 & 0 \end{bmatrix}$$

The lower triangular part of Y^- agrees with G. The forward/backward outputs $\mathbf{y}_p^{\pm}$ can be computed using, for example, the routine **lattice**. They can also be computed by directly convolving the prediction filters with the input. For example, the backward filter of order 4 given in Example 5.3.1 is $\mathbf{a}_4^R = [-0.5,0.5,-0.1875,-0.25,1]^T$. Convolving it with the autocorrelation sequence gives the last column of Y^-

$$[128, -64, 80, -88, 89] * [-0.5, 0.5, -0.1875, -0.25, 1] = [-64, 96, -96, 64, 40.5, \cdots]$$

Convolving the forward filter $\mathbf{a}_4$ with the autocorrelation sequence gives the last column of the matrix Y^+

$$[128, -64, 80, -88, 89] * [1, -0.25, -0.1875, 0.5, -0.5] = [128, -96, 72, -32, 0, \cdots]$$

Note that we are interested only in the outputs for $0 \leqslant k \leqslant M = 4$. The last 4 outputs (in general, the last p outputs for a pth order filter) of these convolutions were not shown. They correspond to the transient behavior of the filter after the input is turned off.

It is also possible to derive a *split* or *immitance-domain* version of the Schur algorithm that achieves a further 50% reduction in computational complexity [46,47]. Thus, with M parallel processors, the complexity of the Schur algorithm can be reduced to $O(M/2)$ operations. We define a symmetrized or split gapped function in terms of the symmetric polynomial $F_p(z)$ defined in Eq. (5.6.1)

$$g_p(k) = \sum_{i=0}^{p} f_{pi} R(k-i), \qquad G_p(z) = F_p(z) S_{yy}(z) \tag{5.10.16}$$

It can be thought of as the output of the filter $F_p(z)$ driven by the autocorrelation sequence. Multiplying both sides of Eq. (5.6.1) by $S_{yy}(z)$ and using the definitions (5.10.3), we obtain $G_p(z) = G_{p-1}^+(z) + z^{-1}G_{p-1}^-(z)$ or, in the time domain

$$g_p(k) = g_{p-1}^+(k) + g_{p-1}^-(k-1) \tag{5.10.17}$$

Similarly, Eq. (5.6.2) gives

$$(1 - \gamma_p) g_p(k) = g_p^+(k) + g_p^-(k) \tag{5.10.18}$$

It follows from Eqs. (5.10.4) and (5.10.18) or from the symmetry property of $F_p(z)$ that $g_p(k) = g_p(p - k)$, and in particular, $g_p(0) = g_p(p)$. The split Levinson algorithm of Section 5.6 requires the computation of the coefficients $\alpha_{p+1} = \tau_{p+1}/\tau_p$. Setting $k = 0$ in the definition (5.10.16) and using the reflection symmetry $R(i) = R(-i)$, we recognize that the inner product of Eq. (5.6.6) is $\tau_p = g_p(0) = g_p(p)$. Therefore, the coefficient α_{p+1} can be written as the ratio of the two gapped function values

$$\alpha_{p+1} = \frac{g_{p+1}(p+1)}{g_p(p)} \tag{5.10.19}$$

Because the forward and backward gapped functions have overlapping gaps, it follows that $g_p(k)$ will have a gap $g_p(k) = 0$, $k = 1,2, \ldots, p - 1$. Therefore, for an Mth order predictor, we only need to know the values of $g_p(k)$, for $p \leqslant k \leqslant M$. These can be computed by the following three-term recurrence, obtained by multiplying the recurrence (5.6.4) by $S_{yy}(z)$

$$g_{p+2}(k) = g_{p+1}(k) + g_{p+1}(k-1) - \alpha_{p+1} g_p(k-1) \tag{5.10.20}$$

Using $F_0(z) = 2$ and $F_1(z) = 1 + z^{-1}$, it follows from the definition that $g_0(k) = 2R(k)$ and $g_1(k) = R(k) + R(k-1)$. To initialize τ_0 correctly, however, we must choose $g_0(0) = R(0)$, so that $\tau_0 = g_0(0) = R(0)$. Thus, we are led to the following *split Schur algorithm*:

0. Initialize by $g_0(k) = 2R(k)$, $g_1(k) = R(k) + R(k-1)$, for $k = 1,2, \ldots ,M$, and $g_0(0) = R(0)$, $\gamma_0 = 0$
1. At stage p, we have available $\gamma_p, g_p(k)$ for $p \leq k \leq M$, and $g_{p+1}(k)$ for $p + 1 \leq k \leq M$
2. Compute α_{p+1} from Eq. (5.10.19) and solve for $\gamma_{p+1} = -1 + \alpha_{p+1}/(1 - \gamma_p)$
3. For $p + 2 \leq k \leq M$, compute $g_{p+2}(k)$ using Eq. (5.10.20)
4. Go to stage $p + 1$

Recalling that $E_p = \tau_p(1 - \gamma_p)$, we may set at the final order $E_M = \tau_M(1 - \gamma_M) = g_M(M)(1 - \gamma_M)$. Step 3 of the algorithm requires only one multiplication for each k, whereas step 3 of the ordinary Schur algorithm requires *two*. This reduces the computational complexity by 50%. The subroutine **schur2** (see Appendix B) is an implementation of this algorithm. The inputs to the routine are the order M and the lags $\{R(0),R(1), \ldots ,R(M)\}$. The outputs are the parameters $\{E_M,\gamma_1,\gamma_2, \ldots ,\gamma_M\}$. The routine can be modified easily to include the computation of the backward gapped functions $g_p^-(k)$, which are the columns of the Cholesky matrix G. This can be done by the recursion

$$g_p^-(k) = g_p^-(k-1) + (1 - \gamma_p) g_p(k) - g_{p+1}(k) \tag{5.10.21}$$

where $p + 1 \leq k \leq M$, with starting value $g_p^-(p) = E_p = g_p(p)(1 - \gamma_p)$. This recursion will generate the lower triangular part of G. Equation (5.10.21) follows by writing Eq. (5.10.17) for order $(p + 1)$ and subtracting it from Eq. (5.10.18). Note, also, that Eq. (5.10.17) and the bound (5.10.15) imply the bound $|g_p(k)| \leq 2R(0)$, which allows a fixed-point implementation.

We finish this section by discussing the connection of the Schur algorithm to Schur's original work. It follows from Eq. (5.10.3) that the ratio of the two gapped functions $G_p^{\pm}(z)$ is an *all-pass stable* transfer function, otherwise known as a *lossless bounded real* function [56].

$$S_p(z) = \frac{G_p^-(z)}{G_p^+(z)} = \frac{A_p^R(z)}{A_p(z)} = \frac{a_{pp} + a_{p,p-1}z^{-1} + \cdots + z^{-p}}{1 + a_{p1}z^{-1} + \cdots + a_{pp}z^{-p}} \tag{5.10.22}$$

The all-pass property follows from the fact that the reverse polynomial $A_p^R(z)$ has the same magnitude response as $A_p(z)$. The stability property follows from the minimal phase property of the polynomials $A_p(z)$, which in turn is equivalent to all reflection coefficients having magnitude less than one. Such functions satisfy the boundedness property

$$|S_p(z)| \leq 1, \quad \text{for} \quad |z| \geq 1 \tag{5.10.23}$$

with equality attained on the unit circle. Taking the limit $z \to \infty$, it follows from Eq. (5.10.22) that the reflection coefficient γ_p is obtainable from $S_p(z)$ by

$$S_p(\infty) = a_{pp} = -\gamma_p \tag{5.10.24}$$

Using the backward Levinson recursion (5.3.23), we obtain a new all-pass function

$$S_{p-1}(z) = \frac{G^-_{p-1}(z)}{G^+_{p-1}(z)} = \frac{A^R_{p-1}(z)}{A_{p-1}(z)} = \frac{z(\gamma_p A_p + A^R_p)}{A_p + \gamma_p A^R_p}$$

or, dividing numerator and denominator by $A_p(z)$

$$S_{p-1}(z) = z\,\frac{S_p(z) + \gamma_p}{1 + \gamma_p S_p(z)} \tag{5.10.25}$$

This is Schur's original recursion [70]. Applying this recursion repeatedly from some initial value $p = M$ down to $p = 0$, with $S_0(z) = 1$, will give rise to the set of reflection or Schur coefficients $\{\gamma_M, \ldots, \gamma_1\}$. The starting all-pass function $S_M(z)$ will be stable if and only if all reflection coefficients have magnitude less than one. We note finally that there is an intimate connection between the Schur algorithm and inverse scattering problems [76,79,80,86,87,90–92,138]. In Section 5.13, we will see that the lattice recursions (5.10.6) describe the forward and backward moving waves incident on a layered structure. The Schur function $S_p(z)$ will correspond to the overall reflection response of the structure, and the recursion (5.10.25) will describe the successive removal of the layers. The coefficients γ_p will represent the elementary reflection coefficients at the layer interfaces. This justifies the term *reflection coefficients* for the γs.

5.11 *Lattice Realizations of FIR Wiener Filters*

In this section, we combine the results of Sections 4.3 and 5.9 to derive alternative realizations of Wiener filters that are based on the Gram-Schmidt lattice structures. Consider the FIR Wiener filtering problem of estimating a desired signal x_n on the basis of the related signal y_n, using an Mth order filter. The I/O equation of the optimal filter is given by Eq. (4.3.8). The vector of optimal weights is determined by solving the set of normal equations, given by Eq.

(4.3.9). The discussion of the previous section suggests that Eq. (4.3.9) can be solved efficiently using the Levinson recursion. Defining the data vector

$$\mathbf{y}(n) = \begin{bmatrix} y_n \\ y_{n-1} \\ \vdots \\ y_{n-M} \end{bmatrix} \tag{5.11.1}$$

we rewrite Eq. (4.3.9) in the compact matrix form

$$R_{yy}\mathbf{h} = \mathbf{r}_{xy} \tag{5.11.2}$$

where R_{yy} is the $(M + 1) \times (M + 1)$ autocorrelation matrix of $\mathbf{y}(n)$, and $\mathbf{r}_{xy}$ the $(M + 1)$-vector of cross-correlations between x_n and $\mathbf{y}(n)$; namely,

$$R_{yy} = E[\mathbf{y}(n)\mathbf{y}(n)^T] \qquad \mathbf{r}_{xy} = E[x_n\mathbf{y}(n)] = \begin{bmatrix} R_{xy}(0) \\ R_{xy}(1) \\ \vdots \\ R_{xy}(M) \end{bmatrix} \tag{5.11.3}$$

and $\mathbf{h}$ is the $(M + 1)$-vector of optimal weights

$$\mathbf{h} = \begin{bmatrix} h_0 \\ h_1 \\ \cdot \\ \cdot \\ h_M \end{bmatrix} \tag{5.11.4}$$

The I/O equation of the filter, Eq. (4.3.8), is

$$\hat{x}_n = \mathbf{h}^T\mathbf{y}(n) = h_0 y_n + h_1 y_{n-1} + \cdots + h_M y_{n-M} \tag{5.11.5}$$

Next, consider the Gram-Schmidt transformation of Eq. (5.9.4) from the data vector $\mathbf{y}(n)$ to the decorrelated vector $\mathbf{e}^-(n)$:

$$\mathbf{e}^-(n) = L\mathbf{y}(n) \qquad \text{or} \qquad \begin{bmatrix} e_0^-(n) \\ e_1^-(n) \\ \vdots \\ e_M^-(n) \end{bmatrix} = L \begin{bmatrix} y_n \\ y_{n-1} \\ \vdots \\ y_{n-M} \end{bmatrix} \tag{5.11.6}$$

Inserting Eq. (5.11.6) into Eq. (5.11.5), we find

$$\hat{x}_n = \mathbf{h}^T L^{-1}\mathbf{e}^-(n)$$

Defining the $(M + 1)$-vector

$$\mathbf{g} = L^{-T}\mathbf{h} \tag{5.11.7}$$

we obtain the alternative I/O equation for the Wiener filter:

$$\begin{aligned} \hat{x}_n &= \mathbf{g}^T\mathbf{e}^-(n) = \sum_{p=0}^{M} g_p e_p^-(n) \\ &= g_0 e_0^-(n) + g_1 e_1^-(n) + \cdots + g_M e_M^-(n) \end{aligned} \tag{5.11.8}$$

This is easily recognized as the projection of x_n onto the subspace spanned by $\{e_0^-(n), e_1^-(n), \ldots, e_M^-(n)\}$ which is the same as that spanned by the data vector $\{y_n, y_{n-1}, \ldots, y_{n-M}\}$. Indeed, it follows from Eqs. (5.11.7) and (5.11.2) that

$$\begin{aligned} \mathbf{g}^T = \mathbf{h}^T L^{-1} &= E[x_n\mathbf{y}(n)^T]E[\mathbf{y}(n)\mathbf{y}(n)^T]^{-1}L^{-1} \\ &= E[x_n\mathbf{e}^-(n)^T]L^{-T}(L^{-1}E[\mathbf{e}^-(n)\mathbf{e}^-(n)^T]L^{-T})^{-1}L^{-1} \\ &= E[x_n\mathbf{e}^-(n)^T]E[\mathbf{e}^-(n)\mathbf{e}^-(n)^T]^{-1} \\ &= [E[x_n e_0^-(n)]/E_0, E[x_n e_1^-(n)]/E_1, \ldots, E[x_n e_M^-(n)]/E_M] \end{aligned}$$

so that the estimate of x_n can be expressed as

$$\hat{x}_n = E[x_n\mathbf{e}^-(n)^T]E[\mathbf{e}^-(n)\mathbf{e}^-(n)^T]^{-1}\mathbf{e}^-(n) = E[x_n\mathbf{y}(n)^T]E[\mathbf{y}(n)\mathbf{y}(n)^T]^{-1}\mathbf{y}(n)$$

The key to the lattice realization of the optimal filtering equation (5.11.8) is the observation that the *analysis lattice filter* of Fig. (5.3) for the process y_n provides, in its successive lattice stages, the signals $e_p^-(n)$ which are required in the sum (5.11.8). Thus, if the weight vector **g** is known, an alternative realization of the optimal filter will be as shown in Fig. 5.5. By comparison, the *direct form* realization using Eq. (5.11.5) operates directly on the vector $\mathbf{y}(n)$, which, at each time instant n, is available at the tap registers of the filter. This is depicted in Fig. 5.6.

Both types of realizations can be formulated *adaptively*, without requiring prior knowledge of the filter coefficients or the correlation matrices R_{yy} and R_{xy}. We will discuss adaptive implentations in Chapter 7. If R_{yy} and R_{xy} are known, or can be estimated, then the design procedure for both the lattice and the direct form realizations is:

1. Using Levinson's algorithm, implemented by the subroutine **lev**, perform the LU Cholesky factorization of R_{yy} to determine the matrices L and D.
2. The vector of weights **g** can be computed in terms of the known quantities L, D, $\mathbf{r}_{xy}$ as follows:

$$\mathbf{g} = L^{-T}\mathbf{h} = L^{-T}R_{yy}^{-1}\mathbf{r}_{xy} = L^{-T}(L^TD^{-1}L)\mathbf{r}_{xy} = D^{-1}L\mathbf{r}_{xy}$$

3. The vector **h** can be recovered from **g** by $\mathbf{h} = L^T\mathbf{g}$.

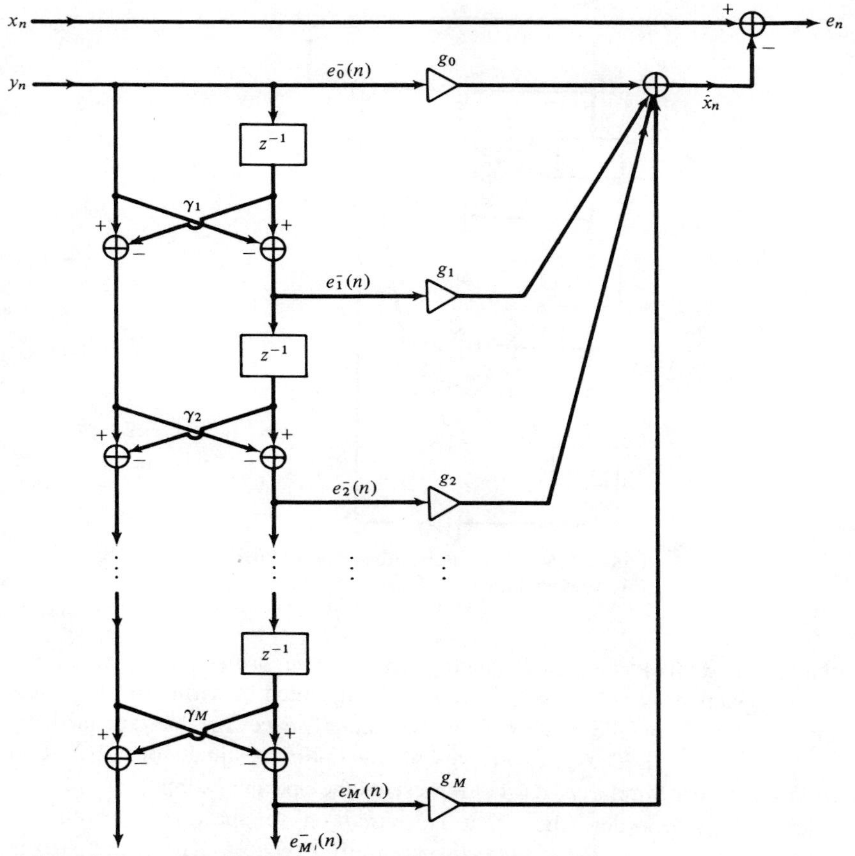

Figure 5.5 Lattice Realization of the FIR Wiener Filter

The subroutine **firw** (see Appendix B) is an implementation of this design procedure. The inputs to the subroutine are the order M, and the correlation lags $\{R_{yy}(0), R_{yy}(1), \ldots, R_{yy}(M)\}$ and $\{R_{xy}(0), R_{xy}(1), \ldots, R_{xy}(M)\}$. The outputs are the quantities L, D, **g**, and **h.**

The estimate (5.11.8) may also be written recursively *in the order* of the filter: If we denote

$$\hat{x}_p(n) = \sum_{i=0}^{p} g_i e_i^-(n) \tag{5.11.9}$$

we obtain the recursion

$$\hat{x}_p(n) = \hat{x}_{p-1}(n) + g_p e_p^-(n), \qquad p = 0,1, \ldots, M \tag{5.11.10}$$

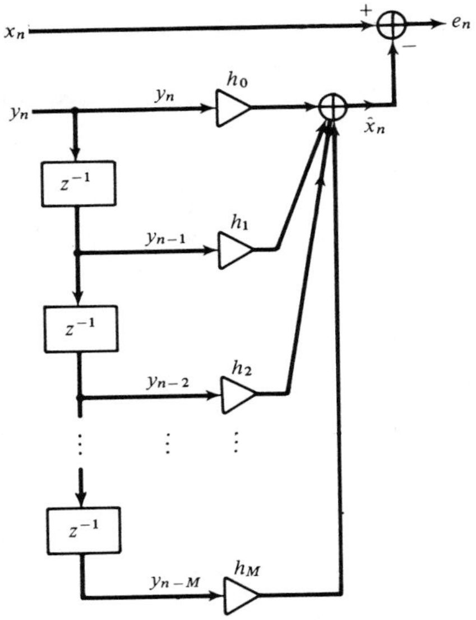

Figure 5.6 Direct Form Realization of the FIR Wiener Filter

initialized as $\hat{x}_{-1}(n) = 0$. The quantity $\hat{x}_p(n)$ is the *projection* of x_n on the subspace spanned by $\{e_0^-(n), e_1^-(n), \ldots, e_p^-(n)\}$ which by virtue of the lower-triangular nature of the matrix L is the *same* space as that spanned by $\{y_n, y_{n-1}, \ldots, y_{n-p}\}$. Thus, $\hat{x}_p(n)$ represents the optimal estimate of x_n based on a *pth order* filter. Similarly, $\hat{x}_{p-1}(n)$ represents the optimal estimate of x_n based on the $(p-1)$th order filter; that is, based on the past $p-1$ samples $\{y_n, y_{n-1}, \ldots, y_{n-p+1}\}$. These two subspaces differ by y_{n-p}. The term $e_p^-(n)$ is by construction the best postdiction error of estimating y_{n-p} from the samples $\{y_n, y_{n-1}, \ldots, y_{n-p+1}\}$; that is, $e_p^-(n)$ is the *orthogonal complement* of y_{n-p} projected on that subspace. Therefore, the term $g_p e_p^-(n)$ in Eq. (5.11.10) represents the improvement in the estimate of x_n that results by taking into account the *additional* past value y_{n-p}; it represents that part of x_n that cannot be estimated in terms of the subspace $\{y_n, y_{n-1}, \ldots, y_{n-p+1}\}$. The estimate $\hat{x}_p(n)$ of x_n is *better* than $\hat{x}_{p-1}(n)$ in the sense that it produces a smaller mean-squared estimation error. To see this, define the estimation errors in the two cases

$$e_p(n) = x_n - \hat{x}_p(n) \qquad e_{p-1}(n) = x_n - \hat{x}_{p-1}(n)$$

Using the recursion (5.11.10) we find

$$e_p(n) = e_{p-1}(n) - g_p e_p^-(n) \tag{5.11.11}$$

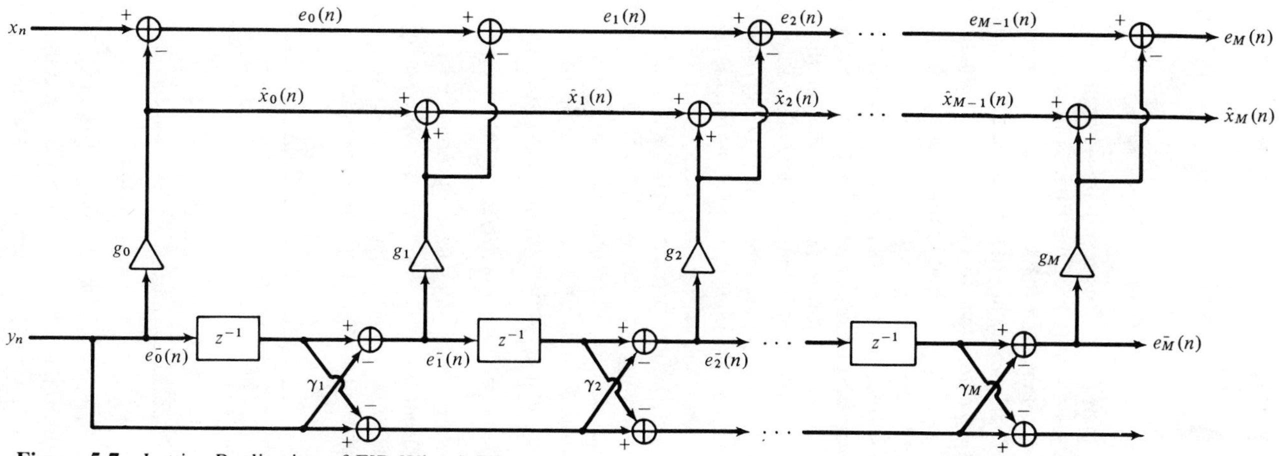

Figure 5.7 Lattice Realization of FIR Wiener Filter

Using $g_p = E[x_n e_p^-(n)]/E_p$, we find for $\mathcal{E}_p = E[e_p(n)^2]$

$$\mathcal{E}_p = E[x_n^2] - \sum_{i=0}^{p} g_i E[e_i^-(n)x_n] = \mathcal{E}_{p-1} - g_p E[e_p^-(n)x_n]$$

$$= \mathcal{E}_{p-1} - (E[x_n e_p^-(n)])^2/E_p = \mathcal{E}_{p-1} - g_p^2 E_p$$

Thus, $\mathcal{E}_p$ is smaller than $\mathcal{E}_{p-1}$. This result shows explicitly how the estimate is constantly improved as the length of the filter is increased. The nice feature of the lattice realization is that the filter length can be increased simply by adding more lattice sections *without* having to recompute the weights g_p of the previous sections. A realization *equivalent* to Fig. 5.5, but which shows explicitly the *recursive* construction (5.11.10) of the estimate of x_n and of the estimation error (5.11.11), is shown in Fig. 5.7.

The subroutine **lwf** (see Appendix B) is an implementation of the lattice Wiener filter of Fig. 5.7. The routine **dwf** implements the direct-form Wiener filter of Fig. 5.6. Each call to these routines transforms a pair of input samples $\{x,y\}$ into the pair of output samples $\{\hat{x},e\}$ and updates the internal state of the filter. Successive calls over $n = 0,1,2, \ldots$ will transform the input sequences $\{x_n,y_n\}$ into the output sequences $\{\hat{x}_n,e_n\}$. In both realizations, the internal state of the filter is taken to be the vector of samples stored in the delays of the filter; that is, $w_p(n) = e_{p-1}^-(n-1)$, $p = 1,2, \ldots ,M$ for the lattice case, and $w_p(n) = y_{n-p}$, $p = 1,2, \ldots ,M$ for the direct-form case. By allowing the filter coefficients to change between calls, these routines can be used in adaptive implementations.

Next, we present a Wiener filter design example for a *noise canceling* application. The primary and secondary signals $x(n)$ and $y(n)$ are of the form

$$x(n) = s(n) + v_1(n) \qquad y(n) = v_2(n)$$

where $s(n)$ is a desired signal corrupted by noise $v_1(n)$. The signal $v_2(n)$ is correlated with $v_1(n)$ but not with $s(n)$, and provides a *reference* noise signal. The noise canceler is to be implemented as a Wiener filter of order M, realized either in the direct or the lattice form. It is shown below:

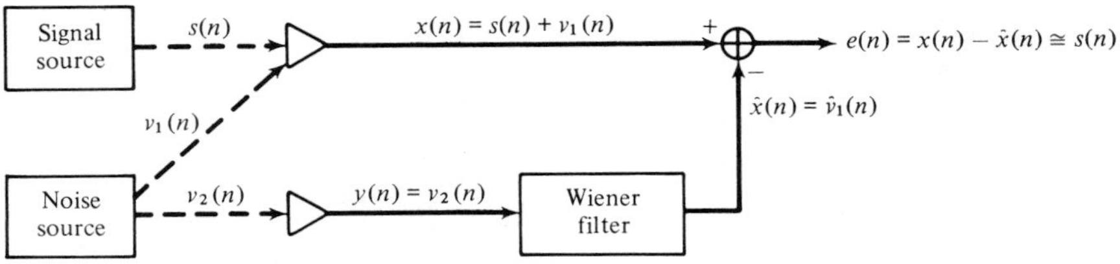

Its basic operation is that of a correlation canceler; that is, the optimally designed filter $H(z)$ will transform the reference noise $v_2(n)$ into the best replica of $v_1(n)$, and then proceed to cancel it from the output, leaving a clean signal $s(n)$. For the purpose of the simulation, we took $s(n)$ to be a simple sinusoid

$$s(n) = \sin(\omega_0 n) \qquad \text{where } \omega_0 = 0.075\pi \text{ [rads/sample]}$$

and $v_1(n)$ and $v_2(n)$ were generated by the difference equations

$$v_1(n) = -0.5v_1(n-1) + v(n)$$

$$v_2(n) = 0.8v_2(n-1) + v(n)$$

driven by a common, zero-mean, unit-variance, uncorrelated sequence $v(n)$. The difference equations establish a correlation between the two noise components v_1 and v_2, which is exploited by the canceler to effect the noise cancellation. Figures 5.8 and 5.9 show 100 samples of the signals $x(n)$, $s(n)$, and $y(n)$, generated by a particular realization of $v(n)$. For $M = 4$ and $M = 6$, the sample autocorrelation and cross-correlation lags, $R_{yy}(k), R_{xy}(k); k = 0, 1, \ldots, M$, were computed and sent through the routine **firw** to get the filter weights **g** and **h**. The reference signal y_n was filtered through H to get the estimate $\hat{x}_n$—which is really an estimate of $v_1(n)$—and the estimation error $e(n) = x(n) - \hat{x}(n)$, which is really an estimate of $s(n)$. This estimate of $s(n)$ is shown in Figs. 5.10 and 5.11, for the cases $M = 4$ and $M = 6$, respectively. The improvement afforded by using a higher order filter is evident. For the particular realization of $x(n)$ and $y(n)$ that we used, the *sample* correlations $R_{yy}(k), R_{xy}(k), k = 0, 1, 2, \ldots, M$ were:

$$R_{yy} = [2.4540,\ 1.9265,\ 1.4636,\ 1.1031,\ 0.8425,\ 0.6557,\ 0.5120]$$

$$R_{xy} = [0.6857,\ -0.3097,\ 0.1496,\ -0.0714,\ 0.0626,\ 0.0105,\ 0.0315]$$

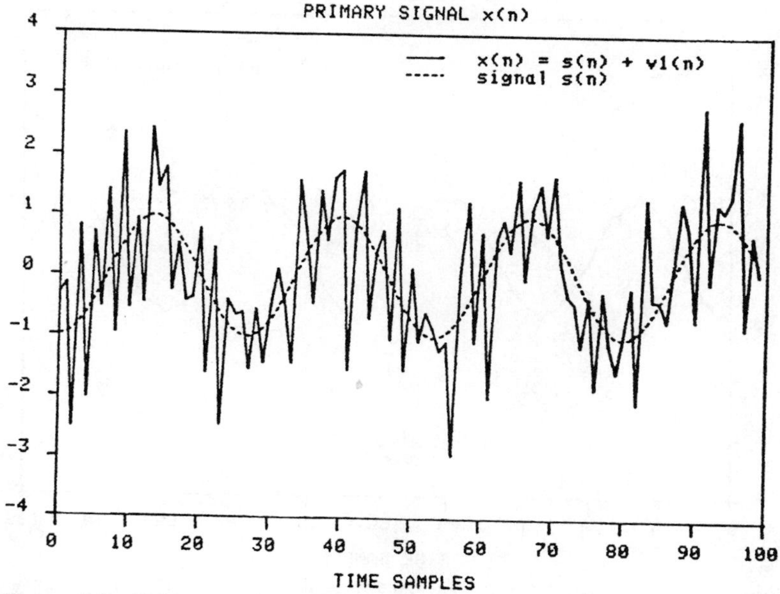

Figure 5.8 Noise Corrupted Sinusoid

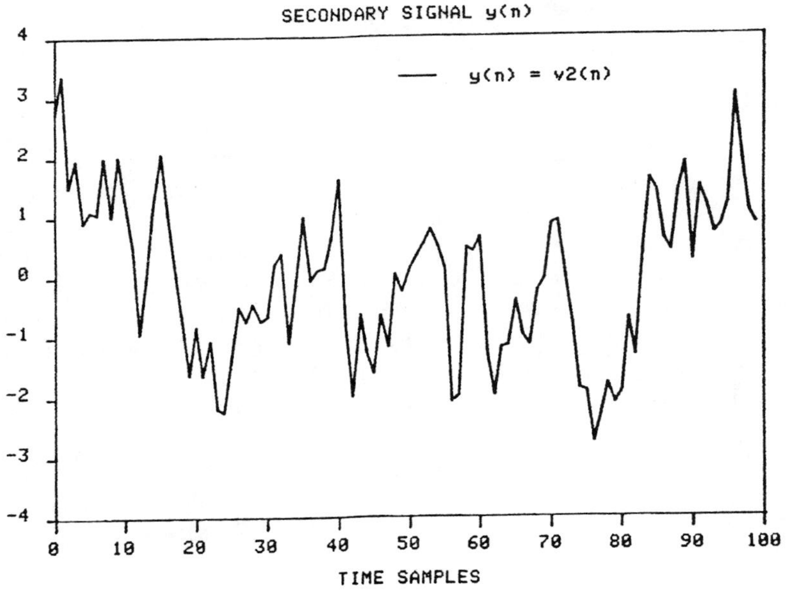

Figure 5.9 Reference Noise

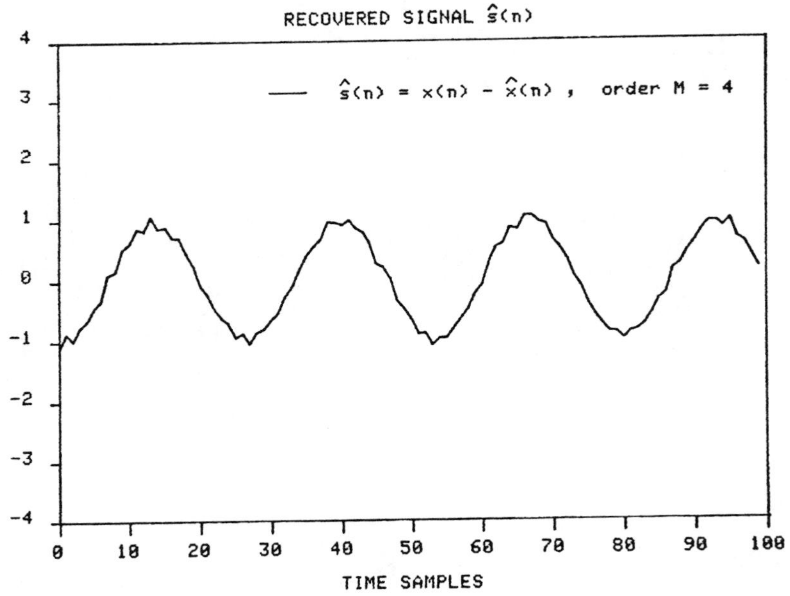

Figure 5.10 Output of Noise Canceler ($M = 4$)

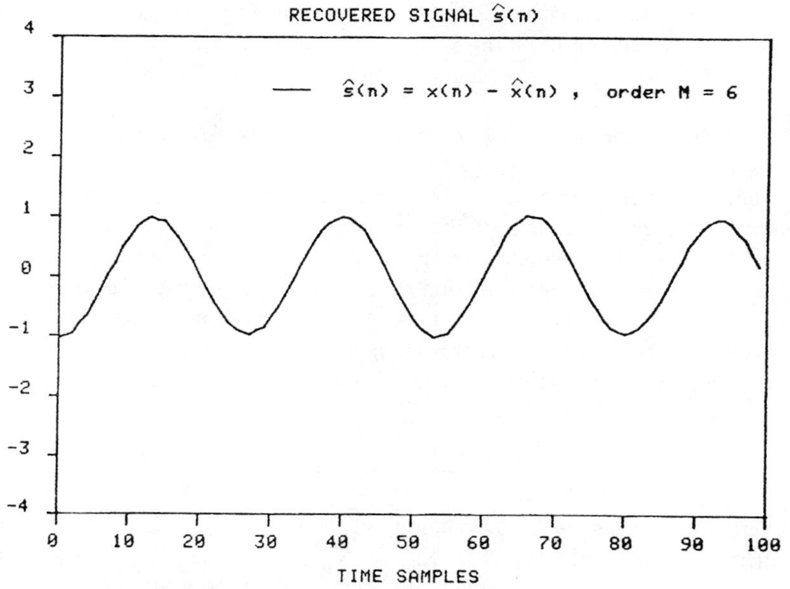

Figure 5.11 Output of Noise Canceler ($M = 6$)

and the resulting vector of lattice weights $g_p, p = 0,1, \ldots, M$, reflection coefficients γ_p; $p = 1,2, \ldots, M$, and direct form weights h_m; $m = 0,1, \ldots, M$ were, for $M = 6$,

$$\mathbf{g} = [0.2794,\ -0.9005,\ 0.4693,\ -0.2186,\ 0.1220,\ -0.0521,\ 0.0290]$$

$$\boldsymbol{\gamma} = [0.7850,\ -0.0518,\ -0.0059,\ 0.0128,\ 0.0114,\ 0.0004]$$

$$\mathbf{h} = [1.0084,\ -1.2964,\ 0.6545,\ -0.3212,\ 0.1663,\ -0.0760,\ 0.0290]$$

To get the **g** and $\boldsymbol{\gamma}$ of the case $M = 4$, simply ignore the last two entries in the above. The corresponding **h** is in this case:

$$\mathbf{h} = [1.0078,\ -1.2963,\ 0.6554,\ -0.3193,\ 0.1220]$$

As we discussed in Section 1.7, the lattice realizations based on the backward orthogonal basis have three major advantages over the direct-form realizations: (a) the filter processes nonredundant information only, and hence adaptive implementations would adapt faster; (b) the design of the optimal filter weights **g** does not require any matrix inversion; and (c) the lower-order portions of **g** are already optimal. Moreover, it appears that adaptive versions of the lattice realizations have better numerical properties than the direct-form versions. In array processing problems, because the data vector $\mathbf{y}(n)$ does not have the tapped-delay line form (5.11.1), the Gram-Schmidt orthogonalization cannot be done by a simple a lattice filter. It requires a more complicated structure that basically amounts to carrying out the lower triangular linear trasformation (5.11.6). The benefits, however, are the same. We discuss adaptive versions of Gram-Schmidt preprocessors for arrays in Chapter 7.

5.12 *Autocorrelation, Covariance, and Burg's Methods*

As mentioned in Section 5.3, the finite order linear prediction problem may be thought of as an *approximation* to the infinite order prediction problem. For large enough order p of the predictor, the prediction-error filter $A_p(z)$ may be considered to be an adequate approximation to the whitening filter $A(z)$ of the process y_n. In this case, the prediction-error sequence $e_p^+(n)$ is approximately white, and the inverse synthesis filter $1/A_p(z)$ is an approximation to the signal model $B(z)$ of y_n. Thus, we have obtained an approximate solution to the signal modeling problem depicted below:

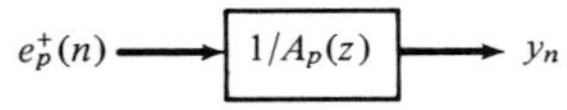

The variance of $e_p^+(n)$ is E_p. Depending on the realization one uses, the model parameters are either the set $\{a_{p1}, a_{p2}, \ldots, a_{pp}; E_p\}$ or $\{\gamma_1, \gamma_2, \ldots, \gamma_p; E_p\}$. Because these model parameters can be determined by solving a simple *linear* system of equations—that is, the normal equations (5.3.7)—this approach to the modeling problem has become widespread.

In this section, we present three widely used methods of extracting the model parameters from a given block of measured signal values y_n [3,6,10,11,93–103]. These methods are:

1. The autocorrelation, or Yule-Walker, method
2. The covariance method
3. Burg's method

We have already discussed the Yule-Walker method, which consists simply of replacing the theoretical autocorrelations $R_{yy}(k)$ with the corresponding sample autocorrelations $\hat{R}_{yy}(k)$ computed from the given frame of data. This method, like the other two, can be justified on the basis of an appropriate *least-squares* minimization criterion obtained by replacing the ensemble averages $E[e_p^+(n)^2]$ by appropriate time averages.

The theoretical minimization criteria for the optimal forward and backward predictors are

$$E[e_p^+(n)^2] = \min \qquad E[e_p^-(n)^2] = \min \tag{5.12.1}$$

where $e_p^+(n)$ and $e_p^-(n)$ are the result of filtering y_n through the prediction-error filter $\mathbf{a} = [1, a_{p1}, \ldots, a_{pp}]^T$ and its reverse $\mathbf{a}^R = [a_{pp}, a_{p,p-1}, \ldots, a_{p1}, 1]^T$, respectively; namely,

$$\begin{aligned} e_p^+(n) &= y_n + a_{p1}y_{n-1} + a_{p2}y_{n-2} + \cdots + a_{pp}y_{n-p} \\ e_p^-(n) &= y_{n-p} + a_{p1}y_{n-p+1} + a_{p2}y_{n-p+2} + \cdots + a_{pp}y_n \end{aligned} \tag{5.12.2}$$

Note that in both cases the mean-squared value of $e_p^{\pm}(n)$ can be expressed in terms of the $(p+1) \times (p+1)$ autocorrelation matrix

$$R(i,j) = R(i-j) = E[y_{n+i-j}y_n] = E[y_{n-j}y_{n-i}], \qquad 0 \leq i,j \leq p$$

as follows

$$E[e_p^+(n)^2] = E[e_p^-(n)^2] = \mathbf{a}^T R\mathbf{a} \tag{5.12.3}$$

Consider a frame of length N of measured values of y_n

$y_0, y_1, \cdots, y_{N-1}$

1. The *Yule-Walker,* or *autocorrelation,* method replaces the ensemble average (5.9.1) by the least-squares time-average criterion

$$\mathcal{E} = \sum_{n=0}^{N+p-1} e_p^+(n)^2 = \min \tag{5.12.4}$$

where $e_p^+(n)$ is obtained by convolving the length-$(p+1)$ prediction-error sequence $\mathbf{a} = [1, a_{p1}, a_{p2}, \ldots, a_{pp}]^T$ with the length-N data sequence y_n. The length of the sequence $e_p^+(n)$ is, therefore, $N + (p+1) - 1 = N + p$, which justifies the upper-limit in the summation of Eq. (5.12.4). This convolution operation is equivalent to assuming that the block of data y_n has been extended both to the left and to the right by padding it with zeros and running the filter over this *extended* sequence. The last p output samples $e_p^+(n); N \leq n \leq N+p-1$ correspond to running the filter off the ends of the data sequence to the right. These terms arise because the prediction-error filter has memory of p samples. This is depicted below:

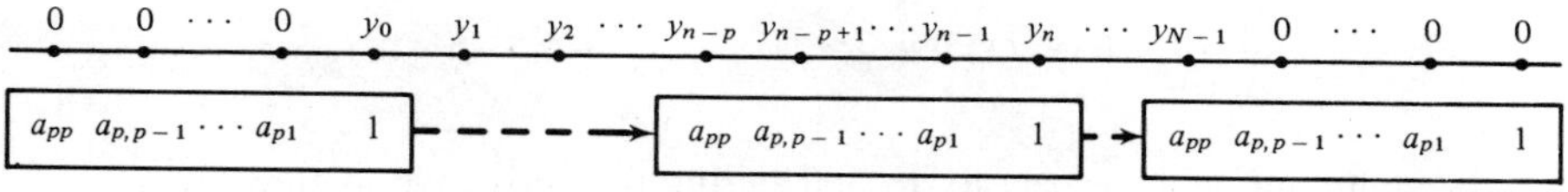

Inserting Eq. (5.12.2) into Eq. (5.12.4), it is easily shown that $\mathcal{E}$ can be expressed in the equivalent form

$$\mathcal{E} = \sum_{n=0}^{N+p-1} e_p^+(n)^2 = \sum_{i,j=0}^{p} a_i \hat{R}(i-j)\, a_j = \mathbf{a}^T \hat{R}\mathbf{a} \tag{5.12.5}$$

where $\hat{R}(k)$ denotes the sample autocorrelation of the length-N data sequence y_n; namely

$$\hat{R}(k) = \hat{R}(-k) = \sum_{n=0}^{N-1-k} y_{n+k}y_n \qquad 0 \leq k \leq N-1$$

where the usual normalization factor $1/N$ has been ignored. This equation is identical to Eq. (5.12.3) with R replaced by $\hat{R}$. Thus, the minimization of the time-average index (5.12.5) with respect to the prediction coefficients will lead exactly to the *same set* of normal equations (5.3.7) with R replaced by $\hat{R}$. The *positive definiteness* of the sample autocorrelation matrix also guarantees that the resulting prediction-error filter be *minimal phase*, and thus also that all reflection coefficients have magnitude *less* than one.

2. The *covariance method* replaces Eq. (5.12.1) by the time average

$$\mathcal{E} = \sum_{n=p}^{N-1} e_p^+(n)^2 = \min \tag{5.12.6}$$

where the summation in n is such that the filter *does not* run off the ends of the data block, as shown below:

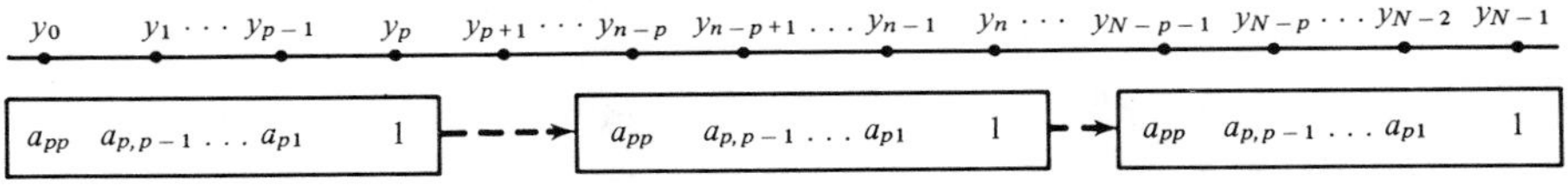

To explain the method and to see its potential problems with stability, consider a simple example of a length-three sequence and a first order predictor:

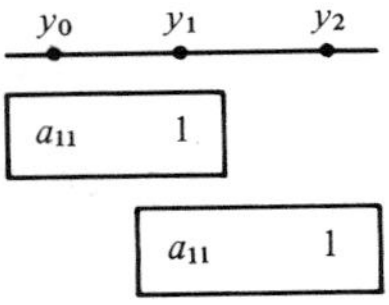

$$\mathcal{E} = \sum_{n=1}^{2} e_1^+(n)^2 = e_1^+(1)^2 + e_1^+(2)^2 = (y_1 + a_{11}y_0)^2 + (y_2 + a_{11}y_1)^2$$

Differentiating with respect to a_{11} and setting the derivative to zero gives

$$(y_1 + a_{11}y_0)y_0 + (y_2 + a_{11}y_1)y_1 = 0$$

$$a_{11} = -\frac{y_1y_0 + y_2y_1}{y_0^2 + y_1^2}$$

Note that the denominator does not depend on the variable y_2 and therefore it is possible, if y_2 is large enough, for a_{11} to have magnitude greater than one, making the prediction-error filter nonminimal phase. Although this potential stability problem exists, this method has been used with good success in speech processing, with few, if any, such stability problems. The autocorrelation method is sometimes preferred in speech processing because the resulting normal equations have a Toeplitz structure and their solution can be obtained efficiently using

Levinson's algorithm. However, similar ways of solving the covariance equations have been developed recently that are just as efficient [98].

3. Although the autocorrelation method is implemented efficiently, and the resulting prediction-error filter is guaranteed to be minimal phase, it suffers from the effect of prewindowing the data sequence y_n by padding it with zeros to the left and to the right. This reduces the accuracy of the method somewhat, especially when the data record N is short. In this case, the effect of prewindowing is felt more strongly. The proper way to extend the sequence y_n, if it must be extended, is a way *compatible* with the signal model generating this sequence. Since we are trying to determine this model, the fairest way of proceeding is to try to use the available data block in a way which is maximally noncommital to what the sequence is like beyond the ends of the block. *Burg's method,* also known as the *maximum entropy method* (MEM), arose from the desire on the one hand not to run off the ends of the data, and, on the other, to always result in a minimal-phase filter. Burg's minimization criterion is to minimize the sum-squared of both the *forward* and the *backward* prediction errors:

$$\mathcal{E} = \sum_{n=p}^{N-1} [e_p^+(n)^2 + e_p^-(n)^2] = \min \tag{5.12.7}$$

where the summation range is the same as in the covariance method, but with both the forward and the reversed filters running over the data, as shown:

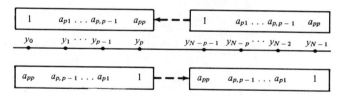

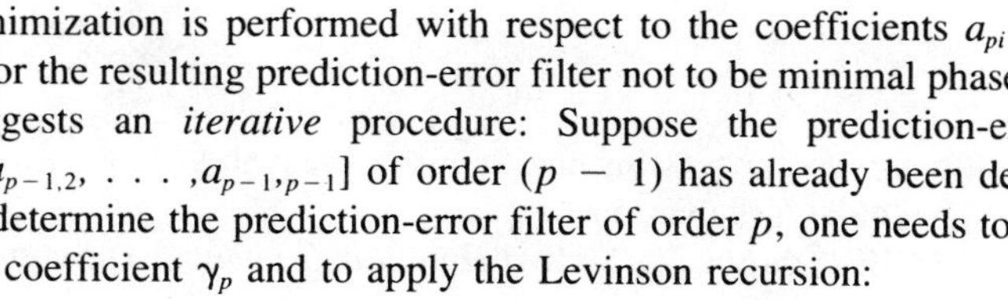

If the minimization is performed with respect to the coefficients a_{pi}, it is still possible for the resulting prediction-error filter not to be minimal phase. Instead, Burg suggests an *iterative* procedure: Suppose the prediction-error filter $[1, a_{p-1,1}, a_{p-1,2}, \ldots, a_{p-1,p-1}]$ of order $(p-1)$ has already been determined. Then, to determine the prediction-error filter of order p, one needs to know the reflection coefficient γ_p and to apply the Levinson recursion:

$$\begin{bmatrix} 1 \\ a_{p,1} \\ a_{p,2} \\ \vdots \\ a_{p,p-1} \\ a_{p,p} \end{bmatrix} = \begin{bmatrix} 1 \\ a_{p-1,1} \\ a_{p-1,2} \\ \vdots \\ a_{p-1,p-1} \\ 0 \end{bmatrix} - \gamma_p \begin{bmatrix} 0 \\ a_{p-1,p-1} \\ a_{p-1,p-2} \\ \vdots \\ a_{p-1,1} \\ 1 \end{bmatrix} \tag{5.12.8}$$

To guarantee the minimal-phase property, the reflection coefficient γ_p must have magnitude less than one. The best choice for γ_p is that which minimizes the performance index (5.12.7). Differentiating with respect to γ_p and setting the derivative to zero we find

$$\frac{\partial \mathcal{E}}{\partial \gamma_p} = 2 \sum_{n=p}^{N-1} \left[e_p^+(n) \frac{\partial e_p^+(n)}{\partial \gamma_p} + e_p^-(n) \frac{\partial e_p^-(n)}{\partial \gamma_p} \right] = 0$$

Using the lattice relationships

$$\begin{aligned} e_p^+(n) &= e_{p-1}^+(n) - \gamma_p e_{p-1}^-(n-1) \\ e_p^-(n) &= e_{p-1}^-(n-1) - \gamma_p e_{p-1}^+(n) \end{aligned} \qquad (5.12.9)$$

both valid for $p \leq n \leq N - 1$ if the filter is not to run off the data, we find the conditions

$$\sum_{n=p}^{N-1} [e_p^+(n)e_{p-1}^-(n-1) + e_p^-(n)e_{p-1}^+(n)] = 0$$

$$\sum_{n=p}^{N-1} [(e_{p-1}^+(n) - \gamma_p e_{p-1}^-(n-1))e_{p-1}^-(n-1) \\ + (e_{p-1}^-(n-1) - \gamma_p e_{p-1}^+(n))e_{p-1}^+(n)] = 0$$

which can be solved for γ_p to give

$$\gamma_p = \frac{2 \sum_{n=p}^{N-1} e_{p-1}^+(n)e_{p-1}^-(n-1)}{\sum_{n=p}^{N-1} [e_{p-1}^+(n)^2 + e_{p-1}^-(n-1)^2]} \qquad (5.12.10)$$

This expression for γ_p is of the form

$$\gamma_p = \frac{2\mathbf{a} \cdot \mathbf{b}}{|\mathbf{a}|^2 + |\mathbf{b}|^2}$$

where **a** and **b** are vectors. Using the Schwarz inequality, it is easily verified that γ_p has magnitude less than one.

Equations (5.12.8) through (5.12.10) define *Burg's method.* The computational steps are summarized below:

0. Initialize as follows:

$$e_0^+(n) = e_0^-(n) = y_n; \text{ for } 0 \leq n \leq N - 1 \text{ and } E_0 = \frac{1}{N} \sum_{n=0}^{N-1} y_n^2$$

1. At stage $(p - 1)$, we have available the quantities:

$$A_{p-1}(z),\ E_{p-1} \text{ and } e_{p-1}^{\pm}(n); \text{ for } p - 1 \leq n \leq N - 1$$

2. Using Eq. (5.12.10), compute the reflection coefficient γ_p
3. Using (5.12.8), compute $A_p(z)$
4. Using (5.12.9), compute $e_p^{\pm}(n)$; for $p \leq n \leq N-1$
5. Update the mean-squared error by $E_p = (1 - \gamma_p^2)E_{p-1}$
6. Go to stage p

The subroutine **burg** (see Appendix B) is an implementation of this method. The inputs to the subroutine are the vector of data samples $\{y_0, y_1, \ldots, y_{N-1}\}$ and the desired final order M of the predictor. The outputs are all the prediction-error filters of order up to M, arranged as usual into the lower triangular matrix L, and the corresponding mean-squared prediction errors $\{E_0, E_1, \ldots, E_M\}$.

Example 5.12.1: The length-six block of data

$$y_n = [4.684, 7.247, 8.423, 8.650, 8.640, 8.392]$$

for $n = 0,1,2,3,4,5$, is known to have been generated by sending zero-mean, unit-variance, white noise ϵ_n through the difference equation

$$y_n - 1.70y_{n-1} + 0.72y_{n-2} = \epsilon_n$$

Thus, the theoretical prediction-error filter and mean-squared error are $A_2(z) = 1 - 1.70z^{-1} + 0.72z^{-2}$, and $E_2 = 1.00$. Using Burg's method, extract the model parameters for a second order model. The reader is urged to go through the algorithm by hand. Sending the above six y_n samples through the routine **burg,** we find the first and second order prediction-error filters and the corresponding errors:

$$A_1(z) = 1 - 0.989z^{-1} \quad \text{and} \quad E_1 = 1.529$$

$$A_2(z) = 1 - 1.757z^{-1} + 0.779z^{-2} \quad \text{and} \quad E_2 = 0.60$$

The resulting set of LPC model parameters, from any of the above analysis methods, can be used in a number of ways as suggested in Section 1.11. One of the most successful applications has been to analysis and synthesis of speech [6,104–112]. Each frame of speech, of duration of the order of 20 msec, is subjected to the Yule-Walker analysis method to extract the corresponding set of model parameters. The order of the predictor is typically $M = 10$–15. Pitch and voiced/unvoiced information are also extracted. The resulting set of parameters represents that speech segment. To synthesize the segment, the set of model parameters are recalled from memory and used in the synthesizer to drive the synthesis filter. The latter is commonly realized as a *lattice filter*. Lattice realizations are preferred because they are much better well-behaved under quantization of their coefficients (i.e., the reflection coefficients) than the direct form realizations [6,108,109]. A typical speech analysis and synthesis system is shown in Fig. 5.12.

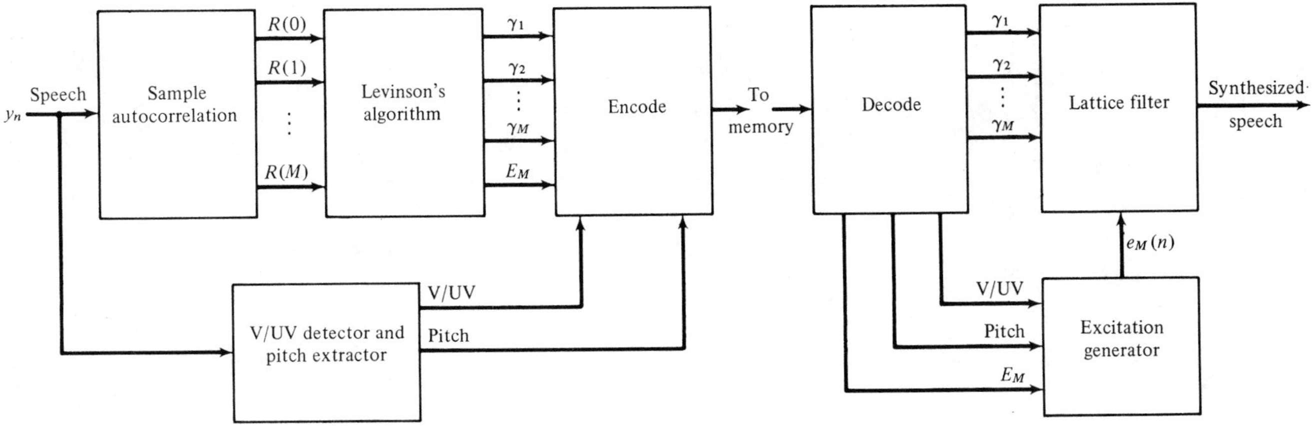

Figure 5.12 LPC Analysis and Synthesis of Speech

Linear predictive modeling techniques have also been applied to EEG signal processing in order to *model* EEG spectra, to *classify* EEGs automatically, to detect EEG *transients* that might have diagnostic significance, and to *predict* the onset of epileptic seizures [113–120].

LPC methods have been applied successfully to *signal classification* problems such as speech recognition [107,121–126] or the automatic classification of EEGs [117]. *Distance measures* between two sets of model parameters extracted from two signal frames can be used as measures of similarity between the frames. Itakura's *LPC distance measure* can be introduced as follows: Consider two *autoregressive* signal sequences, the test sequence $y_T(n)$ to be compared against the reference sequence $y_R(n)$. Let $A_T(z)$ and $A_R(z)$ be the two whitening filters, both of order M. The two signal models are

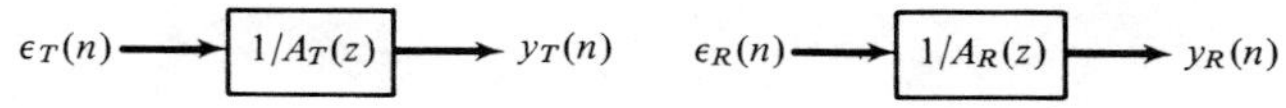

Now, suppose the sequence to be tested, $y_T(n)$, is filtered through the whitening filter of the reference signal

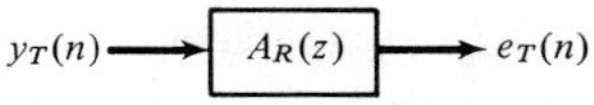

resulting in the output signal $e_T(n)$. The mean output power is easily expressed as

$$
\begin{aligned}
E[e_T(n)^2] &= \mathbf{a}_R^\dagger R_T \mathbf{a}_R = \int_{-\pi}^{\pi} S_{e_Te_T}(\omega)\,\frac{d\omega}{2\pi} \\
&= \int_{-\pi}^{\pi} |A_R(\omega)|^2 S_{y_Ty_T}(\omega)\,\frac{d\omega}{2\pi} \\
&= \int_{-\pi}^{\pi} |A_R(\omega)|^2 \frac{\sigma_{\epsilon_T}^2}{|A_T(\omega)|^2}\,\frac{d\omega}{2\pi}
\end{aligned}
$$

where R_T is the correlation matrix of $y_T(n)$. On the other hand, if $y_T(n)$ is filtered through its own whitening filter it will produce ϵ_T. Thus, in this case

$$
\sigma_{\epsilon_T}^2 = E[\epsilon_T(n)^2] = \mathbf{a}_T^\dagger R_T \mathbf{a}_T
$$

It follows that

$$
\frac{E[e_T(n)^2]}{E[\epsilon_T(n)^2]} = \frac{\mathbf{a}_R^\dagger R_T \mathbf{a}_R}{\mathbf{a}_T^\dagger R_T \mathbf{a}_T} = \int_{-\pi}^{\pi} \left|\frac{A_R(\omega)}{A_T(\omega)}\right|^2 \frac{d\omega}{2\pi} \tag{5.12.11}
$$

The log of this quantity is Itakura's LPC distance measure

$$d(\mathbf{a}_T,\mathbf{a}_R) = \log\left(\frac{E[e_T^2]}{E[\epsilon_T^2]}\right) = \log\left(\frac{\mathbf{a}_R^\dagger R_T \mathbf{a}_R}{\mathbf{a}_T^\dagger R_T \mathbf{a}_T}\right) = \log\left[\int_{-\pi}^{\pi}\left|\frac{A_R(\omega)}{A_T(\omega)}\right|^2 \frac{d\omega}{2\pi}\right]$$

In practice, the quantities $\mathbf{a}_T$, R_T, and $\mathbf{a}_R$ are extracted from a frame of $y_T(n)$ and a frame of $y_R(n)$. If the model parameters are equal, the distance is zero. This distance measure effectively provides a comparison between the two spectra of the processes y_T and y_R, but instead of comparing them directly, a *prewhitening* of $y_T(n)$ is attempted by sending it through the whitening filter of the other signal. If the two spectra are close, the filtered signal $e_T(n)$ will be close to white—that is, with a spectrum close to being flat; a measure of this flatness is precisely the above integrated spectrum of Eq. (5.12.11).

5.13 *Dynamic Predictive Deconvolution—Waves in Layered Media*

The analysis and synthesis lattice filters, implemented via the Levinson recursion, were obtained within the context of linear prediction. Here, we would like to point out the remarkable fact that the same analysis and synthesis lattice structures also occur naturally in the problem of *wave propagation* in *layered media* [6,7,9,59,61,95,104,127–144]. This is perhaps the reason behind the great success of linear prediction methods in speech and seismic signal processing. In fact, historically many linear prediction techniques were originally developed within the context of these two application areas.

In speech, the vocal tract is modeled as an acoustic tube of varying cross-sectional area. It can be approximated by the *piece-wise* constant area approximation shown below:

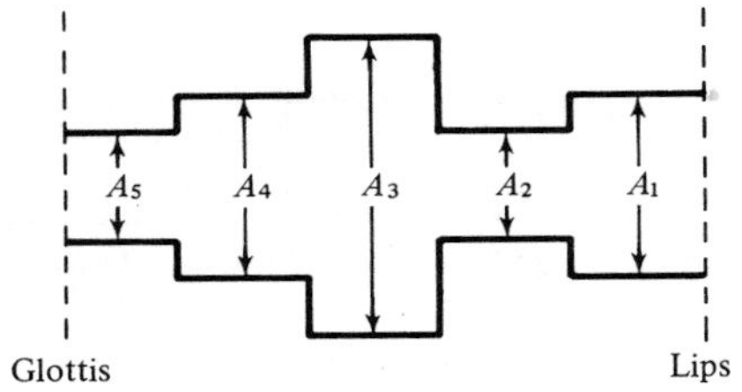

The acoustic impedance of a sound wave varies inversely with the tube area

$$Z = \frac{\rho c}{A}$$

where ρ, c, and A are the air density, speed of sound, and tube area, respectively. Therefore, as the sound wave propagates from the glottis to the lips, it will suffer reflections every time it encounters an interface; that is, every time it enters a tube segment of different diameter. Multiple reflections will be set up within each segment and the tube will *reverberate* in a complicated manner depending on the number of segments and the diameter of each segment. By measuring the speech wave that eventually comes out of the lips, it is possible to remove, or deconvolve, the reverberatory effects of the tube and, in the process, extract the *tube parameters,* such as the areas of the segments or, equivalently, the reflection coefficients at the interfaces. During speech, the configuration of the vocal tract tube changes continuously. But being a mechanical system, it does so fairly slowly, and for short periods of time (of the order of 20–30 msec) it may be assumed to maintain a fixed configuration. From each such short segment of speech, a set of configuration parameters (e.g., reflection coefficients) may be extracted. This set may be used to synthesize the speech segment.

The seismic problem is somewhat different. Here it is not the transmitted wave that is experimentally accessible, but rather the overall reflected wave:

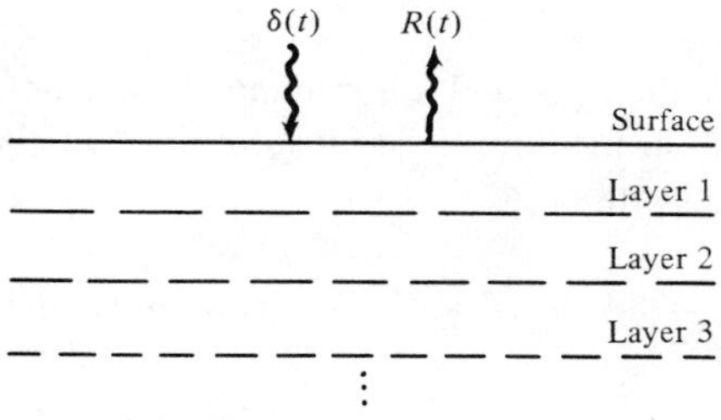

An impulsive input to the earth, such as a dynamite explosion near the surface, will set up seismic elastic waves propagating downwards. As the various earth layers are encountered, reflections will take place. Eventually each layer will be reverberating and an overall reflected wave will be measured at the surface. On the basis of this reflected wave, the layered structure (i.e., reflection coefficients, impedances, etc.) must be extracted by deconvolution techniques. These are essentially identical to the linear prediction methods.

In addition to geophysical and speech applications, this wave problem and the associated *inverse* problem of extracting the structure of the medium from the observed (reflected or transmitted) response have a number of other applications. Examples include the probing of dielectric materials by electromagnetic waves, the study of the optical properties of thin films, the probing of tissues by ultrasound, and the design of broadband terminations of transmission lines.

The mathematical analysis of such wave propagation problems has been done more or less independently in each of these application areas, and is well known dating back to the time of Stokes.

In this type of wave propagation problem there are always *two* associated propagating field quantities, the ratio of which is constant and equal to the corresponding *characteristic impedance* of the propagation medium. Examples of these include the electric and magnetic fields in the case of EM waves, the air pressure and particle volume velocity for sound waves, the stress and particle displacement for seismic waves, and the voltage and current waves in the case of TEM transmission lines.

As a concrete example, we have chosen to present in some detail the case of EM waves propagating in lossless dielectrics. The simplest and most basic scattering problem arises when there is a single interface separating two semi-infinite dielectrics of characteristic impedances Z and Z', as shown

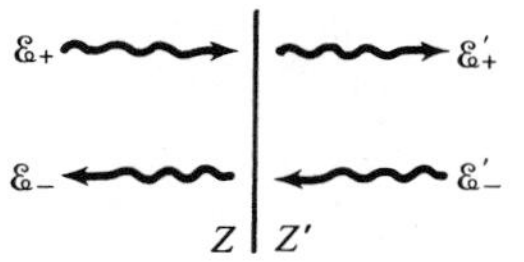

where $\mathcal{E}_+$ and $\mathcal{E}_-$ are the right and left moving electric fields in medium Z, and $\mathcal{E}'_+$ and $\mathcal{E}'_-$ are those in medium Z'. *Matching* the boundary conditions at this interface gives two equations

$$\mathcal{E}_+ + \mathcal{E}_- = \mathcal{E}'_+ + \mathcal{E}'_- \qquad \text{(continuity of electric field)}$$

$$\frac{1}{Z}(\mathcal{E}_+ - \mathcal{E}_-) = \frac{1}{Z'}(\mathcal{E}'_+ - \mathcal{E}'_-) \qquad \text{(continuity of magnetic field)}$$

Introducing the reflection and transmission coefficients

$$\rho = \frac{Z' - Z}{Z' + Z}, \qquad \tau = 1 + \rho, \qquad \rho' = -\rho, \qquad \tau' = 1 + \rho' = 1 - \rho \tag{5.13.1}$$

the above equations can be written in a transmission matrix form

$$\begin{bmatrix} \mathcal{E}_+ \\ \mathcal{E}_- \end{bmatrix} = \frac{1}{\tau} \begin{bmatrix} 1 & \rho \\ \rho & 1 \end{bmatrix} \begin{bmatrix} \mathcal{E}'_+ \\ \mathcal{E}'_- \end{bmatrix} \tag{5.13.2}$$

The flow of energy carried by these waves is given by the Poynting vector

$$P = \frac{1}{2} Re\left[(\mathcal{E}_+ + \mathcal{E}_-)^* \frac{1}{Z}(\mathcal{E}_+ - \mathcal{E}_-)\right] = \frac{1}{Z}(\mathcal{E}_+^*\mathcal{E}_+ - \mathcal{E}_-^*\mathcal{E}_-) \tag{5.13.3}$$

One consequence of the above matching conditions is that the total energy flow to the right is preserved *across* the interface: that is,

$$\frac{1}{Z}(\mathcal{E}_+^*\mathcal{E}_+ - \mathcal{E}_-^*\mathcal{E}_-) = \frac{1}{Z'}(\mathcal{E}_+'^*\mathcal{E}_+' - \mathcal{E}_-'^*\mathcal{E}_-') \qquad (5.13.4)$$

It proves convenient to absorb the factors $1/Z$ and $1/Z'$ into the definitions for the fields by *renormalizing* them as follows:

$$\begin{bmatrix} E_+ \\ E_- \end{bmatrix} = \frac{1}{\sqrt{Z}}\begin{bmatrix} \mathcal{E}_+ \\ \mathcal{E}_- \end{bmatrix}, \qquad \begin{bmatrix} E_+' \\ E_-' \end{bmatrix} = \frac{1}{\sqrt{Z'}}\begin{bmatrix} \mathcal{E}_+' \\ \mathcal{E}_-' \end{bmatrix}$$

Then, Eq. (5.13.4) reads

$$E_+^*E_+ - E_-^*E_- = E_+'^*E_+' - E_-'^*E_-' \qquad (5.13.5)$$

and the matching equations (5.13.2) can be written in the normalized form

$$\begin{bmatrix} E_+ \\ E_- \end{bmatrix} = \frac{1}{t}\begin{bmatrix} 1 & \rho \\ \rho & 1 \end{bmatrix}\begin{bmatrix} E_+' \\ E_-' \end{bmatrix}, \qquad t = \sqrt{1-\rho^2} = \sqrt{\tau\tau'} \qquad (5.13.6)$$

They may also be written in a *scattering matrix* form that relates the *outgoing* fields to the *incoming* fields, as follows:

$$\begin{bmatrix} E_+' \\ E_- \end{bmatrix} = \begin{bmatrix} t & \rho' \\ \rho & t \end{bmatrix}\begin{bmatrix} E_+ \\ E_-' \end{bmatrix} = S\begin{bmatrix} E_+ \\ E_-' \end{bmatrix} \qquad (5.13.7)$$

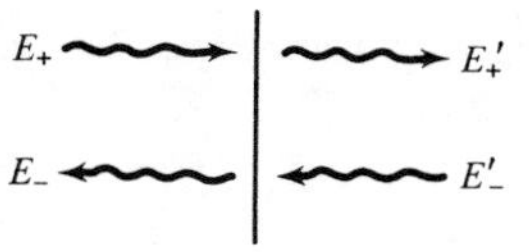

This is the most elementary scattering matrix of all, and ρ and t are the most elementary reflection and transmission responses. From these, the reflection and transmission response of more complicated structures can be built up. In the more general case, we have a dielectric structure consisting of M slabs stacked together as shown in Fig. 5.13.

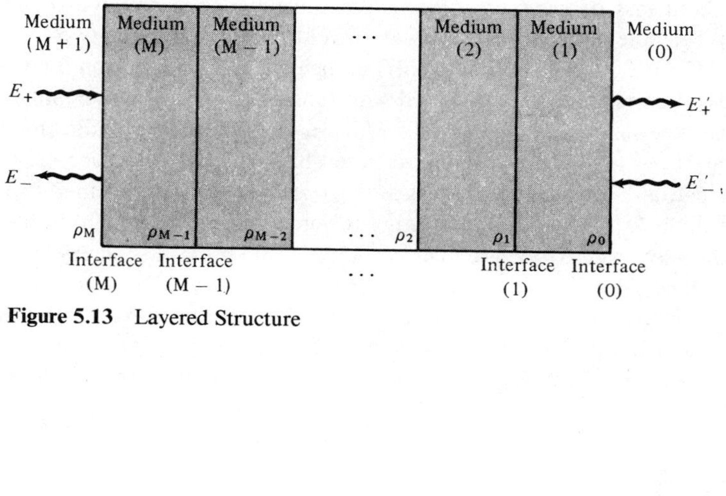

Figure 5.13 Layered Structure

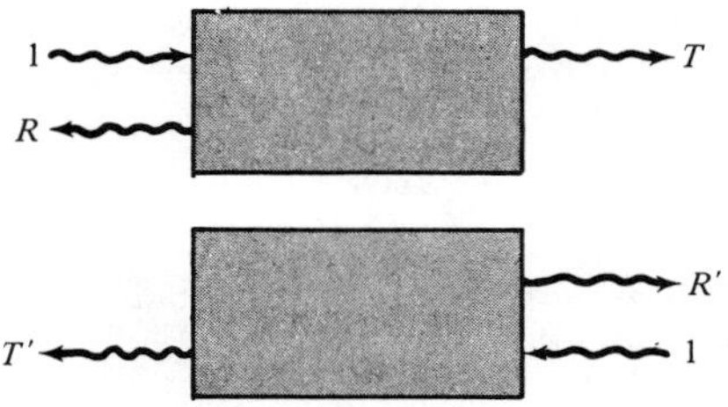

Figure 5.14 Reflection and Transmission Responses

The media to the left and right in the figure are assumed to be semi-infinite. The *reflection* and *transmission responses* (from the *left*, or from the *right*) of the structure are defined as the responses of the structure to an impulse (incident from the left, or from the right) as shown in Fig. 5.14.

The corresponding scattering matrix is defined as

$$S = \begin{bmatrix} T & R' \\ R & T' \end{bmatrix}$$

and by linear superposition, the relationship between arbitrary incoming and outgoing waves is

$$\begin{bmatrix} E'_+ \\ E_- \end{bmatrix} = \begin{bmatrix} T & R' \\ R & T' \end{bmatrix} \begin{bmatrix} E_+ \\ E'_- \end{bmatrix}$$

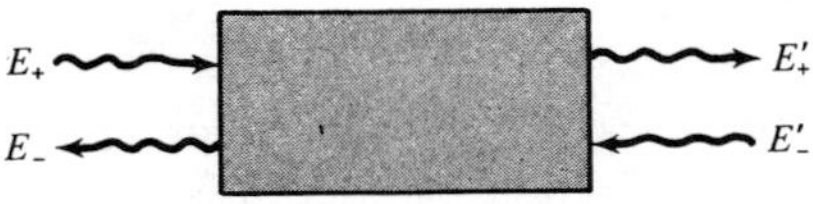

The *inverse scattering problem* that we pose is how to extract the detailed properties of the layered structure, such as the reflection coefficients $\rho_0, \rho_1, \ldots,$ ρ_M, from the knowledge of the scattering matrix S; that is, from observations of the reflection response R or the transmission response T.

Without loss of generality, we may assume the M slabs have *equal travel time*. We denote the common one-way travel time by T_1 and the two-way travel time by $T_2 = 2T_1$. As an impulse $\delta(t)$ is incident from the left on interface M, there will be immediately a reflected wave and a transmitted wave into medium M. When the latter reaches interface $M - 1$, part of it will be transmitted into medium $M - 1$, and part will be reflected back towards interface M where it will be partially rereflected towards $M - 1$ and partially transmitted to the left into medium $M + 1$, thus contributing towards the overall reflection response. Since the wave had to travel to interface $M - 1$ and back, this latter contribution will occur at time T_2. Similarly, another wave will return back to interface M due to reflection from the second interface $M - 2$; this wave will return $2T_2$ seconds later and will add to the contribution from the zig-zag path within medium M which is also returning at $2T_2$, and so on. The timing diagram below shows all the possible return paths up to time $t = 3T_2$, during which the original impulse can only travel as far as interface $M - 3$:

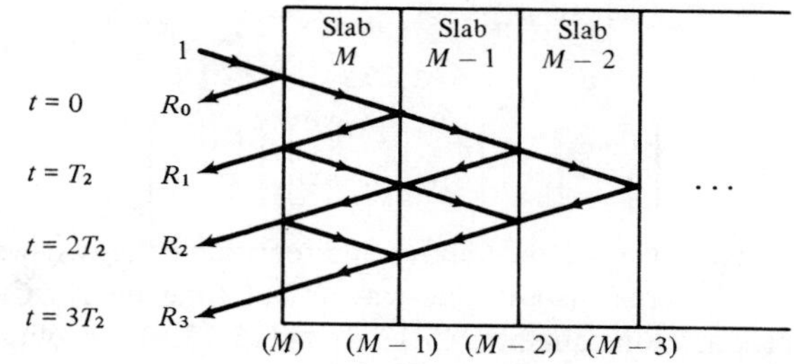

When we add the contributions of all the returned waves we see that the reflection response will be a linear superposition of returned impulses

$$R(t) = \sum_{k=0}^{\infty} R_k \delta(t - kT_2)$$

It has a Fourier transform expressible more conveniently as the z-transform

$$R(z) = \sum_{k=0}^{\infty} R_k z^{-k} \qquad \text{where } z = e^{j\omega T_2}$$

Observe that R is *periodic in frequency* ω with period $2\pi/T_2$, which plays a role analogous to the sampling frequency. Therefore, it is enough to specify R within the *Nyquist interval* $[-\pi/T_2, \pi/T_2]$.

Next, we develop the *lattice recursions* that facilitate the solution of the direct and the inverse scattering problems. Consider the mth slab and let $E_m^{\pm}$ be the right/left moving waves incident on the left side of the mth interface. To relate them to the same quantities $E_{m-1}^{\pm}$ incident on the left side of the $(m - 1)$st interface, first we use the *matching* equations to "pass" to the other side of the mth interface and into the mth slab, and then we *propagate* these quantities to reach the left side of the $(m - 1)$st interface. This is shown below.

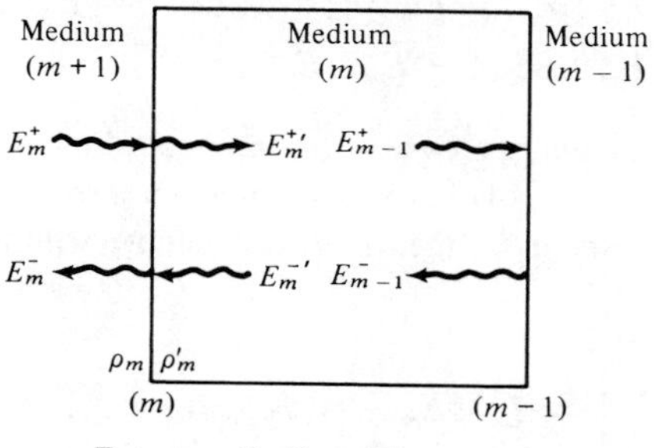

$$\begin{bmatrix} E_m^+ \\ E_m^- \end{bmatrix} = \frac{1}{t_m} \begin{bmatrix} 1 & \rho_m \\ \rho_m & 1 \end{bmatrix} \begin{bmatrix} E_m^{+\prime} \\ E_m^{-\prime} \end{bmatrix}, \qquad t_m = (1 - \rho_m^2)^{1/2} \tag{5.13.8}$$

Since the left-moving wave $E_m^{-\prime}$ is the delayed replica of E_{m-1}^- by T_1 seconds, and $E_m^{+\prime}$ is the advanced replica of E_{m-1}^+ by T_1 seconds, it follows that

$$E_m^{+\prime} = z^{1/2}E_{m-1}^+, \qquad E_m^{-\prime} = z^{-1/2}E_{m-1}^-$$

or, in matrix form,

$$\begin{bmatrix} E_m^{+\prime} \\ E_m^{-\prime} \end{bmatrix} = \begin{bmatrix} z^{1/2} & 0 \\ 0 & z^{-1/2} \end{bmatrix} \begin{bmatrix} E_{m-1}^+ \\ E_{m-1}^- \end{bmatrix} \tag{5.13.9}$$

where the variable z^{-1} was defined above and represents the two-way travel time delay, while $z^{-1/2}$ represents the one-way travel time delay. Combining the matching and propagation equations (5.13.8) and (5.13.9), we obtain the desired relationship between $E_m^\pm$ and $E_{m-1}^\pm$:

$$\begin{bmatrix} E_m^+ \\ E_m^- \end{bmatrix} = \frac{z^{1/2}}{t_m} \begin{bmatrix} 1 & \rho_m z^{-1} \\ \rho_m & z^{-1} \end{bmatrix} \begin{bmatrix} E_{m-1}^+ \\ E_{m-1}^- \end{bmatrix} \tag{5.13.10}$$

Or, introducing some convenient vector notation

$$E_m(z) = \psi_m(z)E_{m-1}(z) \tag{5.13.11}$$

where

$$E_m(z) = \begin{bmatrix} E_m^+(z) \\ E_m^-(z) \end{bmatrix}, \qquad \psi_m(z) = \frac{z^{1/2}}{t_m} \begin{bmatrix} 1 & \rho_m z^{-1} \\ \rho_m & z^{-1} \end{bmatrix} \tag{5.13.12}$$

The "match-and-propagate" transition matrix $\psi_m(z)$ has two interesting properties; namely, defining $\bar{\psi}_m(z) = \psi_m(z^{-1})$

$$\bar{\psi}_m(z)^T J_3 \psi(z) = \psi_m(z^{-1})^T J_3 \psi_m(z) = J_3, \qquad J_3 = \begin{bmatrix} 1 & 0 \\ 0 & -1 \end{bmatrix} \tag{5.13.13}$$

$$\bar{\psi}_m(z) = \psi_m(z^{-1}) = J_1 \psi_m(z) J_1, \qquad J_1 = \begin{bmatrix} 0 & 1 \\ 1 & 0 \end{bmatrix} \tag{5.13.14}$$

From Eq. (5.3.13) we have

$$\begin{aligned} \bar{E}_m^+ E_m^+ - \bar{E}_m^- E_m^- &= \bar{E}_m^T J_3 E_m = \bar{E}_{m-1}^T \bar{\psi}_m^T J_3 \psi_m E_{m-1} = \bar{E}_{m-1}^T J_3 E_{m-1} \\ &= \bar{E}_{m-1}^+ E_{m-1}^+ - \bar{E}_{m-1}^- E_{m-1}^- \end{aligned} \tag{5.13.15}$$

which is equivalent to *energy conservation,* according to Eq. (5.13.5). The second property, Eq. (5.13.14), expresses *time-reversal invariance* and allows the construction of a *second,* linearly independent, solution of the recursive equations (5.13.11):

$$\hat{E}_m = J_1 \bar{E}_m = \begin{bmatrix} \bar{E}_m^- \\ \bar{E}_m^+ \end{bmatrix} = J_1 \bar{\psi}_m \bar{E}_{m-1} = J_1 \bar{\psi}_m J_1 J_1 \bar{E}_{m-1} = \psi_m \hat{E}_{m-1} \tag{5.13.16}$$

The recursions (5.13.11) may be iterated now down to $m = 0$. By an additional boundary match, we may pass to the right side of interface $m = 0$:

$$E_m = \psi_m\psi_{m-1} \cdots \psi_1 E_0 = \psi_m\psi_{m-1} \cdots \psi_1\psi_0 E_0'$$

where we defined ψ_0 by

$$\psi_0 = \frac{1}{t_0}\begin{bmatrix} 1 & \rho_0 \\ \rho_0 & 1 \end{bmatrix}$$

or, more explicitly,

$$\begin{bmatrix} E_m^+ \\ E_m^- \end{bmatrix} = \frac{z^{m/2}}{t_m t_{m-1} \cdots t_1 t_0}\begin{bmatrix} 1 & \rho_m z^{-1} \\ \rho_m & z^{-1} \end{bmatrix} \cdots \begin{bmatrix} 1 & \rho_1 z^{-1} \\ \rho_1 & z^{-1} \end{bmatrix}\begin{bmatrix} 1 & \rho_0 \\ \rho_0 & 1 \end{bmatrix}\begin{bmatrix} E_0^{+\prime} \\ E_0^{-\prime} \end{bmatrix} \tag{5.13.17}$$

To deal with this product of matrices, we define

$$\begin{bmatrix} A_m & C_m \\ B_m & D_m \end{bmatrix} = \begin{bmatrix} 1 & \rho_m z^{-1} \\ \rho_m & z^{-1} \end{bmatrix} \cdots \begin{bmatrix} 1 & \rho_1 z^{-1} \\ \rho_1 & z^{-1} \end{bmatrix}\begin{bmatrix} 1 & \rho_0 \\ \rho_0 & 1 \end{bmatrix} \tag{5.13.18}$$

where A_m, B_m, C_m, D_m are *polynomials* of degree m in the variable z^{-1}. The energy conservation and time-reversal invariance properties of the ψ_m matrices imply similar properties for these polynomials. Writing Eq. (5.13.18) in terms of the ψ_ms, we have

$$\begin{bmatrix} A_m & C_m \\ B_m & D_m \end{bmatrix} = z^{-m/2}\sigma_m\psi_m\psi_{m-1} \cdots \psi_1\psi_0$$

where we defined the quantity

$$\sigma_m = t_m t_{m-1} \cdots t_1 t_0 = \prod_{i=0}^{m} (1 - \rho_i^2)^{1/2} \tag{5.13.19}$$

The property (5.13.13) implies the same for the above product of matrices; that is,

$$\begin{bmatrix} \bar{A}_m & \bar{C}_m \\ \bar{B}_m & \bar{D}_m \end{bmatrix}^T \begin{bmatrix} 1 & 0 \\ 0 & -1 \end{bmatrix}\begin{bmatrix} A_m & C_m \\ B_m & D_m \end{bmatrix} = \begin{bmatrix} 1 & 0 \\ 0 & -1 \end{bmatrix}\sigma_m^2$$

which implies that the quantity

$$\bar{A}_m(z)A_m(z) - \bar{B}_m(z)B_m(z) = \sigma_m^2 \tag{5.13.20}$$

is independent of z. The property (5.13.14) implies that C_m and D_m are the reverse polynomials B_m^R and A_m^R, respectively; in fact

$$\begin{bmatrix} A_m^R & C_m^R \\ B_m^R & D_m^R \end{bmatrix} = z^{-m} \begin{bmatrix} \bar{A}_m & \bar{C}_m \\ \bar{B}_m & \bar{D}_m \end{bmatrix} = z^{-m} z^{m/2} \sigma_m \bar{\psi}_m \cdots \bar{\psi}_0$$

$$= z^{-m/2} \sigma_m J_1 (\psi_m \cdots \psi_0) J_1 = J_1 \begin{bmatrix} A_m & C_m \\ B_m & D_m \end{bmatrix} J_1$$

$$= \begin{bmatrix} 0 & 1 \\ 1 & 0 \end{bmatrix} \begin{bmatrix} A_m & C_m \\ B_m & D_m \end{bmatrix} \begin{bmatrix} 0 & 1 \\ 1 & 0 \end{bmatrix} = \begin{bmatrix} D_m & B_m \\ C_m & A_m \end{bmatrix} \qquad (5.13.21)$$

from which it follows that $C_m(z) = B_m^R(z)$ and $D_m(z) = A_m^R(z)$. The definition (5.13.18) also implies the recursion

$$\begin{bmatrix} A_m & B_m^R \\ B_m & A_m^R \end{bmatrix} = \begin{bmatrix} 1 & \rho_m z^{-1} \\ \rho_m & z^{-1} \end{bmatrix} \begin{bmatrix} A_{m-1} & B_{m-1}^R \\ B_{m-1} & A_{m-1}^R \end{bmatrix}$$

Therefore each column of the *ABCD* matrix satisfies the same recursion.

To summarize, we have

$$\begin{bmatrix} A_m(z) & B_m^R(z) \\ B_m(z) & A_m^R(z) \end{bmatrix} = \begin{bmatrix} 1 & \rho_m z^{-1} \\ \rho_m & z^{-1} \end{bmatrix} \cdots \begin{bmatrix} 1 & \rho_1 z^{-1} \\ \rho_1 & z^{-1} \end{bmatrix} \begin{bmatrix} 1 & \rho_0 \\ \rho_0 & 1 \end{bmatrix} \qquad (5.13.22)$$

with the *lattice recursion*

$$\begin{bmatrix} A_m(z) \\ B_m(z) \end{bmatrix} = \begin{bmatrix} 1 & \rho_m z^{-1} \\ \rho_m & z^{-1} \end{bmatrix} \begin{bmatrix} A_{m-1}(z) \\ B_{m-1}(z) \end{bmatrix} \qquad (5.13.23)$$

and the property (5.13.20). The lattice recursion may be *initialized* at $m = 0$ by

$$A_0(z) = 1, \quad B_0(z) = \rho_0, \quad \text{or} \quad \begin{bmatrix} A_0(z) & B_0^R(z) \\ B_0(z) & A_0^R(z) \end{bmatrix} = \begin{bmatrix} 1 & \rho_0 \\ \rho_0 & 1 \end{bmatrix} \qquad (5.13.24)$$

Furthermore, it follows from the lattice recursion (5.13.23) that the reflection coefficients ρ_m always appear in the *first* and *last* coefficients of the polynomials $A_m(z)$ and $B_m(z)$, as follows:

$$b_m(0) = \rho_m, \quad a_m(0) = 1, \quad b_m(m) = \rho_0, \quad a_m(m) = \rho_0 \rho_m \qquad (5.13.25)$$

Eq. (5.13.17) for the field components reads now

$$\begin{bmatrix} E_m^+ \\ E_m^- \end{bmatrix} = \frac{z^{m/2}}{\sigma_m} \begin{bmatrix} A_m & B_m^R \\ B_m & A_m^R \end{bmatrix} \begin{bmatrix} E_0^{+\prime} \\ E_0^{-\prime} \end{bmatrix}$$

Setting $m = M$, we find the relationship between the fields incident on the dielectric slab structure from the left to those incident from the right:

$$\begin{bmatrix} E_M^+ \\ E_M^- \end{bmatrix} = \frac{z^{M/2}}{\sigma_M} \begin{bmatrix} A_M & B_M^R \\ B_M & A_M^R \end{bmatrix} \begin{bmatrix} E_0^{+\prime} \\ E_0^{-\prime} \end{bmatrix} \tag{5.13.26}$$

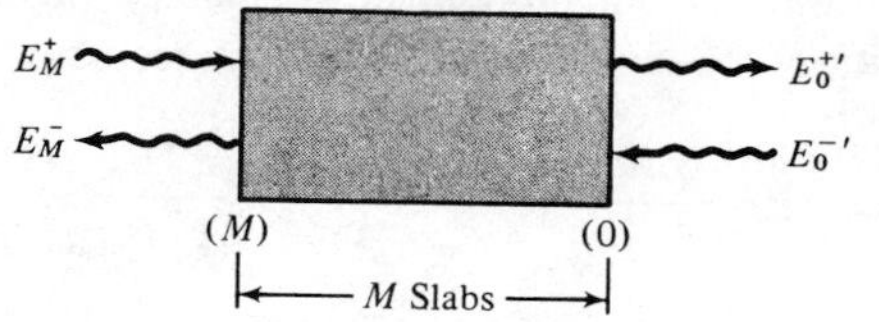

All the multiple reflections and reverberatory effects of the structure are buried in the transition matrix

$$\begin{bmatrix} A_M & B_M^R \\ B_M & A_M^R \end{bmatrix}$$

In reference to Fig. 5.14, the reflection and transmission responses R, T, R', T' of the structure can be obtained from Eq. (5.13.26) by noting that

$$\begin{bmatrix} 1 \\ R \end{bmatrix} = \frac{z^{M/2}}{\sigma_M} \begin{bmatrix} A_M & B_M^R \\ B_M & A_M^R \end{bmatrix} \begin{bmatrix} T \\ 0 \end{bmatrix}, \qquad \begin{bmatrix} 0 \\ T' \end{bmatrix} = \frac{z^{M/2}}{\sigma_M} \begin{bmatrix} A_M & B_M^R \\ B_M & A_M^R \end{bmatrix} \begin{bmatrix} R' \\ 1 \end{bmatrix}$$

which may be combined into one equation

$$\begin{bmatrix} 1 & 0 \\ R & T' \end{bmatrix} = \frac{z^{M/2}}{\sigma_M} \begin{bmatrix} A_M & B_M^R \\ B_M & A_M^R \end{bmatrix} \begin{bmatrix} T & R' \\ 0 & 1 \end{bmatrix}$$

that can be written as follows:

$$\frac{z^{M/2}}{\sigma_M} \begin{bmatrix} A_M & B_M^R \\ B_M & A_M^R \end{bmatrix} = \begin{bmatrix} 1 & 0 \\ R & T' \end{bmatrix} \begin{bmatrix} T & R' \\ 0 & 1 \end{bmatrix}^{-1}$$

$$= \begin{bmatrix} 1 & 0 \\ R & 1 \end{bmatrix} \begin{bmatrix} T^{-1} & 0 \\ 0 & T' \end{bmatrix} \begin{bmatrix} 1 & -R' \\ 0 & 1 \end{bmatrix}$$

Solving these for the reflection and transmission responses, we find

$$R(z) = \frac{B_M(z)}{A_M(z)} \qquad T(z) = \frac{\sigma_M z^{-M/2}}{A_M(z)}$$
$$R'(z) = -\frac{B_M^R(z)}{A_M(z)} \qquad T'(z) = \frac{\sigma_M z^{-M/2}}{A_M(z)} \tag{5.13.27}$$

Note that $T(z) = T'(z)$. Since on physical grounds the transmission response $T(z)$ must be a *stable* and *causal* z-transform, it follows that necessarily the polynomial $A_M(z)$ must be a *minimal-phase polynomial*. The overall delay factor $z^{-M/2}$ in $T(z)$ is of no consequence. It just means that before anything can be transmitted through the structure, it must traverse all M slabs, each with a travel time delay of T_1 seconds; that is, with overall delay of MT_1 seconds.

Let $R_{m-1}(z)$ and $T_{m-1}(z)$ be the reflection and transmission responses based on $m - 1$ layers. The addition of one more layer will change the responses to $R_m(z)$ and $T_m(z)$. Using the lattice recursions, we may derive a recursion for these responses

$$R_m(z) = \frac{B_m(z)}{A_m(z)} = \frac{\rho_m A_{m-1}(z) + z^{-1}B_{m-1}(z)}{A_{m-1}(z) + \rho_m z^{-1}B_{m-1}(z)}$$

dividing numerator and denominator by $A_{m-1}(z)$, we obtain

$$R_m(z) = \frac{\rho_m + z^{-1}R_{m-1}(z)}{1 + \rho_m z^{-1}R_{m-1}(z)} \tag{5.13.28}$$

It describes the effect of adding a layer. Expanding it in a power series, we have

$$R_m(z) = \rho_m + (1-\rho_m^2)\left[z^{-1}R_{m-1}(z)\right] - (1-\rho_m^2)\rho_m\left[z^{-1}R_{m-1}(z)\right]^2 + \cdots$$

It can be verified easily that the various terms in this sum correspond to the multiple reflections taking place within the mth layer.

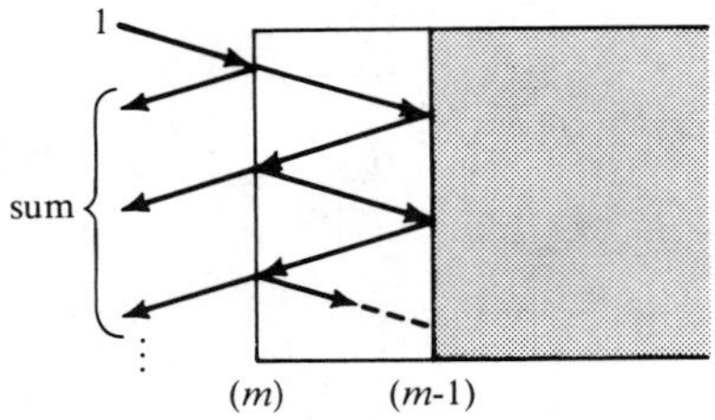

The first term in the expansion is always ρ_m; that is, $\rho_m = R_m(\infty)$. Thus, from the knowledge of $R_m(z)$ we may extract ρ_m. With ρ_m known, we may invert Eq. (5.13.28) to get $R_{m-1}(z)$ from which we extract ρ_{m-1}; and so on, we may extract the series of reflection coefficients. The inverse of Eq. (5.13.28), which describes the effect of removing a layer, is

$$R_{m-1}(z) = z\frac{R_m(z) - \rho_m}{1 - \rho_m R_m(z)} \tag{5.13.29}$$

Up to a difference in the sign of ρ_m, this is recognized as the Schur recursion (5.10.25). It provides a nice physical interpretation of the Schur recursion; namely, the Schur functions are the overall reflection responses at the successive layer interfaces, which on physical grounds must be stable, causal, and bounded $|R_m(z)| \leq 1$ for all z in their region of convergence that includes, at least, the unit circle and all the points outside it. We may also derive a recursion for the transmission responses.

$$T_m(z) = \frac{t_m z^{-1/2} T_{m-1}(z)}{1 + \rho_m z^{-1} R_{m-1}(z)}, \qquad T_{m-1}(z) = z^{1/2} \frac{t_m T_m(z)}{1 - \rho_m R_m(z)} \tag{5.13.30}$$

It requires the simultaneous recursion of $R_m(z)$. The dynamic predictive deconvolution is an alternative method of extracting the sequence of reflection coefficients and will be discussed below.

The equations (5.13.27) for the scattering responses R, T, R', T' imply the *unitarity* of the scattering matrix S

$$S = \begin{bmatrix} T & R' \\ R & T' \end{bmatrix}$$

that is,

$$\bar{S}(z)^T S(z) = S(z^{-1})^T S(z) = I \tag{5.13.31}$$

where I is the 2×2 unit matrix. On the unit circle $z = e^{j\omega}$ the scattering matrix becomes a *unitary* matrix: $S(\omega)^\dagger S(\omega) = I$. Component-wise, Eq. (5.13.31) becomes

$$\bar{T}T + \bar{R}R = \bar{T}'T' + \bar{R}'R' = 1, \qquad \bar{T}R' + \bar{R}T' = 0 \tag{5.13.32}$$

Robinson and Treitel's *dynamic predictive deconvolution method* [59] of solving the *inverse scattering problem* is based on the above unitarity equation. In the inverse problem, it is required to extract the set of reflection coefficients from measurements of either the reflection response R or the transmission response T. In speech processing it is the transmission response that is available. In geophysical applications, or in studying the reflectivity properties of thin films, it is the reflection response that is available. The problem of designing terminations of transmission lines also falls in the latter category. In this case, an appropriate termination is desired that must have a specified reflection response $R(z)$; for example, to be reflectionless over a wide band of frequencies about some operating frequency.

The solution of both types of problems follows the same steps. First, from the knowledge of the reflection response $R(z)$, or the transmission response $T(z)$, the *spectral function* of the structure is defined

$$\Phi(z) = 1 - R(z)\bar{R}(z) = T(z)\bar{T}(z) = \frac{\sigma_M^2}{A_M(z)A_M(z^{-1})} \tag{5.13.33}$$

This is recognized as the *power spectrum* of the *transmission* response, and it is of the autoregressive type. Thus, linear prediction methods can be used in the solution.

In the time domain, the autocorrelation lags $\phi(k)$ of the spectral function are obtained from the sample autocorrelations of the reflection sequence, or the transmission sequence

$$\phi(k) = \delta(k) - C(k) = D(k) \tag{5.13.34}$$

where $C(k)$ and $D(k)$ are the sample autocorrelations

$$C(k) = \sum_n R(n + k)R(n), \qquad D(k) = \sum_n T(n + k)T(n) \tag{5.13.35}$$

In practice, only a *finite record* of the reflection (or transmission) sequence will be available, say $\{R(0), R(1), \ldots, R(N-1)\}$. Then, an approximation to $C(k)$ must be used, as follows:

$$C(k) = \sum_{n=0}^{N-1-k} R(n+k)R(n) \tag{5.13.36}$$

The polynomial $A_M(z)$ may be recovered from the knowledge of the first M lags of the spectral function; that is, $\{\phi(0), \phi(1), \ldots, \phi(M)\}$. The determining equations for the *coefficients* of $A_M(z)$ are precisely the *normal* equations of linear prediction. In the present context, they may be derived directly by noting that $\Phi(z)$ is a stable spectral density and is already factored into its minimal-phase factors, in Eq. (5.13.33). Thus, writing

$$\Phi(z)A_M(z) = \frac{\sigma_M^2}{A_M(z^{-1})}$$

it follows that the right-hand side is expandable in positive powers of z; the negative powers of z in the left-hand side must be set equal to zero. This gives the normal equations:

$$\begin{bmatrix} \phi(0) & \phi(1) & \phi(2) & \cdots & \phi(M) \\ \phi(1) & \phi(0) & \phi(1) & \cdots & \phi(M-1) \\ \phi(2) & \phi(1) & \phi(0) & \cdots & \phi(M-2) \\ \vdots & \vdots & \vdots & & \vdots \\ \phi(M) & \phi(M-1) & \phi(M-2) & \cdots & \phi(0) \end{bmatrix} \begin{bmatrix} 1 \\ a_M(1) \\ a_M(2) \\ \vdots \\ a_M(M) \end{bmatrix} = \begin{bmatrix} \sigma_M^2 \\ 0 \\ 0 \\ \vdots \\ 0 \end{bmatrix} \tag{5.13.37}$$

which can be solved efficiently using Levinson's algorithm.

Having obtained $A_M(z)$ and noting that $B_M(z) = A_M(z)R(z)$, the coefficients of the polynomial $B_M(z)$ may be recovered by *convolution*:

$$b_M(n) = \sum_{m=0}^{n} a_M(n - m)R(m), \qquad n = 0,1, \ldots, M \tag{5.13.38}$$

Having obtained both $A_M(z)$ and $B_M(z)$ and noting that $\rho_M = b_M(0)$, the lattice recursion (5.13.23) may be inverted to recover the polynomials $A_{M-1}(z)$ and

$B_{M-1}(z)$, as well as the next reflection coefficient $\rho_{M-1} = b_{M-1}(0)$, and so on. The inverse of the lattice recursion matrix is

$$\begin{bmatrix} 1 & \rho_m z^{-1} \\ \rho_m & z^{-1} \end{bmatrix}^{-1} = \frac{1}{1-\rho_m^2} \begin{bmatrix} 1 & -\rho_m \\ -\rho_m z & z \end{bmatrix}$$

Therefore, the *backward recursion* becomes

$$\begin{bmatrix} A_{m-1}(z) \\ B_{m-1}(z) \end{bmatrix} = \frac{1}{1-\rho_m^2} \begin{bmatrix} 1 & -\rho_m \\ -\rho_m z & z \end{bmatrix} \begin{bmatrix} A_m(z) \\ B_m(z) \end{bmatrix}, \quad \text{with } \rho_m = b_m(0) \qquad (5.13.39)$$

In this manner, all the reflection coefficients $\rho_0, \rho_1, \ldots, \rho_M$ can be extracted. The computational algorithm is summarized as follows:

1. Measure $R(0), R(1), \ldots, R(N-1)$
2. Select a reasonable value for the number of slabs M
3. Compute the $M+1$ sample autocorrelation lags $C(0), C(1), \ldots, C(M)$ of the reflection response $R(n)$, using Eq. (5.13.36)
4. Compute $\phi(k) = \delta(k) - C(k)$; $k = 0, 1, \ldots, M$
5. Using Levinson's algorithm, solve the normal equations (5.13.37) for the coefficients of $A_M(z)$
6. Convolve $A_M(z)$ with $R(z)$ to find $B_M(z)$
7. Compute $\rho_M = b_M(0)$, and iterate the backward recursion (5.13.39) from $m = M$ down to $m = 0$

The subroutine **dpd** (see Appendix B) is an implementation of the dynamic predictive deconvolution procedure. The inputs to the subroutine are N samples of the reflection response $\{R(0), R(1), \ldots, R(N-1)\}$ and the number of layers M. The outputs are the lattice polynomials $A_i(z)$ and $B_i(z)$, for $i = 0, 1, \ldots, M$, arranged in the two *lower-triangular* matrices A and B whose *rows* hold the coefficients of these polynomials; that is, $A(i,j) = a_i(j)$, or

$$A(i,z) = \sum_{j=0}^{i} A(i,j) z^{-j}; \qquad i = 0, 1, \ldots, M$$

and similarly for $B(i,z)$. The subroutine invokes the routine **lev** to solve the normal equations (5.13.34). The *forward scattering problem* is implemented by the subroutine **scatter,** whose inputs are the set of reflection coefficients $\{\rho_0, \rho_1, \ldots, \rho_M\}$ and whose outputs are the lattice polynomials $A(i,z)$ and $B(i,z)$, for $i = 0, 1, \ldots, M$, as well as a prespecified number N of reflection response samples $R(0), R(1), \ldots, R(N-1)$. It utilizes the forward lattice recursion (5.13.23) to obtain the lattice polynomials, and then computes the reflection response samples by taking the inverse z-transform of Eq. (5.13.27).

Next, we present a number of deconvolution examples simulated by means of the routines **scatter** and **dpd**. In each case, we specified the five reflection coefficients of a structure consisting of four layers. Using **scatter** we gen-

K	$R(K)$
0	0.5000
1	0.3750
2	0.1875
3	0.0234
4	−0.0586
5	−0.1743
6	0.1677
7	0.0265
8	−0.0601
9	−0.0259
10	0.0238
11	0.0314
12	−0.0225
13	−0.0153
14	0.0109
15	0.0097

Exact $A(i,j)$

1.0000	0.0000	0.0000	0.0000	0.0000
1.0000	0.2500	0.0000	0.0000	0.0000
1.0000	0.5000	0.2500	0.0000	0.0000
1.0000	0.7500	0.5625	0.2500	0.0000
1.0000	1.0000	0.9375	0.6250	0.2500

Extracted $A(i,j)$

1.0000	0.0000	0.0000	0.0000	0.0000
1.0000	0.2509	0.0000	0.0000	0.0000
1.0000	0.5009	0.2510	0.0000	0.0000
1.0000	0.7509	0.5638	0.2508	0.0000
1.0000	1.0009	0.9390	0.6263	0.2504

Exact $B(i,j)$

0.5000	0.0000	0.0000	0.0000	0.0000
0.5000	0.5000	0.0000	0.0000	0.0000
0.5000	0.6250	0.5000	0.0000	0.0000
0.5000	0.7500	0.7500	0.5000	0.0000
0.5000	0.8750	1.0313	0.8750	0.5000

Extracted $B(i,j)$

0.5010	0.0000	0.0000	0.0000	0.0000
0.5000	0.5010	0.0000	0.0000	0.0000
0.5000	0.6255	0.5010	0.0000	0.0000
0.5000	0.7505	0.7510	0.5010	0.0000
0.5000	0.8755	1.0323	0.8764	0.5010

Figure 5.15 Reflection Response and Lattice Polynomials

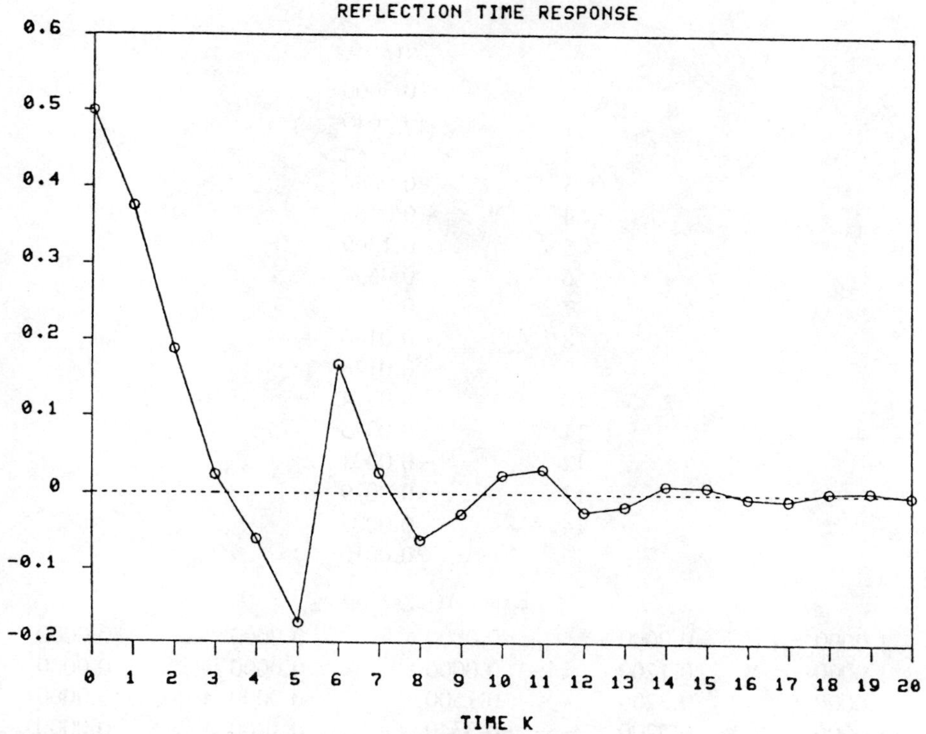

Figure 5.16 Reflection Response in the Time Domain

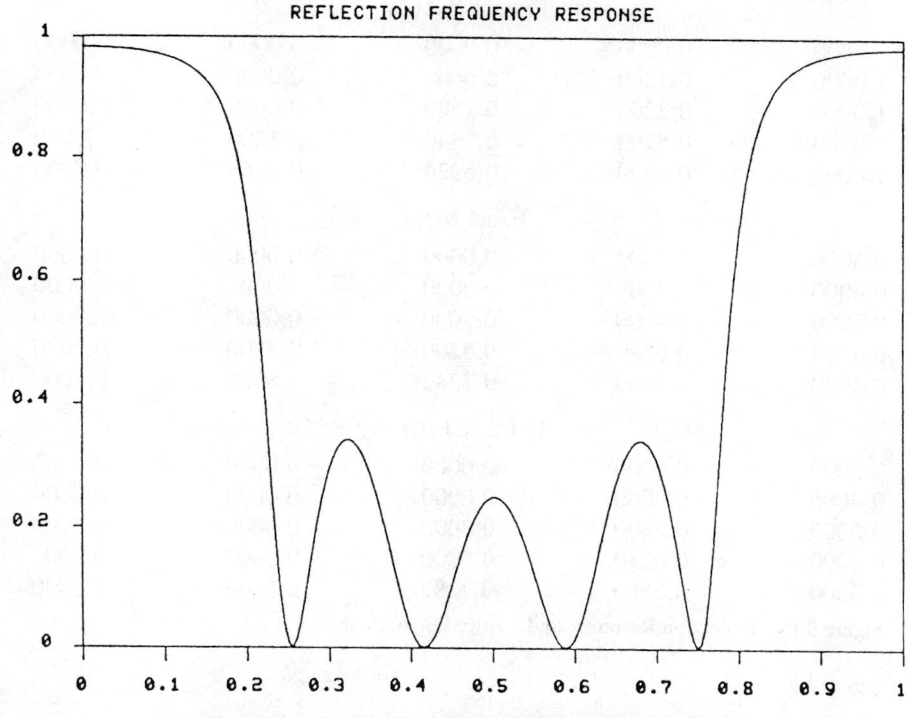

Figure 5.17 Reflection Response in the Frequency Domain

K	$R(K)$
0	0.3000
1	0.3640
2	0.3385
3	0.0664
4	−0.0468
5	−0.1309
6	0.0594
7	0.0373
8	−0.0146
9	−0.0148
10	0.0014
11	0.0075
12	−0.0001
13	−0.0029
14	−0.0003
15	0.0010

Exact $A(i,j)$

1.0000	0.0000	0.0000	0.0000	0.0000
1.0000	0.1200	0.0000	0.0000	0.0000
1.0000	0.3200	0.1500	0.0000	0.0000
1.0000	0.5200	0.3340	0.1200	0.0000
1.0000	0.6400	0.5224	0.2760	0.0900

Extracted $A(i,j)$

1.0000	0.0000	0.0000	0.0000	0.0000
1.0000	0.1200	0.0000	0.0000	0.0000
1.0000	0.3200	0.1500	0.0000	0.0000
1.0000	0.5200	0.3340	0.1200	0.0000
1.0000	0.6400	0.5224	0.2760	0.0900

Exact $B(i,j)$

0.3000	0.0000	0.0000	0.0000	0.0000
0.4000	0.3000	0.0000	0.0000	0.0000
0.5000	0.4600	0.3000	0.0000	0.0000
0.4000	0.6280	0.5200	0.3000	0.0000
0.3000	0.5560	0.7282	0.5560	0.3000

Extracted $B(i,j)$

0.3000	0.0000	0.0000	0.0000	0.0000
0.4000	0.3000	0.0000	0.0000	0.0000
0.5000	0.4600	0.3000	0.0000	0.0000
0.4000	0.6280	0.5200	0.3000	0.0000
0.3000	0.5560	0.7282	0.5560	0.3000

Figure 5.18 Reflection Response and Lattice Polynomials

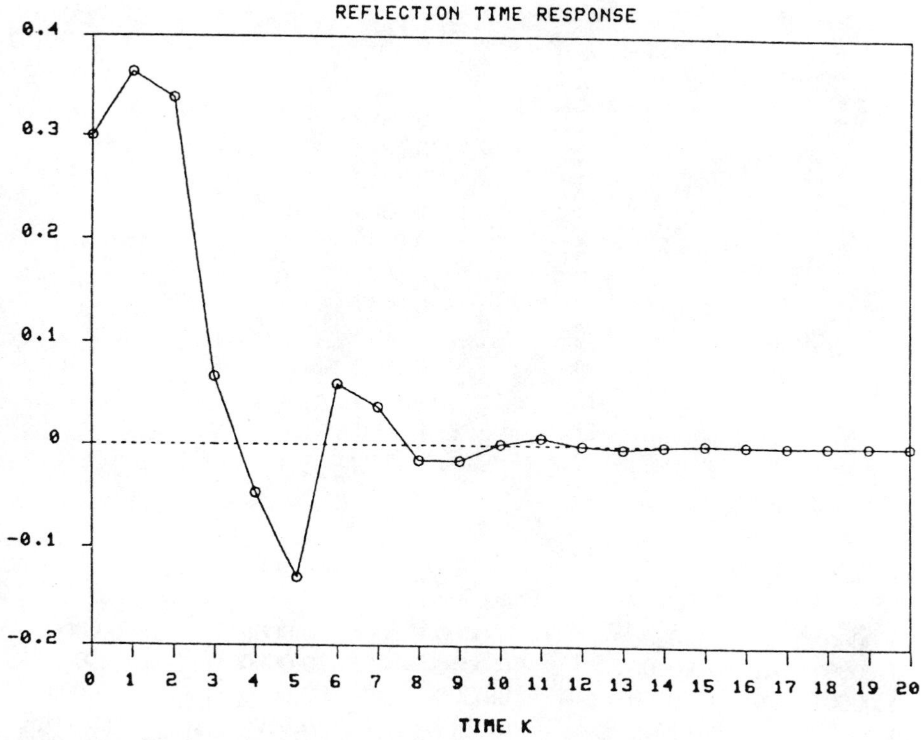

Figure 5.19 Reflection Response in the Time Domain

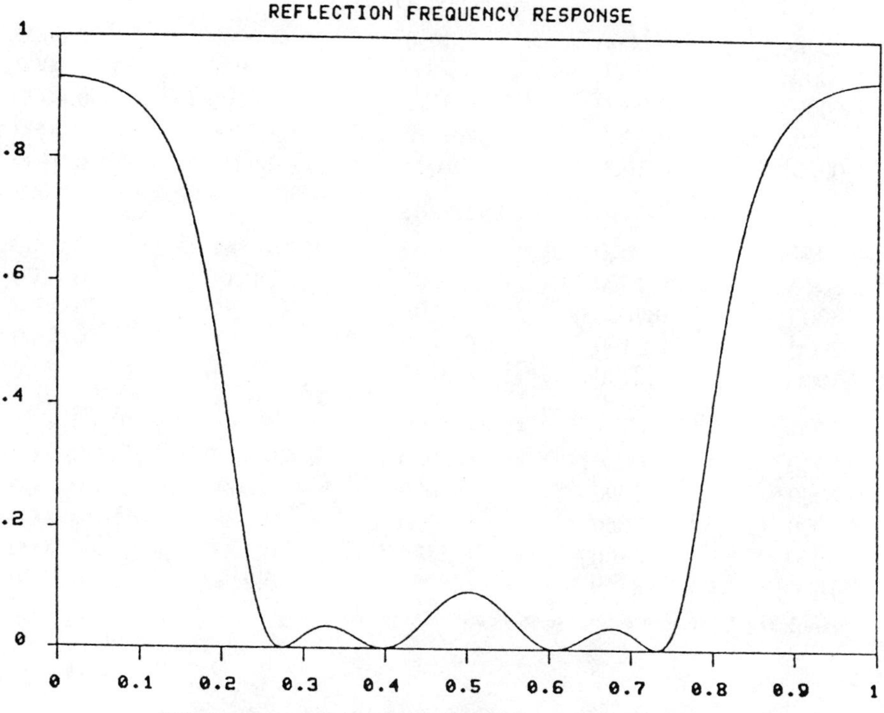

Figure 5.20 Reflection Response in the Frequency Domain

K	$R(K)$
0	0.1000
1	0.1980
2	0.2812
3	0.1445
4	0.0388
5	−0.0346
6	−0.0072
7	0.0017
8	0.0015
9	0.0002
10	−0.0002
11	−0.0001
12	0.0000
13	0.0000
14	0.0000
15	0.0000

Exact $A(i, j)$

1.0000	0.0000	0.0000	0.0000	0.0000
1.0000	0.0200	0.0000	0.0000	0.0000
1.0000	0.0800	0.0300	0.0000	0.0000
1.0000	0.1400	0.0712	0.0200	0.0000
1.0000	0.1600	0.1028	0.0412	0.0100

Extracted $A(i, j)$

1.0000	0.0000	0.0000	0.0000	0.0000
1.0000	0.0200	0.0000	0.0000	0.0000
1.0000	0.0800	0.0300	0.0000	0.0000
1.0000	0.1400	0.0712	0.0200	0.0000
1.0000	0.1600	0.1028	0.0412	0.0100

Exact $B(i, j)$

0.1000	0.0000	0.0000	0.0000	0.0000
0.2000	0.1000	0.0000	0.0000	0.0000
0.3000	0.2060	0.1000	0.0000	0.0000
0.2000	0.3160	0.2120	0.1000	0.0000
0.1000	0.2140	0.3231	0.2140	0.1000

Extracted $B(i, j)$

0.1000	0.0000	0.0000	0.0000	0.0000
0.2000	0.1000	0.0000	0.0000	0.0000
0.3000	0.2060	0.1000	0.0000	0.0000
0.2000	0.3160	0.2120	0.1000	0.0000
0.1000	0.2140	0.3231	0.2140	0.1000

Figure 5.21 Reflection Response and Lattice Polynomials

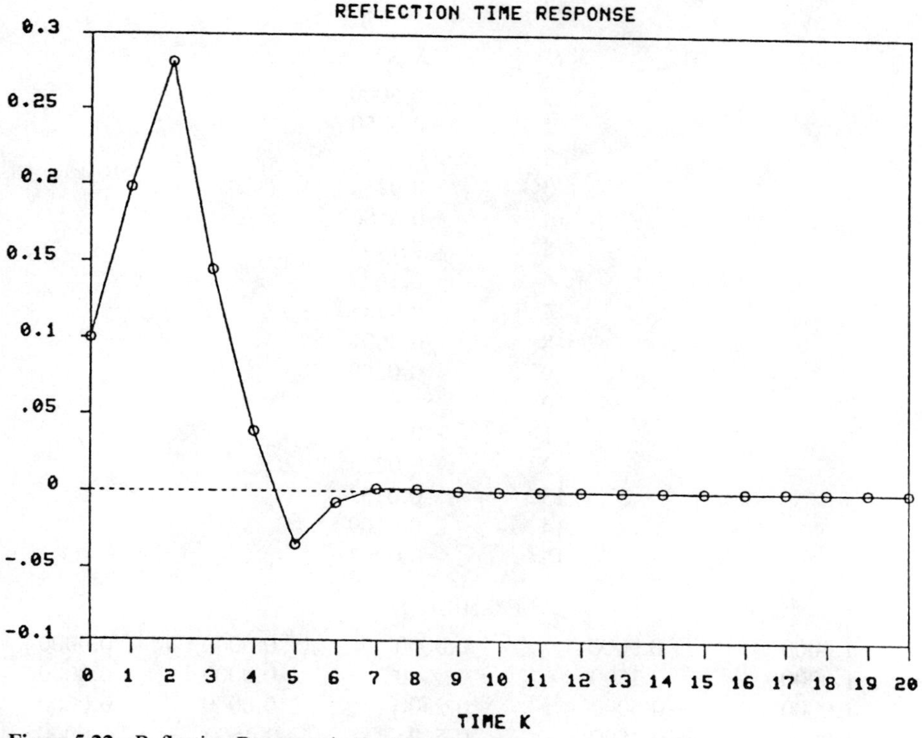

Figure 5.22 Reflection Response in the Time Domain

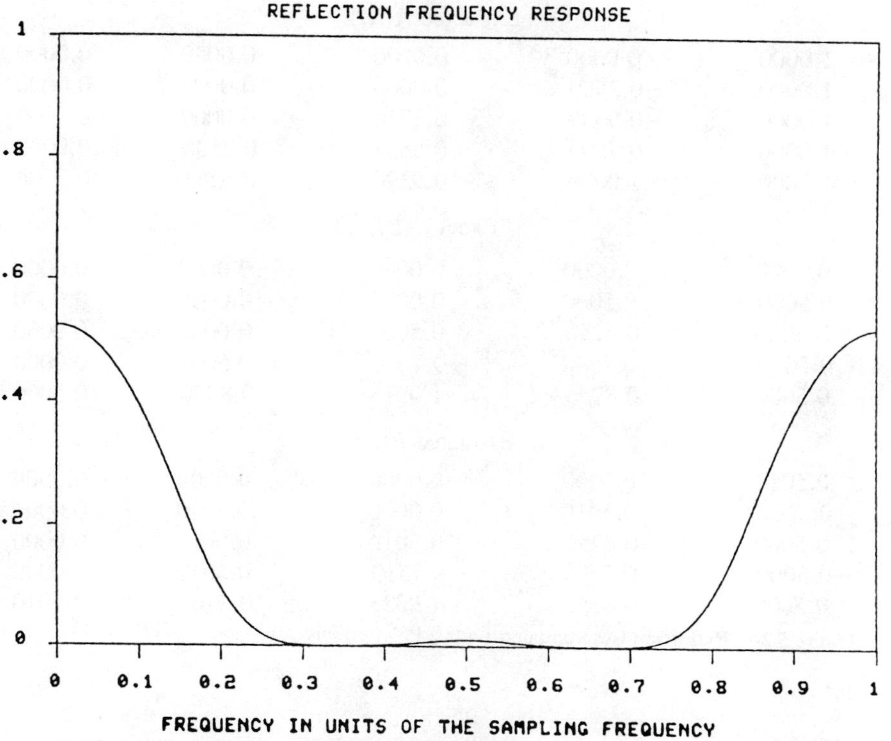

Figure 5.23 Reflection Response in the Frequency Domain

K	$R(K)$
0	0.5000
1	−0.3750
2	0.1875
3	−0.0234
4	−0.0586
5	0.1743
6	0.1677
7	−0.0265
8	−0.0601
9	0.0259
10	0.0238
11	−0.0314
12	−0.0225
13	0.0153
14	0.0109
15	−0.0097

Exact $A(i,j)$

1.0000	0.0000	0.0000	0.0000	0.0000
1.0000	−0.2500	0.0000	0.0000	0.0000
1.0000	−0.5000	0.2500	0.0000	0.0000
1.0000	−0.7500	0.5625	−0.2500	0.0000
1.0000	−1.0000	0.9375	−0.6250	0.2500

Extracted $A(i,j)$

1.0000	0.0000	0.0000	0.0000	0.0000
1.0000	−0.2509	0.0000	0.0000	0.0000
1.0000	−0.5009	0.2510	0.0000	0.0000
1.0000	−0.7509	0.5638	−0.2508	0.0000
1.0000	−1.0009	0.9390	−0.6263	0.2504

Exact $B(i,j)$

0.5000	0.0000	0.0000	0.0000	0.0000
−0.5000	0.5000	0.0000	0.0000	0.0000
0.5000	−0.6250	0.5000	0.0000	0.0000
−0.5000	0.7500	−0.7500	0.5000	0.0000
0.5000	−0.8750	1.0313	−0.8750	0.5000

Extracted $B(i,j)$

0.5010	0.0000	0.0000	0.0000	0.0000
−0.5000	0.5010	0.0000	0.0000	0.0000
0.5000	−0.6255	0.5010	0.0000	0.0000
−0.5000	0.7505	−0.7510	0.5010	0.0000
0.5000	−0.8755	1.0323	−0.8764	0.5010

Figure 5.24 Reflection Response and Lattice Polynomials

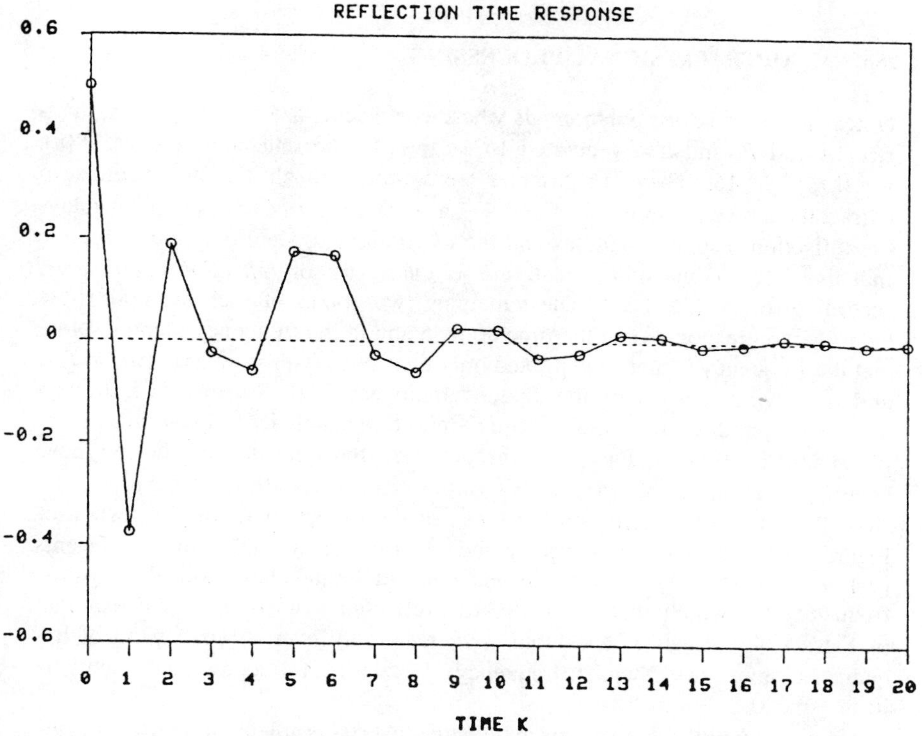

Figure 5.25 Reflection Response in the Time Domain

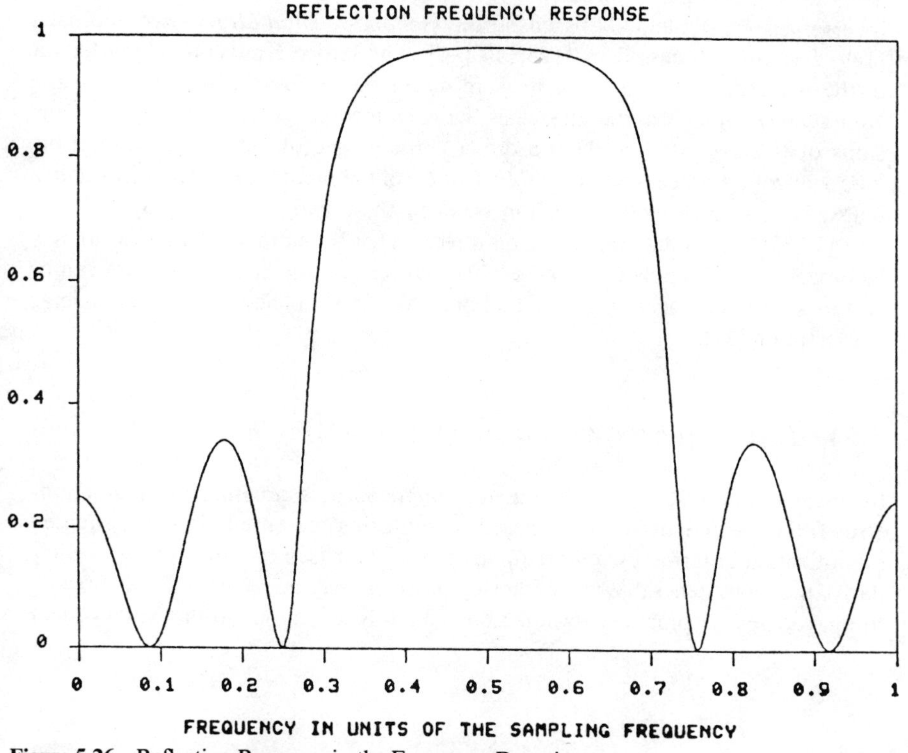

Figure 5.26 Reflection Response in the Frequency Domain

erated the exact lattice polynomials whose coefficients are arranged in the matrices A and B, and also generated 16 samples of the reflection response $R(n)$; $n=0,1,\ldots,15$. These 16 samples were sent through the **dpd** routine to extract the lattice polynomials A and B. The first graph of each example displays the reflection response samples and the exact and extracted polynomials. Note that the *first column* of the matrix B is the vector of *reflection coefficients*, according to Eq. (5.13.25). The remaining two graphs of each example show the reflection response R in the time domain and in the frequency domain. Note that the frequency response is plotted only over one Nyquist interval $[0,2\pi/T_2]$, and it is symmetric about the Nyquist frequency π/T_2. Figures 5.15 through 5.17 correspond to the case of equal reflection coefficients $\{\rho_0,\rho_1,\rho_2,\rho_3,\rho_4\}=\{0.5,0.5,0.5,0.5,0.5\}$. In Figs. 5.18 through 5.20 the reflection coefficients have been tapered somewhat at the ends (windowed) and are $\{0.3,0.4,0.5,0.4,0.3\}$. Note the effect of tapering on the lobes of the reflection frequency response. Figures 5.21 through 5.23 correspond to the set of reflection coefficients $\{0.1,0.2,0.3,0.2,0.1\}$. Note the *broad band* of frequencies about the Nyquist frequency for which there is very little reflection. In contrast, the example in Figs. 5.24 through 5.26 exhibits *high reflectivity* over a broad band of frequencies about the Nyquist frequency. Its set of reflection coefficients is $\{0.5,-0.5,0.5,-0.5,0.5\}$.

In this section we have discussed the inverse problem of unraveling the structure of a medium from the knowledge of its reflection response. The connection of the dynamic predictive deconvolution method to the conventional inverse scattering methods based on the *Gelfand-Levitan-Marchenko* approach [139] has been discussed in [128,140,141]. The lattice recursions characteristic of the wave propagation problem were derived as a *direct* consequence of the *boundary conditions* at the interfaces between media, whereas the lattice recursions of linear prediction were a direct consequence of the Gram-Schmidt orthogonalization process and the *minimization* of the prediction-error performance index. Is there a deeper connection between these two problems [76,79,80,90–92,142,143]? One notable result in this direction has been to show that the Cholesky factorization of Toeplitz or near-Toeplitz matrices via the Schur algorithm can be cast in a wave propagation model and derived as a simple consequence of energy conservation [87].

5.14 *Least-Squares Waveshaping and Spiking Filters*

In linear prediction, the three practical methods of estimating the prediction-error filter coefficients were all based on replacing the ensemble mean-squared minimization criterion by a *least-squares* criterion based on time averages. Similarly, the more general Wiener filtering problem may be recast in terms of such time averages. A practical formulation, which is analogous to the Yule-Walker or autocorrelation method, is as follows [59,60,95,144]: Given a record of available data

$$\boxed{y_0, y_1, \ldots, y_N}$$

find the *best* linear FIR filter of order M

$$\boxed{h_0, h_1, \ldots, h_M}$$

which reshapes y_n into a desired signal x_n, specified in terms of the samples

$$\boxed{x_0, x_1, \ldots, x_{N+M}}$$

where for consistency of convolution we have assumed we know $N + M + 1$ samples of the desired signal. The actual *output* of the waveshaping filter will be

$$\hat{x}_n = \sum_{m=0}^{M} h_m y_{n-m}; \qquad 0 \leq n \leq N + M \tag{5.14.1}$$

The *estimation error* will be

$$e_n = x_n - \hat{x}_n; \qquad 0 \leq n \leq N + M \tag{5.14.2}$$

As the optimality criterion we choose the *least-squares* criterion

$$\mathcal{E} = \sum_{n=0}^{N+M} e_n^2 = \min \tag{5.14.3}$$

The optimal filter weights h_m are selected to minimize $\mathcal{E}$. It is convenient to recast the above in a compact matrix form. Define the $(N + M + 1) \times (M + 1)$ data matrix Y, the $(M + 1) \times 1$ vector of filter weights $\mathbf{h}$, the $(M + N + 1) \times 1$ vector of desired samples $\mathbf{x}$, and estimation errors $\mathbf{e}$, as follows:

$$Y = \overbrace{\begin{bmatrix} y_0 & 0 & 0 & \cdots & 0 \\ y_1 & y_0 & 0 & \cdots & 0 \\ y_2 & y_1 & y_0 & \cdots & 0 \\ \vdots & \vdots & \vdots & & \vdots \\ y_N & y_{N-1} & y_{N-2} & \cdots & y_{N-M} \\ 0 & y_N & y_{N-1} & \cdots & \vdots \\ 0 & 0 & y_N & \cdots & \vdots \\ \vdots & \vdots & \vdots & & \vdots \\ 0 & 0 & 0 & \cdots & y_N \end{bmatrix}}^{\text{M zeros}} \begin{matrix} \\ \\ \\ \\ \\ \Bigg\} \text{M zeros} \\ \\ \\ \\ \end{matrix}, \quad \mathbf{h} = \begin{bmatrix} h_0 \\ h_1 \\ \vdots \\ h_M \end{bmatrix}, \quad \mathbf{x} = \begin{bmatrix} x_0 \\ x_1 \\ x_2 \\ \vdots \\ x_{N+M} \end{bmatrix} \tag{5.14.4}$$

Equations (5.14.1) through (5.14.3) now become

$$\hat{\mathbf{x}} = Y\mathbf{h}, \qquad \mathbf{e} = \mathbf{x} - \hat{\mathbf{x}}, \qquad \mathcal{E} = \mathbf{e}^T\mathbf{e} \tag{5.14.5}$$

Minimizing $\mathcal{E}$ with respect to the weight vector $\mathbf{h}$ results in the *orthogonality* equations

$$Y^T\mathbf{e} = Y^T(\mathbf{x} - Y\mathbf{h}) = 0 \tag{5.14.6}$$

which are equivalent to the *normal* equations

$$Y^TY\mathbf{h} = Y^T\mathbf{x} \tag{5.14.7}$$

Solving for $\mathbf{h}$, we find

$$\mathbf{h} = (Y^TY)^{-1}Y^T\mathbf{x} = R^{-1}\mathbf{r} \tag{5.14.8}$$

where the quantities

$$R = Y^TY, \qquad \mathbf{r} = Y^T\mathbf{x} \tag{5.14.9}$$

may be recognized (see Section 1.10) as the $(M+1)\times(M+1)$ autocorrelation matrix formed by the sample autocorrelations $\hat{R}_{yy}(0), \hat{R}_{yy}(1), \ldots, \hat{R}_{yy}(M)$ of y_n, and as the $(M+1)\times 1$ vector of sample cross-correlations $\hat{R}_{xy}(0), \hat{R}_{xy}(1), \ldots, \hat{R}_{xy}(M)$ between the desired and the available vectors x_n and y_n. We have already used this expression for the weight vector $\mathbf{h}$ in the example of Section 5.11. Here we have justified it in terms of the least-squares criterion (5.14.3). The subroutine **firw** may be used to solve for the weights (5.14.8) and, if so desired, to give the corresponding lattice realization. The actual filter output $\hat{\mathbf{x}}$ is expressed as

$$\hat{\mathbf{x}} = Y\mathbf{h} = YR^{-1}Y^T\mathbf{x} = P\mathbf{x} \tag{5.14.10}$$

where

$$P = YR^{-1}Y^T = Y(Y^TY)^{-1}Y^T \tag{5.14.11}$$

The error vector becomes $\mathbf{e} = (I - P)\mathbf{x}$. The "performance" matrix P is a projection matrix, and thus, so is $(I - P)$. Then, the error squared becomes

$$\mathcal{E} = \mathbf{e}^T\mathbf{e} = \mathbf{x}^T(I - P)^2\mathbf{x} = \mathbf{x}^T(I - P)\mathbf{x} \tag{5.14.12}$$

The $(N + M + 1) \times (N + M + 1)$ matrix P has trace equal to $M + 1$, as can be checked easily. Since its eigenvalues as a projection matrix are either 0 or 1, it follows that in order for the sum of all the eigenvalues (the trace) to be equal to $M + 1$, there must necessarily be $M + 1$ eigenvalues that are equal to 1, and N eigenvalues equal to 0. Therefore the matrix P has rank $M + 1$, and if the desired vector $\mathbf{x}$ is selected to be any of the $M + 1$ eigenvectors belonging to eigenvalue 1, the corresponding estimation error will be zero.

Among all possible waveshapes that may be chosen for the desired vector $\mathbf{x}$, of particular importance are the *spikes*, or impulses. In this case, $\mathbf{x}$ is a unit impulse, say at the origin; that is, $x_n = \delta_n$. The convolution $\hat{x}_n = h_n * y_n$ of the corresponding filter with y_n is the best least-squares approximation to the unit impulse. In other words, h_n is the best *least-squares inverse* filter to y_n that attempts to reshape, or compress, y_n into a unit impulse. Such least squares inverse filters are used extensively in *deconvolution* applications. More generally, the vector **x** may be chosen to be any one of the unit vectors

$$\mathbf{x} = \mathbf{u}_i = \begin{bmatrix} 0 \\ \vdots \\ 0 \\ 1 \\ 0 \\ \vdots \\ 0 \end{bmatrix} \begin{matrix} \\ \\ \\ \leftarrow i\text{th slot}; \\ \\ \\ \\ \end{matrix} \qquad i = 0,1, \ldots ,N + M \tag{5.14.13}$$

which corresponds to a unit impulse occurring at the ith time instant instead of at the origin; that is, $x_n = \delta(n - i)$. The actual output from the spiking filter is given by

$$\hat{\mathbf{x}} = P\mathbf{x} = P\mathbf{u}_i = i\text{th column of } P \tag{5.14.14}$$

Thus, the ith column of the matrix P is the *output* of the *ith spiking filter* which attempts to compress y_n into a spike with i delays. The corresponding ith filter is $\mathbf{h} = R^{-1}Y^T\mathbf{u}_i$. Therefore, the *columns* of the matrix

$$H = R^{-1}Y^T \tag{5.14.15}$$

are *all* the optimal *spiking filters*. The estimation error of the ith filter is

$$\mathcal{E}_i = \mathbf{u}_i^T(I - P)\mathbf{u}_i = 1 - P_{ii} \tag{5.14.16}$$

where P_{ii} is the iith diagonal element of P. Since the delay i may be positioned anywhere from $i = 0$ to $i = N + M$, there are $N + M + 1$ such spiking filters, each with error $\mathcal{E}_i$. Among these, there will be one that has the optimal delay i which corresponds to the smallest of the $\mathcal{E}_i$s; or, equivalently, to the maximum of the diagonal elements P_{ii}. The design procedure for least-squares spiking filters for a given finite signal y_n; $n = 0,1, \ldots ,N$ is summarized as follows:

1. Compute $R = Y^TY$
2. Compute the inverse R^{-1} (preferably by the Levinson recursion)
3. Compute $H = R^{-1}Y^T$ = all the spiking filters
4. Compute $P = YH = YR^{-1}Y^T$ = all spiking filter outputs
5. Select that column i of P for which P_{ii} is the largest

If the Levinson-Cholesky algorithm is used to compute the inverse R^{-1}, this design procedure becomes fairly efficient. An implementation of the procedure is given by the subroutine **spike**. The inputs to the subroutine are the $N+1$ samples $y_0, y_1, \ldots, y_N$, the desired order M of the spiking filter, and a so-called "*prewhitening*" or Backus-Gilbert parameter EPSILON, which will be explained below. The outputs of the subroutine are the matrices P and H.

To explain the role of the parameter ϵ, let us go back to the waveshaping problem. When the data sequence y_n to be reshaped into x_n is inaccurately known—if, for example, it has been contaminated by white noise v_n—the least-squares minimization criterion (5.14.3) can be extended slightly to accomplish the double task of (1) producing the *best estimate* of x_n and (2) reducing the noise *at the output* of the filter h_n as much as possible. The input to the filter is the noisy sequence $y_n + v_n$, and its output is $h_n * y_n + y_n * v_n = \hat{x}_n + u_n$, where we set $u_n = h_n * v_n$. The term u_n represents *the filtered noise*. The minimization criterion (5.14.3) may be replaced by

$$\mathcal{E} = \sum_n e_n^2 + \lambda E[u_n^2] \tag{5.14.17}$$

where λ is a positive parameter which can be chosen by the user. Large λ emphasizes large *reduction* of the output noise, but this is done *at the expense of resolution*; that is, at the expense of obtaining a very good estimate. On the other hand, small λ emphasizes higher resolution but with lesser noise reduction. This tradeoff between *resolution and noise reduction* is the basic property of this performance index. Assuming v_n is white with variance σ_v^2, we have

$$E[u_u^2] = \sigma_v^2 \sum_{n=0}^{M} h_n^2 = \sigma_v^2 \mathbf{h}^T \mathbf{h}$$

Thus, Eq. (5.14.17) may be written as

$$\mathcal{E} = \mathbf{e}^T \mathbf{e} + \lambda \sigma_v^2 \mathbf{h}^T \mathbf{h} \tag{5.14.18}$$

Its minimization with respect to $\mathbf{h}$ gives the normal equations

$$(Y^T Y + \lambda \sigma_v^2 I)\mathbf{h} = Y^T \mathbf{x} \tag{5.14.19}$$

from which it is evident that the diagonal of $Y^T Y$ is shifted by an amount $\lambda \sigma_v^2$; that is

$$\hat{R}_{yy}(0) \rightarrow \hat{R}_{yy}(0) + \lambda \sigma_v^2 = (1 + \epsilon)\hat{R}_{yy}(0), \qquad \epsilon = \frac{\lambda \sigma_v^2}{\hat{R}_{yy}(0)}$$

In practice, ϵ may be taken to be a few percent or less. It is evident from Eq. (5.14.19) that one beneficial effect of the parameter ϵ is the *stabilization* of the inverse of the matrix $Y^T Y + \lambda \sigma_v^2$.

The main usage of spiking filters is in deconvolution problems [59,60,95,144–146], where the desired and the available signals x_n and y_n are related to each other by the convolutional relationship

$$y_n = f_n * x_n = \sum_m f_m x_{n-m} \tag{5.14.20}$$

where f_n is a "blurring" function which is assumed to be approximately *known*. The basic deconvolution problem is to recover x_n from y_n if f_n is known. For example, y_n may represent the image of an object x_n recorded through an optical system with a point-spread function f_n; or y_n might represent the recorded seismic trace arising from the excitation of the layered earth by an impulsive waveform f_n (the source wavelet) which is convolved with the reflection impulse response x_n of the earth. (In the previous section x_n was denoted by R_n.) If the effect of the source wavelet f_n can be "deconvolved away," the resulting reflection sequence x_n may be subjected to the dynamic predictive deconvolution procedure to unravel the earth structure. Or, f_n may represent the impulse response of a channel, or a magnetic recording medium, which broadens and blurs (intersymbol interference) the desired message x_n. The least-squares inverse spiking filters offer a way to solve the deconvolution problem: Simply *design a least-squares* spiking filter h_n corresponding to the blurring function f_n; that is, $h_n*f_n \cong \delta_n$ in the least squares sense. Then, filtering y_n through h_n will recover the desired signal x_n:

$$\hat{x}_n = h_n*y_n = (h_n*f_n)*x_n \cong \delta_n*x_n = x_n \qquad (5.14.21)$$

If the ith spiking filter is used, which compresses f_n into an impulse with i delays, $h_n*f_n \cong \delta(n-i)$, then the desired signal x_n will be recovered with a delay of i units of time.

This and all other approaches to deconvolution work well when the data y_n are not noisy. In presence of noise, Eq. (5.14.20) becomes

$$y_n = f_n*x_n + v_n \qquad (5.14.22)$$

where v_n may be assumed to be zero-mean white noise of variance σ_v^2. Even if the blurring function f_n is known exactly and a good least-squares inverse filter h_n can be designed, the presence of the noise term can distort the deconvolved signal beyond recognition. This may be explained as follows. Filtering y_n through the inverse filter h_n results in

$$h_n*y_n = (h_n*f_n)*x_n + h_n*v_n \cong x_n + u_n$$

where $u_n = h_n*v_n$ is the filtered noise. Its variance is

$$E[u_n^2] = \sigma_v^2\mathbf{h}^T\mathbf{h} = \sigma_v^2 \sum_{m=0}^{M} h_m^2$$

which, depending on the particular shape of h_n, may be much larger than the original variance σ_v^2. This happens, for example, when f_n consists mainly of low frequencies. For h_n to compress f_n into a spike with a high frequency content, the impulse response h_n itself must be very spiky, which can result in values for $\mathbf{h}^T\mathbf{h}$ which are greater than one. To combat the effects of noise, the least-squares design criterion for $\mathbf{h}$ must be changed by adding to it a term $\lambda E[u_n^2]$ as was done in Eq. (5.14.17). The design criterion for $\mathbf{h}$ is then

$$\mathcal{E} = \sum_n (\delta_n - h_n*f_n)^2 + \lambda\sigma_v^2\mathbf{h}^T\mathbf{h} = \min$$

which effectively amounts to changing the autocorrelation lag $\hat{R}_{ff}(0)$ to $(1 + \epsilon)\hat{R}_{ff}(0)$. The first term in this performance index tries to produce a good inverse filter; the second term tries to minimize the output power of the noise after filtering by the deconvolution filter h_n. Note that conceptually this index is somewhat different from that of Eq. (5.14.17), because now v_n represents the noise in the data y_n, whereas there v_n represented inaccuracies in the knowledge of the wavelet f_n. In this approach to deconvolution we are not attempting to determine the best least-squares estimate of the desired signal x_n, but rather the best least-squares inverse to the blurring function f_n. If the second order statistics of x_n were known, we could, of course, determine the optimal (Wiener) estimate $\hat{x}_n$ of x_n. This is also done in many applications.

The performance of the spiking filters and their usage in deconvolution are illustrated by the following example: The blurring function f_n to be spiked was chosen as

$$f_n = g(n - 25);\ n = 0,1,2,\ldots,65$$

$$f_n = 0;\ \text{otherwise}$$

where $g(k)$ was the "gaussian hat"

$$g(k) = \cos(0.15k)\exp(-0.004k^2)$$

The signal x_n to be recovered, was taken to be the series of spikes

$$x_n = \sum_{i=0}^{9} a_i \delta(n - n_i)$$

where the amplitudes a_i and delays n_i were chosen as

$$a_i = 1,\ 0.8,\ 0.5,\ 0.95,\ 0.7,\ 0.5,\ 0.3,\ 0.9,\ 0.5,\ 0.85$$

$$n_i = 25,\ 50,\ 60,\ 70,\ 80,\ 90,\ 100,\ 120,\ 140,\ 160$$

for

$$i = 0,\ 1,\ 2,\ 3,\ 4,\ 5,\ 6,\ 7,\ 8,\ 9$$

Figure 5.27 shows the signal f_n to be spiked. Since the gaussian hat is symmetric about the origin, we chose the spiking delay to be at $i = 25$. The order of the spiking filter h_n was $M = 50$. Figure 5.28 shows the impulse response h_n versus time. Note the spiky nature of h_n which is required here because f_n has a fairly low frequency content. Figure 5.29 shows the results of the convolution $h_n * f_n$, which is the best least-squares approximation to the impulse $\delta(n - 25)$. The "goodness" of the spiking filter is judged by the diagonal entries of the performance matrix P, according to Eq. (5.14.16). For the chosen delay $k = 25$, we find $P(25,25) = 0.97$. To obtain a better picture of the overall performance of the spiking filters, in Fig. 5.30 we have plotted the diagonal elements $P(k,k)$ versus k. It is seen that the chosen delay $k = 25$ is nearly optimal. Figure 5.31 shows the composite signal y_n obtained by convolving f_n and x_n, according to

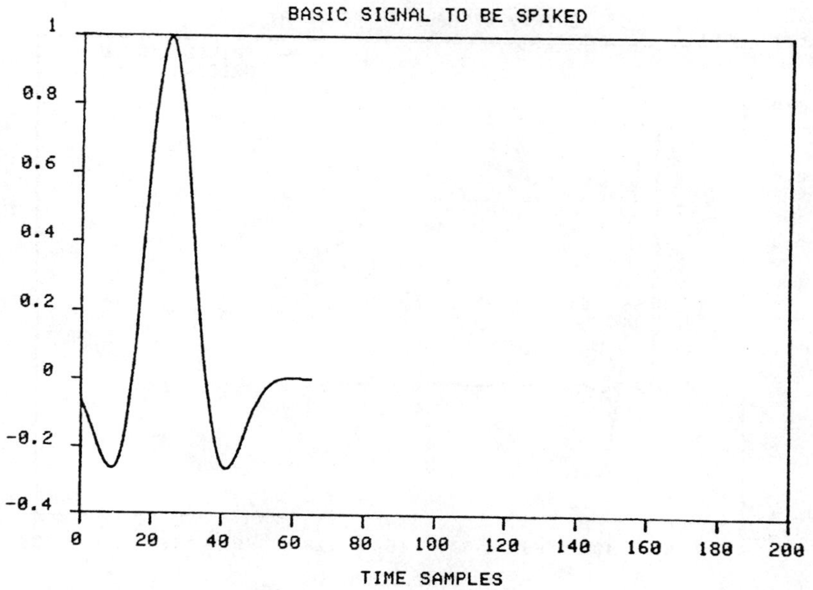

Figure 5.27 Signal f_n To Be Spiked

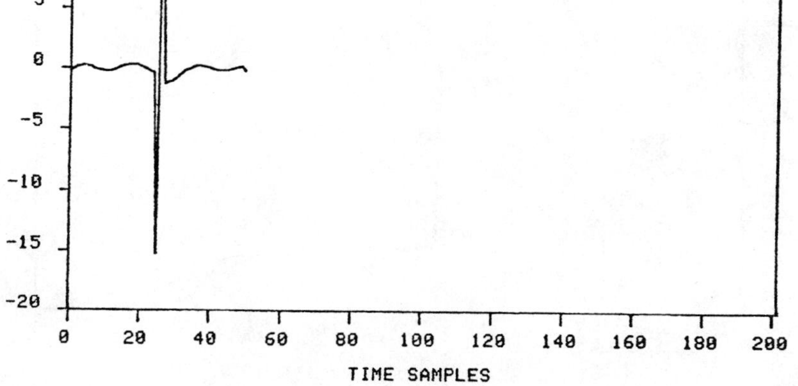

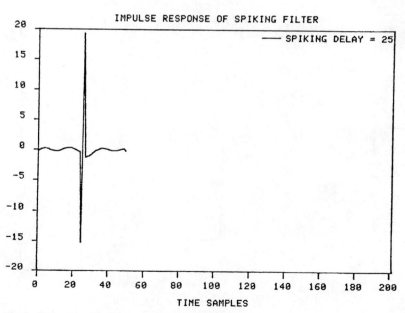

Figure 5.28 Impulse Response h_n of Spiking Filter

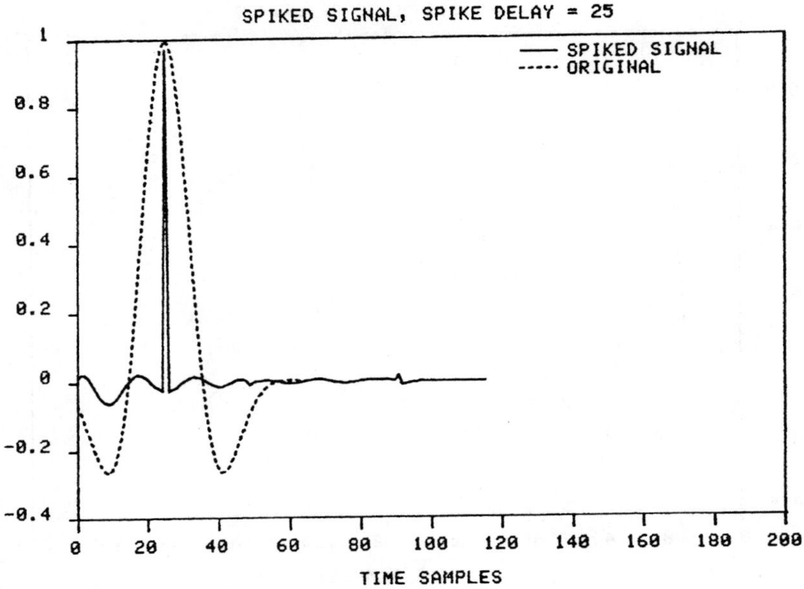

Figure 5.29 The Signal $h_n * f_n$

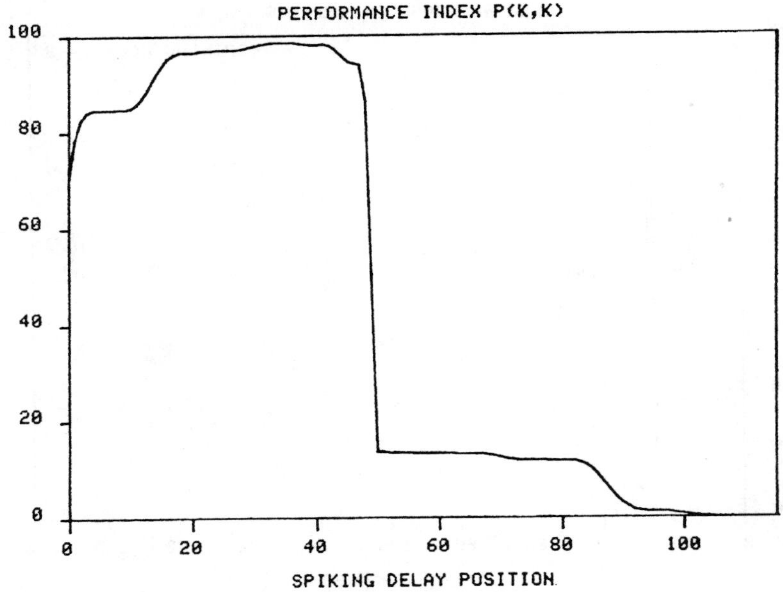

Figure 5.30 Performance of the Spiking Filters for f_n

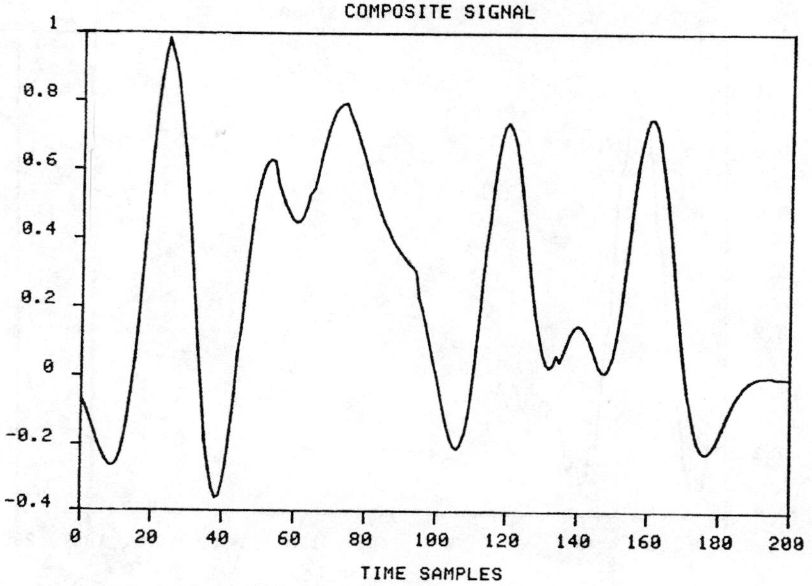

Figure 5.31 Composite Signal $y_n = f_n * x_n$

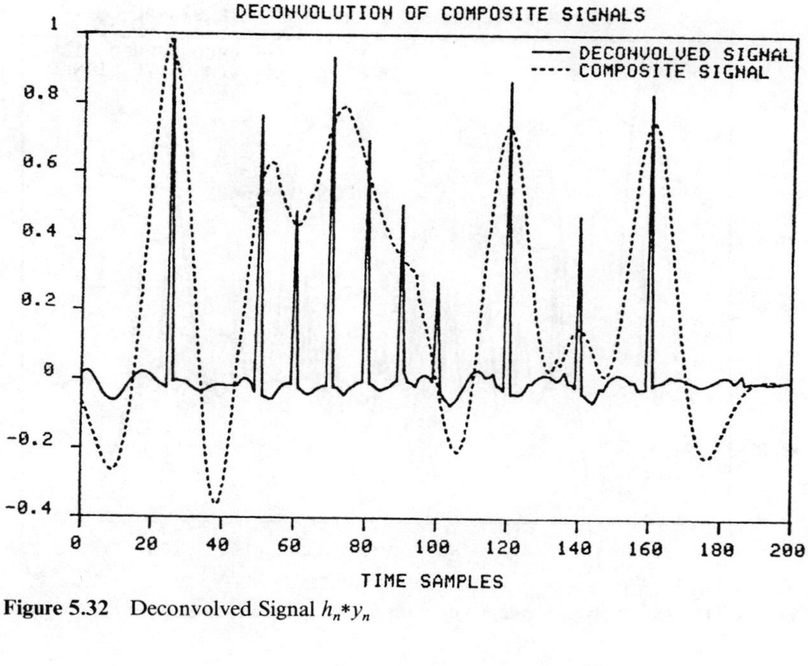

Figure 5.32 Deconvolved Signal $h_n * y_n$

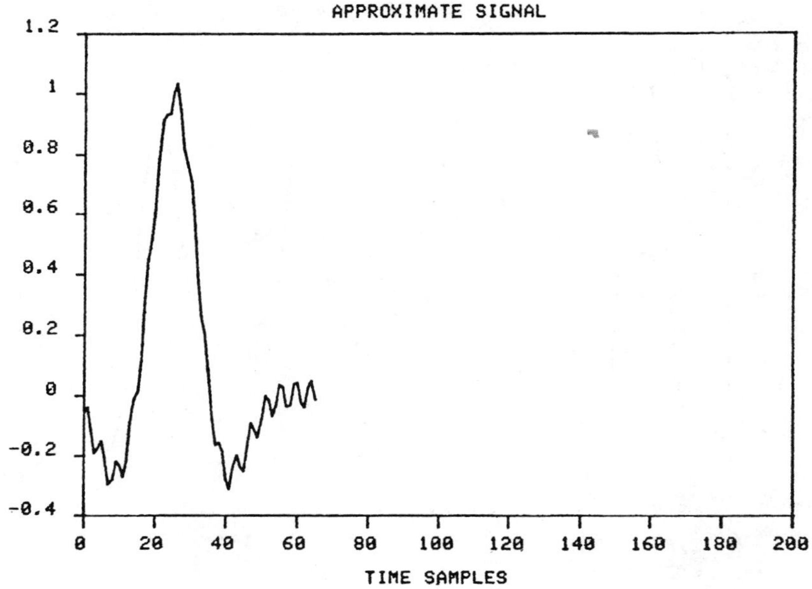

Figure 5.33 Approximately Known Signal f'_n

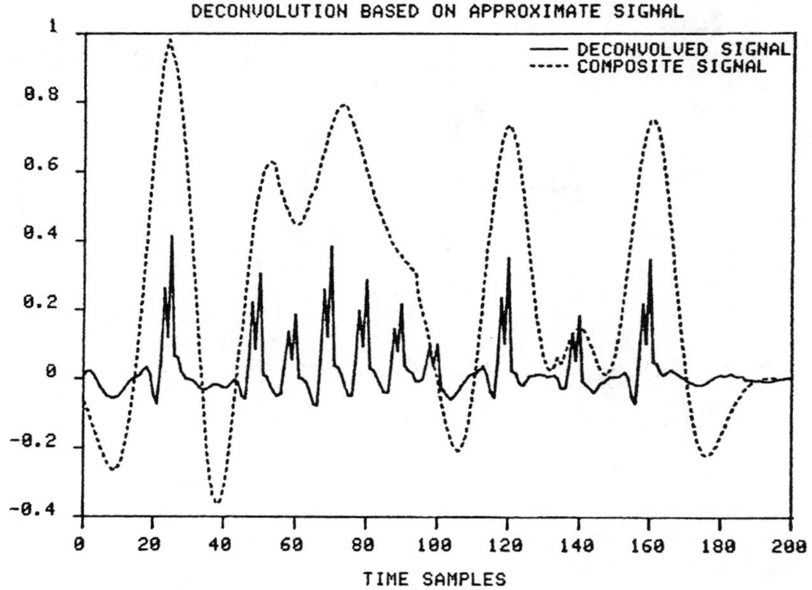

Figure 5.34 Deconvolved Signal $h'_n * y_n$, with h'_n Designed on the Basis of f'_n

Eq. (5.4.20). Figure 5.32 shows the deconvolved signal x_n according to Eq. (5.14.21). The recovery of the amplitudes a_i and delays n_i of x_n is very accurate. These results represent the idealistic case of *noise-free* data y_n and *perfect knowledge* of the blurring function f_n. To study the sensitivity of the deconvolution technique to inaccuracies in the knowledge of the signal f_n, we have added a small high frequency perturbation on f_n as follows:

$$f'_n = f_n + 0.05 \sin[1.5(n - 25)]$$

The approximate signal f'_n is shown in Fig. 5.33. The spiking filter was designed on the basis of f'_n rather than f_n. The result of filtering the *same* composite signal y_n through the corresponding inverse filter is shown in Fig. 5.34. Both the delays and the amplitudes a_i and n_i are not well resolved, but the basic nature of x_n can still be seen. Inspecting Fig. 5.28 we note the large spikes that are present in the impulse response h_n; these can cause the amplification of any additive noise component. Indeed, the noise reduction ratio of the filter h_n is $\mathbf{h}^T\mathbf{h} = 612$, thus it will tend to amplify even small amounts of noise. To study the effect of noise, we have added a noise term v_n, as in Eq. (5.14.22), with variance equal to 10^{-4} (this corresponds to just 1% of the amplitude a_0); the composite signal y_n is shown in Fig. 5.35. One can barely see the noise. Yet, after filtering with the inverse filter h_n of Fig. (5.28), the noise component is amplified to a great extent. The result of deconvolving the noisy y_n with h_n is shown in Fig. 5.36. To reduce the effects of noise, the prewhitening parameter ϵ must be chosen to be nonzero. Even a small nonzero value of ϵ can have a beneficial effect. Figures 5.37 and 5.38 show the deconvolved signal x_n when the filter h_n was designed with the choices $\epsilon = 0.0001$ and $\epsilon = 0.001$, respectively, of the parameter ϵ. Note the trade-off between the noise reduction and the loss of resolution in the recovered spikes of x_n.

Based on the studies of Robinson and Treitel [59], Oldenburg [145], and others, the following summary of the use of the above deconvolution method may be made:

1. If the signal f_n to be spiked is a minimal-phase signal, the optimal spiking delay must be chosen at the origin $i = 0$. The optimality of this choice is not actually seen until the filter order M is sufficiently high. The reason for this choice has to do with the minimal-delay property of such signals which implies that most of their energy is concentrated at the beginning; therefore, they may be more easily compressed to spikes with zero delay.
2. If f_n is a mixed-delay signal, as in the above example, then the optimal spiking delay will have some intermediate value.
3. Even if the shape of f_n is not accurately known, the deconvolution procedure based on the approximate f_n might have some partial success in deconvolving the replicas of f_n.
4. In the presence of noise in the data y_n to deconvolved, some improvement may result by introducing a nonzero value for the prewhitening parameter

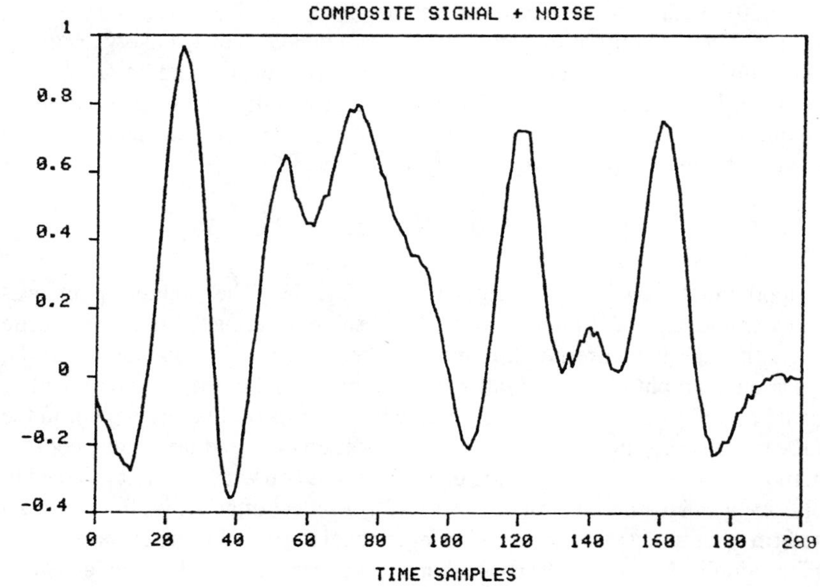

Figure 5.35 Noisy Composite Signal $y_n = f_n * x_n + v_n$

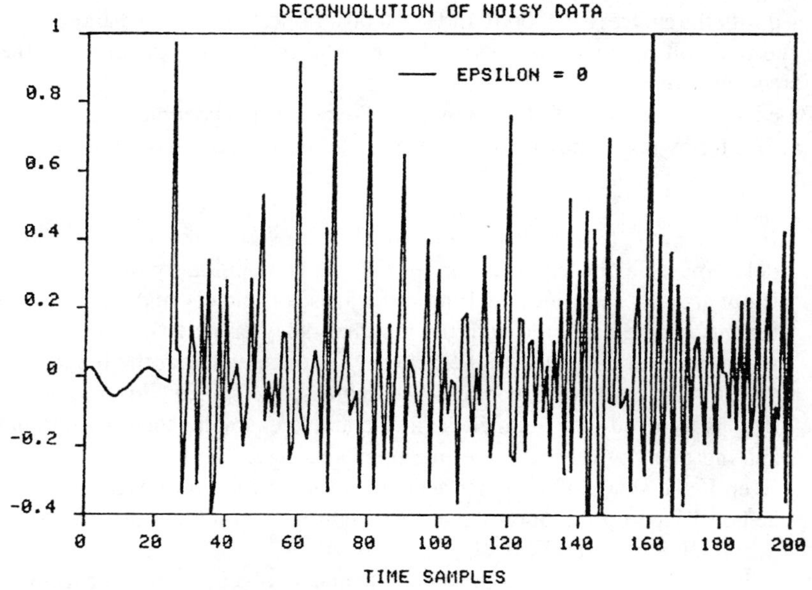

Figure 5.36 Deconvolution of Noisy Data y_n, Using $\epsilon = 0$

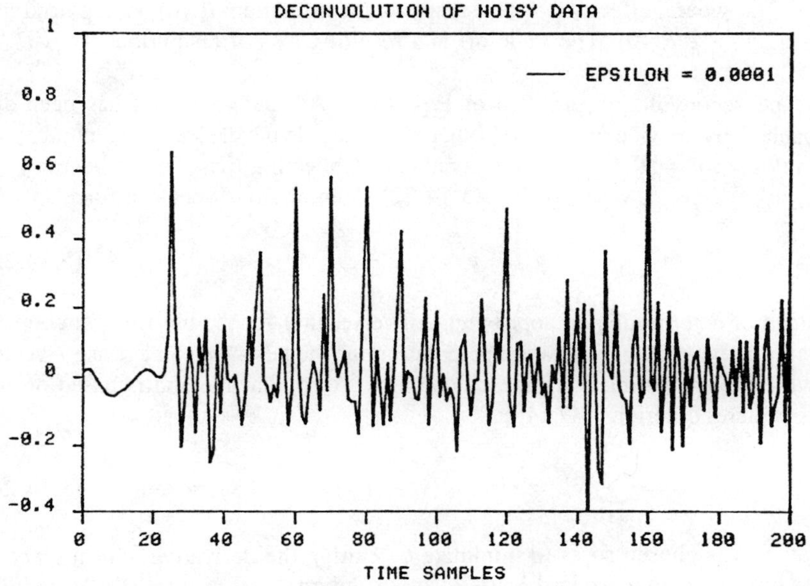

Figure 5.37 Deconvolution of Noisy Data y_n, Using $\epsilon = 0.0001$

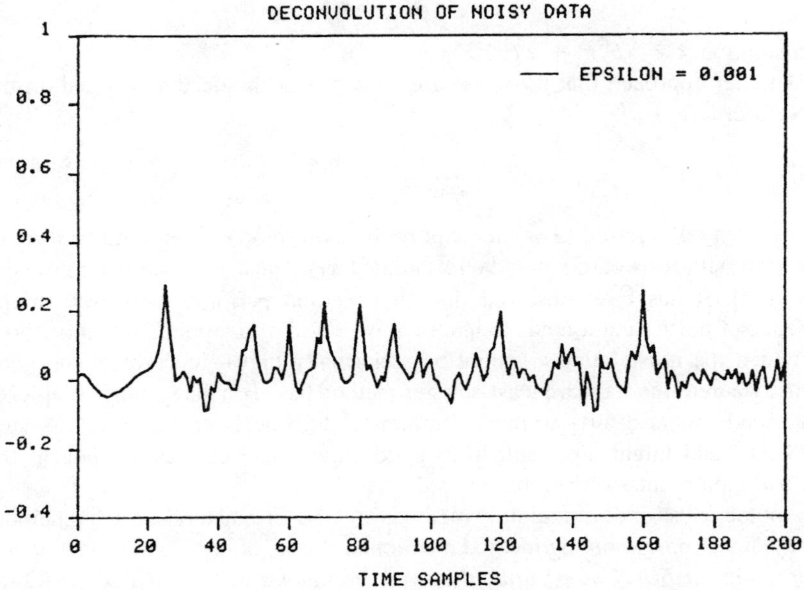

Figure 5.38 Deconvolution of Noisy Data y_n, Using $\epsilon = 0.001$

ϵ, where effectively the sample autocorrelation $\hat{R}_{ff}(0)$ is replaced by $(1 + \epsilon)\hat{R}_{ff}(0)$. The trade-off is a resulting loss of resolution.

The deconvolution problem of Eqs. (5.14.20) and (5.14.22) has been approached by a wide variety of other methods. Typically, a finite number of samples y_n; $n = 0,1, \ldots, N$ is available. Collecting these into a vector $\mathbf{y} = [y_0, y_1, \ldots, y_N]^T$, we write Eq. (5.14.22) in an obvious vectorial form

$$\mathbf{y} = F\mathbf{x} + \mathbf{v} \tag{5.14.23}$$

Instead of determining an approximate inverse filter for the blurring function F, an alternative method is to attempt to determine the best—in some sense—vector $\mathbf{x}$ which is compatible with these equations. A popular method is based on the least-squares criterion [147,148]

$$\mathcal{E} = \sum_{n=0}^{N} v_n^2 = \mathbf{v}^T\mathbf{v} = (\mathbf{y} - F\mathbf{x})^T(\mathbf{y} - F\mathbf{x}) = \min \tag{5.14.24}$$

That is, $\mathbf{x}$ is chosen so as to minimize $\mathcal{E}$. Setting the derivative with respect to $\mathbf{x}$ to zero gives the standard least-squares solution

$$\hat{\mathbf{x}} = (F^TF)^{-1}F^T\mathbf{y}$$

A prewhitening term can be added to the right of the performance index to stabilize the indicated inverse

$$\mathcal{E} = \mathbf{v}^T\mathbf{v} + \lambda\mathbf{x}^T\mathbf{x}$$

with solution $\hat{\mathbf{x}} = (F^TF + \lambda I)^{-1}F^T\mathbf{y}$.

Another approach that has been used recently with success is based on the L_1-norm criterion

$$\mathcal{E} = \sum_{n=0}^{N} |v_n| = \min \tag{5.14.25}$$

This quantity is referred to as the L_1 norm of the vector $\mathbf{v}$. The minimization of this norm with respect to $\mathbf{x}$ may be formulated as a *linear programming* problem [149–155]. It has been observed that this method performs very well in the presence of noise, and it tends to ignore a few "bad" data points—that is, those for which the noise value v_n might be abnormally high—in favor of the good points, whereas the standard least-squares method based on the L_2-norm (5.14.24) will spend all its efforts trying to minimize the few large terms in the sum (5.14.24), and might not result in as good an estimate of $\mathbf{x}$ as it would if the few bad data points were to be ignored.

Another class of deconvolution methods are *iterative* methods. Such methods, like the linear programming method mentioned above, offer the additional option of enforcing *a priori constraints* that may be known to be satisfied by $\mathbf{x}$, for example, *positivity, band-limiting,* or *time-limiting* constraints. The imposition of such constraints can improve the restoration process dramatically. The interested reader is referred to the review article [156].

Problems

Problem 5.1:

(a) Following the methods of Section 5.1, show that the optimal filter for predicting D steps into the future—i.e., estimating $y(n + D)$ on the basis of $\{y(m);\ m \leqslant n\}$—is given by

$$H(z) = \frac{1}{B(z)}\,[z^D B(z)]_+$$

(b) Express $[z^D B(z)]_+$ in terms of $B(z)$ itself and the first $D - 1$ impulse response coefficients b_m; $m = 1,2, \ldots ,D - 1$ of $B(z)$.

(c) For the two random signals y_n defined in Examples 5.1.1 and 5.1.2, find the optimal prediction filters for $D = 2$ and $D = 3$, and write the corresponding I/O filtering equations.

Problem 5.2:

Consider the order-p autoregressive sequence y_n defined by the difference equation (5.2.3). Show that a direct consequence of this difference equation is that the projection of y_n onto the subspace spanned by the entire past $\{y_{n-i};\ 1 \leqslant i < \infty\}$ is the same as the projection of y_n onto the subspace spanned only by the past p samples $\{y_{n-i};\ 1 \leqslant i \leqslant p\}$.

Problem 5.3:

(a) Show that the performance index (5.3.2) may be written as

$$\mathcal{E} = E[e_n^2] = \mathbf{a}^T R \mathbf{a}$$

where $\mathbf{a} = [1,a_1, \ldots ,a_p]^T$ is the order-p prediction-error filter, and R the autocorrelation matrix of y_n; that is, $R_{ij} = E[y_{n-i}y_{n-j}]$.

(b) Derive Eq. (5.3.7) by minimizing the index $\mathcal{E}$ with respect to the weights $\mathbf{a}$, subject to the linear constraint that $a_0 = 1$, and incorporating this constraint by means of a Lagrange multiplier.

Problem 5.4:

Take the inverse z-transform of Eq. (5.3.17) and compare the resulting equation with Eq. (5.3.15).

Problem 5.5:

Verify that Eqs. (5.3.22) and (5.3.23) are inverses of each other.

Problem 5.6:
A fourth order all-pole random signal process $y(n)$ is represented by the following set of signal model parameters (reflection coefficients and input variance):

$$\{\gamma_1,\gamma_2,\gamma_3,\gamma_4,\sigma_\epsilon^2\} = \{0.5,-0.5,0.5,-0.5,40.5\}$$

(a) Using the Levinson recursion, find the prediction error filter $A_4(z)$.

(b) Determine $\sigma_y^2 = R_{yy}(0)$. Using intermediate results from part (a), determine the autocorrelation lags $R_{yy}(k)$; $k = 1,2,3,4$.

Problem 5.7:
The first five lags of the autocorrelation function of a fourth order autoregressive random sequence $y(n)$ are

$$\{R(0),R(1),R(2),R(3),R(4)\} = \{256,128,-32,-16,22\}$$

Determine the best prediction-error filters and the corresponding mean-squared errors of orders $p = 1,2,3,4$ by using Levinson's algorithm in matrix form.

Problem 5.8:
The fourth order prediction-error filter and mean-squared prediction error of a random signal have been determined to be

$$A_4(z) = 1 - 1.25z^{-1} + 1.3125z^{-2} - z^{-3} + 0.5z^{-4}, \qquad E_4 = 0.81$$

Using the subroutine **rlev**, determine the autocorrelation lags $R(k)$; $0 \leq k \leq 4$, the four reflection coefficients, and all the lower order prediction-error filters.

Problem 5.9:
Verify the results of Example (5.3.1) using the subroutines **lev, frwlev, bkwlev,** and **rlev,** as required.

Problem 5.10:

(a) Given the five signal samples

$$\{y_0,y_1,y_2,y_3,y_4\} = \{1,-1,1,-1,1\}$$

compute the corresponding sample autocorrelation lags $\hat{R}(k)$; $k = 0,1,\ldots,4$, and send them through the routine **lev** to determine the fourth order prediction error filter $A_4(z)$.

(b) Predict the sixth sample in this sequence.

(c) Repeat (a) and (b) for the sequence of samples $\{1,2,3,4,5\}$.

Problem 5.11:

Find the infinite autoregressive or maximum entropy extension of the two autocorrelation sequences

(a) $\{R(0),R(1)\} = \{1,0.5\}$
(b) $\{R(0),R(1),R(2)\} = \{4,0,1\}$

In both cases, determine the corresponding power spectrum density $S_{yy}(z)$ and from it calculate the $R(k)$ for all lags k.

Problem 5.12:

Write Eq. (5.3.24) for order $p+1$. Derive Eq. (5.5.1) from Eq. (5.3.24) by replacing the filter $\mathbf{a}_{p+1}$ in terms of the filter $\mathbf{a}_p$ via the Levinson recursion.

Problem 5.13:

Do Problem 5.7 using the split Levinson algorithm.

Problem 5.14:

Draw the lattice realization of the analysis and synthesis filters $A_4(z)$ and $1/A_4(z)$ obtained in Problems 5.6, 5.7, and 5.8.

Problem 5.15:

Test the minimal phase property of the two polynomials

$$A(z) = 1 - 1.08z^{-1} + 0.13z^{-2} + 0.24z^{-3} - 0.5z^{-4}$$

$$A(z) = 1 + 0.18z^{-1} - 0.122z^{-2} - 0.39z^{-3} - 0.5z^{-4}$$

Problem 5.16:

(a) The entropy of an M-dimensional random vector is defined by $S = -\int p(\mathbf{y})\ln p(\mathbf{y})d^M\mathbf{y}$. Show that the entropy of a zero-mean gaussian $\mathbf{y}$ with covariance matrix R is given, up to an additive constant, by $S = \frac{1}{2}\ln(\det R)$.

(b) With the help of the LU factorization (5.9.1), show that ratio of the determinants of an order M autocorrelation matrix and its order $p (p < M)$ submatrix is

$$\frac{\det R_M}{\det R_p} = \prod_{i=p+1}^{M} E_i$$

(c) Consider all possible autocorrelation extensions of the set $\{R(0),R(1), \ldots ,R(p)\}$ up to order M. For gaussian processes, use the results in parts (a) and (b) to show that the particular extension defined by the choice $\gamma_i = 0, i = p+1, \ldots ,M$, maximizes the entropy of the order-M process; hence, the name *maximum entropy* extension.

Problem 5.17:

Consider the LU factorization $LRL^T = D$ of an order-M autocorrelation matrix R. Denote by $\mathbf{b}_p^T$, $p = 0,1, \ldots ,M$ the rows of L. They are the backward prediction filters with zeros padded to their ends to make them $(M+1)$-dimensional vectors.

(a) Show that the inverse factorization $R^{-1} = L^T D^{-1} L$ can be written as

$$R^{-1} = \sum_{p=0}^{M} \frac{1}{E_p} \mathbf{b}_p \mathbf{b}_p^T$$

(b) Define the vectors $\mathbf{s}(z) = [1, z^{-1}, z^{-2}, \ldots , z^{-M}]^T$. Show that the z-transform of an order-M filter and its inverse can be expressed compactly as

$$A(z) = \mathbf{s}(z)^T \mathbf{a}, \qquad \mathbf{a} = \int_{u.c.} A(z)\mathbf{s}(z^{-1}) \frac{dz}{2\pi jz}$$

(c) Define the vector $\mathbf{k}(w) = R^{-1}\mathbf{s}(w)$. The z-transform of this vector is called a *reproducing kernel* [57,58,66]. Show that it can be written in the alternative forms

$$K(z, w) = \mathbf{s}(z)^T \mathbf{k}(w) = \mathbf{k}(z)^T \mathbf{s}(w) = \mathbf{k}(z)^T R \mathbf{k}(w) = \mathbf{s}(z)^T R^{-1} \mathbf{s}(w)$$

(d) Let J denote the $(M+1) \times (M+1)$ reversing matrix. Show that $J\mathbf{s}(z) = z^{-M}\mathbf{s}(z^{-1})$. And that $K(z,w) = z^{-M} w^{-M} K(z^{-1}, w^{-1})$.

(e) Show that $K(z,w)$ admits the following representations in terms of the backward and forward prediction polynomials

$$K(z, w) = \sum_{p=0}^{M} \frac{1}{E_p} B_p(z) B_p(w) = \sum_{p=0}^{M} \frac{1}{E_p} A_p(z) A_p(w)$$

Problem 5.18:

Let $S_{yy}(z)$ be the power spectral density of the autocorrelation function $R(k)$ from which we build the matrix R of the previous problem. Show that R and R^{-1} admit the following representations in terms of the phasing and kernel vectors:

$$R = \int_{u.c.} S_{yy}(z)\mathbf{s}(z^{-1})\mathbf{s}(z)^T \frac{dz}{2\pi jz}, \qquad R^{-1} = \int_{u.c.} S_{yy}(z)\mathbf{k}(z^{-1})\mathbf{k}(z)^T \frac{dz}{2\pi jz}$$

Then, show the *reproducing* kernel property

$$K(z, w) = \int_{u.c.} K(z, u^{-1}) K(w, u) S_{yy}(u) \frac{du}{2\pi ju}$$

Problem 5.19:

(a) Let $\mathbf{s}_p(z) = [1, z^{-1}, \ldots , z^{-p}]^T$. Using the order-updating formulas for R_p^{-1} show that the kernel vector $\mathbf{k}_p(w) = R_p^{-1}\mathbf{s}_p(w)$ satisfies the following order-recursive equations

$$\mathbf{k}_p(w) = \begin{bmatrix} \mathbf{k}_{p-1}(w) \\ 0 \end{bmatrix} + E_p^{-1}\,\mathbf{b}_p\,B_p(w)$$

$$\mathbf{k}_p(w) = \begin{bmatrix} 0 \\ w^{-1}\mathbf{k}_{p-1}(w) \end{bmatrix} + E_p^{-1}\,\mathbf{a}_p\,A_p(w)$$

(b) Show that the corresponding reproducing kernels satisfy

$$K_p(z, w) = K_{p-1}(z, w) + E_p^{-1} B_p(z) B_p(w)$$

$$K_p(z, w) = z^{-1}w^{-1}K_{p-1}(z, w) + E_p^{-1} A_p(z) A_p(w)$$

(c) Using part (b), show the Christoffel–Darboux formula [57,58,66]

$$K_p(z, w) = \frac{1}{E_p}\,\frac{A_p(z)A_p(w) - z^{-1}w^{-1}B_p(z)B_p(w)}{1 - z^{-1}w^{-1}}$$

(d) Let z_i be the ith zero of the prediction polynomial $A_p(z)$. Using part (c), evaluate $K_p(z_i, z_i^*)$ and thereby show that necessarily $|z_i| \leq 1$. This is yet another proof of the minimal phase property of the prediction-error filters. Show further that if the prediction filter $\mathbf{a}_p(z)$ is symmetric; i.e., $\mathbf{a}_p = \mathbf{a}_p^R$, then its zeros lie on the unit circle.

(e) Show the Christoffel–Darboux formula [57,58,66]

$$K_{p-1}(z, w) = \frac{1}{E_p}\,\frac{A_p(z)A_p(w) - B_p(z)B_p(w)}{1 - z^{-1}w^{-1}}$$

and use this expression to prove the result in (d) that $|z_i| \leq 1$.

Problem 5.20:

Do Problem 5.7 using the Schur algorithm, determine the Cholesky factor G, and verify $R = GD^{-1}G^T$ by explicit matrix multiplication.

Problem 5.21:

For the Example 5.10.2, compute the entries of the output matrices $Y^{\pm}$ by directly convolving the forward/backward prediction filters with the input autocorrelation lags.

Problem 5.22:

Do Problem 5.7 using the split Schur algorithm, and determine the Cholesky factor G by the recursion (5.10.21).

Problem 5.23:

(a) Show the identity

$$\left| \frac{-a^* + z^{-1}}{1 - az^{-1}} \right|^2 = 1 - \frac{(1 - |z^{-1}|^2)(1 - |a|^2)}{|1 - az^{-1}|^2}$$

(b) Using part (a), show that the all-pass Schur function $S_p(z)$ defined by Eq. (5.10.22) satisfies the boundedness inequality (5.10.23), with equality attained on the unit circle. Show that it also satisfies $|S_p(z)| > 1$, for $|z| < 1$.

Problem 5.24:

Define the Schur function $S_3(z) = \dfrac{0.125 - 0.875z^{-2} + z^{-3}}{1 - 0.875z^{-1} + 0.125z^{-3}}$. Carry out the recursions (5.10.24) and (5.10.25) to construct the lower order Schur functions $S_p(z)$, $p = 2,1,0$, and in the process extract the corresponding reflection coefficients.

Problem 5.25:

Consider a generalized version of the simulation example discussed in Section 5.11, defined by

$$x(n) = s(n) + v_1(n), \qquad y(n) = v_2(n)$$

where

$$s(n) = \sin(\omega_0 n + \phi)$$

$$v_1(n) = a_1 v_1(n - 1) + v(n)$$

$$v_2(n) = a_2 v_2(n - 1) + v(n)$$

where $v(n)$ is zero-mean, unit-variance, white noise, and ϕ a random phase independent of $v(n)$. This ensures that the $s(n)$ component is uncorrelated with $v_1(n)$ and $v_2(n)$.

(a) Show that

$$R_{xy}(k) = \frac{a_1^k}{1 - a_1 a_2} \qquad k \geq 0$$

$$R_{yy}(k) = \frac{a_2^k}{1 - a_2^2} \qquad k \geq 0$$

(b) Show that the infinite-order Wiener filter for estimating $x(n)$ on the basis of $y(n)$ has a (causal) impulse response

$$h_0 = 1,\ h_k = (a_1 - a_2)a_1^{k-1} \qquad \text{for } k \geq 1$$

(c) Next, consider the order-M FIR Wiener filter. Send the theoretical correlations of part (a) for $k = 0,1, \ldots, M$ through the subroutine **firw** to obtain the theoretical Mth order Wiener filter realized both in the direct and the lattice forms. Draw these realizations. Compare the theoretical values of the weights **h**, **g**, and γ with the simulated values presented in Section 5.11 that correspond to the choice of parameters $M = 4$, $a_1 = -0.5$, and $a_2 = 0.8$. Also compare the answer for **h** with the first $M + 1$ samples of the infinite order Wiener filter impulse response of part (b).

(d) Repeat (c) with $M = 6$.

Problem 5.26:

A closed form solution of Problem 5.25 can be obtained as follows:

(a) Show that the inverse of the $(M+1) \times (M+1)$ autocorrelation matrix defined by the autocorrelation lags $R_{yy}(k)$, $k = 0, 1, \ldots, M$, of Problem 5.25(a) is given by

$$R_{yy}^{-1} = \begin{bmatrix} 1 & -a_2 & 0 & \cdots & 0 & 0 \\ -a_2 & b & -a_2 & \cdots & 0 & 0 \\ 0 & -a_2 & b & \cdots & 0 & 0 \\ \vdots & \vdots & \vdots & \ddots & \vdots & \vdots \\ 0 & 0 & 0 & & b & -a_2 \\ 0 & 0 & 0 & & -a_2 & 1 \end{bmatrix}$$

where $b = 1 + a_2^2$.

(b) Using this inverse, show that the optimal Mth order Wiener filter has impulse response

$$h_0 = 1,\ h_k = (a_1 - a_2)\, a_1^{k-1} \text{ for } 1 \le k \le M - 1, \text{ and } h_M = \frac{(a_1 - a_2)}{1 - a_1 a_2} a_1^{M-1}$$

(c) Show that the lattice weights **g** can be obtained from **h** by the backward substitution

$$g_M = h_M, \text{ and } g_m = a_2 g_{m+1} + h_m,\ m = M - 1, M - 2, \ldots, 1, 0$$

(d) For $M = 4$, $a_1 = -0.5$, $a_2 = 0.8$, compute the numerical values of **h** and **g** using the above expressions and compare them with those of Problem 5.25(c).

Problem 5.27: Computer Experiment

Consider the noise canceling example of Section 5.11 and Problem 5.25, defined by the choice of parameters

$$\omega_0 = 0.075\pi \text{ [rads/sample]}, \qquad \phi = 0,\ a_1 = -0.5,\ a_2 = 0.8,\ M = 4$$

(a) Generate 100 samples of the signals $x(n)$, $s(n)$, and $y(n)$. On the same graph, plot $x(n)$ and $s(n)$ versus n. Plot $y(n)$ versus n.

(b) Using these samples, compute the sample correlations $\hat{R}_{yy}(k)$, $\hat{R}_{xy}(x)$, for

$k = 0, 1, \ldots, M$, and compare them with the theoretical values obtained in Problem 5.25(a).

(c) Send these lags through the routine **firw** to get the optimal Wiener filter weights $\mathbf{h}$ and $\mathbf{g}$, and the reflection coefficients $\boldsymbol{\gamma}$. Draw the lattice and direct form realizations of the Wiener filter.

(d) Filter y_n through the Wiener filter realized in the lattice form, and plot the output $e(n) = x(n) - \hat{x}(n)$ versus n.

(e) Repeat (d) using the direct form realization of the Wiener filter.

(f) Repeat (d) when $M = 6$.

Problem 5.28:

The following six samples

$$\{y_0, y_1, y_2, y_3, y_4, y_5\} = \{4.684,\ 7.247,\ 8.423,\ 8.650,\ 8.640,\ 8.392\}$$

have been generated by sending zero-mean unit-variance white-noise through the difference equation

$$y_n = a_1 y_{n-1} + a_2 y_{n-2} + \epsilon_n$$

where $a_1 = 1.70$, $a_2 = -0.72$. Iterating Burg's method by hand, obtain estimates of the model parameters a_1, a_2, and σ_ϵ^2.

Problem 5.29:

Derive Eq. (5.12.11).

Problem 5.30: Computer Experiment

Ten samples from a fourth order autoregressive process $y(n)$ are given. It is desired to extract the model parameters $\{a_1, a_2, a_3, a_4, \sigma_\epsilon^2\}$ as well as the equivalent parameter set $\{\gamma_1, \gamma_2, \gamma_3, \gamma_4, \sigma_\epsilon^2\}$

(a) Determine these parameters using Burg's method.

(b) Repeat using the Yule-Walker method.

Note: The exact parameter values by which the above simulated samples were generated are

$$\{a_1, a_2, a_3, a_4, \sigma_\epsilon^2\} = \{-2.2137,\ 2.9403,\ -2.1697,\ 0.9606,\ 1\}$$

n	$y(n)$
0	4.503
1	−10.841
2	−24.183
3	−25.662
4	−14.390
5	1.453
6	10.980
7	13.679
8	15.517
9	15.037

Problem 5.31:

Using the continuity equations at an interface, derive the transmission matrix equation (5.13.2) and the energy conservation equation (5.13.4).

Problem 5.32:

Show Eq. (5.13.6).

Problem 5.33:
Figure 5.25 defines the scattering matrix S. Explain how the principle of linear superposition may be used to show the general relationship

$$\begin{bmatrix} E'_+ \\ E_- \end{bmatrix} = S \begin{bmatrix} E_+ \\ E'_- \end{bmatrix}$$

between incoming and outgoing fields.

Problem 5.34:
Show the two properties of the matrix $\psi_m(z)$ stated in Eqs. (5.13.13) and (5.13.14).

Problem 5.35:
Show Eqs. (5.13.25).

Problem 5.36:
The reflection response of a stack of four dielectrics has been found to be

$$R(z) = \frac{-0.25 + 0.0313z^{-1} + 0.2344z^{-2} - 0.2656z^{-3} + 0.25z^{-4}}{1 - 0.125z^{-1} + 0.0664z^{-3} - 0.0625z^{-4}}$$

Determine the reflection coefficients $\{\rho_0, \rho_1, \rho_2, \rho_3, \rho_4\}$.

Problem 5.37:
Prove the recursion (5.13.30). Using the recursions (5.13.29), obtain the reflection coefficients $\{\rho_0, \rho_1, \rho_2, \rho_3, \rho_4\}$ of the previous problem.

Problem 5.38: Computer Experiment
It is desired to probe the structure of a stack of dielectrics from its reflection response. To this end, a unit impulse is sent incident on the stack and the reflection response is measured as a function of time.
It is known in advance (although this is not necessary) that the stack consists of four equal travel-time slabs stacked in front of a semi-infinite medium.
Thirteen samples of the reflection response are collected as shown here. Determine the reflection coefficients $\{\rho_0, \rho_1, \rho_2, \rho_3, \rho_4\}$ by means of the dynamic predictive deconvolution procedure.

k	$R(k)$
0	−0.2500
1	0.0000
2	0.2344
3	−0.2197
4	0.2069
5	0.0103
6	0.0305
7	−0.0237
8	0.0093
9	−0.0002
10	0.0035
11	−0.0017
12	0.0004

Problem 5.39: Computer Experiment
Generate the results of Figures 5.16–5.17 and 5.25–5.26.

Problem 5.40: Computer Experiment

This problem illustrates the use of the dynamic predictive deconvolution method in the design of broadband terminations of transmission lines. The termination is constructed by the cascade of M equal travel-time segments of transmission lines such that the overall reflection response of the structure approximates the desired reflection response. The characteristic impedances of the various segments are obtainable from the reflection coefficients $\{\rho_0, \rho_1, \ldots, \rho_M\}$. The reflection response $R(\omega)$ of the structure is a periodic function of ω with period $\omega_s = 2\pi/T_2$, where T_2 is the two-way travel time delay of each segment. The design procedure is illustrated by the following example: The desired frequency response $R(\omega)$ is defined over one Nyquist period by

$$R(\omega) = \begin{cases} 0 & \text{for} \quad 0.25\omega_s \leq \omega \leq 0.75\omega_s \\ 0.9 & \text{for} \quad 0 \leq \omega < 0.25\omega_s \text{ and } 0.75\omega_s < \omega \leq \omega_s \end{cases}$$

as shown in Fig. 5.39.

(a) Using the Fourier series method of designing digital filters, design a $N = 21$-tap filter with impulse response $R(k)$; $k = 0, 1, \ldots, N - 1$, whose frequency response approximates the desired response defined above. Window the designed reflection impulse response $R(k)$ by a length-N Hamming window. Plot the magnitude frequency response of the windowed reflection series over one Nyquist interval $0 \leq \omega \leq \omega_s$.

(b) For $M = 6$, send the N samples of the windowed reflection series through the dynamic predictive deconvolution routine **dpd** to obtain the polynomials $A_M(z)$ and $B_M(z)$ and the reflection coefficients $\{\rho_0, \rho_1, \rho_2, \ldots, \rho_M\}$. Plot the magnitude response of the structure; that is, plot

$$|R(\omega)| = \left|\frac{B_M(z)}{A_M(z)}\right| \qquad z = \exp(j\omega T_2) = \exp\left(2\pi j \frac{\omega}{\omega_s}\right)$$

and compare it with the windowed response of part (a). To facilitate the comparison, plot both responses of parts (a) and (b) on the same graph.

(c) Repeat part (b) for $M = 2$, $M = 3$, and $M = 10$.

(d) Repeat parts (a) through (c) for $N = 31$ reflection series samples.

(e) Repeat parts (a) through (c) for $N = 51$.

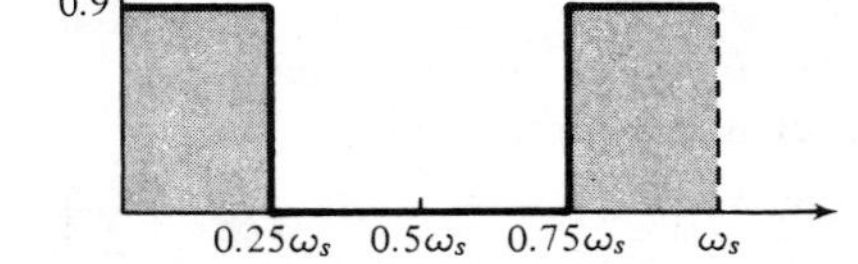

Figure 5.39 Desired Reflection Frequency Response

Problem 5.41:
Show that the performance matrix P defined by Eq. (5.14.11) has trace equal to $M + 1$.

Problem 5.42: Computer Experiment
Reproduce the results of Figs. 5.27 through 5.34.

References

1. G. P. Box and G. M. Jenkins, *Time Series Analysis, Forecasting, and Control*, San Francisco, Holden-Day, 1970.
2. P. Whittle, *Prediction and Regulation*, New York, Van Nostrand Reinhold, 1963.
3. J. Makhoul, Linear Prediction: A Tutorial Review, *Proc. IEEE*, **63,** 56 (1975).
4. N. Levinson, The Wiener RMS Error Criterion in Filter Design and Prediction, *J. Math. Physics*, **25,** 261 (1947).
5. J. Durbin, The Fitting of Time Series Models, *Rev. Inst. Int. Stat.*, **28,** 344–348 (1973).
6. J. D. Markel and A. H. Gray, Jr., *Linear Prediction of Speech*, New York, Springer-Verlag, 1976.
7. E. A. Robinson, *Multichannel Time-Series Analysis with Digital Computer Programs*, San Francisco, Holden-Day, 1967.
8. E. A. Robinson and S. Treitel, *Geophysical Signal Analysis*, Englewood Cliffs, NJ, Prentice-Hall, 1980.
9. E. A. Robinson and S. Treitel, Maximum Entropy and the Relationship of the Partial Autocorrelation to the Reflection Coefficients of a Layered System, *IEEE Trans. Acoust., Speech, Signal Process.*, **ASSP-28,** 22 (1980).
10. S. M. Kay and S. L. Marple, Spectrum Analysis—A Modern Perspective, *Proc. IEEE*, **69,** 1380–1419 (1981).
11. S. Haykin, Ed., *Nonlinear Methods of Spectral Analysis*, New York, Springer-Verlag, 1979.
12. A. Papoulis, Predictable Processes and Wold's Decomposition: A Review, *IEEE Trans. Acoust., Speech, Signal Process.*, **ASSP-33,** 933 (1985).
13. O. Barndorff-Nielsen and G. Schou, On the Parametrization of Autoregressive Models by Partial Autocorrelations, *J. Multiv. Anal.*, **3,** 408 (1973).
14. F. L. Ramsey, Characterization of the Partial Autocorrelation Function,'' *Ann. Stat.*, **2,** 1296–1301 (1974)
15. M. Morf, A. Vieira, and T. Kailath, Covariance Characterization by Partial Autocorrelation Matrices, *Ann. Stat.*, **6,** 643–645 (1978).
16. R. E. Kalman, On Partial Realizations, Transfer Functions, and Canonical Forms, *Acta Polytech. Scandinav.*, Math. Comput. Sci. Series, **13,** 9 (1979).
17. R. E. Kalman, Realization of Covariance Sequences, in I. Gohberg, Ed., *Toeplitz Centennial, Operator Theory: Advances and Applications,* vol. 4, Boston, Birkhäuser, 1982.

18. W. Gragg and A. Lindquist, On the Partial Realization Problem, *Lin. Alg. Appl.*, **50,** 277 (1983).
19. T. K. Citron, A. M. Bruckstein, and T. Kailath, An Inverse Scattering Approach to the Partial Realization Problem, *Proc. 1984 IEEE Int. Conf. Decision and Control,* Las Vegas, NV, p. 1503.
20. T. T. Georgiou, Realization of Power Spectra from Partial Covariance Sequences, *IEEE Trans. Acoust., Speech, Signal Process.,* **ASSP-35,** 438 (1987).
21. S. Saito and K. Nakata, *Fundamentals of Speech Processing,* New York, Academic, 1985.
22. N. I. Aheizer and M. Krein, *Some Questions in the Theory of Moments,* Providence, RI, Am. Math Soc., 1962.
23. R. R. Bitmead and B. D. O. Anderson, Asymptotically Fast Solution of Toeplitz and Related Systems of Linear Equations, *Lin. Alg. Appl.,* **34,** 103 (1980).
24. R. P. Brent, F. G. Gustavson, and D. Y. Y. Yun, Fast Solution of Toeplitz Systems of Equations and Computation of Padé Approximants, *J. Algorithms,* **1,** 259 (1980).
25. H. M. Ahmed, J. M. Delosme, and M. Morf, Highly Concurrent Computing Structures for Matrix Arithmetic and Signal Processing, *Computer Magazine,* **15,** 65–82 (Jan. 1982).
26. H. T. Kung, Why Systolic Architectures?, *Computer Magazine,* **15,** 37–46 (Jan. 1982).
27. R. P. Brent and F. T. Luk, A Systolic Array of the Linear-Time Solution of Toeplitz Systems of Equations, *J. VLSI Comput. Syst.,* **1,** 1 (1983).
28. S. K. Rao and T. Kailath, Orthogonal Digital Filters for VLSI Implementation, *IEEE Trans. Circ. Syst.,* **CAS-31,** 933 (1984).
29. D. R. Sweet, Fast Toeplitz Orthogonalization, *Numer. Math.,* **43,** 1 (1984).
30. S. Y. Kung, On Super Computing with Systolic/Wavefront Array Processors, *Proc. IEEE,* **72,** 867 (1984).
31. S. Y. Kung, VLSI Array Processors, *ASSP Magazine,* **2,** no. 3, 4, (1985).
32. S. Y. Kung, VLSI Signal Processing: From Transversal Filtering to Concurrent Array Processing, in S. Y. Kung, H. J. Whitehouse, and T. Kailath, Eds., *VLSI and Modern Signal Processing,* Englewood Cliffs, NJ, Prentice-Hall, 1985.
33. G. R. Nudd and J. G. Nash, Application of Concurrent VLSI Systems to Two-Dimensional Signal Processing, *Ibid.*
34. R. Schreiber, Systolic Linear Algebra Machines in Digital Signal Processing, *Ibid.*
35. P. Dewilde, E. Deprettere, and R. Nouta, Parallel and Pipelined VLSI Implementation of Signal Processing Algorithms, *Ibid.*
36. R. Kumar, A Fast Algorithm for Solving a Toeplitz System of Equations, *IEEE Trans. Acoust., Speech, Signal Process.,* **ASSP-33,** 254 (1985).
37. J. R. Bunch, Stability of Methods for Solving Toeplitz Systems of Equations, *SIAM J. Sci. Stat. Comput.,* **6,** 349 (1985).
38. A. D. McAulay, Parallel AR Computation with a Reconfigurable Signal Processor, *Proc. 1986 IEEE Int. Conf. Acoust., Speech, Signal Process.,* Tokyo, p. 1365.
39. A. W. Bojanczyk, Systolic Implementation of the Lattice Algorithm for Least Squares Linear Prediction Problems, *Lin. Alg. Appl.,* **77,** 27 (1986).

40. F. De Hoog, A New Algorithm for Solving Toeplitz Systems of Equations, *Lin. Alg. Appl.*, **88/89,** 123 (1987).
41. H. Kimura and T. Osada, Canonical Pipelining of Lattice Filters, *IEEE Trans. Acoust., Speech, Signal Process.*, **ASSP-35,** 878 (1987).
42. P. Dewilde and E. F. Deprettere, Modelling VLSI Interconnects as an Inverse Scattering Problem, *Proc. 1987 IEEE Int. Conf. Circuits and Systems,* Philadelphia, PA, p. 147.
43. Y. Bistritz, Zero Location with Respect to the Unit Circle of Discrete-Time Linear System Polynomials, *Proc. IEEE,* **72,** 1131 (1984).
44. P. Delsarte and Y. Genin, The Split Levinson Algorithm, *IEEE Trans. Acoust., Speech, Signal Process.*, **ASSP-34,** 470, (1986).
45. Y. Bistritz, H. Lev-Ari, and T. Kailath, Immitance-Domain Levinson Algorithms, *Proc. 1986 IEEE Int. Conf. Acoust., Speech, Signal Process.*, Tokyo, p. 253.
46. P. Delsarte and Y. Genin, On the Splitting of Classical Algorithms in Linear Prediction Theory, *IEEE Trans. Acoust., Speech, Signal Process.*, **ASSP-35,** 645 (1987).
47. Y. Bistritz, H. Lev-Ari, and T. Kailath, Complexity Reduced Lattice Filters for Digital Speech Processing, *Proc. 1987 IEEE Int. Conf. Acoust., Speech, Signal Process.*, Dallas, TX, p. 21.
48. Y. Bistritz and T. Kailath, Fast Algorithms for Non-Hermitian Quasi-Toeplitz Matrices, *Proc. 1987 IEEE Int. Conf. Circuits and Systems,* Philadelphia, PA, p. 1068.
49. H. Krishna and S. D. Morgera, The Levinson Recurrence and Fast Algorithms for Solving Toeplitz Systems of Linear Equations, *IEEE Trans. Acoust., Speech, Signal Process.*, **ASSP-35,** 839 (1987).
50. S. D. Morgera and H. Krishna, Generalized Levinson/Szegö Complex Recurrences for a Class of Second-Order Nonstationary Stochastic Processes, *Proc. 1987 IEEE Int. Conf. Circuits and Systems,* Philadelphia, PA, p. 84.
51. G. Martinelli, G. Orlandi, and P. Burrascano, Yule-Walker Equations and Bartlett's Bisection Theory, *IEEE Trans. Circ. Syst.*, **CAS-32,** 1074 (1985).
52. A. J. Berkhout, Stability and Least-Squares Estimation, *Automatica,* **11,** 637–638 (1975).
53. A. Vieira and T. Kailath, Another Approach to the Schur-Cohn Criterion, *IEEE Trans. Circuits and Systems,* **CAS-24,** 218–220 (April 1977).
54. S. A. Tretter, *Introduction to Discrete-Time Signal Processing,* New York, Wiley, 1976.
55. R. J. Duffin, Algorithms for Classical Stability Problems, *SIAM Rev.*, **11,** 196 (1969).
56. P. P. Vaidyanathan and S. K. Mitra, A Unified Structural Interpretation of Some Well-Known Stability-Test Procedures for Linear Systems, *Proc. IEEE,* **75,** 478 (1987).
57. N. I. Achiezer, *The Classical Moment Problem,* Edinburgh, Oliver and Boyd, 1965.
58. G. Szegö, *Orthogonal Polynomials,* Providence, RI, American Mathematical Society, 1958.
59. E. A. Robinson and S. Treitel, Digital Signal Processing in Geophysics, in A. Oppenheim, Ed., *Applications of Digital Signal Processing,* Englewood Cliffs, NJ, Prentice-Hall, 1978.
60. S. Treitel and E. A. Robinson, The Design of High-Resolution Digital Filters, *IEEE Trans. Geosc. Electron.*, **GE-4,** 25–38 (1966).
61. J. Claerbout, *Fundamentals of Geophysical Data Processing,* New York, McGraw-Hill, 1976.

62. I. C. Gohberg and I. A. Fel'dman, *Convolution Equations and Projection Methods for their Solution,* Providence, RI, American Mathematical Society, 1974.
63. W. F. Trench, An Algorithm for the Inversion of Finite Toeplitz Matrices, *J. Soc. Ind. Appl. Math.,* **12,** 515–522 (1964).
64. S. Zohar, Toeplitz Matrix Inversion: The Algorithm of W. F. Trench, *J. Assoc. Comput. Mach.,* **16,** 592–601 (1969).
65. S. Zohar, The Solution of a Toeplitz Set of Linear Equations, *J. Assoc. Comput. Mach.,* **21,** 272–276 (1974).
66. T. Kailath, A. Vieira, and M. Morf, Inverses of Toeplitz Operators, Innovations and Orthogonal Polynomials, *SIAM Rev.,* **20,** 106–119 (1978).
67. H. Lev-Ari and T. Kailath, Triangular Factorization of Structured Hermitian Matrices, in I. Gohberg, Ed., *I. Schur Methods in Operator Theory and Signal Processing, Operator Theory: Advances and Applications,* vol. 18, Boston, Birkhäuser, 1986.
68. I. Gohberg, T. Kailath, and I. Koltracht, Efficient Solution of Linear Systems of Equations with Recursive Structure, *Lin. Alg. Appl.,* **80,** 81 (1986).
69. I. Gohberg, T. Kailath, I. Koltracht, and P. Lancaster, Linear Complexity Parallel Algorithms for Linear Systems of Equations with Recursive Structure, *Lin. Alg. Appl.,* **88/89,** 271 (1987).
70. I. Schur, On Power Series Which Are Bounded in the Interior of the Unit Circle I and II, in I. Gohberg, Ed., *I. Schur Methods in Operator Theory and Signal Processing, Operator Theory: Advances and Applications,* vol. 18, Boston, Birkhäuser, 1986.
71. T. Kailath, A Theorem of I. Schur and Its Impact on Modern Signal Processing, *Ibid.*
72. E. H. Bareiss, Numerical Solution of Linear Equations with Toeplitz and Vector Toeplitz Matrices, *Numer. Math.,* **13,** 404 (1969).
73. J. Rissanen, Algorithms for Triangular Decomposition of Block Hankel and Toeplitz Matrices with Application to Factoring Positive Matrix Polynomials, *Math. Comp.,* **27,** 147 (1973).
74. J. Rissanen, Solution of Linear Equations with Hankel and Toeplitz Matrices, *Numer. Math.,* **22,** 361 (1974).
75. J. Le Roux and C. J. Gueguen, A Fixed Point Computation of Partial Correlation Coefficients, *IEEE Trans. Acoust., Speech, Signal Process.,* **ASSP-25,** 257–259 (1977).
76. P. Dewilde, A. Vieira, and T. Kailath, On the Generalized Szegö-Levinson Realization Algorithm for Optimal Linear Predictors Based on a Network Synthesis Approach, *IEEE Trans. Circuits Syst.,* **CAS-25,** 663–675 (1978).
77. P. Delsarte, Y. Genin, and Y. Kamp, Schur Parametrization of Positive Definite Block-Toeplitz Systems, *SIAM J. Appl. Math.,* **36,** 34 (1979).
78. T. Kailath, S. Y. Kung, and M. Morf, Displacement Rank of Matrices and Linear Equations, *J. Math. Anal. Appl.,* **68,** 395 (1979).
79. P. Dewilde and H. Dym, Schur Recursions, Error Formulas, and Convergence of Rational Estimators for Stationary Stochastic Sequences, *IEEE Trans. Inf. Theory,* **IT-27,** 446–461 (1981).
80. P. Dewilde, J. T. Fokkema, and I. Widya, Inverse Scattering and Linear Prediction: The Continuous Time Case, in M. Hazewinkel and J. C. Willems, Eds., *Stochastic Systems: The Mathematics of Filtering and Identification and Applications,* Boston, Reidel, 1981.

81. E. Jonkheere and P. Delsarte, Inversion of Toeplitz Operators, Levinson Equations, and Gohberg-Krein Factorization—A Simple and Unified Approach for the Rational Case, *J. Math. Anal. Appl.*, **87,** 295 (1982).
82. S. Y. Kung and Y. H. Hu, A Highly Concurrent Algorithm and Pipelined Architecture for Solving Toeplitz Systems, *IEEE Trans. Acoust., Speech, Signal Process.*, **ASSP-31,** 66–75 (1983).
83. H. Lev-Ari and T. Kailath, Lattice Filter Parametrization and Modeling of Nonstationary Processes, *IEEE Trans. Inform. Th.*, **IT-30,** 2 (1984).
84. T. Kailath, Ed. *Modern Signal Processing,* Washington, DC, Hemisphere Publishing, 1985.
85. T. Kailath, Signal Processing in the VLSI Era, in S. Y. Kung, H. J. Whitehouse, and T. Kailath, Eds., *VLSI and Modern Signal Processing,* Englewood Cliffs, NJ, Prentice-Hall, 1985.
86. A. Yagle and B. C. Levy, The Schur Algorithm and Its Applications, *Acta Applic. Math.*, **3,** 255 (1985).
87. T. Kailath, A. M. Bruckstein, and D. Morgan, Fast Matrix Factorization via Discrete Transmission Lines, *Lin. Alg. Appl.*, **75,** 1 (1985).
88. P. P. Vaidyanathan and S. K. Mitra, Discrete Version of Richard's Theorem and Applications to Cascaded Lattice Realization of Digital Filter Transfer Functions, *IEEE Trans. Circ. Syst.*, **CAS-33,** 26 (1986).
89. J. Le Roux, Some Properties of the Schur Recursion for the Direct Computation of the Matricial Spectral Factor, *Signal Processing,* **11,** 359 (1986).
90. A. M. Bruckstein and T. Kailath, An Inverse Scattering Framework for Several Problems in Signal Processing, *ASSP Magazine,* No. 1, 6 (1987).
91. P. Delsarte and Y. Genin, The Tridiagonal Approach to Inverse Scattering Problems, in *Proc. 1987 IEEE Int. Conf. Circuits and Systems,* Philadelphia, PA, p. 140.
92. H. Lev-Ari and T. Kailath, Lossless Cascade Networks: The Crossroads of Stochastic Estimation, Inverse Scattering, and Filter Synthesis, *Proc. 1987 IEEE Int. Conf. Circuits and Systems,* Philadelphia, PA, p. 1088.
93. J. P. Burg, Maximum Entropy Spectral Analysis, Presented at *37th Annual Int. SEG Meeting,* Oklahoma City, (1967).
94. D. Childers, Ed. *Modern Spectrum Analysis,* New York, IEEE Press, 1978.
95. E. R. Kanasewich, *Time Sequence Analysis in Geophysics,* Edmonton, University of Alberta Press, 1975.
96. D. E. Smylie, G. K. C. Clarice, and T. J. Ulrich, Analysis of Irregularities in the Earth's Rotation, in *Methods of Computational Physics,* Vol. 13, New York, Academic, 1973, pp. 391–430.
97. T. J. Ulrich and R. W. Clayton, Time Series Modelling and Maximum Entropy, *Phys. Earth Planet. Inter.*, **12,** 188–200 (1976).
98. M. Morf, B. Dickinson, T. Kailath, and A. Vieira, Efficient Solution of Covariance Equations for Linear Prediction, *IEEE Trans. Acoust., Speech, Signal Process.*, **ASSP-25,** 429–435 (1977).
99. E. T. Jaynes, On the Rationale of Maximum-Entropy Methods, *Proc. IEEE,* **70,** 939 (1982).

100. B. R. Frieden, Dice, Entropy, and Likelihood, *Proc. IEEE,* **73,** 1764 (1985).

101. B. Helme and C. L. Nikias, Improved Spectrum Performance via a Data-Adaptive Weighted Burg Technique, *IEEE Trans. Acoust., Speech, Signal Process.,* **ASSP-33,** 903 (1985).

102. P. F. Fougere, Applications of Maximum Entropy Spectrum Estimation to Air Force Problems, *Proc. Third ASSP Workshop on Spectrum Estimation and Modeling,* Boston, 1986, p. 77.

103. J. Makhoul, Maximum Confusion Spectral Analysis, *Proc. Third ASSP Workshop on Spectrum Estimation and Modeling,* Boston, 1986, p. 6.

104. B. S. Atal and S. Hanauer, Speech Analysis and Synthesis by Linear Prediction of the Speech Wave, *J. Acoust. Soc. Amer.,* **50,** 637 (1971).

105. F. Itakura and S. Saito, A Statistical Method for Estimation of Speech Spectral Density and Formant Frequencies, *Electr. Commun.,* **53-A,** 36–43 (1970).

106. R. Schafer and L. Rabiner, Digital Representation of Speech Signals, *Proc. IEEE,* **63,** 66 (1975).

107. L. R. Rabiner and R. W. Schafer, *Digital Processing of Speech Signals,* Englewood Cliffs, NJ, Prentice-Hall, 1978.

108. J. D. Markel and A. H. Gray, Jr. Roundoff Noise Characteristics of a Class of Orthogonal Polynomial Structures, *IEEE Trans. Acoust., Speech, Signal Process.,* **ASSP-23,** 473–486 (1975).

109. R. Viswanathan and J. Makhoul, Quantization Properties of Transmission Parameters in Linear Predictive Systems, *IEEE Trans. Acoust., Speech, Signal Process.,* **ASSP-23,** 309–321 (1975).

110. N. Morgan, *Talking Chips,* New York, McGraw-Hill, 1984.

111. M. R. Schroeder, Predictive Coding of Speech: Historical Review and Directions for Future Research, *Proc. 1986 IEEE Int. Conf. Acoust., Speech, Signal Process.,* Tokyo, p. 261.

112. P. E. Papamichalis, *Practical Approaches to Speech Coding,* Englewood Cliffs, NJ, Prentice-Hall, 1987.

113. A. Isaksson, A. Wennberg, and L. H. Zetterberg, Computer Analysis of EEG Signals with Parametric Models, *Proc. IEEE,* **69,** 451–461 (1981).

114. W. Gersch, Spectral Analysis of EEG's by Autoregressive Decomposition of Time Series, *Math. Biosci.,* **7,** 205–222 (1970).

115. C. D. McGillem, J. I. Aunon, and D. G. Childers, Signal Processing In Evoked Potential Research: Applications of Filtering and Pattern Recognition, *CRC Critical Reviews of Bioengineering,* **6,** 225–265 (October 1981).

116. A. Isaksson and A. Wennberg, Spectral Properties of Nonstationary EEG Signals, Evaluated by Means of Kalman Filtering: Application Examples from a Vigilance Test, in P. Kellaway and I. Petersen, Eds., *Quantitative Analysis Studies in Epilepsy,* New York, Raven Press, 1976.

117. G. Bodenstein and H. M. Praetorius, Feature Extraction from the Electroencephalogram by Adaptive Segmentation, *Proc. IEEE,* **65,** 642–652 (1977).

118. T. Bohlin, Analysis of EEG Signals with Changing Spectra using a Short-Word Kalman Estimator, *Math. Biosci.,* **35,** 221–259 (1977).

119. F. H. Lopes da Silva, Analysis of EEG Nonstationarities, in W. A. Cobb and H. Van Duijn, Eds., *Contemporary Clinical Neurophysiology* (EEG Suppl. No. 34), Amsterdam, Elsevier, 1978.
120. Z. Rogowski, I. Gath, and E. Bental, On the Prediction of Epileptic Seizures, *Biol. Cybernetics,* **42,** 9–15 (1981).
121. F. Itakura, Minimum Prediction Residual Principle Applied to Speech Recognition, *IEEE Trans. Acoust., Speech, Signal Process.,* **ASSP-23,** 67–72 (1975).
122. J. M. Tribolet, L. R. Robiner, and M. M. Sondhi, Statistical Properties of an LPC Distance Measure, *IEEE Trans. Acoust., Speech, Signal Process.,* **ASSP-27,** 550–558 (1979).
123. P. de Souza and P. J. Thompson, LPC Distance Measures and Statistical Tests with Particular Reference to the Likelihood Ratio, *IEEE Trans. Acoust., Speech, Signal Process.,* **ASSP-30,** 304–315 (1982).
124. R. M. Gray, et al., Distortion Measures for Speech Processing, *IEEE Trans. Acoust., Speech, Signal Process.,* **ASSP-28,** 367–376 (1980).
125. J. L. Flanagan, Talking with Computers: Synthesis and Recognition of Speech by Machines, *IEEE Trans. Biomed. Eng.,* **BME-29,** 223–232 (1982).
126. L. Dusek, T. B. Schalk, and M. McMahan, Voice Recognition Joins Speech on Programmable Board, *Electronics,* **56**(8), 128–132 (April 1983).
127. H. Wakita, Direct Estimation of the Vocal Tract Shape by Inverse Filtering of Acoustic Speech Waveforms, *IEEE Trans. Audio Electroacoust.,* **AU-21,** 417 (1973).
128. J. A. Ware and K. Aki, Continuous and Discrete Inverse Scattering Problems in a Stratified Elastic Medium. I. Plane Waves at Normal Incidence, *J. Acoust. Soc. Am.,* **45,** 91 (1969).
129. L. C. Wood and S. Treitel, Seismic Signal Processing, *Proc. IEEE,* **63,** 649–661 (1975).
130. P. L. Goupillaud, An Approach to Inverse Filtering of Near-Surface Layer Effects from Seismic Records, *Geophysics,* **26,** 754–760 (1961).
131. J. F. Claerbout, Synthesis of a Layered Medium from Its Acoustic Transmission Response, *Geophysics,* **33,** 264–269 (1968).
132. F. Koehler and M. T. Taner, Direct and Inverse Problems Relating Reflection Coefficients and Reflection Response for Horizontally Layered Media, *Geophysics,* **42,** 1199–1206 (1977).
133. E. A. Robinson and S. Treitel, The Fine Structure of the Normal Incidence Synthetic Seismogram, *Geophys. J. R. Astron. Soc.,* **53,** 289–309 (1978).
134. S. Treitel and E. A. Robinson, Maximum Entropy Spectral Decomposition of a Seismogram into Its Minimum Entropy Component Plus Noise, *Geophysics,* **46,** 1108 (1981).
135. J. M. Mendel and F. Habibi-Ashrafi, A Survey of Approaches to Solving Inverse Problems for Lossless Layered Media Systems, *IEEE Trans. Geosci. Electron.,* **GE-18,** 320–330 (1980).
136. K. P. Bube and R. Burridge, The One-Dimensional Problem of Reflection Seismology, *SIAM Rev.,* **25,** 497 (1983).
137. S. H. Gray, The Relationship Between "Direct, Discrete" and "Iterative, Continuous" One-Dimensional Inverse Methods, *Geophysics,* **49,** 54 (1984).

138. A. M. Bruckstein, B. C. Lévy, and T. Kailath, Differential Methods for Inverse Scattering, *SIAM J. Appl. Math.,* **45,** 312 (1985).

139. R. G. Newton, Inversion of Reflection Data for Layered Media: A Review of Exact Methods, *Geophys. J. R. Astron. Soc.,* **65,** 191–215 (1981).

140. E. A. Robinson, A Spectral Approach to Geophysical Inversion by Lorentz, Fourier, and Radon Transforms, *Proc. IEEE,* **70,** 1039–1054 (1982).

141. J. G. Berryman and R. R. Greene, Discrete Inverse Methods for Elastic Waves in Layered Media, *Geophysics,* **45,** 213–233 (1980).

142. F. J. Dyson, Old and New Approaches to the Inverse Scattering Problem, in E. H. Lieb, B. Simon, and A. S. Wightman, Eds., *Studies in Mathematical Physics,* Princeton, Princeton University Press, 1976.

143. K. M. Case, Inverse Scattering, Orthogonal Polynomials, and Linear Estimation, in I. C. Gohberg and M. Kac, Eds., *Topics in Functional Analysis, Advances in Mathematics Supplementary Studies,* Vol. 3, New York, Academic, 1978.

144. M. T. Silvia and E. A. Robinson, *Deconvolution of Geophysical Time Series in the Exploration for Oil and Natural Gas,* Amsterdam, Elsevier, 1979.

145. D. W. Oldenburg, A Comprehensive Solution to the Linear Deconvolution Problem,'' *Geophys. J. R. Astron. Soc.,* **65,** 331–357 (1981).

146. S. Treitel and L. R. Lines, Linear Inverse Theory and Deconvolution, *Geophysics,* **47,** 115 (1982).

147. S. Twomey, *Introduction to the Mathematics of Inversion in Remote Sensing and Indirect Measurements,* Amsterdam, Elsevier, 1977.

148. B. R. Frieden, Image Enhancement and Restoration, in T. S. Huang, Ed., *Picture Processing and Digital Filtering,* New York, Springer-Verlag, 1975.

149. J. F. Claerbout and F. Muir, Robust Modeling with Erratic Data, *Geophysics,* **38,** 826–844 (1973).

150. H. L. Taylor, S. C. Banks, and J. F. McCoy, Deconvolution with the L_1 Norm, *Geophysics,* **44,** 39–52 (1979).

151. R. Mammone and G. Eichmann, Superresolving Image Restoration Using Linear Programming, *Applied Optics,* **21,** 496–501 (1982).

152. R. Mammone and G. Eichmann, Restoration of Discrete Fourier Spectra Using Linear Programming, *J. Optical Soc. Am.,* **72,** 987–992 (1982).

153. I. Barrodale and F. D. K. Roberts, An Improved Algorithm for the Discrete L_1 Linear Approximation, *SIAM J. Numer. Anal.,* **10,** 839 (1973).

154. I. Barrodale and F. D. K. Roberts, Algorithm 478: Solution of an Overdetermined System of Equations in the L_1 Norm, *Commun. ACM,* **17,** 319 (1974).

155. B. Drachman, Two Methods to Deconvolve: L_1–Method Using Simplex Algorithm and L_2–Method Using Least Squares and a Parameter, *IEEE Trans. Antenn. Propag.,* **AP-32,** 219 (1984).

156. R. W. Schafer, R. M. Mersereau, and M. A. Richards, Constrained Iterative Restoration Algorithms, *Proc. IEEE,* **69,** 432–450 (1981).

6

Spectrum Estimation

6.1 *Spectrum Estimation by Autoregressive Modeling*

When a block of signal samples is available, it may be too short to provide enough frequency resolution in the periodogram spectrum. Often, it may not even be correct to extend the length by collecting more samples, since this might come into conflict with the stationarity of the segment. In cases such as these, parametric representation of the spectra by means of autoregressive models can provide much better frequency resolution than the classical periodogram method [1–15]. This approach was discussed briefly in Section 1.11. The spectrum estimation procedure is as follows: First, the given data segment $\{y_0, y_1, \ldots, y_{N-1}\}$ is subjected to one of the analysis methods discussed in Section 5.12 to extract estimates of the LPC model parameters $\{a_1, a_2, \ldots, a_M; E_M\}$. The choice of order M is an important consideration. There are a number of criteria for model order selection [1], but there is no single one that works well under all circumstances. In fact, selecting the right order M is more of an art than science. As an example, we mention Akaike's *final prediction error* (FPE) criterion which selects the M that minimizes the quantity

$$E_M \cdot \frac{N + M + 1}{N - M - 1} = \min$$

where E_M is the estimate of the mean-squared prediction error for the Mth order predictor, and N is the length of the sequence y_n. As M increases, the factor E_M

decreases and the second factor increases, thus, there is a minimum value. The spectrum estimate is then given by

$$S_{AR}(\omega) = \frac{E_M}{|A_M(\omega)|^2} = \frac{E_M}{|1 + a_1 e^{-j\omega} + a_2 e^{-2j\omega} + \dots + a_M e^{-jM\omega}|^2} \tag{6.1.1}$$

Note that this would be the exact spectrum if y_n were autoregressive with the above set of model parameters. Generally, spectra that have a few dominant spectral peaks can be modeled quite successfully by such all-pole autoregressive models. One can also fit the given block of data to more general ARMA models. The decision to model a spectrum by ARMA, AR, or MA models should ultimately depend on some prior information regarding the physics of the process y_n. The reader is referred to the exhaustive review article of Kay and Marple [1], to the special issue [10], and to [2,4,11,13–15], for the discussion of essentially all currently available spectrum estimation techniques, and to Robinson's interesting historical account [12].

Next, we compare by means of a simulation example the classical periodogram method, the Yule-Walker method, and Burg's method of computing spectrum estimates. Generally, the rule of thumb to follow is that Burg's method should work better than the other methods on short records of data, and that all three methods tend to improve as the data record becomes longer. For our simulation example, we chose a fourth order autoregressive model characterized by two very sharp peaks in its spectrum. The signal generator for the sequence y_n was

$$y_n + a_1 y_{n-1} + a_2 y_{n-2} + a_3 y_{n-3} + a_4 y_{n-4} = \epsilon_n$$

where ϵ_n was zero-mean, unit-variance, white noise. The prediction-error filter $A(z)$ was defined in terms of its four zeros

$$\begin{aligned} A(z) &= 1 + a_1 z^{-1} + a_2 z^{-2} + a_3 z^{-3} + a_4 z^{-4} \\ &= (1 - z_1 z^{-1})(1 - z_1^* z^{-1})(1 - z_2 z^{-1})(1 - z_2^* z^{-1}) \end{aligned}$$

where the zeros were chosen as

$$z_1 = 0.99 \exp(0.2\pi j) \qquad z_2 = 0.99 \exp(0.4\pi j)$$

This gives for the filter coefficients

$$a_1 = -2.2137, \quad a_2 = 2.9403, \quad a_3 = -2.1697, \quad a_4 = 0.9606$$

The exact spectrum is given by Eq. (6.1.1) with $E_4 = \sigma_\epsilon^2 = 1$. Since the two zeros z_1 and z_2 are near the unit circle, the spectrum will have two very sharp peaks at the normalized frequencies

$$\omega_1 = 0.2\pi, \quad \omega_2 = 0.4\pi \qquad \text{[radians/sample]}$$

Using the above difference equation and a realization of ϵ_n, a sequence of length 20 of y_n samples was generated (the filter was run for a while until its transients died out and stationarity of y_n was reached). The *same* set of 20 samples was used to compute the ordinary periodogram spectrum and the autoregressive spectra using the Yule-Walker and Burg methods of extracting the model parameters. The resulting spectra are shown together with the exact spectrum in Figs. 6.1 through 6.3. Figures 6.4 through 6.6 show the spectra obtained by increasing the length of the data sequence y_n to 100 samples. The lack of sufficient resolution of both the periodogram and the Yule-Walker spectrum estimates for the shorter data record is attributed to the *windowing* of the sequence y_n. But as the length increases the effects of windowing become less and less pronounced and both methods improve. Burg's method is remarkable in that it works very well even on the basis of very short data records. The Burg spectral estimate is sometimes called the "maximum entropy" spectral estimate. The connection to entropy concepts is discussed in the above references.

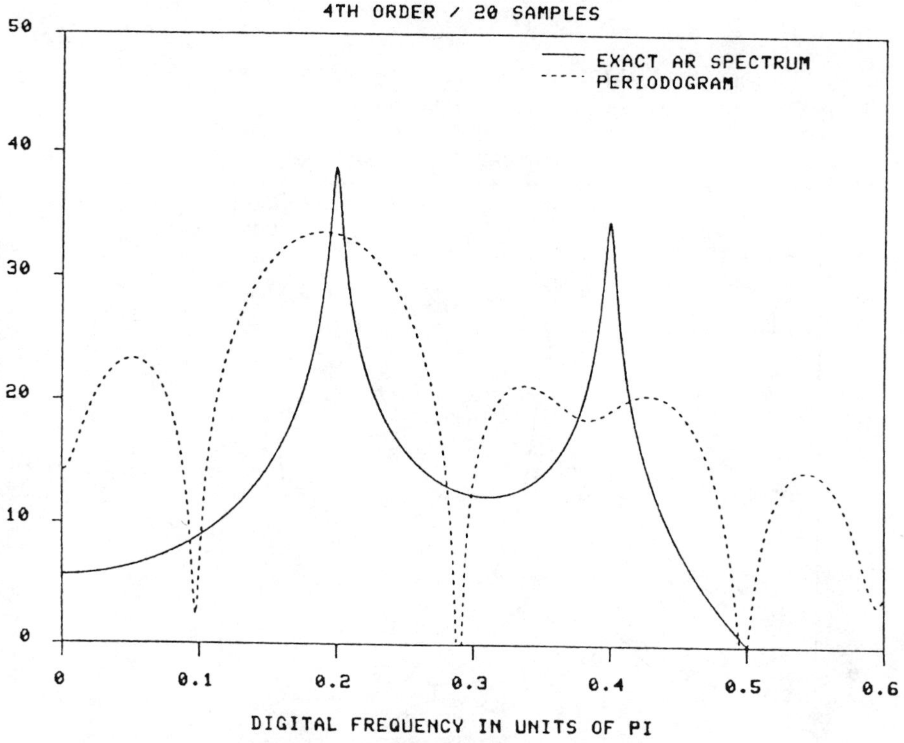

Figure 6.1 Ordinary Periodogram Based on 20 Samples

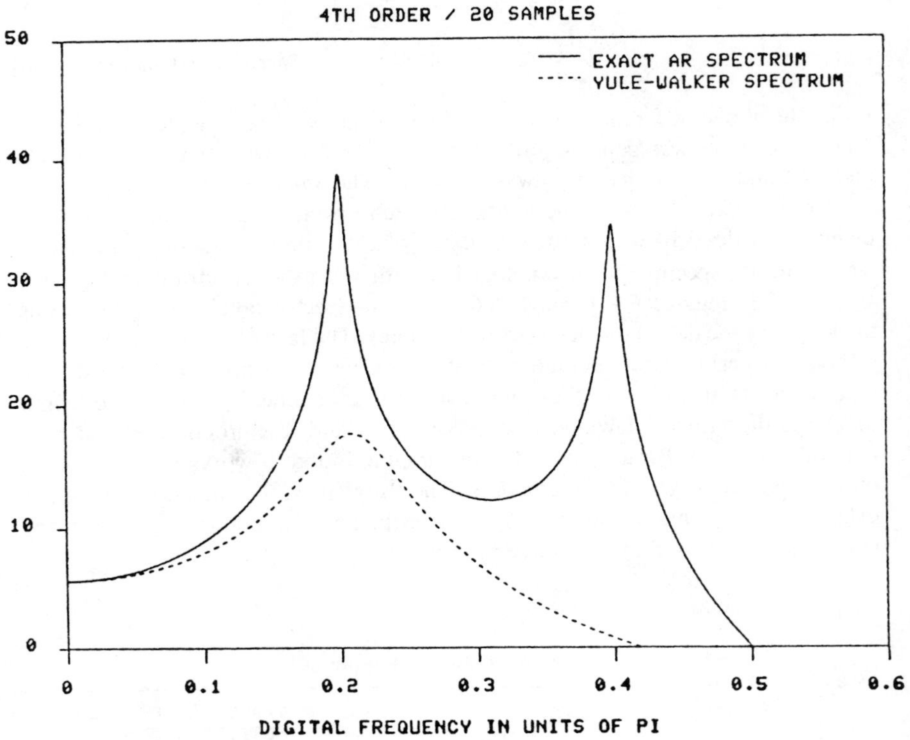

Figure 6.2 Yule-Walker Spectrum Based on 20 Samples

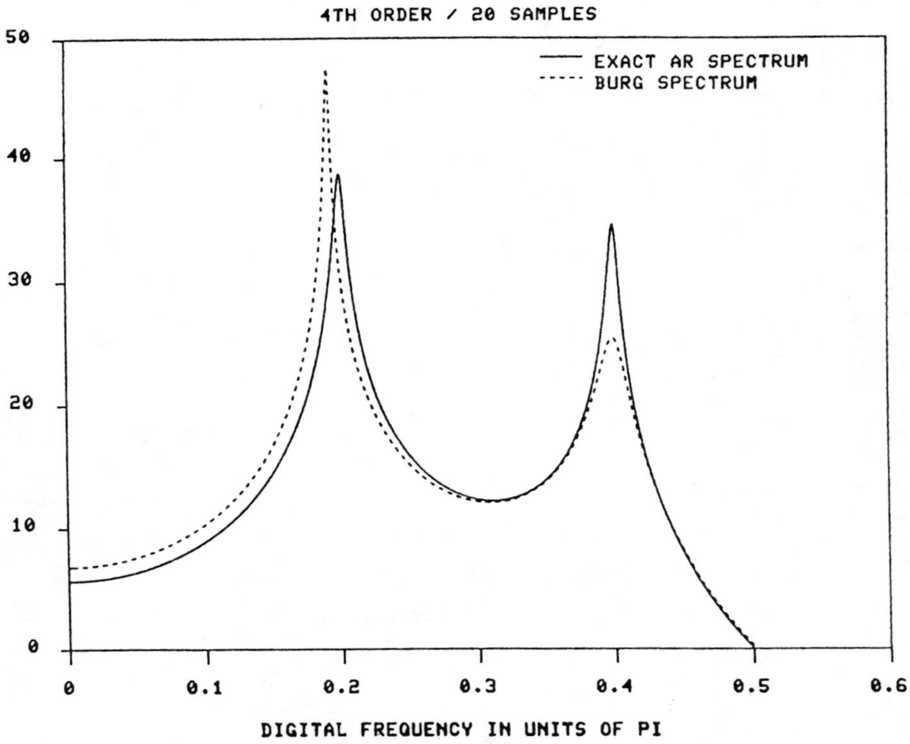

Figure 6.3 Burg Spectrum Based on 20 Samples

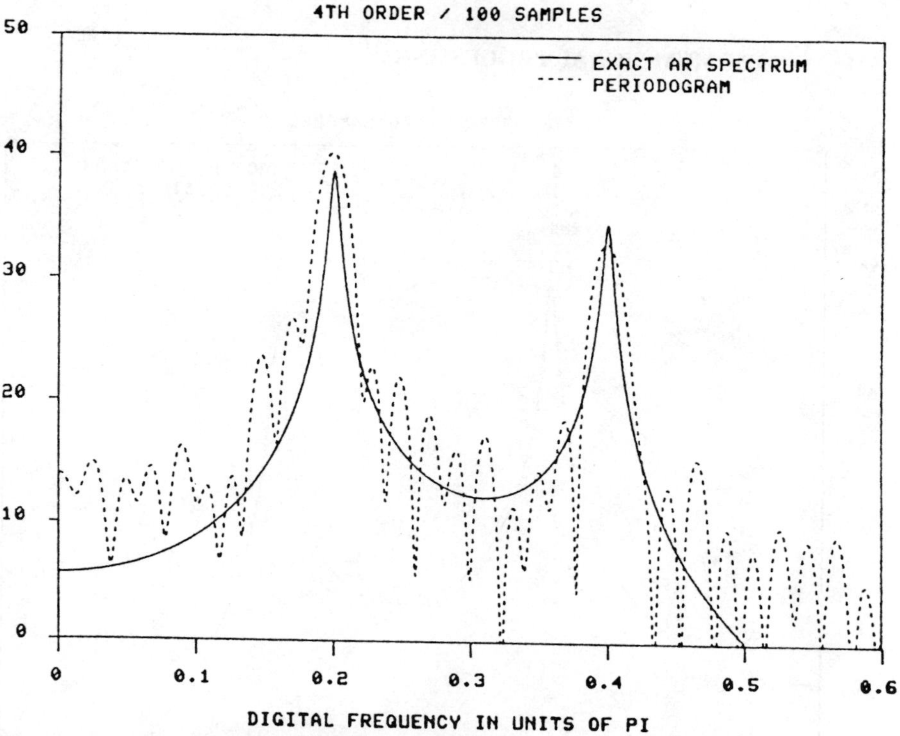

Figure 6.4 Ordinary Periodogram Based on 100 Samples

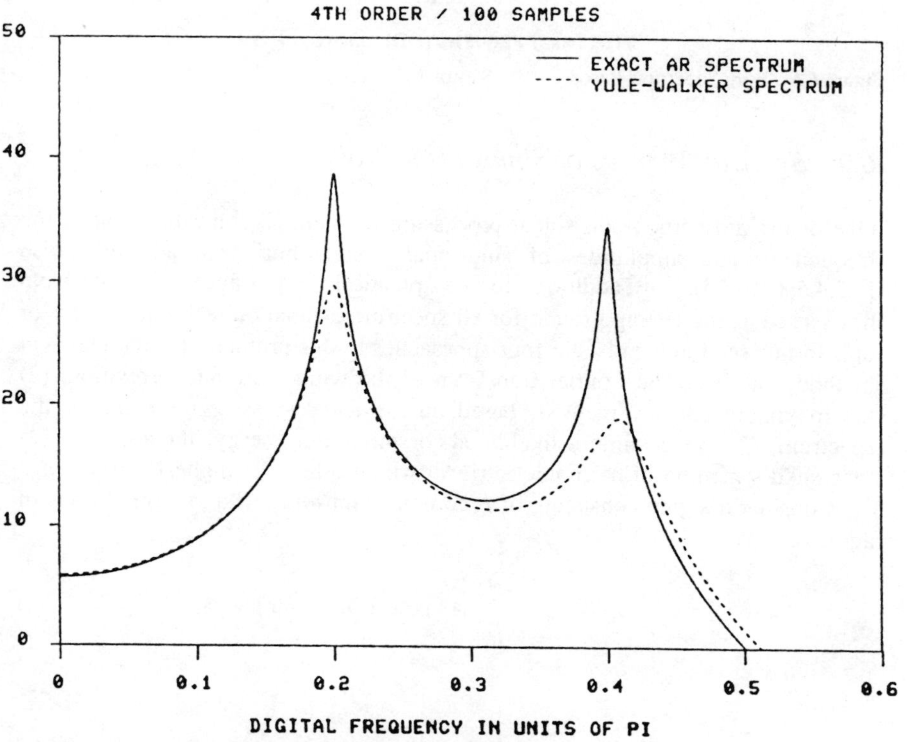

Figure 6.5 Yule-Walker Spectrum Based on 100 Samples

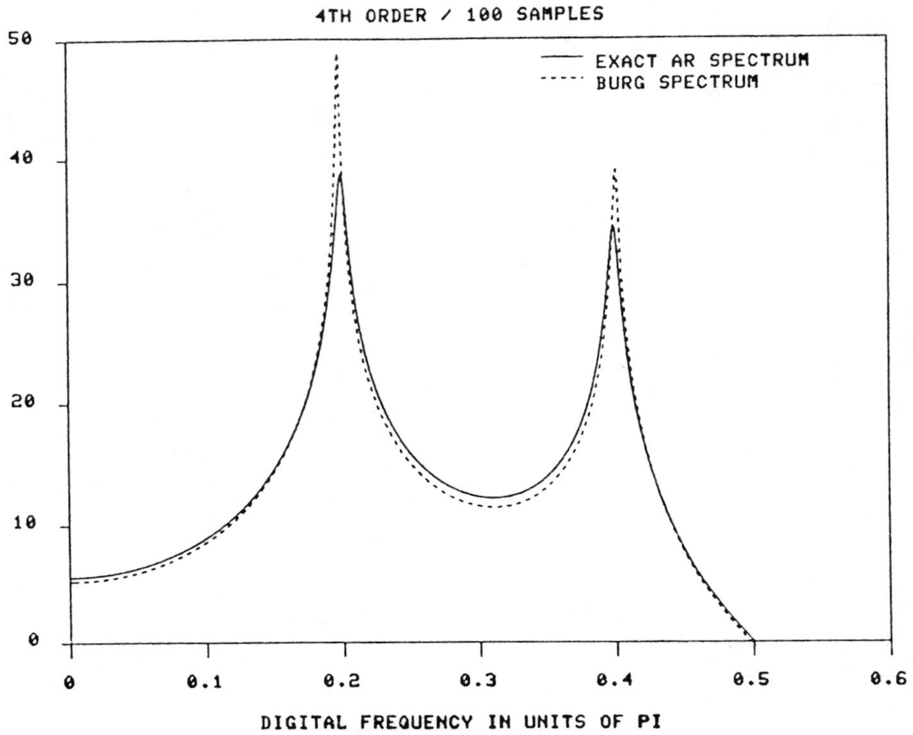

Figure 6.6 Burg Spectrum Based on 100 Samples

6.2 *Spectral Analysis of Sinusoids in Noise*

One of the most important signal processing problems is the estimation of the frequencies and amplitudes of sinusoidal signals buried in additive noise [1,2,4,5,8,10–24]. In addition to its practical importance, this problem has served as the testing ground for all spectrum estimation techniques, new or old. In this section we discuss four approaches to this problem: (1) the classical method, based on the Fourier transform of the windowed autocorrelation; (2) the maximum entropy method, based on the autoregressive modeling of the spectrum; (3) the maximum likelihood, or minimum energy, method; and (4) Pisarenko's method of harmonic retrieval which offers the highest resolution.

Consider a signal consisting of L complex sinusoids with random phases in additive noise:

$$y_n = v_n + \sum_{i=1}^{L} A_i \exp(j\omega_i n + j\phi_i) \tag{6.2.1}$$

where the phases ϕ_i are uniformly distributed and independent of each other, and v_n is zero-mean white noise of variance σ_v^2, assumed to be independent of the phases ϕ_i:

$$E[v_n^* v_m] = \sigma_v^2 \delta_{nm}, \qquad E[\phi_i v_n] = 0 \tag{6.2.2}$$

Under these assumptions, the autocorrelation of y_n is easily found to be

$$R(k) = E[y_{n+k} y_n^*] = \sigma_v^2 \delta(k) + \sum_{i=1}^{L} P_i \exp(j\omega_i k) \tag{6.2.3}$$

where P_i denotes the power level of the ith sinusoid; that is, $P_i = |A_i|^2$. The basic problem is to extract the set of frequencies $\{\omega_1, \omega_2, \ldots, \omega_L\}$ and powers $\{P_1, P_2, \ldots, P_L\}$ by appropriate processing of a segment of signal samples y_n. The theoretical power spectrum is a line spectrum superimposed on a white-noise spectrum:

$$S(\omega) = \sigma_v^2 + \sum_{i=1}^{L} P_i \, 2\pi\delta(\omega - \omega_i), \qquad -\pi \leqslant \omega \leqslant \pi \tag{6.2.4}$$

which is obtained by Fourier transforming (6.2.3):

$$S(\omega) = \sum_{k=-\infty}^{\infty} R(k) \exp(-j\omega k) \tag{6.2.5}$$

Given a finite set of autocorrelation lags $\{R(0), R(1), \ldots, R(M)\}$, the classical spectrum analysis method consists of windowing these lags by an appropriate window and then computing the sum (6.2.5), truncated to $-M \leqslant k \leqslant M$. We will use the triangular or Bartlett window which corresponds to the mean value of the ordinary periodogram spectrum [25]. This window is defined by

$$w_B(k) = \begin{cases} \dfrac{1}{M+1}(M + 1 - |k|), & \text{if } -M \leqslant k \leqslant M \\ 0 & \text{otherwise} \end{cases}$$

Replacing $R(k)$ by $w_B(k)R(k)$ in Eq. (6.2.5), we obtain the classical Bartlett spectrum estimate:

$$\hat{S}_B(\omega) = \sum_{k=-M}^{M} w_B(k) R(k) \exp(-j\omega k) \tag{6.2.6}$$

We choose the Bartlett window because this expression can be written in a compact matrix form by introducing the $(M + 1)$-dimensional phase vector

$$\mathbf{s}_\omega = \begin{bmatrix} 1 \\ e^{j\omega} \\ e^{2j\omega} \\ \vdots \\ e^{j\omega M} \end{bmatrix}$$

and the $(M + 1) \times (M + 1)$ autocorrelation matrix R, defined as

$$R(k,m) = R(k - m) = \sigma_v^2 \delta(k - m) + \sum_{i=1}^{L} P_i \exp[j\omega_i(k - m)]$$

for $0 \leq k, m \leq M$. Ignoring the $1/(M + 1)$ scale factor arising from the definition of the Bartlett window, we may write Eq. (6.2.6) as

$$\hat{S}_B(\omega) = \mathbf{s}_\omega^\dagger R \mathbf{s}_\omega \qquad \text{(classical Bartlett spectrum)} \qquad (6.2.7)$$

The autocorrelation matrix R of the sinusoids can also be written in terms of the phasing vectors as

$$R = \sigma_v^2 I + \sum_{i=1}^{L} P_i \mathbf{s}_{\omega_i} \mathbf{s}_{\omega_i}^\dagger \qquad (6.2.8)$$

where I is the $(M + 1) \times (M + 1)$ identity matrix. It can be written even more compactly by introducing the $L \times L$ diagonal *power matrix*, and the $(M + 1) \times L$ *sinusoid matrix*

$$P = \text{diag}\{P_1, P_2, \ldots, P_L\}, \qquad S = [\mathbf{s}_{\omega_1}, \mathbf{s}_{\omega_2}, \ldots, \mathbf{s}_{\omega_L}]$$

Then, Eq. (6.2.8) becomes

$$R = \sigma_v^2 I + SPS^\dagger \qquad (6.2.9)$$

Inserting Eq. (6.2.8) into Eq. (6.2.7) we find

$$\hat{S}_B(\omega) = \sigma_v^2 \mathbf{s}_\omega^\dagger \mathbf{s}_\omega + \sum_{i=1}^{L} P_i \mathbf{s}_\omega^\dagger \mathbf{s}_{\omega_i} \mathbf{s}_{\omega_i}^\dagger \mathbf{s}_\omega$$

Defining the function

$$W(\omega) = \sum_{m=0}^{M} \exp(-j\omega m) = \frac{1 - e^{-j\omega(M+1)}}{1 - e^{-j\omega}}$$

$$= \frac{\sin\left[\dfrac{\omega(M + 1)}{2}\right]}{\sin\left(\dfrac{\omega}{2}\right)} e^{-j\omega M/2} \qquad (6.2.10)$$

we note that

$$\mathbf{s}_\omega^\dagger \mathbf{s}_{\omega_i} = W(\omega - \omega_i) \qquad \text{and} \qquad \mathbf{s}_\omega^\dagger \mathbf{s}_\omega = W(0) = M + 1$$

Then, in this notation the Bartlett spectrum (6.2.7) becomes

$$\hat{S}_B(\omega) = \sigma_v^2(M + 1) + \sum_{i=1}^{L} P_i |W(\omega - \omega_i)|^2 \tag{6.2.11}$$

The effect of $W(\omega - \omega_i)$ is to smear each spectral line $\delta(\omega - \omega_i)$ of the true spectrum. If the frequencies ω_i are too close to each other the smeared peaks will tend to overlap with a resulting loss of resolution. The function $W(\omega)$ is the Fourier transform of the *rectangular* window and it is depicted below:

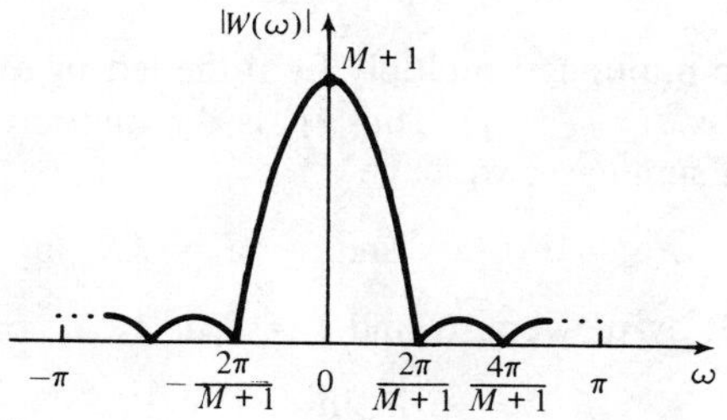

It has an effective resolution width $\Delta\omega = 2\pi/(M + 1)$. For fairly large Ms, the first side lobe is about 13 dB down from the main lobe. As M increases, the main lobe becomes higher and thinner, resembling more and more a delta function, which improves the frequency resolution capability of this estimate.

Next, we derive a closed form expression [20,24] for the AR, or maximum entropy, spectral estimate. It is given by Eq. (6.1.1) and is obtained by fitting an order-M autoregressive model to the autocorrelation lags $\{R(0), R(1), \ldots, R(M)\}$. This can be done for any desired value of M. Autoregressive spectrum estimates generally work well in modeling "peaked" or resonant spectra; therefore, it is expected that they will work in this case, too. However, it should be kept in mind that AR models are not really appropriate for such sinusoidal signals. Indeed, AR models are characterized by all-pole stable filters that always result in autocorrelation functions $R(k)$ which decay exponentially with the lag k; whereas Eq. (6.2.3) is persistent in k and never decays. As a rule, AR modeling of sinusoidal spectra works very well as long as the signal to noise ratios (SNRs) are fairly high. Pisarenko's method, to be discussed later, provides unbiased frequency estimates *regardless* of the SNRs.

The LPC model parameters for the AR spectrum estimate (6.1.1) are obtained by minimizing the mean-squared prediction error:

$$\mathcal{E} = E[e_n^* e_n] = \mathbf{a}^\dagger R \mathbf{a} = \min, \quad e_n = \sum_{m=0}^{M} a_m y_{n-m} \tag{6.2.12}$$

where $\mathbf{a} = [1, a_1, a_2, \ldots, a_M]^T$ is the prediction-error filter and R the autocorrelation matrix (6.2.9). The minimization of $\mathcal{E}$ must be subject to the linear constraint that the first entry of $\mathbf{a}$ be unity. This constraint can be expressed in vector form

$$a_0 = \mathbf{u}_0^\dagger \mathbf{a} = 1 \tag{6.2.13}$$

where $\mathbf{u}_0 = [1, 0, 0, \ldots, 0]^T$ is the unit vector consisting of one followed by M zeros. Incorporating this constraint with a Lagrange multiplier, we solve the minimization problem

$$\mathcal{E} = \mathbf{a}^\dagger R \mathbf{a} + \mu(1 - \mathbf{u}_0^\dagger \mathbf{a}) = \min$$

Differentiating with respect to $\mathbf{a}$ we obtain the normal equations

$$R\mathbf{a} = \mu \mathbf{u}_0$$

To fix the Lagrange multiplier, multiply from the left by $\mathbf{a}^\dagger$ and use Eq. (6.2.13) to get $\mathbf{a}^\dagger R \mathbf{a} = \mu \mathbf{a}^\dagger \mathbf{u}_0$, or $\mathcal{E} = \mu$. Thus, μ is the minimized value of $\mathcal{E}$ which we denote by E; in summary, we have

$$R\mathbf{a} = E\mathbf{u}_0 \qquad \text{and} \qquad \mathbf{a} = ER^{-1}\mathbf{u}_0 \tag{6.2.14}$$

Acting from the left by $\mathbf{u}_0^T$ we also find $1 = E\mathbf{u}_0^T R^{-1} \mathbf{u}_0$, or

$$E^{-1} = \mathbf{u}_0^T R^{-1} \mathbf{u}_0 = (R^{-1})_{00} \tag{6.2.15}$$

which is, of course, the same as Eq. (5.9.18). The special structure of R allows the computation of $\mathbf{a}$ and the AR spectrum in closed form. Applying the matrix inversion lemma to Eq. (6.2.9), we find the inverse of R,

$$R^{-1} = \frac{1}{\sigma_v^2}(I + SDS^\dagger) \tag{6.2.16}$$

where D is a $L \times L$ matrix given by

$$D = -[\sigma_v^2 P^{-1} + S^\dagger S]^{-1} \tag{6.2.17}$$

Equation (6.2.16) can also be derived directly by making such an Ansatz for R^{-1} and then fixing D. The quantity $\sigma_v^2 P^{-1}$ in D is a matrix of noise to signal ratios. Inserting Eq. (6.2.16) into Eq. (6.2.14), we find for $\mathbf{a}$

$$\mathbf{a} = ER^{-1}\mathbf{u}_0 = \frac{E}{\sigma_v^2}[\mathbf{u}_0 + SDS^\dagger \mathbf{u}_0] = \frac{E}{\sigma_v^2}[\mathbf{u}_0 + S\mathbf{d}]$$

where we used the fact that $\mathbf{s}_{\omega_i}^\dagger \mathbf{u}_0 = 1$, which implies that

$$S^\dagger \mathbf{u}_0 = \begin{bmatrix} \mathbf{s}_{\omega_1}^\dagger \\ \mathbf{s}_{\omega_2}^\dagger \\ \vdots \\ \mathbf{s}_{\omega_L}^\dagger \end{bmatrix} \mathbf{u}_0 = \begin{bmatrix} 1 \\ 1 \\ \vdots \\ 1 \end{bmatrix} = \mathbf{v}; \qquad \text{i.e., a column of } L \text{ ones}$$

and defined

$$\mathbf{d} = \begin{bmatrix} d_1 \\ d_2 \\ \vdots \\ d_L \end{bmatrix} = D\mathbf{v} \qquad \text{or} \qquad d_i = \sum_{j=1}^{L} D_{ij}$$

Using Eq. (6.2.15) we have also

$$\begin{aligned} E^{-1} &= \mathbf{u}_0^T R^{-1} \mathbf{u}_0 = \frac{1}{\sigma_v^2} \mathbf{u}_0^T [I + SDS^\dagger] \mathbf{u}_0 \\ &= \frac{1}{\sigma_v^2} [1 + \mathbf{v}^T D \mathbf{v}] \\ &= \frac{1}{\sigma_v^2} [1 + \mathbf{v}^T \mathbf{d}] = \frac{1}{\sigma_v^2} \left[1 + \sum_{i=1}^{L} d_i \right] \end{aligned}$$

and, therefore,

$$E = \sigma_v^2 \left[1 + \sum_{i=1}^{L} d_i \right]^{-1} \tag{6.2.18}$$

We finally find for the prediction-error filter

$$\mathbf{a} = \frac{\mathbf{u}_0 + S\mathbf{d}}{1 + \mathbf{v}^T \mathbf{d}} = \frac{\mathbf{u}_0 + \sum_{i=1}^{L} d_i \mathbf{s}_{\omega_i}}{1 + \sum_{i=1}^{L} d_i} \tag{6.2.19}$$

The frequency response $A(\omega)$ of the filter is obtained by dotting the phasing vector $\mathbf{s}_\omega$ into $\mathbf{a}$:

$$A(\omega) = \sum_{m=0}^{M} a_m \exp(-j\omega m) = \mathbf{s}_\omega^\dagger \mathbf{a} = \frac{1 + \sum_{i=1}^{L} d_i\, \mathbf{s}_\omega^\dagger \mathbf{s}_{\omega_i}}{1 + \sum_{i=1}^{L} d_i}$$

and using the result $\mathbf{s}_\omega^\dagger \mathbf{s}_{\omega_i} = W(\omega - \omega_i)$, we finally find

$$A(\omega) = \frac{1 + \sum_{i=1}^{L} d_i W(\omega - \omega_i)}{1 + \sum_{i=1}^{L} d_i} \tag{6.2.20}$$

and for the AR, or maximum entropy, spectrum estimate:

$$\hat{S}_{AR}(\omega) = \frac{E}{|A(\omega)|^2} = \sigma_v^2 \frac{1 + \sum_{i=1}^{L} d_i}{\left|1 + \sum_{i=1}^{L} d_i W(\omega - \omega_i)\right|^2} \tag{6.2.21}$$

The frequency dependence is shown explicitly. Note, that the matrix $S^\dagger S$, appearing in the definition of D, can also be expressed in terms of $W(\omega)$. Indeed, the ijth element of $S^\dagger S$ is

$$(S^\dagger S)_{ij} = \mathbf{s}_{\omega_i}^\dagger \mathbf{s}_{\omega_j} = W(\omega_i - \omega_j)$$

One interesting consequence of Eq. (6.2.21) is that in the limit of very weak noise $\sigma_v^2 \to 0$, it vanishes. In this limit the mean-squared prediction error (6.2.18) vanishes. This is to be expected, since in this case the noise term v_n is absent from the sum (6.2.1), rendering y_n a deterministic signal; that is, one that can be predicted from a few past values with zero prediction error. To avoid such behavior when σ_v^2 is small, the factor E is sometimes dropped altogether from the spectral estimate resulting in the "pseudo-spectrum"

$$\hat{S}_{AR}(\omega) = \frac{1}{|A(\omega)|^2} \qquad \text{(AR spectrum estimate)} \tag{6.2.22}$$

This expression will exhibit fairly sharp peaks at the sinusoid frequencies, but the magnitude of these peaks will no longer be representative of the power levels P_i. This expression can only be used to extract the frequencies ω_i. Up to a scale factor, Eq. (6.2.22) can also be written in the form

$$\hat{S}_{AR}(\omega) = \frac{1}{|\mathbf{s}_\omega^\dagger R^{-1} \mathbf{u}_0|^2}$$

Example 6.2.1: To see the effect of the SNR on the sharpness of the peaks in the AR spectrum, consider the case $M = L = 1$. Then,

$$S^\dagger S = \mathbf{s}_{\omega_1}^\dagger \mathbf{s}_{\omega_1} = [1, e^{-j\omega_1}] \begin{bmatrix} 1 \\ e^{j\omega_1} \end{bmatrix} = M + 1 = 2$$

$$D = -[\sigma_v^2 P_1^{-1} + 2]^{-1}$$

$$\mathbf{a} = \frac{\mathbf{u}_0 + d_1 \mathbf{s}_{\omega_1}}{1 + d_1} = \begin{bmatrix} 1 \\ \dfrac{d_1}{1 + d_1} e^{j\omega_1} \end{bmatrix}$$

Using $d_1 = D$, we find

$$\mathbf{a} = \begin{bmatrix} 1 \\ \dfrac{-P_1}{P_1 + \sigma_v^2} e^{j\omega_1} \end{bmatrix}, \qquad A(z) = 1 + a_1 z^{-1}$$

The prediction-error filter has a zero at

$$z_1 = -a_1 = \frac{P_1}{P_1 + \sigma_v^2} \exp(j\omega_1)$$

The zero z_1 is inside the unit circle, as it should. The lower the SNR = P_1/σ_v^2, the more inside it lies, resulting in a more smeared peak about ω_1. As the SNR increases, the zero moves closer to the unit circle at the right frequency ω_1, resulting in a very sharp peak in the spectrum (6.2.22)

Example 6.2.2: For the case of a single sinusoid and arbitrary order M, compute the 3 dB width of the spectral peak of AR spectrum and compare it with the width of the Bartlett spectrum. Using Eq. (6.2.20), we have

$$A(\omega) = \frac{1 + d_1 W(\omega - \omega_1)}{1 + d_1}, \quad d_1 = -[SNR^{-1} + M + 1]^{-1}$$

where we set $SNR = P_1/\sigma_v^2$. The value of $A(\omega)$ at the sinusoid frequency is

$$A(\omega_1) = \frac{1 + d_1 W(0)}{1 + d_1} = \frac{1}{1 + SNR \cdot M}$$

It is small in the limit of high signal to noise ratio resulting in a high peak in the spectrum. The half-width at half-maximum of the AR spectrum is defined by the condition

$$\frac{S(\omega_1 + \Delta\omega)}{S(\omega_1)} = \frac{1}{2}, \quad \text{or, equivalently} \quad \frac{|A(\omega_1 + \Delta\omega)|^2}{|A(\omega_1)|^2} = 2$$

To first order in $\Delta\omega$, we have

$$W(\Delta\omega) = \sum_{m=0}^{M} e^{-j\Delta\omega m} \approx \sum_{m=0}^{M} (1 - jm\Delta\omega) = (M+1) - j\Delta\omega M(M+1)/2$$

where we used $\sum_{m=0}^{M} m = M(M+1)/2$. This gives

$$\frac{A(\omega_1 + \Delta\omega)}{A(\omega_1)} = \frac{1 + d_1 W(\Delta\omega)}{1 + d_1 W(0)} = 1 - j\Delta\omega SNR \cdot M(M+1)/2$$

The condition for half-maximum requires that the above imaginary part be unity, which gives for the full 3 dB width [18]

$$(\Delta\omega)_{3\text{dB}} = 2\Delta\omega = \frac{4}{SNR\cdot M(M+1)}$$

Thus, the peak becomes narrower both for increasing *SNR* and order *M*. Note that it depends on *M* like $O(1/M^2)$, which is a factor of *M smaller* than the Bartlett width that behaves like $O(1/M)$.

More generally, in the case of multiple sinusoids, if the SNRs are high the spectrum (6.2.22) will exhibit sharp peaks at the desired sinusoid frequencies. The mechanism by which this happens can be seen qualitatively from Eq. (6.2.20) as follows: The matrix $S^\dagger S$ in D introduces cross-coupling among the various frequencies ω_i. However, if these frequencies are well separated from each other (by more than $2\pi/(M+1)$), then the off-diagonal elements of $S^\dagger S$, namely $W(\omega_i - \omega_j)$, will be small, and for the purpose of this argument may be taken to be zero. This makes the matrix $S^\dagger S$ diagonal. Since $W(0) = M + 1$, it follows that $S^\dagger S = (M+1)I$, and D will become diagonal with diagonal elements

$$d_i = D_{ii} = -[\sigma_v^2 P_i^{-1} + M + 1]^{-1} = -\frac{P_i}{\sigma_v^2 + (M+1)P_i}$$

Evaluating $A(\omega)$ at ω_i and keeping only the ith contribution in the sum we find, approximately,

$$A(\omega_i) \simeq \frac{1 + d_i W(0)}{1 + \sum_{j=1}^{L} d_j} = \frac{1}{1 + \sum_{j=1}^{L} d_j}\,\frac{1}{1 + (M+1)\left(\dfrac{P_i}{\sigma_v^2}\right)}$$

which shows that if the SNRs P_i/σ_v^2 are high, $A(\omega_i)$ will be very small, resulting in large spectral peaks in Eq. (6.2.22). The resolvability properties of the AR estimate improve *both* when the *SNRs increase* and when the *order M increases*. The mutual interaction of the various sinusoid components cannot be ignored altogether. One effect of this interaction is *biasing* in the estimates of the frequencies; that is, even if two nearby peaks are clearly separated, the peaks may not occur exactly at the desired sinusoid frequencies, but may be slightly shifted. The degree of bias depends on the *relative separation* of the peaks and on *the SNRs*. With the above qualifications in mind, we can state that the LPC approach to this problem is one of the most successful ones.

The maximum likelihood (ML), or minimum energy, spectral estimator is given by the expression [16]

$$\hat{S}_{ML}(\omega) = \frac{1}{\mathbf{s}_\omega^\dagger R^{-1}\mathbf{s}_\omega} \qquad \text{(ML spectrum estimate)} \qquad (6.2.23)$$

It can be justified by envisioning a bank of narrowband filters, each designed to allow a sinewave through at the filter's center frequency and to attenuate all other frequency components. Thus, the narrowband filter with center frequency ω is required to let this frequency go through unchanged, that is,

$$A(\omega) = \mathbf{s}_\omega^\dagger \mathbf{a} = 1$$

while at the same time it is required to minimize the output power

$$\mathbf{a}^\dagger R \mathbf{a} = \min$$

The solution of this minimization problem subject to the above constraint is readily found to be

$$\mathbf{a} = \frac{R^{-1}\mathbf{s}_\omega}{\mathbf{s}_\omega^\dagger R^{-1}\mathbf{s}_\omega}$$

which gives for the minimized output power at this frequency

$$\mathbf{a}^\dagger R \mathbf{a} = \frac{1}{\mathbf{s}_\omega^\dagger R^{-1}\mathbf{s}_\omega}$$

Using Eq. (6.2.16), we find

$$\begin{aligned}\mathbf{s}_\omega^\dagger R^{-1}\mathbf{s}_\omega &= \frac{1}{\sigma_v^2}\left[\mathbf{s}_\omega^\dagger\mathbf{s}_\omega + \sum_{i,j=1}^{L} D_{ij}\mathbf{s}_\omega^\dagger\mathbf{s}_{\omega_i}\mathbf{s}_{\omega_j}^\dagger\mathbf{s}_\omega\right] \\ &= \frac{1}{\sigma_v^2}\left[(M+1) + \sum_{i,j=1}^{L} D_{ij}W(\omega-\omega_i)W(\omega-\omega_j)^*\right]\end{aligned}$$

and the theoretical ML spectrum becomes in this case

$$\hat{S}_{ML}(\omega) = \frac{\sigma_v^2}{(M+1) + \sum_{i,j=1}^{L} D_{ij}W(\omega-\omega_i)W(\omega-\omega_j)^*} \tag{6.2.24}$$

Example 6.2.3: Determine the matrix D and vector $\mathbf{d}$ for the case of $L=2$ and arbitrary M. The matrix $S^\dagger S$ is in this case

$$S^\dagger S = \begin{bmatrix} W(0) & W(\omega_1-\omega_2) \\ W(\omega_2-\omega_1) & W(0)\end{bmatrix} \equiv \begin{bmatrix} M+1 & W_{12} \\ W_{12}^* & M+1\end{bmatrix}$$

so that D becomes

$$D = -\begin{bmatrix} \sigma_v^2 P_1^{-1} + M + 1 & W_{12} \\ W_{12}^* & \sigma_v^2 P_2^{-1} + M + 1 \end{bmatrix}^{-1}$$

$$= \frac{1}{|W_{12}|^2 - (\sigma_v^2 P_1^{-1} + M + 1)(\sigma_v^2 P_2^{-1} + M + 1)}$$

$$\times \begin{bmatrix} \sigma_v^2 P_2^{-1} + M + 1 & -W_{12} \\ -W_{12}^* & \sigma_v^2 P_1^{-1} + M + 1 \end{bmatrix}$$

and

$$\mathbf{d} = D\mathbf{v} = D\begin{bmatrix} 1 \\ 1 \end{bmatrix} = \frac{1}{|W_{12}|^2 - (\sigma_v^2 P_1^{-1} + M + 1)(\sigma_v^2 P_2^{-1} + M + 1)}$$

$$\times \begin{bmatrix} \sigma_v^2 P_2^{-1} + M + 1 - W_{12} \\ \sigma_v^2 P_1^{-1} + M + 1 - W_{12}^* \end{bmatrix}$$

Using the results of Example 6.2.3, we have carried out a computation illustrating the three spectral estimates: Figure 6.7 shows the theoretical autoregressive, Bartlett, and maximum likelihood spectral estimates given by Eqs. (6.2.11), (6.2.22), and (6.2.24), respectively, for two sinusoids of frequencies

$$\omega_1 = 0.4\pi, \qquad \omega_2 = 0.6\pi$$

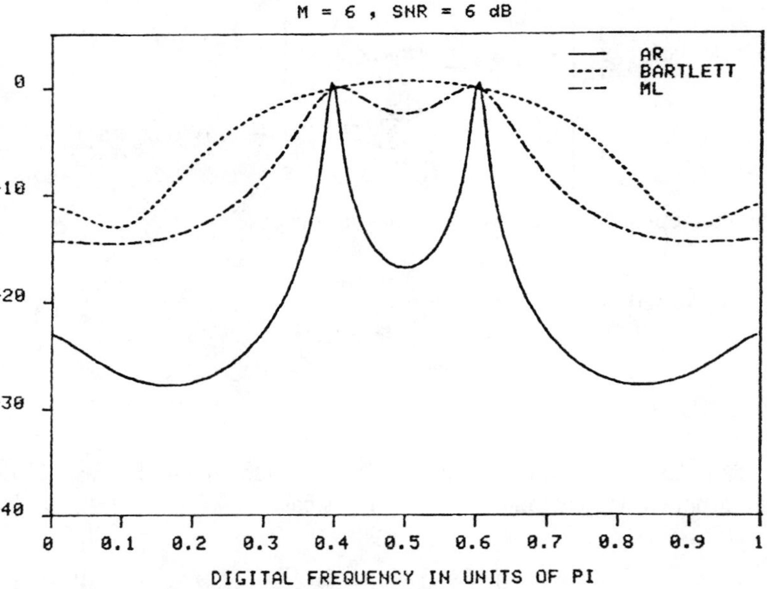

Figure 6.7 Maximum Entropy, Bartlett, and Maximum Likelihood Spectrum Estimates of Two Sinusoids in Noise

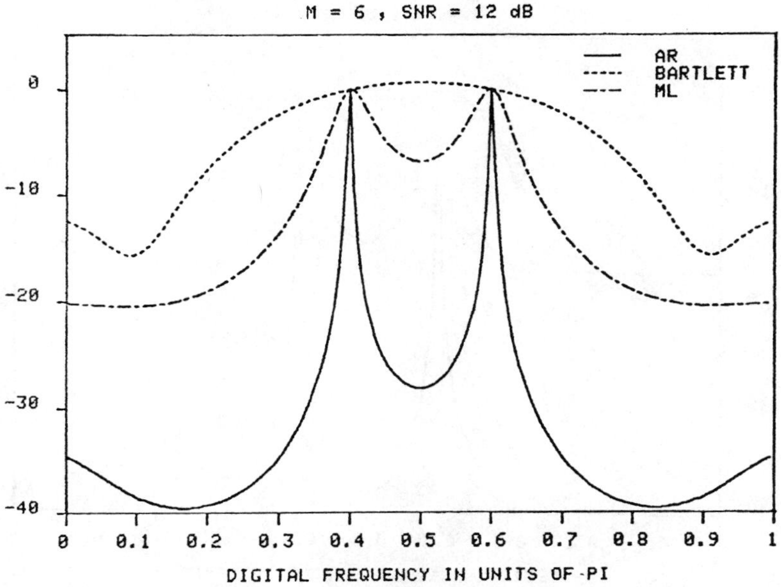

Figure 6.8 Effect of Increasing SNR on the Resolution Capability of the Three Spectrum Estimates

and equal powers SNR = 10 $\log_{10}(P_1/\sigma_v^2)$ = 6 dB, and $M = 6$. To facilitate the comparison, all three spectra have been *normalized* to 0 dB at the frequency ω_1 of the first sinusoid. It is seen that the length $M = 6$ is too short for the Bartlett spectrum to resolve the two peaks. The AR spectrum is the best (however, close inspection of the graph will reveal a small *bias* in the frequency of the peaks, arising from the mutual interaction of the two sinewaves). The effect of increasing the SNR is shown in Fig. 6.8, where the SNR has been changed to SNR = 12 dB. It is seen that the AR spectral peaks become narrower, thus increasing their resolvability. To show the effect of increasing the length M, we kept SNR = 6 dB, and increased M to $M = 12$ and $M = 18$. The resulting spectra are shown in Figs. 6.9 and 6.10. It is seen that all spectra tend to become better. The interplay between resolution, order, SNR, and bias has been studied in [18,20,23].

The main motivation behind the definition (6.2.22) for the pseudospectrum was to obtain an expression that exhibits very sharp spectral peaks at the sinusoid frequencies ω_i. Infinite resolution can, in principle, be achieved if we can find a polynomial $A(z)$ that has zeros *on the unit circle* at the desired frequency angles; namely,

$$z_i = \exp(j\omega_i); \qquad i = 1,2, \ldots, L \tag{6.2.25}$$

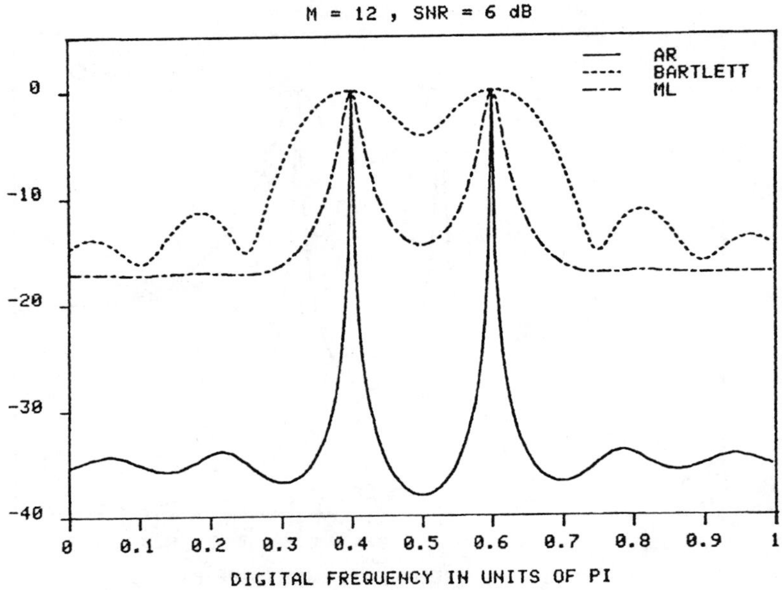

Figure 6.9 Effect of Increasing the Order on the Resolution Capability

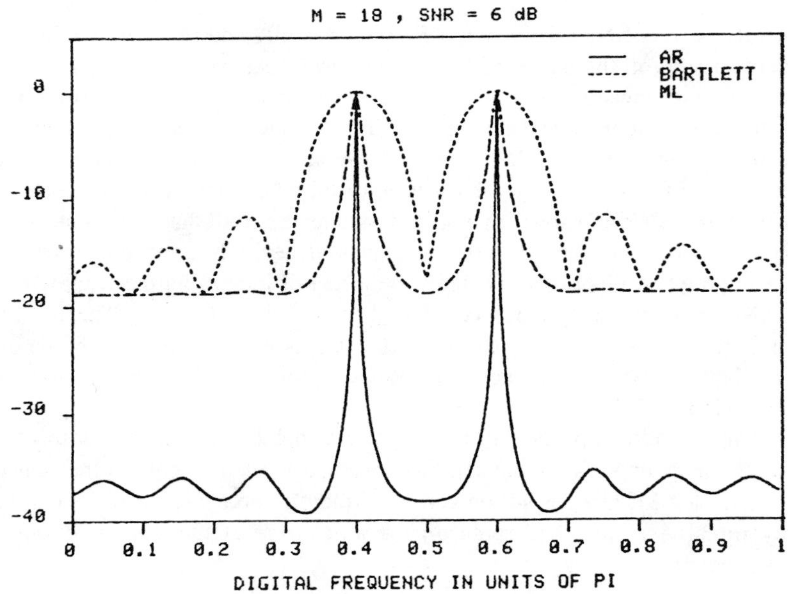

Figure 6.10 Further Increase of the Order M

Pisarenko's method determines such a polynomial on the basis of the autocorrelation matrix R. The desired conditions on the polynomial are

$$A(z_i) = A(\omega_i) = 0; \qquad i = 1,2, \ldots ,L \tag{6.2.26}$$

where we slightly abuse the notation and write $A(e^{j\omega}) = A(\omega)$. To satisfy these conditions, the degree M of the polynomial $A(z)$ must necessarily be $M \geq L$; then, the remaining $M - L$ zeros of $A(z)$ could be arbitrary. Let $\mathbf{a}$ be the vector of coefficients of $A(z)$, so that

$$\mathbf{a} = \begin{bmatrix} a_0 \\ a_1 \\ \vdots \\ a_M \end{bmatrix} \qquad A(z) = a_0 + a_1 z^{-1} + \cdots + a_M z^{-M}$$

Noting that $A(\omega) = \mathbf{s}_\omega^\dagger \mathbf{a}$, Eqs. (6.2.26) may be combined into one vectorial equation

$$S^\dagger \mathbf{a} = \begin{bmatrix} A(\omega_1) \\ A(\omega_2) \\ \vdots \\ A(\omega_L) \end{bmatrix} = 0 \tag{6.2.27}$$

But then, Eq. (6.2.9) implies that

$$R\mathbf{a} = \sigma_v^2 \mathbf{a} + SPS^\dagger \mathbf{a} = \sigma_v^2 \mathbf{a}$$

or that σ_v^2 must be an *eigenvalue* of R with $\mathbf{a}$ the corresponding *eigenvector*:

$$R\mathbf{a} = \sigma_v^2 \mathbf{a} \tag{6.2.28}$$

The quantity σ_v^2 is actually the *smallest* eigenvalue of R. To see this, consider any other eigenvector $\mathbf{a}$ of R, and normalize it to unit norm

$$R\mathbf{a} = \lambda \mathbf{a}, \qquad \text{with } \mathbf{a}^\dagger \mathbf{a} = 1 \tag{6.2.29}$$

Then, (6.2.9) implies that

$$\lambda = \lambda \mathbf{a}^\dagger \mathbf{a} = \mathbf{a}^\dagger R \mathbf{a} = \sigma_v^2 \mathbf{a}^\dagger \mathbf{a} + \mathbf{a}^\dagger SPS^\dagger \mathbf{a}$$

$$= \sigma_v^2 + [A(\omega_1)^*, A(\omega_2)^*, \ldots , A(\omega_L)^*]\, P \begin{bmatrix} A(\omega_1) \\ A(\omega_2) \\ \vdots \\ A(\omega_L) \end{bmatrix}$$

$$= \sigma_v^2 + \sum_{i=1}^{L} P_i |A(\omega_i)|^2$$

which shows that any λ is equal to σ_v^2 shifted by a nonnegative amount. If the eigenvector satisfies the conditions (6.2.26), then the shift in λ vanishes. Thus, the desired polynomial $A(z)$ can be found by solving the *eigenvalue problem* (6.2.29) and selecting the eigenvector belonging to the *minimum eigenvalue.* This is Pisarenko's method [19]. As a byproduct of the procedure, the noise power level σ_v^2 is also determined, which in turn allows the determination of the power matrix P, as follows: Writing Eq. (6.2.9) as

$$R - \sigma_v^2 I = SPS^\dagger$$

and acting by $S^\dagger$ and S from the left and right, we obtain

$$P = U^\dagger(R - \sigma_v^2 I)U \qquad \text{where } U = S(S^\dagger S)^{-1} \tag{6.2.30}$$

Since there is a freedom in selecting the *remaining* $M - L$ zeros of the polynomial $A(z)$, it follows that there are $(M - L) + 1$ eigenvectors all belonging to the minimum eigenvalue σ_v^2. Thus, the $(M + 1)$-dimensional eigenvalue problem (6.2.29) has: (a) $M+1-L$ *degenerate eigenvalues* equal to σ_v^2, and (b) L additional eigenvalues which are strictly greater than σ_v^2. The $(M + 1 - L)$-dimensional subspace spanned by the degenerate eigenvectors belonging to σ_v^2 is called the *noise* subspace. The L-dimensional subspace spanned by the eigenvectors belonging to the remaining L eigenvalues is called the *signal* subspace. Since the signal subspace is orthogonal to the noise subspace, and the L linearly independent signal vectors $\mathbf{s}_{\omega_i}$; $i = 1,2, \ldots ,L$, are also orthogonal to the noise subspace, it follows that the signal subspace is *spanned* by the $\mathbf{s}_{\omega_i}s$. In the special case when $L = M$, there is no degeneracy in the minimum eigenvalue, and there is a *unique* minimum eigenvector. In this case, all $M = L$ zeros of $A(z)$ lie on the unit circle at the desired angles ω_i.

Example 6.2.4: Consider the case $L=M=2$. The matrix R is written explicitly as

$$R = \sigma_v^2 I + P_1 \mathbf{s}_{\omega_1}\mathbf{s}_{\omega_1}^\dagger + P_2 \mathbf{s}_{\omega_2}\mathbf{s}_{\omega_2}^\dagger$$

$$= \begin{bmatrix} \sigma_v^2 + P_1 + P_2 & P_1 e^{-j\omega_1} + P_2 e^{-j\omega_2} & P_1 e^{-2j\omega_1} + P_2 e^{-2j\omega_2} \\ P_1 e^{j\omega_1} + P_2 e^{j\omega_2} & \sigma_v^2 + P_1 + P_2 & P_1 e^{-j\omega_1} + P_2 e^{-j\omega_2} \\ P_1 e^{2j\omega_1} + P_2 e^{2j\omega_2} & P_1 e^{j\omega_1} + P_2 e^{j\omega_2} & \sigma_v^2 + P_1 + P_2 \end{bmatrix}$$

It is easily verified that the (unnormalized) vector

$$\mathbf{a} = \begin{bmatrix} 1 \\ -(e^{j\omega_1} + e^{j\omega_2}) \\ e^{j\omega_1} e^{j\omega_2} \end{bmatrix}$$

is an eigenvector of R belonging to $\lambda = \sigma_v^2$. In this case, the polynomial $A(z)$ is

$$A(z) = a_0 + a_1 z^{-1} + a_2 z^{-2} = 1 - (e^{j\omega_1} + e^{j\omega_2})\, z^{-1} + e^{j\omega_1} e^{j\omega_2} z^{-2}$$

$$= (1 - e^{j\omega_1} z^{-1})\,(1 - e^{j\omega_2} z^{-1})$$

exhibiting the two desired zeros at the sinusoid frequencies.

Example 6.2.5: Consider the case $M = 2$, $L = 1$. The matrix R is

$$R = \sigma_v^2 I + P_1 \mathbf{s}_{\omega_1} \mathbf{s}_{\omega_1}^\dagger = \begin{bmatrix} \sigma_v^2 + P_1 & P_1 e^{-j\omega_1} & P_1 e^{-2j\omega_1} \\ P_1 e^{j\omega_1} & \sigma_v^2 + P_1 & P_1 e^{-j\omega_1} \\ P_1 e^{2j\omega_1} & P_1 e^{j\omega_1} & \sigma_v^2 + P_1 \end{bmatrix}$$

It is easily verified that the three eigenvectors of R are

$$\mathbf{e}_0 = \begin{bmatrix} 1 \\ -e^{j\omega_1} \\ 0 \end{bmatrix}, \qquad \mathbf{e}_1 = \begin{bmatrix} 0 \\ 1 \\ -e^{j\omega_1} \end{bmatrix}, \qquad \mathbf{e}_2 = \begin{bmatrix} 1 \\ e^{j\omega_1} \\ e^{2j\omega_1} \end{bmatrix} = \mathbf{s}_{\omega_1}$$

belonging to the eigenvalues

$$\lambda = \sigma_v^2, \qquad \lambda = \sigma_v^2, \qquad \lambda = \sigma_v^2 + 3P_1$$

The first two eigenvectors span the noise subspace and the third the signal subspace. *Any* linear combination of the noise eigenvectors also belongs to $\lambda = \sigma_v^2$. For example, if we take

$$\mathbf{a} = \begin{bmatrix} a_0 \\ a_1 \\ a_2 \end{bmatrix} = \begin{bmatrix} 1 \\ -e^{j\omega_1} \\ 0 \end{bmatrix} - \rho \begin{bmatrix} 0 \\ 1 \\ -e^{j\omega_1} \end{bmatrix} = \begin{bmatrix} 1 \\ -(\rho + e^{j\omega_1}) \\ \rho e^{j\omega_1} \end{bmatrix}$$

the corresponding polynomial is

$$A(z) = 1 - (e^{j\omega_1} + \rho)\, z^{-1} + e^{j\omega_1} \rho z^{-2} = (1 - e^{j\omega_1} z^{-1})\,(1 - \rho z^{-1})$$

showing one desired zero at $z_1 = e^{j\omega_1}$ and a *spurious* zero.

The Pisarenko method can also be understood in terms of a *minimization criterion* of the type (6.2.12), as follows: For any set of coefficients $\mathbf{a}$, define the output signal

$$e_n = a_0 y_n + a_1 y_{n-1} + \cdots + a_M y_{n-M}$$

Then, the mean output power is expressed as

$$\mathcal{E} = E[e_n^* e_n] = \mathbf{a}^\dagger R \mathbf{a} = \sigma_v^2\, \mathbf{a}^\dagger \mathbf{a} + \sum_{i=1}^{L} P_i |A(\omega_i)|^2$$

Imposing the quadratic constraint

$$\mathbf{a}^\dagger \mathbf{a} = 1 \tag{6.2.31}$$

we obtain

$$\mathcal{E} = E[e_n^* e_n] = \mathbf{a}^\dagger R \mathbf{a} = \sigma_v^2 + \sum_{i=1}^{L} P_i |A(\omega_i)|^2 \tag{6.2.32}$$

It is evident that the *minimum* of this expression is obtained when conditions (6.2.26) are satisfied. Thus, an *equivalent* formulation of the Pisarenko method is to *minimize the performance index* (6.2.32) subject to the *quadratic constraint* (6.2.31). The AR and the Pisarenko spectrum estimation techniques differ only in the *type* of constraint imposed on the filter weights **a**.

We observed earlier that the AR spectral peaks become sharper as the SNR increases. One way to explain this is to note that in the high SNR limit or, equivalently, in the *noiseless* limit $\sigma_v^2 \to 0$, the linear prediction filter tends to the Pisarenko filter, which has infinite resolution. This can be seen as follows. In the limit $\sigma_v^2 \to 0$, the matrix D defined in Eq. (6.2.17) tends to

$$D \to -(S^\dagger S)^{-1}$$

and therefore, R^{-1} given by Eq. (6.2.16) becomes singular, converging to

$$R^{-1} \to \frac{1}{\sigma_v^2}[I - S(S^\dagger S)^{-1} S^\dagger]$$

Thus, up to a scale factor the linear prediction solution, $R^{-1}\mathbf{u}_0$, will converge to

$$\mathbf{a} = [I - S(S^\dagger S)^{-1} S^\dagger]\mathbf{u}_0 \tag{6.2.33}$$

The matrix $[I - S(S^\dagger S)^{-1} S^\dagger]$ is the *projection* matrix onto the noise subspace, and therefore, **a** will lie in that subspace, that is, $S^\dagger \mathbf{a} = 0$. In the limit $\lambda_{\min} = \sigma_v^2 = 0$, the noise subspace of R consists of all the eigenvectors with zero eigenvalue, $R\mathbf{a} = 0$. We note that the particular noise subspace eigenvector given in Eq. (6.2.33) corresponds to the so-called *minimum-norm* eigenvector, discussed in Section 6.6. In his original method, Pisarenko considered the special case when the number of sinusoids was equal to the filter order, $L = M$. This implies that the noise subspace is one-dimensional, $M + 1 - L = 1$, consisting of a single eigenvector with zero eigenvalue, such that $R\mathbf{a} = 0$. In this case, the $(M + 1) \times (M + 1)$ singular matrix R has rank M and all its principal submatrices are nonsingular. As we mentioned in Section 5.5, such singular Toeplitz matrices admit a general sinusoidal representation. It is obtained by setting $\sigma_v^2 = 0$ and $L = M$ in Eq. (6.2.8)

$$R = \sum_{i=1}^{M} P_i\, \mathbf{s}_{\omega_i} \mathbf{s}_{\omega_i}^\dagger\,, \quad \text{or,} \quad R(k) = \sum_{i=1}^{M} P_i\, e^{j\omega_i k}$$

In summary, we have discussed the theoretical aspects of four methods of estimating the frequencies of sinusoids in noise. In practice, an *estimate* of the correlation matrix R can be obtained in terms of the sample autocorrelations from a block of data values y_n,

$$\hat{R}(k) = \frac{1}{N} \sum_{n=0}^{N-1-k} y_{n+k} y_n^* , \quad k = 0, 1, \cdots, M$$

The quality of the resulting estimates of the eigenvectors will be discussed in Section 6.11. The AR and Pisarenko methods can also be implemented *adaptively*. The adaptive approach is based on the minimization criteria (6.2.12) and (6.2.32) and will be discussed in Chapter 7, where also some simulations will be presented.

6.3 *Superresolution Array Processing*

One of the main signal processing functions of sonar, radar, or seismic arrays of sensors is to detect the presence of one or more radiating point-sources. This is a problem of spectral analysis, and it is the *spatial frequency* analog of the problem of extracting sinusoids in noise discussed in the previous section. The same spectral analysis techniques can be applied to this problem. All methods aim at producing a high-resolution estimate of the *spatial* frequency power spectrum of the signal field incident on the array of sensors. The *directions* of point-source emitters can be extracted by identifying the sharpest peaks in this spectrum. In this section, we discuss conventional (Bartlett) *beamforming*, as well as the *maximum-likelihood, linear prediction*, and *eigenvector* based methods, all of which are of current interest [28–88]. We also discuss some aspects of *optimum beamforming* for interference nulling [29–31,103–107].

Consider a *linear array* of $M+1$ sensors *equally spaced* at distances d, and a plane wave incident on the array at an angle θ_1 with respect to the array normal, as shown below.

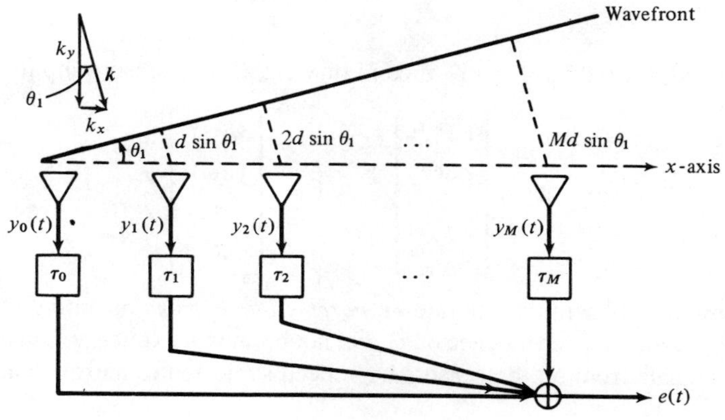

The conventional *beamformer* introduces appropriate delays at the outputs of each sensor to compensate the propagation delays of the wavefront reaching the array. The output of the beamformer (the "beam") is the sum

$$e(t) = \sum_{m=0}^{M} y_m(t - \tau_m) \tag{6.3.1}$$

where $y_m(t)$; $m = 0,1, \ldots, M$ is the signal at the mth sensor. To reach sensor 1, the wavefront must travel an extra distance $d \sin\theta_1$; to reach sensor 2 it must travel distance $2\, d \sin \theta_1$, and so on. Thus, it reaches these sensors with a propagation delay of $d \sin \theta_1/c$, $2\, d \sin \theta_1/c$, and so on. The last sensor is reached with a delay of $M\, d \sin \theta_1/c$ seconds. Thus, to time-align the first and the last sensor, the output of the first sensor must be delayed by $\tau_0 = M\, d \sin \theta_1/c$, and similarly, the mth sensor is time-aligned with the last one, with a delay of

$$\tau_m = (M - m)d \sin\theta_1/c; \qquad m = 0,1, \ldots, M \tag{6.3.2}$$

In this case, all terms in the sum (6.3.1) are equal to the value measured at the last sensor—that is, $y_m(t - \tau_m) = y_M(t)$—and the output of the beamformer is $e(t) = (M + 1)\, y_M(t)$, thus enhancing the received signal by a factor of $M + 1$ and hence its power by a factor $(M + 1)^2$. The concept of beamforming is the same as that of *signal averaging* discussed in Example (2.3.5). If there is additive noise present, it will contribute incoherently to the output power—that is, by a factor of $(M + 1)$, whereas the signal power is enhanced by $(M + 1)^2$. Thus, the *gain* in the signal to noise ratio at the output of the array (the array gain) is a factor of $M + 1$.

In the frequency domain, the above delay-and-sum operation becomes equivalent to linear weighting. Fourier transforming Eq. (6.3.1) we have

$$e(\omega) = \sum_{m=0}^{M} y_m(\omega) e^{-j\omega\tau_m}$$

which can be written compactly as

$$e = \mathbf{a}^T \mathbf{y} \tag{6.3.3}$$

where $\mathbf{a}$ and $\mathbf{y}$ are the $(M + 1)$-vectors of weights and sensor outputs

$$\mathbf{a} = \begin{bmatrix} e^{-j\omega\tau_0} \\ e^{-j\omega\tau_1} \\ \vdots \\ e^{-j\omega\tau_M} \end{bmatrix}, \qquad \mathbf{y} = \begin{bmatrix} y_0(\omega) \\ y_1(\omega) \\ \vdots \\ y_M(\omega) \end{bmatrix}$$

From now on, we will concentrate on *narrow-band* arrays operating at a given frequency ω and the dependence on ω will not be shown explicitly. This assumes that the signals from all the sensors have been subjected to narrow-band prefil-

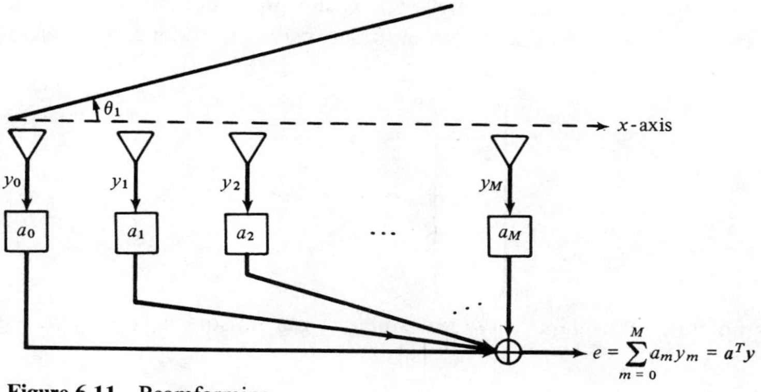

Figure 6.11 Beamforming

tering that leaves only the narrow operating frequency band. The beamformer now acts as a linear combiner, as shown in Fig. 6.11. A plane wave at the operating frequency ω, of amplitude A_1, and incident at the above angle θ_1, will have a value at the space-time point $(t,\mathbf{r})$ given by

$$A_1 e^{j\omega t - j\mathbf{k}\cdot\mathbf{r}}$$

Dropping the sinusoidal t-dependence and evaluating this expression on the x-axis, we have

$$A_1 e^{-jk_x x}$$

where k_x is the x-component of the wavenumber $\mathbf{k}$

$$k_x = \frac{\omega}{c} \sin \theta_1$$

The value of this field at the mth sensor, $x_m = md$, is then

$$A_1 \, e^{-jmk_1}$$

where k_1 denotes the *normalized* wavenumber

$$k_1 = k_x d = \frac{\omega d}{c} \sin \theta_1 = \frac{2\pi d}{\lambda} \sin \theta_1 \tag{6.3.4}$$

This is the analog of the digital frequency. To avoid aliasing effects arising from the spatial sampling process, the spatial sampling frequency $1/d$ must be greater than or equal to twice the spatial frequency of the wave; namely, $1/\lambda$. Thus, we must have $1/d \geqslant 2(1/\lambda)$, or $d \leqslant \lambda/2$. Since $\sin \theta_1$ has magnitude less than one, the sampling condition forces k_1 to lie within the Nyquist interval

$$-\pi \leqslant k_1 \leqslant \pi$$

In this case the correspondence between k_1 and θ_1 is unique. For any angle θ and corresponding normalized wavenumber k, we introduce the phasing, or *steering vector*,

$$\mathbf{s}_k = \begin{bmatrix} 1 \\ e^{jk} \\ e^{2jk} \\ \vdots \\ e^{Mjk} \end{bmatrix}, \qquad k = \frac{2\pi d}{\lambda}\sin\theta \tag{6.3.5}$$

In this notation, the plane wave measured at the sensors is represented by the vector

$$\mathbf{y} = A_1\,\mathbf{s}_{k_1}^* = A_1 \begin{bmatrix} 1 \\ e^{-jk_1} \\ e^{-2jk_1} \\ \vdots \\ e^{-Mjk_1} \end{bmatrix}$$

The steering vector of array weights $\mathbf{a}$, steered towards an arbitrary direction θ, is also expressed in terms of the phasing vector $\mathbf{s}_k$; we have

$$a_m = e^{-j\omega\tau_m} = e^{-j\omega(M-m)(d\sin\theta/c)} = e^{-jMk}\,e^{+jmk}$$

or, ignoring the overall common phase e^{-jMk}, we have

$$\mathbf{a} = \mathbf{s}_k \qquad \left(\text{steering vector towards } k = \frac{2\pi d}{\lambda}\sin\theta\right) \tag{6.3.6}$$

The output of the beamformer, steered towards θ, is

$$e = \mathbf{a}^T\mathbf{y} = \mathbf{s}_k^T\mathbf{y} = A_1\mathbf{s}_k^T\mathbf{s}_{k_1}^* = A_1\mathbf{s}_{k_1}^\dagger\mathbf{s}_k = A_1W(k - k_1)^*$$

where $W(\cdot)$ was defined in Section 6.2. The mean output of the beamformer steered towards k is

$$S(k) = E[e^*e] = \mathbf{a}^\dagger E[\mathbf{y}^*\mathbf{y}^T]\mathbf{a} = \mathbf{a}^\dagger R\mathbf{a} = \mathbf{s}_k^\dagger R\mathbf{s}_k$$

Using $\mathbf{y} = A_1\mathbf{s}_{k_1}^*$, we find $R = E[\mathbf{y}^*\mathbf{y}^T] = P_1\mathbf{s}_{k_1}\mathbf{s}_{k_1}^\dagger$, where $P_1 = E[|A_1|^2]$; and

$$\begin{aligned} S(k) &= \mathbf{s}_k^\dagger R\mathbf{s}_k = P_1\mathbf{s}_k^\dagger\mathbf{s}_{k_1}\mathbf{s}_{k_1}^\dagger\mathbf{s}_k \\ &= P_1|W(k - k_1)|^2 \end{aligned}$$

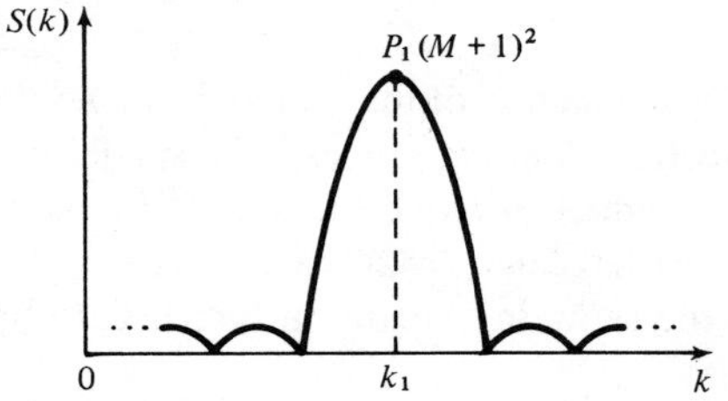

If the beam is steered on target, that is, if $\theta = \theta_1$ or $k = k_1$, then $S(k_1) = P_1 (M + 1)^2$, and the output power is enhanced. The response pattern of the array has the same shape as $W(k)$, and therefore its resolution capability is limited to the width $\Delta k = 2\pi/(M + 1)$ of the main lobe of the smearing function $W(k)$. Using $\Delta k = (2\pi d/\lambda)\Delta\theta$ we find the basic angular resolution to be $\Delta\theta = [\lambda/(M + 1)d]$, or $\Delta\theta = \lambda/D$, where $D = (M + 1)d$ is the effective *aperture* of the array. This is the classic Rayleigh limit on the resolving power of an optical system with aperture D[28].

Next, we consider the problem of resolving the directions of arrival of *multiple* plane waves incident on an array in the presence of background noise. We assume L planes waves incident on an array of $M + 1$ sensors from angles θ_i; $i = 1,2, \ldots ,L$. The incident field is sampled at the sensors giving rise to a series of "snapshots." At the nth snapshot time instant, the field received at the mth sensor is of the form [35]

$$y_m(n) = v_m(n) + \sum_{i=1}^{L} A_i(n)e^{-jmk_i}, \qquad m = 0,1, \ldots ,M \tag{6.3.7}$$

where $A_i(n)$ is the amplitude of the ith wave (it would be a constant independent of time if we had exact sinusoidal dependence at the operating frequency), and k_i are the normalized wavenumbers related to the angles of arrival by

$$k_i = \frac{2\pi d}{\lambda} \sin \theta_i; \; i = 1,2, \ldots ,L \tag{6.3.8}$$

and $v_m(n)$ is the background noise, which is assumed to be *spatially incoherent*, and also uncorrelated with the signal amplitudes $A_i(n)$; that is,

$$E[v_m(n)^* v_k(n)] = \sigma_v^2\delta_{mk}; \qquad E[v_m(n)^* A_i(n)] = 0 \tag{6.3.9}$$

Eq. (6.3.7) can be written in vector form as

$$\mathbf{y}(n) = \mathbf{v}(n) + \sum_{i=1}^{L} A_i(n)\mathbf{s}_{k_i}^* \tag{6.3.10}$$

The autocorrelation matrix of the signal field sensed by the array is

$$R = E[\mathbf{y}(n)^*\mathbf{y}(n)^T] = \sigma_v^2 I + \sum_{i,j=1}^{L} \mathbf{s}_{k_i} P_{ij} \mathbf{s}_{k_j}^\dagger \tag{6.3.11}$$

where I is the $(M + 1) \times (M + 1)$ unit matrix, and P_{ij} is the amplitude correlation matrix

$$P_{ij} = E[A_i(n)^* A_j(n)] \qquad 1 \leq i,j \leq L \tag{6.3.12}$$

If the sources are uncorrelated with respect to each other, the power matrix P_{ij} is diagonal. Introducing the $(M + 1) \times L$ signal matrix

$$S = [\mathbf{s}_{k_1}, \mathbf{s}_{k_2}, \ldots, \mathbf{s}_{k_L}]$$

we write Eq. (6.3.11) as

$$R = \sigma_v^2 I + SPS^\dagger \tag{6.3.13}$$

which is the same as Eq. (6.2.9) of the previous section. Therefore, the analytical expressions of the various spectral estimators can be transferred to this problem as well. We summarize the various spectrum estimators below:

$$\hat{S}_B(k) = \mathbf{s}_k^\dagger R \mathbf{s}_k \qquad \text{(conventional Bartlett beamformer)}$$

$$\hat{S}_{LP}(k) = \frac{1}{|\mathbf{s}_k^\dagger R^{-1} \mathbf{u}_0|^2} \qquad \text{(LP spectral estimate)}$$

$$\hat{S}_{ML}(k) = \frac{1}{\mathbf{s}_k^\dagger R^{-1} \mathbf{s}_k} \qquad \text{(ML beamformer)}$$

For example, for uncorrelated sources $P_{ij} = P_i \delta_{ij}$, the Bartlett spatial spectrum will be

$$\hat{S}_B(k) = \mathbf{s}_k^\dagger R \mathbf{s}_k = \sigma_v^2 (M + 1) + \sum_{i=1}^{L} P_i |W(k - k_i)|^2$$

which gives rise to peaks at the desired wavenumbers k_i from which the angles θ_i can be extracted. When the beam is steered towards the ith plane wave, the measured power at the output of the beamformer will be

$$\hat{S}_B(k_i) = \sigma_v^2 (M + 1) + P_i (M + 1)^2 + \sum_{j \neq i} P_j |W(k_i - k_j)|^2$$

Ignoring the third term for the moment, we observe the basic *improvement* in the SNR offered by beamforming:

$$\frac{P_i (M + 1)^2}{\sigma_v^2 (M + 1)} = \frac{P_i}{\sigma_v^2} (M + 1)$$

If the sources are too close to each other [closer than the beamwidth of $W(k)$], the resolution ability of the beamformer worsens. In such cases, the alternative spectral estimates offer better resolution, with the LP estimate typically having a better performance. The resolution capability of both the ML and the LP estimates improves with higher SNR, whereas that of the conventional beamformer does not.

The Pisarenko method can also be applied here. As discussed in the previous section, the $(M + 1)$-dimensional eigenvalue problem $R\mathbf{a} = \lambda \mathbf{a}$ has an L-dimensional *signal subspace* with eigenvalues greater than σ_v^2, and a $(M + 1 - L)$-dimensional *noise subspace* spanned by the degenerate eigenvectors belonging to the minimum eigenvalue of σ_v^2. *Any* vector $\mathbf{a}$ in the *noise subspace* will have at least L zeros at the desired wavenumber frequencies k_i; that is, the polynomial

$$A(z) = a_0 + a_1 z^{-1} + \cdots + a_M z^{-M}$$

will have L zeros at

$$z_i = \exp(jk_i); \qquad i = 1,2, \ldots ,L$$

and $(M - L)$ other spurious zeros. This can be seen as follows: If $R\mathbf{a} = \sigma_v^2 \mathbf{a}$, then Eq. (6.3.13) implies

$$(\sigma_v^2 I + SPS^\dagger)\mathbf{a} = \sigma_v^2 \mathbf{a} \qquad \text{or} \qquad SPS^\dagger \mathbf{a} = 0$$

dotting with $\mathbf{a}^\dagger$ we find $\mathbf{a}^\dagger SPS^\dagger \mathbf{a} = 0$, and since P is assumed to be strictly positive definite, it follows that $S^\dagger \mathbf{a} = 0$, or

$$S^\dagger \mathbf{a} = \begin{bmatrix} A(k_1) \\ A(k_2) \\ \vdots \\ A(k_L) \end{bmatrix} = 0$$

The L largest eigenvalues of R correspond to the signal subspace eigenvectors and can be determined by reducing the original $(M+1) \times (M+1)$ eigenvalue problem for R into a smaller $L \times L$ eigenvalue problem. Let $\mathbf{e}$ be any eigenvector in the signal subspace, that is, $R\mathbf{e} = \lambda \mathbf{e}$, with $\lambda > \sigma_v^2$. It follows that $SPS^\dagger \mathbf{e} = (\lambda - \sigma_v^2)\mathbf{e}$. Multiplying both sides by $S^\dagger$ we obtain $(S^\dagger SP)(S^\dagger \mathbf{e}) = (\lambda - \sigma_v^2)(S^\dagger \mathbf{e})$, which states that the L-dimensional vector $S^\dagger \mathbf{e}$ is an eigenvector of the $L \times L$ matrix $S^\dagger SP$. We can turn this into a hermitian eigenvalue problem by factoring the power matrix P into its square root factors, $P = GG^\dagger$, and multiplying both sides of the reduced eigenvalue problem by $G^\dagger$. This gives $(G^\dagger S^\dagger SG)(G^\dagger S^\dagger \mathbf{e}) = (\lambda - \sigma_v^2)(G^\dagger S^\dagger \mathbf{e})$. Thus, we obtain the $L \times L$ hermitian eigenvalue problem

$$F\mathbf{f} = (\lambda - \sigma_v^2)\mathbf{f}, \quad \text{where} \quad F = G^\dagger S^\dagger SG, \quad \mathbf{f} = G^\dagger S^\dagger \mathbf{e} \tag{6.3.14}$$

The L signal subspace eigenvalues are obtained from the solution of this reduced eigenproblem. From each L-dimensional eigenvector $\mathbf{f}$, one can also construct the corresponding $(M+1)$-dimensional eigenvector $\mathbf{e}$. Because $\mathbf{e}$ lies in the signal subspace, it can be expressed as a linear combination of the planewaves

$$\mathbf{e} = \sum_{i=1}^{L} c_i \mathbf{s}_{k_i} = [\mathbf{s}_{k_1}, \cdots, \mathbf{s}_{k_L}] \begin{bmatrix} c_1 \\ \cdot \\ \vdots \\ c_L \end{bmatrix} = S\mathbf{c}$$

It follows from Eq. (6.3.14) that

$$\mathbf{f} = G^{\dagger}S^{\dagger}\mathbf{e} = G^{\dagger}S^{\dagger}S\mathbf{c} \quad \Rightarrow \quad \mathbf{c} = (S^{\dagger}S)^{-1}G^{-\dagger}\mathbf{f}$$

and therefore,

$$\mathbf{e} = S\mathbf{c} = S(S^{\dagger}S)^{-1}G^{-\dagger}\mathbf{f} \qquad (6.3.15)$$

Example 6.3.1: Using the above reduction method, determine the signal subspace eigenvectors and eigenvalues for the case of two equal-power planewaves and arbitrary M. The 2×2 matrix P becomes proportional to the identity matrix $P = P_1 I$. The reduced matrix F is then

$$F = P_1 S^{\dagger}S = P_1 \begin{bmatrix} \mathbf{s}_1^{\dagger}\mathbf{s}_1 & \mathbf{s}_1^{\dagger}\mathbf{s}_2 \\ \mathbf{s}_2^{\dagger}\mathbf{s}_1 & \mathbf{s}_2^{\dagger}\mathbf{s}_2 \end{bmatrix} = P_1 \begin{bmatrix} M+1 & W_{12} \\ W^*_{12} & M+1 \end{bmatrix}$$

where $W_{12} = W(k_1 - k_2)$. In the equal-power case, F is always proportional to $S^{\dagger}S$, and therefore, $\mathbf{f}$ is an eigenvector of that. It follows that $(S^{\dagger}S)^{-1}\mathbf{f}$ will be a scalar multiple of $\mathbf{f}$ and that Eq. (6.3.15) can be simplified (up to a scalar factor) to $\mathbf{e} = S\mathbf{f}$. The two eigenvalues and eigenvectors of F are easily found to be

$$\lambda - \sigma_v^2 = P_1(M+1 \pm |W_{12}|), \quad \mathbf{f} = \begin{bmatrix} 1 \\ \pm e^{-j\theta_{12}} \end{bmatrix}$$

where θ_{12} is the phase of W_{12}. Using $\mathbf{e} = S\mathbf{f}$ it follows that the two signal subspace eigenvectors will be

$$\mathbf{e} = \mathbf{s}_1 \pm e^{-j\theta_{12}}\,\mathbf{s}_2$$

The eigenvalue spread of R is in this case

$$\frac{\lambda_{\max}}{\lambda_{\min}} = \frac{\sigma_v^2 + P_1(M+1+|W_{12}|)}{\sigma_v^2} = 1 + SNR\cdot(M+1+|W(k_1-k_2)|)$$

where $SNR = P_1/\sigma_v^2$. It can be written in the form

$$\frac{\lambda_{\max}}{\lambda_{\min}} = 1 + SNR_{\text{eff}}\,(1 + |\cos\phi_{12}|)$$

where $SNR_{\text{eff}} = SNR \cdot (M+1)$ is the effective SNR of the array, or the array gain, and $\cos\phi_{12}$ is the cosine of the angle between the two signal vectors; that is, $\cos\phi_{12} = \mathbf{s}_1^{\dagger}\mathbf{s}_2/\|\mathbf{s}_1\| \cdot \|\mathbf{s}_2\|$.

In practice, *estimates* of the covariance matrix R are used. For example, if the sensor outputs are recorded over N snapshots—that is, $\mathbf{y}(n)$; $n = 0, 1, \ldots, N-1$, then, the covariance matrix R may be estimated by replacing the ensemble average of Eq. (6.3.11) with the *time-average:*

$$\hat{R} = \frac{1}{N}\sum_{n=0}^{N-1} \mathbf{y}(n)^*\,\mathbf{y}(n)^T = \text{empirical } R$$

Since the empirical R will not be of the exact theoretical form of Eq. (6.3.11), the degeneracy of the noise subspace will be lifted somewhat. The degree to which this happens depends on how much the empirical R differs from the theoretical R. One can still use the *minimum eigenvector* **a** to define the polynomial $A(z)$ and from it an approximate Pisarenko spectral estimator

$$\hat{S}_P(k) = \frac{1}{|A(z)|^2} \qquad \text{where } z = e^{jk}$$

which will have sharp and possibly biased peaks at the desired wavenumber frequencies.

Example 6.3.2: Consider the case $L = M = 1$, defined by the theoretical autocorrelation matrix

$$R = \sigma_v^2 I + P_1 \mathbf{s}_{k_1} \mathbf{s}_{k_1}^\dagger = \begin{bmatrix} \sigma_v^2 + P_1 & P_1 e^{-jk_1} \\ P_1 e^{jk_1} & \sigma_v^2 + P_1 \end{bmatrix}$$

Its eigenvectors are

$$\mathbf{e}_0 = \begin{bmatrix} 1 \\ -e^{jk_1} \end{bmatrix}, \qquad \mathbf{e}_1 = \mathbf{s}_{k_1} = \begin{bmatrix} 1 \\ e^{jk_1} \end{bmatrix}$$

belonging to the eigenvalues $\lambda_0 = \sigma_v^2$ and $\lambda_1 = \sigma_v^2 + 2P_1$, respectively. Selecting as the array vector

$$\mathbf{a} = \mathbf{e}_0 = \begin{bmatrix} 1 \\ -e^{jk_1} \end{bmatrix}$$

we obtain a polynomial with a zero at the desired location:

$$A(z) = 1 + a_1 z^{-1} = 1 - e^{jk_1} z^{-1}$$

Now, suppose that the analysis is based on an empirical autocorrelation matrix $\hat{R}$ which differs from the theoretical one by a small amount:

$$\hat{R} = R + \Delta R$$

Using standard first-order perturbation theory, we find the correction to the minimum eigenvalue λ_0 and eigenvector $\mathbf{e}_0$

$$\hat{\lambda}_0 = \lambda_0 + \Delta\lambda_0, \qquad \hat{\mathbf{e}}_0 = \mathbf{e}_0 + \Delta c \mathbf{e}_1$$

where the first-order correction terms are

$$\Delta\lambda_0 = \frac{\mathbf{e}_0^\dagger \Delta R \mathbf{e}_0}{\mathbf{e}_0^\dagger \mathbf{e}_0} \qquad \text{and} \qquad \Delta c = \frac{\mathbf{e}_1^\dagger \Delta R \mathbf{e}_0}{(\lambda_0 - \lambda_1)\mathbf{e}_1^\dagger \mathbf{e}_1}$$

The change induced in the zero of the eigenpolynomial is found as follows

$$\hat{\mathbf{a}} = \hat{\mathbf{e}}_0 = \begin{bmatrix} 1 \\ -e^{jk_1} \end{bmatrix} + \Delta c \begin{bmatrix} 1 \\ e^{jk_1} \end{bmatrix} = \begin{bmatrix} 1 + \Delta c \\ -(1 - \Delta c)e^{jk_1} \end{bmatrix}$$

so that

$$\hat{A}(z) = (1 + \Delta c) - (1 - \Delta c)e^{jk_1}z^{-1}$$

and the zero is now at $z_1 = e^{jk_1}\dfrac{1 - \Delta c}{1 + \Delta c} = e^{jk_1}(1 - 2\Delta c)$ to first order in Δc. Since Δc is generally complex, the factor $(1 - 2\Delta c)$ will cause both a change (bias) in the phase of the zero e^{jk_1}, and will move it off the unit circle reducing the resolution. Another way to see this is to compute the value of the polynomial steered on target; that is,

$$\hat{A}(k_1) = \mathbf{s}_{k_1}^{\dagger}\hat{\mathbf{a}} = \mathbf{s}_{k_1}^{\dagger}(\mathbf{e}_0 + \Delta c\mathbf{e}_1) = \Delta c\mathbf{s}_{k_1}^{\dagger}\mathbf{e}_1 = 2\Delta c$$

which is small but not zero.

The high resolution properties of the Pisarenko and other eigenvector methods depend directly on the assumption that the background noise field is *spatially incoherent,* resulting in the special structure of the autocorrelation matrix R. When the noise is spatially coherent, a different eigen-analysis must be carried out. Suppose the covariance matrix of the noise field $\mathbf{v}$ is

$$E[\mathbf{v}^*\mathbf{v}^T] = \sigma_v^2 Q$$

where Q reflects the spatial coherence of $\mathbf{v}$. Then the covariance matrix of Eq. (6.3.13) is replaced by

$$R = \sigma_v^2 Q + SPS^{\dagger} \tag{6.3.16}$$

The relevant eigenvalue problem is now the *generalized* eigenvalue problem

$$R\mathbf{a} = \lambda Q\mathbf{a} \tag{6.3.17}$$

Consider any such generalized eigenvector $\mathbf{a}$, and assume it is normalized such that

$$\mathbf{a}^{\dagger}Q\mathbf{a} = 1 \tag{6.3.18}$$

Then, the corresponding eigenvalue is expressed as

$$\lambda = \lambda\, \mathbf{a}^{\dagger}Q\mathbf{a} = \mathbf{a}^{\dagger}R\mathbf{a} = \sigma_v^2\mathbf{a}^{\dagger}Q\mathbf{a} + \mathbf{a}^{\dagger}SPS^{\dagger}\mathbf{a}$$

$$= \sigma_v^2 + \sum_{i=1}^{L} P_i|A(k_i)|^2$$

which shows that the minimum eigenvalue is σ_v^2 and it is attained whenever $A(k_i) = 0$; $i = 1,2, \ldots ,L$. Therefore, the eigenpolynomial $A(z)$ can be used to determine the wavenumbers k_i. Thus, the procedure is to solve the generalized eigenvalue problem and select the minimum eigenvector. This eigenvalue problem is also equivalent to the minimization problem

$$\mathcal{E} = \mathbf{a}^\dagger R\mathbf{a} = \min, \qquad \text{subject to } \mathbf{a}^\dagger Q\mathbf{a} = 1 \tag{6.3.19}$$

This criterion, and its solution as the minimum eigenvector, is equivalent to the *unconstrained* minimization of the Rayleigh quotient; that is,

$$\frac{\mathbf{a}^\dagger R\mathbf{a}}{\mathbf{a}^\dagger Q\mathbf{a}} = \min \quad \Leftrightarrow \quad R\mathbf{a} = \lambda_{\min} Q\mathbf{a} \tag{6.3.20}$$

The practical implementation of the method requires knowledge of the noise covariance matrix Q, which is not always possible to obtain. Covariance difference methods [71–74] can be used in the case of unknown Q. Such methods work with measurements from *two* different arrays, translated or rotated with respect to each other. Assuming that the background noise is invariant under translation or rotation, the covariance matrices of the two arrays will be $R_1 = S_1P_1S_1^\dagger + \sigma_v^2 Q$ and $R_2 = S_2P_2S_2^\dagger + \sigma_v^2 Q$. The eigenstructure of the covariance difference $R_1 - R_2 = S_1P_1S_1^\dagger - S_2P_2S_2^\dagger$ can be used to extract the signal information.

The two spectral analysis problems discussed in this and the previous section—direction finding and harmonic retrieval—are *dual* to each other; one dealing with spatial frequencies and the other with time frequencies. The optimum processing part is the same in both cases. The optimum processor does not care how its inputs are supplied, it only "sees" the *correlations* among the inputs and its function is to "break down" these correlations thereby extracting the sinusoidal components. The two cases differ only in the way the inputs to the optimum processor are supplied. This conceptual separation between the input part and the optimum processing part is shown in Fig. 6.12. In the time series case, the correlations among the inputs are sequential correlations in time, whereas in the array case they are spatial correlations, such as those that exist along a coherent wavefront.

A problem related but not identical to direction finding is that of *optimum beamforming* for interference nulling [29–31,103–107]. In this case, one of the plane waves, say, $\mathbf{s}_{k_1}$, is assumed to be a desired plane wave with *known* direction of arrival θ_1 or wavenumber k_1. The other plane waves are considered as interferers or jammers to be nulled. Assuming for simplicity uncorrelated sources, the covariance matrix (6.3.11) may be decomposed into a part due to the desired signal and a part due to the noise plus interference

$$R = \sigma_v^2 I + \sum_{i=1}^{L} P_i\mathbf{s}_i\mathbf{s}_i^\dagger = P_1\mathbf{s}_1\mathbf{s}_1^\dagger + [\sigma_v^2 I + \sum_{i=2}^{L} P_i\mathbf{s}_i\mathbf{s}_i^\dagger] = P_1\mathbf{s}_1\mathbf{s}_1^\dagger + R_n$$

where we denoted $\mathbf{s}_i = \mathbf{s}_{k_i}$. The output power of the array with weights $\mathbf{a}$ will be

$$\mathcal{E} = \mathbf{a}^\dagger R\mathbf{a} = P_1|\mathbf{s}_1^\dagger\mathbf{a}|^2 + \mathbf{a}^\dagger R_n\mathbf{a} \tag{6.3.21}$$

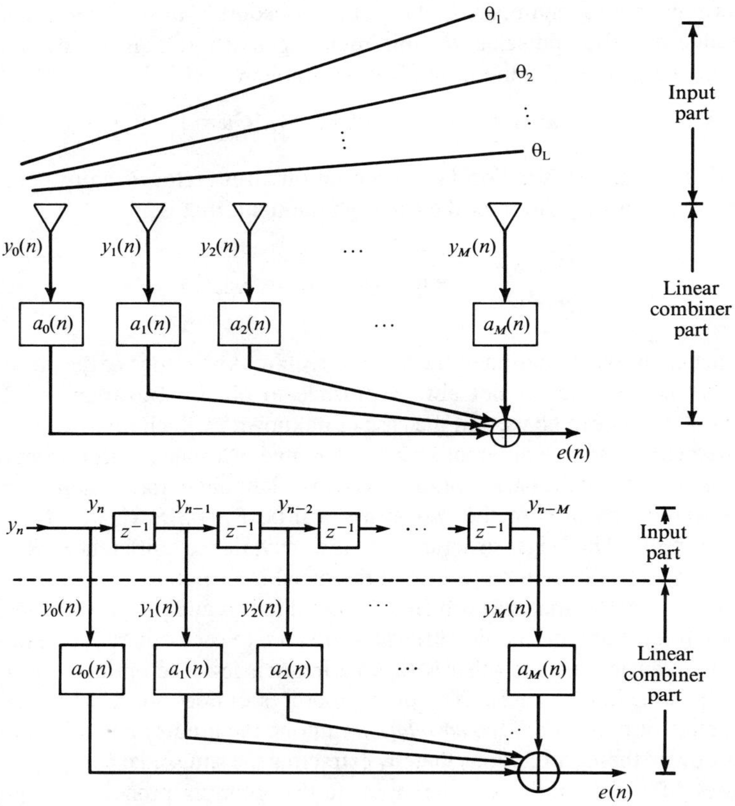

Figure 6.12 Duality Between Time Series and Array Problems

The first term is the output power due to the desired signal; the second term is due to the presence of noise plus interference. This expression suggests two possible optimization criteria for **a**. First, choose **a** to maximize the relative signal to noise plus interference ratio (SNIR)

$$SNIR = \frac{P_1 \,|\, \mathbf{s}_1^{\dagger}\mathbf{a} \,|^2}{\mathbf{a}^{\dagger}R_n\mathbf{a}} = \max \tag{6.3.22}$$

The second criterion is to keep the output of the array toward the look direction $\mathbf{s}_1$ fixed, while minimizing the output power

$$\mathbf{s}_1^{\dagger}\mathbf{a} = 1 \qquad \text{and} \qquad \mathcal{E} = \mathbf{a}^{\dagger}R\mathbf{a} = P_1 + \mathbf{a}^{\dagger}R_n\mathbf{a} = \min \tag{6.3.23}$$

Clearly, this is equivalent to minimizing the noise plus interference term $\mathbf{a}^{\dagger}R_n\mathbf{a}$. These two criteria are essentially equivalent. This is seen as follows. Equation (6.3.22) is equivalent to *minimizing* the inverse function $(SNIR)^{-1}$. Adding one to it, we obtain the equivalent criterion

$$1 + (SNIR)^{-1} = 1 + \frac{\mathbf{a}^\dagger R_n \mathbf{a}}{P_1 \, |\mathbf{s}_1^\dagger \mathbf{a}|^2} = \frac{\mathbf{a}^\dagger R \mathbf{a}}{P_1 \, |\mathbf{s}_1^\dagger \mathbf{a}|^2} = \min$$

This is identical to the Rayleigh quotient (6.3.20) with the choice $Q = P_1 \mathbf{s}_1 \mathbf{s}_1^\dagger$. It is equivalent to the minimum eigenvector solution of

$$R\mathbf{a} = \lambda Q \mathbf{a} = \lambda P_1 \mathbf{s}_1 (\mathbf{s}_1^\dagger \mathbf{a}) = \mu \mathbf{s}_1 \quad \Rightarrow \quad \mathbf{a} = \mu R^{-1} \mathbf{s}_1$$

where we put all the scalar factors into μ. Similarly, the constraint $\mathbf{s}_1^\dagger \mathbf{a} = 1$ implies $\mathbf{a}^\dagger Q_1 \mathbf{a} = 1$ with $Q_1 = \mathbf{s}_1 \mathbf{s}_1^\dagger$. It follows from Eq. (6.3.19), applied with Q_1, that the solution is again the generalized eigenvector

$$R\mathbf{a} = \lambda_1 Q_1 \mathbf{a} = \lambda_1 \mathbf{s}_1 (\mathbf{s}_1^\dagger \mathbf{a}) = \mu_1 \mathbf{s}_1 \quad \Rightarrow \quad \mathbf{a} = \mu_1 R^{-1} \mathbf{s}_1$$

Thus, up to a scale factor, the optimum solution for both criteria is

$$\mathbf{a} = R^{-1} \mathbf{s}_1 \tag{6.3.24}$$

This solution admits, yet, a third interpretation as the *Wiener solution* of an ordinary mean-square estimation problem. The term $\mathbf{y}_1(n) = A_1(n)\mathbf{s}_1^*$ of Eq. (6.3.10) is the desired signal. A reference signal $x(n)$ could be chosen to correlate highly with this term and not at all with the other terms in Eq. (6.3.10). For example, $x(n) = f(n)A_1(n)$. The array weights can be designed by demanding that the scalar output of the array, $\mathbf{a}^T\mathbf{y}(n)$, be the best mean-square estimate of $x(n)$. This gives the criterion

$$E[\,|x(n) - \mathbf{a}^T \mathbf{y}(n)|^2] = E[\,|x(n)|^2] - \mathbf{a}^\dagger \mathbf{r} - \mathbf{r}^\dagger \mathbf{a} + \mathbf{a}^\dagger R \mathbf{a} = \min$$

where we set $\mathbf{r} = E[x(n)\mathbf{y}(n)^*]$. Minimizing with respect to $\mathbf{a}$ (and $\mathbf{a}^*$) gives the Wiener solution $\mathbf{a} = R^{-1}\mathbf{r}$. Now, because $x(n)$ is correlated only with $\mathbf{y}_1(n)$, it follows that $\mathbf{r}$ will be proportional to $\mathbf{s}_1$

$$\mathbf{r} = E[x(n)\mathbf{y}(n)^*] = E[x(n)\mathbf{y}_1(n)^*] = E[x(n)A_1(n)^*]\,\mathbf{s}_1$$

Thus, again up to a scale, we obtain the solution (6.3.24). Using the matrix inversion lemma (see Problem 6.6), we can write the inverse of $R = P_1 \mathbf{s}_1 \mathbf{s}_1^\dagger + R_n$ in the form

$$R^{-1} = R_n^{-1} - c R_n^{-1} \mathbf{s}_1 \mathbf{s}_1^\dagger R_n^{-1}, \quad c = (P_1^{-1} + \mathbf{s}_1^\dagger R_n^{-1} \mathbf{s}_1)^{-1}$$

Acting by both sides on $\mathbf{s}_1$, we find

$$R^{-1}\mathbf{s}_1 = c_1 R_n^{-1} \mathbf{s}_1, \quad c_1 = c P_1^{-1}$$

Therefore, the optimal solution can also be written (up to another scale factor) in terms of the noise plus interference covariance matrix R_n

$$\mathbf{a} = R_n^{-1} \mathbf{s}_1 \tag{6.3.25}$$

These solutions are sometimes modified to include arbitrary tapering weights for the array—replacing the steering vector $\mathbf{s}_1$ with a generalized steering vector

$$\mathbf{s} = \begin{bmatrix} b_0 \\ b_1 e^{jk_1} \\ \vdots \\ b_M e^{jMk_1} \end{bmatrix} = B\mathbf{s}_1\,, \quad B = \mathrm{diag}\{b_0, b_1, \cdots, b_M\} \tag{6.3.26}$$

The weights b_m can be chosen to attain a prescribed shape for the quiescent response of the array in absence of interference. Typical choices are (with $k_1 = 0$)

$$\mathbf{s} = [1, 0, 0, \cdots, 0]^T\,, \quad \mathbf{s} = [1, 1, \cdots, 1]^T$$

To appreciate the properties of the optimum solution, we consider the case of one jammer, so that

$$R = P_1\mathbf{s}_1\mathbf{s}_1^\dagger + R_n\,, \quad R_n = \sigma_v^2 I + P_2\mathbf{s}_2\mathbf{s}_2^\dagger$$

Using the matrix inversion lemma on R_n^{-1}, we obtain

$$R_n^{-1} = \frac{1}{\sigma_v^2}\left[I - \frac{1}{\sigma_v^2 P_2^{-1} + \mathbf{s}_2^\dagger\mathbf{s}_2}\mathbf{s}_2\mathbf{s}_2^\dagger\right]$$

Therefore, the optimum solution given by Eq. (6.3.25) becomes

$$\mathbf{a} = R_n^{-1}\mathbf{s}_1 = \frac{1}{\sigma_v^2}\left[\mathbf{s}_1 - \frac{P_2 W(k_2 - k_1)}{\sigma_v^2 + P_2(M+1)}\mathbf{s}_2\right]$$

where we used $\mathbf{s}_2^\dagger\mathbf{s}_2 = M + 1$ and $\mathbf{s}_2^\dagger\mathbf{s}_1 = W(k_2 - k_1)$. Dropping the overall factor of $1/\sigma_v^2$, we find for the array pattern as a function of wavenumber k or angle θ

$$A(k) = \mathbf{s}_k^\dagger\mathbf{a} = W(k - k_1) - \frac{P_2 W(k_2 - k_1)}{\sigma_v^2 + P_2(M+1)} W(k - k_2) \tag{6.3.27}$$

In the absence of the jammer, $P_2 = 0$, we obtain the usual quiescent Bartlett response, $W(k - k_1)$. The presence of the second term, called a *retrodirective* beam, will partially distort the quiescent pattern but it will suppress the jammer. Indeed, the array response steered toward the jammer at $k = k_2$ becomes

$$A(k_2) = W(k_2 - k_1) - \frac{P_2 W(k_2 - k_1)}{\sigma_v^2 + P_2(M+1)} W(0) = \frac{W(k_2 - k_1)}{\sigma_v^2 + P_2(M+1)}$$

The ratio $A(k_2)/W(k_2 - k_1)$ is the array response, in the direction of the jammer, relative to the quiescent response. Thus, if the signal to noise ratio $SNR_2 = P_2/\sigma_v^2$ is large, the jammer will be suppressed. Only in the limit of infinite SNR is the jammer completely nulled. The reason for the incomplete nulling can be traced, as in the case of linear prediction, to the linear constraint on the weights (6.3.23). To get exact nulling of the jammers, we must force the zeros of the polynomial **a** to lie on the unit circle at the jammer positions. As suggested by Problem 6.13, this can be accomplished by imposing a *quadratic* constraint $\mathbf{a}^\dagger Q\mathbf{a} = const.$ where Q must be chosen as $Q = \sigma_v^2 I + P_1\mathbf{s}_1\mathbf{s}_1^\dagger$ instead of $Q = P_1\mathbf{s}_1\mathbf{s}_1^\dagger$. The optimum weight is the minimum eigenvector solution of the generalized eigenproblem $R\mathbf{a} = \lambda Q\mathbf{a}$ and will have exact zeros at the jammer positions. As in the linear prediction case, the linearly constrained optimum beamformer solution tends to this eigenvector solution in the limit $\sigma_v^2 \to 0$.

6.4 *Eigenvector Methods*

The single most important property of eigenvector methods is that, at least in principle, they produce unbiased frequency estimates with infinite resolution, regardless of the signal to noise ratios. This property is not shared by the older methods. For example, the resolution of the Bartlett method is limited by the array aperture, and the resolution of the linear prediction and maximum likelihood methods degenerates with decreasing SNRs. Because of this property, eigenvector methods have received considerable attention in signal processing and have been applied to several problems, such as harmonic retrieval, direction finding, echo resolution, and pole identification [19,45–99]. In the remainder of this chapter, we discuss the theoretical aspects of eigenvector methods in further detail, and present several versions of such methods, such as MUSIC, Minimum-Norm, and ESPRIT.

We have seen that the eigenspace of the covariance matrix R consists of two mutually orthogonal parts: the $(M + 1 - L)$-dimensional noise subspace spanned by the eigenvectors belonging to the minimum eigenvalue σ_v^2, and the L-dimensional signal subspace spanned by the remaining L eigenvectors having eigenvalues strictly greater than σ_v^2. Let $\mathbf{e}_i, i = 0,1, \ldots, M$, denote the *orthonormal* eigenvectors of R in order of *increasing* eigenvalue, and let $K = M + 1 - L$ denote the dimension of the noise subspace. Then, the first K eigenvectors $\{\mathbf{e}_i, i = 0,1, \ldots, K-1\}$ form an orthonormal basis for the noise subspace, and the last L eigenvectors $\{\mathbf{e}_i, i = K, K+1, \ldots, M\}$ form a basis for the signal subspace. We arrange these basis vectors into the eigenvector matrices

$$E_N = [\mathbf{e}_0, \mathbf{e}_1, \cdots, \mathbf{e}_{K-1}], \qquad E_S = [\mathbf{e}_K, \mathbf{e}_{K+1}, \cdots, \mathbf{e}_M] \tag{6.4.1}$$

Their dimensions are $(M + 1) \times K$ and $(M + 1) \times L$. The full eigenvector matrix of R is

$$E = [E_N, E_S] = [\mathbf{e}_0, \mathbf{e}_1, \cdots, \mathbf{e}_{K-1}, \mathbf{e}_K, \cdots, \mathbf{e}_M] \tag{6.4.2}$$

The orthonormality of the eigenvectors is expressed by the unitarity property $E^\dagger E = I$, where I is the $(M + 1)$-dimensional unit matrix. It can be written in terms of the submatrices (6.4.1)

$$E_N^\dagger E_N = I_K, \qquad E_N^\dagger E_S = 0, \qquad E_S^\dagger E_S = I_L \tag{6.4.3}$$

where I_K and I_L are the $K \times K$ and $L \times L$ unit matrices. The completeness of the eigenvectors is expressed also by the unitarity of E; i.e, $EE^\dagger = I$. In terms of the submatrices, it reads

$$E_N E_N^\dagger + E_S E_S^\dagger = I \tag{6.4.4}$$

These two terms are the *projection* matrices onto the noise and signal subspaces. We have seen that the L signal direction vectors $\mathbf{s}_{k_i}$ belong to the signal subspace, and therefore, are expressible as linear combinations of E_S. It follows that the signal matrix $S = [\mathbf{s}_{k_1}, \ldots, \mathbf{s}_{k_L}]$ is a nonorthogonal basis of the signal subspace and must be related to E_S by $S = E_S C$, where C is an $L \times L$ invertible matrix. Using the orthonormality of E_S, it follows that $S^\dagger S = C^\dagger E_S^\dagger E_S C = C^\dagger C$. Thus, the projector onto the signal subspace may be written as

$$P_S = E_S E_S^\dagger = (SC^{-1})(C^{-\dagger} S^\dagger) = S(C^\dagger C)^{-1} S^\dagger = S(S^\dagger S)^{-1} S^\dagger \tag{6.4.5}$$

We may also obtain a nonorthogonal, but useful, basis for the noise subspace. We have seen that an $(M+1)$-dimensional vector $\mathbf{e}$ lies in the noise subspace—equivalently, it is an eigenvector belonging to the minimum eigenvalue σ_v^2—if and only if the corresponding order-M eigenfilter $E(z)$ has L zeros on the unit circle at the desired signal zeros, $z_i = e^{jk_i}, i = 1,2, \ldots, L$, and $M - L = K - 1$ other spurious zeros. Such a polynomial will factor into the product

$$E(z) = A(z)F(z) = A(z)[f_0 + f_1 z^{-1} + \cdots + f_{K-1} z^{-(K-1)}] \tag{6.4.6}$$

where the zeros of $F(z)$ are the spurious zeros, and $A(z)$ is the *reduced-order* polynomial of order L whose zeros are the desired zeros; that is,

$$A(z) = \prod_{i=1}^{L} (1 - z_i z^{-1}) = 1 + a_1 z^{-1} + \cdots + a_L z^{-L} \tag{6.4.7}$$

Introducing the K delayed polynomials

$$B_i(z) = z^{-i} A(z), \quad i = 0, 1, \cdots, K-1 \tag{6.4.8}$$

we may write Eq. (6.4.6) in the form

$$E(z) = f_0 B_0(z) + f_1 B_1(z) + \cdots + f_{K-1} B_{K-1}(z) = \sum_{i=0}^{K-1} f_i B_i(z) \tag{6.4.9}$$

and in coefficient form

$$\mathbf{e} = \sum_{i=0}^{K-1} f_i \mathbf{b}_i = [\mathbf{b}_0, \mathbf{b}_1, \cdots, \mathbf{b}_{K-1}] \begin{bmatrix} f_0 \\ f_1 \\ \vdots \\ f_{K-1} \end{bmatrix} = B\mathbf{f} \tag{6.4.10}$$

Because each of the polynomials $B_i(z)$ has L desired zeros, it follows that the corresponding vectors $\mathbf{b}_i$ will lie in the noise subspace. Thus, the matrix B defined in Eq. (6.4.10) will be a nonorthogonal basis of the noise subspace. It is a useful basis because the expansion coefficients $\mathbf{f}$ of any noise subspace vector $\mathbf{e}$ are the coefficients of the spurious polynomial $F(z)$ in the factorization (6.4.6). Put differently, Eq. (6.4.10) parametrizes explicitly the spurious degrees of freedom arising from the K-fold degeneracy of the minimum eigenvalue. The basis vectors $\mathbf{b}_i$, considered as $(M+1)$-dimensional vectors, are simply the delayed versions of the vector of coefficients, $\mathbf{a} = [1, a_1, \ldots, a_L]^T$, of the polynomial $A(z)$; that is,

$$\mathbf{b}_i = [\underbrace{0, \cdots, 0}_{i \text{ zeros}}, 1, a_1, \cdots, a_L, \underbrace{0, \cdots, 0}_{K-1-i \text{ zeros}}]^T \tag{6.4.11}$$

For example, in the case $L = 2$ and $M = 5$, we have $K = M + 1 - L = 4$ and B is

$$B = [\mathbf{b}_0, \mathbf{b}_1, \mathbf{b}_2, \mathbf{b}_3] = \begin{bmatrix} 1 & 0 & 0 & 0 \\ a_1 & 1 & 0 & 0 \\ a_2 & a_1 & 1 & 0 \\ 0 & a_2 & a_1 & 1 \\ 0 & 0 & a_2 & a_1 \\ 0 & 0 & 0 & a_2 \end{bmatrix}$$

It follows that the basis B must be linearly related to the orthonormal basis E_N by $B = E_N C$, where C is a $K \times K$ invertible matrix. Then, $B^\dagger B = C^\dagger C$ and the projector onto the noise subspace becomes

$$P_N = E_N E_N^\dagger = (BC^{-1})(C^{-\dagger}B^\dagger) = B(C^\dagger C)^{-1}B^\dagger = B(B^\dagger B)^{-1}B^\dagger \tag{6.4.12}$$

Combining Eqs. (6.4.12) and (6.4.5), we may write the completeness relation (6.4.4) in terms of the nonorthogonal bases B and S

$$B(B^\dagger B)^{-1}B^\dagger + S(S^\dagger S)^{-1}S^\dagger = I \tag{6.4.13}$$

The objective of all eigenvector methods is to estimate the signal zeros $z_i = e^{jk_i}$, $i = 1, 2, \ldots, L$. All methods begin with an eigenanalysis of R, such that E_N and E_S are available. In practice, the eigenanalysis is based on the sample covariance matrix $\hat{R}$ defined on the basis of a finite number of snapshots, say N,

$$\hat{R} = \frac{1}{N} \sum_{n=0}^{N-1} \mathbf{y}(n)^* \mathbf{y}(n)^T \tag{6.4.14}$$

Sometimes, a symmetrized version is preferred, obtained from $\hat{R}$ by

$$\hat{R}_s = \frac{1}{2}(\hat{R} + J\hat{R}^* J) \tag{6.4.15}$$

where J is the $(M+1)$-dimensional reversing matrix. This matrix is invariant under reversal, that is, $J\hat{R}_s J = \hat{R}_s^*$. This version is appropriate when the theoretical R is

Toeplitz. This case arises if and only if the $L \times L$ power matrix P is diagonal; that is, when the L sources are mutually uncorrelated. As the number of snapshots increases, the eigenstructure of $\hat{R}$ or $\hat{R}_s$ becomes a better and better approximation of the eigenstructure of R. Such asymptotic statistical properties will be discussed in Section 6.11. Next, we discuss several practical approaches.

6.5 *MUSIC Method*

Let $E_i(z)$ denote the eigenfilters of the noise subspace eigenvectors $\mathbf{e}_i, i = 0,1, \ldots, K-1$. According to Eq. (6.4.5), we can write $E_i(z) = A(z)F_i(z)$, which shows that $E_i(z)$ have a common set of L zeros at the desired signal locations, but each may have a different set of $K-1$ spurious zeros. It is possible for these spurious zeros to lie very close to or on the unit circle. Therefore, if only one eigenfilter is used, there may be an ambiguity in distinguishing the desired zeros from the spurious ones. The multiple signal classification (MUSIC) method [46,48] attempts to average out the effect of the spurious zeros by forming the sum of the *magnitude responses* of the K eigenfilters, that is, with $z = e^{jk}$,

$$\frac{1}{K}\sum_{i=0}^{K-1} |E_i(k)|^2 = |A(k)|^2 \frac{1}{K}\sum_{i=0}^{K-1} |F_i(k)|^2$$

Because the polynomials $F_i(z)$ are all different, the averaging operation will tend to smear out any spurious zero of any individual term in the sum. Thus, the above expression will effectively vanish only at the L desired zeros of the common factor $|A(k)|^2$. The MUSIC pseudospectrum is defined as the inverse

$$S_{MUS}(k) = \frac{1}{\dfrac{1}{K}\displaystyle\sum_{i=0}^{K-1} |E_i(k)|^2} \tag{6.5.1}$$

It will exhibit peaks at the L desired wavenumbers $k_i, i = 1,2, \ldots, L$. The sum may also be replaced by a weighted sum [54]. The sum may be written compactly in terms of the projection matrices onto the noise or signal subspaces. Noting that $|E_i(k)|^2 = |\mathbf{s}_k^\dagger \mathbf{e}_i|^2 = \mathbf{s}_k^\dagger(\mathbf{e}_i\mathbf{e}_i^\dagger)\mathbf{s}_k$, we find

$$\sum_{i=0}^{K-1} |E_i(k)|^2 = \mathbf{s}_k^\dagger\left[\sum_{i=0}^{K-1} \mathbf{e}_i\mathbf{e}_i^\dagger\right]\mathbf{s}_k = \mathbf{s}_k^\dagger E_N E_N^\dagger \mathbf{s}_k = \mathbf{s}_k^\dagger\mathbf{s}_k - \mathbf{s}_k^\dagger E_S E_S^\dagger \mathbf{s}_k$$

where we used Eq. (6.4.4). Note that $\mathbf{s}_k^\dagger\mathbf{s}_k = M + 1$. The practical version of the MUSIC method is summarized below.

1. Based on a finite number of snapshots, compute the sample covariance matrix $\hat{R}$, solve its eigenproblem, and obtain the estimated eigenvector matrix E with eigenvalues arranged in increasing order.

2. Estimate the dimension K of the noise subspace as the number of the smallest, approximately equal, eigenvalues. This can be done systematically using the AIC or

MDL criteria discussed later. The estimated number of planewaves will be $L = M + 1 - K$. Divide E into its noise and signal subspace parts, E_N and E_S.

3. Compute the spectrum (6.5.1) and extract the desired wavenumbers k_i from the L peaks in this spectrum.

The Akaike (AIC) and minimum description length (MDL) information-theoretic criteria have been suggested to determine the number of planewaves that are present, or equivalently, the dimension of the noise subspace [61]. They are defined by

$$\begin{aligned} AIC(k) &= -2NkL(k) + 2(M+1-k)(M+1+k) \\ MDL(k) &= -NkL(k) + \frac{1}{2}(M+1-k)(M+1+k)\log(N) \end{aligned} \tag{6.5.2}$$

for $k = 1, 2, \ldots, M+1$, where N is the number of snapshots and $L(k)$ is a likelihood function defined as the log of the ratio of the harmonic and arithmetic means of the first k estimated eigenvalues $\{\hat{\lambda}_0, \hat{\lambda}_1, \ldots, \hat{\lambda}_{k-1}\}$ of $\hat{R}$; namely,

$$L(k) = \log\left[\frac{(\hat{\lambda}_0 \hat{\lambda}_1 \cdots \hat{\lambda}_{k-1})^{1/k}}{(\hat{\lambda}_0 + \hat{\lambda}_1 + \cdots + \hat{\lambda}_{k-1})/k}\right]$$

The dimension K of the noise subspace is chosen to be that k that *minimizes* the functions $AIC(k)$ or $MDL(k)$. The above definition is equivalent to that of [61], but produces the value of K instead of L. The routine **aicmdl** (see Appendix B) takes as inputs the $M + 1$ estimated eigenvalues in increasing order and the number N, and computes the values of the AIC and MDL functions. Once K is known, an estimate of the minimum eigenvalue can be obtained by

$$\hat{\sigma}_v^2 = \hat{\lambda}_{\min} = \frac{1}{K}(\hat{\lambda}_0 + \hat{\lambda}_1 + \cdots + \hat{\lambda}_{K-1}) \tag{6.5.3}$$

Next, we present some simulation examples. The required eigenproblems were solved using the EISPACK package. First, we compare the MUSIC method against the linear prediction method. We considered two uncorrelated equal-power planewaves incident on an array of 8 sensors ($M = 7$). The SNR of the waves, defined by $SNR_i = 10\log_{10}(P_i/\sigma_v^2)$, was -5 dB and their wavenumbers $k_1 = 0.2\pi$ and $k_2 = 0.4\pi$. For half-wavelength array spacing ($d = \lambda/2$), these correspond, through Eq. (6.3.8), to the angles of arrival $\theta_1 = 11.54°$ and $\theta_2 = 23.58°$. The number of snapshots was $N = 500$. The snapshots were simulated using Eq. (6.3.10). Each $\mathbf{v}(n)$ was generated as a complex vector of $M + 1$ zero-mean independent gaussian components of variance $\sigma_v^2 = 1$. Note that to generate a zero-mean complex random variable v of variance σ_v^2, one must generate two zero-mean independent real random variables v_1 and v_2 each with variance $\sigma_v^2/2$ and set $v = v_1 + jv_2$; then, $E[v^* v] = E[v_1^2] + E[v_2^2] = 2(\sigma_v^2/2) = \sigma_v^2$. The amplitudes $A_i(n)$ were assumed to have only random phases; that is, $A_i(n) = (P_i)^{1/2}e^{j\phi_{in}}$, where ϕ_{in} were independent angles uniformly distributed in $[0,\pi]$. The routine **snap** (see Appendix B) takes as input an integer seed, generates a snapshot vector $\mathbf{y}$, and updates the seed. Successive calls to **snap,** in conjunction with the (complex version) of the routine **sampcov,** can be used to generate the sample covariance matrix $\hat{R}$. In this particular example, we used the

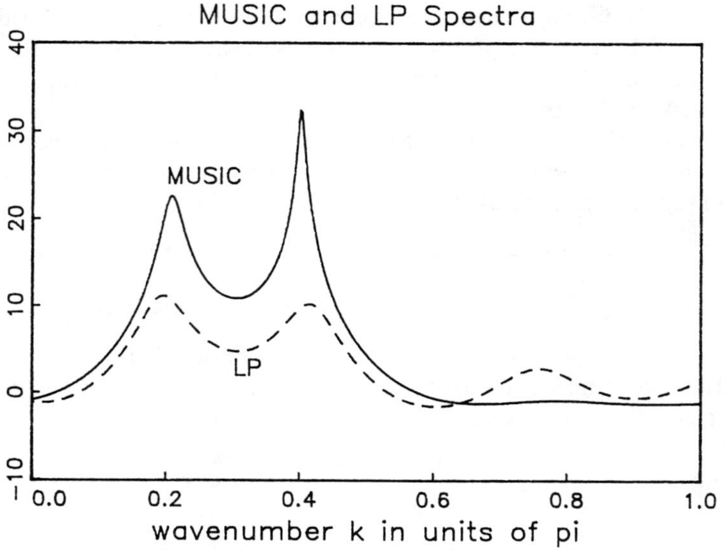

Figure 6.13 MUSIC and LP Spectra

symmetrized version $\hat{R}_s$ because the two sources were uncorrelated. Figure 6.13 shows the MUSIC spectrum computed using Eq. (6.5.1) together with the LP spectrum $S_{LP}(k) = 1/|A(k)|^2 = 1/|\mathbf{s}_k^\dagger \mathbf{a}|^2$, where $\mathbf{a} = \hat{R}_s^{-1}\mathbf{u}_0$. Because each term in the average sum (6.5.1) arises from a unit-norm eigenvector, we have normalized the LP vector **a** also to unit norm for the purpose of plotting the two spectra on the same graph. Increasing the number of snapshots will improve the MUSIC spectrum because the covariance matrix $\hat{R}$ will become a better estimate of R, but it will not improve the LP spectrum because the *theoretical* LP spectrum does not perform well at low SNRs.

To facilitate the computation and manipulation of spectra, we have included the following small routines. The routine **norm** converts a vector **a** to a unit-norm vector. The routine **fresp** computes the magnitude response squared, $|A(k)|^2 = |\mathbf{s}_k^\dagger \mathbf{a}|^2$, of an Mth order filter **a** at a specified number of equally-spaced frequency points within the right-half of the Nyquist interval, $0 \leq k \leq \pi$. It can be modified easily to include the entire Nyquist interval or any subinterval. The routine **invresp** inverts a given spectrum, $S(k) \rightarrow 1/S(k)$. The routines **abs2db** and **db2abs** convert a spectrum from absolute units to decibels and back, $S(k) \leftrightarrow 10\log_{10} S(k)$. The routine **select** picks out any eigenvector from the $M + 1$ ones of the eigenvector matrix E. The routine **music** computes Eq. (6.5.1) over a specified number of frequency points. It is built out of the routines **select, fresp,** and **invresp.**

In the second simulation example, we increased the SNR of the two plane waves to 10 dB and reduced the number of snapshots to $N = 100$. The theoretical and empirical eigenvalues of R and $\hat{R}_s$ were found to be

i	0	1	2	3	4	5	6	7
λ_i	1.00	1.00	1.00	1.00	1.00	1.00	61.98	100.02
$\hat{\lambda}_i$	0.70	0.78	0.93	1.09	1.12	1.16	61.87	99.50

The values of the AIC and MDL functions were

k	1	2	3	4	5	6	7	8
$AIC(k)$	126.00	120.59	114.15	107.48	94.60	77.13	2446.76	3184.04
$MDL(k)$	145.06	138.45	128.72	116.26	98.10	75.04	1242.92	1592.02

Both functions achieve their minimum value at $K = 6$ and therefore, $L = M + 1 - K = 2$. The estimated value of σ_v^2, computed by Eq. (6.5.3), was $\hat{\sigma}_v^2 = 0.96$. Figure 6.14 shows the spectra of the first three noise subspace eigenvectors; namely, $S_i(k) = 1/|E_i(k)|^2 = 1/|\mathbf{s}_k^\dagger \mathbf{e}_i|^2$ for $i = 0,1,2$. They were computed by calling the spectrum manipulation routines **select, fresp, invresp,** and **abs2db**. We note the presence of a common set of peaks at the two desired wavenumbers and several spurious peaks. The spurious peaks are *different,* however, in each spectrum and therefore, the averaging operation will tend to eliminate them. The averaged MUSIC spectrum, based on all $K = 6$ noise subspace eigenvectors, is plotted in Figure 6.15 using the same scale as in Fig. 6.14. The averaging operation has had two effects.

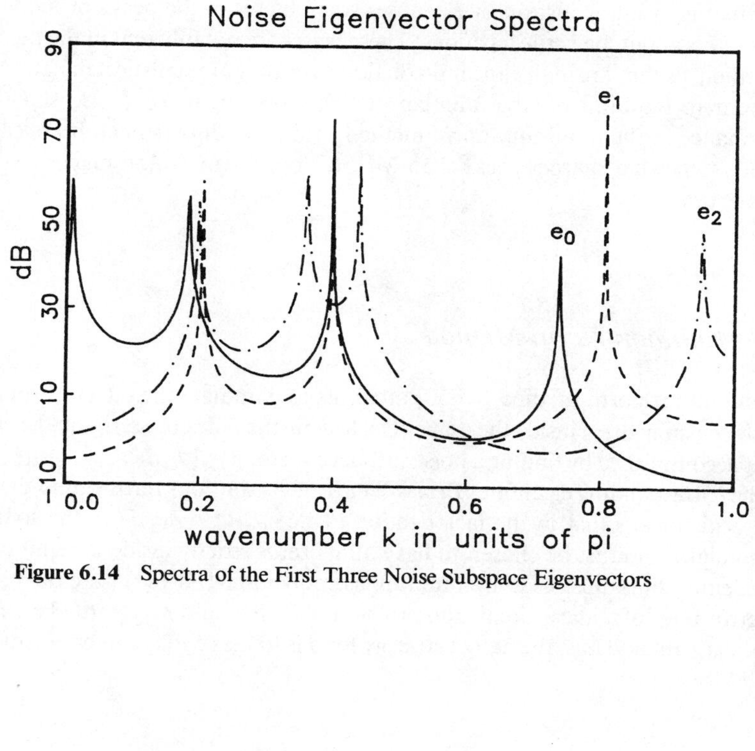

Figure 6.14 Spectra of the First Three Noise Subspace Eigenvectors

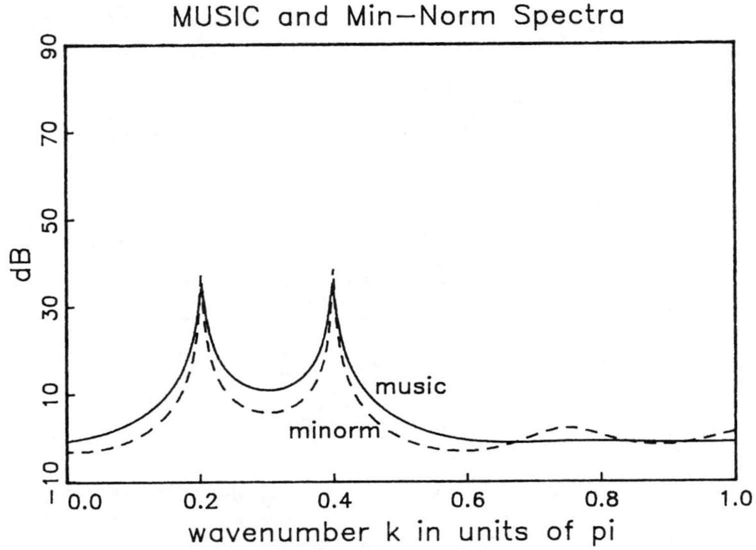

Figure 6.15 MUSIC and Minimum-Norm Spectra

First, the removal of all spurious peaks and second, the broadening and reduction in sharpness of the two desired peaks. This broadening is the result of statistical sampling; that is, using $\hat{R}$ instead of R, causes small biases in the peaks of individual eigenvectors about their true locations. These biases are not inherent in the theoretical method, as they are in the linear prediction case; they are statistical in nature and disappear in the limit of large number of snapshots. Figure 6.15 also shows the performance of the minimum-norm method, which we discuss next. It appears to produce somewhat sharper peaks than MUSIC, but it can exhibit higher levels of spurious peaks.

6.6 *Minimum-Norm Method*

The minimum-norm method [47,53] attempts to eliminate the effect of spurious zeros by pushing them inside the unit circle, leaving the L desired zeros on the circle. This is accomplished by finding a noise subspace vector $\mathbf{d} = [d_0, d_1, \ldots, d_M]^T$ such that the corresponding eigenfilter $D(z)$ will have all its spurious zeros within the unit circle. This means that in the factorization (6.4.6), $D(z) = A(z)F(z)$, the spurious polynomial $F(z)$ must be chosen to have all its zeros strictly inside the unit circle, equivalently, $F(z)$ must be a minimum phase polynomial. If $F(z)$ were the prediction-error filter of a linear prediction problem, then it would necessarily be a minimum phase filter. Thus, the design strategy for $\mathbf{d}$ is to make $F(z)$ a linear prediction filter. This can be done by requiring that $\mathbf{d}$ have minimum norm subject to the constraint that its first coefficient be unity; that is,

$$\mathbf{d}^\dagger\mathbf{d} = \min, \quad \text{subject to} \quad \mathbf{u}_0^\dagger\mathbf{d} = d_0 = 1 \tag{6.6.1}$$

The minimization is carried over the noise subspace vectors. In the B basis (6.4.10), the vector $\mathbf{d}$ is expressed by $\mathbf{d} = B\mathbf{f}$, where $\mathbf{f}$ are the coefficients of $F(z)$, and the constraint equation becomes $\mathbf{u}_0^\dagger B\mathbf{f} = 1$. With the exception of $\mathbf{b}_0$, all basis vectors $\mathbf{b}_i$ start with zero; therefore, $\mathbf{u}_0^\dagger B = [\mathbf{u}_0^\dagger\mathbf{b}_0, \mathbf{u}_0^\dagger\mathbf{b}_1, \ldots, \mathbf{u}_0^\dagger\mathbf{b}_{K-1}] = [1, 0, \ldots, 0] = \mathbf{u}^\dagger$; that is, a K-dimensional unit vector. Therefore, in the B basis Eq. (6.6.1) becomes

$$\mathbf{d}^\dagger\mathbf{d} = \mathbf{f}^\dagger R_{aa}\mathbf{f} = \min, \quad \text{subject to} \quad \mathbf{u}^\dagger\mathbf{f} = 1 \tag{6.6.2}$$

where we set $R_{aa} = B^\dagger B$. This is recognized as the Toeplitz matrix of autocorrelations of the filter $\mathbf{a}$, as defined in Section 3.3. For the 6×4 example above, we verify

$$B^\dagger B = \begin{bmatrix} R_{aa}(0) & R_{aa}(1)^* & R_{aa}(2)^* & 0 \\ R_{aa}(1) & R_{aa}(0) & R_{aa}(1)^* & R_{aa}(2)^* \\ R_{aa}(2) & R_{aa}(1) & R_{aa}(0) & R_{aa}(1)^* \\ 0 & R_{aa}(2) & R_{aa}(1) & R_{aa}(0) \end{bmatrix}$$

where $R_{aa}(0) = 1 + |a_0|^2 + |a_1|^2$, $R_{aa}(1) = a_1a_0^* + a_2a_1^*$, $R_{aa}(2) = a_2a_0^*$, and $R_{aa}(3) = 0$. Note that the autocorrelation function of a length-L filter $\mathbf{a}$ vanishes for lags greater than L. It follows that Eq. (6.6.2) represents an ordinary linear prediction problem and its solution $\mathbf{f}$ will be a minimum phase filter with all its zeros inside the unit circle. Up to a scale factor, we write this solution as $\mathbf{f} = R_{aa}^{-1}\mathbf{u} = (B^\dagger B)^{-1}\mathbf{u}$. Writing $\mathbf{u} = B^\dagger\mathbf{u}_0$, we have $\mathbf{f} = (B^\dagger B)^{-1}B^\dagger\mathbf{u}_0$, and the solution for $\mathbf{d}$ becomes

$$\mathbf{d} = B\mathbf{f} = B(B^\dagger B)^{-1}B^\dagger\mathbf{u}_0 = E_N E_N^\dagger\mathbf{u}_0 \tag{6.6.3}$$

This is the solution of criterion (6.6.1) up to a scale. Interestingly, the locations of the spurious zeros do not depend on the signal to noise ratios, but depend only on the desired zeros on the unit circle. This follows from the fact that the solution for $\mathbf{f}$ depends only on B. Using Eq. (6.4.13), we may also write $\mathbf{d}$ in terms of the signal subspace bases

$$\mathbf{d} = [I - E_S E_S^\dagger]\,\mathbf{u}_0 = [I - S(S^\dagger S)^{-1}S^\dagger]\,\mathbf{u}_0$$

Recall from Section 6.2 that this is the large SNR limit of the LP solution. Noting that $E_N^\dagger\mathbf{u}_0$ is the complex conjugate of the top row of the eigenvector matrix E_N, we write Eq. (6.6.3) explicitly as a linear combination of noise subspace eigenvectors

$$\mathbf{d} = \sum_{i=0}^{K-1} E_{0i}{}^*\,\mathbf{e}_i \tag{6.6.4}$$

where E_{0i}^* is the conjugate of the $0i$th matrix element of E. The subroutine **minorm** computes $\mathbf{d}$ using Eq. (6.6.4). The corresponding pseudospectrum estimate is defined as the inverse magnitude response of the filter $\mathbf{d}$

$$S_{MIN}(k) = \frac{1}{|D(k)|^2} = \frac{1}{|\mathbf{s}_k^\dagger\mathbf{d}|^2} \tag{6.6.5}$$

The practical implementation of this method requires the same two initial steps as MUSIC; namely, eigenanalysis of $\hat{R}$ and estimation of K. In Fig. 6.15, the minimum-norm spectrum was computed by calling the routines **minorm, norm, fresp, invresp,** and **abs2db.** The vector $\mathbf{d}$ was normalized to unit norm to make a fair comparison with the MUSIC spectrum. Looking at the spectra is not the best way to evaluate this method because the spurious zeros—even though inside the unit circle—interact with the desired zeros to modify the shape of the spectrum. The minimum-norm method is better judged by comparing the theoretical and empirical zeros of the polynomial $D(z)$, computed from R and $\hat{R}$. They are shown in the following table. The first two zeros are the desired ones.

Zeros of $D(z)$			
theoretical		empirical	
$\lvert z_i \rvert$	$\arg z_i/\pi$	$\lvert z_i \rvert$	$\arg z_i/\pi$
1.000	0.400	0.996	0.400
1.000	0.200	1.005	0.202
0.816	0.746	0.818	0.747
0.816	-0.146	0.815	-0.144
0.781	-0.425	0.784	-0.424
0.781	-0.975	0.787	-0.973
0.771	-0.700	0.764	-0.698

The main idea of the minimum-norm method was to separate the desired zeros from the spurious ones by pushing the latter inside the unit circle. In some applications of eigenvector methods, such as pole identification, the desired zeros lie themselves *inside* the unit circle (being the poles of a stable and causal system) and therefore, cannot be separated from the spurious ones. To separate them, we need a modification of the method that places all the spurious zeros to the *outside* of the unit circle. This can be done by replacing the vector $\mathbf{f}$ by its reverse $\mathbf{f}^R = J\mathbf{f}^*$, where J is the $K \times K$ reversing matrix. The resulting polynomial will be the reverse of $F(z)$, with all its zeros reflected to the outside of the unit circle. The reverse vector $\mathbf{f}^R$ is the *backward* prediction filter obtained by minimizing (6.6.2) subject to the constraint that its *last* element be unity. Using the reversal invariance of R_{aa}, namely, $JR_{aa}J = R_{aa}^*$, we find

$$\mathbf{f}^R = J\mathbf{f}^* = J(R_{aa}^{-1})^*\mathbf{u} = R_{aa}^{-1}J\mathbf{u} = R_{aa}^{-1}\mathbf{v}$$

where $\mathbf{v} = J\mathbf{u} = [0, \ldots, 0, 1]^T$ is the reverse of $\mathbf{u}$. With the exception of $\mathbf{b}_{K-1}$, the last element of all basis vectors $\mathbf{b}_i$ is zero. Denoting by $\mathbf{v}_0$ the reverse of $\mathbf{u}_0$, it follows that $\mathbf{v}_0^\dagger B = [0, \ldots, 0, a_L] = a_L\mathbf{v}^\dagger$. Thus, up to a scale factor, $\mathbf{v}$ can be replaced by $B^\dagger\mathbf{v}_0$, and hence, $\mathbf{f}^R = R_{aa}^{-1}B^\dagger\mathbf{v}_0 = (B^\dagger B)^{-1}B^\dagger\mathbf{v}_0$. The vector $\mathbf{d}$ becomes

$$\mathbf{d} = B\mathbf{f}^R = B(B^\dagger B)^{-1}B^\dagger\mathbf{v}_0 = E_N E_N^\dagger \mathbf{v}_0 \qquad (6.6.6)$$

Up to a scale, this is the minimum-norm vector subject to the constraint that its *last* element be unity; that is, $\mathbf{v}_0^\dagger \mathbf{d} = d_M = 1$. In terms of the matrix elements of the eigenvector matrix E, it reads

$$\mathbf{d} = \sum_{i=0}^{K-1} E_{Mi}{}^* \mathbf{e}_i \tag{6.6.7}$$

where E_{Mi}^* is the conjugate of the last row of E. The spurious zeros of this vector will lie outside the unit circle. We may refer to this method as the *modified minimum-norm* method.

6.7 *Reduced-Order Method*

The basis B of the noise subspace has very special structure, being constructed in terms of the delayed replicas of the *same* reduced-order vector $\mathbf{a}$. It is evident from Eq. (6.4.11) that $\mathbf{a}$ can be extracted from *any* column $\mathbf{b}_i$ of B by advancing it by i units. The B basis is linearly related to the orthonormal eigenvector basis by $B = E_N C$ with some $K \times K$ invertible matrix C. Thus, the vector $\mathbf{b}_i$ is expressible as a linear combination of the noise subspace eigenvectors

$$\mathbf{b}_i = \sum_{j=0}^{K-1} \mathbf{e}_j C_{ji}\,, \quad i = 0, 1, \cdots, K\text{-}1$$

This vector has a total of $K - 1$ vanishing coefficients, namely, the first i and the last $K - 1 - i$ coefficients. Component-wise, we may write $b_{im} = 0$, for $0 \leqslant m \leqslant i - 1$ and for $i + L + 1 \leqslant m \leqslant M$. This vector can be specified only up to an overall scale factor because we are interested only in the zeros of the reduced-order vector $\mathbf{a}$. Therefore, we may arbitrarily fix one of the coefficients C_{ji} to unity. For example, we may single out the 0th eigenvector.

$$\mathbf{b}_i = \mathbf{e}_0 + \sum_{j=1}^{K-1} \mathbf{e}_j C_{ji} \tag{6.7.1}$$

If $\mathbf{e}_0$ happens to be absent from the sum, we may single out $\mathbf{e}_1$, and so on. The coefficient b_{ii} will no longer be unity, but may be normalized so later. The $K - 1$ unknown coefficients $C_{ji}, j = 1,2, \ldots, K - 1$ can be determined by the $K - 1$ conditions that the first i and last $K - 1 - i$ coefficients of $\mathbf{b}_i$ be zero. Written in terms of the matrix elements of the eigenvector matrix E, these conditions read for each $i = 0,1, \ldots, K - 1$

$$E_{m0} + \sum_{j=1}^{K-1} E_{mj} C_{ji} = 0\,, \quad \text{for} \quad 0 \leq m \leq i\text{-}1 \ \text{ and } \ L+1+i \leq m \leq M \tag{6.7.2}$$

Thus, solving the linear Eqs. (6.7.2) for the coefficients C_{ji} and substituting in Eq. (6.7.1), we obtain $\mathbf{b}_i$ and, advancing it by i units, the reduced-order vector $\mathbf{a}$. Because $B_i(z) = z^{-i}A(z)$, the polynomial $B_i(z)$ has no spurious zeros. In effect, forming the linear combination Eq. (6.7.1) of noise subspace eigenvectors removes the spurious zeros completely by placing them at the origin of the z-plane. In a sense, this procedure carries the philosophy of the minimum-norm method further.

When the theoretical R is replaced by the empirical $\hat{R}$ and the corresponding E_N is replaced by the estimated $\hat{E}_N$, it is no longer possible to linearly transform the basis $\hat{E}_N$ to a B basis constructed from a *single* reduced-order vector **a**. It is still possible, however, to form linear combinations of the estimated eigenvectors.

$$\hat{\mathbf{b}}_i = \sum_{j=0}^{K-1} \hat{\mathbf{e}}_j C_{ji}\,, \quad i = 0, 1, \cdots, K\text{-}1 \tag{6.7.3}$$

such that the resulting vectors $\hat{\mathbf{b}}_i$ will have vanishing first i and last $K-1-i$ coefficients; that is, of the form

$$\hat{\mathbf{b}}_i = [\underbrace{0, \cdots, 0}_{i \text{ zeros}}, 1, a_{i1}, \cdots, a_{iL}, \underbrace{0, \cdots, 0}_{K\text{-}1\text{-}i \text{ zeros}}]^T \tag{6.7.4}$$

This can be done by solving Eq. (6.7.2) with E replaced by its estimate, $\hat{E}$, obtained from $\hat{R}$. The resulting K reduced-order vectors $\mathbf{a}_i = [1, a_{i1}, a_{i2}, \ldots, a_{iL}]^T$, $i = 0, 1, \ldots, K-1$ will not be the same necessarily. But, each can be considered as an approximate *estimate* of the true reduced-order vector **a**; and its L zeros will be estimates of the true desired zeros. It turns out that individually none of the $\mathbf{a}_i$ is a particularly good estimate of **a**. They may be combined, however, to produce a better estimate. This is analogous to MUSIC, where individual spectra of noise eigenvectors are not good, but combining them by averaging produces a better spectrum. To see how we may best combine the $\mathbf{a}_i$s, we form a new basis of the estimated noise subspace in terms of the vectors $\hat{\mathbf{b}}_i$, namely, $\hat{B} = [\hat{\mathbf{b}}_0, \hat{\mathbf{b}}_1, \ldots, \hat{\mathbf{b}}_{K-1}]$. For our 6×4 example, we have

$$\hat{B} = [\hat{\mathbf{b}}_0, \hat{\mathbf{b}}_1, \hat{\mathbf{b}}_2, \hat{\mathbf{b}}_3] = \begin{bmatrix} 1 & 0 & 0 & 0 \\ a_{01} & 1 & 0 & 0 \\ a_{02} & a_{11} & 1 & 0 \\ 0 & a_{12} & a_{21} & 1 \\ 0 & 0 & a_{22} & a_{31} \\ 0 & 0 & 0 & a_{32} \end{bmatrix}$$

The linear transformations (6.7.3) may be written compactly as $\hat{B} = \hat{E}_N C$. Note that $\hat{B}^\dagger \hat{B}$ is no longer Toeplitz and therefore, the LP solution **f** of Eq. (6.6.2) will not necessarily have minimum phase. Thus, the empirical minimum-norm solution can have spurious zeros outside or near the unit circle. Because the basis $\hat{B}$ is an estimate of the true B, we may try to fit $\hat{B}$ to a matrix of the type B having the special structure (6.4.11) by minimizing the distance between the two matrices according to some matrix norm. For example, we may minimize the Frobenius matrix distance [102]

$$\|\hat{B} - B\|^2 = \mathrm{tr}\left[(\hat{B} - B)^\dagger(\hat{B} - B)\right] = \sum_{i=0}^{K-1} \|\hat{\mathbf{b}}_i - \mathbf{b}_i\|^2 = \min$$

Because $\hat{\mathbf{b}}_i$ and $\mathbf{b}_i$ are the delayed versions of the reduced-order vectors $\mathbf{a}_i$ and $\mathbf{a}$, it follows that $\|\hat{\mathbf{b}}_i - \mathbf{b}_i\|^2 = \|\mathbf{a}_i - \mathbf{a}\|^2$. Therefore,

$$\|\hat{B} - B\|^2 = \sum_{i=0}^{K-1} \|\mathbf{a}_i - \mathbf{a}\|^2 = \min \tag{6.7.5}$$

Minimizing with respect to $\mathbf{a}$ gives the result

$$\hat{\mathbf{a}} = \frac{1}{K}\sum_{i=0}^{K-1} \mathbf{a}_i\,, \qquad \hat{A}(z) = \frac{1}{K}\sum_{i=0}^{K-1} A_i(z) \tag{6.7.6}$$

that is, the average of the K filters. Thus, we obtain the following *reduced-order* algorithm [75]:

1. Solve the eigenproblem for the estimated covariance matrix $\hat{R}$.
2. Using the estimated noise subspace eigenvectors, solve Eq. (6.7.2) for the coefficients C_{ji} and using Eq. (6.7.3) obtain the basis vectors $\hat{\mathbf{b}}_i$ and hence the reduced-order vectors $\mathbf{a}_i, i = 0, 1, \ldots, K-1$.
3. Use the average (6.7.6) to get an estimate $\hat{A}(z)$ of the reduced-order polynomial $A(z)$. Obtain estimates of the desired zeros by a root-finding procedure on $\hat{A}(z)$, or, by finding the peaks in the pseudospectrum

$$\hat{S}(k) = \frac{1}{|\hat{A}(k)|^2} = \frac{1}{|\mathbf{s}_k^\dagger \hat{\mathbf{a}}|^2} \tag{6.7.7}$$

Figure 6.16 shows a comparison between the reduced-order algorithm and MUSIC for the same example considered in Figs. 6.13 and 6.15, where, again, for the pur-

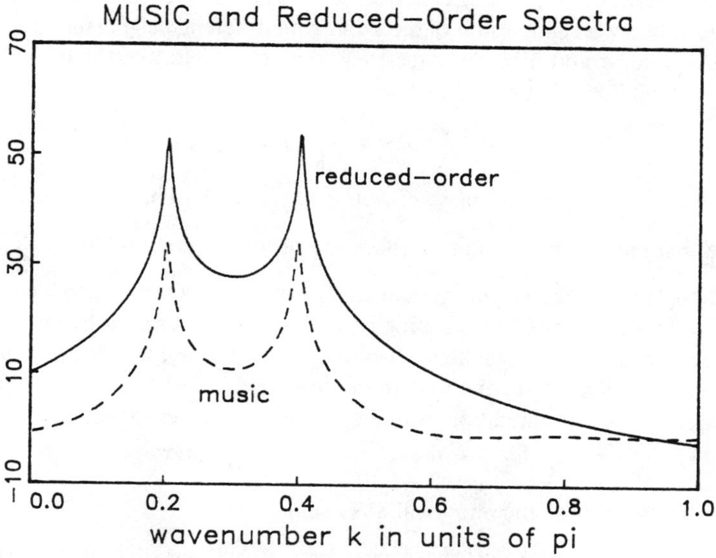

Figure 6.16 MUSIC and Reduced-Order Method

poses of comparison the vector $\hat{\mathbf{a}}$ was normalized to unit norm. As in the case of MUSIC, the spectrum of any individual reduced-order vector $\mathbf{a}_i$ is not good, but the spectrum based on the average $\hat{\mathbf{a}}$ is better. This can be appreciated by comparing the two zeros ($L = 2$) of the six ($K = 6$) individual filters $A_i(z), i = 0, 1, \ldots, 5$ with the two zeros of the averaged polynomial $\hat{A}(z)$ and with the theoretical zeros. They are shown in the table below.

zeros	$\hat{A}_0$	$\hat{A}_1$	$\hat{A}_2$	$\hat{A}_3$	$\hat{A}_4$	$\hat{A}_5$	$\hat{A}$	A
$\lvert z_1 \rvert$	0.971	1.091	0.891	1.123	0.917	1.030	1.008	1.000
$\arg z_1/\pi$	0.420	0.393	0.385	0.385	0.393	0.420	0.404	0.400
$\lvert z_2 \rvert$	0.991	1.116	0.875	1.143	0.896	1.009	1.009	1.000
$\arg z_2/\pi$	0.204	0.208	0.215	0.215	0.208	0.204	0.205	0.200

An alternative method of combining the K estimates is as follows [99]. Form the $(L+1) \times K$ matrix $A = [\mathbf{a}_0, \mathbf{a}_1, \ldots, \mathbf{a}_{K-1}]$ and note that if $\mathbf{a}_i$ were computed on the basis of the theoretical covariance matrix R, then A would have rank one because each $\mathbf{a}_i$ would be exactly equal to $\mathbf{a}$. But if the empirical matrix $\hat{R}$ is used, then the matrix A will only approximately have rank one, in the sense of its *singular value decomposition* (SVD)[102]. Thus, we may replace A by its rank-one SVD approximant, namely, the rank-one matrix closest to A with respect to the Frobenius or Euclidean matrix norms. This amounts to finding the largest eigenvalue of the $(L+1) \times (L+1)$ matrix

$$AA^{\dagger} = \sum_{i=0}^{K-1} \mathbf{a}_i \mathbf{a}_i^{\dagger} \tag{6.7.8}$$

and choosing the corresponding eigenvector to be the estimate of $\mathbf{a}$. This eigenvector is expressible as a weighted sum of the $\mathbf{a}_i$ but with different weights than Eq. (6.7.6). To see this, let σ and $\hat{\mathbf{a}}$ be the largest eigenvalue and eigenvector of $AA^{\dagger}$. Using $AA^{\dagger}\hat{\mathbf{a}} = \sigma\hat{\mathbf{a}}$, and defining $\mathbf{w} = A^{\dagger}\hat{\mathbf{a}}/\sigma$, we find

$$\hat{\mathbf{a}} = A\mathbf{w} = \sum_{i=0}^{K-1} w_i \mathbf{a}_i \tag{6.7.9}$$

where w_i are the components of $\mathbf{w} = [w_0, w_1, \ldots, w_{K-1}]^T$. The constraint that $\hat{\mathbf{a}}$ and $\mathbf{a}_i$ have first coefficients of unity implies the normalization condition $\sum_{i=0}^{K-1} w_i = 1$. Even though this method is computationally more complex than Eq. (6.7.6), it allows one to judge the quality of the resulting estimate. This may be done by inspecting the relative magnitudes of the singular values of A, equivalently, the $L + 1$ eigenvalues of $AA^{\dagger}$. Theoretically, all but the maximum eigenvalue must be zero. Applying this method to the above simulation example, we find for the estimated zeros

$$z_1 = 1.017 e^{j0.403\pi}, \qquad z_2 = 1.018 e^{j0.205\pi}$$

and for the theoretical and empirical SVD values

theoretical	0.000	0.000	33.708
empirical	0.000	0.106	34.599

6.8 *Maximum Likelihood Method*

The maximum likelihood method is not, strictly speaking, an eigenvector method; however, some of the ideas we have been discussing apply to it. The method determines the planewave frequencies and amplitudes by fitting them *directly* to the measured snapshot data using a criterion, such as maximum likelihood or least-squares [76–79]. Each snapshot is modeled according to Eq. (6.3.10), which can be written compactly as

$$\mathbf{y}(n) = [\mathbf{s}_{k_1}{}^*, \cdots, \mathbf{s}_{k_L}{}^*]\begin{bmatrix} A_1(n) \\ \vdots \\ A_L(n) \end{bmatrix} + \mathbf{v}(n) = S^*\mathbf{A}(n) + \mathbf{v}(n) \tag{6.8.1}$$

The unknown amplitudes $\mathbf{A}(n)$ and wavenumbers $k_i, i = 1, 2, \ldots, L$ are treated as deterministic parameters to be fitted to the snapshot data $Y = \{\mathbf{y}(n), n = 0, 1, \ldots, N-1\}$. The maximum likelihood estimates of these parameters are obtained by maximizing the joint density of the snapshots, $p(Y) = \max$. If the wave parameters are deterministic, then the randomness in $\mathbf{y}(n)$ arises only from $\mathbf{v}(n)$. Assuming $\mathbf{v}(n)$ are complex gaussian (see Problem 6.16) and independent, the joint density of Y is the product of marginal densities:

$$p(Y) = \prod_{n=0}^{N-1} p(\mathbf{v}(n)) = (\pi\sigma_v^2)^{-N(M+1)} \exp\left[-\frac{1}{\sigma_v^2}\sum_{n=0}^{N-1} \|\mathbf{v}(n)\|^2\right]$$

$$= (\pi\sigma_v^2)^{-N(M+1)} \exp\left[-\frac{1}{\sigma_v^2}\sum_{n=0}^{N-1} \|\mathbf{y}(n) - S^*\mathbf{A}(n)\|^2\right]$$

Thus, under gaussian statistics, the maximum likelihood criterion is equivalent to the least-squares minimization criterion.

$$J = \sum_{n=0}^{N-1} \|\mathbf{y}(n) - S^*\mathbf{A}(n)\|^2 = \min \tag{6.8.2}$$

According to the general discussion of [101], the simultaneous minimization of J with respect to k_i and $\mathbf{A}(n)$ can be done in two steps. First, minimize with respect to the amplitudes $\mathbf{A}(n)$ and then, minimize with respect to the wavenumbers k_i. Setting the gradients with respect to $\mathbf{A}(n)$ to zero, we obtain

$$\frac{\partial J}{\partial \mathbf{A}(n)} = -S^\dagger[\mathbf{y}(n)^* - S\mathbf{A}(n)^*] = 0 \quad \Rightarrow \quad \mathbf{A}(n)^* = (S^\dagger S)^{-1}S^\dagger\mathbf{y}(n)^*$$

Inserting in Eq. (6.8.2) we find

$$J = \sum_{n=0}^{N-1} \|\mathbf{y}(n)^* - S\mathbf{A}(n)^*\|^2 = \sum_{n=0}^{N-1} \|[I - S(S^\dagger S)^{-1}S^\dagger]\mathbf{y}(n)^*\|^2$$

Using Eq. (6.4.13), we may rewrite it in terms of the projector onto the noise subspace, namely, $P_N = B(B^\dagger B)^{-1}B^\dagger$

$$J = \sum_{n=0}^{N-1} \|B(B^\dagger B)^{-1}B^\dagger \mathbf{y}(n)^*\|^2 = \sum_{n=0}^{N} \|P_N \mathbf{y}(n)^*\|^2$$

Using the projection property $P_N^\dagger P_N = P_N$, and the definition (6.4.14) of the sample covariance matrix, we find

$$J = \sum_{n=0}^{N} \mathbf{y}(n)^T P_N \mathbf{y}(n)^* = \mathrm{tr}\left[\sum_{n=0}^{N} P_N \mathbf{y}(n)^* \mathbf{y}(n)^T\right] = N\mathrm{tr}(P_N\hat{R})$$

The minimization of J with respect to the coefficients of the reduced-order vector $\mathbf{a}$ is a highly nonlinear problem. It may be solved, however, iteratively by the solution of a succession of simpler problems, by the following procedure [91,77–79,95,97]. Write $\mathbf{y}(n)^T B = [\mathbf{y}(n)^T\mathbf{b}_0, \mathbf{y}(n)^T\mathbf{b}_1, \ldots, \mathbf{y}(n)^T\mathbf{b}_{K-1}]$ and note that $\mathbf{y}(n)^T\mathbf{b}_i = \mathbf{a}^T\mathbf{y}_i(n)$, where $\mathbf{y}_i(n)$ is the $(L+1)$-dimensional portion of $\mathbf{y}(n)$ starting at the ith position, namely,

$$\mathbf{y}_i(n) = [y_i(n), y_{i+1}(n), \cdots, y_{i+L}(n)]^T, \quad i = 0, 1, \cdots, K\text{-}1$$

Then, $\mathbf{y}(n)^T B = \mathbf{a}^T[\mathbf{y}_0(n), \mathbf{y}_1(n), \ldots, \mathbf{y}_{K-1}(n)] \equiv \mathbf{a}^T Y(n)$. And, J may be written as

$$J = \sum_{n=0}^{N-1} \mathbf{y}(n)^T B(B^\dagger B)^{-1}B^\dagger \mathbf{y}(n)^* = \mathbf{a}^T\left[\sum_{n=0}^{N-1} Y(n)(B^\dagger B)^{-1}Y(n)^\dagger\right]\mathbf{a}^*$$

The minimization of J is obtained by solving the succession of problems: for $i = 1, 2, \ldots,$

$$J_i = \mathbf{a}_i^T\left[\sum_{n=0}^{N-1} Y(n)(B_{i-1}^\dagger B_{i-1})^{-1}Y(n)^\dagger\right]\mathbf{a}_i^* = \min \qquad (6.8.3)$$

where $B_{i-1}^\dagger B_{i-1}$ is constructed from the solution $\mathbf{a}_{i-1}$ of the previous iteration. The iteration is initialized by $\mathbf{a}_0 = [1, 0, \ldots, 0]^T$, which gives $B_0^\dagger B_0 = I_K$. At each iteration, Eq. (6.8.3) is subject to an appropriate constraint on $\mathbf{a}_i$, such as that its first coefficient be unity, or, that its zeros lie on the unit circle. Note that $B^\dagger B$ is Toeplitz and therefore, its inverse can be computed efficiently by the Levinson recursion.

6.9 *ESPRIT Method*

There exist a number of eigenvector methods that employ *two* or more sets of snapshot measurements obtained from two or more arrays related to each other either by translation or by rotation. Examples are the estimation of signal parameters via rotational invariance techniques (ESPRIT) method [80–82], the covariance difference method [71–74], and the spatial smoothing method for dealing with coherent signals [55,62].

Consider two arrays related to each other by an overall translation by distance Δ along the x-axis. The effect of translation shows up as an overall phase change in each direction vector. For example, the value of a wave on the x-axis with respect to the original and translated x-axes will be

$$A_1 e^{-jk_x x} \to A_1 e^{-jk_x(x+\Delta)} = A_1 e^{-jk_x x} e^{-jk_x \Delta}$$

Setting $x_m = md$ and letting $\delta = \Delta/d$ be the displacement in units of d, we obtain at the original and translated mth array elements

$$A_1 e^{-jk_1 m} \to A_1 e^{-jk_1(m+\delta)} = A_1 e^{-jk_1 m} e^{-jk_1 \delta}$$

or, in terms of the direction vectors

$$A_1 \mathbf{s}_1{}^* \to A_1 \mathbf{s}_1{}^* e^{-jk_1 \delta}$$

It follows that the matrix $S = [\mathbf{s}_{k_1}, \ldots, \mathbf{s}_{k_L}]$ transforms under translation as

$$S \to SD_\delta, \qquad D_\delta = \text{diag}\{e^{jk_1\delta}, e^{jk_2\delta}, \cdots, e^{jk_L\delta}\} \tag{6.9.1}$$

Therefore, the snapshot measurements at the original and translated arrays are

$$\mathbf{y}(n) = S^*\mathbf{A}(n) + \mathbf{v}(n), \qquad \mathbf{y}_\delta(n) = S^*D_\delta{}^*\mathbf{A}(n) + \mathbf{v}_\delta(n) \tag{6.9.2}$$

The covariance and cross-covariance matrices are

$$R_{yy} = E[\mathbf{y}(n)^*\mathbf{y}(n)^T] = SPS^\dagger + \sigma_v^2 I$$
$$R_{y_\delta y_\delta} = E[\mathbf{y}_\delta(n)^*\mathbf{y}_\delta(n)^T] = SD_\delta PD_\delta^\dagger S^\dagger + \sigma_v^2 I \tag{6.9.3}$$

$$R_{yy_\delta} = E[\mathbf{y}(n)^*\mathbf{y}_\delta(n)^T] = SPD_\delta^\dagger S^\dagger \tag{6.9.4}$$

where we used $E[\mathbf{v}_\delta(n)^*\mathbf{v}_\delta(n)^T] = E[\mathbf{v}(n)^*\mathbf{v}(n)^T] = \sigma_v^2 I$ and $E[\mathbf{v}(n)^*\mathbf{v}_\delta(n)^T] = 0$.

The ESPRIT method works with the matrix pencil, $C(\lambda) = C - \lambda C_\delta$, defined by the pair of matrices

$$C = R_{yy} - \sigma_v^2 I = SPS^\dagger, \qquad C_\delta = R_{yy_\delta} = SPD_\delta^\dagger S^\dagger \tag{6.9.5}$$

The generalized eigenvalues of this matrix pencil are, by definition [102], the solutions of $\det(C - \lambda C_\delta) = 0$, and the corresponding generalized eigenvectors satisfy $C\mathbf{e} = \lambda C_\delta \mathbf{e}$. The ESPRIT method is based on the observation that the *nonzero* generalized eigenvalues of $C(\lambda)$ are simply

$$\lambda_i = e^{jk_i\delta}, \quad i = 1, 2, \cdots L \tag{6.9.6}$$

and therefore, the desired wavenumbers k_i can be extracted from the knowledge of the λs. Note that $\lambda = 0$ is a generalized eigenvalue because $\det(C) = \det(SPS^\dagger) = 0$. This follows from the fact that $SPS^\dagger$ is an $(M+1) \times (M+1)$ matrix of rank $L < M+1$. The generalized eigenvectors corresponding to $\lambda = 0$ are the vectors in the null space of $SPS^\dagger$; namely, they satisfy $SPS^\dagger\mathbf{e} = 0$ or, equivalently, $S^\dagger\mathbf{e} = 0$. These are the noise subspace eigenvectors of R_{yy}. Next, we show that the only *nonzero* generalized eigenvalues are those in Eq. (6.9.6). The corresponding generalized eigenvector $\mathbf{e}$ must satisfy

$$SPS^\dagger\mathbf{e} = \lambda SPD_\delta^\dagger S^\dagger\mathbf{e}$$

multiplying both sides by $S^\dagger$ and removing the common matrix factor $(S^\dagger S)P$, we obtain $S^\dagger\mathbf{e} = \lambda D_\delta^\dagger S^\dagger\mathbf{e}$. Using the fact that $D_\delta^\dagger = D_\delta^{-1}$, and defining the L-dimensional vector $\mathbf{f} = S^\dagger\mathbf{e}$, we obtain

$$D_\delta \mathbf{f} = \lambda \mathbf{f}$$

Clearly, if $\mathbf{e}$ is not in the noise subspace, then $\mathbf{f} = S^\dagger\mathbf{e} \neq 0$; therefore, λ must be an eigenvalue of D_δ which is already diagonal. This proves Eq. (6.9.6). The eigenvectors of D_δ will be the L-dimensional unit vectors; that is, the columns of the $L \times L$ unit matrix, $\mathbf{f}_i = \mathbf{u}_i, i = 1,2, \ldots, L$. The generalized eigenvectors will be $\mathbf{e}_i = S(S^\dagger S)^{-1}\mathbf{u}_i$. These are obtained by an argument similar to Eq. (6.3.15). Thus, the L columns of the matrix $S(S^\dagger S)^{-1}$ are simply the generalized eigenvectors corresponding to the generalized eigenvalues (6.9.6).

In the practical implementation of the method, we assume we have two sets of snapshots, $\mathbf{y}(n)$ and $\mathbf{y}_\delta(n), n = 0,1, \ldots, N-1$, measured at the original and translated arrays. The covariance R_{yy} is estimated by Eq. (6.4.14) and the cross-covariance by

$$\hat{C}_\delta = \hat{R}_{yy_\delta} = \frac{1}{N}\sum_{n=0}^{N-1} \mathbf{y}(n)^* \mathbf{y}_\delta(n)^T$$

From the eigenproblem of $\hat{R}_{yy}$, we obtain an estimate $\hat{\sigma}_v^2$, either as the minimum eigenvalue or, as the average of the eigenvalues of the noise subspace. Then, set $\hat{C} = \hat{R}_{yy} - \hat{\sigma}_v^2 I$ and solve the generalized eigenproblem for the pair $\{\hat{C}, \hat{C}_\delta\}$ (e.g., using the EISPACK package). The L generalized eigenvalues closest to the unit circle are used to extract estimates of the desired wavenumbers k_i by Eq. (6.9.6).

Unlike the minimum-norm and reduced-order methods that require equally spaced linear arrays, the MUSIC and ESPRIT methods can be applied to arrays of arbitrary geometry.

6.10 *Spatial Smoothing*

Eigenvector methods rely on the property that the noise subspace eigenvectors have at least L zeros on the unit circle at the desired frequency locations. As we saw in Section 6.3, this property requires that the $L \times L$ power matrix P have full rank equal to L. To repeat the argument, the condition $R\mathbf{a} = \sigma_v^2\mathbf{a}$ implies that $SPS^\dagger\mathbf{a} = 0$, but what we want is $S^\dagger\mathbf{a} = 0$. Multiplying by $\mathbf{a}^\dagger$, we obtain $(S^\dagger\mathbf{a})^\dagger P(S^\dagger\mathbf{a}) = 0$, but this does not necessarily imply that $S^\dagger\mathbf{a} = 0$ unless P has full rank. The case of diagonal P corresponds to mutually *uncorrelated* sources for the L plane waves. The case of a nondiagonal P of full rank implies that the sources are *partially correlated.* The case of a nondiagonal P with less than full rank implies that some or all of the sources are *coherent* with each other. This case commonly arises in multipath situations, as shown in the diagram

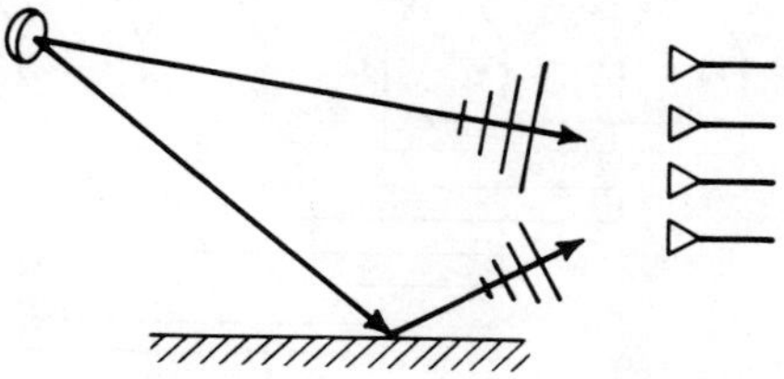

To see how eigenvector methods fail if P does not have full rank, consider the worst case when all the sources are coherent, which means that the wave amplitudes $A_i(n)$ are all proportional to each other, say, $A_i(n) = c_i A_1(n), i = 1, 2, \ldots, L$, where the $c_i \neq 0$ ($c_1 = 1$) are attenuation factors corresponding to the different paths. Compactly, we may write $\mathbf{A}(n) = A_1(n)\mathbf{c}$. Then, the power matrix becomes

$$P = E[\mathbf{A}(n)^* \mathbf{A}(n)^T] = E[\,|A_1(n)|^2]\mathbf{c}^* \mathbf{c}^T = P_1 \mathbf{c}^* \mathbf{c}^T \tag{6.10.1}$$

It has rank one. The corresponding covariance matrix is

$$R = SPS^\dagger + \sigma_v^2 I = P_1 S \mathbf{c}^* \mathbf{c}^T S^\dagger + \sigma_v^2 I = P_1 \mathbf{s}\mathbf{s}^\dagger + \sigma_v^2 I \tag{6.10.2}$$

where $\mathbf{s} = S\mathbf{c}^* = \sum_{l=1}^{L} \mathbf{s}_{k_l} c_l^*$. Similarly, $\mathbf{y}(n) = A_1(n) S^* \mathbf{c} + \mathbf{v}(n) = A_1(n)\mathbf{s}^* + \mathbf{v}(n)$. Because R is a rank-one modification of the identity matrix, it will have a one-dimensional signal subspace spanned by $\mathbf{s}$, and a noise subspace of dimension $K = M + 1 - 1 = M$ spanned by the eigenvectors belonging to the minimum eigenvalue σ_v^2. Thus, although we have L different signals, the solution of the eigenproblem will result in a one-dimensional signal subspace. Moreover, the noise eigenvectors, will *not* necessarily have zeros at the L desired locations. This can be seen as follows. If $R\mathbf{a} = \sigma_v^2 \mathbf{a}$ then $P_1 \mathbf{s}\mathbf{s}^\dagger \mathbf{a} = 0$, or, $\mathbf{s}^\dagger \mathbf{a} = \mathbf{c}^T S^\dagger \mathbf{a} = 0$, which gives

$$\mathbf{c}^T S^\dagger \mathbf{a} = [c_1, \cdots, c_L] \begin{bmatrix} A(k_1) \\ \vdots \\ A(k_L) \end{bmatrix} = \sum_{l=1}^{L} c_l A(k_l) = 0$$

This does not imply that the individual terms in the sum are zero. One solution to this problem is the method of spatial smoothing [55,62], which *restores* P to full rank, so that the eigenstructure methods can be applied as usual. The method is as follows. The given array of $M + 1$ sensors is subdivided into J subarrays each having $\bar{M} + 1$ sensors. The first subarray consists of the first $\bar{M} + 1$ elements of the given array. Each subsequent subarray is obtained by shifting ahead one array element at a time, as shown in this diagram

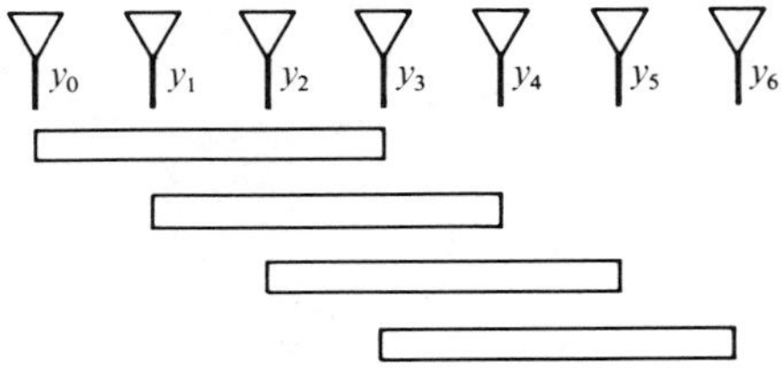

Formally, we define the J subarrays by

$$\bar{\mathbf{y}}_i(n) = [y_i(n), y_{i+1}(n), \cdots, y_{i+\bar{M}}(n)]^T, \qquad i = 0, 1, \cdots, J\text{-}1 \tag{6.10.3}$$

where the bar indicates that the size of the subarray is $\bar{M}+1$. That is the $(\bar{M}+1)$-dimensional portion of $\mathbf{y}(n)$ starting at the ith array element. Using Eq. (6.9.2), we may write compactly

$$\bar{\mathbf{y}}_i(n) = \bar{S}^* D_i^* \mathbf{A}(n) + \bar{\mathbf{v}}_i(n)$$

where $\bar{S}$ is the same as S but of dimension $\bar{M}+1$. The matrix D_i is given by Eq. (6.9.1) with $\delta = i$, corresponding to translation by i units. The covariance matrix of the ith subarray will be

$$\bar{R}_i = E[\bar{\mathbf{y}}_i(n)^* \bar{\mathbf{y}}_i(n)^T] = \bar{S} D_i P D_i^\dagger \bar{S}^\dagger + \sigma_v^2 \bar{I}$$

where $\bar{I}$ is the $(\bar{M}+1)$-dimensional identity matrix. The average of the subarray covariances is

$$\bar{R} = \frac{1}{J}\sum_{i=0}^{J-1} \bar{R}_i = \bar{S}\bar{P}\bar{S}^\dagger + \sigma_v^2 \bar{I} \tag{6.10.4}$$

where

$$\bar{P} = \frac{1}{J}\sum_{i=0}^{J-1} D_i P D_i^\dagger \tag{6.10.5}$$

To be able to resolve L sources by the $(\bar{M}+1)$-dimensional eigenproblem (6.10.4), we must have $\bar{M} \geq L$, and the rank of $\bar{P}$ must be L. It has been shown [62] that if the number of subarrays J is greater than the number of signals, $J \geq L$, then, $\bar{P}$ has full rank. If the J subarrays are to fit within the original array of length $M+1$, then we must have $M+1 \geq (\bar{M}+1)+(J-1)$; that is, the length of the first subarray plus the $J-1$ subsequent shifts. Thus, $M+1 \geq \bar{M}+J$. If both J and $\bar{M}$ are greater than L, then we must have $M+1 \geq 2L$. Therefore, the price for restoring the rank of P is that we must use twice as long an array as in the ordinary full-rank case with L sources. A somewhat stronger result is that $J \geq L+1-\rho$, where ρ is the rank of P [86]; equivalently, we have $J \geq \nu+1$, where $\nu = L-\rho$ is the nullity of P. This would give for the minimum number of array elements $M+1 \geq 2L+1-\rho$ [63,79,86].

Following [62], we derive the condition $J \geq L$ for the worst case, when all the signals are coherent. In that case, P has rank one ($\rho = 1$) and is given by Eq. (6.10.1); $\bar{P}$ becomes

$$\bar{P} = \frac{P_1}{J}\sum_{i=0}^{J-1} D_i \mathbf{c}^* \mathbf{c}^T D_i^\dagger = \frac{P_1}{J}\sum_{i=0}^{J-1} \mathbf{d}_i \mathbf{d}_i^\dagger\,, \qquad \mathbf{d}_i = D_i \mathbf{c}^*$$

Writing $\sum_{i=0}^{J-1} \mathbf{d}_i \mathbf{d}_i^\dagger = DD^\dagger$, where $D = [\mathbf{d}_0, \mathbf{d}_1, \ldots, \mathbf{d}_{J-1}]$, it follows that the rank of $\bar{P}$ is the same as the rank of D. The matrix element D_{li} is the lth component of the ith column; that is, $D_{li} = (\mathbf{d}_i)_l = c_l^* e^{jk_l i}$. Thus, D can be written as the product, $D = C^* V$, of the diagonal matrix $C^* = \mathrm{diag}\{c_1^*, \ldots, c_L^*\}$ and the $L \times J$ Vandermonde matrix V with matrix elements $V_{li} = e^{jk_l i}$; for example, if $L = 3$ and $J = 4$,

$$V = \begin{bmatrix} 1 & e^{jk_1} & e^{2jk_1} & e^{3jk_1} \\ 1 & e^{jk_2} & e^{2jk_2} & e^{3jk_2} \\ 1 & e^{jk_3} & e^{2jk_3} & e^{3jk_3} \end{bmatrix}$$

The rank of Vandermonde matrices is always full; that is, it is the minimum of the column and row dimensions, $\min(L,J)$. It follows that the rank of $\bar{P}$ is equal to $\min(L,J)$, therefore, it is equal to L only if $J \geq L$.

To appreciate the mechanism by which the rank is restored, let us consider an example with two ($L = 2$) fully coherent sources. The minimum number of subarrays needed to *decohere* the sources is $J = L = 2$. This implies $\bar{M} = M + 1 - J = M - 1$. The covariance matrix of the full array is

$$R = P_1 [\mathbf{s}_1, \mathbf{s}_2][c_1^*, c_2^*] \begin{bmatrix} c_1 \\ c_2 \end{bmatrix} \begin{bmatrix} \mathbf{s}_1^\dagger \\ \mathbf{s}_2^\dagger \end{bmatrix} + \sigma_v^2 I$$

The covariance matrices of the two subarrays are

$$\bar{R}_0 = P_1 [\bar{\mathbf{s}}_1, \bar{\mathbf{s}}_2][c_1^*, c_2^*] \begin{bmatrix} c_1 \\ c_2 \end{bmatrix} \begin{bmatrix} \bar{\mathbf{s}}_1^\dagger \\ \bar{\mathbf{s}}_2^\dagger \end{bmatrix} + \sigma_v^2 \bar{I}$$

$$\bar{R}_1 = P_1 [\bar{\mathbf{s}}_1, \bar{\mathbf{s}}_2][e^{jk_1} c_1^*, e^{jk_2} c_2^*] \begin{bmatrix} e^{-jk_1} c_1 \\ e^{-jk_2} c_2 \end{bmatrix} \begin{bmatrix} \bar{\mathbf{s}}_1^\dagger \\ \bar{\mathbf{s}}_2^\dagger \end{bmatrix} + \sigma_v^2 \bar{I}$$

Their average becomes

$$\bar{R} = \frac{1}{2}(\bar{R}_0 + \bar{R}_1) = [\bar{\mathbf{s}}_1, \bar{\mathbf{s}}_2]\bar{P} \begin{bmatrix} \bar{\mathbf{s}}_1^\dagger \\ \bar{\mathbf{s}}_2^\dagger \end{bmatrix} + \sigma_v^2 \bar{I}$$

where

$$\bar{P} = \frac{1}{2}[c_1^*, c_2^*] \begin{bmatrix} c_1 \\ c_2 \end{bmatrix} + \frac{1}{2}[e^{jk_1} c_1^*, e^{jk_2} c_2^*] \begin{bmatrix} e^{-jk_1} c_1 \\ e^{-jk_2} c_2 \end{bmatrix} =$$

$$= \begin{bmatrix} c_1^* c_1 & c_1^* c_2 (1 + e^{j(k_1 - k_2)})/2 \\ c_1 c_2^* (1 + e^{j(k_2 - k_1)})/2 & c_2^* c_2 \end{bmatrix}$$

Clearly, $\bar{P}$ is nonsingular. The presence of the translation phases makes the two column vectors $[c_1^*, c_2^*]^T$ and $[e^{jk_1}c_1^*, e^{jk_2}c_2^*]^T$ linearly independent. The determinant of $\bar{P}$ is easily found to be

$$\det\bar{P} = |c_1c_2|^2\sin^2(\frac{k_1 - k_2}{2})$$

Perhaps, an even simpler example is to consider the two quadratic forms

$$Q_0 = (f_1 + f_2)^2 = \mathbf{f}^T\begin{bmatrix}1\\1\end{bmatrix}[1,\ 1]\mathbf{f}, \qquad \mathbf{f} = \begin{bmatrix}f_1\\f_2\end{bmatrix}$$

$$Q_1 = f_1^2 = \mathbf{f}^T\begin{bmatrix}1\\0\end{bmatrix}[1,\ 0]\mathbf{f}$$

Separately, they have rank one, but their sum has full rank

$$Q = Q_0 + Q_1 = (f_1 + f_2)^2 + f_1^2 = 2f_1^2 + 2f_1f_2 + f_2^2 = \mathbf{f}^T\begin{bmatrix}2 & 1\\1 & 1\end{bmatrix}\mathbf{f}$$

where the 2×2 coefficient matrix has rank two, being the sum of two rank-one matrices defined by two linearly independent two-dimensional vectors

$$\begin{bmatrix}2 & 1\\1 & 1\end{bmatrix} = \begin{bmatrix}1\\1\end{bmatrix}[1,\ 1] + \begin{bmatrix}1\\0\end{bmatrix}[1,\ 0]$$

Such quadratic forms can be formed, for example, by $\mathbf{a}^\dagger SPS^\dagger\mathbf{a} = \mathbf{f}^\dagger P\mathbf{f}$, where $\mathbf{f} = S^\dagger\mathbf{a}$.

In the practical implementation of the method, the subarray covariances are computed by sample averages over N snapshots; that is,

$$\hat{\bar{R}}_i = \frac{1}{N}\sum_{n=0}^{N-1}\bar{\mathbf{y}}_i(n)^*\bar{\mathbf{y}}_i(n)^T$$

and the average

$$\hat{\bar{R}} = \frac{1}{J}\sum_{i=0}^{J-1}\hat{\bar{R}}_i$$

In addition to spatial smoothing, there exist other methods for dealing with the problem of coherent signal sources [83,84,87,88].

6.11 *Asymptotic Properties*

Statistically, the sample covariance matrix $\hat{R}$ approximates the theoretical R, and therefore, the linear predictor based on $\hat{R}$ will approximate the one based on R. Similarly, the eigenstructure of $\hat{R}$ will approximate that of R. In this section, we derive the asymptotic statistical properties that justify such approximations [108–142]. The basic technique for deriving asymptotic results is to perform a linearization of the empirical solution about the theoretical one and then use the asymptotic statistical properties of $\hat{R}$. In Section 1.5, we obtained the asymptotic covariance of $\hat{R}$ for a large number of snapshots N,

$$E[\Delta R_{ij}\Delta R_{kl}] = \frac{1}{N}(R_{ik}R_{jl} + R_{il}R_{jk}) \tag{6.11.1}$$

where $\Delta R = \hat{R} - R$ is the deviation of $\hat{R}$ from its mean. This was valid in the real-valued case; the complex-valued version will be considered shortly.

The normal equations of linear prediction based on $\hat{R}$ and R are

$$\hat{R}\hat{\mathbf{a}} = \hat{E}\mathbf{u}_0\,, \quad \hat{\mathbf{a}} = \begin{bmatrix} 1 \\ \hat{\boldsymbol{\alpha}} \end{bmatrix} \qquad \text{and} \qquad R\mathbf{a} = E\mathbf{u}_0\,, \quad \mathbf{a} = \begin{bmatrix} 1 \\ \boldsymbol{\alpha} \end{bmatrix}$$

where $\hat{E}$ and E are the minimized values of mean-square prediction errors given by $\hat{E} = \hat{\mathbf{a}}^T\hat{R}\hat{\mathbf{a}}$ and $E = \mathbf{a}^T R\mathbf{a}$. Setting $\hat{\mathbf{a}} = \mathbf{a} + \Delta\mathbf{a}$ and $\hat{E} = E + \Delta E$, we obtain

$$(R + \Delta R)(\mathbf{a} + \Delta\mathbf{a}) = (E + \Delta E)\mathbf{u}_0 \quad \Longrightarrow \quad R\Delta\mathbf{a} + \Delta R\mathbf{a} = \Delta E\mathbf{u}_0 \tag{6.11.2}$$

where we kept only the first-order terms. Because $\hat{\mathbf{a}}$ and $\mathbf{a}$ have first coefficient of unity, $\Delta\mathbf{a} = \hat{\mathbf{a}} - \mathbf{a}$ will have zero first coefficient, that is, $\mathbf{u}_0^T\Delta\mathbf{a} = 0$. Multiplying both sides of Eq. (6.11.2) by $\mathbf{a}^T$, we obtain $\mathbf{a}^T R\Delta\mathbf{a} + \mathbf{a}^T\Delta R\mathbf{a} = \Delta E$. Using the normal equations for $\mathbf{a}$, we have $\mathbf{a}^T R\Delta\mathbf{a} = E\mathbf{u}_0^T\Delta\mathbf{a} = 0$. Thus, $\Delta E = \mathbf{a}^T\Delta R\mathbf{a}$. Solving Eq. (6.11.2) for $\Delta\mathbf{a}$ and using $R^{-1}\mathbf{u}_0 = E^{-1}\mathbf{a}$, we find

$$\Delta\mathbf{a} = E^{-1}\Delta E\mathbf{a} - R^{-1}\Delta R\mathbf{a}\,, \qquad \Delta E = \mathbf{a}^T\Delta R\mathbf{a} \tag{6.11.3}$$

For the purpose of computing the asymptotic covariances of $\Delta\mathbf{a}$ and ΔE, it proves convenient to express Eq. (6.11.3) in terms of the vector $\delta\mathbf{a} \equiv \Delta R\mathbf{a}$. Then,

$$\Delta\mathbf{a} = E^{-1}\Delta E\mathbf{a} - R^{-1}\delta\mathbf{a}\,, \qquad \Delta E = \mathbf{a}^T\delta\mathbf{a} \tag{6.11.4}$$

Using Eq. (6.11.1), we find for the covariance of $\delta\mathbf{a}$

$$E[\delta a_i\delta a_k] = E[\sum_j \Delta R_{ij}a_j \sum_l \Delta R_{kl}a_l] = \sum_{jl} E[\Delta R_{ij}\Delta R_{kl}]a_j a_l$$

$$= \frac{1}{N}\sum_{jl}(R_{ik}R_{jl} + R_{jk}R_{il})a_j a_l = \frac{1}{N}[R_{ik}(\mathbf{a}^T R\mathbf{a}) + (R\mathbf{a})_i(\mathbf{a}^T R)_k]$$

or,

$$E[\delta\mathbf{a}\,\delta\mathbf{a}^T] = \frac{1}{N}[RE + R\mathbf{a}\mathbf{a}^T R] \tag{6.11.5}$$

Writing $\Delta E = \delta\mathbf{a}^T\mathbf{a}$, we find

$$E[\delta\mathbf{a}\Delta E] = E[\delta\mathbf{a}\delta\mathbf{a}^T]\mathbf{a} = \frac{1}{N}[RE + R\mathbf{a}\mathbf{a}^T R]\mathbf{a} = \frac{1}{N}[ER\mathbf{a} + R\mathbf{a}(\mathbf{a}^T R\mathbf{a})] = \frac{2E}{N}R\mathbf{a}$$

Using this result, we find for the asymptotic variance of $\hat{E}$

$$E[(\Delta E)^2] = \mathbf{a}^T E[\delta\mathbf{a}\Delta E] = \frac{2E}{N}\mathbf{a}^T R\mathbf{a} = \frac{2E^2}{N} \tag{6.11.6}$$

This generalizes Eq. (1.15.2). Similarly, we find for the cross-covariance between $\hat{E}$ and $\hat{\mathbf{a}}$

$$E[\Delta\mathbf{a}\Delta E] = E[(E^{-1}\Delta E\mathbf{a} - R^{-1}\delta\mathbf{a})\Delta E] = E^{-1}E[(\Delta E)^2]\mathbf{a} - R^{-1}E[\delta\mathbf{a}\Delta E]$$

or,

$$E[\Delta\mathbf{a}\Delta E] = E^{-1}\frac{2E^2}{N}\mathbf{a} - R^{-1}(\frac{2E}{N}R\mathbf{a}) = 0 \tag{6.11.7}$$

Finally, we find for the covariance of the predictor $\hat{\mathbf{a}}$

$$E[\Delta\mathbf{a}\Delta\mathbf{a}^T] = E[\Delta\mathbf{a}(E^{-1}\Delta E\mathbf{a}^T - \delta\mathbf{a}^T R^{-1})] = -E[\Delta\mathbf{a}\,\delta\mathbf{a}^T]R^{-1}$$

$$= -E[(E^{-1}\mathbf{a}\Delta E - R^{-1}\delta\mathbf{a})\delta\mathbf{a}^T] = -[E^{-1}\mathbf{a}\frac{2E}{N}\mathbf{a}^T R - R^{-1}\frac{1}{N}(RE + R\mathbf{a}\mathbf{a}^T R)]R^{-1}$$

or,

$$E[\Delta\mathbf{a}\Delta\mathbf{a}^T] = \frac{E}{N}(R^{-1} - E^{-1}\mathbf{a}\mathbf{a}^T) = \frac{E}{N}\begin{bmatrix} 0 & \mathbf{0}^T \\ \mathbf{0} & \tilde{R}^{-1} \end{bmatrix}$$

where we used Eq. (5.9.16) or Eq. (1.7.35), and $\tilde{R}$ is the lower-order portion of R. Such a result was expected because $\Delta\mathbf{a}$ is of the form $\Delta\mathbf{a} = \begin{bmatrix} 0 \\ \Delta\boldsymbol{\alpha} \end{bmatrix}$, where $\Delta\boldsymbol{\alpha} = \hat{\boldsymbol{\alpha}} - \boldsymbol{\alpha}$. Thus,

$$E[\Delta\boldsymbol{\alpha}\Delta\boldsymbol{\alpha}^T] = \frac{E}{N}\tilde{R}^{-1} \tag{6.11.8}$$

This is a well-known result, and although we obtained it for sample covariance matrices of the type (1.5.21), where the *snapshots* $\mathbf{y}_n$ were assumed to be independent, it can be proved in the case of autoregressive models where $\hat{R}$ is built out of the sample autocorrelation function [108,118,119,120,121,125–128,133]. It can also be shown that asymptotically $\hat{E}$ and $\hat{\boldsymbol{\alpha}}$ are the *maximum likelihood* estimates of the LP parameters E and $\boldsymbol{\alpha}$, having all the good properties of such estimates, namely, asymptotic unbiasedness, consistency, efficiency, and gaussian distribution about the theoretical values with covariances given by Eqs. (6.11.6) through (6.11.8), which are none other than the Cramér-Rao bounds of these parameters. It is instructive to use the general formula (1.17.17) to derive these bounds, where the parameter vector is defined as $\boldsymbol{\lambda} = [E, \boldsymbol{\alpha}]^T$. We must determine the dependence of R on these parameters and then compute the derivatives $\partial R/\partial E$ and $\partial R/\partial/\boldsymbol{\alpha}$. We write the UL factorization of R in the form of Eq. (1.7.33)

$$R = \begin{bmatrix} \rho_a & \mathbf{r}_a^T \\ \mathbf{r}_a & \tilde{R} \end{bmatrix} = U^{-1} D_a U^{-T} = \begin{bmatrix} 1 & \alpha^T \\ 0 & \tilde{U} \end{bmatrix}^{-1} \begin{bmatrix} E & 0^T \\ 0 & \tilde{D} \end{bmatrix} \begin{bmatrix} 1 & 0^T \\ \alpha & \tilde{U}^T \end{bmatrix}^{-1}$$

The parametrization of R on the parameters E and $\boldsymbol{\alpha}$ is shown explicitly. It is evident that the entries ρ_a and $\mathbf{r}_a$ depend on E and $\boldsymbol{\alpha}$, whereas $\tilde{R}$ does not. We have

$$\mathbf{r}_a = -\tilde{R}\alpha\,, \qquad \rho_a = E - \alpha^T \mathbf{r}_a = E + \alpha^T \tilde{R}\alpha$$

Working with differentials, we find $d\mathbf{r}_a = -\tilde{R}d\boldsymbol{\alpha}$ and $d\rho_a = dE + 2\boldsymbol{\alpha}^T\tilde{R}d\boldsymbol{\alpha}$. Differentiating R entry by entry and using Eq. (1.7.35) for R^{-1}, we find

$$R^{-1}dR = E^{-1}\begin{bmatrix} dE + \alpha^T\tilde{R}d\alpha & -d\alpha^T\tilde{R} \\ (dE + \alpha^T\tilde{R}d\alpha)\alpha - Ed\alpha & -\alpha d\alpha^T\tilde{R} \end{bmatrix} \tag{6.11.9}$$

Writing a similar expression for a second differential $R^{-1}\delta R$, multiplying the two, and taking the trace, we find

$$\mathrm{tr}[R^{-1}dRR^{-1}\delta R] = E^{-2}dE\,\delta E + 2E^{-1}d\alpha^T\tilde{R}\delta\alpha \tag{6.11.10}$$

This gives for the matrix elements of the Fisher information matrix

$$J_{EE} = \frac{1}{2}N\,\mathrm{tr}[R^{-1}\frac{\partial R}{\partial E}R^{-1}\frac{\partial R}{\partial E}] = \frac{N}{2E^2}$$

$$J_{\alpha E} = \frac{1}{2}N\,\mathrm{tr}[R^{-1}\frac{\partial R}{\partial \alpha}R^{-1}\frac{\partial R}{\partial E}] = 0$$

$$J_{\alpha\alpha} = \frac{1}{2}N\,\mathrm{tr}[R^{-1}\frac{\partial R}{\partial \alpha}R^{-1}\frac{\partial R}{\partial \alpha^T}] = \frac{N}{E}\tilde{R}$$

As we know, the inverse of the information matrix is the Cramér-Rao bound for unbiased estimates. This inverse agrees with Eqs. (6.11.6) through (6.11.8). Following the discussion of [123,129], we may also derive the asymptotic covariances of the reflection coefficients. The forward and backward Levinson recursion establishes a one-to-one correspondence between the prediction coefficients $\boldsymbol{\alpha}$ and the vector of reflection coefficients $\boldsymbol{\gamma}$. Therefore, we have the differential correspondence $\Delta\boldsymbol{\gamma} = \Gamma\Delta\boldsymbol{\alpha}$, where Γ is the matrix of partial derivatives $\Gamma_{ij} = \partial\gamma_i/\partial\alpha_j$. It follows that the asymptotic covariance of $\boldsymbol{\gamma}$ will be

$$E[\Delta\gamma\Delta\gamma^T] = \Gamma E[\Delta\alpha\Delta\alpha^T]\Gamma^T = \frac{E}{N}\Gamma\tilde{R}^{-1}\Gamma^T \tag{6.11.11}$$

Example 6.11.1 For the first-order case, we have $\tilde{R} = [R(0)]$ and $E_1 = R(0)(1 - \gamma_1^2)$, where $\gamma_1 = -a_{11}$. Thus, we obtain Eq. (1.15.2) as a special case

$$E[(\Delta a_{11})^2] = E[(\Delta\gamma_1)^2] = \frac{1-\gamma_1^2}{N}$$

For the second-order case, $\Delta\boldsymbol{\alpha} = [\Delta a_{21}, \Delta a_{22}]^T$, and we have $E_2 = R(0)(1 - \gamma_1^2)(1 - \gamma_2^2)$ and $\tilde{R}$ is the order-one autocorrelation matrix. Thus, we find

$$E[\Delta\boldsymbol{\alpha}\Delta\boldsymbol{\alpha}^T] = \frac{E_2}{N}\tilde{R}^{-1} = \frac{E_2}{N}\begin{bmatrix} R(0) & R(1) \\ R(1) & R(0) \end{bmatrix}^{-1} =$$

$$= \frac{(1-\gamma_1^2)(1-\gamma_2^2)}{N(1-\gamma_1^2)}\begin{bmatrix} 1 & -\gamma_1 \\ -\gamma_1 & 1 \end{bmatrix} = \frac{1-\gamma_2^2}{N}\begin{bmatrix} 1 & -\gamma_1 \\ -\gamma_1 & 1 \end{bmatrix}$$

From the Levinson recursion, we find for the second-order predictor $a_{21} = -\gamma_1(1 - \gamma_2)$ and $a_{22} = -\gamma_2$. Differentiating, we have

$$d\boldsymbol{\alpha} = \begin{bmatrix} da_{21} \\ da_{22} \end{bmatrix} = \begin{bmatrix} -(1-\gamma_2) & \gamma_1 \\ 0 & -1 \end{bmatrix}\begin{bmatrix} d\gamma_1 \\ d\gamma_2 \end{bmatrix}$$

Inverting, we find

$$d\boldsymbol{\gamma} = \begin{bmatrix} d\gamma_1 \\ d\gamma_2 \end{bmatrix} = \frac{1}{1-\gamma_2}\begin{bmatrix} -1 & -\gamma_1 \\ 0 & -(1-\gamma_2) \end{bmatrix} d\boldsymbol{\alpha} = \Gamma d\boldsymbol{\alpha}$$

Forming the product $\Gamma\tilde{R}^{-1}\Gamma^T$ we finally find

$$E[\Delta\boldsymbol{\gamma}\Delta\boldsymbol{\gamma}^T] = \frac{1}{N}\frac{1-\gamma_2^2}{(1-\gamma_2)^2}\begin{bmatrix} 1-\gamma_1^2 & 0 \\ 0 & (1-\gamma_2)^2 \end{bmatrix}$$

which gives component-wise

$$E[(\Delta\gamma_1)^2] = \frac{1}{N}\frac{(1+\gamma_2)(1-\gamma_1^2)}{1-\gamma_2}, \quad E[\Delta\gamma_1\Delta\gamma_2] = 0, \quad E[(\Delta\gamma_2)^2] = \frac{1-\gamma_2^2}{N}$$

Setting $\gamma_2 = 0$, the variance of γ_1 becomes equal to that of the first-order case and $E[(\Delta\gamma_2)^2] = 1/N$. More generally, for an autoregressive process of order M, all reflection coefficients of order greater than M vanish, but their asymptotic variances are equal to $1/N$[123,129].

Next, we consider the asymptotic properties of the eigenstructure of $\hat{R}$[134–142]. In the complex-valued case $\hat{R}$ is given by Eq. (6.4.14), and Eq. (6.11.1) is replaced by

$$E[\Delta R_{ij}\Delta R_{kl}] = \frac{1}{N}R_{il}R_{kj} \tag{6.11.12}$$

where again $\Delta R = \hat{R} - R$. This can be shown in the same way as Eq. (1.5.23) using the following expression for the expectation value of the product of four complex gaussian random variables arising from the (independent) snapshots $\mathbf{y}(n)$ and $\mathbf{y}(m)$

$$E[y_i(n)^* y_j(n) y_k(m)^* y_l(m)] = R_{ij}R_{kl} + \delta_{nm}R_{il}R_{kj}$$

Equation (6.11.12) may be written more conveniently in the form

$$E[(\mathbf{a}^\dagger \Delta R \mathbf{b})(\mathbf{c}^\dagger \Delta R \mathbf{d})] = \frac{1}{N}(\mathbf{a}^\dagger R \mathbf{d})(\mathbf{c}^\dagger R \mathbf{b}) \tag{6.11.13}$$

for any four $(M+1)$-dimensional vectors **a, b, c, d.** In particular, we may apply it to four eigenvectors of R. Let $\mathbf{e}_i$ denote the orthonormal eigenvectors of R, $R\mathbf{e}_i = \lambda_i \mathbf{e}_i$, with eigenvalues arranged in increasing order. Then,

$$E[(\mathbf{e}_i^\dagger \Delta R \mathbf{e}_j)(\mathbf{e}_k^\dagger \Delta R \mathbf{e}_l)] = \frac{1}{N}(\mathbf{e}_i^\dagger R \mathbf{e}_l)(\mathbf{e}_k^\dagger R \mathbf{e}_j) = \frac{1}{N}\lambda_i \lambda_j \delta_{il}\delta_{kj}$$

where we used $(\mathbf{e}_i^\dagger R)\mathbf{e}_l = \lambda_i \mathbf{e}_i^\dagger \mathbf{e}_l = \lambda_i \delta_{il}$. Arranging the eigenvectors into the eigenvector matrix $E = [\mathbf{e}_0, \mathbf{e}_1, \ldots, \mathbf{e}_M]$, we recognize that the quantities $\mathbf{e}_i^\dagger \Delta R \mathbf{e}_j$ are the matrix elements of ΔR in the E basis; that is, the elements of the matrix $\Delta V = E^\dagger \Delta R E$. Thus, we obtain the *diagonalized* version of Eq. (6.11.12)

$$E[\Delta V_{ij} \Delta V_{kl}] = \frac{1}{N}\lambda_i \lambda_j \delta_{il}\delta_{kj} \tag{6.11.14}$$

The asymptotic properties of the eigenstructure of $\hat{R}$ are obtained by using Eq. (6.11.14) coupled with standard first-order perturbation theory. The eigenproblems for R and $\hat{R}$ are

$$\hat{R}\hat{E} = \hat{E}\hat{\Lambda} \quad \text{and} \quad RE = E\Lambda \tag{6.11.15}$$

where $\hat{E}, E$ are the eigenvector matrices and $\hat{\Lambda}, \Lambda$ the diagonal matrices of the eigenvalues. Because the eigenvectors E form a complete set, it follows that the eigenvectors $\hat{E}$ can be expanded as linear combinations of the former; that is, $\hat{E} = EF$. The orthonormality and completeness of $\hat{E}$ and E requires that F be a unitary matrix, satisfying $F^\dagger F = FF^\dagger = I$. This is easily shown; for example, $\hat{E}^\dagger \hat{E} = F^\dagger E^\dagger E F = F^\dagger I F = F^\dagger F = I$. In carrying out the first-order perturbation analysis, we shall assume initially that all the eigenvalues of R are distinct. This corresponds to the Pisarenko case, where the noise subspace is one-dimensional and thus, $L = M$. The assumption of distinct eigenvalues means that, under a perturbation, $\hat{R} = R + \Delta R$, each eigenvector changes by a small correction of the form $\hat{E} = E + \Delta E$. By the completeness of the basis E, we may write $\Delta E = E \Delta C$ so that $\hat{E} = E(I + \Delta C)$. The unitarity of the matrix $F = I + \Delta C$ requires that ΔC be antihermitian; that is, $\Delta C + \Delta C^\dagger = 0$. This follows from the first-order approximation $F^\dagger F = I + \Delta C + \Delta C^\dagger$. The perturbation changes the eigenvalues by $\hat{\lambda}_i = \lambda_i + \Delta\lambda_i$ or $\hat{\Lambda} = \Lambda + \Delta\Lambda$. To determine the first-order corrections we use Eq. (6.11.15)

$$(R + \Delta R)(E + \Delta E) = (E + \Delta E)(\Lambda + \Delta\Lambda) \quad \Longrightarrow \quad \Delta R E + R \Delta E = \Delta E \Lambda + E \Delta\Lambda$$

where we kept only the first-order terms. Multiplying both sides by $E^\dagger$ and using $E^\dagger RE = \Lambda$ and the definition $\Delta V = E^\dagger \Delta RE$, we obtain

$$\Delta V + \Lambda\Delta C = \Delta C\Lambda + \Delta\Lambda \quad \Longrightarrow \quad \Delta\Lambda + \Delta C\Lambda - \Lambda\Delta C = \Delta V$$

or, component-wise

$$\Delta\lambda_i \delta_{ij} + (\lambda_j - \lambda_i)\Delta C_{ij} = \Delta V_{ij}$$

Setting $i = j$ and then $i \neq j$, we find

$$\Delta\lambda_i = \Delta V_{ii}\,, \qquad \Delta C_{ij} = -\frac{\Delta V_{ij}}{\lambda_i - \lambda_j}\,, \quad \text{for} \quad i \neq j \tag{6.11.16}$$

Using Eq. (6.11.14), we obtain the asymptotic variances of the eigenvalues

$$E[(\Delta\lambda_i)^2] = E[\Delta V_{ii}\Delta V_{ii}] = \frac{\lambda_i^2}{N} \tag{6.11.17}$$

For the eigenvectors, we write

$$\Delta\mathbf{e}_i = \hat{\mathbf{e}}_i - \mathbf{e}_i = \sum_{j\neq i} \mathbf{e}_j \Delta C_{ji}$$

and their covariances are

$$E[\Delta\mathbf{e}_i \Delta\mathbf{e}_i^\dagger] = \sum_{j\neq i}\sum_{k\neq i} \mathbf{e}_j \mathbf{e}_k^\dagger E[\Delta C_{ji}\Delta C_{ki}^*]$$

Using the antihermiticity of ΔC and Eq. (6.11.14), we find

$$E[\Delta C_{ji}\Delta C_{ki}^*] = -\frac{E[\Delta V_{ji}\Delta V_{ik}]}{(\lambda_j - \lambda_i)(\lambda_i - \lambda_k)} = \frac{1}{N}\frac{\lambda_i\lambda_j}{(\lambda_i - \lambda_j)^2}\delta_{jk}$$

which gives

$$E[\Delta\mathbf{e}_i \Delta\mathbf{e}_i^\dagger] = \frac{1}{N}\sum_{j\neq i}\frac{\lambda_i\lambda_j}{(\lambda_i - \lambda_j)^2}\mathbf{e}_j\mathbf{e}_j^\dagger \tag{6.11.18}$$

Separating out the minimum eigenvalue λ_0 and eigenvector $\mathbf{e}_0$, and denoting the remaining signal subspace eigenvectors and eigenvalues by $E_S = [\mathbf{e}_1, \ldots, \mathbf{e}_M]$ and $\Lambda_S = \text{diag}\{\lambda_1, \ldots, \lambda_M\}$, we may write Eq. (6.11.18) compactly

$$E[\Delta\mathbf{e}_0 \Delta\mathbf{e}_0^\dagger] = \frac{1}{N} E_S \lambda_0 \Lambda_S (\Lambda_S - \lambda_0 I_M)^{-2} E_S^\dagger \tag{6.11.19}$$

where I_M is the M-dimensional unit matrix. The zeros of the polynomial $\mathbf{e}_0$ contain the desired frequency information. The asymptotic variances for the zeros can be obtained by writing

$$\Delta z_i = \left(\frac{\partial z_i}{\partial \mathbf{e}_0}\right)^T \Delta\mathbf{e}_0$$

which gives

$$E[\,|\Delta z_i|^2] = \left(\frac{\partial z_i}{\partial \mathbf{e}_0}\right)^T E[\Delta\mathbf{e}_0 \Delta\mathbf{e}_0^\dagger]\left(\frac{\partial z_i}{\partial \mathbf{e}_0}\right)^* \tag{6.11.20}$$

Example 6.11.2: In the $L = M = 1$ Example 6.3.1, we have for the eigenvalues and orthonormal eigenvectors of R

$$\lambda_0 = \sigma_v^2\,, \quad \lambda_1 = \sigma_v^2 + 2P_1\,, \quad \mathbf{e}_0 = \frac{1}{\sqrt{2}}\begin{bmatrix} 1 \\ -e^{jk_1} \end{bmatrix}, \quad \mathbf{e}_1 = \frac{1}{\sqrt{2}}\begin{bmatrix} 1 \\ e^{jk_1} \end{bmatrix}$$

It follows from Eq. (6.11.19)

$$E[\Delta\mathbf{e}_0 \Delta\mathbf{e}_0^\dagger] = \frac{1}{N}\,\mathbf{e}_1\mathbf{e}_1^\dagger\,\frac{\lambda_1\lambda_0}{(\lambda_1 - \lambda_0)^2}$$

Using the general formula for the sensitivities of zeros with respect to the coefficients of a polynomial [25]

$$\frac{\partial z_i}{\partial a_m} = -\frac{1}{a_0}\,\frac{z_i^{M-m}}{\prod_{j\neq i}(z_i - z_j)}$$

we find for the zero $z_1 = e^{jk_1}$ of $\mathbf{e}_0$

$$\frac{\partial z_1}{\partial \mathbf{e}_0} = -\sqrt{2}\begin{bmatrix} z_1 \\ 1 \end{bmatrix}$$

Using this into Eq. (6.11.20), we find

$$E[\,|\Delta z_1|^2] = \frac{1}{N}\,\frac{4\lambda_1\lambda_0}{(\lambda_1 - \lambda_0)^2} = \frac{1}{N}\,\frac{1 + 2SNR}{SNR^2}\,, \qquad SNR = \frac{P_1}{\sigma_v^2}$$

This implies that the quality of the estimated zero improves either by increasing the number of snapshots N or the signal to noise ratio. For low SNR, the denominator $(\lambda_1 - \lambda_0)^2$ becomes small and the variance of z_1 increases, resulting in degradation of performance. For a given level of quality there is a *tradeoff* between the number of snapshots and SNR. In general, the signal subspace eigenvalues Λ_S will be separated from $\lambda_0 = \sigma_v^2$ by a term that depends on the signal powers, say, $\Lambda_S = \lambda_0 I_M + P_S$. Then,

$$\lambda_0\Lambda_S(\Lambda_S - \lambda_0 I_M)^{-2} = (I_M + P_S/\sigma_v^2)(P_S/\sigma_v^2)^{-2}$$

and Eq. (6.11.19) implies that estimate of $\mathbf{e}_0$ is better for larger SNRs.

When the noise subspace has dimension $K = M + 1 - L$ and the minimum eigenvalue λ_0 has K-fold degeneracy, the first-order perturbation analysis becomes somewhat more complicated. The eigenproblem for R is divided into its noise and signal subspace parts

$$RE_N = \lambda_0 E_N\,, \qquad RE_S = E_S\Lambda_S$$

where E_N consists of the K degenerate eigenvectors belonging to the minimum eigenvalue $\lambda_0 = \sigma_v^2$ and E_S consists of the remaining L signal subspace eigenvectors. Under a perturbation $\hat{R} = R + \Delta R$, the degeneracy of E_N is lifted and the noise subspace eigenvalues become unequal $\hat{\lambda}_i = \lambda_0 + \Delta\lambda_i$, $i = 0, 1, \ldots, K-1$, or $\hat{\Lambda}_N = \lambda_0 I_K + \Delta\Lambda_N$. Similarly, the signal subspace eigenvalues change to $\hat{\Lambda}_S = \Lambda_S + \Delta\Lambda_S$. The signal subspace eigenvectors, belonging to distinct eigenvalues, change in the usual way; namely, each eigenvector changes by receiving small contributions from all other eigenvectors. The noise subspace eigenvectors, however, being degenerate, are mixed up by the perturbation into linear combinations of themselves, and in addition, they receive small corrections from the signal subspace eigenvectors. Thus, the eigenproblem for the perturbed matrix $\hat{R}$ is

$$\hat{R}\hat{E}_N = \hat{E}_N\hat{\Lambda}_N\,, \qquad \hat{R}\hat{E}_S = \hat{E}_S\hat{\Lambda}_S \tag{6.11.21}$$

where the corrections of the eigenvectors are of the form

$$\hat{E}_N = E_N C + E_S \Delta C\,, \qquad \hat{E}_S = E_S + E_S\Delta B + E_N \Delta D \tag{6.11.22}$$

In absence of the perturbation ΔR, the choice of the degenerate basis E_N is arbitrary and can be replaced by any linear combination $E_N C$. The presence of the perturbation fixes this particular linear combination by the requirement that the change in the eigenvectors be small. Combining the two equations into the full eigenvector matrices, we have

$$\hat{E} = [\hat{E}_N, \hat{E}_S] = [E_N, E_S]\begin{bmatrix} C & \Delta D \\ \Delta C & I_L + \Delta B \end{bmatrix} = EF$$

The orthonormality and completeness requirements for $\hat{E}$ imply that $F^\dagger F = FF^\dagger = I$. To first order, these conditions are equivalent to

$$C^\dagger C = I_K\,, \qquad \Delta C + \Delta D^\dagger C = 0\,, \qquad \Delta B + \Delta B^\dagger = 0 \tag{6.11.23}$$

Thus, C must be unitary. Inserting Eq. (6.11.22) into the first term of Eq. (6.11.21) and using Eg. (6.11.23), we find

$$(R + \Delta R)(E_N C - E_S \Delta D^\dagger C) = (E_N C - E_S\Delta D^\dagger C)(\lambda_0 I_K + \Delta\Lambda_N)$$

and equating first-order terms,

$$\Delta R E_N C - E_S \Lambda_S \Delta D^\dagger C = E_N C \Delta\Lambda_N - E_S \Delta D^\dagger C \lambda_0$$

Multiplying both sides first by $E_N^\dagger$ and then by $E_S^\dagger$ and using the orthonormality properties (6.4.3), we obtain

$$\Delta V_{NN} C = C\Delta\Lambda_N \tag{6.11.24}$$

where $\Delta V_{NN} = E_N^\dagger \Delta R E_N$, and

$$\Delta V_{SN} C - \Lambda_S \Delta D^\dagger C = -\Delta D^\dagger C \lambda_0$$

where $\Delta V_{SN} = E_S^\dagger \Delta R E_N$, and solving for $\Delta D^\dagger$

$$\Delta D^\dagger = (\Lambda_S - \lambda_0 I_L)^{-1}\Delta V_{SN} \tag{6.11.25}$$

Similarly, from the second term of Eq. (6.11.21), we find for ΔB

$$\Delta\Lambda_S + \Delta B \Lambda_S - \Lambda_S \Delta B = \Delta V_{SS}\,, \qquad \Delta V_{SS} = E_S^\dagger \Delta R E_S \tag{6.11.26}$$

which can be solved as in Eq. (6.11.16). To summarize, the corrections to noise subspace eigenvalues $\Delta\Lambda_N$ and the unitary matrix C are obtained from the solution of the $K \times K$ eigenproblem (6.11.24), ΔD is constructed by (6.11.25), then ΔC is constructed by (6.11.23), and ΔB by (6.11.26). Because the corrections to the signal subspace eigenvectors are obtained from the nondegenerate part of the perturbation analysis, it follows that Eq. (6.11.18) is still valid for the signal eigenvectors. More specifically, because we index the noise subspace eigenvectors for $0 \le i \le K-1$ and the signal subspace eigenvectors for $K \le i \le M$, we split the sum over the noise and signal subspace parts

$$E[\Delta\mathbf{e}_i\Delta\mathbf{e}_i^\dagger] = \frac{1}{N}\frac{\lambda_0\lambda_i}{(\lambda_0-\lambda_i)^2}\sum_{j=0}^{K-1}\mathbf{e}_j\mathbf{e}_j^\dagger + \frac{1}{N}\sum_{\substack{j\neq i\\ j=K}}^{M}\frac{\lambda_j\lambda_i}{(\lambda_j-\lambda_i)^2}\mathbf{e}_j\mathbf{e}_j^\dagger$$

where we used the fact that all noise subspace eigenvalues are equal to λ_0. The first term is recognized as the projector onto the noise subspace. Thus,

$$E[\Delta\mathbf{e}_i\Delta\mathbf{e}_i^\dagger] = \frac{1}{N}\frac{\lambda_i\lambda_0}{(\lambda_i-\lambda_0)^2}E_N E_N^\dagger + \frac{1}{N}\sum_{\substack{j\neq i\\ j=K}}^{M}\frac{\lambda_i\lambda_j}{(\lambda_i-\lambda_j)^2}\mathbf{e}_j\mathbf{e}_j^\dagger \qquad (6.11.27)$$

for $K \le i \le M$. Because most eigenvector methods can also be formulated in terms of the signal subspace eigenvectors, it is enough to consider only the asymptotic covariances of these eigenvectors. For example, in the reduced-order method of Section 6.7, the reduced order polynomials $\mathbf{a}_i$ may alternatively be computed by requiring that the corresponding shifted vectors $\mathbf{b}_i$ be orthogonal to the signal subspace [75]; namely, $E_S^\dagger\mathbf{b}_i = 0$, $i = 0, 1, \ldots, K-1$, and similarly, for the empirical quantities $\hat{E}_S^\dagger\hat{\mathbf{b}}_i = 0$. If we denote by G_i the part of E_S consisting of $L+1$ rows starting with the ith row, then, these conditions become $G_i^\dagger\mathbf{a}_i = 0$. Because the first coefficient of $\mathbf{a}_i$ is unity, these give rise to L linear equations for the L last coefficients of $\mathbf{a}_i$. It follows that $\mathbf{a}_i$ can be constructed as a function of the signal eigenvectors, and thus, one can obtain the corresponding covariance of $\mathbf{a}_i$ using Eq. (6.11.27). An example will illustrate this remark.

Example 6.11.3: Consider the case of one plane wave ($L = 1$) and arbitrary M. The covariance matrix $R = \sigma_v^2 I + P_1\mathbf{s}_{k_1}\mathbf{s}_{k_1}^\dagger$ has a one-dimensional signal subspace spanned by $\mathbf{s}_{k_1}$. The normalized signal subspace eigenvector is $\mathbf{e}_M = \mathbf{s}_{k_1}/\sqrt{M+1}$, so that $E_S = [\mathbf{e}_M]$. Its eigenvalue is $\lambda_M = \sigma_v^2 + (M+1)P_1$. The matrix G_i is formed by row i to row $i + L$, inclusive. That is,

$$G_i = \begin{bmatrix} e_{Mi} \\ e_{M,i+1}\end{bmatrix} = \frac{1}{\sqrt{M+1}}\begin{bmatrix} e^{jk_1 i} \\ e^{jk_1(i+1)}\end{bmatrix}$$

The equation $G_i^\dagger\mathbf{a}_i = 0$ becomes for the first-order filters $\mathbf{a}_i$

$$G_i^\dagger\mathbf{a}_i = \frac{1}{\sqrt{M+1}}[e^{-jk_1 i}, e^{-jk_1(i+1)}]\begin{bmatrix}1\\ a_{i1}\end{bmatrix} = 0 \quad\Rightarrow\quad a_{i1} = -e^{jk_1}$$

and therefore, all the reduced-order polynomials are equal to the theoretical one, $A_i(z) = 1 - e^{jk_1}z^{-1}$. Now, if the empirical $\hat{\mathbf{e}}_M$ is used, then a similar calculation gives $a_{i1} = -\hat{e}^*_{Mi}/\hat{e}^*_{M,i+1}$, and therefore, the estimated zero will be $\hat{z}_1 = -a_{i1} = \hat{e}^*_{Mi}/\hat{e}^*_{M,i+1}$. Differentiating, we obtain $dz_1 = de^*_{Mi}/e^*_{M,i+1} - e^*_{Mi}de^*_{M,i+1}/e^{2}_{M,i+1}{}^*$; therefore, its covariance will be

$$E[\,|\Delta z_1|^2] = \frac{1}{|e_{M,i+1}|^2}E[\,|\Delta e_{Mi}|^2] + \frac{|e_{Mi}|^2}{|e_{M,i+1}|^4}E[\,|\Delta e_{M,i+1}|^2] -$$

$$-\ 2\mathrm{Re}\left(\frac{e_{Mi}{}^*}{|e_{M,i+1}|^2 e_{M,i+1}{}^*}E[\Delta e_{Mi}\Delta e_{M,i+1}{}^*]\right)$$

This simplifies to

$$E[\,|\Delta z_1|^2] = (M+1)\Big[E[\,|\Delta e_{Mi}|^2] + E[\,|\Delta e_{M,i+1}|^2] - 2\mathrm{Re}(e^{jk_1}E[\Delta e_{Mi}\Delta e_{M,i+1}{}^*])\Big]$$

Because the signal subspace is one-dimensional, the second term in Eq. (6.11.27) is absent. The noise projector can be expressed in terms of the signal projector $E_N E_N^\dagger = I - E_S E_S^\dagger$. Thus, Eq. (6.11.27) becomes

$$E[\Delta \mathbf{e}_M \Delta \mathbf{e}_M^\dagger] = \frac{1}{N}\frac{\lambda_M\lambda_0}{(\lambda_M - \lambda_0)^2}\left(I - \frac{1}{M+1}\mathbf{s}_{k_1}\mathbf{s}_{k_1}^\dagger\right)$$

Extracting the ith and $(i+1)$st components, we get for the variance of the estimated zero

$$E[\,|\Delta z_1|^2] = \frac{1}{N}\frac{2(M+1)\lambda_M\lambda_0}{(\lambda_M - \lambda_0)^2} = \frac{1}{N}\frac{2[1 + (M+1)SNR]}{(M+1)\,SNR^2}$$

where $SNR = P_1/\sigma_v^2$. Setting $M = 1$, we recover the result of Example 6.11.2.

Problems

Problem 6.1: Computer Experiment

A fourth order autoregressive process is defined by the difference equation

$$y_n + a_1 y_{n-1} + a_2 y_{n-2} + a_3 y_{n-3} + a_4 y_{n-4} = \epsilon_n$$

where ϵ_n is zero-mean, unit-variance, white gaussian noise. The filter parameters $\{a_1, a_2, a_3, a_4\}$ are chosen such that the prediction error filter

$$A(z) = 1 + a_1 z^{-1} + a_2 z^{-2} + a_3 z^{-3} + a_4 z^{-4}$$

has zeros at the locations

$$0.99\exp(\pm 0.2\pi j) \quad \text{and} \quad 0.99\exp(\pm 0.4\pi j)$$

(a) Determine $\{a_1, a_2, a_3, a_4\}$.

(b) Using a random number generator for ϵ_n, generate a realization of y_n consisting of 50 samples. To avoid transient effects, be sure to let the filter run for a while. For instance, discard the first 500 or 1000 outputs and keep the last 50.

(c) Compute the sample autocorrelation of y_n based on the above block of data.

(d) Solve the normal equations by means of Levinson's algorithm to determine the Yule-Walker estimates of the model parameters $\{a_1, a_2, a_3, a_4, \sigma_\epsilon^2\}$ and compare them with the exact values.

(e) Compute the corresponding Yule-Walker spectrum and plot it together with the exact autoregressive spectrum versus frequency. Be sure to allow for a sufficiently dense grid of frequencies to be able to resolve the narrow peaks of this example. Plot all spectra in decibels.

(f) Using the same finite block of y_n data, determine estimates of the model parameters $\{a_1, a_2, a_3, a_4, \sigma_\epsilon^2\}$ using Burg's method, and compare them with the Yule-Walker estimates and with the exact values.

(g) Compute the corresponding Burg spectrum and plot it together with the exact spectrum versus frequency.

(h) Using the same block of y_n data, compute the ordinary periodogram spectrum and plot it together with the exact spectrum.

(i) Window the y_n data with a Hamming window and then compute the corresponding periodogram spectrum and plot it together with the exact spectrum.

(j) Repeat parts (b) through (i) using a longer realization of length 100.

(k) Repeat parts (b) through (i) using a length-200 realization of y_n.

(l) Evaluate the various results of this experiment.

Problem 6.2:

Show that the classical Bartlett spectrum of Eq. (6.2.6) can be written in the compact matrix form of Eq. (6.2.7).

Problem 6.3:

Show that in the limit of large M, the first sidelobe of the smearing function $W(\omega)$ of Eq. (6.2.10) is approximately 13 dB down from the main lobe.

Problem 6.4: Computer Experiment

(a) Reproduce the spectra shown in Figures 6.7 through 6.10.

(b) For the AR case, let $M = 6$, and take the SNRs of both sinusoids to be 6 dB, but change the sinusoid frequencies to

$$\omega_1 = 0.5 + \Delta\omega, \qquad \omega_2 = 0.5 - \Delta\omega$$

where $\Delta\omega$ is variable. Study the dependence of bias of the spectral peaks on the frequency separation $\Delta\omega$ by computing and plotting the spectra for various values of $\Delta\omega$. (Normalize all spectra to 0 dB at the sinusoid frequency ω_1).

Problem 6.5:
Derive Equation (6.2.30).

Problem 6.6:
Let

$$R = \sigma_v^2 I + \sum_{i=1}^{L} P_i \mathbf{s}_{\omega_i} \mathbf{s}_{\omega_i}^{\dagger}$$

be the autocorrelation matrix of Eq. (6.2.8). Show that the inverse R^{-1} can be computed recursively as follows:

$$R_k^{-1} = R_{k-1}^{-1} - \frac{R_{k-1}^{-1} \mathbf{s}_{\omega_k} \mathbf{s}_{\omega_k}^{\dagger} R_{k-1}^{-1}}{\mathbf{s}_{\omega_k}^{\dagger} R_{k-1}^{-1} \mathbf{s}_{\omega_k} + P_k^{-1}}$$

for $k = 1, \ldots, L$, initialized by $R_0 = \sigma_v^2 I$.

Problem 6.7:
Consider the case of one sinusoid ($L = 1$) in noise and arbitrary filter order $M > 2$, so that the $(M + 1) \times (M + 1)$ autocorrelation matrix is

$$R = \sigma_v^2 I + P_1 \mathbf{s}_{\omega_1} \mathbf{s}_{\omega_1}^{\dagger}$$

(a) Show that the $(L = 1)$ – dimensional signal subspace is spanned by the eigenvector

$$\mathbf{e}_M = \mathbf{s}_{\omega_1}$$

and determine the corresponding eigenvalue.

(b) Show that the $M + 1 - L = M$ dimensional noise subspace is spanned by the M linearly independent eigenvectors

$$
\mathbf{e}_0 = \begin{bmatrix} 1 \\ -e^{j\omega_1} \\ 0 \\ 0 \\ \vdots \\ 0 \\ 0 \\ 0 \end{bmatrix} \Bigg\updownarrow \mathrm{M}-1, \quad \mathbf{e}_1 = \begin{bmatrix} 0 \\ 1 \\ -e^{j\omega_1} \\ 0 \\ \vdots \\ 0 \\ 0 \\ 0 \end{bmatrix},
$$

$$
\mathbf{e}_2 = \begin{bmatrix} 0 \\ 0 \\ 1 \\ -e^{j\omega_1} \\ \vdots \\ 0 \\ 0 \\ 0 \end{bmatrix}, \qquad \mathbf{e}_{M-1} = \begin{bmatrix} 0 \\ 0 \\ 0 \\ 0 \\ \vdots \\ 0 \\ 1 \\ -e^{j\omega_1} \end{bmatrix}
$$

all belonging to the minimum eigenvalue σ_v^2.

(c) Show that the eigenpolynomial $A(z)$ corresponding to an arbitrary linear combination of the M noise eigenvectors

$$
\mathbf{a} = \mathbf{e}_0 + c_1\mathbf{e}_1 + c_2\mathbf{e}_2 + \cdots + c_{M-1}\mathbf{e}_{M-1}
$$

can be factored in the form

$$
A(z) = (1 - e^{j\omega_1}z^{-1})(1 + c_1z^{-1} + c_2z^{-2} + \cdots + c_{M-1}z^{-M+1})
$$

exhibiting one zero at the desired sinusoid frequency ω_1 on the unit circle, and $M - 1$ additional spurious zeros with arbitrary locations that depend on the particular choice of the coefficients c_i.

Problem 6.8:

The constraint (6.2.31) can be incorporated into the performance index (6.2.32) by means of a Lagrange multiplier

$$
\mathcal{E} = \mathbf{a}^\dagger R\mathbf{a} + \lambda(1 - \mathbf{a}^\dagger\mathbf{a})
$$

Show that the minimization of $\mathcal{E}$ is equivalent to the Pisarenko eigenvalue problem of Eq. (6.2.29), with the multiplier λ playing the role of the eigenvalue. Show that the minimum of $\mathcal{E}$ is the minimum eigenvalue.

Problem 6.9:
Show Equation (6.3.11).

Problem 6.10:
Consider a singular $(M+1) \times (M+1)$ autocorrelation matrix R having nonsingular principal submatrices, and let $\mathbf{a}$ be the symmetric or antisymmetric order-M prediction filter satisfying $R\mathbf{a} = 0$, as discussed in Section 5.5. First, argue that the M zeros of this filter lie on the unit circle $z_i = e^{j\omega_i}$, $i = 1,2, \ldots, M$. Then, consider the eigenvalue decomposition of this matrix in the form $R = E^\dagger \Lambda E$, where Λ is the diagonal matrix of the M *nonzero* eigenvalues of R and E is the $(M+1) \times M$ matrix whose columns are the M corresponding eigenvectors. Let $S = [\mathbf{s}_{\omega_1}, \mathbf{s}_{\omega_2}, \ldots, \mathbf{s}_{\omega_M}]$ be the matrix of phasing vectors defined by the zeros of $\mathbf{a}$. Argue that E is linearly related to S and that R can be written in the form $R = S^\dagger P S$, where P is an $M \times M$ positive-definite matrix. Finally, show that the requirement that R be Toeplitz implies that P must be diagonal, and therefore, R admits the sinusoidal representation

$$R = \sum_{i=1}^{M} P_i \mathbf{s}_{\omega_i} \mathbf{s}_{\omega_i}^\dagger \text{ with } P_i \text{ positive.}$$

Problem 6.11: Computer Experiment
To simulate Eq. (6.3.7), the signal amplitudes $A_i(n)$ may be generated by

$$A_i(n) = A_i \exp(j\phi_{in})$$

where ϕ_{in} are independent random phases distributed uniformly over the interval $[0,2\pi]$, and A_i are deterministic amplitudes related to the assumed signal to noise ratios (SNR) in units of decibels by

$$(\text{SNR})_i = 10 \log_{10}\left[\frac{|A_i|^2}{\sigma_v^2}\right], \qquad i = 1,2, \ldots, L$$

(a) Consider one plane wave incident on an array of seven sensors from an angle $\theta_1 = 30°$. The sensors are equally spaced at half-wavelength spacings; i.e., $d = \lambda/2$. For each of the following values of the SNR of the wave

$$\text{SNR} = 0 \text{ dB}, \quad 10 \text{ dB}, \quad 20 \text{ dB}$$

generate $N = 1000$ snapshots of Eq. (6.3.7) and compute the empirical spatial correlation matrix across the array by

$$R = \frac{1}{N} \sum_{n=0}^{N-1} \mathbf{y}(n)^* \mathbf{y}(n)^T$$

Compute and plot on the same graph the three spatial spectra: Bartlett, autoregressive (AR), and maximum likelihood (ML), versus wavenumber k.

(b) Repeat for two plane waves incident from angles $\theta_1 = 25°$ and $\theta_2 = 35°$, and with equal powers of 30 dB.

(c) Repeat part (b) for angles $\theta_1 = 28°$ and $\theta_2 = 32°$.

(d) Repeat part (c) by gradually decreasing the (common) SNR of the two plane waves to the values of 20 dB, 10 dB, and 0 dB.

(e) For parts (a) through (d), also plot all the theoretical spectra.

Note: The empirical R is Hermitian but not Toeplitz. If you find it difficult to compute R^{-1} required in the AR and ML spectra, you may work with a Toeplitz version of R obtained by replacing each diagonal by the average of the entries along that diagonal, and then develop a complex-valued version of the routine LEV to obtain R^{-1}.

Problem 6.12:

Consider L plane waves incident on a linear array of $M+1$ sensors ($L \leq M$) in the presence of spatially coherent noise. As discussed in Section 6.3, the corresponding covariance matrix is given by

$$R = \sigma_v^2 Q + \sum_{i=1}^{L} P_i \mathbf{s}_{k_i} \mathbf{s}_{k_i}^{\dagger}$$

where the waves are assumed to be mutually uncorrelated.

(a) Show that the generalized eigenvalue problem

$$R\mathbf{a} = \lambda Q \mathbf{a}$$

has (1) an $(M + 1 - L)$-dimensional noise subspace spanned by $M + 1 - L$ linearly independent degenerate eigenvectors all belonging to the eigenvalue $\lambda = \sigma_v^2$ and (2) an L-dimensional signal subspace with L eigenvalues greater than σ_v^2.

(b) Show that any two eigenvectors $\mathbf{a}_1$ and $\mathbf{a}_2$ belonging to distinct eigenvalues λ_1 and λ_2 are orthogonal to each other with respect to the inner product defined by the matrix Q; that is, show that

$$\mathbf{a}_1^{\dagger} Q \mathbf{a}_2 = 0$$

(c) Show that the L-dimensional signal subspace is spanned by the L vectors

$$Q^{-1}\mathbf{s}_{k_i}; \qquad i = 1,2, \ldots, L$$

(d) Show that any vector $\mathbf{a}$ in the noise subspace corresponds to a polynomial $A(z)$ that has L of its M zeros on the unit circle at locations

$$z_i = \exp(jk_i); \qquad i = 1,2, \ldots, L$$

The remaining $M - L$ zeros can have arbitrary locations.

Problem 6.13:

The previous problem suggests the following approach to the problem of "selectively nulling" some of the sources and not nulling others. Suppose L_1 of the sources are not to be nulled and have known SNRs and directions of arrival, and L_2 of the sources are to be nulled. The total number of sources is then $L = L_1 + L_2$, and assuming incoherent background noise, the incident field will have covariance matrix

$$R = \sigma_v^2 I + \sum_{i=1}^{L_1} P_i \mathbf{s}_{k_i} \mathbf{s}_{k_i}^\dagger + \sum_{i=L_1+1}^{L_1+L_2} P_i \mathbf{s}_{k_i} \mathbf{s}_{k_i}^\dagger$$

Define Q by means of

$$\sigma_v^2 Q = \sigma_v^2 I + \sum_{i=1}^{L_1} P_i \mathbf{s}_{k_i} \mathbf{s}_{k_i}^\dagger$$

so that we may write R as follows

$$R = \sigma_v^2 Q + \sum_{i=L_1+1}^{L_1+L_2} P_i \mathbf{s}_{k_i} \mathbf{s}_{k_i}^\dagger$$

Then, the nulling of the L_2 sources at wavenumbers k_i; $i = L_1 + 1, \ldots, L_1 + L_2$, can be effected by the $(M+1-L_2)$-dimensional *noise* subspace of the generalized eigenvalue problem

$$R\mathbf{a} = \lambda Q \mathbf{a}$$

having minimum eigenvalue equal to σ_v^2.

(a) As an example, consider the case $M = 2$, $L_1 = L_2 = 1$. Then,

$$R = \sigma_v^2 Q + P_2 \mathbf{s}_{k_2} \mathbf{s}_{k_2}^\dagger, \qquad \sigma_v^2 Q = \sigma_v^2 I + P_1 \mathbf{s}_{k_1} \mathbf{s}_{k_1}^\dagger$$

Show that the $(M + 1 - L_2 = 2)$-dimensional noise subspace is spanned by the two eigenvectors

$$\mathbf{e}_1 = \begin{bmatrix} 1 \\ -e^{jk_2} \\ 0 \end{bmatrix}, \qquad \mathbf{e}_2 = \begin{bmatrix} 0 \\ 1 \\ -e^{jk_2} \end{bmatrix}$$

(b) Show that an arbitrary linear combination

$$\mathbf{a} = \mathbf{e}_1 + \rho_1 \mathbf{e}_2$$

corresponds to a filter $A(z)$ having one zero at the desired location $z_2 = \exp(jk_2)$, and a spurious zero with arbitrary location.

(c) Show that the $(L_2 = 1)$-dimensional signal subspace is spanned by the vector

$$\mathbf{e}_3 = Q^{-1} \mathbf{s}_{k_2}$$

and that the corresponding generalized eigenvalue is

$$\lambda = \sigma_v^2 + P_2 \mathbf{s}_{k_2}^\dagger Q^{-1} \mathbf{s}_{k_2}$$

(d) Verify the orthogonality properties $\mathbf{e}_i^\dagger Q \mathbf{e}_3 = 0$, $i = 1,2$, for the three eigenvectors $\mathbf{e}_1$, $\mathbf{e}_2$, $\mathbf{e}_3$ defined in parts (a) and (c).

(e) As another example, consider the case $M = 3$, and $L_1 = L_2 = 1$. Show that the $(M + 1 - L_2 = 3)$-dimensional noise subspace is spanned by the three eigenvectors

$$\mathbf{e}_1 = \begin{bmatrix} 1 \\ -e^{jk_2} \\ 0 \\ 0 \end{bmatrix}, \quad \mathbf{e}_2 = \begin{bmatrix} 0 \\ 1 \\ -e^{jk_2} \\ 0 \end{bmatrix}, \quad \mathbf{e}_3 = \begin{bmatrix} 0 \\ 0 \\ 1 \\ -e^{jk_2} \end{bmatrix}$$

and the signal eigenvector is $\mathbf{e}_4 = Q^{-1}\mathbf{s}_{k_2}$. Generalize this part and part (a), to the case of arbitrary M and $L_1 = L_2 = 1$.

(f) As a final example that corresponds to a unique noise eigenvector, consider the case $M = 2$, and $L_1 = 1$, $L_2 = 2$, so that

$$R = \sigma_v^2 Q + P_2 \mathbf{s}_{k_2}\mathbf{s}_{k_2}^\dagger + P_3 \mathbf{s}_{k_3}\mathbf{s}_{k_3}^\dagger, \qquad \sigma_v^2 Q = \sigma_v^2 I + P_1 \mathbf{s}_{k_1}\mathbf{s}_{k_1}^\dagger$$

with k_2 and k_3 to be nulled. Show that the $(M + 1 - L_2 = 1)$-dimensional noise subspace is spanned by

$$\mathbf{a} = \mathbf{e}_1 = \begin{bmatrix} 1 \\ -(e^{jk_2} + e^{jk_3}) \\ e^{jk_2}e^{jk_3} \end{bmatrix}$$

and that the corresponding polynomial $A(z)$ factors into the two desired zeros

$$A(z) = (1 - e^{jk_2}z^{-1})(1 - e^{jk_3}z^{-1})$$

Problem 6.14: Computer Experiment

Consider a nine-element ($M = 8$) linear array with half-wavelength spacing and two mutually uncorrelated incident plane waves with wavenumbers $k_1 = 0.3\pi$, $k_2 = 0.5\pi$ and equal powers of 20 dB. The background noise is incoherent with variance $\sigma_v^2 = 1$.

(a) Construct the theoretical matrix R of Eq. (6.3.13) and solve its eigenproblem determining the nine eigenvectors and eigenvalues. Using a root finder (see e.g.,[143]), compute the eight zeros of each of the seven noise subspace eigenvectors and verify that the desired zeros lie on the unit circle.

(b) Generate $N = 100$ snapshots, construct the sample covariance matrix $\hat{R}$ of Eq. (6.4.14), solve its eigenproblem, use the AIC and MDL criteria to check the dimension of the noise subspace, but regardless of these criteria take that dimension to be seven. Compare the empirical eigenvalues with the theoretical ones found above. Compute the zeros of the noise subspace eigenvectors and decide if the desired zeros are among them and if any spurious ones lie close to the unit circle. Also, compute the zeros of the Min-Norm vector $\mathbf{d}$.

(c) On the same graph, plot in dB the pseudospectra of a few of the noise subspace eigenvectors, say, the first three. On a separate graph, but using the same vertical scales as the previous one, plot the MUSIC and Min-Norm spectra.

(d) Using the same set of snapshots, repeat parts (b,c) for the symmetrized sample covariance matrix of Eq. (6.4.15).

(e) For fixed SNR, repeat parts (b,c,d) for the following choices of number of snapshots: $N = 20, 50, 150, 200, 500$.

(f) With number of snapshots fixed at $N = 100$, repeat parts (a,b,c,d) for the following values of the (common) signal to noise ratio: $SNR = -10, 5, 0, 5, 10, 30$ dB.

(g) Repeat parts (a–f) for three 20 dB planewaves with $k_1 = 0.3\pi$, $k_2 = 0.4\pi$, $k_3 = 0.5\pi$.

Problem 6.15:
Show Eqs. (6.11.9) and (6.11.10).

Problem 6.16:
Consider an M-dimensional complex random vector $\mathbf{y}$ with real and imaginary parts ξ and η, $\mathbf{y} = \xi + j\eta$. With this vector we associate a $(2M)$-dimensional real random vector $\tilde{\mathbf{y}} = \begin{bmatrix} \xi \\ \eta \end{bmatrix}$. The corresponding covariance matrices are defined by

$$R = E[\mathbf{y}^* \mathbf{y}^T], \qquad \tilde{R} = E[\tilde{\mathbf{y}}\tilde{\mathbf{y}}^T]$$

(a) Show that the conditions $E[\xi\xi^T] = E[\eta\eta^T]$ and $E[\xi\eta^T] = -E[\eta\xi^T]$ are equivalent to the condition $E[\mathbf{y}\mathbf{y}^T] = 0$. And that in this case the covariance matrices can be written as follows

$$R = 2(A + jB), \quad \tilde{R} = \begin{bmatrix} A & B \\ -B & A \end{bmatrix}, \quad A = E[\xi\xi^T], \quad B = E[\xi\eta^T]$$

The matrix A is symmetric and B antisymmetric. Show the equality of the quadratic forms $\mathbf{y}^T R^{-1} \mathbf{y}^* = \frac{1}{2}\tilde{\mathbf{y}}^T \tilde{R}^{-1} \tilde{\mathbf{y}}$. Also, show the relationship between the determinants $\det R = 2^M (\det \tilde{R})^{1/2}$. *Hint:* Apply a correlation canceling transformation on $\tilde{R}$ and use the matrix identity $A + BA^{-1}B = (A + jB)A^{-1}(A - jB)$.

(b) A complex gaussian random vector $\mathbf{y}$ is defined by the requirement that the corresponding real vector $\tilde{\mathbf{y}}$ be gaussian [112,144,145]. Equating the elemental probabilities $p(\mathbf{y})d^{2M}\mathbf{y} = p(\tilde{\mathbf{y}})d^{2M}\tilde{\mathbf{y}}$ and using the results of part (a), show that if $p(\tilde{\mathbf{y}})$ is an ordinary (zero-mean) gaussian with covariance $\tilde{R}$, then the density of $\mathbf{y}$ is

$$p(\mathbf{y}) = (\pi^M \det R)^{-1} e^{-\mathbf{y}^T R^{-1} \mathbf{y}^*}$$

(c) Using this density show for any four components of $\mathbf{y}$

$$E[y_i^* y_j y_k^* y_l] = R_{ij} R_{kl} + R_{il} R_{kj}$$

(d) Use this result to prove Eq. (6.11.12)

Problem 6.17:
Show that the log-likelihood function based on N independent complex gaussian snapshots is given by (up to a constant)

$$\ln p = -N\mathrm{tr}[\ln R + R^{-1}\hat{R}]$$

where $\hat{R}$ is given by Eq. (6.4.14). Note that it differs by a factor of two from the real-valued case. From the discussion of Section 1.17, it follows that $\hat{R}$ is the maximum likelihood estimate of R. Moreover, the trace formula for the Fisher information matrix also differs by a factor of two, namely,

$$J_{ij} = N\,\mathrm{tr}[R^{-1}\frac{\partial R}{\partial \lambda_i}R^{-1}\frac{\partial R}{\partial \lambda_j}]$$

Problem 6.18:
Using Eq. (6.11.12), show that the covariance of the complex-valued LP parameters E and **a** are

$$E[(\Delta E)^2] = \frac{E^2}{N}, \quad E[\Delta \mathbf{a}\Delta E] = 0, \quad E[\Delta\mathbf{a}\Delta\mathbf{a}^\dagger] = \frac{E}{N}(R^{-1} - E^{-1}\mathbf{a}\mathbf{a}^\dagger)$$

Problem 6.19:
Let $S(k) = \mathbf{s}_k^\dagger R\mathbf{s}_k$ be the Bartlett spectrum. Using Eq. (6.11.13), show that its variance is

$$E[(\Delta S(k))^2] = \frac{1}{N}S(k)^2$$

Show that the variance of the ML spectrum $S(k) = 1/\mathbf{s}_k^\dagger R^{-1}\mathbf{s}_k$ is also given by a similar formula.

Problem 6.20:
(a) Let $A(k) = \mathbf{s}_k^\dagger\mathbf{a}$ be the frequency response of the LP polynomial in the complex-valued case. Using the results of Problem 6.18, show that its variance is

$$E[\,|\Delta A(k)|^2\,] = \frac{E}{N}\left(\mathbf{s}_k^\dagger R^{-1}\mathbf{s}_k - E^{-1}|A(k)|^{-2}\right)$$

Use the kernel representation of Problem 5.17 to argue that the right-hand side is positive. Alternatively, show that it is positive by writing $A(k) = E\mathbf{s}_k^\dagger R^{-1}\mathbf{u}_0$ and $E = (\mathbf{u}_0^\dagger R^{-1}\mathbf{u}_0)^{-1}$, and using the Schwarz inequality.

(b) In the complex case, show that $E[\Delta\mathbf{a}\Delta\mathbf{a}^T] = 0$. Then, show that the variance of the AR spectrum $S(k) = E/|A(k)|^2$ is given by

$$E[(\Delta S(k))^2] = \frac{1}{N}S(k)^2[2S(k)(\mathbf{s}_k^\dagger R^{-1}\mathbf{s}_k) - 1]$$

and show again that the right-hand side is positive.

References

1. S. M. Kay and S. L. Marple, Spectrum Analysis—A Modern Perspective, *Proc. IEEE,* **69,** 1380–1419 (1981).
2. S. Haykin, Ed., *Nonlinear Methods of Spectral Analysis,* New York, Springer-Verlag, 1979.
3. J. P. Burg, Maximum Entropy Spectral Analysis, presented at *37th Annual Int. SEG Meeting,* Oklahoma City, (1967).
4. D. Childers, Ed., *Modern Spectrum Analysis,* New York, IEEE Press, 1978.
5. D. E. Smylie, G. K. C. Clarice, and T. J. Ulrich, Analysis of Irregularities in the Earth's Rotation, in *Methods of Computational Physics,* vol. 13, New York, Academic, 1973, pp. 391–430.
6. T. J. Ulrich and R. W. Clayton, Time Series Modelling and Maximum Entropy, *Phys. Earth Planet. Inter.,* **12,** 188–200 (1976).
7. W. Gersch and D. R. Sharpe, Estimation of Power Spectra with Finite Order Autoregressive Models, *IEEE Trans. Autom. Control,* **AC-13,** 367–369 (1973).
8. O. L. Frost, Power Spectrum Estimation, in G. Tacconi, Ed., *Aspects of Signal Processing*, Boston, Reidel, 1977.
9. P. R. Gutowski, E. A. Robinson, and S. Treitel, Spectral Estimation: Fact or Fiction?, *IEEE Trans. Geosci. Electron.,* **GE-16,** 80–84 (1978).
10. *Proc. IEEE,* **70**(9) (September 1982), Special Issue on Spectral Estimation.
11. A. Papoulis, Maximum Entropy and Spectral Estimation: A Review, *IEEE Trans. Acoust., Speech, Signal Process.,* **ASSP-29,** 1176–1186 (1981).
12. E. A. Robinson, A Historical Perspective of Spectrum Estimation, *Proc. IEEE,* **70,** 885–907 (1982).
13. S. B. Kesler, Ed., *Modern Spectrum Analysis, II,* New York, IEEE Press, 1986.
14. S. L. Marple, *Digital Spectral Analysis with Applications,* Englewood Cliffs, NJ, Prentice-Hall, 1987.
15. S. M. Kay, *Modern Spectral Estimation,* Englewood Cliffs, NJ, Prentice-Hall, 1988.
16. J. Capon, High Resolution Frequency Wavenumber Spectrum Analysis, *Proc. IEEE,* **57,** 1408–1418 (1969).
17. J. Capon, Maximum Likelihood Spectral Estimation, in S. Haykin, Ed., *Nonlinear Methods of Spectral Analysis,* New York, Springer-Verlag, 1979.
18. R. T. Lacoss, Data Adaptive Spectral Analysis Methods, *Geophysics,* **36,** 661–675 (1971).
19. V. F. Pisarenko, The Retrieval of Harmonics from a Covariance Function, *Geoph. J. R. Astron. Soc.,* **33,** 347–366 (1973).
20. E. H. Satorius and J. R. Zeidler, Maximum Entropy Spectral Analysis of Multiple Sinusoids in Noise, *Geophysics,* **43,** 1111–1118 (1978).
21. D. W. Tufts and R. Kumaresan, Singular Value Decomposition and Improved Frequency Estimation Using Linear Prediction, *IEEE Trans. Acoust., Speech, Signal Process.,* **ASSP-30,** 671–675 (1982).

22. D. W. Tufts and R. Kumaresan, Estimation of Frequencies of Multiple Sinusoids: Making Linear Prediction Perform like Maximum Likelihood, *Proc. IEEE,* **70,** 975–989 (1982).

23. S. L. Marple, Frequency Resolution of Fourier and Maximum Entropy Spectral Estimates, *Geophysics,* **47,** 1303–1307 (1982).

24. M. Quirk and B. Liu, On the Resolution of Autoregressive Spectral Estimation, *Proc. IEEE Int. Conf. Acoust., Speech, Signal Process.,* 1095–1097 (1983).

25. A. V. Oppenheim and R. W. Schafer, *Digital Signal Processing,* Englewood Cliffs, NJ, Prentice-Hall, 1975.

26. S. Y. Kung and Y. H. Hu, Improved Pisarenko's Sinusoidal Spectrum Estimate via SVD Subspace Approximation Methods, *Proc. 21st IEEE Int. Conf. Decision and Control,* Orlando, FL, (1982), p. 1312.

27. Y. H. Hu and S. Y. Kung, Toeplitz Eigensystem Solver, *IEEE Trans. Acoust., Speech, Signal Process.,* **ASSP-33,** 1264 (1985)

28. B. D. Steinberg, *Principles of Aperture and Array System Design,* New York, Wiley, 1976.

29. J. E. Hudson, *Adaptive Array Principles,* Stevenage, UK, Peter Peregrinus, 1981.

30. D. E. N. Davies, K. G. Corless, D. S. Hicks, and K. Milne, Array Signal Processing, in A. W. Rudge, K. Milne, A. D. Olver, and P. Knight, Eds., *The Handbook of Antenna Design,* vol. 2, London, Peter Peregrinus, 1983.

31. N. L. Owsley, Sonar Array Processing, in S. Haykin, Ed., *Array Signal Processing,* Englewood Cliffs, NJ, Prentice-Hall, 1985.

32. S. Haykin, Radar Signal Processing, *ASSP Magazine,* **2,** no.2, 2 (1985).

33. B. L. Lewis, F. F. Kretschmer, and W. W. Shelton, Eds., *Aspects of Radar Signal Processing,* Norwood, MA, Artech House, 1986.

34. W. C. Knight, R. G. Pridham, and S. M. Kay, Digital Signal Processing for Sonar, *Proc. IEEE,* **69,** 1451–1506 (1981).

35. W. F. Gabriel, Spectral Analysis and Adaptive Array Superresolution Techniques, *Proc. IEEE,* **68,** 654–666 (1980).

36. R. N. McDonough, Application of the Maximum Likelihood Method and the Maximum Entropy Method to Array Processing, in S. Haykin, Ed., *Nonlinear Methods of Spectral Analysis,* New York, Springer-Verlag, 1979.

37. D. H. Johnson, The Application of Spectral Estimation Methods to Bearing Estimation Problems, *Proc. IEEE,* **70,** 1018–1028 (1982).

38. A. J. Berni, Angle-of-Arrival Estimation Using an Adaptive Antenna Array, *IEEE Trans. Aerosp. Electron. Syst.,* **AES-11,** 278–284 (March 1975).

39. T. Thorvaldsen, Maximum Entropy Spectral Analysis in Antenna Spatial Filtering, *IEEE Trans. Antennas Propag.,* **AP-28,** 552–560 (1980).

40. T. E. Barnard, Two Maximum Entropy Beamforming Algorithms for Equally Spaced Line Arrays, *IEEE Trans. Acoust., Speech, Signal Process.,* **ASSP-30,** 175–189 (1980).

41. N. L. Owsley, Spectral Signal Set Extraction, in G. Tacconi, Ed., *Aspects of Signal Processing,* Boston, D. Reidel, 1977.

42. J. E. Evans, Aperture Sampling Techniques for Precision Direction Finding, *IEEE Trans. Aerosp. Electron. Syst.,* **AES-15,** 899 (1979).

43. W. D. White, Angular Spectra in Radar Applications, *IEEE Trans. Aerosp. Electron. Syst.,* **AES-15,** 895 (1979).

44. J. E. Evans, Comments on "Angular Spectra in Radar Applications," *IEEE Trans. Aerosp. Electron. Syst.,* **AES-15,** 891 (1979).

45. W. S. Ligget, Passive Sonar: Fitting Models to Multiple Time Series, in J. W. R. Griffiths, et al., Eds., *Signal Processing,* New York, Academic, 1973.

46. R. O. Schmidt, Multiple Emitter Location and Signal Parameter Estimation, *Proc. 1979 RADC Spectral Estimation Workshop,* Rome, NY, p. 243. Reprinted in the Special Issue on Adaptive Processing Antenna Systems, *IEEE Trans. Antennas and Propagation,* **AP-34,** 276 (1986).

47. S. S. Reddi, Multiple Source Location—A Digital Approach, *IEEE Trans. Aerosp. Electron. Syst.,* **AES-15,** 95–105 (1979).

48. G. Bienvenu and L. Kopp, Adaptivity to Background Noise Spatial Coherence for High Resolution Passive Methods, *Proc. IEEE Int. Conf. Acoust., Speech, Signal Process.,* 307–310 (1980).

49. A Cantoni and L. Godara, Resolving the Directions of Sources in a Correlated Field Incident on an Array, *J. Acoust. Soc. Am.,* **67,** 1247–1255 (1980).

50. D. Bordelon, Complementarity of the Reddi Method of Source Direction Estimation with those of Pisarenko and Cantoni and Godara, I., *J. Acoust., Soc. Am.,* **69,** 1355–1359 (May 1981).

51. T. S. Durrani and K. C. Sharman, Extraction of an Eigenvector-Oriented 'Spectrum' for the MESA Coefficients, *IEEE Trans. Acoust., Speech, Signal Process.,* **ASSP-30,** 649–651 (1982).

52. T. P. Bronez and J. A. Cadzow, An Algebraic Approach to Superresolution Adaptive Array Processing, *IEEE Trans. Aerosp. Electron. Syst.,* **AES-19,** 123–133 (1983).

53. R. Kumaresan and D. W. Tufts, Estimating the Angles of Arrival of Multiple Plane Waves, *IEEE Trans. Aerosp. Electron. Syst.,* **AES-19,** 134–139 (1983).

54. D. H. Johnson and S. R. DeGraaf, Improving the Resolution of Bearing in Passive Sonar Arrays by Eigenvalue Analysis, *IEEE Trans. Acoust., Speech, Signal Process.,* **ASSP-30,** 638-647 (1982).

55. T. E. Evans, et al., High Resolution Angular Spectrum Estimation Techniques for Terrain Scattering Analysis and Angle of Arrival Estimation, *Proc. 1st ASSP Spectral Estimation Workshop,* Hamilton, Ontario, (1981), p. 134.

56. K. C. Sharman and T. S. Durrani, Eigenfilter Approaches to Adaptive Array Processing, *Proc. IEE, part F,* **130,** 22 (1983).

57. M. Wax and T. Kailath, Optimum Localization of Multiple Sources by Passive Arrays, *IEEE Trans. Acoust., Speech, Signal Process.,* **ASSP-31,** 1210 (1983).

58. G. Bienvenu and L. Kopp, Optimality of High Resolution Array Processing Using the Eigensystem Approach, *IEEE Trans. Acoust., Speech, Signal Process.,* **ASSP-31,** 1235 (1983).

59. G. Bienvenu and H. Mermoz, Principles of High-Resolution Array Processing, in S. Y.

Kung, H. J. Whitehouse, and T. Kailath, Eds., *VLSI and Modern Signal Processing,* Englewood Cliffs, NJ, Prentice-Hall, 1985.

60. N. L. Owsley, High-Resolution Spectrum Analysis by Dominant-Mode Enhancement, *Ibid.*
61. M. Wax and T. Kailath, Detection of Signals by Information Theoretic Criteria, *IEEE Trans. Acoust., Speech, Signal Process.,* **ASSP-33,** 387 (1985).
62. T. J. Shan, M. Wax, and T. Kailath, On Spatial Smoothing for Direction-of-Arrival Estimation of Coherent Signals, *IEEE Trans. Acoust., Speech, Signal Process.,* **ASSP-33,** 806 (1985).
63. A. Di, Multiple Source Location—A Matrix Decomposition Approach, *IEEE Trans. Acoust., Speech, Signal Process.,* **ASSP-33,** 1086 (1985).
64. S. R. De Graaf and D. H. Johnson, Capability of Array Processing Algorithms to Estimate Source Bearings, *IEEE Trans. Acoust., Speech, Signal Process.,* **ASSP-33,** 1368 (1985).
65. W. F. Gabriel, Using Spectral Estimation Techniques in Adaptive Processing Antenna Systems, *IEEE Trans. Antennas Propag.,* **AP-34,** 291 (1986).
66. I. Karasalo, Estimating the Covariance Matrix by Signal Subspace Averaging, *IEEE Trans. Acoust., Speech, Signal Process.,* **ASSP-34,** 8 (1986).
67. G. Vezzosi, Estimation of Phase Angles from the Cross-Spectral Matrix, *IEEE Trans. Acoust., Speech, Signal Process.,* **ASSP-34,** 405 (1986).
68. G. Su and M. Morf, Modal Decomposition Signal Subspace Algorithms, *IEEE Trans. Acoust., Speech, Signal Process.,* **ASSP-34,** 585 (1986).
69. K. C. Sharman and T. S. Durrani, A Comparative Study of Modern Eigenstructure Methods for Bearing Estimation—A New High Performance Approach, *Proc. 1986 IEEE Int. Conf. Decision and Control,* Athens, p. 1737.
70. U. Nickel, Angular Superresolution with Phased Array Radar: A Review of Algorithms and Operational Constraints, *IEE Proc.,* **134,** Pts. F, 53 (1987).
71. A. Paulraj and T. Kailath, Eigenstructure Methods for Direction of Arrival Estimation in the Presence of Unknown Noise Fields, *IEEE Trans. Acoust., Speech, Signal Process.,* **ASSP-34,** 13 (1986).
72. F. B. Tuteur and Y. Rockah, A New Method for Signal Detection and Estimation Using the Eigenstructure of the Covariance Difference, *Proc. 1986 IEEE Int. Conf. Acoust., Speech, Signal Process.,* Tokyo, p. 2811.
73. F. B. Tuteur and Y. Rockah, The Covariance Difference Method in Signal Detection, *Proc. Third ASSP Workshop on Spectrum Estimation and Modeling,* Boston, 1986, p. 120.
74. S. Prasad, R. Williams, A. Mahalanabis, and L. Sibul, A Transform Based Covariance Differencing Approach to Bearing Estimation, *Proc. 1987 IEEE Int. Conf. Acoust., Speech, Signal Process.,* Dallas, p. 1119.
75. S. J. Orfanidis, A Reduced MUSIC Algorithm, *Proc. Third ASSP Workshop on Spectrum Estimation and Modeling,* Boston, 1986, p. 165.
76. M. Wax and T. Kailath, Extending the Threshold of the Eigenstructure Methods, *Proc. 1985 IEEE Int. Conf Acoust., Speech, Signal Process.,* Tampa, FL, p. 556.
77. R. Kumaresan and A. K. Shaw, High Resolution Bearing Estimation Without Eigende-

composition, *Proc. 1985 IEEE Int. Conf Acoust., Speech, Signal Process.,* Tampa, FL, p. 576.

78. Y. Bresler and A. Macovski, Exact Maximum Likelihood Parameter Estimation of Superimposed Exponential Signals in Noise, *IEEE Trans. Acoust., Speech, Signal Process.,* **ASSP-34,** 1081 (1986).
79. Y. Bresler and A. Macovski, On the Number of Signals Resolvable by a Uniform Linear Array, *IEEE Trans. Acoust., Speech, Signal Process.,* **ASSP-34,** 1361 (1986).
80. R. Roy, A. Paulraj, and T. Kailath, Estimation of Signal Parameters via Rotational Invariance Techniques—ESPRIT, *Proc. 19th Asilomar Conf. Circ., Syst. and Computers,* Asilomar, CA, 1985, p. 83.
81. R. Roy, A. Paulraj, and T. Kailath, ESPRIT—A Subspace Rotation Approach to Estimation of Parameters of Cisoids in Noise, *IEEE Trans. Acoust., Speech, Signal Process.,* **ASSP-34,** 1340 (1986).
82. R. Roy, A. Paulraj, and T. Kailath, Comparative Performance of ESPRIT and MUSIC for Direction-of-Arrival Estimation, *Proc. 1987 IEEE Int. Conf. Acoust., Speech, Signal Process.,* Dallas, p. 2344.
83. F. Haber and M. Zoltowski, Spatial Spectrum Estimation in a Coherent Signal Environment Using an Array in Motion, *IEEE Trans. Antennas Propag.,* **AP-34,** 301 (1986).
84. A. J. Luthra, A Solution to the Adaptive Nulling Problem with a Look-Direction Constraint in the Presence of Coherent Jammers, *IEEE Trans. Antennas Propag.,* **AP-34,** 702 (1986).
85. S. Kesler, J. Kesler, and G. Levita, Experiments in Resolving Coherent Targets in the Near Field, *Proc. Third ASSP Workshop on Spectrum Estimation and Modeling,* Boston, 1986, p. 168.
86. S. S. Reddi, On a Spatial Smoothing Technique for Multiple Source Location, *IEEE Trans. Acoust., Speech, Signal Process.,* **ASSP-35,** 709 (1987), and *ibid.,* p. 1352.
87. J. A. Cadzow, Y. S. Kim, D. C. Shiue, Y. Sun, and G. Xu, Resolution of Coherent Signals Using a Linear Array, *Proc. 1987 IEEE Int. Conf. Acoust., Speech, Signal Process.,* Dallas, p. 1597.
88. R. Williams, S. Prasad, A. Mahalanabis, and L. Sibul, Localization of Coherent Sources Using a Modified Spatial Smoothing Technique. *Proc. 1987 IEEE Int. Conf. Acoust., Speech, Signal Process.,* Dallas, p. 2352.
89. A. M. Bruckstein, T. J. Shan, and T. Kailath, The Resolution of Overlapping Echos, *IEEE Trans. Acoust., Speech, Signal Process.,* **ASSP-33,** 1357 (1985).
90. I. Isenberg and R. D. Dyson, The Analysis of Fluorescent Decay by a Method of Moments, *Biophys. J.,* **9,** 1337 (1969).
91. A. J. Evans and R. Fischl, Optimal Least-Squares Time-Domain Synthesis of Recursive Digital Filters, *IEEE Trans. Audio Electroacoust.,* **AU-21,** 61 (1973).
92. A. J. Berni, Target Identification by Natural Resonance Estimation, *IEEE Trans. Aerosp. Electron. Syst.,* **AES-11,** 147 (1975).
93. M. L. Van Blaricum and R. Mittra, Problems and Solutions Associated with Prony's Method for Processing Transient Data, *IEEE Trans. Antennas Propag.,* **AP-26,** 174 (1978).
94. T. L. Henderson, Geometric Methods for Determining System Poles from Transient Response, *IEEE Trans. Acoust., Speech, Signal Process.,* **ASSP-29,** 982 (1981).

95. R. Kumaresan and D. W. Tufts, Estimating the Parameters of Exponentially Damped Sinusoids and Pole-Zero Modeling in Noise, *IEEE Trans. Acoust., Speech, Signal Process.,* **ASSP-30,** 833 (1982).

96. M. Wax, R. O. Schmidt, and T. Kailath, Eigenstructure Method for Retrieving the Poles from the Natural Response, *Proc. 1983 IEEE Int. Conf. Decision and Control,* San Antonio, TX, p. 1343.

97. R. Kumaresan, L. L. Scharf, and A. K. Shaw, An Algorithm for Pole-Zero Modeling and Spectral Analysis, *IEEE Trans. Acoust., Speech, Signal Process.,* **ASSP-34,** 637 (1986).

98. J. A. Cadzow and M. M. Wu, Analysis of Transient Data in Noise, *IEE Proc.,* **134,** Pt. F, 69 (1987).

99. S. J. Orfanidis, Pole Retrieval by Eigenvector Methods, *Proc. 1987 IEEE Int. Conf. Acoust., Speech, Signal Process.,* Dallas, p. 1505.

100. B. N. Parlett, *The Symmetric Eigenvalue Problem,* Englewood Cliffs, NJ, Prentice-Hall, 1980.

101. G. H. Golub and V. Pereyra, The Differentiation of Pseudo-Inverses and Non-Linear Least-Squares Problems Whose Variables Separate, *SIAM J. Numer. Anal.,* **10,** 413 (1973).

102. G. H. Golub and C. F. Van Loan, *Matrix Computations,* Baltimore, Johns Hopkins University Press, 1983.

103. S. P. Applebaum, Adaptive Arrays, *IEEE Trans. Antennas Prop.,* **AP-24,** 585–598 (1976).

104. H. Cox, Resolving Power and Sensitivity to Mismatch of Optimum Array Processors, *J. Acoust. Soc. Am.,* **54,** 771–785 (1973).

105. F. Gabriel, Adaptive Arrays—An Introduction, *Proc. IEEE,* **64,** 239–272 (1976).

106. B. Widrow, et al., Adaptive Antenna Systems, *Proc. IEEE,* **55,** 2143–2159 (1967).

107. C. L. Zham, Application of Adaptive Arrays to Suppress Strong Jammers in the Presence of Weak Signals, *IEEE Trans. Aerosp. Electron. Syst.,* **AES-9,** 260 (1973).

108. T. W. Anderson, *The Statistical Analysis of Time Series,* New York, Wiley, 1971.

109. D. N. Lawley and A. E. Maxwell, *Factor Analysis as a Statistical Method,* London, Butterworth, 1971.

110. C. R. Rao, *Linear Statistical Inference and Its Applications,* (2nd ed.), New York, Wiley, 1973.

111. D. R. Cox and D. V. Hinkley, *Theoretical Statistics,* London, Chapman and Hall, 1974.

112. D. R. Brillinger, *Time Series, Data Analysis and Theory,* New York, Holt, Rinehart and Winston, 1975.

113. M. G. Kendall and A. Stuart, *The Advanced Theory of Statistics,* vol. 2, (4th edition), London, Griffin, 1979.

114. M. G. Kendall and A. Stuart, *The Advanced Theory of Statistics,* vol. 3, (3d edition), New York, Hafner Press, 1976.

115. M. S. Srivastava and C. G. Khatri, *An Introduction to Multivariate Statistics,* New York, North Holland, 1979.

116. T. W. Anderson, *An Introduction to Multivariate Statistical Analysis,* (2nd ed.), New York, Wiley 1984.

117. J. Cryer, *Times Series Analysis,* Boston, Duxbury Press, 1986.

118. K. Dzhaparidze, *Parameter Estimation and Hypothesis Testing in Spectral Analysis of Stationary Time Series,* New York, Springer-Verlag, 1986.
119. P. J. Brockwell and R. A. Davis, *Time Series: Theory and Methods,* New York, Springer-Verlag, 1987.
120. H. B. Mann and A. Wald, On the Statistical Treatment of Linear Stochastic Difference Equations, *Econometrica,* **11,** 173 (1943).
121. P. Whittle, The Analysis of Multiple Stationary Time Series, *J. Roy. Stat. Soc.,* Ser. B, **15,** 125 (1953).
122. J. Capon and N. R. Goodman, Probability Distributions for Estimators of the Frequency-Wavenumber Spectrum, *Proc. IEEE,* **58,** 1785 (1971).
123. O. Barndorff-Nielsen and G. Schou, On the Parametrization of Autoregressive Models by Partial Autocorrelations, *J. Multiv. Anal.,* **3,** 408 (1973).
124. M. Pagano, Estimation of Models of Autoregressive Signal Plus White Noise, *Ann. Stat.,* **2,** 99 (1974).
125. K. N. Berk, Consistent Autoregressive Spectral Estimates, *Ann. Stat.,* **2,** 489 (1974).
126. A. B. Baggeroer, Confidence Intervals for Regression (MEM) Spectral Estimates, *IEEE Trans. Inform. Th.,* **IT-22,** 534 (1976).
127. H. Sakai, Statistical Properties of AR Spectral Analysis, *IEEE Trans. Acoust., Speech, Signal Process.,* **ASSP-27,** 402 (1979).
128. R. D. Martin, The Cramér-Rao Bound and Robust M-Estimates for Autoregressions, *Biometrika,* **69,** 437 (1982).
129. S. M. Kay and J. Makhoul, On the Statistics of the Estimated Reflection Coefficients of an Autoregressive Process, *IEEE Trans. Acoust., Speech, Signal Process.,* **ASSP-31,** 1447 (1983).
130. M. Aktar, B. Sankur, and Y. Istefanopulos, Properties of the Maximum Likelihood and Pisarenko Spectral Estimates, *Signal Processing,* **8**, 401 (1985).
131. B. Porat and B. Friedlander, Computation of the Exact Information Matrix of Gaussian Time Series with Stationary Random Components, *IEEE Trans. Acoust., Speech, Signal Process.,* **ASSP-34,** 118 (1986).
132. S. Kay and D. Sengupta, Spectral Estimation of Non-Gaussian Autoregressive Processes, in *Proc. Third ASSP Workshop on Spectrum Estimation and Modeling,* Boston, 1986, p. 10.
133. D. Burshtein and E. Weinstein, Confidence Intervals for the Maximum Entropy Spectrum, *IEEE Trans. Acoust., Speech, Signal Process.,* **ASSP-35,** 504 (1987).
134. M. A. Girschick, On the Sampling Theory of Roots of Determinantal Equations, *Ann. Math. Stat.,* **10,** 203 (1939).
135. D. N. Lawley, Tests of Significance for the Latent Roots of Covariance and Correlation Matrices, *Biometrika,* **43,** 128 (1956).
136. T. W. Anderson, Asymptotic Theory for Principal Component Analysis, *Ann. Math. Stat.,* **34,** 122 (1963).
137. R. P. Gupta, Asymptotic Theory for Principal Component Analysis in the Complex Case, *J. Indian Stat. Assoc.,* **3,** 97 (1965).
138. D. E. Tyler, Asymptotic Inference for Eigenvectors, *Ann. Stat.,* **9,** 725 (1981).

139. H. Sakai, Statistical Analysis of Pisarenko's Method for Sinusoidal Frequency Estimation, *IEEE Trans. Acoust., Speech, Signal Process.,* **ASSP-32,** 95 (1984).

140. K. Sharman, T. S. Durrani, M. Wax, and T. Kailath, Asymptotic Performance of Eigenstructure Spectral Analysis Methods, *Proc. 1984 IEEE Int. Conf. Acoust., Speech, Signal Process.,* San Diego, CA, p. 455.

141. D. J. Jeffries and D. R. Farrier, Asymptotic Results for Eigenvector Methods, *IEE Proc.,* **132,** Pt. F, 589 (1985).

142. M. Kaveh and A. J. Barabell, The Statistical Performance of the MUSIC and the Minimum-Norm Algorithms for Resolving Plane Waves in Noise, *IEEE Trans. Acoust., Speech, Signal Process.,* **ASSP-34,** 331 (1986).

143. W. H. Press, B. P. Flannery, S. A. Teukolsky, and W. T. Vetterling, *Numerical Recipes,* New York, Springer-Verlag, 1986.

144. N. R. Goodman, Statistical Analysis Based on a Certain Multivariate Complex Gaussian Distribution, *Ann. Math. Stat.,* **34,** 152 (1963).

145. K. S. Miller, *Complex Stochastic Processes,* Reading, MA, Addison-Wesley, 1974.

7

Adaptive Filters

7.1 *Adaptive Implementation of Wiener Filters*

We review briefly the solution of the Wiener filtering problem.

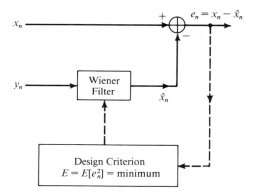

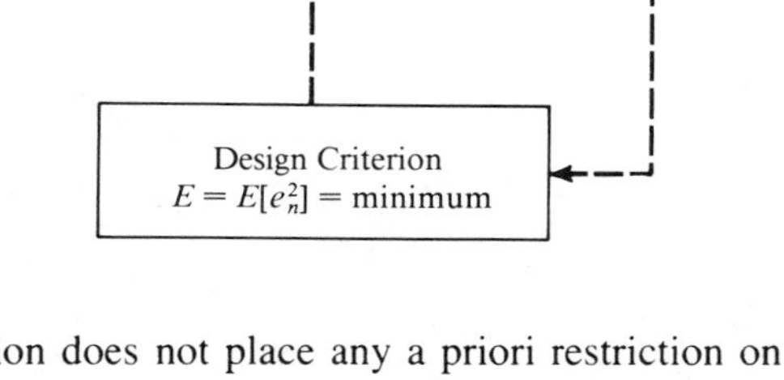

The general solution does not place any a priori restriction on the order of the Wiener filter. In general, an infinite number of weights is required to achieve the lowest estimation error. However, in adaptive implementations we must insist in advance that the number of filter weights be finite. This is so because the adaptation algorithm adapts each weight individually. Obviously, we cannot adapt an infinite number of weights.

We will assume then, that the optimal Wiener filter is an FIR filter, say with $M + 1$ weights

$$\mathbf{h} = [h_0, h_1, \ldots, h_M]^T \rightarrow H(z) = h_0 + h_1 z^{-1} + h_2 z^{-2} + \cdots + h_M z^{-M}$$

This filter processes the available observations y_n to produce the estimate

$$\hat{x}_n = \sum_{m=0}^{M} h_m y_{n-m} = h_0 y_n + h_1 y_{n-1} + h_2 y_{n-2} + \cdots + h_M y_{n-M}$$

The weights h_m are chosen optimally so that the mean-squared estimation error is minimized; that is,

$$\mathcal{E} = E[e_n^2] = \text{minimum}, \qquad e_n = x_n - \hat{x}_n$$

This minimization criterion leads to the orthogonality equations, which are the determining equations for the optimal weights. Writing the estimate in vector notation

$$\hat{x}_n = [h_0, h_1, \ldots, h_M] \begin{bmatrix} y_n \\ y_{n-1} \\ \vdots \\ y_{n-M} \end{bmatrix} = \mathbf{h}^T \mathbf{y}(n)$$

we may write the orthogonality equations as

$$E[e_n y_{n-m}] = 0, \qquad 0 \leq m \leq M$$

or equivalently,

$$E[e_n \mathbf{y}(n)] = 0$$

These give the normal equations

$$E[(x_n - \hat{x}_n)\mathbf{y}(n)] = E[(x_n - \mathbf{h}^T\mathbf{y}(n))\mathbf{y}(n)] = 0$$

$$E[\mathbf{y}(n)\mathbf{y}(n)^T]\mathbf{h} = E[x_n \mathbf{y}(n)]$$

or

$$R\mathbf{h} = \mathbf{r}, \qquad R = E[\mathbf{y}(n)\mathbf{y}(n)^T], \qquad \mathbf{r} = E[x_n \mathbf{y}(n)]$$

The optimal weights are obtained then by

$$\mathbf{h} = R^{-1}\mathbf{r} \tag{7.1.1}$$

The corresponding minimal value of the estimation error is computed by

$$\mathcal{E} = E[e_n^2] = E[e_n(x_n - \mathbf{h}^T\mathbf{y}(n))] = E[e_n x_n]$$

$$= E[x_n^2] - \mathbf{h}^T E[\mathbf{y}(n) x_n] = E[x_n^2] - \mathbf{r}^T R^{-1} \mathbf{r}$$

The normal equations, and especially the orthogonality equations, have their usual *correlation canceling* interpretations. The signal x_n being estimated can be written as

$$x_n = e_n + \hat{x}_n = e_n + \mathbf{h}^T\mathbf{y}(n)$$

It is composed of two parts, the term e_n, which because of the orthogonality equations is entirely uncorrelated with $\mathbf{y}(n)$, and the second term, which is correlated with $\mathbf{y}(n)$. In effect, the filter removes from x_n any part of it that is correlated with the secondary input $\mathbf{y}(n)$; what is left, e_n, is uncorrelated with $\mathbf{y}(n)$. The Wiener filter acts as a correlation canceler. If the primary signal x_n and the secondary signal $\mathbf{y}(n)$ are in any way correlated, the filter will cancel from the output e_n any such correlations.

One difficulty with the above solution is that the statistical quantities R and $\mathbf{r}$ must be known, or at least estimated, in advance. This can be done either by block processing or adaptive processing methods. The principal advantages of block processing methods are that the design is based on a *single,* fixed, data record and that the length of the data record may be very *short.* Thus, such methods are most appropriate in applications where the *availability* of data is limited, as for example, in parametric spectrum estimation based on a single block of data, or in deconvolution applications where the data to be deconvolved are already available, for example, a still distorted picture or a recorded segment of a seismic response.

Availability of data, however, is not the only consideration. In a *changing* environment, even if more data could be collected, it may not be correct to use them in the design because *stationarity* may not be valid for the longer data block. Block processing methods can still be used in such cases, but the optimum filters must be *redesigned* every time the environment changes, so that the filter is always matched to the data being processed by it. This is, for example, what is done in speech processing. The input speech signal is divided into fairly short segments, with each segment assumed to arise from a stationary process, then the statistical correlations are estimated by sample correlations and the optimal prediction coefficients corresponding to each segment are computed. In a sense, this procedure is data-adaptive, but more precisely, it is block-by-block adaptive.

In other applications, however, we do not know how often to redesign and must use *adaptive* implementations that provide an automatic way of redesigning the optimum processors to continually *track* the environment. For example, communications and radar antennas are vulnerable to jamming through their sidelobes. Adaptive sidelobe cancelers continuously adjust themselves to steer nulls toward the jammers even when the jammers may be changing positions or new jammers may be coming into play. Another example is the equalization of unknown or changing channels, or both. In switched telephone lines the exact transmission channel is not known in advance but is established at the moment the connection is made. Similarly, in fading communications channels the channel is continuously changing. To undo the effects of the channel, such as amplitude and phase distortions, an equalizer filter must be used at the receiving end that effectively acts as an inverse to the channel. Adaptive equalizers determine automatically the characteristics of the channel and provide the required inverse response. Other applications, well-suited to adaptive implementations, are noise canceling, echo canceling, linear prediction and spectrum estimation, and system identification and control.

In this chapter we discuss several adaptation algorithms, such as the Widrow–Hoff least mean square (LMS) algorithm, the conventional recursive least squares (RLS) algorithm, the fast RLS algorithms, and the adaptive lattice algorithms and present some of their applications [1–9, 155]. A typical adaptive implementation of a Wiener filter is depicted in Fig. 7.1. The adaptation algorithm continuously monitors the output error signal e_n and attempts to minimize the output power $E[e_n^2]$, or, equivalently tries to decorrelate e_n from the secondary input y_n. At each time instant n, the current values of the weights are used to perform the filtering operation. The computed output e_n is then used by the adaptation part of the algorithm to change the weights in the direction of their optimum values. As processing of the input signals x_n and y_n takes place and the filter gradually *learns* the statistics of these inputs, its weights gradually converge to their optimum values given by the Wiener solution (7.1.1). Clearly, the input statistics must remain unchanged for at least as long as it takes the filter to learn it and converge to its optimum configuration. If, after convergence, the input statistics should change, the filter will respond by readjusting its weights to their new optimum values, and so on. In other words, the adaptive filter will track the nonstationary changes of the input statistics as long as such changes occur slowly enough for the filter to converge between changes. The three basic issues in any adaptive implementation are:

1. The learning or convergence speed of the algorithm
2. The computational complexity of the algorithm
3. The numerical accuracy and stability of the algorithm

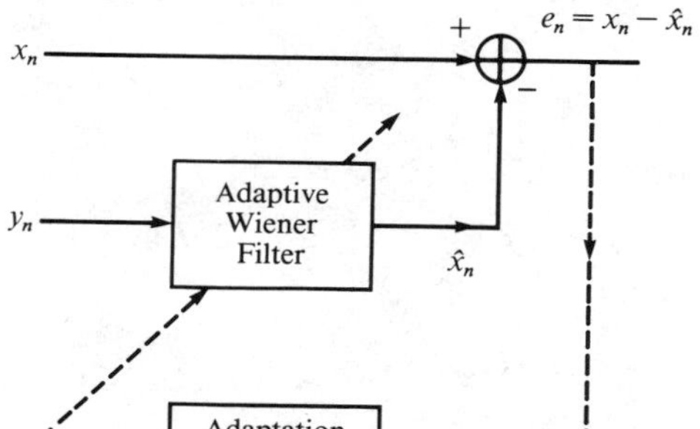

Figure 7.1 Adaptive Wiener Filter

The convergence speed is an important factor because it determines the maximum rate of change of the input nonstationarities that can be usefully tracked by the filter. The computational complexity refers to the number of operations required to update the filter from one time instant to the next. The table below shows how various adaptive algorithms fare under these requirements

algorithm	speed	complexity	stability
LMS	slow	simple	stable
RLS	fast	complex	stable
Fast RLS	fast	simple	unstable
Lattice	fast	simple	stable

Only adaptive lattice algorithms satisfy all three requirements. We will discuss these algorithms in detail later on. In the next section we begin with the LMS algorithm because it is the simplest and most widely used. We finish this section with the obvious remark that adaptive or block processing optimal filter designs, regardless of type, cannot do any better than the theoretical Wiener solution. The optimal filter, therefore, should be first analyzed theoretically to determine if it is worth using it in the application at hand.

7.2 *Correlation Canceler Loop* (*CCL*)

To illustrate the basic principles behind adaptive filters, consider the simplest possible filter; that is, a filter with only one weight

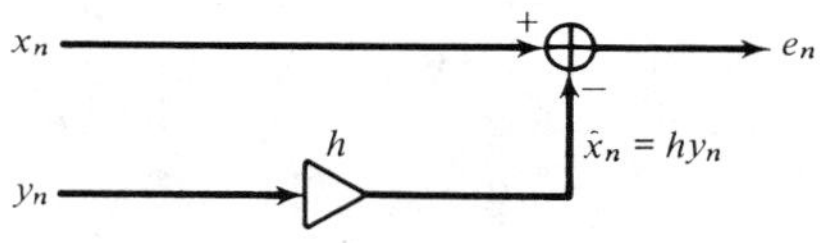

The weight h must be selected optimally so as to produce the best possible estimate

$$\hat{x}_n = hy_n$$

of x_n. The estimation error is expressed as

$$\begin{aligned}\mathcal{E}(h) &= E[e_n^2] = E[(x_n - hy_n)^2] = E[x_n^2] - 2hE[x_n y_n] + h^2 E[y_n^2] \\ &= E[x_n^2] - 2hr + h^2 R\end{aligned} \tag{7.2.1}$$

The minimization condition is

$$\frac{\partial \mathcal{E}(h)}{\partial h} = 2E\left[e_n \frac{\partial e_n}{\partial h}\right] = -2E[e_n y_n] = -2r + 2Rh = 0 \tag{7.2.2}$$

which gives the solution $h = R^{-1}r$, and also shows the correlation cancellation condition $E[e_n y_n] = 0$.

The adaptive implementation is based on solving the equation

$$\frac{\partial \mathcal{E}(h)}{\partial h} = 0 \tag{7.2.3}$$

iteratively, using a gradient-descent method. The dependence of the error $\mathcal{E}$ on the filter parameter is parabolic, with an absolute minimum occurring at the above optimal value $h = R^{-1}r$. This is shown below

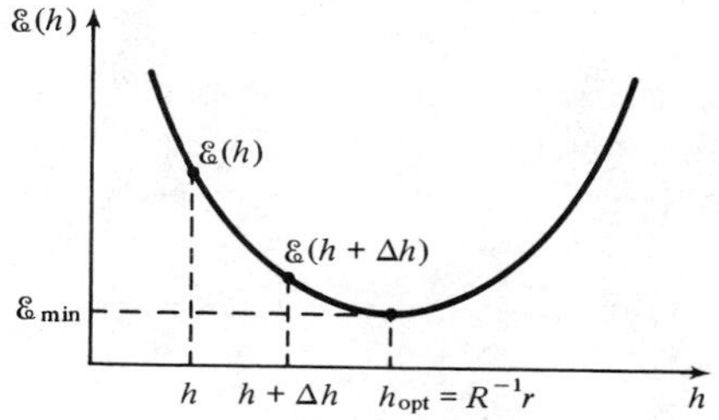

In the adaptive version, the filter parameter h is made *time-dependent, $h(n)$*, and is updated from one time instant to the next as follows

$$h(n + 1) = h(n) + \Delta h(n) \tag{7.2.4}$$

where $\Delta h(n)$ is a correction term that must be chosen properly in order to ensure that eventually the time-varying weight $h(n)$ will converge to the optimal value

$$h(n) \to h = R^{-1}r \qquad \text{as } n \to \infty$$

The filtering operation is now given by the still *linear* but *time noninvariant* form

$$\hat{x}_n = h(n) y_n \tag{7.2.5}$$

The computation of the estimate at the next time instant should be made with the new weight; that is,

$$\hat{x}_{n+1} = h(n + 1) y_{n+1}$$

and so on. The simplest way to choose the correction term $\Delta h(n)$, is the *gradient-descent,* or steepest-descent, method. The essence of the method is this: It is required that the change $h \to h + \Delta h$ must move the performance index closer to its minimum than before; that is, Δh must be such that

$$\mathcal{E}(h + \Delta h) \leq \mathcal{E}(h)$$

Therefore, if we always demand this, the repetition of the procedure will lead to smaller and smaller values of $\mathcal{E}$ until the smallest value has been attained. Assuming that Δh is sufficiently small, we may expand to first order and obtain the condition

$$\mathcal{E}(h) + \Delta h \frac{\partial \mathcal{E}(h)}{\partial h} \leq \mathcal{E}(h)$$

If Δh is selected as the *negative gradient* $-\mu(\partial\mathcal{E}/\partial h)$, then this inequality will be guaranteed; that is, if we choose

$$\Delta h = -\mu \frac{\partial \mathcal{E}(h)}{\partial h} \tag{7.2.6}$$

then the inequality is indeed satisfied

$$\mathcal{E}(h) + \Delta h \frac{\partial \mathcal{E}(h)}{\partial h} = \mathcal{E}(h) - \mu \left| \frac{\partial \mathcal{E}(h)}{\partial h} \right|^2 \leq \mathcal{E}(h)$$

The adaptation parameter μ must be small enough to *justify* keeping only the *first order* terms in the above Taylor expansion. Applying this idea to our little adaptive filter, we choose the correction $\Delta h(n)$ according to Eq. (7.2.6), so that

$$h(n+1) = h(n) + \Delta h(n) = h(n) - \mu \frac{\partial \mathcal{E}(h(n))}{\partial h} \tag{7.2.7}$$

Inserting the expression for the gradient $\dfrac{\partial \mathcal{E}}{\partial h} = -2r + 2Rh$, we find

$$\begin{aligned} h(n+1) &= h(n) - \mu[-2r + 2Rh(n)] \\ &= (1 - 2\mu R)h(n) + 2\mu r \end{aligned}$$

This difference equation may be solved in closed form; for example, using z-transforms with any initial conditions $h(0)$ we find

$$h(n) = h + (1 - 2\mu R)^n (h(0) - h) \tag{7.2.8}$$

where h is the optimal value $h = R^{-1}r$. The coefficient $h(n)$ will *converge* to its optimal value h, regardless of the starting value $h(0)$, provided μ is selected such that

$$|1 - 2\mu R| < 1$$

or $-1 < 1 - 2\mu R < 1$, or since μ must be positive (to be in the negative direction of the gradient), μ must satisfy

$$0 < \mu < \frac{1}{R} \tag{7.2.9}$$

To select μ one must have some a priori knowledge of the magnitude of the input variance $R = E[y_n^2]$. Such choice for μ will guarantee convergence, but the *speed of convergence* is controlled by how close the number $1 - 2\mu R$ is to one. The closer it is to unity the slower the speed of convergence. As μ is selected closer to zero, the closer $1 - 2\mu R$ moves to one, and thus the slower the convergence rate. The adaptation parameter must be selected small enough to guarantee convergence but not too small to cause a very *slow* convergence.

7.3 *The Widrow-Hoff LMS Adaptation Algorithm*

The purpose of the discussion in Section 7.2 was to show how the original Wiener filtering problem could be recast in an iterative form. From the practical point of view, this reformulation is still not computable since the adaptation of the weights requires a priori knowledge of the correlations R and r. In the Widrow-Hoff algorithm the above adaptation algorithm is replaced with one that is computable [1,2]. The gradient that appears in Eq. (7.2.7)

$$h(n+1) = h(n) - \mu \frac{\partial \mathcal{E}(h(n))}{\partial h}$$

is replaced by an *instantaneous* gradient by *ignoring* the expectation instructions; that is,

$$\frac{\partial \mathcal{E}(h(n))}{\partial h} = -2E[e_n y_n] = -2r + 2Rh(n) = -2E[x_n y_n] + 2E[y_n^2]h(n)$$

is *replaced* by

$$\frac{\partial \mathcal{E}}{\partial h} = -2e_n y_n = -2x_n y_n + 2y_n^2 h(n) \tag{7.3.1}$$

so that the weight-adjustment algorithm becomes

$$h(n+1) = h(n) + 2\mu e_n y_n \tag{7.3.2}$$

In summary, the required computations are done in the following order:

1. At time n, the filter weight $h(n)$ is available
2. Compute the filter output $\hat{x}_n = h(n)y_n$
3. Compute the estimation error $e_n = x_n - \hat{x}_n$
4. Compute the next filter weight $h(n+1) = h(n) + 2\mu e_n y_n$
5. Go to next time instant $n \to n+1$

The following remarks are in order:

1. The output error e_n is fed back and used to *control* the adaptation of the filter weight.

2. The filter tries to decorrelate the secondary signal from the output e_n. This, is easily seen as follows: If the weight $h(n)$ has more or less reached its optimum value, then $h(n+1) \simeq h(n)$, and the adaptation equation implies also approximately $e_n y_n \simeq 0$.

3. Actually the weight $h(n)$ never really reaches the theoretical limiting value $h = R^{-1}r$. Instead, it stabilizes about this value, and continuously fluctuates about it.

4. The approximation of ignoring the expectation instruction in the gradient is known as the *stochastic approximation*. It complicates the mathematical aspects of the problem considerably. Indeed, the difference equation

$$h(n+1) = h(n) + 2\mu e_n y_n = h(n) + 2\mu(x_n - h(n)y_n)y_n$$

makes $h(n)$ depend on the random variable y_n in highly nonlinear fashion, and it is very difficult to discuss even the average behavior of $h(n)$.

5. In discussing the average behavior of the weight $h(n)$, the following approximation is typically (almost invariably) made in the literature

$$\begin{aligned} E[h(n+1)] &= E[h(n)] + 2\mu E[x_n y_n] - 2\mu E[h(n)y_n^2] \\ &= E[h(n)] + 2\mu E[x_n y_n] - 2\mu E[h(n)]E[y_n^2] \\ &= E[h(n)] + 2\mu r - 2\mu E[h(n)]R \end{aligned}$$

where in the last term, the expectation $E[h(n)]$ was factored out, as though $h(n)$ were independent of y_n^2. With this approximation, the average $E[h(n)]$ satisfies the same difference equation as before. Typically, the weight $h(n)$ will be fluctuating about the theoretical convergence curve as it converges to the optimal value, as shown here.

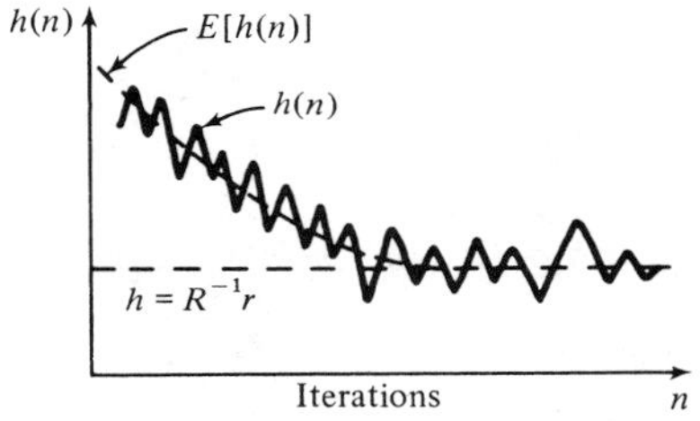

After convergence, the adaptive weight $h(n)$ continuously fluctuates about the Wiener solution h. A measure of these fluctuations is the quantity $E[(h(n) - h)^2]$. Under some restrictive conditions, this quantity has been calculated [10] to be

$$E[(h(n) - h)^2] = \mu\mathcal{E}_{\min} \qquad \text{(for large } n\text{)}$$

Thus, the adaptation parameter μ controls the *size* of these fluctuations. This gives rise to the basic *trade-off* of the LMS algorithm: to obtain high accuracy in the converged weights (small fluctuations), a small value of μ is required, but this will slow down the convergence rate.

A realization of the CCL is shown in Fig. 7.2. The filtering part of the realization must be clearly distinguished from the feedback control loop that performs the adaptation of the filter weight.

Historically, the correlation canceler loop was introduced in adaptive antennas

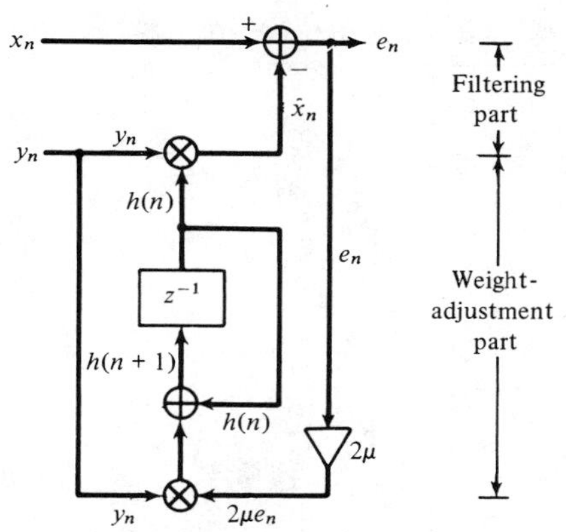

Figure 7.2 Correlation Canceler Loop

as a *sidelobe canceler* [11–17]. It is the simplest possible adaptive filter, and forms the elementary *building block* of more complicated, higher order adaptive filters.

We finish this section by presenting a simulation example of the CCL loop. The primary signal x_n was defined by

$$x_n = -0.8y_n + u_n$$

where the first term represents that part of x_n which is correlated with y_n. The part u_n is not correlated with y_n. The theoretical value of the CCL weight is found as follows:

$$r = E[x_n y_n] = -0.8E[y_n y_n] + E[u_n y_n] = -0.8R$$

where $R = E[y_n y_n]$. Thus, $h = R^{-1}r = -0.8$. The corresponding output of the CCL will be $\hat{x}_n = hy_n = -0.8y_n$, and therefore it will completely cancel the first term of x_n, leaving at the output $e_n = x_n - \hat{x}_n = u_n$.

In the simulation we generated 200 samples of a zero-mean white-noise signal y_n of variance 0.1, and another independent set of 200 samples of a zero-mean white-noise signal u_n also of variance 0.1, and computed x_n. The adaptation algorithm was initialized, as is usually done, to zero initial weight $h(0) = 0$. Fig. 7.3 shows the transient behavior of the adaptive weight $h(n)$ as a function of the number of iterations n, for the two values of μ, $\mu = 0.03$ and $\mu = 0.01$. Note that in both cases, the adaptive weight converges to the theoretical value $h = -0.8$, and that the smaller μ is slower but the fluctuations are also smaller. After the adaptive weight has reached its asymptotic value, the CCL begins to operate optimally, removing the correlated part of x_n from the output e_n.

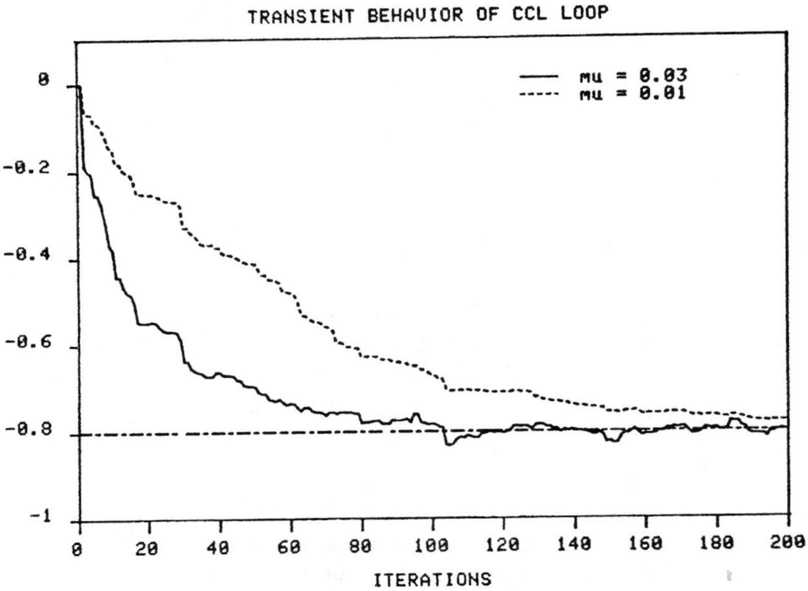

Figure 7.3 Transient Behavior of the Adaptive Weight $h(n)$

Later on we will consider the complex-valued version of adaptive Wiener filters. Their elementary building block is the *complex* CCL shown below

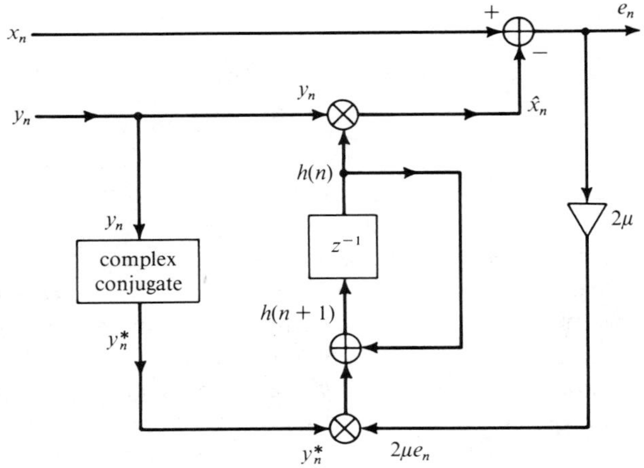

The performance index is now

$$\mathcal{E} = E[|e_n|^2] = E[|x_n - hy_n|^2] = \min$$

with optimum solution

$$h = R^{-1}r, \qquad R = E[y_n y_n^*], \qquad r = E[x_n y_n^*]$$

Analog implementations of the CCL are used in adaptive antennas. An *analog* CCL is shown below

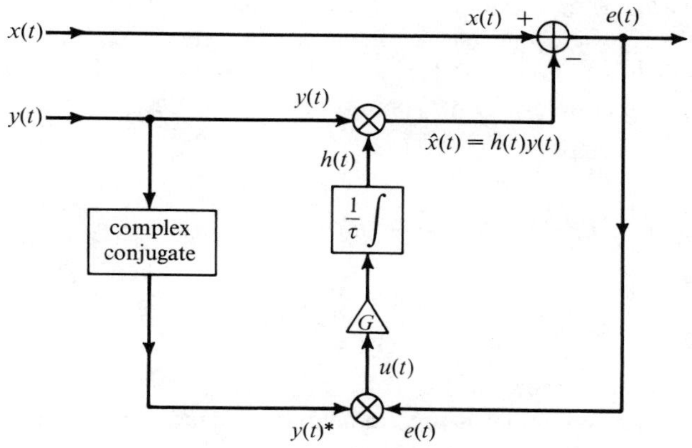

where a high gain amplifier and an ordinary *RC*-type integrator are used. If τ is the *RC* time constant of the integrator, the weight updating part of the CCL is

$$\tau \dot{h}(t) + h(t) = Gu(t) = Ge(t)y(t)^*$$

The performance of the analog CCL can be analyzed by replacing the adaptive weight $h(t)$ by its statistical average, satisfying

$$\tau \dot{h}(t) + h(t) = GE[e(t)y(t)^*] = GE[(x(t) - h(t)y(t))y(t)^*]$$

or, defining $R = E[y(t)y(t)^*]$ and $r = E[x(t)y(t)^*]$,

$$\tau \dot{h}(t) + h(t) = Gr - GRh(t)$$

with solution

$$h(t) = h + (h(0) - h)e^{-at}$$

where h is the asymptotic value

$$h = \frac{Gr}{1 + GR} = (R + G^{-1})^{-1}r$$

Thus, a high gain G is needed to produce an asymptotic value close to the theoretical Wiener solution $R^{-1}r$. The *time constant* of adaptation is given by

$$\frac{1}{a} = \frac{\tau}{GR}$$

Note that this particular implementation always converges and the speed of convergence is still inversely dependent on R.

7.4 *Adaptive Linear Combiner*

A straightforward generalization of the correlation canceler loop is the adaptive linear combiner, where one has available a main signal x_n, and a number of secondary signals $y_m(n)$, $m = 0,1,2, \ldots, M$. These $(M + 1)$ secondary signals are to be linearly combined with appropriate weights $(h_0, h_1, \ldots, h_M)$ to form an estimate of x_n:

$$\hat{x}_n = h_0 y_0(n) + h_1 y_1(n) + \cdots + h_M y_M(n) = [h_0, h_1, \cdots, h_M] \begin{bmatrix} y_0(n) \\ y_1(n) \\ \vdots \\ y_M(n) \end{bmatrix}$$

$$= \mathbf{h}^T \mathbf{y}(n)$$

A realization of this is shown in Fig. 7.4.

The adaptive linear combiner is used in adaptive radar and sonar arrays [11–17]. It also encompasses the case of the ordinary FIR, or transversal, Wiener filter [2].

The optimal weights h_m are those which minimize the estimation error squared

$$\mathcal{E} = E[e_n^2] = \min$$

The corresponding othogonality equations state that the estimation error be orthogonal (decorrelated) to each secondary signal $y_m(n)$

$$\frac{\partial \mathcal{E}}{\partial h_m} = 2E\left[e_n \frac{\partial e_n}{\partial h_m}\right] = -2E[e_n y_m(n)] = 0, \qquad 0 \leq m \leq M$$

or in matrix form

$$E[e_n \mathbf{y}(n)] = 0 = E[x_n \mathbf{y}(n)] - E[\mathbf{y}(n)\mathbf{y}(n)^T]\mathbf{h} = \mathbf{r} - R\mathbf{h}$$

with optimal solution $\mathbf{h} = R^{-1}\mathbf{r}$.

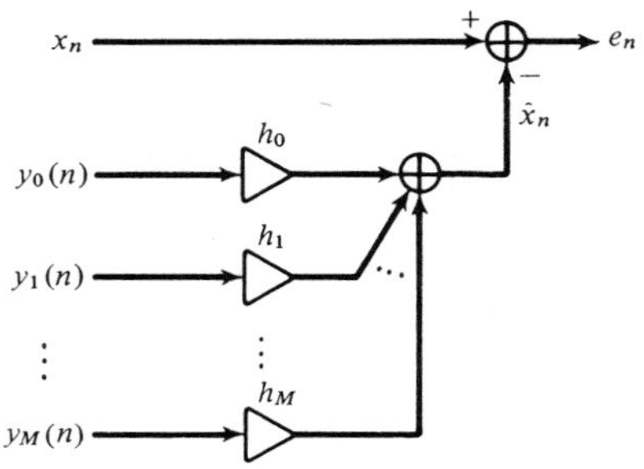

Figure 7.4 Linear Combiner

The adaptive implementation is easily obtained by allowing the weights to become time-dependent, $\mathbf{h}(n)$, and updating them in time according to the gradient descent algorithm

$$\mathbf{h}(n+1) = \mathbf{h}(n) - \mu \frac{\partial \mathcal{E}(\mathbf{h}(n))}{\partial \mathbf{h}}$$

with instantaneous gradient

$$\frac{\partial \mathcal{E}}{\partial \mathbf{h}} = -2E[e_n \mathbf{y}(n)] \rightarrow -2e_n \mathbf{y}(n)$$

so that

$$\mathbf{h}(n+1) = \mathbf{h}(n) + 2\mu e_n \mathbf{y}(n)$$

or component-wise

$$h_m(n+1) = h_m(n) + 2\mu e_n y_m(n), \qquad \text{for } 0 \leq m \leq M \tag{7.4.1}$$

The computational algorithm is outlined below

1. $\hat{x}_n = h_0(n)y_0(n) + h_1(n)y_1(n) + \cdots + h_M(n)y_M(n)$
2. $e_n = x_n - \hat{x}_n$
3. $h_m(n+1) = h_m(n) + 2\mu e_n y_m(n),\ 0 \leq m \leq M$

It is evident that each weight $h_m(n)$ is being adapted by *its own* correlation canceler loop, while all weights use the *same* feedback error e_n to control their loops. The case of two weights ($M = 1$) is shown in Fig. 7.5. The adaptive linear combiner has two major applications:

1. Adaptive sidelobe canceler
2. Adaptive FIR Wiener filter

The two cases differ only in the way the *inputs* to the linear combiner are supplied. The linear combiner part, performing the optimum processing, is the same in both cases. The time series case is discussed in the next section. The array problem is depicted below.

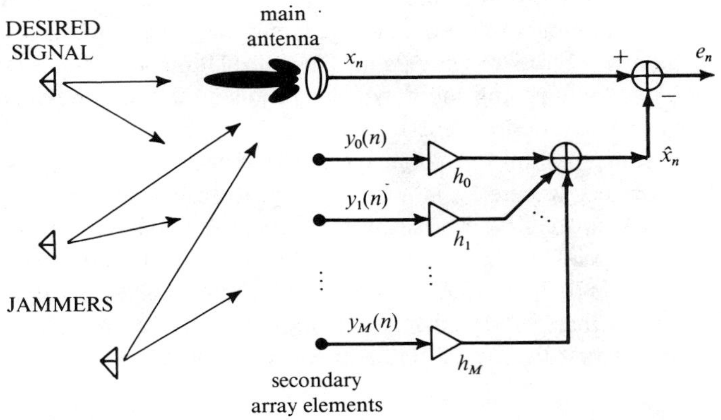

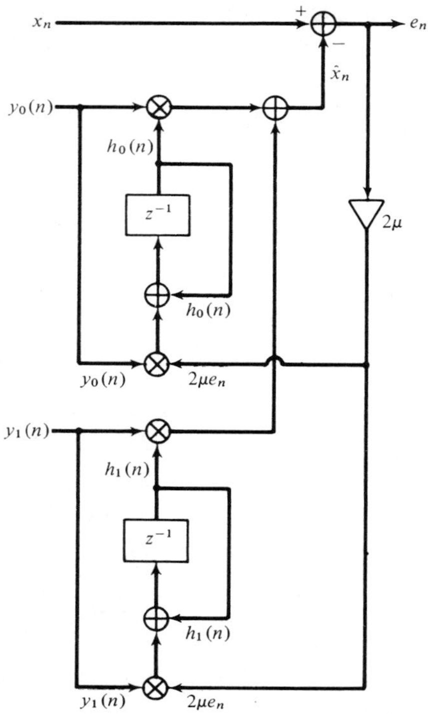

Figure 7.5 Adaptive Linear Combiner

It consists of a main and a number of secondary antennas. The main antenna is highly directional and oriented toward the desired signal. Jammers picked up by the sidelobes of the main antenna and by the secondary antennas will tend to be canceled because the adaptive linear combiner, acting as a correlation canceler, will adjust itself to cancel that part of the main signal that is correlated with the secondary ones. The desired signal may also be canceled partially if it is picked up by the secondary antennas. Strong jammers, however, will generally dominate and as a result the canceler will configure itself to cancel them. The cancellation of the desired signal can also be prevented by imposing additional constraints on the filter weights that can sustain the beam in the desired look-direction.

The adaptation speed of the adaptive canceler is affected by the relative power levels of the jammers. If there are jammers with greatly differing powers, the overall adaptation speed may be slow. The stronger jammers tend to be canceled faster; the weaker ones more slowly. Qualitatively this may be understood by inspecting, for example, expression (6.2.32). The power levels P_i of the plane waves act as *penalty* factors in the performance index; that is, the minimization of the performance index will tend to favor first the largest terms in the sum. This limitation of the LMS algorithm has led to the development of alternative algorithms, such as adaptive Gram–Schmidt preprocessors or RLS, in which all jammers get canceled equally fast.

7.5 *Adaptive FIR Wiener Filter*

The adaptive transversal filter is a special case of the adaptive linear combiner. In this case, there is only *one* secondary signal y_n. The required $M + 1$ signals $y_m(n)$ are provided as *delayed replicas* of y_n; that is,

$$y_m(n) = y_{n-m}, \qquad \text{for } 0 \leqslant m \leqslant M \tag{7.5.1}$$

A realization is shown in Fig. 7.6.
The estimate of x_n is

$$\hat{x}_n = \sum_{m=0}^{M} h_m(n) y_{n-m} = h_0(n) y_n + h_1(n) y_{n-1} + \cdots + h_M(n) y_{n-M}$$

The time-varying filter weights $h_m(n)$ are continuously updated according to the gradient-descent LMS algorithm

$$h_m(n+1) = h_m(n) + 2\mu e_n y_m(n), \qquad 0 \leqslant m \leqslant M$$

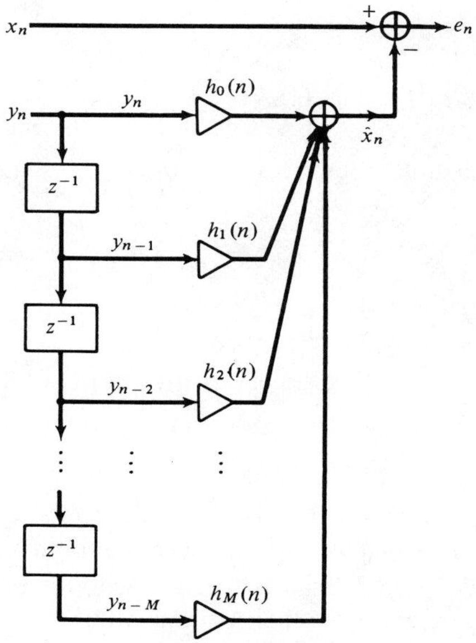

Figure 7.6 Adaptive FIR Wiener Filter

or

$$h_m(n+1) = h_m(n) + 2\mu e_n y_{n-m}, \qquad \text{for } 0 \le m \le M \tag{7.5.2}$$

Each weight is therefore updated by *its own CCL.*

Again, we would like to summarize the computational steps in this case:

1. Compute $\hat{x}_n = \sum_{m=0}^{M} h_m(n) y_{n-m}$
2. Compute the error signal $e_n = x_n - \hat{x}_n$
3. Adjust weights $h_m(n+1) = h_m(n) + 2\mu e_n y_{n-m}$, $0 \le m \le M$

The subroutine **lms** (see Appendix B) is an implementation of the algorithm. With a minor modification it can also be used for the more general adaptive linear combiner. Each call to the routine reads a pair of input samples $\{x_n, y_n\}$, performs the filtering operation to produce the output pair $\{\hat{x}_n, e_n\}$, updates the filter coefficients $h_m(n)$ to their new values $h_m(n+1)$ to be used by the next call, and updates the internal state of the filter. It is essentially the routine **dwf** with the weight adaptation part added to it.

Next, we present the same simulation example as that given in Section 7.3, but it is now approached with a two-tap adaptive filter ($M = 1$). The filtering equation is in this case

$$\hat{x}_n = h_0(n) y_n + h_1(n) y_{n-1}$$

The theoretical Wiener solution is found as follows: First note that

$$\begin{aligned} R_{xy}(k) &= E[x_{n+k} y_n] = E[(-0.8 y_{n+k} + u_{n+k}) y_n] = -0.8 E[y_{n+k} y_n] \\ &= -0.8 R_{yy}(k) = -0.8 R(k) \end{aligned}$$

Thus, the cross-correlation vector $\mathbf{r}$ is $\mathbf{r} = -0.8 \begin{bmatrix} R(0) \\ R(1) \end{bmatrix}$ and the Wiener solution becomes

$$\begin{aligned} \mathbf{h} = R^{-1}\mathbf{r} &= \begin{bmatrix} R(0) & R(1) \\ R(1) & R(0) \end{bmatrix}^{-1} \begin{bmatrix} -0.8R(0) \\ -0.8R(1) \end{bmatrix} \\ &= \frac{-0.8}{R(0)^2 - R(1)^2} \begin{bmatrix} R(0) & -R(1) \\ -R(1) & R(0) \end{bmatrix} \begin{bmatrix} R(0) \\ R(1) \end{bmatrix} = \begin{bmatrix} -0.8 \\ 0 \end{bmatrix} \end{aligned}$$

We could have expected that h_1 is zero, since the signal x_n does not depend on y_{n-1} but only on y_n. The adaptive weights were both initialized to zero, and the value of μ was 0.03. Figure 7.7 shows the two adaptive weights $h_0(n)$ and $h_1(n)$ as a function of n, converging to their optimal values.

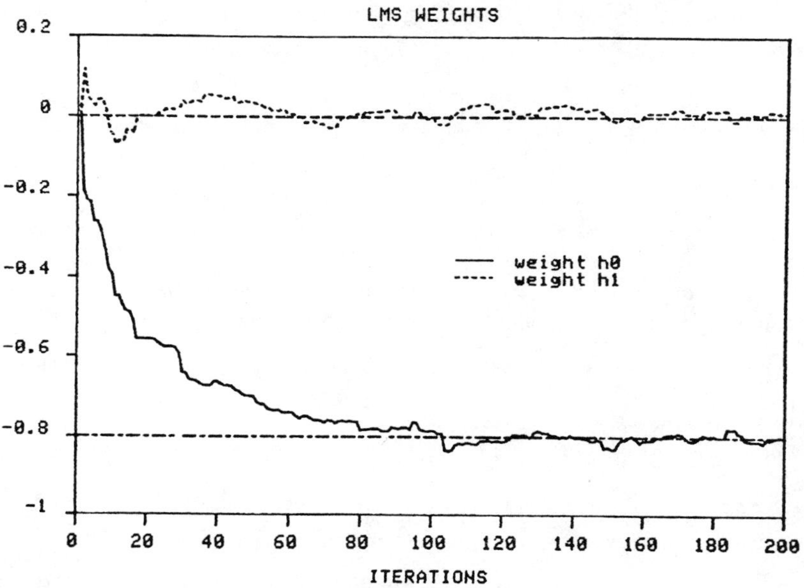

Figure 7.7 Transient Behavior of FIR Adaptive Filter

How does one select the filter order M? The rule is that the filter must have at least as many delays as that part of x_n which is correlated with y_n. To see this, suppose x_n is related to y_n by

$$x_n = c_0 y_n + c_1 y_{n-1} + \cdots + c_L y_{n-L} + u_n \qquad (7.5.3)$$

where u_n is uncorrelated with y_n. Then, the filter order must be *at least* L. If $M \geq L + 1$, we can write

$$x_n = c_0 y_n + c_1 y_{n-1} + \cdots + c_M y_{n-M} + u_n = \mathbf{c}^T \mathbf{y}(n) + u_n$$

where $\mathbf{c}$ is the extended vector having $c_i = 0$ for $L + 1 \leq i \leq M$. The cross-correlation between x_n and $\mathbf{y}(n)$ is

$$\mathbf{r} = E[x_n \mathbf{y}(n)] = E[(\mathbf{y}(n)^T \mathbf{c})\mathbf{y}(n)] = E[\mathbf{y}(n)\mathbf{y}(n)^T]\mathbf{c} = R\mathbf{c}$$

Thus, the Wiener solution will be $\mathbf{h} = R^{-1}\mathbf{r} = \mathbf{c}$. This, in turn, implies the complete cancellation of the y-dependent part of x_n. Indeed, $\hat{x}_n = \mathbf{h}^T\mathbf{y}(n) = \mathbf{c}^T\mathbf{y}(n)$ and

$$e_n = x_n - \hat{x}_n = (\mathbf{c}^T\mathbf{y}(n) + u_n) - \mathbf{c}^T\mathbf{y}(n) = u_n$$

What happens if we underestimate the filter order and choose $M < L$? In this case, we expect to cancel completely the first M terms of Eq. (7.5.3) and to cancel the remaining terms as much as possible. To see this, we separate out the first M terms writing

$$x_n = [c_0, \cdots, c_M]\begin{bmatrix} y_n \\ \vdots \\ y_{n-M} \end{bmatrix} + [c_{M+1}, \cdots, c_L]\begin{bmatrix} y_{n-M-1} \\ \vdots \\ y_{n-L} \end{bmatrix} + u_n$$

$$= \mathbf{c}_1^T \mathbf{y}_1(n) + \mathbf{c}_2^T \mathbf{y}_2(n) + u_n$$

The problem of estimating x_n using an Mth order filter is equivalent to the problem of estimating x_n from $\mathbf{y}_1(n)$. The cross-correlation between x_n and $\mathbf{y}_1(n)$ is

$$E[x_n \mathbf{y}_1(n)] = E[\mathbf{y}_1(n)\mathbf{y}_1(n)^T]\mathbf{c}_1 + E[\mathbf{y}_1(n)\mathbf{y}_2(n)^T]\mathbf{c}_2$$

It follows that the optimum estimate of x_n is

$$\hat{x}_n = E[x_n \mathbf{y}_1(n)^T]E[\mathbf{y}_1(n)\mathbf{y}_1(n)^T]^{-1}\mathbf{y}_1(n) = \mathbf{c}_1^T \mathbf{y}_1(n) + \mathbf{c}_2^T \hat{\mathbf{y}}_{2/1}(n)$$

where $\hat{\mathbf{y}}_{2/1}(n) = E[\mathbf{y}_2(n)\mathbf{y}_1(n)^T]E[\mathbf{y}_1(n)\mathbf{y}_1(n)^T]^{-1}\mathbf{y}_1(n)$ is recognized as the optimum estimate of $\mathbf{y}_2(n)$ based on $\mathbf{y}_1(n)$. Thus, the estimation error will be

$$e_n = x_n - \hat{x}_n = \mathbf{c}_2^T[\mathbf{y}_2(n) - \hat{\mathbf{y}}_{2/1}(n)] + u_n$$

which shows that the $\mathbf{y}_1(n)$ part is removed completely, and the $\mathbf{y}_2(n)$ part is removed as much as possible.

7.6 *Speed of Convergence*

The *convergence properties* of the LMS algorithm [2,10,18] may be discussed by restoring the expectation values where they should be

$$\frac{\partial \mathcal{E}}{\partial \mathbf{h}} = -2E[e_n \mathbf{y}(n)], \qquad \mathbf{y}(n) = \begin{bmatrix} y_0(n) \\ y_1(n) \\ \vdots \\ y_M(n) \end{bmatrix} = \begin{bmatrix} y_n \\ y_{n-1} \\ \vdots \\ y_{n-M} \end{bmatrix}$$

$$\begin{aligned}
\mathbf{h}(n+1) &= \mathbf{h}(n) - \mu \frac{\partial \mathcal{E}}{\partial \mathbf{h}} \\
&= \mathbf{h}(n) + 2\mu E[e_n \mathbf{y}(n)] \\
&= \mathbf{h}(n) + 2\mu\{E[x_n \mathbf{y}(n)] - E[\mathbf{y}(n)\mathbf{y}(n)^T]\mathbf{h}(n)\} \\
&= \mathbf{h}(n) + 2\mu \mathbf{r} - 2\mu R \mathbf{h}(n)
\end{aligned}$$

or

$$\mathbf{h}(n+1) = (I - 2\mu R)\mathbf{h}(n) + 2\mu \mathbf{r} \tag{7.6.1}$$

where the covariance matrix R is defined by

$$R = E[\mathbf{y}(n)\mathbf{y}(n)^T]$$
$$R_{ij} = E[y_i(n)y_j(n)] = E[y_{n-i}y_{n-j}] = R_{yy}(i - j), \qquad 0 \leqslant i, j \leqslant M$$

The difference equation (6.6.1) has solution

$$\mathbf{h}(n) = \mathbf{h} + (I - 2\mu R)^n(\mathbf{h}(0) - \mathbf{h})$$

Convergence requires that the quantity $(1 - 2\mu\lambda)$, for every eigenvalue λ of R, have magnitude less than one

$$|1 - 2\mu\lambda| < 1, \qquad \text{or } -1 < 1 - 2\mu\lambda < 1, \qquad \text{or } 0 < \mu < \frac{1}{\lambda}$$

for every eigenvalue λ of R. This condition is guaranteed, for example, if we require this inequality for $\lambda_{\max}$, the maximum eigenvalue

$$0 < \mu < \frac{1}{\lambda_{\max}} \tag{7.6.2}$$

Note that $\lambda_{\max}$ can be bounded from above by

$$\lambda_{\max} < \text{Tr}[R] = \sum_{i=0}^{M} R(i,i) = \sum_{i=0}^{M} R(0) = (M + 1)R(0)$$

and one may require instead $\mu < [(M + 1)R(0)]^{-1}$. As for the *speed* of convergence, suppose that μ is selected half-way within its range (7.6.2), near $0.5/\lambda_{\max}$, then the rate of convergence will depend on the *slowest* converging term of the form $(1 - 2\mu\lambda)^n$; that is, the term having $(1 - 2\mu\lambda)$ as close to one as possible. This occurs for the smallest eigenvalue $\lambda = \lambda_{\min}$. Thus, the *slowest* converging term is effectively given by $[1 - 2\mu\lambda_{\min}]^n = [1 - \lambda_{\min}/\lambda_{\max}]^n$. The effective *time constant* in seconds is obtained by writing $t = nT$, where T is the sampling period, and using the approximation

$$\left(1 - \frac{\lambda_{\min}}{\lambda_{\max}}\right)^n \approx \exp(-\frac{\lambda_{\min}}{\lambda_{\max}} n) = e^{-t/\tau}$$

where

$$\tau = T\frac{\lambda_{\max}}{\lambda_{\min}}$$

The eigenvalue spread $\lambda_{\max}/\lambda_{\min}$ controls, therefore, the *speed of convergence.* The convergence can be as fast as one sampling instant T if the eigenvalue spread is small, i.e., $\lambda_{\max}/\lambda_{\min} \approx 1$. But, the convergence will be *slow* if the eigenvalue spread is large. As we shall see shortly, a large spread in the eigenvalues of the covariance matrix R corresponds to a *highly self-correlated* signal y_n. Thus, we obtain the general qualitative result that in situations where the secondary signal is *strongly self-correlated,* the convergence of the gradient-based LMS algorithm *will be slow.* In many applications, such as channel equalization, the convergence must be as quick as possible. Alternative adaptation schemes exist that combine the computational simplicity of the LMS algorithm with a fast speed of convergence. Examples are the fast RLS and the adaptive lattice algorithms.

The possibility of accelerating the convergence rate may be seen by considering a more general version of the gradient descent algorithm in which the time update for the weight vector is chosen as

$$\Delta\mathbf{h} = -M\frac{\partial\mathcal{E}}{\partial\mathbf{h}} \tag{7.6.3}$$

where M is a *positive definite* and *symmetric* matrix. The LMS steepest descent case is obtained as a special case of this when M is proportional to the unit matrix I, $M = \mu I$. This choice guarantees convergence towards the minimum of the performance index $\mathcal{E}(\mathbf{h})$; indeed,

$$\mathcal{E}(\mathbf{h}+\Delta\mathbf{h}) = \mathcal{E}(\mathbf{h}) + \Delta\mathbf{h}^T\frac{\partial\mathcal{E}}{\partial\mathbf{h}} = \mathcal{E}(\mathbf{h}) - \left(\frac{\partial\mathcal{E}}{\partial\mathbf{h}}\right)^T M\left(\frac{\partial\mathcal{E}}{\partial\mathbf{h}}\right) \leq \mathcal{E}(\mathbf{h})$$

Since the performance index is

$$\mathcal{E} = E[e_n^2] = E[(x_n - \mathbf{h}^T\mathbf{y}(n))^2] = E[x_n^2] - 2\mathbf{h}^T\mathbf{r} + \mathbf{h}^T R\mathbf{h}$$

it follows that $\partial\mathcal{E}/\partial\mathbf{h} = -2(\mathbf{r} - R\mathbf{h})$, and the difference equation for the adaptive weights becomes

$$\begin{aligned}\mathbf{h}(n+1) &= \mathbf{h}(n) + \Delta\mathbf{h}(n)\\ &= \mathbf{h}(n) + 2M(\mathbf{r} - R\mathbf{h}(n))\end{aligned}$$

or

$$\mathbf{h}(n+1) = (I - 2MR)\mathbf{h}(n) + 2M\mathbf{r} \tag{7.6.4}$$

with solution

$$\mathbf{h}(n) = \mathbf{h} + (I - 2MR)^n(\mathbf{h}(0) - \mathbf{h}) \tag{7.6.5}$$

where $\mathbf{h} = R^{-1}\mathbf{r}$ is the asymptotic value. It is evident from Eq. (7.6.4) or Eq. (7.6.5) that the choice of M can *drastically* affect the speed of convergence. For example, if M is chosen as

$$M = (2R)^{-1} \tag{7.6.6}$$

then $I - 2MR = 0$, and the convergence occurs in just one step! This choice of M is equivalent to *Newton's method* of solving the system of equations

$$\mathbf{f}(\mathbf{h}) = \frac{\partial\mathcal{E}}{\partial\mathbf{h}} = 0$$

for the optimal weights. Indeed, Newton's method linearizes about each point $\mathbf{h}$ to get the next point; that is, $\Delta\mathbf{h}$ is selected such that

$$\mathbf{f}(\mathbf{h} + \Delta\mathbf{h}) \approx \mathbf{f}(\mathbf{h}) + \frac{\partial \mathbf{f}}{\partial \mathbf{h}} \Delta\mathbf{h} = 0$$

where we expanded to first order in $\Delta\mathbf{h}$. Solving for $\Delta\mathbf{h}$ we find

$$\Delta\mathbf{h} = -\left(\frac{\partial \mathbf{f}}{\partial \mathbf{h}}\right)^{-1} \mathbf{f}(\mathbf{h})$$

But since $\mathbf{f}(\mathbf{h}) = -2(\mathbf{r} - R\mathbf{h})$, we have $\partial\mathbf{f}/\partial\mathbf{h} = 2R$. Therefore, the choice $M = (2R)^{-1}$ corresponds precisely to Newton's update. Newton's method is depicted below for the one-dimensional case.

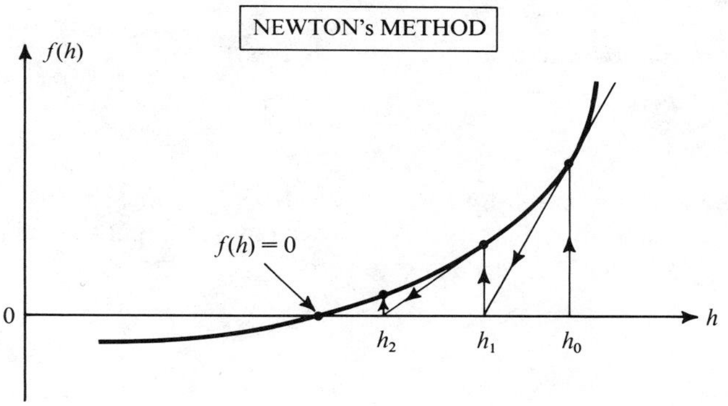

Note that the property that Newton's method converges in one step is a well-known property valid for *quadratic* performance indices (in this case, the gradient $\mathbf{f}(\mathbf{h})$ is already linear in $\mathbf{h}$ and therefore Newton's local linearization is exact). The important property about the choice $M = (2R)^{-1}$ is that M is proportional to the *inverse* of R. An alternative choice could have been $M = \alpha R^{-1}$. In this case $I - 2MR$ becomes proportional to the identity matrix:

$$I - 2MR = (1 - 2\alpha)I$$

having *equal* eigenvalues. Stability requires $|1 - 2\alpha| < 1$, or equivalently, $0 < \alpha < 1$, with Newton's choice corresponding exactly to the middle of this interval, $\alpha = 1/2$. Therefore, the disparity between the eigenvalues that could slow down the convergence rate is eliminated, and all eigenmodes converge at the *same* rate (which is faster the more M resembles $(2R)^{-1}$). The implementation of such Newton-like methods requires knowledge of R, which we do not have. (If we did, we would simply compute the Wiener solution $\mathbf{h} = R^{-1}\mathbf{r}$.) However, as we shall see later, the so-called *least-squares algorithms* effectively provide an implementation of Newton-type methods, and that is the reason for their extremely fast convergence. *Adaptive lattice filters* also have very fast convergence properties. In that case, because of the orthogonalization of the successive lattice stages of the filter, the matrix R is diagonal and the matrix M can also be chosen to be diagonal so as to equalize and speed up the convergence rate of all the filter coefficients. Recursive least-squares and adaptive lattice filters are discussed in Sections 7.13 and 7.18, respectively.

Finally, we would like to demonstrate the previous statement that a strongly correlated signal y_n has a large spread in the eigenvalue spectrum of its covariance matrix. For simplicity, consider the 2×2 case

$$R = E[\mathbf{y}(n)\mathbf{y}(n)^T] = E\left[\begin{pmatrix} y_n \\ y_{n-1} \end{pmatrix} (y_n, y_{n-1})\right] = \begin{bmatrix} R(0) & R(1) \\ R(1) & R(0) \end{bmatrix}$$

The two eigenvalues are easily found to be

$$\lambda_{\min} = R(0) - |R(1)|$$

$$\lambda_{\max} = R(0) + |R(1)|$$

and therefore, the ratio $\lambda_{\min}/\lambda_{\max}$ is given by

$$\frac{\lambda_{\min}}{\lambda_{\max}} = \frac{R(0) - |R(1)|}{R(0) + |R(1)|}$$

Since for an autocorrelation function we always have $|R(1)| \leq R(0)$, it follows that the largest value of $R(1)$ is $\pm R(0)$, implying that for highly correlated signals the ratio $\lambda_{\min}/\lambda_{\max}$ will be very close to zero.

7.7 *Adaptive Channel Equalizers*

Channels used in digital data transmissions can be modeled very often by linear time-invariant systems. The standard model for such a channel including channel noise is shown here.

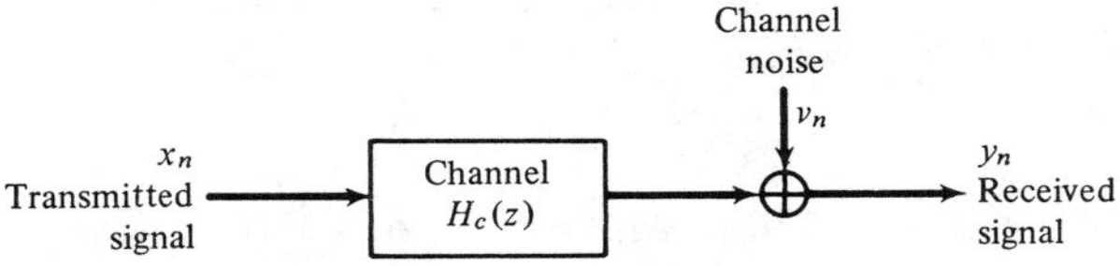

In the Figure, $H_c(z)$ is the transfer function for the channel and v_n is the channel noise, assumed to be additive white gaussian noise. The transfer function $H_c(z)$ incorporates the effects of the modulator and demodulator filters, as well as the channel distortions. The purpose of a channel equalizer is to undo the distorting effects of the channel and recover, from the received waveform y_n, the signal x_n that was transmitted. Typically, a channel equalizer will be a transversal filter with enough taps to approximate the inverse transfer function of the channel.

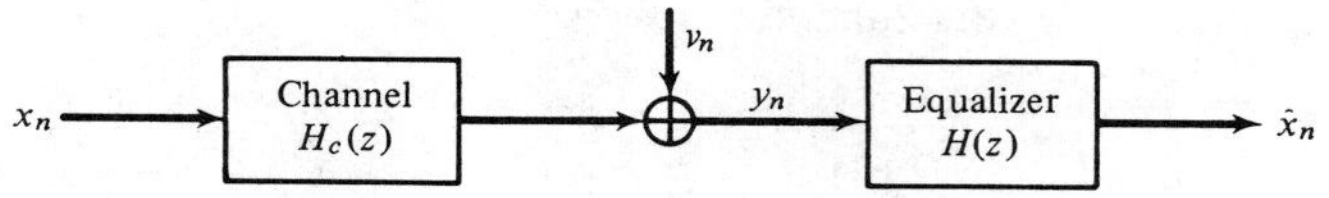

In the diagram shown here, $H(z)$ is the desired transfer function of the equalizer. In many situations, such in the telephone network, the channel is not known in advance, or it may be time-varying as in the case of multipath channels. Therefore it is desirable to design equalizers adaptively [19–21].

A channel equalizer, adaptive or not, is an optimal filter since it tries to produce as good an estimate $\hat{x}_n$ of the transmitted signal x_n as possible. The Wiener filtering concepts that we developed thus far are ideally suited to this problem. This is shown below

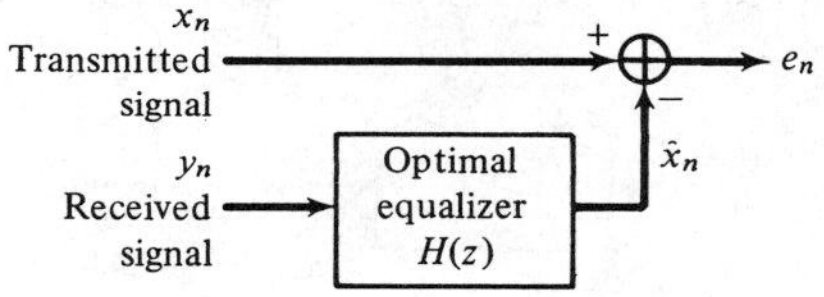

The design of the optimal filter requires two things: first, the autocorrelation of the received signal y_n, and second, the cross-correlation of the transmitted signal x_n with the received signal. Since the transmitted signal is not available at the receiver, the following procedure is used: After the channel connection is established, a "training" sequence x_n, which is also known to the receiver, is transmitted over the channel. Then, the equalizer may be designed, and then the actual message transmitted. To appreciate the equalizer's action as an inverse filter, suppose that the training sequence x_n is a white-noise sequence of variance σ_x^2. According to the theory developed in Chapter 4, the optimal filter estimating x_n on the basis of y_n is given by

$$H(z) = \frac{1}{\sigma_\epsilon^2 B(z)} \left[\frac{S_{xy}(z)}{B(z^{-1})} \right]_+$$

where $B(z)$ is the spectral factor of $S_{yy}(z) = \sigma_\epsilon^2 B(z) B(z^{-1})$. To simplify the discussion, let us ignore the causal instruction:

$$H(z) = \frac{S_{xy}(z)}{\sigma_\epsilon^2 B(z) B(z^{-1})} = \frac{S_{xy}(z)}{S_{yy}(z)}$$

Since we have $Y(z) = H_c(z)X(z) + V(z)$, we find

$$S_{xy}(z) = S_{xx}(z)H_c(z^{-1}) + S_{xv}(z) = S_{xx}(z)H_c(z^{-1}) = \sigma_x^2 H_c(z^{-1})$$

$$S_{yy}(z) = H_c(z)H_c(z^{-1})S_{xx}(z) + S_{vv}(z) = H_c(z)H_c(z^{-1})\sigma_x^2 + \sigma_v^2$$

and the equalizer's transfer function is then

$$H(z) = \frac{S_{xy}(z)}{S_{yy}(z)} = \frac{\sigma_x^2 H_c(z^{-1})}{H_c(z)H_c(z^{-1})\sigma_x^2 + \sigma_v^2}$$

It is seen that when the channel noise is weak (small σ_v^2), the equalizer essentially behaves as the inverse filter $1/H_c(z)$ of the channel.

In an adaptive implementation, we must use a filter with a finite number of weights. These weights are adjusted adaptively until they converge to their optimal values. Again, during this "training mode" a known pilot signal is sent over the channel and is received as y_n. At the receiving end, the pilot signal is locally generated and used in the adaptation algorithm. This implementation is shown below.

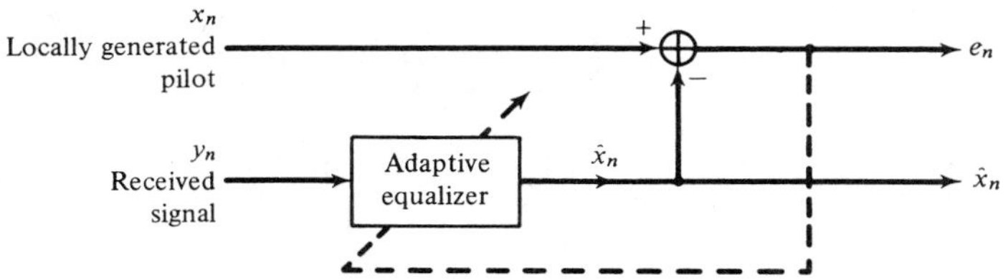

7.8 *Adaptive Echo Cancelers*

Consider two speakers A and B connected to each other by the telephone network. As a result of various impedance mismatches, when A's speech reaches B, it manages to "leak" through and echoes back to speaker A, as though it were B's speech.

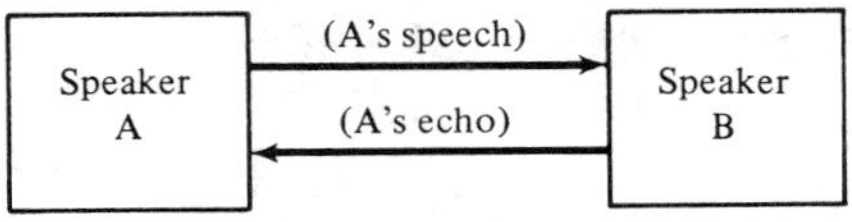

An echo canceler may be placed near B's end, as shown.

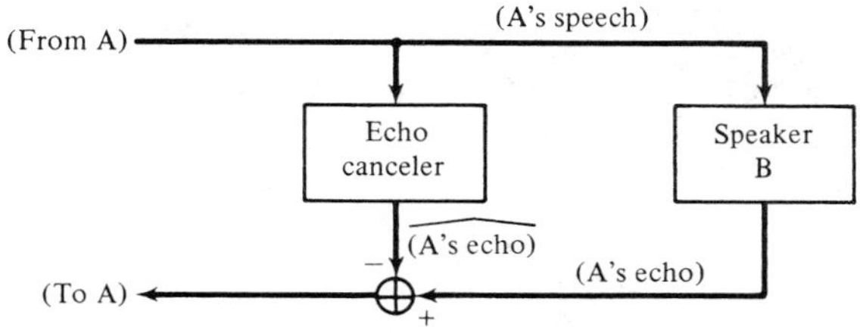

This should produce an *estimate* of A's echo through B's circuits, and then proceed to cancel it. Again, this is another case for which optimal filtering ideas are ideally suited. That is, it should produce the *best* possible estimate of A's echo. An adaptive echo canceler is an adaptive FIR filter placed as shown [22–27].

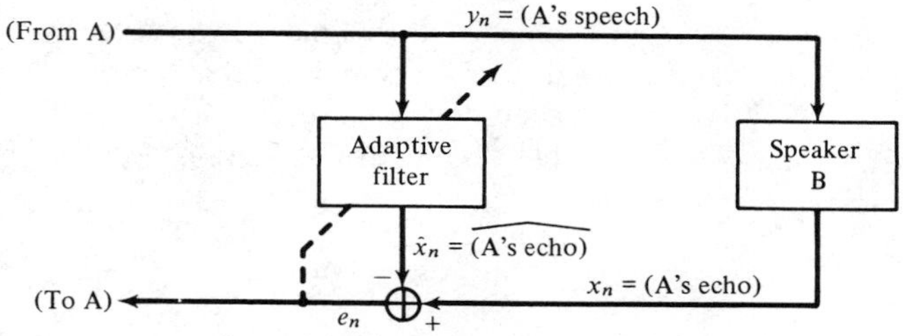

As always, the adaptive filter will adjust itself to cancel any correlations that might exist between its input (A's speech) and the main signal (A's echo).

7.9 *Adaptive Noise Canceling*

In many applications, two signals are available; one is composed of a desired signal plus undesired noise interference, and the other is composed only of noise interference which, if not identical with the noise part of the first signal, is *correlated* with it. This is shown in Fig. 7.8. An adaptive noise canceler [10] is an adaptive filter as shown in the Figure. Its operation as a correlation canceler should be clear. If the signals x_n and y_n are in any way correlated (i.e., the noise component of x_n with y_n), then the filter will respond by adapting its weights until such correlations are canceled from the output e_n. It does so by producing the best possible replica of the noise component of x_n, and proceeding to cancel it. The output e_n will now consist mainly of the desired signal.

There are many applications of adaptive noise canceling, such as adaptive sidelobe cancellation, acoustic noise cancellation [28–32], canceling 60 Hz interference in EKG recordings, plasma estimation [33], and ghost cancellation in television [34].

An interesting property of the adaptive noise canceler is that when the secondary signal y_n is purely sinusoidal at some frequency ω_0, the adaptive filter behaves as a *notch filter* [10,35] at the sinusoid's frequency; that is, the transfer

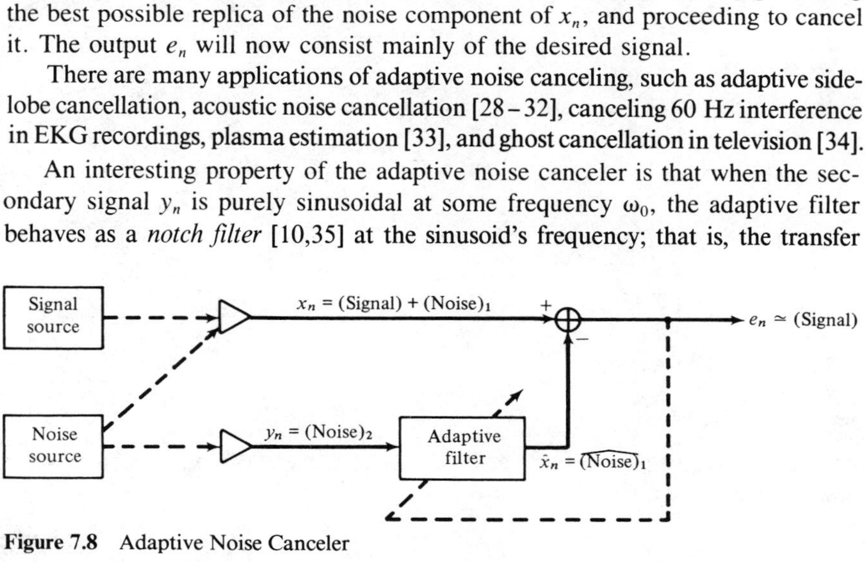

Figure 7.8 Adaptive Noise Canceler

relationship between the primary input x_n and the output e_n becomes the *time-invariant* transfer function of a notch filter. This is a surprising property since the adaptation equations for the weights and the filtering I/O equation are in general time-noninvariant. To understand this effect, it proves convenient to work with complex-valued signals using a complex-valued reformulation of the LMS algorithm [36]. We make a short digression on this, first.

We assume that x_n, y_n, and the weights $\mathbf{h}(n)$ are complex valued. The performance index is replaced by

$$\mathcal{E} = E[e_n^* e_n] = \min$$

where the I/O filtering equation is still given by

$$\hat{x}_n = \sum_{m=0}^{M} h_m y_{n-m} = \mathbf{h}^T \mathbf{y}(n)$$

Since the weights $\mathbf{h}$ are complex, the index $\mathcal{E}$ depends on both the real and the imaginary parts of $\mathbf{h}$. Equivalently, we may think of $\mathcal{E}$ as a function of the two independent variables $\mathbf{h}$ and $\mathbf{h}^*$. A complex change in the weights $\Delta\mathbf{h}$ will change the index to

$$\mathcal{E}(\mathbf{h} + \Delta\mathbf{h}, \mathbf{h}^* + \Delta\mathbf{h}^*) = \mathcal{E}(\mathbf{h}, \mathbf{h}^*) + \Delta\mathbf{h}^T \frac{\partial\mathcal{E}}{\partial\mathbf{h}} + \Delta\mathbf{h}^\dagger \frac{\partial\mathcal{E}}{\partial\mathbf{h}^*}$$

Choosing $\Delta\mathbf{h}$ to be proportional to the *complex conjugate* of the negative gradient; that is,

$$\Delta\mathbf{h} = -2\mu \frac{\partial\mathcal{E}}{\partial\mathbf{h}^*}$$

will move the index $\mathcal{E}$ towards its minimum value; indeed,

$$\mathcal{E}(\mathbf{h} + \Delta\mathbf{h}, \mathbf{h}^* + \Delta\mathbf{h}^*) = \mathcal{E}(\mathbf{h}, \mathbf{h}^*) - 4\mu \left(\frac{\partial\mathcal{E}}{\partial\mathbf{h}}\right)^\dagger \left(\frac{\partial\mathcal{E}}{\partial\mathbf{h}}\right) \leq \mathcal{E}(\mathbf{h}, \mathbf{h}^*)$$

Thus, the complex version of the LMS algorithm consists simply in replacing the *instantaneous gradient by its complex conjugate* [36]. We summarize the algorithm as follows:

1. Compute $\hat{x}_n = \mathbf{h}(n)^T \mathbf{y}(n)$
2. Compute $e_n = x_n - \hat{x}_n$
3. Update weights $\mathbf{h}(n+1) = \mathbf{h}(n) + 2\mu e_n \mathbf{y}(n)^*$

Using this complex version, we now discuss the notching behavior of the adaptive filter. Suppose y_n is sinusoidal

$$y_n = A e^{j\omega_0 n} \tag{7.9.1}$$

at a given frequency ω_0. Then, the weight-update equation becomes

$$h_m(n+1) = h_m(n) + 2\mu e_n y^*_{n-m} = h_m(n) + 2\mu e_n A^* e^{-j\omega_0(n-m)}$$

for $m = 0,1,\ldots,M$. The factor $e^{-j\omega_0(n-m)}$ suggests that we look for a solution of the form

$$h_m(n) = f_m(n)e^{-j\omega_0(n-m)}$$

Then, $f_m(n)$ must satisfy the difference equation

$$e^{-j\omega_0} f_m(n+1) = f_m(n) + 2\mu A^* e_n \tag{7.9.2}$$

As a difference equation in n, this equation has *constant coefficients,* and therefore may be solved by z-transform techniques. Taking z-transforms of both sides we find

$$e^{-j\omega_0} z F_m(z) = F_m(z) + 2\mu A^* E(z)$$

which may be solved for $F_m(z)$ in terms of $E(z)$ to give

$$F_m(z) = E(z)\frac{2\mu A^* e^{j\omega_0}}{z - e^{j\omega_0}}$$

On the other hand, the I/O filtering equation from y_n to the output $\hat{x}_n$ is

$$\hat{x}_n = \sum_{m=0}^{M} h_m(n) y_{n-m} = \sum_{m=0}^{M} f_m(n)e^{-j\omega_0(n-m)} A e^{j\omega_0(n-m)} = \sum_{m=0}^{M} f_m(n)A$$

or, in the z-domain,

$$\hat{X}(z) = \sum_{m=0}^{M} F_m(z)A = E(z)\frac{2\mu(M+1)|A|^2 e^{j\omega_0}}{z - e^{j\omega_0}}$$

Finally, the I/O equation from x_n to the output e_n becomes

$$e_n = x_n - \hat{x}_n$$

or, in the z-domain,

$$E(z) = X(z) - \hat{X}(z) = X(z) - E(z)\frac{2\mu(M+1)|A|^2 e^{j\omega_0}}{z - e^{j\omega_0}}$$

which may be solved for the transfer function $E(z)/X(z)$

$$\frac{E(z)}{X(z)} = \frac{z - e^{j\omega_0}}{z - e^{j\omega_0}(1 - 2\mu(M+1)|A|^2)} \tag{7.9.3}$$

This filter has a *zero* at $z = e^{j\omega_0}$ which corresponds to the *notch* at the frequency ω_0. For sufficiently small values of μ and A, the filter is stable; its pole is at $z = e^{j\omega_0}(1 - 2\mu|A|^2(M+1))$ and can be made to lie inside the unit circle. If the primary input x_n happens to have a sinusoidal component at frequency ω_0, this component will be completely notched away from the output. This will take place even when the sinusoidal reference signal is very weak (i.e., when A is small). The implications of this property for *jamming by signal cancellation* in adaptive array processing have been discussed in [37]. The notching behavior of the adaptive noise canceler when the reference signal consists of a sinusoid plus noise has been discussed in [38].

A related recent result is that the adaptive noise canceler behaves as a time-invariant *comb* filter whenever its secondary input y_n is a periodic train of impulses separated by some period [39]. This property can be used to cancel periodic interference. Because the method of signal averaging can be thought of as comb filtering, the above property may also be used as an alternative method to perform signal averaging for pulling weak periodic signals from background noise, such as evoked potentials [40].

7.10 *Adaptive Line Enhancer* (*ALE*) [10,41–43]

A special case of adaptive noise canceling is when there is only *one* signal x_n available which is contaminated by noise. In such a case, the signal x_n provides *its own reference* signal y_n, which is taken to be a *delayed* replica of $x_n : y_n = x_{n-\Delta}$, as shown in Fig. 7.9. Will such arrangement be successful? The adaptive filter will respond by canceling any components of the main signal x_n that are in any way correlated with the secondary signal $y_n = x_{n-\Delta}$. Suppose the signal x_n consists of two components: a *narrowband* component that has *long-range* correlations such as a sinusoid, and a *broadband* component which will tend to have *short-range* correlations. One of these could represent the desired signal and the other an undesired interfering noise. Pictorially the autocorrelations of the two components could look as follows,

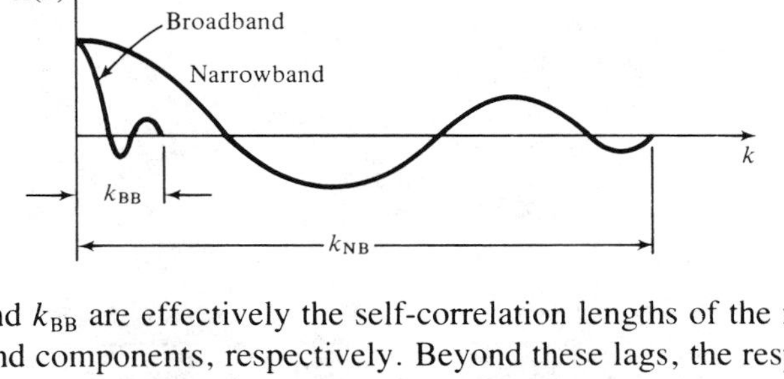

where k_{NB} and k_{BB} are effectively the self-correlation lengths of the narrowband and broadband components, respectively. Beyond these lags, the respective correlations die out quickly. Suppose the delay Δ is selected so that

$$k_{BB} \leqslant \Delta \leqslant k_{NB}$$

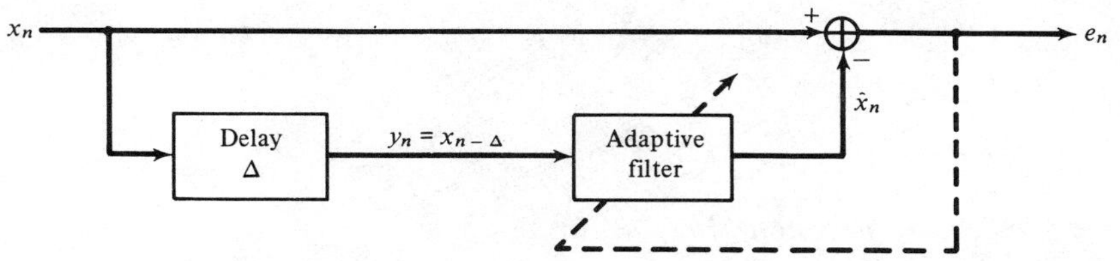

Figure 7.9 Adaptive Line Enhancer

Since Δ is longer than the effective correlation length of the BB component, then the delayed replica BB(n − Δ) will be entirely uncorrelated with the BB part of the main signal. The adaptive filter will not be able to respond to this component. On the other hand, since Δ is shorter than the correlation length of the NB component, the delayed replica NB(n − Δ) that appears in the secondary input will still be correlated with the NB part of the main signal, and the filter will respond to cancel it. Thus, the filter outputs will be as shown:

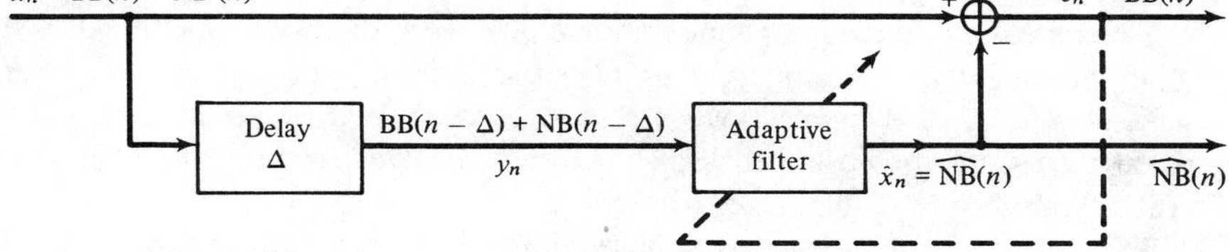

Note that if Δ is selected to be longer than both correlation lengths, the secondary input will become uncorrelated with the primary input, and the adaptive filter will turn itself off. In the opposite case, when the delay Δ is selected to be less than both correlation lengths, then both components of the secondary signal will be correlated with the primary signal, and therefore the adaptive filter will respond to cancel the primary x_n completely. The computational algorithm for the ALE is

1. $\hat{x}_n = \Sigma_{m=0}^{M} h_m(n)y(n - m) = \Sigma_{m=0}^{M} h_m(n)x(n - m - \Delta)$
2. $e_n = x_n - \hat{x}_n$
3. $h_m(n + 1) = h_m(n) + 2\mu e_n x(n - m - \Delta), \qquad m = 0,1,2, \ldots ,M$

The Wiener solution for the steady-state weights is $\mathbf{h} = R^{-1}\mathbf{r}$, where the matrix R and vector $\mathbf{r}$ are *both* expressible in terms of the autocorrelation of the signal x_n, as follows:

$$R_{ij} = E[y_{n-i}y_{n-j}] = E[x_{n-\Delta-i}x_{n-\Delta-j}] = R_{xx}(i - j)$$

$$r_i = E[x_n y_{n-i}] = E[x_n x_{n-\Delta-i}] = R_{xx}(i + \Delta)$$

for $i,j = 0,1, \ldots ,M$. When the input signal consists of multiple sinusoids in additive white noise, the inverse R^{-1} may be obtained using the methods of

Section 6.2, thus resulting in a closed form expression for the steady-state optimal weights [43].

7.11 *Adaptive Linear Prediction*

A linear predictor is a special case of the ALE with the delay $\Delta = 1$. It is shown in Fig. 7.10, where to be consistent with our past notation on linear predictors we have denoted the main signal by y_n. The secondary signal, the input to the adaptive filter, is then y_{n-1}. Due to the special sign convention used for linear predictors, the adaptation algorithm now reads [44,45]

1. $\hat{y}_n = -\sum_{m=1}^{M} a_m(n) y_{n-m}$
2. $e_n = y_n - \hat{y}_n = y_n + a_1(n)y_{n-1} + a_2(n)y_{n-2} + \cdots + a_M(n)y_{n-M}$
3. $a_m(n+1) = a_m(n) - 2\mu e_n y_{n-m}, \qquad 1 \leq m \leq M$

The realization of Fig. 7.10 can be redrawn more explicitly as in Fig. 7.11.

The routine **lmsap** is an implementation of the LMS adaptive predictor. At each call, the routine reads a sample y_n, computes the filter output e_n, updates the filter coefficients $a_m(n)$ to their new values $a_m(n+1)$ to be used by the next call, and updates the registers of the tapped delay line. With a small modification it can be used in the adaptive array problem (see below).

Because of the importance of the adaptive predictor, we present a direct derivation of the LMS algorithm as it applies to this case. The weights a_m are chosen optimally to minimize the mean output power of the filter; that is, the mean squared prediction error:

$$\mathcal{E} = E[e_n^2] = \mathbf{a}^T R \mathbf{a} = \min \tag{7.11.1}$$

where $\mathbf{a} = [1, a_1, a_2, \ldots, a_M]^T$ is the prediction error filter. The performance index (7.11.1) is minimized with respect to the M weights a_m. The gradient with respect to a_m is the mth component of the vector $2R\mathbf{a}$; namely,

$$\frac{\partial \mathcal{E}}{\partial a_m} = 2(R\mathbf{a})_m = 2(E[\mathbf{y}(n)\mathbf{y}(n)^T]\mathbf{a})_m = 2(E[\mathbf{y}(n)\mathbf{y}(n)^T\mathbf{a}])_m$$

$$= 2(E[\mathbf{y}(n)e_n])_m = 2E[y_{n-m}e_n]$$

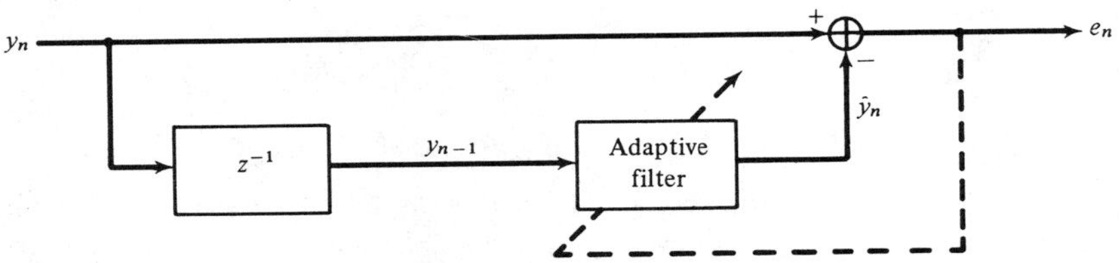

Figure 7.10 Adaptive Linear Predictor

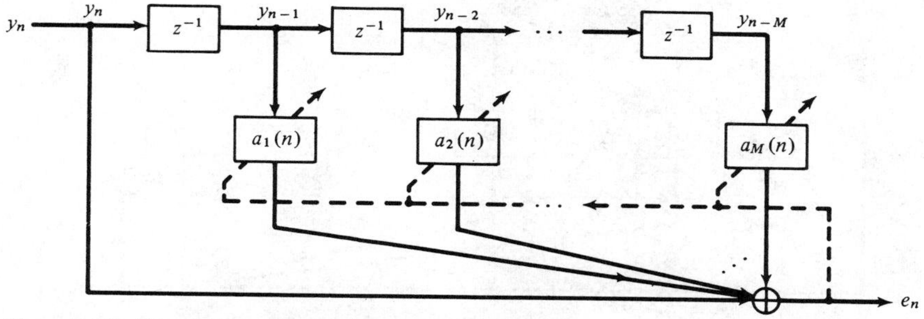

Figure 7.11 Direct Form Realization of Adaptive Predictor

The instantaneous gradient is obtained by *ignoring* the expectation instruction. This gives for the LMS time-update of the mth weight

$$\Delta a_m(n) = -\mu \frac{\partial \mathcal{E}}{\partial a_m} = -2\mu e_n y_{n-m} \qquad m = 1,2, \ldots ,M \qquad (7.11.2)$$

The adaptive predictor may be thought of as an *adaptive whitening filter*, or an analysis filter which determines the LPC model parameters adaptively. As processing of the signal y_n takes place, the autoregressive model parameters a_m are extracted *on-line*. This is but one example of on-line system identification methods [46–54]. The extracted model parameters may be used in any desired way—for example, to provide the *autoregressive spectrum estimate* of the signal y_n. One of the advantages of the adaptive implementation is that it offers the possibility of *tracking* slow changes in the spectra of *nonstationary* signals. The only requirement for obtaining meaningful spectrum estimates is that the nonstationary changes of the spectrum be slow enough for the adaptive filter to have a chance to converge between changes. Typical applications are the *tracking of sinusoids in noise* whose frequencies may be slowly changing [44,45,55], or tracking the time development of the spectra of nonstationary EEG signals [56,57]. At *each* time instant n, the adaptive weights $a_m(n)$; $m = 1,2, \ldots ,M$ may be used to obtain an *instantaneous* autoregressive estimate of the spectrum of y_n, in the form

$$S_n(\omega) = \frac{1}{|1 + a_1(n)e^{-j\omega} + a_2(n)e^{-2j\omega} + \cdots + a_M(n)e^{-Mj\omega}|^2}$$

This is the adaptive implementation of the LP spectrum estimate discussed in Section 6.2. The same adaptive approach to LP spectrum estimation may also be used in the problem of *multiple source location,* discussed in Section 6.3. The only difference in the algorithm is to replace y_{n-m} by $y_m(n)$—that is, by the signal recorded at the mth sensor at time n—and to use the complex-valued version of the LMS algorithm. For completeness, we summarize the computational steps in this case, following the notation of Section 6.3.

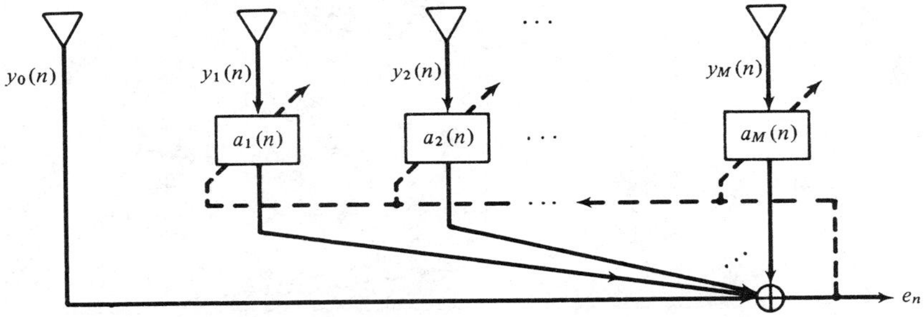

Figure 7.12 Adaptive Array Processor

1. $e_n = y_0(n) + a_1(n)y_1(n) + \cdots + a_M(n)y_M(n)$
2. $a_m(n+1) = a_m(n) - 2\mu e_n y_m(n)^*; \qquad m = 1,2,\ldots,M$

At *each* time instant n, the corresponding *spatial spectrum* estimate may be computed by

$$S_n(k) = \frac{1}{|1 + a_1(n)e^{-jk} + a_2(n)e^{-2jk} + \cdots + a_M(n)e^{-Mjk}|^2}$$

where the wavenumber k and its relationship to the angle of bearing was defined in Section 6.3. Figure 7.12 shows the corresponding adaptive array processing configuration.

The time-adaptive as well as the block-data adaptive methods of superresolution array processing have been reviewed in [58,59]. The above LMS algorithm for the array weights is effectively equivalent to the Howells-Applebaum algorithm [11–17]. Adaptive predictors may also be used to improve the performance of spread-spectrum systems [60–66].

7.12 *Adaptive Implementation of Pisarenko's Method*

In Section 6.2, we noted that the Pisarenko eigenvalue problem was equivalent to the minimization of the performance index

$$\mathcal{E} = E[e_n^* e_n] = \mathbf{a}^\dagger R\mathbf{a} = \min \tag{7.12.1}$$

subject to the quadratic constraint

$$\mathbf{a}^\dagger\mathbf{a} = 1 \tag{7.12.2}$$

where

$$e_n = \sum_{m=0}^{M} a_m y_{n-m} = [a_0,a_1,a_2,\ .\ .\ .\ ,a_M] \begin{bmatrix} y_n \\ y_{n-1} \\ y_{n-2} \\ \vdots \\ y_{n-M} \end{bmatrix} = \mathbf{a}^T\mathbf{y}(n)$$

The solution of the minimization problem shown in Eqs. (7.12.1) and (7.12.2) is the eigenvector **a** belonging to the *minimum* eigenvalue of the covariance matrix R. If there are L sinusoids of frequencies ω_i; $i = 1,2,\ .\ .\ .\ ,L$, and we use a filter with M weights, such that $M \geqslant L$, then the eigenpolynomial $A(z)$ corresponding to the minimum eigenvector **a** will have L zeros on the unit circle at precisely the desired set of frequencies; that is,

$$A(z_i) = 0 \qquad \text{where } z_i = \exp(j\omega_i), \qquad i = 1,2,\ .\ .\ .\ ,L$$

The adaptive implementation [67] of the Pisarenko eigenvalue problem is based on the above minimization criterion. The LMS gradient descent algorithm can be used to update the weights, but some care must be taken to satisfy the essential quadratic constraint (7.12.2) at *each* iteration of the algorithm. Any infinitesimal change $d\mathbf{a}$ of the weights must respect the constraint. This means the $d\mathbf{a}$ cannot be arbitrary but must satisfy the condition

$$d(\mathbf{a}^\dagger\mathbf{a}) = \mathbf{a}^\dagger d\mathbf{a} + d\mathbf{a}^\dagger\mathbf{a} = 0 \tag{7.12.3}$$

so that the new weight $\mathbf{a} + d\mathbf{a}$ still lies on the quadratic surface $\mathbf{a}^\dagger\mathbf{a} = 1$. The ordinary gradient of the performance index $\mathcal{E}$ is

$$\frac{\partial \mathcal{E}}{\partial \mathbf{a}^*} = R\mathbf{a}$$

Projecting this onto the surface $\mathbf{a}^\dagger\mathbf{a} = 1$ by the projection matrix $(I - \mathbf{a}\mathbf{a}^\dagger)$, where I is the $(M + 1)$-dimensional unit matrix, we obtain the "constrained" gradient

$$\left(\frac{\partial \mathcal{E}}{\partial \mathbf{a}^*}\right)_c = (I - \mathbf{a}\mathbf{a}^\dagger)\frac{\partial \mathcal{E}}{\partial \mathbf{a}^*} = (I - \mathbf{a}\mathbf{a}^\dagger)R\mathbf{a} = R\mathbf{a} - \mathcal{E}\mathbf{a} \tag{7.12.4}$$

which is *tangent* to the constraint surface at the point **a**. The vanishing of the constrained gradient is *equivalent* to the Pisarenko eigenvalue problem. The weight update can now be chosen to be proportional to the constrained gradient

$$\Delta\mathbf{a} = -\mu\left(\frac{\partial \mathcal{E}}{\partial \mathbf{a}^*}\right)_c = -\mu(R\mathbf{a} - \mathcal{E}\mathbf{a})$$

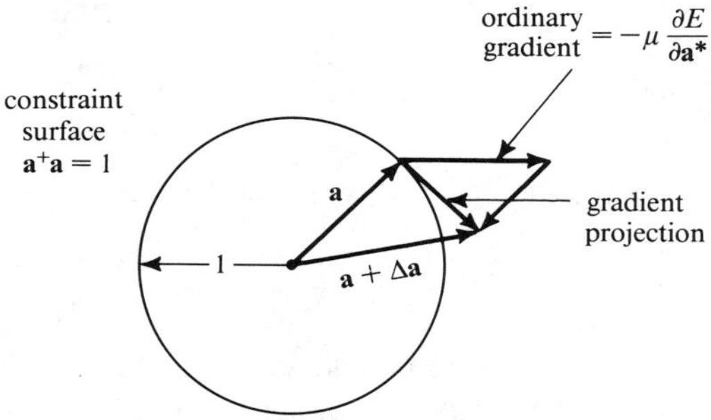

This choice guarantees that $\Delta\mathbf{a}$ satisfies Eq. (7.12.3); indeed, because of the projection matrix in front of the gradient, it follows that $\mathbf{a}^\dagger\Delta\mathbf{a} = 0$. Actually, since $\Delta\mathbf{a}$ is not infinitesimal, it will correspond to a *finite* motion along the tangent to the surface at the point $\mathbf{a}$. Thus, the new point $\mathbf{a} + \Delta\mathbf{a}$ will be slightly off the surface and must be *renormalized* to have unit norm. Using

$$R\mathbf{a} = E[\mathbf{y}(n)^*\mathbf{y}(n)^T]\mathbf{a} = E[\mathbf{y}(n)^* e_n], \qquad \text{and} \qquad \mathcal{E} = E[e_n^* e_n]$$

we write the update as

$$\Delta\mathbf{a} = -\mu(E[e_n\mathbf{y}(n)^*] - E[e_n^* e_n]\mathbf{a})$$

The LMS algorithm is obtained by *ignoring* the indicated ensemble expectation values. The weight adjustment procedure consists of two steps: first, shift the old weight $\mathbf{a}(n)$ by $\Delta\mathbf{a}(n)$, and then renormalize it to unit norm:

$$\begin{aligned} \mathbf{b}(n+1) &= \mathbf{a}(n) + \Delta\mathbf{a}(n) \\ \mathbf{a}(n+1) &= \mathbf{b}(n+1)/\|\mathbf{b}(n+1)\| \end{aligned} \tag{7.12.5}$$

where the weight update is computed by

$$\Delta\mathbf{a}(n) = -\mu[e_n\mathbf{y}(n)^* - e_n^* e_n\mathbf{a}(n)] \tag{7.12.6}$$

In summary, the computational steps are as follows:

1. At time n, $\mathbf{a}(n)$ is available and normalized to unit norm
2. Compute the output $e_n = \sum_{m=0}^{M} a_m(n)y_{n-m} = \mathbf{a}(n)^T\mathbf{y}(n)$
3. Update the filter weights using Eqs. (7.12.5) and (7.12.6)
4. Go to the next time instant, $n \to n+1$

A realization of the adaptive filter is shown in Fig. 7.13. After a number of iterations, the algorithm may be stopped and the Pisarenko spectrum estimate computed

$$S_n(\omega) = \frac{1}{|a_0(n) + a_1(n)e^{-j\omega} + a_2(n)e^{-2j\omega} + \cdots + a_M(n)e^{-Mj\omega}|^2}$$

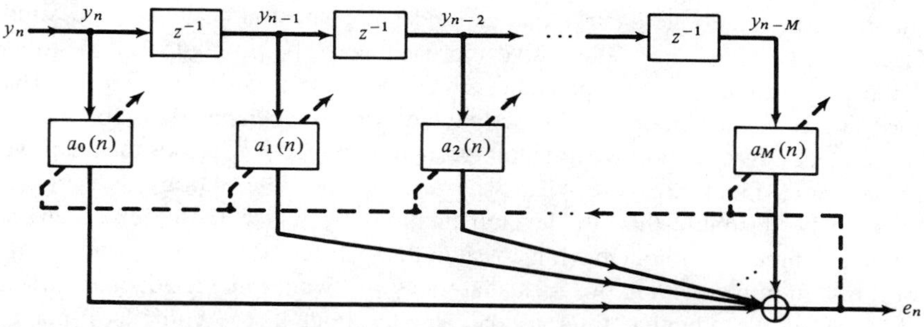

Figure 7.13 Adaptive Implementation of Pisarenko's Method

After convergence, $S_n(\omega)$ should exhibit very sharp peaks at the sought frequency angles ω_i; $i = 1,2, \ldots, L$. The convergence properties of this algorithm have been studied in [68]. Alternative adaptation schemes for the weights have been proposed in [69,70]. The algorithm may also be applied to the array problem of *multiple source location* [71]. Again, the only change is to replace y_{n-m} by $y_m(n)$.

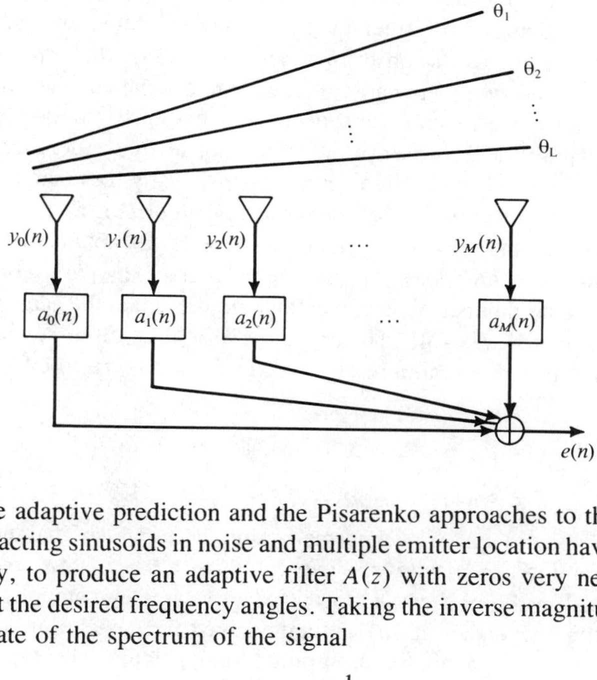

Both the adaptive prediction and the Pisarenko approaches to the two problems of extracting sinusoids in noise and multiple emitter location have a common aim; namely, to produce an adaptive filter $A(z)$ with zeros very near or on the unit circle at the desired frequency angles. Taking the inverse magnitude response as an estimate of the spectrum of the signal

$$S(\omega) = \frac{1}{|A(\omega)|^2}$$

is a simple device to get a curve that exhibits sharp spectral peaks at the desired frequencies. A satisfactory alternative approach would be simply to find the roots of the polynomial $A(z)$ and pick those that are closest to the unit circle. The phase angles of these roots are precisely the desired frequencies. In other words, the frequency information we are attempting to extract by means of the adaptive filter is more directly represented by the zeros of the filter than by its weights. It would be desirable then to develop methods by which these zeros can be estimated directly without having to submit the filter $A(z)$ to root-finding algorithms. In implementing this idea adaptively, we would like to adapt and track the zeros of the adaptive filter as they move about in the complex z-plane, converging to their final destinations which are the desired zeros. In this way, the frequency information can be extracted directly. Such "zero-tracking" adaptation algorithms have been proposed recently [72,73]. Even though the representations of the filter in terms of its zeros and in terms of its weights are mathematically equivalent, the zero representation may be more appropriate in some applications, in the sense that a better insight into the nature of the underlying processes may be gained from it than from the weight representation. As an example we mention the problem of predicting epileptic seizures by LPC modeling of the EEG signal where it was found [74] that the trajectories of the zeros of the prediction-error filter in the z-plane exhibited an unexpected behavior; namely, prior to the onset of a seizure, one of the zeros became the "most mobile" and moved towards the unit circle, whereas the other zeros of the filter did not move much. The trajectory of the most mobile zero could be used as a signature for the onset of the oncoming seizure. Such behavior could not be easily discerned by the frequency response or by the final zero location.

Next, we describe briefly the *zero-tracking algorithm* as it applies to the Pisarenko problem and present a simulation example. Its application to *adaptive prediction* and to *emitter location* has been discussed in [73]. For simplicity, we assume that the number of sinusoids that are present is the same as the order of the filter **a**; that is, $L = M$. The case $L < M$ will be discussed later on. The eigenpolynomial of the minimum eigenvector **a** may be factored into its zeros as follows:

$$\begin{aligned} A(z) &= a_0 + a_1 z^{-1} + a_2 z^{-2} + \cdots + a_M z^{-M} \\ &= a_0(1 - z_1 z^{-1})(1 - z_2 z^{-1}) \cdots (1 - z_M z^{-1}) \end{aligned} \tag{7.12.7}$$

where a_0 may be thought of as a normalization factor which guarantees the unit norm constraint (7.12.2), and $z_i = \exp(j\omega_i)$, $i = 1,2, \ldots ,M$ are the desired sinusoid zeros on the unit circle. In the adaptive implementation, the weights a_m become time dependent $a_m(n)$ and are adapted from each time instant to the next until they converge to the asymptotic values defined by Eq. (7.12.7). At each n, the corresponding polynomial can be factored into its zeros as follows:

$$\begin{aligned} &a_0(n) + a_1(n) z^{-1} + a_2(n) z^{-2} + \cdots + a_M(n) z^{-M} \\ &\quad = a_0(n)(1 - z_1(n) z^{-1})(1 - z_2(n) z^{-1}) \cdots (1 - z_M(n) z^{-1}) \end{aligned} \tag{7.12.8}$$

where again the factor $a_0(n)$ ensures the unit norm constraint. In the zero-tracking algorithm, the weight update equation (7.12.5) is replaced by a *zero-update equation* of the form

$$z_i(n + 1) = z_i(n) + \Delta z_i(n), \qquad i = 1,2, \ldots ,M \qquad (7.12.9)$$

where the zero updates $\Delta z_i(n)$ must be such that to ensure the convergence of the zeros to their asymptotic values z_i. One way to do this is to make the algorithm equivalent to the LMS algorithm. The functional dependence of $z_i(n)$ on $a_m(n)$ defined by Eq. (7.12.8) implies that if the weights $a_m(n)$ are changed by a small amount $\Delta a_m(n)$ given by Eq. (7.12.6), then a small change $\Delta z_i(n)$ will be induced on the corresponding zeros. This is given as follows:

$$\Delta z_i(n) = \sum_{m=0}^{M} \frac{\partial z_i(n)}{\partial a_m} \Delta a_m(n) \qquad (7.12.10)$$

where the partial derivatives are given by [75]

$$\frac{\partial z_i(n)}{\partial a_m} = -\frac{1}{a_0(n)} \frac{z_i(n)^{M-m}}{\prod_{j\neq i} (z_i(n) - z_j(n))} \qquad (7.12.11)$$

for $0 \leq m \leq M$. Equation (7.12.10) is strictly valid for infinitesimal changes, but for small μ, it can be taken to be an adequate approximation for the purpose of computing $\Delta z_i(n)$. The advantage of this expression is that only the *current* zeros $z_i(n)$ are needed to compute $\Delta z_i(n)$. The complete algorithm is summarized as follows:

1. At time n, the zeros $z_i(n)$; $i = 1,2, \ldots ,M$ are available
2. Using convolution, compute the corresponding filter weights and normalize them to unit norm. That is, first convolve the factors of Eq. (7.12.8) to obtain the vector

$$\begin{aligned}\mathbf{b}(n)^T &= [1,b_1(n), b_2(n), \ldots ,b_M(n)] \\ &= [1,-z_1(n)] * [1,-z_2(n)] * \cdots * [1,-z_M(n)]\end{aligned}$$

   and then normalize the vector $\mathbf{b}(n)$ to unit norm

$$\mathbf{a}(n) = \frac{\mathbf{b}(n)}{\|\mathbf{b}(n)\|}$$

3. Compute the filter output $e_n = \sum_{m=0}^{M} a_m(n) y_{n-m}$
4. Compute the LMS coefficient update $\Delta a_m(n)$ using Eq. (7.12.6). Compute the zero update $\Delta z_i(n)$ using Eqs. (7.12.10) and (7.12.11), and update the zeros using Eq. (7.12.9)

The algorithm may be initialized by a random selection of the initial zeros inside the unit circle in the z-plane. Next, we present a simulation example consisting of a fourth order filter and four sinusoids

$$y_n = v_n + e^{j\omega_1 n} + e^{j\omega_2 n} + e^{j\omega_3 n} + e^{j\omega_4 n}$$

with frequencies

$$\omega_1 = 0.25\pi, \quad \omega_2 = -0.25\pi, \quad \omega_3 = 0.75\pi, \quad \omega_4 = -0.75\pi$$

and a zero-mean, unit-variance, white noise sequence v_n (this corresponds to all sinusoids having 0 dB signal to noise ratio). The value of μ was 0.001. Figure 7.14 shows the adaptive trajectories of the four filter zeros as they converge onto the unit circle at the above frequency values. After convergence, the adaptive zeros remain within small neighborhoods about the asymptotic zeros. The diameter of these neighborhoods decreases with smaller μ, but so does the speed of convergence [73]. The transient behavior of the zeros can be seen by plotting $z_i(n)$ versus iteration number n. Figure 7.15 shows the real and imaginary parts of the adaptive trajectory $z_3(n)$ converging to the real and imaginary parts of the asymptotic zero $z_3 = \exp(j\omega_3)$.

When the number L of sinusoids is less than the order M of the filter, only L of the M zeros $z_i(n)$ of the filter will be driven to the unit circle at the right frequency angles. The remaining $(M - L)$ zeros correspond to spurious degrees of freedom (the degeneracy of the minimum eigenvalue σ_v^2), and are affected by the adaptation process only insofar as the M zero trajectories are not entirely independent of each other but are mutually coupled through Eq. (7.12.10). Where these spurious zeros converge depends on the particular initialization. For some

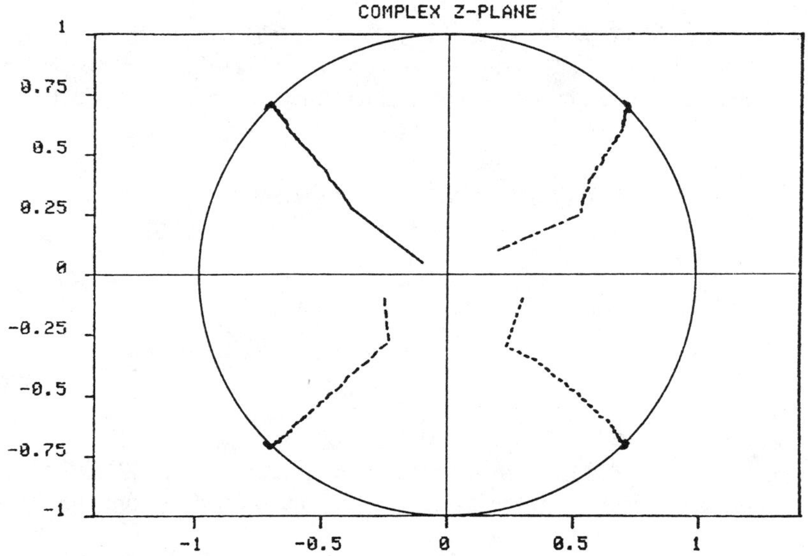

Figure 7.14 z-Plane Trajectories of the Four Adaptive Zeros $z_i(n)$, $i = 1, 2, 3, 4$

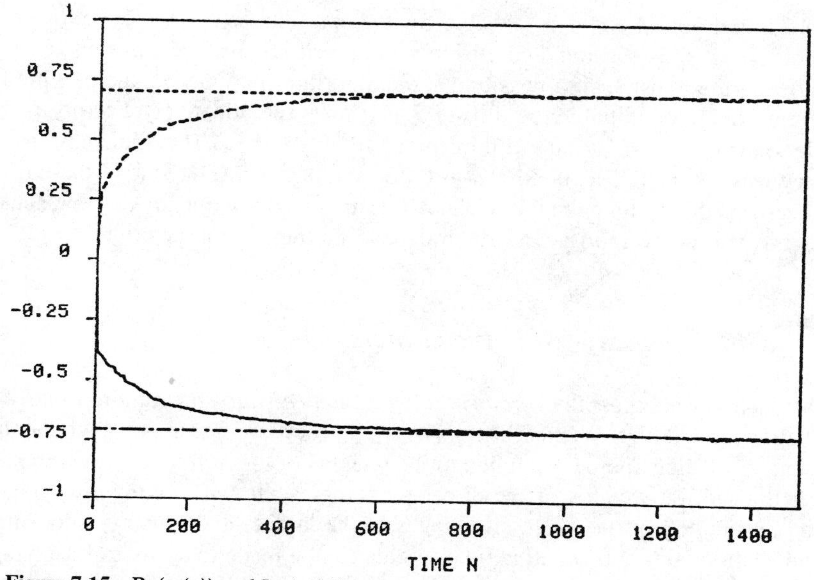

Figure 7.15 Re($z_3(n)$) and Im($z_3(n)$) versus n

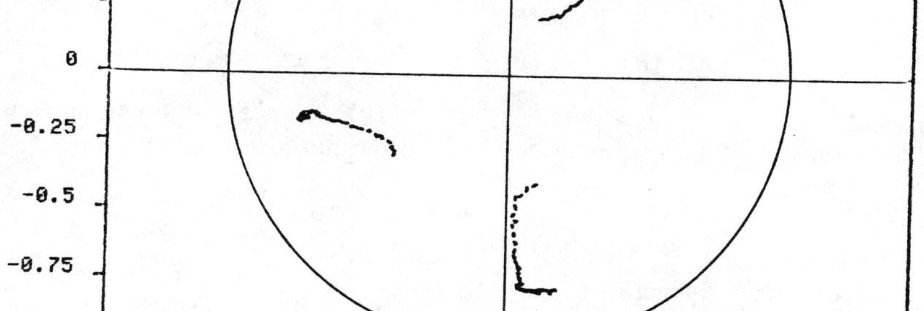

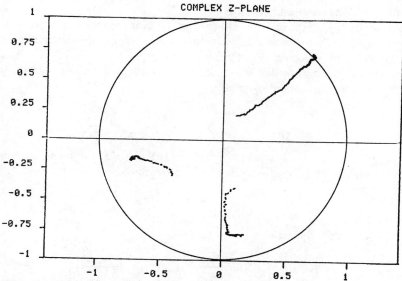

Figure 7.16 Single Sinusoid with Order-3 Adaptive Filter

special initial conditions it is possible for the spurious zeros to move close to the unit circle, thus causing a confusion as to which are the true sinusoid zeros. To safeguard against such a possibility, the algorithm may be run again with a different choice of initial zeros. Figure 7.16 shows the adaptive trajectory of a single sinusoid, $L = 1$, using a third order filter, $M = 3$. The sinusoid's frequency was $\omega_1 = 0.25\pi$, its SNR was 0 dB, and μ was 0.001. One of the three filter zeros is driven to the unit circle at the desired angle, while the two spurious zeros traverse fairly short paths which depend on their initial positions.

7.13 *Gradient Adaptive Lattice Filters*

In this section we discuss the "*gradient adaptive lattice*" implementations of linear prediction and lattice Wiener filters [76–81]. They are based on a gradient-descent, LMS-like approach applied to the weights of the *lattice representations* rather than to the weights of the direct form representation. Taking advantage of the decoupling of the successive stages of the lattice, and properly choosing the adaptation constants μ, all lattice weights can be made to converge fast and, in contrast to the LMS weights, with a convergence rate that is essentially *independent* of the *eigenvalue spread* of the *input* covariance matrix. The gradient lattice algorithms are very similar but not identical to the recursive least-squares lattice algorithms [102–110], and they share the same properties of fast convergence and computational efficiency with the latter. Typically, the gradient lattice converges somewhat more slowly than RLSL. Some comparisons between the two types of algorithms are given in [81,109].

We start by casting the ordinary lattice filter of linear prediction in a gradient-adaptive form, and then discuss the gradient-adaptive form of the lattice Wiener filter, the stationary version of which was presented in Section 5.11.

The lattice recursion for an Mth order prediction-error filter of a stationary signal y_n was found in Section 5.7 to be

$$\begin{aligned} e_{p+1}^{+}(n) &= e_p^{+}(n) - \gamma_{p+1} e_p^{-}(n-1) \\ e_{p+1}^{-}(n) &= e_p^{-}(n-1) - \gamma_{p+1} e_p^{+}(n) \end{aligned} \tag{7.13.1}$$

for $p = 0, 1, \ldots, M-1$, where $e_0^{+}(n) = e_0^{-}(n) = y_n$. The optimal value of the reflection coefficient γ_{p+1} can be obtained by minimizing the performance index

$$\mathcal{E}_{p+1} = E[e_{p+1}^{+}(n)^2 + e_{p+1}^{-}(n)^2] \tag{7.13.2}$$

Differentiating with respect to γ_{p+1} we find

$$\frac{\partial \mathcal{E}_{p+1}}{\partial \gamma_{p+1}} = 2E\left[e_{p+1}^{+}(n) \frac{\partial e_{p+1}^{+}(n)}{\partial \gamma_{p+1}} + e_{p+1}^{-}(n) \frac{\partial e_{p+1}^{-}(n)}{\partial \gamma_{p+1}} \right]$$

and, using Eq. (7.13.1),

$$\frac{\partial \mathcal{E}_{p+1}}{\partial \gamma_{p+1}} = -2E\left[e_{p+1}^{+}(n)e_p^{-}(n-1) + e_{p+1}^{-}(n)e_p^{+}(n)\right] \tag{7.13.3}$$

Inserting Eq. (7.13.1) into Eq. (7.13.3), we rewrite the latter as

$$\frac{\partial \mathcal{E}_{p+1}}{\partial \gamma_{p+1}} = -2(C_{p+1} - \gamma_{p+1}D_{p+1}) \tag{7.13.4}$$

where

$$C_{p+1} = 2E[e_p^{+}(n)e_p^{-}(n-1)] \tag{7.13.5}$$

$$D_{p+1} = E[e_p^{+}(n)^2 + e_p^{-}(n-1)^2] \tag{7.13.6}$$

Setting the gradient (7.13.4) to zero, we find the *optimal value* of γ_{p+1}

$$\gamma_{p+1} = \frac{C_{p+1}}{D_{p+1}} = \frac{2E[e_p^{+}(n)e_p^{-}(n-1)]}{E[e_p^{+}(n)^2 + e_p^{-}(n-1)^2]} \tag{7.13.7}$$

which, due to the assumed *stationarity,* agrees with Eq. (5.7.4). Replacing the numerator and denominator of Eq. (7.13.7) by time averages leads to Burg's method.

The *gradient lattice* is obtained by solving $(\partial \mathcal{E}_{p+1}/\partial \gamma_{p+1}) = 0$ iteratively by the *gradient descent* method

$$\gamma_{p+1}(n+1) = \gamma_{p+1}(n) - \mu_{p+1}\frac{\partial \mathcal{E}_{p+1}}{\partial \gamma_{p+1}(n)} \tag{7.13.8}$$

where μ_{p+1} is a small positive adaptation constant. Before we drop the expectation instructions in Eq. (7.13.3), we use the result of Eq. (7.13.4) to discuss *qualitatively* the convergence rate of the algorithm. Inserting Eq. (7.13.4) into Eq. (7.13.8), we find

$$\gamma_{p+1}(n+1) = \gamma_{p+1}(n) + 2\mu_{p+1}(C_{p+1} - \gamma_{p+1}(n)D_{p+1})$$

or

$$\gamma_{p+1}(n+1) = (1 - 2\mu_{p+1}D_{p+1})\,\gamma_{p+1}(n) + 2\mu_{p+1}C_{p+1} \tag{7.13.9}$$

Actually, if we replace γ_{p+1} by $\gamma_{p+1}(n)$ in Eq. (7.13.1), the stationarity of the lattice is lost, and it is *not correct* to assume that C_{p+1} and D_{p+1} are independent of n. The implicit dependence of D_{p+1} and C_{p+1} on the (time-varying) reflection coefficients of the previous lattice stages makes Eq. (7.13.9) a nonlinear difference equation in the reflection coefficients. In the analogous discussion of the LMS case in Section 7.6, the corresponding difference equation for the weights was linear with *constant* coefficients—because of the tapped delay line structure, the stationarity of the input signal $\mathbf{y}(n)$ was not affected by the time-varying weights. Nevertheless, we will use Eq. (7.13.9) in a qualitative manner, replacing D_{p+1} and C_{p+1} by their constant asymptotic values, but only for the purpose of *motivating* the final choice of the adaptation parameter μ_{p+1}. The solution of Eq. (7.13.9), then, is

$$\gamma_{p+1}(n) = \gamma_{p+1} + (1 - 2\mu_{p+1}D_{p+1})^n(\gamma_{p+1}(0) - \gamma_{p+1}) \tag{7.13.10}$$

where γ_{p+1} is the asymptotic value of the weight, given in Eq. (7.13.7). The stability of Eqs. (7.13.9) and (7.13.10) requires that

$$|1 - 2\mu_{p+1}D_{p+1}| < 1 \tag{7.13.11}$$

If we choose μ_{p+1} as

$$2\mu_{p+1} = \frac{\alpha}{D_{p+1}} \qquad 0 < \alpha < 1 \tag{7.13.12}$$

then $1 - 2\mu_{p+1}D_{p+1} = 1 - \alpha$ will satisfy Eq. (7.13.11). Note that α was chosen to be independent of the order p. This implies that all reflection coefficients γ_{p+1} will essentially converge at the same rate. Using Eqs. (7.13.3) and (7.13.12), we write Eq. (7.13.8) as follows:

$$\gamma_{p+1}(n+1) = \gamma_{p+1}(n) + \frac{\alpha}{D_{p+1}} E[e_{p+1}^{+}(n)e_p^{-}(n-1) + e_{p+1}^{-}(n)e_p^{+}(n)] \tag{7.13.13}$$

The *practical implementation* of this method consists of *ignoring* the expectation instruction, and using a *least-squares approximation* for D_{p+1} of the form [76–78]

$$D_{p+1}(n) = (1 - \lambda) \sum_{k=0}^{n} \lambda^{n-k} [e_p^{+}(k)^2 + e_p^{-}(k-1)^2] \tag{7.13.14}$$

where $0 < \lambda < 1$. It may also be computed *recursively* by

$$D_{p+1}(n) = \lambda D_{p+1}(n-1) + (1-\lambda)[e_p^{+}(n)^2 + e_p^{-}(n-1)^2] \tag{7.13.15}$$

This quantity is a measure of D_{p+1} of Eq. (7.13.6); indeed, taking expectations of both sides and assuming stationarity, we find

$$\begin{aligned} E[D_{p+1}(n)] &= (1-\lambda)\sum_{k=0}^{n} \lambda^{n-k} E[e_p^{+}(k)^2 + e_p^{-}(k-1)^2] \\ &= D_{p+1}(1-\lambda)\sum_{k=0}^{n}\lambda^{n-k} \\ &= D_{p+1}(1-\lambda^{n+1}) \end{aligned}$$

which reduces to D_{p+1} for large n. With the above changes, we obtain the adaptive version of Eq. (7.13.13),

$$\gamma_{p+1}(n+1) = \gamma_{p+1}(n) + \frac{\alpha}{D_{p+1}(n)} [e_{p+1}^{+}(n)e_p^{-}(n-1) + e_{p+1}^{-}(n)e_p^{+}(n)] \quad (7.13.16)$$

It can be written in a slightly different form by defining the quantity

$$\begin{aligned} d_{p+1}(n) &= \sum_{k=0}^{n} \lambda^{n-k} [e_p^{+}(k)^2 + e_p^{-}(k-1)^2] \\ &= \lambda d_{p+1}(n-1) + [e_p^{+}(n)^2 + e_p^{-}(n-1)^2] \end{aligned} \quad (7.13.17)$$

and noting that $D_{p+1}(n) = (1-\lambda)d_{p+1}(n)$. Defining the new parameter $\beta = \alpha/(1-\lambda)$, we rewrite Eq. (7.13.16) in the form

$$\gamma_{p+1}(n+1) = \gamma_{p+1}(n) + \frac{\beta}{d_{p+1}(n)} [e_{p+1}^{+}(n)e_p^{-}(n-1) + e_{p+1}^{-}(n)e_p^{+}(n)] \quad (7.13.18)$$

This is usually operated with $\beta = 1$ or, equivalently, $\alpha = 1 - \lambda$. This choice makes Eq. (7.13.18) equivalent to a recursive reformulation of Burg's method [76–78]. This may be seen as follows: Define the quantity $c_{p+1}(n)$ by

$$c_{p+1}(n) = \beta \sum_{k=0}^{n} \lambda^{n-k}[2e_p^{+}(k)e_p^{-}(k-1)] + (1-\beta)d_{p+1}(n)$$

Then, inserting Eq. (7.13.1), with γ_{p+1} replaced by $\gamma_{p+1}(n)$, into Eq. (7.13.18), we find after some algebra

$$\gamma_{p+1}(n+1) = \frac{c_{p+1}(n)}{d_{p+1}(n)}$$

Setting $\beta = 1$, we obtain

$$\gamma_{p+1}(n+1) = \frac{2\sum_{k=0}^{n} \lambda^{n-k} e_p^{+}(k)e_p^{-}(k-1)}{\sum_{k=0}^{n} \lambda^{n-k}[e_p^{+}(k)^2 + e_p^{-}(k-1)^2]} \quad (7.13.19)$$

which corresponds to Burg's method, and also guarantees that the magnitude of $\gamma_{p+1}(n+1)$ will remain less than one at each iteration. The adaptive lattice is depicted in Fig. 7.17.

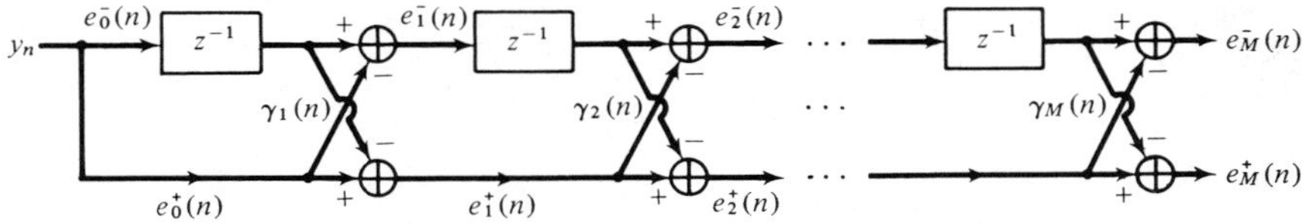

Figure 7.17 Adaptive Lattice Predictor

At each time instant n, the order recursions are

$$e_{p+1}^+(n) = e_p^+(n) - \gamma_{p+1}(n)e_p^-(n-1)$$
$$e_{p+1}^-(n) = e_p^-(n-1) - \gamma_{p+1}(n)e_p^+(n) \tag{7.13.20}$$

for $p=0,1, \ldots ,M-1$, with $\gamma_{p+1}(n)$ updated in time using Eq. (7.13.18) or Eq. (7.13.19). Initialize Eq. (7.13.20) by $e_0^+(n)=e_0^-(n)=y_n$. We summarize the computational steps as follows:

1. At time n, the coefficients $\gamma_{p+1}(n)$ and $d_{p+1}(n-1)$ are available
2. Iterate Eq. (7.13.20) for $p=0,1, \ldots ,M-1$
3. Using Eq. (7.13.17), compute $d_{p+1}(n)$, for $p=0,1, \ldots ,M-1$
4. Using Eq. (7.13.18), compute $\gamma_{p+1}(n+1)$, for $p=0,1, \ldots ,M-1$
5. Go to $n \rightarrow n+1$

Next, we discuss the *adaptive lattice realization* of the *FIR Wiener filter* of Section 5.11. We use the same notation as in that section. The time-invariant lattice weights g_p are chosen optimally to minimize the mean-squared estimation error

$$\mathcal{E} = E[e_n^2] = \min \tag{7.13.21}$$

where $e_n = x_n - \hat{x}_n$, and

$$\hat{x}_n = \sum_{p=0}^{M} g_p e_p^-(n) = [g_0, g_1, \ldots ,g_M] \begin{bmatrix} e_0^-(n) \\ e_1^-(n) \\ \vdots \\ e_M^-(n) \end{bmatrix} = \mathbf{g}^T\mathbf{e}^-(n) \tag{7.13.22}$$

The gradient with respect to $\mathbf{g}$ is

$$\frac{\partial \mathcal{E}}{\partial \mathbf{g}} = -2E[e_n \mathbf{e}^-(n)] \tag{7.13.23}$$

Inserting Eq. (7.13.22) into Eq. (7.13.23), we rewrite the latter as

$$\frac{\partial \mathcal{E}}{\partial \mathbf{g}} = -2(\mathbf{r} - R\mathbf{g}) \tag{7.13.24}$$

where **r** and R are defined in terms of the *backward* lattice signals $e_p^-(n)$ as

$$\mathbf{r} = E[x_n \mathbf{e}^-(n)], \qquad R = E[\mathbf{e}^-(n)\mathbf{e}^-(n)^T] \tag{7.13.25}$$

The gradient-descent method applied to the weights **g** is

$$\mathbf{g}(n+1) = \mathbf{g}(n) - M\frac{\partial \mathcal{E}}{\partial \mathbf{g}(n)} \tag{7.13.26}$$

where, following the discussion of Section 7.6, we have used a positive definite symmetric adaptation matrix M, to be chosen below. Then, Eq. (7.13.26) becomes

$$\mathbf{g}(n+1) = (I - 2MR)\mathbf{g}(n) + 2M\mathbf{r} \tag{7.13.27}$$

The orthogonality of the backward prediction errors $\mathbf{e}^-(n)$ causes their covariance matrix R to be *diagonal*

$$R = \mathrm{diag}[E_0, E_1, \ldots, E_M] \tag{7.13.28}$$

where E_p are the variances of $e_p^-(n)$

$$E_p = E[e_p^-(n)^2] \tag{7.13.29}$$

for $p = 0, 1, \ldots, M$. If we chose M to be diagonal, $M = \mathrm{diag}[\mu_0, \mu_1, \ldots, \mu_M]$, the state matrix $(I - 2MR)$ of Eq. (7.13.27) will also be diagonal and therefore Eq. (7.13.27) decouples into its individual components

$$g_p(n+1) = (1 - 2\mu_p E_p)\, g_p(n) + 2\mu_p r_p \tag{7.13.30}$$

for $p = 0, 1, \ldots, M$, where $r_p = E[x_n e_p^-(n)]$. Its solution is

$$g_p(n) = g_p + (1 - 2\mu_p E_p)^n\,(g_p(0) - g_p) \tag{7.13.31}$$

where $g_p = r_p/E_p$ are the *optimal weights*. The convergence *rate* depends on the quantity $(1 - 2\mu_p E_p)$. Choosing μ_p by

$$2\mu_p = \frac{\alpha}{E_p} \qquad 0 < \alpha < 1 \tag{7.13.32}$$

implies that all lattice weights $g_p(n)$ will have the *same* rate of convergence. Using Eqs. (7.13.32) and (7.13.23) we can rewrite Eq. (7.13.26) componentwise as follows

$$g_p(n+1) = g_p(n) + \frac{\alpha}{E_p} E[e_n e_p^-(n)]$$

Ignoring the expectation instruction, and replacing E_p by its *time average*

$$\begin{aligned} E_p(n) &= (1-\lambda)\sum_{k=0}^{n} \lambda^{n-k} e_p^-(k)^2 \\ &= \lambda\, E_p(n-1) + (1-\lambda) e_p^-(n)^2 \end{aligned} \tag{7.13.33}$$

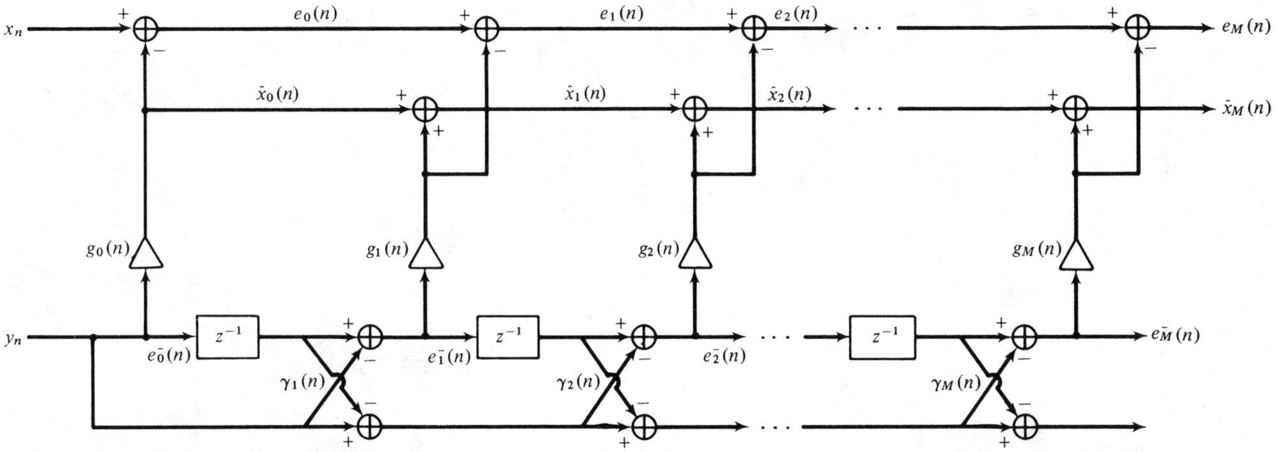

Figure 7.18 Adaptive Lattice Wiener Filter

we obtain the adaptation equation for the pth weight

$$g_p(n+1) = g_p(n) + \frac{\alpha}{E_p(n)} e_n e_p^-(n) \tag{7.13.34}$$

for $p = 0,1,\ldots,M$. Defining

$$d_p^-(n) = \sum_{k=0}^{n} \lambda^{n-k} e_p^-(k)^2 = \lambda d_p^-(n-1) + e_p^-(n)^2 \tag{7.13.35}$$

and noting $E_p(n) = (1-\lambda)d_p^-(n)$, we rewrite Eq. (7.13.34) as

$$g_p(n+1) = g_p(n) + \frac{\beta}{d_p^-(n)} e_n e_p^-(n) \tag{7.13.36}$$

where $\beta = \alpha/(1-\lambda)$. Typically, Eq. (7.13.36) is operated with $\beta = 1$, or $\alpha = 1-\lambda$ [76,78]. The realization of the adaptive lattice Wiener filter is shown in Fig. 7.18.

A slightly different version of the algorithm is obtained by replacing e_n in Eq. (7.13.36) by $e_p(n)$; that is, the estimation error based on a pth order filter:

$$e_p(n) = x_n - \hat{x}_p(n), \quad \hat{x}_p(n) = \sum_{i=0}^{p} g_i(n) e_i^-(n)$$

It satisfies the recursions (5.11.10) through (5.11.11). This version arises by minimizing the order-p performance index $\mathcal{E}_p = E[e_p(n)^2]$ rather than the order-M performance index (7.13.21). This version is justified by the property that all lower order portions of $\mathbf{g}$ are already optimal; if $\{g_0, g_1, \ldots, g_{p-1}\}$ are already optimal, then to go to the next order p it is only necessary to determine the optimal value of the new weight g_p, which is obtained by minimizing $\mathcal{E}_p$ with respect to g_p. The overall algorithm is summarized below:

1. At time n, the quantities $\gamma_p(n)$, $d_p(n)$, for $p = 1,2,\ldots,M$ and $g_p(n)$, $d_p^-(n)$, for $p = 0,1,\ldots,M$ are available, and also x_n and y_n
2. Initialize in order by

$$e_0^{\pm}(n) = y_n, \quad \hat{x}_0(n) = g_0(n)e_0^-(n), \quad e_0(n) = x_n - \hat{x}_0(n)$$

$$d_0^-(n) = \lambda d_0^-(n-1) + e_0^-(n)^2$$

$$g_0(n+1) = g_0(n) + \frac{\beta}{d_0^-(n)} e_0(n) e_0^-(n)$$

3. For $p = 1,2, \ldots, M$ compute

$$e_p^+(n) = e_{p-1}^+(n) - \gamma_p(n) e_{p-1}^-(n-1)$$

$$e_p^-(n) = e_{p-1}^-(n-1) - \gamma_p(n) e_{p-1}^+(n)$$

$$d_p(n) = \lambda d_p(n-1) + e_{p-1}^+(n)^2 + e_{p-1}^-(n-1)^2$$

$$\gamma_p(n+1) = \gamma_p(n) + \frac{\beta}{d_p(n)} \left[e_p^+(n) e_{p-1}^-(n-1) + e_p^-(n) e_{p-1}^+(n) \right]$$

$$\hat{x}_p(n) = \hat{x}_{p-1}(n) + g_p(n) e_p^-(n)$$

$$e_p(n) = e_{p-1}(n) - g_p(n) e_p^-(n)$$

$$d_p^-(n) = \lambda d_p^-(n-1) + e_p^-(n)^2$$

$$g_p(n+1) = g_p(n) + \frac{\beta}{d_p^-(n)} e_p(n) e_p^-(n)$$

4. Go to the next time instant, $n \to n+1$

The adaptation of the reflection coefficients $\gamma_p(n)$ provides a gradual *orthogonalization* of the backward error signals $e_p^-(n)$, which in turn drive the adaptation equations for the lattice weights $g_p(n)$.

The algorithm is initialized in time by setting $\gamma_p(0) = 0$, $d_p(-1) = 0$, $g_p(0) = 0$, and $d_p^-(-1) = 0$. Because initially all the γs and the delay registers of the lattice are zero, it follows that the backward output of the pth lattice section, $e_p^-(n)$, will be zero for $n < p$. The corresponding $d_p^-(n)$ will also be zero and thus cannot be used in the updating of $g_p(n)$. During this startup period, we keep $g_p(n) = 0$, $n < p$. A similar problem does not arise for the γs because $d_p(n)$ contains contributions from the forward lattice outputs, which are not zero.

The subroutine **glwf** (see Appendix B) is an implementation of the gradient lattice Wiener filter. It is the same as **lwf** with the weight adaptation parts added to it. Next, we present a simulation example. The signals x_n and y_n were generated by

$$x_n = y_n + 1.5y_{n-1} - 2y_{n-2} + u_n, \qquad y_n = 0.75y_{n-1} - 0.5y_{n-2} + \epsilon_n$$

where u_n and ϵ_n were mutually independent, zero-mean, unit-variance, white noises. It follows from our general discussion in Section 7.5 that we must use a Wiener filter of order at least $M = 2$ to cancel completely the y-dependent part of x_n. Solving the order-two linear prediction problem for y_n using **bkwlev**, we find the theoretical L matrix and reflection coefficients

$$L = \begin{bmatrix} 1 & 0 & 0 \\ -0.5 & 1 & 0 \\ 0.5 & -0.75 & 1 \end{bmatrix}, \qquad \gamma_1 = 0.5, \quad \gamma_2 = -0.5 \tag{7.13.37}$$

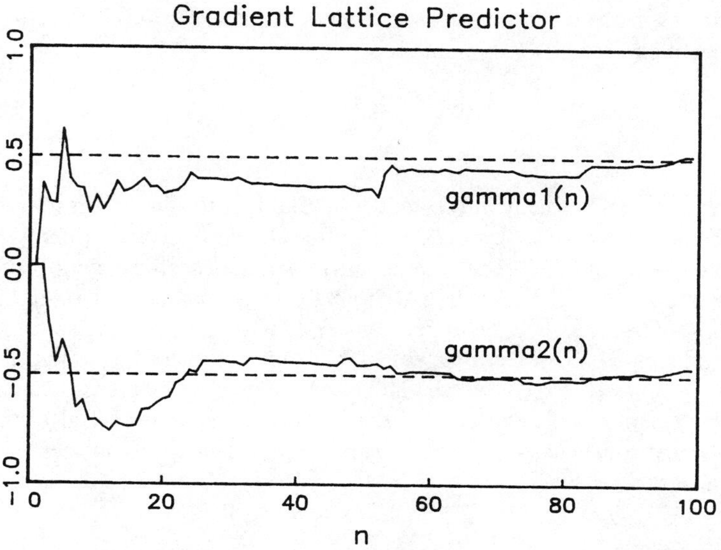

Figure 7.19 Reflection Coefficients $\gamma_1(n)$ and $\gamma_2(n)$ Versus n

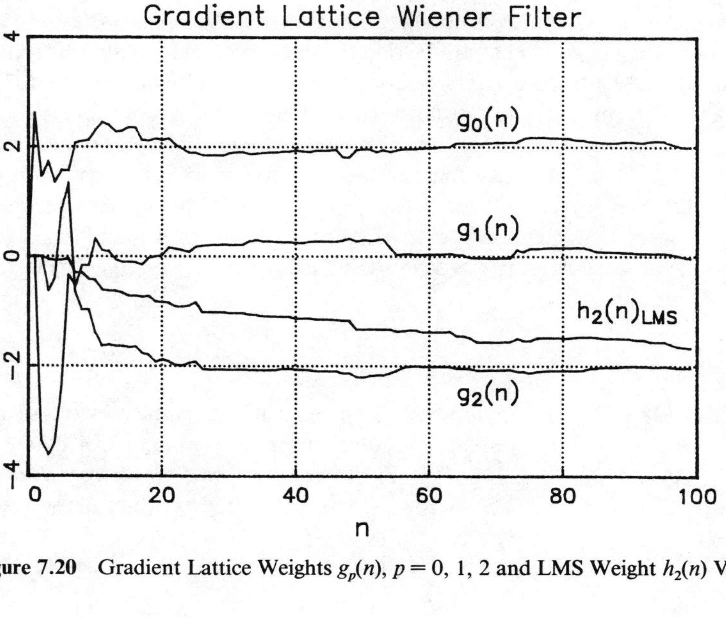

Figure 7.20 Gradient Lattice Weights $g_p(n)$, $p = 0, 1, 2$ and LMS Weight $h_2(n)$ Versus n

The direct-form coefficients of the Wiener filter are precisely the coefficients of the y-dependent part of x_n. Thus, we have

$$\mathbf{h} = \begin{bmatrix} 1 \\ 1.5 \\ -2 \end{bmatrix} \quad \text{and} \quad \mathbf{g} = L^{-T}\mathbf{h} = \begin{bmatrix} 2 \\ 0 \\ -2 \end{bmatrix} \tag{7.13.38}$$

In the simulation we generated 100 samples of x_n and y_n (after letting the transients of the difference equation of y_n die out). The routine **glwf** was run on these samples with $\lambda = 1$ and $\beta = 1$. Figure 7.19 shows the adaptive reflection coefficients $\gamma_1(n)$ and $\gamma_2(n)$ versus iteration number n. Figure 7.20 shows the three coefficients $g_p(n)$, $p = 0,1,2$, versus n, converging to their theoretical values $\mathbf{g}$ above. For comparison purposes, we have also included the direct-form weight $h_2(n)$ adapted according to the standard LMS algorithm with $\mu = 0.01$. It should be compared to $g_2(n)$ because by construction the last elements of $\mathbf{g}$ and $\mathbf{h}$ are the same; here, $g_2 = h_2$. The LMS algorithm can be accelerated somewhat by using a larger μ, but at the expense of increasing the noisiness of the weights.

7.14 *Adaptive Gram-Schmidt Preprocessors*

In this section we derive the *spatial* analogs of the gradient adaptive lattice algorithms. The main function of the adaptive lattice filter is to decorrelate the tapped delay-line data vector $\mathbf{y}(n) = [y_n, y_{n-1}, \ldots, y_{n-M}]^T$. In effect, it carries out the Gram-Schmidt orthogonalization of the components of $\mathbf{y}(n)$ at *each* time instant n. In array processing problems, because the data vector $\mathbf{y}(n) = [y_0(n), y_1(n), \ldots, y_M(n)]^T$ does not have the tapped-delay line property, the Gram-Schmidt orthogonalization cannot be done by a simple a lattice filter. It requires a more complicated structure that basically amounts to carrying out the lower triangular linear transformation $\mathbf{y} = B\boldsymbol{\epsilon}$ which decorrelates the covariance matrix of $\mathbf{y}$.

The Gram-Schmidt construction of an arbitrary random vector $\mathbf{y}$ was discussed in Section 1.5. Here, we recast these results in a way that can be used directly in gradient-adaptive implementations. The Gram-Schmidt construction proceeds recursively starting at one end, say, $\epsilon_0 = y_0$. At the mth step of the recursion, we have available the mutually decorrelated components $\{\epsilon_0, \epsilon_1, \ldots, \epsilon_{m-1}\}$. The next component ϵ_m is defined by

$$\epsilon_m = y_m - \sum_{i=0}^{m-1} b_{mi}\epsilon_i, \qquad b_{mi} = \frac{1}{E_i} E[y_m \epsilon_i] \tag{7.14.1}$$

where $E_i = E[\epsilon_i^2]$. By construction, ϵ_m is decorrelated from all the previous ϵs; that is, $E[\epsilon_m \epsilon_i] = 0$, $i = 0,1, \ldots, m-1$. The summation term in Eq. (7.14.1) represents the optimum estimate of y_m based on the previous ϵs, and ϵ_m represents the estimation error. Therefore, the coefficients b_{mi} can also be derived by the mean-square criterion

$$\mathcal{E}_m = E[\epsilon_m^2] = \min \tag{7.14.2}$$

The gradient with respect to b_{mi} is

$$\frac{\partial \mathcal{E}_m}{\partial b_{mi}} = -2E[\epsilon_m \epsilon_i] = -2(E[y_m \epsilon_i] - b_{mi} E_i), \qquad i = 0,1, \ldots, m-1 \tag{7.14.3}$$

where we used the fact that the previous ϵs are already decorrelated, so that $E[\epsilon_i \epsilon_j] = \delta_{ij} E_i$ for $i,j = 0,1, \ldots, m-1$. Setting the gradient to zero gives the optimum solution (7.14.1) for b_{mi}. In a gradient-adaptive approach, the coefficients b_{mi} will be time-dependent, $b_{mi}(n)$, and updated by

$$b_{mi}(n+1) = b_{mi}(n) - \mu_{mi} \frac{\partial \mathcal{E}_m}{\partial b_{mi}(n)} \tag{7.14.4}$$

Using the above expression for the gradient, we find the difference equation

$$b_{mi}(n+1) = (1 - 2\mu_{mi} E_i) b_{mi}(n) + 2\mu_{mi} E[y_m \epsilon_i]$$

with solution

$$b_{mi}(n) = b_{mi} + (1 - 2\mu_{mi} E_i)^n (b_{mi}(0) - b_{mi})$$

where b_{mi} is the optimum solution (7.14.1). As in Section 7.13, because of the diagonal nature of the covariance matrix of the previous ϵs, the system of difference equations for the b_{mi}s decouples into separate scalar equations. Choosing μ_{mi} by

$$2\mu_{mi} = \frac{\alpha}{E_i}, \qquad 0 < \alpha < 1$$

implies that all coefficients $b_{mi}(n)$ will converge at the *same* rate. With this choice, Eq. (7.14.4) becomes

$$b_{mi}(n+1) = b_{mi}(n) + \frac{\alpha}{E_i} E[\epsilon_m \epsilon_i]$$

As before, we may replace E_i by its time average $E_i(n) = (1 - \lambda) d_i(n)$, where

$$d_i(n) = \sum_{k=0}^{n} \lambda^{n-k} \epsilon_i(k)^2 = \lambda d_i(n-1) + \epsilon_i(n)^2$$

Setting $\beta = \alpha/(1 - \lambda)$ and dropping the expectation values, we obtain the adaptive Gram–Schmidt algorithm

1. At time n, $b_{mi}(n)$ and $d_i(n-1)$ are available, and also the current data vector $\mathbf{y}(n) = [y_0(n), y_1(n), \ldots, y_M(n)]^T$
2. $\epsilon_0(n) = y_0(n)$
3. For $m = 1,2, \ldots, M$ compute

$$\epsilon_m(n) = y_m(n) - \sum_{i=0}^{m-1} b_{mi}(n) \epsilon_i(n)$$

$$d_{m-1}(n) = \lambda d_{m-1}(n-1) + \epsilon_{m-1}(n)^2$$

For $i = 0,1, \ldots, m-1$ compute

$$b_{mi}(n+1) = b_{mi}(n) + \frac{\beta}{d_i(n)} \epsilon_m(n)\epsilon_i(n)$$

4. Go to the next time instant, $n \to n+1$

The algorithm is initialized in time by $b_{mi}(0) = 0$ and $d_i(-1) = 0$. The conventional Gram–Schmidt construction builds up the matrix B row-wise; for example in the case $M = 3$

$$B = \begin{bmatrix} 1 & 0 & 0 & 0 \\ b_{10} & 1 & 0 & 0 \\ b_{20} & b_{21} & 1 & 0 \\ b_{30} & b_{31} & b_{32} & 1 \end{bmatrix}$$

According to Eq. (7.14.1), ϵ_m is constructed from the entries of the mth row of B. This gives rise to the block-diagram realization of the Gram-Schmidt construction shown in Fig. 7.21. We will see shortly that each circular block represents an elementary *correlation canceling* operation of the type [15,82–86]

$$e = u - bv$$

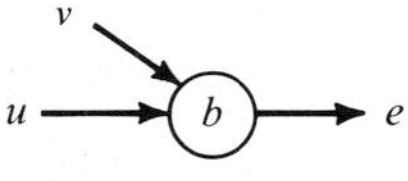

with

$$E[ev] = 0 \quad \Longrightarrow \quad b = \frac{E[uv]}{E[v^2]}$$

Therefore, each block can be replaced by an ordinary adaptive CCL or by an accelerated CCL, as discussed below. This point of view leads to an alternative way of

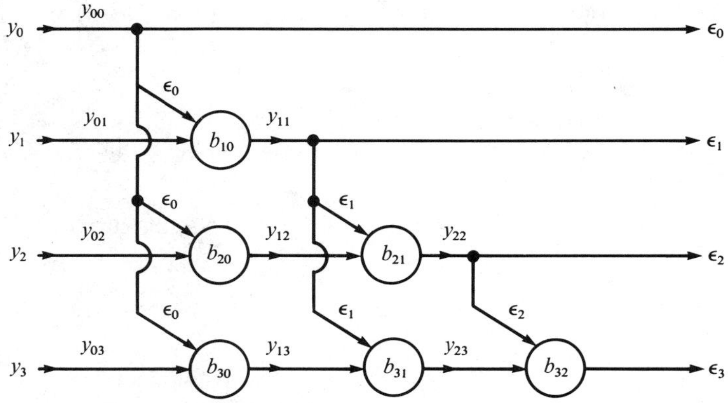

Figure 7.21 Gram-Schmidt Preprocessor

organizing the Gram-Schmidt construction with better numerical properties, known as the *modified Gram-Schmidt* procedure [87], which builds up the matrix B column-wise. Let $\mathbf{b}_i$ be the ith column of B, so that

$$\mathbf{y} = B\boldsymbol{\epsilon} = [\mathbf{b}_0, \mathbf{b}_1, \ldots, \mathbf{b}_M]\begin{bmatrix} \epsilon_0 \\ \epsilon_1 \\ \vdots \\ \epsilon_M \end{bmatrix} = \sum_{j=0}^{M} \mathbf{b}_j \epsilon_j$$

Removing the contribution of the first i columns, we define for $i = 1, 2, \ldots, M$

$$\mathbf{y}_i = \mathbf{y} - \sum_{j=0}^{i-1} \mathbf{b}_j \epsilon_j = \sum_{j=i}^{M} \mathbf{b}_j \epsilon_j \tag{7.14.5}$$

Component-wise, we write

$$y_{im} = \sum_{j=i}^{M} b_{mj}\epsilon_j, \qquad m = 0, 1, \ldots, M$$

It follows from the lower-triangular nature of B that $y_{im} = 0$ for $m < i$. Moreover, because B has unit diagonal, we have at $m = i$, $y_{ii} = b_{ii}\epsilon_i = \epsilon_i$. Thus,

$$\epsilon_i = y_{ii} \tag{7.14.6}$$

Equation (7.14.5) can be written recursively as follows

$$\mathbf{y}_i = \mathbf{b}_i\epsilon_i + \sum_{j=i+1}^{M} \mathbf{b}_j\epsilon_j = \mathbf{b}_i\epsilon_i + \mathbf{y}_{i+1}$$

or,

$$\mathbf{y}_{i+1} = \mathbf{y}_i - \mathbf{b}_i\epsilon_i \tag{7.14.7}$$

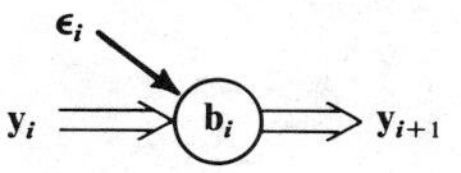

and component-wise, $y_{i+1,m} = y_{im} - b_{mi}\epsilon_i$. It is initialized by $\mathbf{y}_0 = \mathbf{y}$. It is evident by inspecting Fig. 7.21 that $\mathbf{y}_i$ represents the output column vector after each column operation. Equation (7.14.7) shows also that each circular block is an elementary correlation canceler. This follows by noting that $\mathbf{y}_{i+1}$ is built out of ϵ_j, $j \geq i+1$, each being uncorrelated with ϵ_i. Thus,

$$E[\epsilon_i \mathbf{y}_{i+1}] = E[\epsilon_i \mathbf{y}_i] - \mathbf{b}_i E_i = 0 \rightarrow \mathbf{b}_i = \frac{1}{E_i} E[\epsilon_i \mathbf{y}_i]$$

or, component-wise

$$b_{mi} = \frac{1}{E_i} E[\epsilon_i y_{im}], \qquad m = i+1, \ldots, M \tag{7.14.8}$$

An adaptive implementation can be obtained easily by writing

$$\mathbf{b}_i(n+1) = \mathbf{b}_i(n) + 2\mu_i E[\epsilon_i \mathbf{y}_{i+1}] = (1 - 2\mu_i E_i)\mathbf{b}_i(n) + 2\mu_i E[\epsilon_i \mathbf{y}_i]$$

As usual, we set $2\mu_i = \alpha/E_i$, replace E_i by $E_i(n) = (1-\lambda)d_i(n)$, and drop the expectation values to obtain the following algorithm, which adapts the matrix elements of B column-wise:

1. At time n, $b_{mi}(n)$ and $d_i(n-1)$ are available, and also the current data vector $\mathbf{y}(n) = [y_0(n), y_1(n), \ldots, y_M(n)]^T$
2. Define $y_{0m}(n) = y_m(n)$ for $m = 0, 1, \ldots, M$
3. For $i = 0, 1, \ldots, M$ compute

$$\epsilon_i(n) = y_{ii}(n)$$
$$d_i(n) = \lambda d_i(n-1) + \epsilon_i(n)^2$$

For $i+1 \leq m \leq M$ compute

$$y_{i+1,m}(n) = y_{im}(n) - b_{mi}(n)\epsilon_i(n)$$

$$b_{mi}(n+1) = b_{mi}(n) + \frac{\beta}{d_i(n)}\epsilon_i(n)y_{i+1,m}(n)$$

4. Go to the next time instant, $n \rightarrow n+1$

The algorithm may be appended to provide an overall Gram-Schmidt implementation of the *adaptive linear combiner* of Section 7.4. In the decorrelated basis, the estimate of x_n and estimation error may be written order recursively as

$$\hat{x}_i(n) = \hat{x}_{i-1}(n) + g_i(n)\epsilon_i(n), \qquad e_i(n) = e_{i-1}(n) - g_i(n)\epsilon_i(n) \qquad (7.14.9)$$

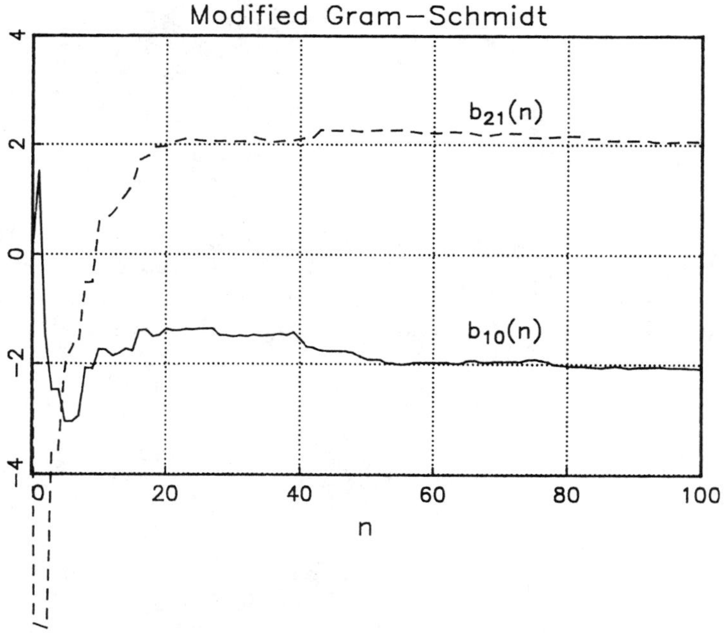

Figure 7.22 Gram-Schmidt Weights $b_{10}(n)$ and $b_{21}(n)$ Versus n Adapted by the Modified Gram-Schmidt Algorithm

with the weights $g_i(n)$ adapted by

$$g_i(n+1) = g_i(n) + \frac{\beta}{d_i(n)} e_i(n)\epsilon_i(n), \qquad i = 0, 1, \ldots, M \tag{7.14.10}$$

The subroutine **mgs** (see Appendix B) is an implementation of the adaptive modified Gram-Schmidt procedure. At each call, the routine reads the snapshot vector **y**, computes the decorrelated vector $\boldsymbol{\epsilon}$, and updates the matrix elements of B in preparation for the next call. An LMS-like version can be obtained by replacing the accelerated CCLs by ordinary CCLs [15]

$$b_{mi}(n+1) = b_{mi}(n) + 2\mu\epsilon_i(n)y_{i+1,m}(n) \tag{7.14.11}$$

An exact recursive least squares version of the modified Gram-Schmidt algorithm can also be derived [86]. It bears the same relationship to the above gradient-based version that the exact RLS lattice filter bears to the gradient lattice filter. The computational complexity of the algorithm is high because there are $M(M+1)/2$ coefficients to be adapted at each time instant, namely, the matrix elements in the strictly lower triangular part of B. By contrast, in the lattice structure there are only M reflection coefficients to be adapted. Despite its computational complexity, the algorithm is quite modular, built out of elementary CCLs.

Next, we present a simulation example of order $M = 2$. The vectors **y** were constructed by

$$\mathbf{y} = \begin{bmatrix} y_0 \\ y_1 \\ y_2 \end{bmatrix} = \begin{bmatrix} 1 & 0 & 0 \\ -2 & 1 & 0 \\ 1 & 2 & 1 \end{bmatrix} \begin{bmatrix} \epsilon_0 \\ \epsilon_1 \\ \epsilon_2 \end{bmatrix} = B\boldsymbol{\epsilon}$$

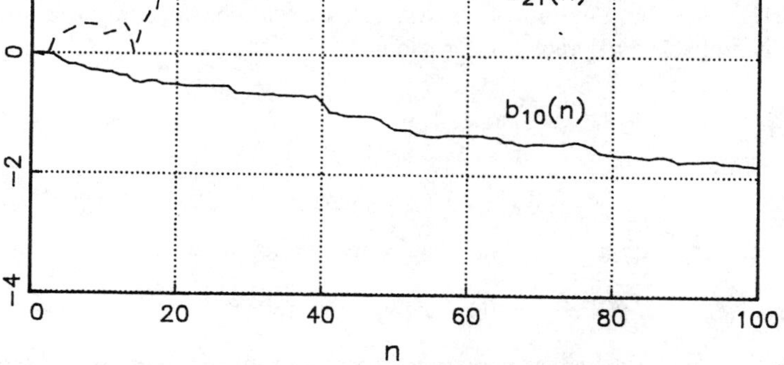

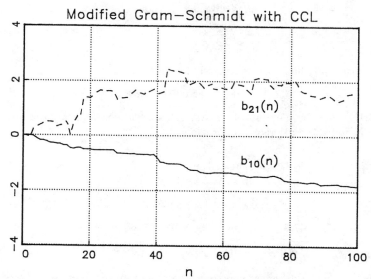

Figure 7.23 Same Weights Adapted According to the LMS Algorithm of Eq. (7.14.11), with $\mu = 0.01$

with the components of $\boldsymbol{\epsilon}$ having variances $E_0 = 1$, $E_1 = 4$, and $E_2 = 9$. We generated 100 independent snapshots $\boldsymbol{\epsilon}$ and computed the corresponding $\mathbf{y} = B\boldsymbol{\epsilon}$. Figure 7.22 shows the two matrix elements $b_{10}(n)$ and $b_{21}(n)$ adapted by running **mgs** on the 100 snapshots with $\lambda = 1$ and $\beta = 1$. They are converging to the theoretical values $b_{10} = -2$ and $b_{21} = 2$. Figure 7.23 shows the same two matrix elements adapted by the LMS algorithm (7.14.11) with $\mu = 0.01$.

7.15 *Rank-One Modification of Covariance Matrices*

All recursive least-squares (RLS) algorithms, conventional, lattice, and fast direct-form structures, can be derived from the rank-one updating properties of covariance matrices. In this section we discuss these properties and derive all the necessary algebraic steps and computational reductions that make the fast RLS versions possible. In the succeeding sections, we couple these results with the so-called *shift-invariance* property to *close the loop,* as it were, and complete the derivation of the fast RLS algorithms.

The rank-one modification of a covariance matrix R_0 is obtained by adding the rank-one term

$$R_1 = R_0 + \mathbf{y}\mathbf{y}^T \tag{7.15.1}$$

where $\mathbf{y}$ is a vector of the same dimension as R_0. Similarly, the modification of a cross-correlation vector $\mathbf{r}_0$ will be defined as

$$\mathbf{r}_1 = \mathbf{r}_0 + x\mathbf{y} \tag{7.15.2}$$

where x is a scalar. We define the *Wiener solutions* based on the pairs $\{R_0, \mathbf{r}_0\}$ and $\{R_1, \mathbf{r}_1\}$ by

$$\mathbf{h}_0 = R_0^{-1}\mathbf{r}_0\,, \qquad \mathbf{h}_1 = R_1^{-1}\mathbf{r}_1 \tag{7.15.3}$$

and the corresponding *estimates* of x and estimation errors

$$\hat{x}_0 = \mathbf{h}_0^T\mathbf{y}\,, \quad e_0 = x - \hat{x}_0 \quad \text{and} \quad \hat{x}_1 = \mathbf{h}_1^T\mathbf{y}\,, \quad e_1 = x - \hat{x}_1 \tag{7.15.4}$$

Similarly, using the notation of Section 1.7, we will consider the solution of the forward and backward prediction problems

$$R_0\mathbf{a}_0 = E_{0a}\mathbf{u}\,, \qquad R_1\mathbf{a}_1 = E_{1a}\mathbf{u} \tag{7.15.5}$$

and

$$R_0\mathbf{b}_0 = E_{0b}\mathbf{v}\,, \qquad R_1\mathbf{b}_1 = E_{1b}\mathbf{v} \tag{7.15.6}$$

and the corresponding forward and backward prediction errors

$$e_{0a} = \mathbf{a}_0^T\mathbf{y}\,, \quad e_{1a} = \mathbf{a}_1^T\mathbf{y} \quad \text{and} \quad e_{0b} = \mathbf{b}_0^T\mathbf{y}\,, \quad e_{1b} = \mathbf{b}_1^T\mathbf{y} \tag{7.15.7}$$

The basic question is how to construct the solution of the filtering and prediction problems 1 from the solution of the corresponding problems 0; that is, to construct $\mathbf{h}_1$

from $\mathbf{h}_0$, $\mathbf{a}_1$ from $\mathbf{a}_0$, and $\mathbf{b}_1$ from $\mathbf{b}_0$. We will generally refer to the various quantities of problem-0 as *a priori* and to the corresponding quantities of problem-1 as *a posteriori.* The constructions are carried out with the help of the so-called a priori and a posteriori *Kalman gain* vectors defined by

$$\mathbf{k}_0 = R_0^{-1}\mathbf{y}\,, \quad \mathbf{k}_1 = R_1^{-1}\mathbf{y} \tag{7.15.8}$$

We also define the so-called *likelihood* variables

$$\nu = \mathbf{y}^T R_0^{-1}\mathbf{y} = \mathbf{y}^T\mathbf{k}_0\,, \qquad \mu = \frac{1}{1+\nu} = \frac{1}{1+\mathbf{y}^T R_0^{-1}\mathbf{y}} \tag{7.15.9}$$

Note that the positivity condition $\nu > 0$ is equivalent to $0 < \mu < 1$. Multiplying Eq. (7.15.1) from the left by R_1^{-1} and from the right by R_0^{-1}, we obtain

$$R_0^{-1} = R_1^{-1} + R_1^{-1}\mathbf{y}\mathbf{y}^T R_0^{-1} = R_1^{-1} + \mathbf{k}_1\mathbf{k}_0^T \tag{7.15.10}$$

Acting on $\mathbf{y}$ and using the definitions (7.15.8) through (7.15.9), we find $\mathbf{k}_0 = \mathbf{k}_1 + \mathbf{k}_1\nu = (1+\nu)\mathbf{k}_1$, or,

$$\mathbf{k}_1 = \mu\mathbf{k}_0 \tag{7.15.11}$$

It follows that $\mathbf{y}^T R_1^{-1}\mathbf{y} = \mathbf{k}_1^T\mathbf{y} = \mu\mathbf{k}_0^T\mathbf{y} = \mu\nu = \nu/(1+\nu) = 1-\mu$. Thus,

$$\mu = 1 - \mathbf{y}^T R_1^{-1}\mathbf{y} = \frac{1}{1+\mathbf{y}^T R_0^{-1}\mathbf{y}} \tag{7.15.12}$$

Solving Eq. (7.15.10) for R_1^{-1}, we obtain

$$R_1^{-1} = R_0^{-1} - \mu\mathbf{k}_0\mathbf{k}_0^T = R_0^{-1} - \frac{1}{1+\mathbf{y}^T R_0^{-1}\mathbf{y}} R_0^{-1}\mathbf{y}\mathbf{y}^T R_0^{-1} \tag{7.15.13}$$

which is recognized as the application of the matrix inversion lemma to Eq. (7.15.1). It provides the rank-one update of the *inverse* matrices. Denoting $P_0 = R_0^{-1}$ and $P_1 = R_1^{-1}$, we may rewrite Eq. (7.15.13) in the form

$$P_1 = P_0 - \mu\mathbf{k}_0\mathbf{k}_0^T\,, \quad \mathbf{k}_0 = P_0\mathbf{y}\,, \quad \mu = \frac{1}{1+\mathbf{y}^T P_0\mathbf{y}} \tag{7.15.14}$$

Before we derive the relationship between the Wiener solutions (7.15.3), we may obtain the relationship between the a priori and a posteriori estimation errors. Noting that $\hat{x}_0 = \mathbf{h}_0^T\mathbf{y} = \mathbf{r}_0^T R_0^{-1}\mathbf{y} = \mathbf{r}_0^T\mathbf{k}_0$, and similarly $\hat{x}_1 = \mathbf{r}_1^T\mathbf{k}_1$, we obtain

$$\hat{x}_1 = \mathbf{k}_1^T\mathbf{r}_1 = (\mu\mathbf{k}_0)^T(\mathbf{r}_0 + x\mathbf{y}) = \mu\hat{x}_0 + \mu\nu x = \mu\hat{x}_0 + (1-\mu)x = x - \mu e_0$$

from which it follows that

$$e_1 = \mu e_0 \tag{7.15.15}$$

The *standard trick,* or simplest method, of relating the solutions of problem-1 to the solutions of problem-0 is to act on the solution of problem-0 by the covariance matrix of problem-1; that is,

$$R_1\mathbf{h}_0 = (R_0 + \mathbf{y}\mathbf{y}^T)\mathbf{h}_0 = \mathbf{r}_0 + \hat{x}_0\mathbf{y} = (\mathbf{r}_1 - x\mathbf{y}) + \hat{x}_0\mathbf{y} = \mathbf{r}_1 - e_0\mathbf{y}$$

multiplying by R_1^{-1} we find $\mathbf{h}_0 = \mathbf{h}_1 - e_0\mathbf{k}_1$, or using Eqs. (7.15.11) and (7.15.15)

$$\mathbf{h}_1 = \mathbf{h}_0 + e_0\mathbf{k}_1 = \mathbf{h}_0 + \mu e_0\mathbf{k}_0 = \mathbf{h}_0 + e_1\mathbf{k}_0 \tag{7.15.16}$$

Note that the update term can be expressed either in terms of the a priori estimation error e_0 and a posteriori Kalman gain $\mathbf{k}_1$, or the a posteriori error e_1 and a priori Kalman gain $\mathbf{k}_0$. Next, we summarize what may be called the *conventional* RLS computational sequence:

1. $\mathbf{k}_0 = P_0\mathbf{y}$
2. $\nu = \mathbf{k}_0^T\mathbf{y}\,, \qquad \mu = \dfrac{1}{1+\nu}$
3. $\mathbf{k}_1 = \mu\mathbf{k}_0$
4. $P_1 = P_0 - \mathbf{k}_1\mathbf{k}_0^T$
5. $\hat{x}_0 = \mathbf{h}_0^T\mathbf{y}\,, \qquad e_0 = x - \hat{x}_0\,, \qquad e_1 = \mu e_0\,, \qquad \hat{x}_1 = x - e_1$
6. $\mathbf{h}_1 = \mathbf{h}_0 + e_0\mathbf{k}_1$

Because in step 4 an entire matrix is updated, the computational complexity of the algorithm grows *quadratically* with the matrix order; that is, $O(M^2)$ operations.

Next, we consider the forward and backward prediction solutions. Equations (1.7.28) and (1.7.35) applied to R_0 become

$$R_0^{-1} = \begin{bmatrix} 0 & \mathbf{0}^T \\ \mathbf{0} & \tilde{R}_0^{-1} \end{bmatrix} + \frac{1}{E_{0a}}\mathbf{a}_0\mathbf{a}_0^T = \begin{bmatrix} \bar{R}_0^{-1} & \mathbf{0} \\ \mathbf{0}^T & 0 \end{bmatrix} + \frac{1}{E_{0b}}\mathbf{b}_0\mathbf{b}_0^T$$

Acting on $\mathbf{y}$ and using Eq. (7.15.7), we find

$$\mathbf{k}_0 = \begin{bmatrix} 0 \\ \tilde{\mathbf{k}}_0 \end{bmatrix} + \frac{e_{0a}}{E_{0a}}\mathbf{a}_0 = \begin{bmatrix} \bar{\mathbf{k}}_0 \\ 0 \end{bmatrix} + \frac{e_{0b}}{E_{0b}}\mathbf{b}_0 \tag{7.15.17}$$

where $\tilde{\mathbf{k}}_0 = \tilde{R}_0^{-1}\tilde{\mathbf{y}}$, and $\bar{\mathbf{k}}_0 = \bar{R}_0^{-1}\bar{\mathbf{y}}$. Similarly, we obtain for the a posteriori gains

$$\mathbf{k}_1 = \begin{bmatrix} 0 \\ \tilde{\mathbf{k}}_1 \end{bmatrix} + \frac{e_{1a}}{E_{1a}}\mathbf{a}_1 = \begin{bmatrix} \bar{\mathbf{k}}_1 \\ 0 \end{bmatrix} + \frac{e_{1b}}{E_{1b}}\mathbf{b}_1 \tag{7.15.18}$$

Because $\mathbf{b}_0$ and $\mathbf{b}_1$ have last coefficients of unity, it follows that the *last* coefficients of the Kalman gains will be

$$k_{0b} = \frac{e_{0b}}{E_{0b}}\,, \qquad k_{1b} = \frac{e_{1b}}{E_{1b}} \tag{7.15.19}$$

Similarly, the *first* coefficients will be

$$k_{0a} = \frac{e_{0a}}{E_{0a}}, \qquad k_{1a} = \frac{e_{1a}}{E_{1a}} \tag{7.15.20}$$

Taking the dot product of Eq. (7.15.17) with $\mathbf{y}$ and using the definition (7.15.9) and (7.15.7), we obtain

$$\nu = \tilde{\nu} + \frac{e_{0a}^2}{E_{0a}} = \bar{\nu} + \frac{e_{0b}^2}{E_{0b}} \quad \text{or,} \quad \nu = \tilde{\nu} + e_{0a}k_{0a} = \bar{\nu} + e_{0b}k_{0b} \tag{7.15.21}$$

where $\tilde{\nu} = \tilde{\mathbf{k}}_0^T\tilde{\mathbf{y}}$ and $\bar{\nu} = \bar{\mathbf{k}}_0^T\bar{\mathbf{y}}$. Similarly, using $\mathbf{k}_1^T\mathbf{y} = 1 - \mu$ and taking the dot product of Eq. (7.15.18) with $\mathbf{y}$, we find

$$1 - \mu = 1 - \tilde{\mu} + \frac{e_{1a}^2}{E_{1a}} = 1 - \bar{\mu} + \frac{e_{1b}^2}{E_{1b}}$$

or,

$$\mu = \tilde{\mu} - \frac{e_{1a}^2}{E_{1a}} = \bar{\mu} - \frac{e_{1b}^2}{E_{1b}} \tag{7.15.22}$$

This is equivalent to Eq. (7.15.21). To relate $\mathbf{a}_1$ and $\mathbf{a}_0$ we apply the standard method

$$R_1\mathbf{a}_0 = (R_0 + \mathbf{y}\mathbf{y}^T)\mathbf{a}_0 = E_{0a}\mathbf{u} + e_{0a}\mathbf{y}$$

Multiplying by R_1^{-1} and using $R_1^{-1}\mathbf{u} = \mathbf{a}_1/E_{1a}$, we obtain

$$\mathbf{a}_0 = \frac{E_{0a}}{E_{1a}}\mathbf{a}_1 + e_{0a}\mathbf{k}_1 \tag{7.15.23}$$

It has five useful consequences. First, equating first coefficients and using Eq. (7.15.20), we obtain

$$1 = \frac{E_{0a}}{E_{1a}} + e_{0a}k_{1a} = \frac{E_{0a}}{E_{1a}} + \frac{e_{0a}e_{1a}}{E_{1a}} \tag{7.15.24}$$

or,

$$E_{1a} = E_{0a} + e_{0a}e_{1a} \tag{7.15.25}$$

Second, writing Eq. (7.15.24) in the form $E_{0a}/E_{1a} = 1 - e_{0a}k_{1a}$, we rewrite Eq. (7.15.23) as

$$\mathbf{a}_0 = (1 - e_{0a}k_{1a})\mathbf{a}_1 + e_{0a}\mathbf{k}_1 = \mathbf{a}_1 + e_{0a}(\mathbf{k}_1 - k_{1a}\mathbf{a}_1) = \mathbf{a}_1 + e_{0a}\begin{bmatrix} 0 \\ \tilde{\mathbf{k}}_1 \end{bmatrix}$$

where we used Eq. (7.15.18). Thus,

$$\mathbf{a}_1 = \mathbf{a}_0 - e_{0a}\begin{bmatrix} 0 \\ \tilde{\mathbf{k}}_1 \end{bmatrix} \tag{7.15.26}$$

Third, taking the dot product with $\mathbf{y}$ and using $\tilde{\mathbf{k}}_1^T\tilde{\mathbf{y}} = 1 - \tilde{\mu}$, we find $e_{1a} = e_{0a} - (1-\tilde{\mu})e_{0a} = \tilde{\mu}e_{0a}$, or

$$e_{1a} = \tilde{\mu}e_{0a} \tag{7.15.27}$$

This is analogous to Eq. (7.15.15). Fourth, writing $e_{0a} = e_{1a}/\tilde{\mu} = (1+\tilde{\nu})e_{1a}$, it follows by adding one to Eq. (7.15.21) that

$$(1+\nu) = (1+\tilde{\nu}) + (1+\tilde{\nu})e_{1a}\frac{e_{0a}}{E_{0a}} = (1+\tilde{\nu})\frac{E_{0a} + e_{1a}e_{0a}}{E_{0a}} = (1+\tilde{\nu})\frac{E_{1a}}{E_{0a}}$$

and inverting,

$$\mu = \tilde{\mu}\frac{E_{0a}}{E_{1a}} \tag{7.15.28}$$

This, in turn, is equivalent to Eq. (7.15.22) as can be seen by

$$\mu = \tilde{\mu}\frac{E_{1a} - e_{0a}e_{1a}}{E_{1a}} = \tilde{\mu} - (\tilde{\mu}e_{0a})\frac{e_{1a}}{E_{1a}} = \tilde{\mu} - \frac{e_{1a}^2}{E_{1a}}$$

Fifth, using Eq. (7.15.27) and the result $\tilde{\mathbf{k}}_1 = \tilde{\mu}\tilde{\mathbf{k}}_0$, we may rewrite Eq. (7.15.26) in terms of the a posteriori error e_{1a} and the a priori gain $\tilde{\mathbf{k}}_0$, as follows

$$\mathbf{a}_1 = \mathbf{a}_0 - e_{1a}\begin{bmatrix} 0 \\ \tilde{\mathbf{k}}_0 \end{bmatrix} \tag{7.15.29}$$

Defining the inverse matrices $\tilde{P}_0 = \tilde{R}_0^{-1}$ and $\tilde{P}_1 = \tilde{R}_1^{-1}$, we summarize the conventional RLS computational sequence for the *forward predictor*:

1. $\tilde{\mathbf{k}}_0 = \tilde{P}_0\tilde{\mathbf{y}}$
2. $\tilde{\nu} = \tilde{\mathbf{k}}_0^T\tilde{\mathbf{y}}, \quad \tilde{\mu} = \dfrac{1}{1+\tilde{\nu}}$
3. $\tilde{\mathbf{k}}_1 = \tilde{\mu}\tilde{\mathbf{k}}_0$
4. $\tilde{P}_1 = \tilde{P}_0 - \tilde{\mathbf{k}}_1\tilde{\mathbf{k}}_0^T$
5. $e_{0a} = \mathbf{a}_0^T\mathbf{y}, \quad e_{1a} = \tilde{\mu}e_{0a}$
6. $\mathbf{a}_1 = \mathbf{a}_0 - e_{0a}\begin{bmatrix} 0 \\ \tilde{\mathbf{k}}_1 \end{bmatrix}$

The fast RLS algorithms make use also of the backward predictors. Starting with $R_1\mathbf{b}_0 = (R_0 + \mathbf{y}\mathbf{y}^T)\mathbf{b}_0 = E_{0b}\mathbf{v} + e_{0b}\mathbf{y}$, and following similar steps as for the forward case, we obtain parallel results for the backward predictor; that is,

$$\mathbf{b}_0 = \frac{E_{0b}}{E_{1b}}\mathbf{b}_1 + e_{0b}\mathbf{k}_1 \tag{7.15.30}$$

from which it follows

$$1 = \frac{E_{0b}}{E_{1b}} + e_{0b}k_{1b} = \frac{E_{0b}}{E_{1b}} + \frac{e_{0b}e_{1b}}{E_{1b}} \tag{7.15.31}$$

or,

$$E_{1b} = E_{0b} + e_{0b}e_{1b} \tag{7.15.32}$$

Similarly, we have $\bar{\mathbf{k}}_1 = \bar{\mu}\bar{\mathbf{k}}_0$, and

$$e_{1b} = \bar{\mu} e_{0b} \tag{7.15.33}$$

and the equivalences

$$\nu = \bar{\nu} + \frac{e_{0b}^2}{E_{0b}} \quad \Leftrightarrow \quad \mu = \bar{\mu} - \frac{e_{1b}^2}{E_{1b}} \quad \Leftrightarrow \quad \mu = \bar{\mu}\frac{E_{0b}}{E_{1b}} \tag{7.15.34}$$

Finally, the update equations for $\mathbf{b}_1$ are

$$\mathbf{b}_1 = \mathbf{b}_0 - e_{0b}\begin{bmatrix} \mathbf{k}_1 \\ 0 \end{bmatrix} = \mathbf{b}_0 - e_{1b}\begin{bmatrix} \mathbf{k}_0 \\ 0 \end{bmatrix} \tag{7.15.35}$$

Writing Eq. (7.15.31) in the form $E_{1b}/E_{0b} = 1/(1 - e_{0b}k_{1b})$ and solving Eq. (7.15.30) for $\mathbf{b}_1$, we have the alternative expression

$$\mathbf{b}_1 = \frac{E_{1b}}{E_{0b}}(\mathbf{b}_0 - e_{0b}\mathbf{k}_1) = (\mathbf{b}_0 - e_{0b}\mathbf{k}_1)/(1 - e_{0b}k_{1b}) \tag{7.15.36}$$

This is used in the *fast Kalman* (FK) [88,89] computational sequence, which we summarize below:

1. $e_{0a} = \mathbf{a}_0^T\mathbf{y}$

2. $\mathbf{a}_1 = \mathbf{a}_0 - e_{0a}\begin{bmatrix} 0 \\ \bar{\mathbf{k}}_1 \end{bmatrix}$

3. $e_{1a} = \mathbf{a}_1^T\mathbf{y}$

4. $E_{1a} = E_{0a} + e_{0a}e_{1a}$

5. Compute the first element of $\mathbf{k}_1$, $k_{1a} = \dfrac{e_{1a}}{E_{1a}}$

6. $\mathbf{k}_1 = \begin{bmatrix} 0 \\ \bar{\mathbf{k}}_1 \end{bmatrix} + k_{1a}\mathbf{a}_1$, extract the last element of $\mathbf{k}_1$, k_{1b}

7. $e_{0b} = \mathbf{b}_0^T\mathbf{y}$

8. $\mathbf{b}_1 = (\mathbf{b}_0 - e_{0b}\mathbf{k}_1)/(1 - e_{0b}k_{1b})$

9. $\begin{bmatrix} \mathbf{k}_1 \\ 0 \end{bmatrix} = \mathbf{k}_1 - k_{1b}\,\mathbf{b}_1$

10. $\hat{x}_0 = \mathbf{h}_0^T\mathbf{y}, \quad e_0 = x - \hat{x}_0, \quad \mathbf{h}_1 = \mathbf{h}_0 + e_0\mathbf{k}_1, \quad \hat{x}_1 = \mathbf{h}_1^T\mathbf{y}, \quad e_1 = x - \hat{x}_1$

Step 9 is obtained from Eq. (7.15.18). Steps 1 through 9 perform the calculation and update of the Kalman gain vector $\mathbf{k}_1$, which is used in step 10 for the Wiener filtering part. The computationally intensive parts of the algorithm are the computation of the inner products and the vector updates. Steps 1, 2, 3, 6, 7, and 9 require M operations each, and step 8 requires $2M$ operations. Thus, the gain calculation in steps 1 through 9 requires a total of $8M$ operations. The Wiener filtering and updating part in step 10 requires an additional $3M$ operations. Thus, the overall complexity grows like $8M + 3M = 11M$ operations; that is, *linearly* in the order M.

Several of the above operations can be avoided. In particular, the computation of the error e_{1a} in step 3 can be done by Eq. (7.15.27), thus, avoiding the inner product. Similarly, the inner product in step 7 can be avoided by solving Eq. (7.17.19) for e_{0b}, that is, $e_{0b} = k_{ob}E_{0b}$. Also, the division by the overall scalar factor $(1 - e_{0b}k_{1b})$ in step 8 can be avoided by using Eq. (7.15.35) instead. This saves $3M$ out of the $8M$ computations—a 40% reduction. Similarly, the operation $\hat{x}_1 = \mathbf{h}_1^T\mathbf{y}$ in the Wiener filtering part can be avoided by $e_1 = \mu e_0$, and $\hat{x}_1 = x - e_1$. The resulting computational sequence is the *fast a posteriori error sequential technique* (FAEST) [90]. It uses the a posteriori errors and the a priori Kalman gains. It is summarized below:

1. $e_{0a} = \mathbf{a}_0^T\mathbf{y}$

2. $e_{1a} = \bar{\mu} e_{0a} = e_{0a}/(1 + \bar{\nu})$

3. Compute the first element of $\mathbf{k}_0$, $k_{0a} = \dfrac{e_{0a}}{E_{0a}}$

4. $E_{1a} = E_{0a} + e_{0a}e_{1a}$

5. $\mathbf{k}_0 = \begin{bmatrix} 0 \\ \bar{\mathbf{k}}_0 \end{bmatrix} + k_{0a}\mathbf{a}_0$, extract the last element of $\mathbf{k}_0$, k_{0b}

6. $e_{0b} = k_{0b}E_{0b}$

7. $\begin{bmatrix} \mathbf{k}_0 \\ 0 \end{bmatrix} = \mathbf{k}_0 - k_{0b}\mathbf{b}_0$

8. $\nu = \bar{\nu} + e_{0a}k_{0a}, \quad \bar{\nu} = \nu - e_{0b}k_{0b}$

9. $e_{1b} = \bar{\mu} e_{0b} = e_{0b}/(1+\bar{\nu})$

10. $E_{1b} = E_{0b} + e_{0b} e_{1b}$

11. $\mathbf{a}_1 = \mathbf{a}_0 - e_{1a} \begin{bmatrix} 0 \\ \tilde{\mathbf{k}}_0 \end{bmatrix}$

12. $\mathbf{b}_1 = \mathbf{b}_0 - e_{1b} \begin{bmatrix} \bar{\mathbf{k}}_0 \\ 0 \end{bmatrix}$

13. $\hat{x}_0 = \mathbf{h}_0^T \mathbf{y}, \quad e_0 = x - \hat{x}_0, \quad e_1 = \mu e_0 = e_0/(1+\nu), \quad \hat{x}_1 = x - e_1$

14. $\mathbf{h}_1 = \mathbf{h}_0 + e_1 \mathbf{k}_0$

Step 8 was obtained from Eq. (7.15.21). Steps 1, 5, 7, 11, and 12 require M operations each. Therefore, the gain calculation can be done with $5M$ operations. The last two Wiener filtering steps require an additional $2M$ operations. Thus, the total operation count grows like $5M + 2M = 7M$. The so-called *fast transversal filter* (FTF) [91] computational sequence is essentially identical to FAEST, but works directly with the variables μ instead of ν. The only change is to replace step 8 by the following:

8. $\mu = \tilde{\mu} \dfrac{E_{0a}}{E_{1a}}, \qquad \bar{\mu} = \dfrac{\mu}{1 - e_{0b} k_{0b} \mu}$ (FTF)

The second equation is obtained from (7.15.34), (7.15.31), and the proportionality $\mathbf{k}_1 = \mu \mathbf{k}_0$, which implies the same for the last elements of these vectors, $k_{1b} = \mu k_{0b}$. We have

$$\bar{\mu} = \mu \frac{E_{1b}}{E_{0b}} = \frac{\mu}{1 - e_{0b} k_{1b}} = \frac{\mu}{1 - e_{0b} k_{0b} \mu}$$

The above computational sequences are organized to start with the tilde quantities, such as $\tilde{\nu}$ and $\tilde{\mathbf{k}}_0$, and end up with the bar quantities such as $\bar{\nu}$ and $\bar{\mathbf{k}}_0$. The reason has to do with the shift invariance property, which implies that all bar quantities computed at the present iteration become the corresponding tilde quantities of the *next* iteration; for example,

$$\tilde{\nu}(n+1) = \bar{\nu}(n), \qquad \tilde{\mathbf{k}}_0(n+1) = \bar{\mathbf{k}}_0(n)$$

This property allows the repetition of the computational cycle from one time instant to the next. As we have seen, the computational savings of FAEST over FK, and FK over conventional RLS, have nothing to do with shift invariance but rather are consequences of the rank-one updating properties. The FAEST, FTF, and FK algorithms are the fastest known RLS algorithms. Unfortunately, they can exhibit numerically unstable behavior and require the use of *rescue* devices and reinitializations for continuous operation [92–101].

Next, we consider the lattice formulations. Equations (1.7.50) can be applied to the *a priori* lattice

$$e_{0a} = \bar{e}_{0a} - \gamma_{0b}\,\bar{e}_{0b}\,, \qquad e_{0b} = \bar{e}_{0b} - \gamma_{0a}\,\bar{e}_{0a} \tag{7.15.37}$$

and *a posteriori* lattice

$$e_{1a} = \bar{e}_{1a} - \gamma_{1b}\,\bar{e}_{1b}\,, \qquad e_{1b} = \bar{e}_{1b} - \gamma_{1a}\,\bar{e}_{1a} \tag{7.15.38}$$

with the reflection coefficients computed by

$$\gamma_{0a} = \frac{\Delta_0}{\bar{E}_{0a}}\,, \quad \gamma_{0b} = \frac{\Delta_0}{\bar{E}_{0b}} \quad \text{and} \quad \gamma_{1a} = \frac{\Delta_1}{\bar{E}_{1a}}\,, \quad \gamma_{1b} = \frac{\Delta_1}{\bar{E}_{1b}} \tag{7.15.39}$$

To find the relationship between Δ_1 and Δ_0, we use Eq. (1.7.44) applied to R_1

$$R_1\begin{bmatrix}0\\ \bar{\mathbf{b}}_1\end{bmatrix} = \Delta_1\mathbf{u} + \bar{E}_{1b}\mathbf{v}\,, \qquad R_1\begin{bmatrix}\bar{\mathbf{a}}_1\\ 0\end{bmatrix} = \Delta_1\mathbf{v} + \bar{E}_{1a}\mathbf{u} \tag{7.15.40}$$

Applying Eq. (1.7.44) to R_0 we obtain

$$R_1\begin{bmatrix}\bar{\mathbf{a}}_0\\ 0\end{bmatrix} = (R_0 + \mathbf{y}\mathbf{y}^T)\begin{bmatrix}\bar{\mathbf{a}}_0\\ 0\end{bmatrix} = \Delta_0\mathbf{v} + \bar{E}_{0a}\mathbf{u} + \bar{e}_{0a}\mathbf{y} \tag{7.15.41}$$

and

$$R_1\begin{bmatrix}0\\ \bar{\mathbf{b}}_0\end{bmatrix} = (R_0 + \mathbf{y}\mathbf{y}^T)\begin{bmatrix}0\\ \bar{\mathbf{b}}_0\end{bmatrix} = \Delta_0\mathbf{u} + \bar{E}_{0b}\mathbf{v} + \bar{e}_{0b}\mathbf{y} \tag{7.15.42}$$

Forming the dot products $[0,\tilde{\mathbf{b}}_1^T]R_1\begin{bmatrix}\bar{\mathbf{a}}_0\\ 0\end{bmatrix}$ and $[0,\tilde{\mathbf{b}}_0^T]R_1\begin{bmatrix}\bar{\mathbf{a}}_1\\ 0\end{bmatrix}$, we obtain the two alternative expressions

$$\Delta_1 = \Delta_0 + \tilde{e}_{1b}\,\bar{e}_{0a}\,, \qquad \Delta_1 = \Delta_0 + \bar{e}_{1a}\,\tilde{e}_{0b} \tag{7.15.43}$$

They represent the least-squares modifications of the partial correlation (1.7.53). The two expressions are equivalent to each other. Applying Eq. (7.15.33) to $\tilde{e}_{1b}$, we have $\tilde{e}_{1b} = \bar{\tilde{\mu}}\tilde{e}_{0b}$. Applying Eq. (7.15.27) to $\bar{e}_{1a}$, we have $\bar{e}_{1a} = \tilde{\bar{\mu}}\bar{e}_{0a}$. But, $\bar{\tilde{\nu}} = \tilde{\bar{\nu}}$ because, as is evident from Eq. (1.7.51), the tilde part of $\bar{\mathbf{y}}$ is the same as the bar part of $\tilde{\mathbf{y}}$, namely, $\mathbf{y}_c$. Thus, $\bar{\tilde{\nu}} = \tilde{\bar{\nu}} = \mathbf{y}_c^T R_{0c}^{-1}\mathbf{y}_c$, which implies $\bar{\tilde{\mu}} = \tilde{\bar{\mu}}$. Applying Eq. (7.15.34), we have the updating equation $\tilde{\mu} = \bar{\tilde{\mu}} - \tilde{e}_{1b}^2/E_{1b}$. As for the Wiener filtering part, we can apply the order-updating equations (1.7.24) through (1.7.27) to the a priori and a posteriori problems to get

$$\begin{aligned}\hat{x}_0 &= \bar{x}_0 + g_{0b}e_{0b}\,, \quad e_0 = \bar{e}_0 - g_{0b}e_{0b}\\ \hat{x}_1 &= \bar{x}_1 + g_{1b}e_{1b}\,, \quad e_1 = \bar{e}_1 - g_{1b}e_{1b}\end{aligned} \tag{7.15.44}$$

where g_{0b} and g_{1b} are the *last* components of the lattice weight vectors $\mathbf{g}_0$ and $\mathbf{g}_1$. Because of the relationship $\mathbf{h} = L^T\mathbf{g}$, it follows that the last component of $\mathbf{h}$ is equal to the last component of **g**. Thus, extracting the last components of $\mathbf{h}_1 = \mathbf{h}_0 + e_0\mathbf{k}_1$, we find

$$g_{1b} = g_{0b} + e_0 k_{1b} = g_{0b} + e_0 \frac{e_{1b}}{E_{1b}} \tag{7.15.45}$$

This provides a direct way to update the *g*s. The more conventional updating method is indirect; it is obtained by writing

$$g_{0b} = \frac{\rho_{0b}}{E_{0b}}, \qquad g_{1b} = \frac{\rho_{1b}}{E_{1b}} \tag{7.15.46}$$

Using Eq. (7.15.44), we can find a recursion for the ρs as follows

$$\rho_{1b} = E_{1b} g_{1b} = E_{1b} g_{0b} + (\bar{e}_0 - g_{0b} e_{0b}) e_{1b} = (E_{1b} - e_{0b} e_{1b}) g_{0b} + \bar{e}_0 e_{1b}$$

or, using $E_{1b} - e_{0b}e_{1b} = E_{0b}$

$$\rho_{1b} = \rho_{0b} + \bar{e}_0 e_{1b} = \rho_{0b} + \bar{e}_1 e_{1b}/\bar{\mu} \tag{7.15.47}$$

The conventional *RLS lattice* (RLSL) [102–110] computational sequence is summarized below:

1. $\Delta_1 = \Delta_0 + \tilde{e}_{1b}\bar{e}_{0a} = \Delta_0 + \tilde{e}_{1b}\bar{e}_{1a}/\bar{\mu}$.

2. $\gamma_{1a} = \dfrac{\Delta_1}{\bar{E}_{1a}}, \qquad \gamma_{1b} = \dfrac{\Delta_1}{\bar{E}_{1b}}$

3. $e_{1a} = \bar{e}_{1a} - \gamma_{1b}\bar{e}_{1b}, \qquad e_{1b} = \bar{e}_{1b} - \gamma_{1a}\bar{e}_{1a}$

4. $E_{1a} = \bar{E}_{1a} - \gamma_{1b}\Delta_1, \qquad E_{1b} = \bar{E}_{1b} - \gamma_{1a}\Delta_1$

5. $\mu = \bar{\mu} - \dfrac{\bar{e}_{1b}^2}{\bar{E}_{1b}}$

6. $\rho_{1b} = \rho_{0b} + \bar{e}_1 e_{1b}/\bar{\mu}$

7. $g_{1b} = \dfrac{\rho_{1b}}{E_{1b}}$

8. $e_1 = \bar{e}_1 - g_{1b}e_{1b}, \qquad \hat{x}_1 = x - e_1$

It is referred to as the *a posteriori* RLS lattice because it uses the a posteriori lattice equations (7.15.38). There are 14 multiplication/division operations in this sequence. We will see later that the use of the so-called *forgetting* factor λ requires 2 more multiplications. Thus, the total number of operations is 16. Because this sequence must be performed once per order, it follows that, for an order-M problem, the computational complexity of the RLS lattice will be $16M$ operations per time update. This is to be compared with $7M$ for the FAEST direct-form version. However, as we have already mentioned, the direct-form versions can exhibit numerical instabilities. By contrast, the lattice algorithms are numerically stable [97,111].

Many other variations of the RLS lattice are possible. For example, there is a version based on Eq. (7.15.37), called the *a priori* RLS lattice algorithm [20,106,110], or a version called the *double* (*a priori/a posteriori*) RLS algorithm [107,110] that uses Eqs. (7.15.37) and (7.15.38) simultaneously. This version avoids the computation of the likelihood parameter μ. Like Eq. (7.15.45), we can also obtain direct updating formulas for the reflection coefficients, thereby avoiding the recursion (7.15.43) for the partial correlations Δ. Using the second term of Eqs. (7.15.43) and (7.15.25) applied to $\bar{E}_{1a}$; that is, $\bar{E}_{1a} = \bar{E}_{0a} + \bar{e}_{0a}\bar{e}_{1a}$, we find

$$\gamma_{1a} = \frac{\Delta_1}{\bar{E}_{1a}} = \frac{\Delta_0 + \bar{e}_{1a}\tilde{e}_{0b}}{\bar{E}_{1a}} = \frac{\gamma_{0a}\bar{E}_{0a} + \bar{e}_{1a}\tilde{e}_{0b}}{\bar{E}_{1a}} =$$

$$= \frac{\gamma_{0a}(\bar{E}_{1a} - \bar{e}_{0a}\bar{e}_{1a}) + \bar{e}_{1a}\tilde{e}_{0b}}{\bar{E}_{1a}} = \gamma_{0a} + \frac{\bar{e}_{1a}}{\bar{E}_{1a}}(\tilde{e}_{0b} - \gamma_{0a}\bar{e}_{0a})$$

and using Eq. (7.15.37), we obtain

$$\gamma_{1a} = \gamma_{0a} + e_{0b}\frac{\bar{e}_{1a}}{\bar{E}_{1a}} \tag{7.15.48}$$

Similarly, working with the first term of Eq. (7.15.43), we find

$$\gamma_{1b} = \gamma_{0b} + e_{0a}\frac{\tilde{e}_{1b}}{\tilde{E}_{1b}} \tag{7.15.49}$$

Replacing $\bar{e}_{1a} = \tilde{\bar{\mu}}\bar{e}_{0a}$ and $\tilde{e}_{1b} = \tilde{\bar{\mu}}\tilde{e}_{0b}$ in the above equations gives rise to the so-called *a priori direct-updating* RLS lattice [111], also called the a priori *error-feedback* lattice because the outputs e_{0a} and e_{0b} of the a priori lattice equations (7.15.37) are used to update the reflection coefficients. An *a posteriori* direct or error-feedback algorithm [111] can also be obtained by working with the a posteriori lattice Eq. (7.15.38). In this case, we must express e_{0a} and e_{0b} in terms of the a posteriori quantities as follows: $e_{0a} = \bar{e}_{0a} - \gamma_{0b}\tilde{e}_{0b} = (\bar{e}_{1a} - \gamma_{0b}\tilde{e}_{1b})/\tilde{\bar{\mu}}$, and similarly, $e_{0b} = (\tilde{e}_{1b} - \gamma_{0a}\bar{e}_{1a})/\tilde{\bar{\mu}}$. The a priori and a posteriori error-feedback lattice algorithms are computationally somewhat more expensive—requiring $O(20M)$ operations—than the conventional RLS lattice. But, they have much better *numerical accuracy* under quantization [111] and, of course, their long-term behavior is numerically stable. Below we list the computational sequence of what may be called the *double/direct* RLS lattice algorithm that, on the one hand, uses direct-updating for increased numerical accuracy, and on the other, has the same computational complexity as the conventional a posteriori RLS lattice, namely, $16M$ operations [156]:

1. $e_{0a} = \bar{e}_{0a} - \gamma_{0b}\,\bar{e}_{0b}\,, \qquad e_{0b} = \bar{e}_{0b} - \gamma_{0a}\,\bar{e}_{0a}$

2. $\gamma_{1a} = \gamma_{0a} + e_{0b}\dfrac{\bar{e}_{1a}}{\bar{E}_{1a}}\,, \qquad \gamma_{1b} = \gamma_{0b} + e_{0a}\dfrac{\bar{e}_{1b}}{\bar{E}_{1b}}$

3. $e_{1a} = \bar{e}_{1a} - \gamma_{1b}\,\bar{e}_{1b}\,, \qquad e_{1b} = \bar{e}_{1b} - \gamma_{1a}\,\bar{e}_{1a}$

4. $E_{1a} = E_{0a} + e_{1a}e_{0a}\,, \qquad E_{1b} = E_{0b} + e_{1b}e_{0b}$

5. $e_0 = \bar{e}_0 - g_{0b}e_{0b}$

6. $g_{1b} = g_{0b} + e_0\dfrac{e_{1b}}{E_{1b}}$

7. $e_1 = \bar{e}_1 - g_{1b}e_{1b}\,, \qquad \hat{x}_1 = x - e_1$

It uses simultaneously the a priori and a posteriori lattice equations (7.15.37) and (7.15.38). There are 14 operations (plus 2 for the forgetting factor) per order per time update, that is, a total of $16M$ per time update.

Finally, we discuss the sense in which the a priori and a posteriori backward errors e_{0b}, e_{1b} provide a decorrelation of the covariance matrices R_0 and R_1. Following Eqs. (1.7.13) and (1.7.17), we write the LU factorizations of the a priori and a posteriori problems

$$L_0R_0L_0^T = D_{0b}\,, \qquad L_1R_1L_1^T = D_{1b} \tag{7.15.50}$$

where L_0 and L_1 have as rows the backward predictors $\mathbf{b}_0^T = [\boldsymbol{\beta}_0^T, 1]$ and $\mathbf{b}_1^T = [\boldsymbol{\beta}_1^T, 1]$

$$L_0 = \begin{bmatrix} \bar{L}_0 & \mathbf{0} \\ \boldsymbol{\beta}_0^T & 1 \end{bmatrix}, \qquad L_1 = \begin{bmatrix} \bar{L}_1 & \mathbf{0} \\ \boldsymbol{\beta}_1^T & 1 \end{bmatrix} \tag{7.15.51}$$

The corresponding backward basis vectors are constructed by

$$\mathbf{e}_{0b} = L_0\mathbf{y} = \begin{bmatrix} \bar{L}_0 & \mathbf{0} \\ \boldsymbol{\beta}_0^T & 1 \end{bmatrix}\begin{bmatrix} \bar{\mathbf{y}} \\ y_b \end{bmatrix} = \begin{bmatrix} \bar{L}_0\bar{\mathbf{y}} \\ \mathbf{b}_0^T\mathbf{y} \end{bmatrix} = \begin{bmatrix} \bar{\mathbf{e}}_{0b} \\ e_{0b} \end{bmatrix} \tag{7.15.52}$$

and

$$\mathbf{e}_{1b} = L_1\mathbf{y} = \begin{bmatrix} \bar{L}_1 & \mathbf{0} \\ \boldsymbol{\beta}_1^T & 1 \end{bmatrix}\begin{bmatrix} \bar{\mathbf{y}} \\ y_b \end{bmatrix} = \begin{bmatrix} \bar{L}_1\bar{\mathbf{y}} \\ \mathbf{b}_1^T\mathbf{y} \end{bmatrix} = \begin{bmatrix} \bar{\mathbf{e}}_{1b} \\ e_{1b} \end{bmatrix} \tag{7.15.53}$$

The rank-one updating property (7.15.1) for the Rs can be translated into an updating equation for the LU factorizations [112–114], in the following form

$$L_1 = LL_0 \tag{7.15.54}$$

It turns out that the unit lower triangular matrix L can be built entirely out of the a priori backward errors $\mathbf{e}_{0b}$, as we show below. The determining equation for L may be found by

$$D_{1b} = L_1 R_1 L_1^T = L L_0 (R_0 + \mathbf{y}\mathbf{y}^T) L_0^T L^T = L(D_{0b} + \mathbf{e}_{0b}\mathbf{e}_{0b}^T) L^T \tag{7.15.55}$$

Thus, L performs the LU factorization of the rank-one update of a diagonal matrix, namely, $D_{0b} + \mathbf{e}_{0b}\mathbf{e}_{0b}^T$. The solution is easily found by introducing the block decompositions

$$L = \begin{bmatrix} \bar{L} & 0 \\ \boldsymbol{\beta}^T & 1 \end{bmatrix}, \quad D_{1b} = \begin{bmatrix} \bar{D}_{1b} & 0 \\ 0^T & E_{1b} \end{bmatrix}, \quad D_{0b} + \mathbf{e}_{0b}\mathbf{e}_{0b}^T = \begin{bmatrix} \bar{D}_{0b} + \bar{\mathbf{e}}_{0b}\bar{\mathbf{e}}_{0b}^T & e_{0b}\bar{\mathbf{e}}_{0b} \\ e_{0b}\bar{\mathbf{e}}_{0b}^T & E_{0b} + e_{0b}^2 \end{bmatrix}$$

Using the methods of Section 1.7, e.g., Eqs. (1.7.7) and (1.7.11) applied to this problem, we find the solution

$$\boldsymbol{\beta} = -\bar{\mu} e_{0b} \bar{D}_{0b}^{-1} \bar{\mathbf{e}}_{0b}, \quad \bar{\mu} = \frac{1}{1 + \bar{\mathbf{e}}_{0b}^T \bar{D}_{0b}^{-1} \bar{\mathbf{e}}_{0b}} \tag{7.15.56}$$

Using $\bar{R}_0^{-1} = \bar{L}_0^T \bar{D}_{0b}^{-1} \bar{L}_0$, we recognize

$$\bar{\mathbf{e}}_{0b}^T \bar{D}_{0b}^{-1} \bar{\mathbf{e}}_{0b} = \bar{\mathbf{y}}^T \bar{L}_0^T \bar{D}_{0b}^{-1} \bar{L}_0 \bar{\mathbf{y}} = \bar{\mathbf{y}}^T \bar{R}_0^{-1} \bar{\mathbf{y}} = \bar{\nu}$$

Therefore, the quantity $\bar{\mu}$ defined above is the usual one. Similarly, we find

$$\bar{E}_{1b} = (E_{0b} + e_{0b}^2) + e_{0b}\bar{\mathbf{e}}_{0b}^T \boldsymbol{\beta} = E_{0b} + e_{0b}^2 - \bar{\mu} e_{0b}^2 \bar{\nu}$$

Using $1 - \bar{\mu}\bar{\nu} = \bar{\mu}$ and $e_{1b} = \bar{\mu} e_{0b}$, this reduces to (7.15.32). Writing $\bar{D}_{0b}^{-1}\bar{\mathbf{e}}_{0b} = \bar{L}_0^{-T} \bar{R}_0^{-1} \bar{\mathbf{y}} = \bar{\mathbf{L}}_0^{-T} \bar{\mathbf{k}}_0$, we can express $\boldsymbol{\beta}$ in terms of the Kalman gain vector:

$$\boldsymbol{\beta} = -\bar{\mu} e_{0b} \bar{L}_0^{-T} \bar{\mathbf{k}}_0 \tag{7.15.57}$$

It easy to verify that the block-decomposed form of Eq. (7.15.54) is equivalent to

$$\bar{L}_1 = \bar{L}\bar{L}_0, \quad \boldsymbol{\beta}_1 = \boldsymbol{\beta}_0 + \bar{L}_0^T \boldsymbol{\beta} \tag{7.15.58}$$

Because of Eq. (7.15.57), the updating equation for the $\boldsymbol{\beta}$s is equivalent to Eq. (7.15.35). Using this formalism, we may show the proportionality between the a posteriori and a priori backward errors. We have $\mathbf{e}_{1b} = L_1 \mathbf{y} = L L_0 \mathbf{y} = L \mathbf{e}_{0b}$, and in block form

$$\mathbf{e}_{1b} = \begin{bmatrix} \bar{L} & 0 \\ \boldsymbol{\beta}^T & 1 \end{bmatrix} \begin{bmatrix} \bar{\mathbf{e}}_{0b} \\ e_{0b} \end{bmatrix} = \begin{bmatrix} \bar{L}\bar{\mathbf{e}}_{0b} \\ e_{0b} + \boldsymbol{\beta}^T \bar{\mathbf{e}}_{0b} \end{bmatrix}$$

Therefore, $e_{1b} = e_{0b} + \boldsymbol{\beta}^T \bar{\mathbf{e}}_{0b} = e_{0b} - \bar{\mu} e_{0b} \bar{\nu} = \bar{\mu} e_{0b}$. It follows that L acting on $\mathbf{e}_{0b}$ can be replaced by the diagonal matrix of $\bar{\mu}$s acting on $\mathbf{e}_{0b}$. The double/direct lattice algorithm effectively provides the error signals required to build L. For example, Eq. (7.15.56) can be written in a form that avoids the computation of the μs

$$\boldsymbol{\beta} = -\bar{\mu} e_{0b} \bar{D}_{0b}^{-1} \bar{\mathbf{e}}_{0b} = -e_{1b} \bar{D}_{0b}^{-1} \bar{\mathbf{e}}_{0b} \tag{7.15.59}$$

The a priori and a posteriori estimates $\hat{x}_0$ and $\hat{x}_1$ may also be expressed in the backward bases. Defining $\mathbf{g}_0 = L_0^{-T}\mathbf{h}_0$, we find $\hat{x}_0 = \mathbf{h}_0^T\mathbf{y} = \mathbf{g}_0^T L_0 \mathbf{y} = \mathbf{g}_0^T \mathbf{e}_{0b}$ and similarly, defining $\mathbf{g}_1 = L_1^{-T}\mathbf{h}_1$, we find $\hat{x}_1 = \mathbf{g}_1^T\mathbf{e}_{1b}$. Thus,

$$\mathbf{g}_1 = L_1^{-T}\mathbf{h}_1\,, \qquad \mathbf{g}_0 = L_0^{-T}\mathbf{h}_0 \tag{7.15.60}$$

and

$$\hat{x}_1 = \mathbf{g}_1^T\mathbf{e}_{1b}\,, \qquad \hat{x}_0 = \mathbf{g}_0^T\mathbf{e}_{0b} \tag{7.15.61}$$

Finally, the updating Eq. (7.15.16) for the direct-form weights translates into an updating equation for the lattice weights:

$$\mathbf{g}_1 = L_1^{-T}\mathbf{h}_1 = L_1^{-T}(\mathbf{h}_0 + e_0\mathbf{k}_1) = L^{-T}L_0^{-T}\mathbf{h}_0 + e_0 L_1^{-T}\mathbf{k}_1$$

where we used the factorization (7.15.54) for the first term. Using $R_1^{-1} = L_1^T D_{1b}^{-1} L_1$, we find for the second term $L_1^{-T}\mathbf{k}_1 = L_1^{-T}R_1^{-1}\mathbf{y} = D_{1b}^{-1}L_1\mathbf{y} = D_{1b}^{-1}\mathbf{e}_{1b}$. Therefore,

$$\mathbf{g}_1 = L^{-T}\mathbf{g}_0 + e_0 D_{1b}^{-1}\mathbf{e}_{1b} \tag{7.15.62}$$

Extracting the last elements we obtain Eq. (7.15.45).

7.16 *RLS Adaptive Filters*

The LMS and gradient lattice adaptation algorithms, based on the steepest-descent method, provide a gradual, iterative, minimization of the performance index. The adaptive weights are not optimal at each time instant, but only after convergence. In this section we discuss recursive least-squares adaptation algorithms that are based on the *exact* minimization of least-squares criteria. The filter weights are optimal at *each* time instant n.

Adaptive RLS algorithms are the time-recursive analogs of the block processing methods of linear prediction and FIR Wiener filtering that we discussed in Sections 5.12 and 5.14. They may be used, in place of LMS, in any adaptive filtering application. Because of their fast convergence they have been proposed for use in fast start-up channel equalization [115–118]. They are also routinely used in real-time *system identification* applications [46–52,119]. Their main disadvantage is that they require a fair amount of computation ($O(M^2)$, for M-tap filters) per time update. In biomedical applications, they can be easily implemented on minicomputers [56,57]. In other applications, such as the equalization of rapidly varying channels or adaptive arrays [15,120–122], they may be too costly for implementation.

The recent fast reformulations of RLS algorithms, such as the RLSL, FK, FAEST, and FTF, have $O(M)$ computational complexity. The fast RLS algorithms combine the best of the LMS and RLS, namely, the computational efficiency of the former and the fast convergence of the latter. Among the fast RLS algorithms, it appears that the RLS lattice has better numerical stability properties than the direct-form versions.

We start with the RLS formulation of the FIR Wiener filtering problem. The estimation criterion $\mathcal{E} = E[e(n)^2] = min$ is replaced with a least-squares time average that includes all estimation errors from the initial time instant to the current time n; that is, $e(k), k = 0,1, \ldots, n$.

$$\mathcal{E}_n = \sum_{k=0}^{n} e(k)^2 = \min \tag{7.16.1}$$

where

$$e(k) = x(k) - \hat{x}(k)$$

and $\hat{x}(k)$ is the estimate of $x(k)$ produced by the (order-M) Wiener filter

$$\hat{x}(k) = \sum_{m=0}^{M} h_m y_{k-m} = [h_0, h_1, \cdots, h_M] \begin{bmatrix} y_k \\ y_{k-1} \\ \vdots \\ y_{k-M} \end{bmatrix} = \mathbf{h}^T \mathbf{y}(k)$$

Note that in adaptive array problems, $\mathbf{y}(k)$ represents the vector of measurements at the array elements, namely, $\mathbf{y}(k) = [y_0(k), y_1(k), \ldots, y_M(k)]^T$. To better track possible nonstationarities in the signals, the performance index is sometimes modified by introducing exponential weighting

$$\mathcal{E}_n = \sum_{k=0}^{n} \lambda^{n-k} e(k)^2 = e(n)^2 + \lambda e(n-1)^2 + \cdots + \lambda^n e(0)^2 \tag{7.15.2}$$

where the *forgetting factor* λ is positive and less than one. This performance index emphasizes the *most recent* observations and exponentially ignores the older ones. We will base our discussion on this criterion. Setting the derivative with respect to $\mathbf{h}$ to zero, we find the least-square analogs of the *orthogonality equations*

$$\frac{\partial \mathcal{E}_n}{\partial \mathbf{h}} = -2 \sum_{k=0}^{n} \lambda^{n-k} e(k) \mathbf{y}(k) = 0$$

which may be cast in a *normal equation* form

$$\sum_{k=0}^{n} \lambda^{n-k} [x(k) - \mathbf{h}^T \mathbf{y}(k)] \mathbf{y}(k) = 0$$

$$\left[\sum_{k=0}^{n} \lambda^{n-k} \mathbf{y}(k) \mathbf{y}(k)^T \right] \mathbf{h} = \sum_{k=0}^{n} \lambda^{n-k} x(k) \mathbf{y}(k)$$

Defining the quantities

$$\begin{aligned} R(n) &= \sum_{k=0}^{n} \lambda^{n-k} \mathbf{y}(k) \mathbf{y}(k)^T \\ \mathbf{r}(n) &= \sum_{k=0}^{n} \lambda^{n-k} x(k) \mathbf{y}(k) \end{aligned} \tag{7.16.3}$$

we write the normal equations as $R(n)\mathbf{h} = \mathbf{r}(n)$, with solution $\mathbf{h} = R(n)^{-1}\mathbf{r}(n)$. Note that the n-dependence of $R(n)$ and $\mathbf{r}(n)$ makes $\mathbf{h}$ depend on n; we shall write, therefore,

$$\mathbf{h}(n) = R(n)^{-1}\mathbf{r}(n) \tag{7.16.4}$$

These are the least-squares analogs of the ordinary Wiener solution, with $R(n)$ and $\mathbf{r}(n)$ playing the role of the covariance matrix $R = E[\mathbf{y}(n)\mathbf{y}(n)^T]$ and cross-correlation vector $\mathbf{r} = E[x(n)\mathbf{y}(n)^T]$. These quantities satisfy the rank-one updating properties

$$R(n) = \lambda R(n-1) + \mathbf{y}(n)\mathbf{y}(n)^T \tag{7.16.5}$$

$$\mathbf{r}(n) = \lambda \mathbf{r}(n-1) + x(n)\mathbf{y}(n) \tag{7.16.6}$$

Thus, the general results of the previous section can be applied. We have the correspondences:

$\mathbf{y} \to \mathbf{y}(n)$	$x \to x(n)$
$R_1 \to R(n)$	$R_0 \to \lambda R(n-1)$
$P_1 \to P(n) = R(n)^{-1}$	$P_0 \to \lambda^{-1}P(n-1) = \lambda^{-1}R(n-1)^{-1}$
$\mathbf{r}_1 \to \mathbf{r}(n)$	$\mathbf{r}_0 \to \lambda\mathbf{r}(n-1)$
$\mathbf{h}_1 \to \mathbf{h}(n)$	$\mathbf{h}_0 \to \mathbf{h}(n-1) = R(n-1)^{-1}\mathbf{r}(n-1)$
$\hat{x}_1 \to \hat{x}(n) = \mathbf{h}(n)^T\mathbf{y}(n)$	$\hat{x}_0 \to \hat{x}(n/n-1) = \mathbf{h}(n-1)^T\mathbf{y}(n)$
$e_1 \to e(n) = x(n) - \hat{x}(n)$	$e_0 \to e(n/n-1) = x(n) - \hat{x}(n/n-1)$
$\mathbf{k}_1 \to \mathbf{k}(n) = R(n)^{-1}\mathbf{y}(n)$	$\mathbf{k}_0 \to \mathbf{k}(n/n-1) = \lambda^{-1}R(n-1)^{-1}\mathbf{y}(n)$
$\nu \to \nu(n) = \mathbf{k}(n/n-1)^T\mathbf{y}(n) =$ $= \lambda^{-1}\mathbf{y}(n)^T R(n-1)^{-1}\mathbf{y}(n)$	$\mu \to \mu(n) = \dfrac{1}{1+\nu(n)} = 1 - \mathbf{k}(n)^T\mathbf{y}(n) =$ $= 1 - \mathbf{y}(n)^T R(n)^{-1}\mathbf{y}(n)$
$e_1 = \mu e_0 \to e(n) = \mu(n)e(n/n-1)$	$\mathbf{k}_1 = \mu\mathbf{k}_0 \to \mathbf{k}(n) = \mu(n)\mathbf{k}(n/n-1)$
$P_1 = P_0 - \mathbf{k}_1\mathbf{k}_0^T \to$ $\to P(n) = \lambda^{-1}P(n-1) - \mathbf{k}(n)\mathbf{k}(n/n-1)^T$	$\mathbf{h}_1 = \mathbf{h}_0 + e_0\mathbf{k}_1 \to$ $\to \mathbf{h}(n) = \mathbf{h}(n-1) + e(n/n-1)\mathbf{k}(n)$

We used the notation $\hat{x}(n/n-1)$, $e(n/n-1)$, $\mathbf{k}(n/n-1)$ to denote the *a priori* estimate, estimation error, and Kalman gain. Note that R_0 and $\mathbf{r}_0$ are the quantities $R(n-1)$ and $\mathbf{r}(n-1)$ scaled by the forgetting factor λ. In the a priori Wiener solution $\mathbf{h}_0 = R_0^{-1}\mathbf{r}_0$, the factors λ cancel to give $[\lambda R(n-1)]^{-1}[\lambda\mathbf{r}(n-1)] = R(n-1)^{-1}\mathbf{r}(n-1) = \mathbf{h}(n-1)$. Thus, the a priori Wiener solution is the solution at the *previous* time instant $n-1$. With the above correspondences, the conventional RLS algorithm listed in the previous section becomes

1. $\mathbf{k}(n/n-1) = \lambda^{-1}P(n-1)\mathbf{y}(n)$

2. $\nu(n) = \mathbf{k}(n/n-1)^T\mathbf{y}(n)\,, \qquad \mu(n) = \dfrac{1}{1+\nu(n)}$

3. $\mathbf{k}(n) = \mu(n)\mathbf{k}(n/n-1)$

4. $P(n) = \lambda^{-1} P(n\text{-}1) - \mathbf{k}(n)\mathbf{k}(n/n\text{-}1)^T$

5. $\hat{x}(n/n\text{-}1) = \mathbf{h}(n\text{-}1)^T \mathbf{y}(n)\,, \quad e(n/n\text{-}1) = x(n) - \hat{x}(n/n\text{-}1)\,,$

   $e(n) = \mu(n) e(n/n\text{-}1)\,, \quad \hat{x}(n) = x(n) - e(n)$

6. $\mathbf{h}(n) = \mathbf{h}(n\text{-}1) + e(n/n\text{-}1)\mathbf{k}(n)$

The algorithm may be initialized in time by taking $R(-1) = 0$, which would imply $P(-1) = \infty$. Instead, we may use $P(-1) = 1/\delta$, where δ is a very small number. The algorithm is quite insensitive to the choice of δ. Typical values are $\delta = 0.1$ or $\delta = 0.01$.

The subroutine **rls** (see Appendix B) is an implementation of the algorithm. Because the algorithm can also be used in array problems, we have designed the routine so that its inputs are the old weights $\mathbf{h}(n-1)$, the current sample $x(n)$, and the *entire* data vector $\mathbf{y}(n)$ (in time series problems only the current time sample y_n is needed, the past samples $y_{n-i}, i = 1, \ldots, M$ being stored in the tapped delay line). The outputs of the routine are $\mathbf{h}(n)$, $\hat{x}(n)$, and $e(n)$. A simulation example will be presented in the next section.

The terminology *Kalman gain* arises by interpreting $\mathbf{h}(n) = \mathbf{h}(n-1) + e(n/n-1)\mathbf{k}(n)$ as a Kalman predictor/corrector algorithm, where the first term $\mathbf{h}(n-1)$ is a prediction of the weight $\mathbf{h}(n)$ based on the past, $e(n/n-1) = x(n) - \mathbf{h}(n-1)^T\mathbf{y}(n)$ is the tentative estimation error made on the basis of the prediction $\mathbf{h}(n-1)$, and the second term $e(n/n-1)\mathbf{k}(n)$ is the correction of the prediction. The fast convergence properties of the algorithm can be understood by replacing $\mathbf{k}(n) = R(n)^{-1}\mathbf{y}(n)$ in the update equation

$$\mathbf{h}(n) = \mathbf{h}(n\text{-}1) + R(n)^{-1}\mathbf{y}(n)e(n/n\text{-}1) \tag{7.16.7}$$

It differs from the LMS algorithm by the presence of $R(n)^{-1}$ in front of the weight update term. Because $R(n)$ is an estimate of the covariance matrix $R = E[\mathbf{y}(n)\mathbf{y}(n)^T]$, the presence of $R(n)^{-1}$ makes the RLS algorithm behave like Newton's method, hence its fast convergence properties [123,124]. Another important conceptual difference is that in the RLS algorithm the filters $\mathbf{h}(n)$ and $\mathbf{h}(n-1)$ are the exact Wiener solutions of two different minimization criteria; namely, $\mathcal{E}_n = min$ and $\mathcal{E}_{n-1} = min$, whereas in the LMS algorithm they are successive gradient-descent approximations of a single optimum solution.

The role of the forgetting factor λ may be understood qualitatively, by considering the quantity

$$n_\lambda = \frac{\sum_{n=0}^{\infty} n\lambda^n}{\sum_{n=0}^{\infty} \lambda^n} = \frac{\lambda}{1-\lambda}$$

to be a *measure* of the effective memory of the performance index $\mathcal{E}_n$. Smaller λs correspond to shorter memory n_λ, and can track better the nonstationary changes of the underlying signals. The memory of the performance index n_λ should be as short as the effective duration of the nonstationary segments, but not shorter because the performance index will not be taking full advantage of all the available samples (which could extend over the entire nonstationary segment); as a result, the computed weights $\mathbf{h}(n)$ will exhibit more noisy behavior. In particular, if the signals are stationary, the best value of λ is unity.

In Section 7.12, we considered the adaptive implementation of eigenvector methods based on an LMS gradient-projection method. Adaptive eigenvector methods can also be formulated based on the rank-one updating property (7.16.5). For example, one may use standard numerical analysis methods for the rank-one updating of the entire eigenproblem of $R(n)$ [87,125,126].

If one is interested only in a few largest or smallest eigenvalues and corresponding eigenvectors, one can use the more efficient *power method* or *inverse power method* and their generalizations, such as the *simultaneous and subspace iterations,* or *Lanczos methods,* which are essentially the subspace iteration improved by Rayleigh-Ritz methods [127,128].

The basic procedure for making these numerical analysis methods adaptive is as follows [129–135]. The power method generates the maximum eigenvector by the iteration $\mathbf{e}(n) = R\mathbf{e}(n-1)$, followed by normalization of $\mathbf{e}(n)$ to unit norm. Similarly, the minimum eigenvector may be generated by the inverse power iteration $\mathbf{e}(n) = R^{-1}\mathbf{e}(n-1)$. Because R and R^{-1} are not known, they may be *replaced* by their estimates $R(n)$ and $P(n) = R(n)^{-1}$, which are being updated from one time instant to the next by Eq. (7.16.5) or by step 4 of the RLS algorithm, so that one has $\mathbf{e}(n) = R(n)\mathbf{e}(n-1)$ or $\mathbf{e}(n) = P(n)\mathbf{e}(n-1)$. This can be generalized to the simultaneous iteration case. For example, to generate adaptively the K minimum eigenvectors spanning the noise subspace one starts at each iteration n with K mutually *orthonormalized* vectors $\mathbf{e}_i(n-1)$, $i = 0, 1, \ldots, K-1$. Each is subjected to the inverse power iteration $\mathbf{e}_i(n) = P(n)\mathbf{e}_i(n-1)$ and finally, the K updated vectors $\mathbf{e}_i(n)$ are mutually orthonormalized using the Gram-Schmidt or modified Gram-Schmidt procedure for vectors. Similar simultaneous iteration methods can also be applied to the gradient-projection method of Section 7.12. The main limitation of applying the simultaneous iteration methods is that one must know in advance the dimension K of the noise subspace.

7.17 *Fast RLS Filters [88–91,102–111,136–145]*

The fast direct-form RLS algorithms make use of the forward and backward predictors. The subblock decompositions of the $(M+1)$-dimensional data vector $\mathbf{y}(n)$ are

$$\mathbf{y}(n) = \begin{bmatrix} y_n \\ y_{n-1} \\ \vdots \\ y_{n-M} \end{bmatrix} = \begin{bmatrix} \bar{\mathbf{y}}(n) \\ y_{n-M} \end{bmatrix} = \begin{bmatrix} y_n \\ \tilde{\mathbf{y}}(n) \end{bmatrix} \tag{7.17.1}$$

Therefore,

$$\bar{\mathbf{y}}(n) = \begin{bmatrix} y_n \\ y_{n-1} \\ \vdots \\ y_{n-M+1} \end{bmatrix}, \qquad \tilde{\mathbf{y}}(n) = \begin{bmatrix} y_{n-1} \\ y_{n-2} \\ \vdots \\ y_{n-M} \end{bmatrix} \tag{7.17.2}$$

The corresponding covariance matrices will be

$$\bar{R}(n) = \sum_{k=0}^{n} \lambda^{n-k}\,\bar{\mathbf{y}}(k)\,\bar{\mathbf{y}}(k)^T, \qquad \tilde{R}(n) = \sum_{k=0}^{n} \lambda^{n-k}\,\tilde{\mathbf{y}}(k)\tilde{\mathbf{y}}(k)^T \tag{7.15.3}$$

The definitions (7.17.2) imply the *shift invariance* property

$$\tilde{\mathbf{y}}(n+1) = \bar{\mathbf{y}}(n) \tag{7.17.4}$$

Using this property we find

$$\tilde{R}(n+1) = \sum_{k=0}^{n+1} \lambda^{n+1-k}\,\tilde{\mathbf{y}}(k)\tilde{\mathbf{y}}(k)^T = \sum_{k=-1}^{n} \lambda^{n-k}\,\tilde{\mathbf{y}}(k+1)\tilde{\mathbf{y}}(k+1)^T =$$

$$= \sum_{k=-1}^{n} \lambda^{n-k}\,\bar{\mathbf{y}}(k)\,\bar{\mathbf{y}}(k)^T = \bar{R}(n) + \lambda^{n+1}\,\bar{\mathbf{y}}(-1)\,\bar{\mathbf{y}}(-1)^T$$

If we make the *prewindowing* assumption that $\bar{\mathbf{y}}(-1) = 0$, we obtain the shift invariance property for the covariance matrices

$$\tilde{R}(n+1) = \bar{R}(n) \tag{7.17.5}$$

Before we use the shift invariance properties, we make some additional correspondences from the previous section

$\bar{\mathbf{y}} \to \bar{\mathbf{y}}(n), \quad \tilde{\mathbf{y}} \to \tilde{\mathbf{y}}(n)$
$R_1\mathbf{a}_1 = E_{1a}\mathbf{u} \to R(n)\mathbf{a}(n) = E^+(n)\mathbf{u}$
$R_1\mathbf{b}_1 = E_{1b}\mathbf{v} \to R(n)\mathbf{b}(n) = E^-(n)\mathbf{v}$
$R_0\mathbf{a}_0 = E_{0a}\mathbf{u} \to \lambda R(n-1)\mathbf{a}(n-1) = \lambda E^+(n-1)\mathbf{u}$
$R_0\mathbf{b}_0 = E_{0b}\mathbf{v} \to \lambda R(n-1)\mathbf{b}(n-1) = \lambda E^-(n-1)\mathbf{v}$
$e_{1a} = \mathbf{a}_1^T\mathbf{y} \to e^+(n) = \mathbf{a}(n)^T\mathbf{y}(n)$
$e_{1b} = \mathbf{b}_1^T\mathbf{y} \to e^-(n) = \mathbf{b}(n)^T\mathbf{y}(n)$
$e_{0a} = \mathbf{a}_0^T\mathbf{y} \to e^+(n/n-1) = \mathbf{a}(n-1)^T\mathbf{y}(n)$
$e_{0b} = \mathbf{b}_0^T\mathbf{y} \to e^-(n/n-1) = \mathbf{b}(n-1)^T\mathbf{y}(n)$
$E_{1a} = E_{0a} + e_{1a}e_{0a} \to E^+(n) = \lambda E^+(n-1) + e^+(n)e^+(n/n-1)$
$E_{1b} = E_{0b} + e_{1b}e_{0b} \to E^-(n) = \lambda E^-(n-1) + e^-(n)e^-(n/n-1)$
$\tilde{\mathbf{k}}_1 = \tilde{R}_1^{-1}\tilde{\mathbf{y}} \to \tilde{\mathbf{k}}(n) = \tilde{R}(n)^{-1}\tilde{\mathbf{y}}(n)$
$\bar{\mathbf{k}}_1 = \bar{R}_1^{-1}\bar{\mathbf{y}} \to \bar{\mathbf{k}}(n) = \bar{R}(n)^{-1}\bar{\mathbf{y}}(n)$
$\tilde{\mathbf{k}}_0 = \tilde{R}_0^{-1}\tilde{\mathbf{y}} \to \tilde{\mathbf{k}}(n/n-1) = \lambda^{-1}\tilde{R}(n-1)^{-1}\tilde{\mathbf{y}}(n)$
$\bar{\mathbf{k}}_0 = \bar{R}_0^{-1}\bar{\mathbf{y}} \to \bar{\mathbf{k}}(n/n-1) = \lambda^{-1}\bar{R}(n-1)^{-1}\bar{\mathbf{y}}(n)$
$\tilde{\nu} = \tilde{\mathbf{k}}_0^T\tilde{\mathbf{y}} \to \tilde{\nu}(n) = \tilde{\mathbf{k}}(n/n-1)^T\tilde{\mathbf{y}}(n)$
$\bar{\nu} = \bar{\mathbf{k}}_0^T\bar{\mathbf{y}} \to \bar{\nu}(n) = \bar{\mathbf{k}}(n/n-1)^T\bar{\mathbf{y}}(n)$
$\tilde{\mu} = 1/(1+\tilde{\nu}) \to \tilde{\mu}(n) = 1/(1+\tilde{\nu}(n))$
$\bar{\mu} = 1/(1+\bar{\nu}) \to \bar{\mu}(n) = 1/(1+\bar{\nu}(n))$

We have used the superscripts $\pm$ to indicate the forward and backward quantities. Again, note the cancellation of the factors λ from the a priori normal equations, which implies that the a priori predictors are the predictors of the previous time instant; that is, $\mathbf{a}_0 \to \mathbf{a}(n-1)$ and $\mathbf{b}_0 \to \mathbf{b}(n-1)$.

Using the shift invariance properties (7.17.4) and (7.17.5), we find that all the tilde quantities at the next time instant are equal to the bar quantities at the present instant; for example,

$$\tilde{\mathbf{k}}(n+1) = \tilde{R}(n+1)^{-1}\tilde{\mathbf{y}}(n+1) = \bar{R}(n)^{-1}\bar{\mathbf{y}}(n) = \bar{\mathbf{k}}(n)$$

Similarly,

$$\tilde{\mathbf{k}}(n+1/n) = \lambda^{-1}\tilde{R}(n)^{-1}\tilde{\mathbf{y}}(n+1) = \lambda^{-1}\bar{R}(n-1)^{-1}\bar{\mathbf{y}}(n) = \bar{\mathbf{k}}(n/n-1)$$

and for the likelihood variables

$$\tilde{\nu}(n+1) = \tilde{\mathbf{k}}(n+1/n)^T\tilde{\mathbf{y}}(n+1) = \bar{\mathbf{k}}(n/n-1)^T\bar{\mathbf{y}}(n) = \bar{\nu}(n)$$

and similarly for the μs. We summarize,

$$\begin{aligned} \tilde{\mathbf{k}}(n+1) &= \bar{\mathbf{k}}(n)\,, \qquad \tilde{\mathbf{k}}(n+1/n) = \bar{\mathbf{k}}(n/n-1) \\ \tilde{\nu}(n+1) &= \bar{\nu}(n)\,, \qquad \tilde{\mu}(n+1) = \bar{\mu}(n) \end{aligned} \tag{7.17.6}$$

These equations can be added at ends of the computational sequences of the previous section to complete the computational cycle at each time instant. In the present notation, the complete *FK algorithm* [88,89] is:

0. At time n, we have available the quantities $\mathbf{h}(n-1)$, $\mathbf{a}(n-1)$, $\mathbf{b}(n-1)$, $\tilde{\mathbf{k}}(n)$, $E^+(n-1)$, $x(n)$, and $\mathbf{y}(n)$

1. $e^+(n/n-1) = \mathbf{a}(n-1)^T\mathbf{y}(n)$

2. $\mathbf{a}(n) = \mathbf{a}(n-1) - e^+(n/n-1)\begin{bmatrix} 0 \\ \tilde{\mathbf{k}}(n) \end{bmatrix}$

3. $e^+(n) = \mathbf{a}(n)^T\mathbf{y}(n)$

4. $E^+(n) = \lambda E^+(n-1) + e^+(n)e^+(n/n-1)$

5. Compute the first element of $\mathbf{k}(n)$, $k_0(n) = \dfrac{e^+(n)}{E^+(n)}$

6. $\mathbf{k}(n) = \begin{bmatrix} 0 \\ \tilde{\mathbf{k}}(n) \end{bmatrix} + k_0(n)\,\mathbf{a}(n)\,,$ extract the last element, $k_M(n)$

7. $e^-(n/n-1) = \mathbf{b}(n-1)^T\mathbf{y}(n)$

8. $\mathbf{b}(n) = \dfrac{\mathbf{b}(n-1) - e^{-}(n/n-1)\,\mathbf{k}(n)}{1 - e^{-}(n/n-1)k_M(n)}$

9. $\begin{bmatrix} \bar{\mathbf{k}}(n) \\ 0 \end{bmatrix} = \mathbf{k}(n) - k_M(n)\,\mathbf{b}(n)$

10. $\hat{x}(n/n-1) = \mathbf{h}(n-1)^T\mathbf{y}(n)\,, \qquad e(n/n-1) = x(n) - \hat{x}(n/n-1)$

11. $\mathbf{h}(n) = \mathbf{h}(n-1) + e(n/n-1)\mathbf{k}(n)$

12. $\hat{x}(n) = \mathbf{h}(n)^T\mathbf{y}(n)\,, \qquad e(n) = x(n) - \hat{x}(n)$

13. $\tilde{\mathbf{k}}(n+1) = \bar{\mathbf{k}}(n)\,,$ go to the next time instant, $n \rightarrow n+1$

The first and last entries of the a posteriori Kalman gain vector $\mathbf{k}(n)$ were denoted by $k_0(n)$ and $k_M(n)$; that is, $\mathbf{k}(n) = [k_0(n), k_1(n), \ldots, k_M(n)]^T$. Similarly, we obtain the complete *FAEST algorithm* [90]:

0. At time n, we have available the quantities $\mathbf{h}(n-1)$, $\mathbf{a}(n-1)$, $\mathbf{b}(n-1)$, $\tilde{\mathbf{k}}(n/n-1)$, $\tilde{\nu}(n)$, $E^{\pm}(n-1)$, $x(n)$, and $\mathbf{y}(n)$

1. $e^{+}(n/n-1) = \mathbf{a}(n-1)^T\mathbf{y}(n)$

2. $e^{+}(n) = \tilde{\mu}(n)e^{+}(n/n-1) = e^{+}(n/n-1)/(1 + \tilde{\nu}(n))$

3. Compute the first element of $\mathbf{k}(n/n-1)$, $k_0(n/n-1) = \dfrac{e^{+}(n/n-1)}{\lambda E^{+}(n-1)}$

4. $E^{+}(n) = \lambda E^{+}(n-1) + e^{+}(n)e^{+}(n/n-1)$

5. $\mathbf{k}(n/n-1) = \begin{bmatrix} 0 \\ \tilde{\mathbf{k}}(n/n-1) \end{bmatrix} + k_0(n/n-1)\,\mathbf{a}(n-1)\,,$ extract last element, $k_M(n/n-1)$

6. $e^{-}(n/n-1) = k_M(n/n-1)\,[\lambda E^{-}(n-1)]$

7. $\begin{bmatrix} \bar{\mathbf{k}}(n/n-1) \\ 0 \end{bmatrix} = \mathbf{k}(n/n-1) - k_M(n/n-1)\,\mathbf{b}(n-1)$

8. $\nu(n) = \tilde{\nu}(n) + e^{+}(n/n-1)k_0(n/n-1)\,, \qquad \bar{\nu}(n) = \nu(n) - e^{-}(n/n-1)k_M(n/n-1)$

9. $e^-(n) = \bar{\mu}(n)e^-(n/n\text{-}1) = e^-(n/n\text{-}1)/(1 + \bar{\nu}(n))$

10. $E^-(n) = \lambda E^-(n\text{-}1) + e^-(n)e^-(n/n\text{-}1)$

11. $$\mathbf{a}(n) = \mathbf{a}(n\text{-}1) - e^+(n)\begin{bmatrix} 0 \\ \tilde{\mathbf{k}}(n/n\text{-}1) \end{bmatrix}$$

12. $$\mathbf{b}(n) = \mathbf{b}(n\text{-}1) - e^-(n)\begin{bmatrix} \tilde{\mathbf{k}}(n/n\text{-}1) \\ 0 \end{bmatrix}$$

13. $\hat{x}(n/n\text{-}1) = \mathbf{h}(n\text{-}1)^T\mathbf{y}(n)\,, \quad e(n/n\text{-}1) = x(n) - \hat{x}(n/n\text{-}1)$

14. $e(n) = \mu(n)e(n/n\text{-}1) = e(n/n\text{-}1)/(1 + \nu(n))\,, \quad \hat{x}(n) = x(n) - e(n)$

15. $\mathbf{h}(n) = \mathbf{h}(n\text{-}1) + e(n)\,\mathbf{k}(n/n\text{-}1)$

16. $\tilde{\mathbf{k}}(n+1/n) = \mathbf{k}(n/n\text{-}1)\,, \quad \tilde{\nu}(n+1) = \bar{\nu}(n)\,, \quad \text{go to } n \to n+1$

The algorithm is initialized in time by clearing the tapped delay line of the filter and setting $\mathbf{h}(-1) = 0$, $\mathbf{a}(-1) = \mathbf{u} = [1,\mathbf{0}^T]^T$, $\mathbf{b}(-1) = \mathbf{v} = [\mathbf{0}^T,1]^T$, $\tilde{\mathbf{k}}(0/-1) = 0$, $\tilde{\nu}(0) = 0$, and $E^{\pm}(-1) = \delta$, where δ is a small constant. Exact initialization procedures have been discussed in [91]. The *FTF algorithm* [91] is obtained by replacing step 8 by the following:

$$\mu(n) = \tilde{\mu}(n)\frac{\lambda E^+(n\text{-}1)}{E^+(n)}\,, \qquad \bar{\mu}(n) = \frac{\mu(n)}{1 - e^-(n/n\text{-}1)\,k_M(n/n\text{-}1)\,\mu(n)} \qquad \text{(FTF)}$$

The subroutine **faest** (see Appendix B) is an implementation of the FAEST algorithm. The routine transforms an input pair of samples $\{x,y\}$ into an output pair $\{\hat{x},e\}$, updates the tapped delay line of the filter, and updates the filter $\mathbf{h}(n)$. Next, we present a simulation example comparing the FAEST and LMS algorithms. The example (and input data) is exactly the same as that discussed in Section 7.13 and defined theoretically by Eqs. (7.13.37) and (7.13.38). Figure 7.24 shows two of the adaptive weights, $h_1(n)$ and $h_2(n)$, adapted by FAEST and LMS. The weights are converging to their theoretical values $h_1 = 1.5$ and $h_2 = -2$. The RLS parameters were $\lambda = 1$ and $\delta = 0.01$; the LMS parameter was $\mu = 0.01$. The RLS weight $h_2(n)$ should also be compared with the lattice weight $g_2(n)$ of Fig. 7.20 adapted by the gradient lattice algorithm. Except for initialization differences, the two behave very similarly.

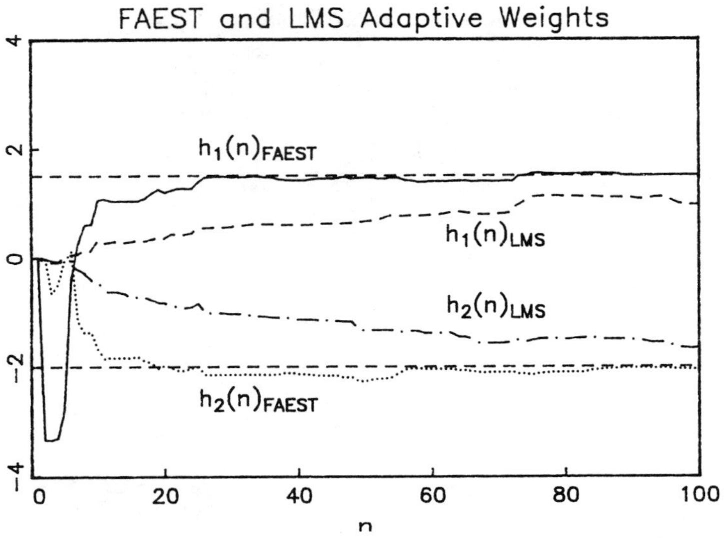

Figure 7.24 Direct-Form Weights Adapted by FAEST and LMS Algorithms

7.18 *RLS Lattice Filters [102–111]*

The fast direct-form RLS filters were fixed-order filters. By contrast, the RLS lattice algorithms, for each time instant n, do a recursion in the order, $p = 0, 1, \ldots, M$. Therefore, it is necessary to indicate the order p by using an extra index in all the quantities of the past two sections. For example, the order-p data vector and its bar and tilde parts will be denoted by

$$\mathbf{y}_p(n) = \begin{bmatrix} y_n \\ y_{n-1} \\ \cdot \\ \cdot \\ y_{n-p} \end{bmatrix}, \quad \bar{\mathbf{y}}_p(n) = \begin{bmatrix} y_n \\ y_{n-1} \\ \cdot \\ \cdot \\ y_{n-p+1} \end{bmatrix}, \quad \tilde{\mathbf{y}}_p(n) = \begin{bmatrix} y_{n-1} \\ y_{n-2} \\ \cdot \\ \cdot \\ y_{n-p} \end{bmatrix} \tag{7.18.1}$$

Therefore, we have

$$\bar{\mathbf{y}}_p(n) = \mathbf{y}_{p-1}(n), \qquad \tilde{\mathbf{y}}_p(n) = \bar{\mathbf{y}}_p(n-1) = \mathbf{y}_{p-1}(n-1) \tag{7.18.2}$$

Similarly, the covariance matrices will be

$$\bar{R}_p(n) = R_{p-1}(n), \qquad \tilde{R}_p(n) = R_{p-1}(n-1) \tag{7.18.3}$$

The order-p predictors will be denoted by $\mathbf{a}_p(n)$ and $\mathbf{b}_p(n)$, with error signals $e_p^+(n) = \mathbf{a}_p(n)^T\mathbf{y}_p(n)$ and $e_p^-(n) = \mathbf{b}_p(n)^T\mathbf{y}_p(n)$. The corresponding mean-square errors will be denoted by $E_p^{\pm}(n)$. Similarly, the a priori estimation errors are denoted by $e_p^+(n/n-1)=\mathbf{a}_p(n-1)^T\mathbf{y}_p(n)$ and $e_p^-(n/n-1)=\mathbf{b}_p(n-1)^T\mathbf{y}_p(n)$. Using Eq. (7.18.3), we find the following correspondences between the order-$(p-1)$ and order-p problems:

$$
\begin{array}{l}
\bar{R}_1 \to R_{p-1}(n)\,,\quad \bar{\mathbf{a}}_1 \to \mathbf{a}_{p-1}(n)\,,\quad \bar{E}_{1a} \to E_{p-1}^+(n)\\
\bar{R}_0 \to \lambda R_{p-1}(n-1)\,,\quad \bar{\mathbf{a}}_0 \to \mathbf{a}_{p-1}(n-1)\,,\quad \bar{E}_{0a} \to \lambda E_{p-1}^+(n-1)\\
\tilde{R}_1 \to R_{p-1}(n-1)\,,\quad \tilde{\mathbf{b}}_1 \to \mathbf{b}_{p-1}(n-1)\,,\quad \tilde{E}_{1b} \to E_{p-1}^-(n-1)\\
\tilde{R}_0 \to \lambda R_{p-1}(n-2)\,,\quad \tilde{\mathbf{b}}_0 \to \mathbf{b}_{p-1}(n-2)\,,\quad \tilde{E}_{0b} \to \lambda E_{p-1}^-(n-2)\\
\bar{e}_{1a} = \bar{\mathbf{a}}_1^T\bar{\mathbf{y}} \to e_{p-1}^+(n) = \mathbf{a}_{p-1}(n)^T\mathbf{y}_{p-1}(n)\\
\tilde{e}_{1b} = \tilde{\mathbf{b}}_1^T\tilde{\mathbf{y}} \to e_{p-1}^-(n-1) = \mathbf{b}_{p-1}(n-1)^T\mathbf{y}_{p-1}(n-1)\\
\bar{e}_{0a} = \bar{\mathbf{a}}_0^T\bar{\mathbf{y}} \to e_{p-1}^+(n/n-1) = \mathbf{a}_{p-1}(n-1)^T\mathbf{y}_{p-1}(n)\\
\tilde{e}_{0b} = \tilde{\mathbf{b}}_0^T\tilde{\mathbf{y}} \to e_{p-1}^-(n-1/n-2) = \mathbf{b}_{p-1}(n-2)^T\mathbf{y}_{p-1}(n-1)\\
\gamma_{1a} \to \gamma_p^+(n)\,,\quad \gamma_{0a} \to \gamma_p^+(n-1)\\
\gamma_{1b} \to \gamma_p^-(n)\,,\quad \gamma_{0b} \to \gamma_p^-(n-1)\\[1em]
\mathbf{a}_1 = \begin{bmatrix}\bar{\mathbf{a}}_1\\0\end{bmatrix} - \gamma_{1b}\begin{bmatrix}0\\\tilde{\mathbf{b}}_1\end{bmatrix} \to \mathbf{a}_p(n) = \begin{bmatrix}\mathbf{a}_{p-1}(n)\\0\end{bmatrix} - \gamma_p^-(n)\begin{bmatrix}0\\\mathbf{b}_{p-1}(n-1)\end{bmatrix}\\[1em]
\mathbf{b}_1 = \begin{bmatrix}0\\\tilde{\mathbf{b}}_1\end{bmatrix} - \gamma_{1a}\begin{bmatrix}\bar{\mathbf{a}}_1\\0\end{bmatrix} \to \mathbf{b}_p(n) = \begin{bmatrix}0\\\mathbf{b}_{p-1}(n-1)\end{bmatrix} - \gamma_p^+(n)\begin{bmatrix}\mathbf{a}_{p-1}(n)\\0\end{bmatrix}\\[1em]
e_{1a} = \bar{e}_{1a} - \gamma_{1b}\tilde{e}_{1b} \to e_p^+(n) = e_{p-1}^+(n) - \gamma_p^-(n)e_{p-1}^-(n-1)\\
e_{1b} = \tilde{e}_{1b} - \gamma_{1a}\bar{e}_{1a} \to e_p^-(n) = e_{p-1}^-(n-1) - \gamma_p^+(n)e_{p-1}^+(n)\\[1em]
\mathbf{a}_0 = \begin{bmatrix}\bar{\mathbf{a}}_0\\0\end{bmatrix} - \gamma_{0b}\begin{bmatrix}0\\\tilde{\mathbf{b}}_0\end{bmatrix} \to \mathbf{a}_p(n-1) = \begin{bmatrix}\mathbf{a}_{p-1}(n-1)\\0\end{bmatrix} - \gamma_p^-(n-1)\begin{bmatrix}0\\\mathbf{b}_{p-1}(n-2)\end{bmatrix}\\[1em]
\mathbf{b}_0 = \begin{bmatrix}0\\\tilde{\mathbf{b}}_0\end{bmatrix} - \gamma_{0a}\begin{bmatrix}\bar{\mathbf{a}}_0\\0\end{bmatrix} \to \mathbf{b}_p(n-1) = \begin{bmatrix}0\\\mathbf{b}_{p-1}(n-2)\end{bmatrix} - \gamma_p^+(n-1)\begin{bmatrix}\mathbf{a}_{p-1}(n-1)\\0\end{bmatrix}\\[1em]
e_{0a} = \bar{e}_{0a} - \gamma_{0b}\tilde{e}_{0b} \to e_p^+(n/n-1) = e_{p-1}^+(n/n-1) - \gamma_p^-(n-1)e_{p-1}^-(n-1/n-2)\\
e_{0b} = \tilde{e}_{0b} - \gamma_{0a}\bar{e}_{0a} \to e_p^-(n/n-1) = e_{p-1}^-(n-1/n-2) - \gamma_p^+(n-1)e_{p-1}^+(n/n-1)\\
\gamma_{1a} = \gamma_{0a} + e_{0b}\dfrac{\bar{e}_{1a}}{\bar{E}_{1a}} \to \gamma_p^+(n) = \gamma_p^+(n-1) + e_p^-(n/n-1)\dfrac{e_{p-1}^+(n)}{E_{p-1}^+(n)}\\
\gamma_{1b} = \gamma_{0b} + e_{0a}\dfrac{\tilde{e}_{1b}}{\tilde{E}_{1b}} \to \gamma_p^-(n) = \gamma_p^-(n-1) + e_p^+(n/n-1)\dfrac{e_{p-1}^-(n-1)}{E_{p-1}^-(n-1)}\\
e_0 = \bar{e}_0 - g_{0b}e_{0b} \to e_p(n/n-1) = e_{p-1}(n/n-1) - g_p(n-1)e_p^-(n/n-1)\\
g_{1b} = g_{0b} + e_0\dfrac{e_{1b}}{E_{1b}} \to g_p(n) = g_p(n-1) + e_p(n/n-1)\dfrac{e_p^-(n)}{E_p^-(n)}\\
e_1 = \bar{e}_1 - g_{1b}e_{1b} \to e_p(n) = e_{p-1}(n) - g_p(n)e_p^-(n)
\end{array}
$$

We have denoted the forward/backward reflection coefficients by $\gamma_p^{\pm}(n)$, and the lattice weights by $g_p(n)$. The order-p a priori and a posteriori estimation errors are $e_p(n/n-1)=x(n)-\hat{x}_p(n/n-1)$ and $e_p(n)=x(n)-\hat{x}_p(n)$. The likelihood variable $\mu = 1-\mathbf{y}^T R_1^{-1}\mathbf{y}$ is

$$\mu_p(n) = 1 - \mathbf{y}_p(n)^T R_p(n)^{-1}\mathbf{y}_p(n) \tag{7.18.4}$$

and can also be written as

$$\mu_p(n) = \frac{1}{1+\nu_p(n)} = \frac{1}{1+\lambda^{-1}\mathbf{y}_p(n)^T R_p(n-1)^{-1}\mathbf{y}_p(n)}$$

Similarly, we have

$$\tilde{\mu}_p(n) = 1 - \tilde{\mathbf{y}}_p(n)^T \tilde{R}_p(n)^{-1}\tilde{\mathbf{y}}_p(n) = 1 - \mathbf{y}_{p-1}(n-1)^T R_{p-1}(n-1)^{-1}\mathbf{y}_{p-1}(n-1) = \mu_{p-1}(n-1)$$

and

$$\bar{\mu}_p(n) = 1 - \bar{\mathbf{y}}_p(n)^T \bar{R}_p(n)^{-1}\bar{\mathbf{y}}_p(n) = 1 - \mathbf{y}_{p-1}(n)^T R_{p-1}(n)^{-1}\mathbf{y}_{p-1}(n) = \mu_{p-1}(n)$$

We summarize,

$$\tilde{\mu}_p(n) = \mu_{p-1}(n-1)\,, \qquad \bar{\mu}_p(n) = \mu_{p-1}(n) \tag{7.18.5}$$

Thus, the proportionality between a posteriori and a priori errors will be

$$e_p^+(n) = \tilde{\mu}_p(n)e_p^+(n/n-1)\,, \qquad e_p^-(n) = \bar{\mu}_p(n)e_p^-(n/n-1) \tag{7.18.6}$$

Using either of Eq. (7.18.5), we find for the quantity $\bar{\tilde{\mu}} = \tilde{\bar{\mu}}$

$$\bar{\tilde{\mu}}_p(n) = \bar{\mu}_{p-1}(n-1) = \tilde{\mu}_{p-1}(n) = \mu_{p-2}(n-1) \tag{7.18.7}$$

Based on the above correspondences, we can obtain all versions of RLS lattice algorithms, such as the conventional a posteriori, a priori, double, and a priori and a posteriori error-feedback. As an example, we summarize the *double/direct RLS lattice algorithm* [156]:

0. At time n, we have available the quantities $\gamma_p^{\pm}(n-1)$, and $g_p(n-1)$, $E_p^{\pm}(n-1)$, $x(n)$, and y_n
1. Initialize in order by

$$e_0^{\pm}(n/n-1) = e_0^{\pm}(n) = y_n$$

$$E_0^{\pm}(n) = \lambda E_0^{\pm}(n-1) + e_0^{\pm}(n)e_0^{\pm}(n/n-1)$$

$$e_0(n/n-1) = x(n) - g_0(n-1)e_0^-(n/n-1)$$

$$g_0(n) = g_0(n-1) + e_0(n/n-1)\frac{e_0^-(n)}{E_0^-(n)}$$

$$e_0(n) = x(n) - g_0(n)e_0^-(n)$$

2. For $p = 1,2, \ldots, M$ compute

$$e_p^+(n/n-1) = e_{p-1}^+(n/n-1) - \gamma_p^-(n-1)e_{p-1}^-(n-1/n-2)$$

$$e_p^-(n/n-1) = e_{p-1}^-(n-1/n-2) - \gamma_p^+(n-1)e_{p-1}^+(n/n-1)$$

$$\gamma_p^+(n) = \gamma_p^+(n-1) + e_p^-(n/n-1)\frac{e_{p-1}^+(n)}{E_{p-1}^+(n)}$$

$$\gamma_p^-(n) = \gamma_p^-(n\text{-}1) + e_p^+(n/n\text{-}1)\frac{e_{p\text{-}1}^-(n\text{-}1)}{E_{p\text{-}1}^-(n\text{-}1)}$$

$$e_p^+(n) = e_{p\text{-}1}^+(n) - \gamma_p^-(n)e_{p\text{-}1}^-(n\text{-}1)$$

$$e_p^-(n) = e_{p\text{-}1}^-(n\text{-}1) - \gamma_p^+(n)e_{p\text{-}1}^+(n)$$

$$E_p^\pm(n) = \lambda E_p^\pm(n\text{-}1) + e_p^\pm(n)e_p^\pm(n/n\text{-}1)$$

$$e_p(n/n\text{-}1) = e_{p\text{-}1}(n/n\text{-}1) - g_p(n\text{-}1)e_p^-(n/n\text{-}1)$$

$$g_p(n) = g_p(n\text{-}1) + e_p(n/n\text{-}1)\frac{e_p^-(n)}{E_p^-(n)}$$

$$e_p(n) = e_{p\text{-}1}(n) - g_p(n)e_p^-(n)$$

3. $\hat{x}_M(n) = x(n) - e_M(n)$, and go to $n \to n+1$.

The algorithm is initialized in time by clearing the delay registers of both lattices and setting $\gamma_p^\pm(-1) = 0$, $E_p^\pm(-1) = 0$, and $g_p(-1) = 0$. As in the case of the gradient lattice, it follows that the backward outputs from the pth lattice section, $e_p^-(n/n-1)$, will be zero for $n < p$; therefore, we must keep $\gamma_p^-(n) = g_p(n) = 0$ for $n < r$, because these quantities require divisions by $E_p^-(n)$. There are 16 multiplications/divisions in step 2; therefore, the complexity of the algorithm grows like $16M$ per time update.

The subroutine **rlsl** (see Appendix B) is an implementation of the above algorithm. It is essentially the same as **lwf** used twice for the a priori and a posteriori lattices and with the weight adaptation parts added to it. Figure 7.25 shows the reflection coefficients $\gamma_1^\pm(n)$ and $\gamma_2^\pm(n)$ adapted by the RLS lattice algorithm, for the same example (and input data) presented in Section 7.13, which was also used in the FAEST simulation. Note that, after some initial transients, the forward and backward reflection coefficients become more or less the same as they converge to their theoretical values. Compare also with the reflection coefficients of Fig. 7.19 adapted by the gradient lattice. The version of the gradient lattice that we presented uses one set of reflection coefficients, which may be thought of as some sort of *average* combination of the forward/backward ones. Indeed, the curves for the gradient lattice reflection coefficients fall mostly between the curves of the forward and backward ones. Similarly, the lattice Wiener weights $g_p(n)$ have almost the same behavior as those of Fig. 7.20.

We finish this section by discussing the LU factorizations. Equations (7.15.20) become

$$L_p(n)R_p(n)L_p(n)^T = D_p^-(n)\,,\quad \lambda L_p(n\text{-}1)R_p(n\text{-}1)L_p(n\text{-}1)^T = \lambda D_p^-(n\text{-}1) \qquad (7.18.8)$$

where

$$D_p^-(n) = \text{diag}\{E_0^-(n), E_1^-(n), \cdots, E_p^-(n)\}$$

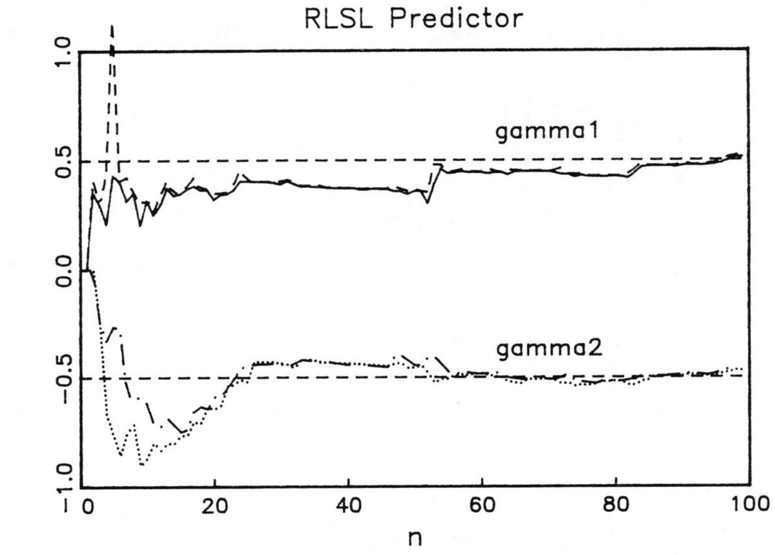

Figure 7.25 Reflection Coefficients Adapted by the Double/Direct RLS Lattice Algorithm

The vectors of a posteriori and a priori backward error signals are constructed by

$$\mathbf{e}_p^-(n) = \begin{bmatrix} e_0^-(n) \\ e_1^-(n) \\ \vdots \\ e_p^-(n) \end{bmatrix} = L_p(n)\,\mathbf{y}_p(n)\,, \qquad \mathbf{e}_p^-(n/n\text{-}1) = \begin{bmatrix} e_0^-(n/n\text{-}1) \\ e_1^-(n/n\text{-}1) \\ \vdots \\ e_p^-(n/n\text{-}1) \end{bmatrix} = L_p(n\text{-}1)\,\mathbf{y}_p(n)$$

This follows from the fact that the rows of the matrices L are the backward predictors of successive orders. The L matrices are related by Eq. (7.15.54), which reads

$$L_p(n) = L_p(n/n\text{-}1)\,L_p(n\text{-}1) \tag{7.18.9}$$

The rows of the unit lower triangular updating matrix $L_p(n/n-1)$ are constructed by (7.15.59), i.e.,

$$\boldsymbol{\beta}_p = -e_p^-(n)\,[\lambda D_{p\text{-}1}(n\text{-}1)]^{-1}\,\mathbf{e}_{p\text{-}1}^-(n/n\text{-}1) \tag{7.18.10}$$

or, component-wise

$$\beta_{pi} = -e_p^-(n)\,\frac{e_i^-(n/n\text{-}1)}{\lambda E_i^-(n\text{-}1)} = -\bar{\mu}_p(n)\,e_p^-(n/n\text{-}1)\,\frac{e_i^-(n/n\text{-}1)}{\lambda E_i^-(n\text{-}1)}\,, \qquad i = 0, 1, \cdots, p\text{-}1$$

The direct and lattice Wiener weights are related by Eq. (7.15.60), i.e., $\mathbf{g}_p(n) = L_p(n)^{-T}\mathbf{h}_p(n)$, and the a posteriori and a priori estimation errors are given by Eq. (7.15.61)

$$\hat{x}_p(n) = \mathbf{g}_p(n)^T\mathbf{e}_p^-(n)\,, \qquad \hat{x}_p(n/n\text{-}1) = \mathbf{g}_p(n\text{-}1)^T\mathbf{e}_p^-(n/n\text{-}1) \qquad (7.18.11)$$

and satisfy the recursions in order

$$\hat{x}_p(n) = \hat{x}_{p\text{-}1}(n) + g_p(n)e_p^-(n)\,, \qquad \hat{x}_p(n/n\text{-}1) = \hat{x}_{p\text{-}1}(n/n\text{-}1) + g_p(n\text{-}1)e_p^-(n/n\text{-}1)$$

This implies the following recursions for the estimation errors

$$e_p(n) = e_{p\text{-}1}(n) - g_p(n)e_p^-(n)\,, \qquad e_p(n/n\text{-}1) = e_{p\text{-}1}(n/n\text{-}1) - g_p(n\text{-}1)e_p^-(n/n\text{-}1)$$

Finally, the time updating Eq. (7.15.62) of the lattice weights takes the form

$$\mathbf{g}_p(n) = L_p(n/n\text{-}1)^{-T}\mathbf{g}_p(n\text{-}1) + e_p(n/n\text{-}1)D_p^-(n)^{-1}\mathbf{e}_p^-(n)$$

and extracting the last component, we obtain

$$g_p(n) = g_p(n\text{-}1) + e_p(n/n\text{-}1)\frac{e_p^-(n)}{E_p^-(n)}$$

RLS lattice and gradient adaptive lattice filters may be used in any Wiener filtering application. Their attractive features are: (a) computational *efficiency;* (b) very *fast* rate of convergence, which is essentially *independent* of the eigenvalue spread of the input covariance matrix; (c) *modularity* of structure admitting parallel VLSI implementations [146–154]; and (d) numerical *stability and accuracy* under quantization.

Problems

Problem 7.1: Computer Experiment

(a) Reproduce the results of Fig. 7.3.

(b) On the same graph of part (a), plot the theoretical convergence curve of the weight $h(n)$ obtained by using Eq. (7.2.8).

(c) Using 10 different realizations of x_n and y_n, compute 10 different realizations of the adaptive weight of Eq. (7.3.2). Compute the average weight over the 10 realizations and plot it versus n, together with the theoretical weight of Eq. (7.2.8). Use $\mu = 0.03$.

(d) Reproduce the results of Fig. 7.7.

Problem 7.2:

In steered adaptive arrays [16] and other applications, one has to solve a constrained Wiener filtering problem. Suppose the $(M+1)$-dimensional weight vector $\mathbf{h} = [h_0, h_1, \ldots, h_M]^T$ satisfies the L linear constraints $\mathbf{c}_i^T\mathbf{h} = f_i$, $i = 1, \ldots, L$, where

$L \leq M$ and $\mathbf{c}_i$ are given $(M+1)$ dimensional vectors and f_i given scalars. The set of constraints may be written compactly $C^T\mathbf{h} = \mathbf{f}$, where $C = [\mathbf{c}_1, \ldots, \mathbf{c}_L]$ and $\mathbf{f} = [f_1, \ldots, f_L]^T$.

(a) Show that the solution of the minimization problem $\mathcal{E} = E[e_n^2] = min$ subject to the constraint $C^T\mathbf{h} = \mathbf{f}$ is given by

$$\mathbf{h} = \mathbf{h}_u + R^{-1}C(C^TR^{-1}C)^{-1}(\mathbf{f} - C^T\mathbf{h}_u)$$

where $\mathbf{h}_u = R^{-1}\mathbf{r}$ is the unconstrained Wiener solution and $R = E[\mathbf{y}(n)\mathbf{y}(n)^T]$, $\mathbf{r} = E[x_n\mathbf{y}(n)^T]$.

(b) In an adaptive implementation, $\mathbf{h}(n+1) = \mathbf{h}(n) + \Delta\mathbf{h}(n)$, the constraint must be satisfied at each iteration. The time update term, therefore, must satisfy $C^T\Delta\mathbf{h}(n) = 0$. Show that the following (gradient projection) choice satisfies this condition

$$\Delta\mathbf{h}(n) = -\mu P\frac{\partial\mathcal{E}}{\partial\mathbf{h}(n)}, \quad P = I - C(C^TC)^{-1}C$$

Moreover, show that this choice moves the performance index closer to its minimum at each iteration.

(c) Show that the resulting difference equation can be written as

$$\mathbf{h}(n+1) = P(\mathbf{h}(n) - 2\mu R\mathbf{h}(n) + 2\mu\mathbf{r}) + \mathbf{h}_{LS}$$

where $\mathbf{h}_{LS} = C(C^TC)^{-1}\mathbf{f}$ is recognized as the *least-squares* solution of the linear equation $C^T\mathbf{h} = \mathbf{f}$. And, show that $C^T\mathbf{h}(n+1) = \mathbf{f}$.

(d) Show that the LMS adaptive algorithm resulting by dropping the expectation values is

$$\mathbf{h}(n+1) = P(\mathbf{h}(n) - 2\mu e_n\mathbf{y}(n)) + \mathbf{h}_{LS}$$

Problem 7.3:

Rederive the results in parts (c) and (d) of Problem 7.2 using the following approach. Introduce a Lagrange multiplier vector $\boldsymbol{\lambda} = [\lambda_1, \ldots, \lambda_L]^T$ into the performance index enforcing the constraint equations; that is, $\mathcal{E} = E[e_n^2] + \boldsymbol{\lambda}^T(\mathbf{f} - C^T\mathbf{h})$. Show that the *ordinary* unconstrained gradient descent $\mathbf{h}(n+1) = \mathbf{h}(n) - \mu\partial\mathcal{E}/\partial\mathbf{h}(n)$ gives rise to the difference equation

$$\mathbf{h}(n+1) = (I - 2\mu R)\mathbf{h}(n) + 2\mu\mathbf{r} - \mu C\boldsymbol{\lambda}(n)$$

Impose the constraint $C^T\mathbf{h}(n+1) = \mathbf{f}$, eliminate $\boldsymbol{\lambda}(n)$, and show that this equation is equivalent to that in part (c) of the previous problem.

Problem 7.4:

Verify that Eq. (7.6.5) is the solution of Eq. (7.6.4).

Problem 7.5:
Consider an adaptive filter with two taps:

$$\hat{x}_n = h_0(n)y_n + h_1(n)y_{n-1} = [h_0(n), h_1(n)]\begin{bmatrix} y_n \\ y_{n-1} \end{bmatrix} = \mathbf{h}(n)^T\mathbf{y}(n)$$

The optimal filter weights are found adaptively by the gradient descent algorithm

$$\mathbf{h}(n+1) = \mathbf{h}(n) - \mu\frac{\partial\mathcal{E}}{\partial\mathbf{h}(n)}$$

where $\mathcal{E} = E[e_n^2]$, and e_n is the estimation error.

(a) Show that the above difference equation may be written as

$$\mathbf{h}(n+1) = \mathbf{h}(n) + 2\mu(\mathbf{r} - R\mathbf{h}(n))$$

where

$$\mathbf{r} = \begin{bmatrix} R_{xy}(0) \\ R_{xy}(1) \end{bmatrix}, \qquad R = \begin{bmatrix} R_{yy}(0) & R_{yy}(1) \\ R_{yy}(1) & R_{yy}(0) \end{bmatrix}$$

(b) Suppose $R_{xy}(0) = 10$, $R_{xy}(1) = 5$, $R_{yy}(0) = 3$, $R_{yy}(1) = 2$. Find the optimal weights $\mathbf{h} = \lim \mathbf{h}(n)$ as $n \to \infty$.

(c) Select $\mu = 1/6$. Explain why such a value is sufficiently small to guarantee convergence of the difference equation of part (a). What other values of μ also guarantee convergence?

(d) With $\mu = 1/6$, solve the difference equation of part (a) in closed form for $n = 0,1, \ldots$. Discuss the rate of convergence.

Problem 7.6:
Consider a single CCL as shown in Fig. 7.2.

(a) Suppose the reference signal is set equal to a unit step signal; that is, $y(n) = u(n)$. Show that the CCL will behave as a time-invariant linear filter with input x_n and output e_n. Determine the transfer function $H(z)$ from x_n to e_n.

(b) Find and interprete the poles and zeros of $H(z)$.

(c) Determine the range of μ-values for which $H(z)$ is stable.

Problem 7.7:
Repeat Problem 7.6 when the reference signal is the alternating unit step; that is, $y(n) = (-1)^n u(n)$.

Problem 7.8:
Let $\mathbf{h}_R$ and $\mathbf{h}_I$ be the real and imaginary parts of the complex weight vector $\mathbf{h} = \mathbf{h}_R + j\mathbf{h}_I$. Show that

$$\frac{\partial \mathcal{E}}{\partial \mathbf{h}^*} = \frac{1}{2}\left[\frac{\partial \mathcal{E}}{\partial \mathbf{h}_R} + j\frac{\partial \mathcal{E}}{\partial \mathbf{h}_I}\right]$$

Consider the simultaneous gradient descent with respect to $\mathbf{h}_R$ and $\mathbf{h}_I$; namely, $\mathbf{h}_R \rightarrow \mathbf{h}_R + \Delta\mathbf{h}_R$ and $\mathbf{h}_I \rightarrow \mathbf{h}_I + \Delta\mathbf{h}_I$, with

$$\Delta\mathbf{h}_R = -\mu\frac{\partial \mathcal{E}}{\partial \mathbf{h}_R}, \quad \Delta\mathbf{h}_I = -\mu\frac{\partial \mathcal{E}}{\partial \mathbf{h}_I}$$

Show that it is equivalent to the gradient descent $\mathbf{h} \rightarrow \mathbf{h} + \Delta\mathbf{h}$, where $\Delta\mathbf{h} = -2\mu\partial\mathcal{E}/\partial\mathbf{h}^*$. Note the conjugation and the factor of two.

Problem 7.9:
Using the transfer function of Eq. (7.9.3), derive an approximate expression for the 3-dB width of the notch. You may work to lowest order in μ.

Problem 7.10: Computer Experiment
Consider the noise canceling example discussed in Section 5.11 and in Problems 5.25–5.27 and defined by the following choice of parameters:

$$\omega_0 = 0.075\pi \text{ [rads/sample]}, \quad \phi = 0, \quad a_1 = -0.5, \quad a_2 = 0.8, \quad M = 4$$

(a) Generate a realization of the signals $x(n)$ and $y(n)$ and process them through the adaptive noise canceler of Section 7.9, using an Mth order adaptive filter and adaptation parameter μ. By trial and error select a value for μ that makes the LMS algorithm convergent, but not too small as to make the convergence too slow. Plot one of the filter weights $h_m(n)$ versus iteration number n, and compare the asymptotic value with the theoretical value obtained in Problem 5.26.

(b) After the weights have converged, plot 100 output samples of the error signal e_n, and observe the noise cancellation property.

(c) Repeat (a) and (b) using an adaptive filter of order $M = 6$.

Problem 7.11: Computer Experiment

(a) Plot the magnitude of the frequency response of the adaptive noise canceler notch filter of Eq. (7.9.3) versus frequency $\omega (z = e^{j\omega})$. Generate several such plots for various values of μ and observe the effect of μ on the width of the notch.

(b) Let $x(n) = e^{j\omega_0 n}$, and $y(n) = Ae^{j\omega_0 n}$ and select the parameters as

$$\omega_0 = 0.075\pi, \quad M = 2, \quad A = 0.01, \quad \mu = 0.1$$

Process $x(n)$ and $y(n)$ through the adaptive noise canceler of Section 7.9, and plot the output $e(n)$ versus n and observe the cancellation of the signal $x(n)$ due to the notch filter created by the presence of the weak sinusoidal reference signal $y(n)$.

Problem 7.12: Computer Experiment
Let $x(n) = x_1(n) + x_2(n)$, where $x_1(n)$ is a narrowband component defined by

$$x_1(n) = \sin(\omega_0 n + \phi), \qquad \omega_0 = 0.075\pi \text{ [rads/sample]}$$

where ϕ is a random phase uniformly distributed over $[0,2\pi]$, and $x_2(n)$ is a fairly broadband component generated by sending zero-mean, unit-variance, white noise $\epsilon(n)$ through the filter

$$x_2(n) = \epsilon(n) + 2\epsilon(n-1) + \epsilon(n-2)$$

(a) Compute the autorcorrelation functions of $x_1(n)$ and $x_2(n)$, and sketch them versus lag k. Based on this computation, select a value for the delay Δ to be used in the adaptive line enhancer discussed in Section 7.10.

(b) Generate a realization of $x(n)$ and process it through the ALE with an appropriately chosen adaptation parameter μ. Plot the output signals $\hat{x}(n)$ and $e(n)$ and compare them with the components $x_1(n)$ and $x_2(n)$, respectively.

Problem 7.13:
The response of the ALE to an input sinusoid in noise can be studied as follows: Let the input be

$$x_n = A_1 \exp(j\omega_1 n + \phi) + v_n$$

where ϕ is a random phase independent of the zero-mean white noise v_n. The optimum Wiener filter weights of the ALE are given by

$$\mathbf{h} = R^{-1}\mathbf{r}$$

where $R_{ij} = R_{xx}(i-j)$ and $r_i = R_{xx}(i+\Delta)$, as discussed in Section 7.10.

(a) Using the methods of Section 6.2, show that the optimum filter $\mathbf{h}$ is given by

$$\mathbf{h} = \frac{e^{j\omega_1\Delta}}{\dfrac{\sigma_v^2}{P_1} + M + 1}\,\mathbf{s}_{\omega_1}$$

where the phasing vector $\mathbf{s}_{\omega_1}$ was defined in Section 6.2, and $P_1 = |A_1|^2$ is the power of the sinusoid.

(b) Show that the mean output power of the ALE is given by

$$E[|\hat{x}_n|^2] = \mathbf{h}^\dagger R\mathbf{h} = \sigma_v^2\mathbf{h}^\dagger\mathbf{h} + P_1|\mathbf{h}^\dagger\mathbf{s}_{\omega_1}|^2$$

(c) Show that the SNR at the output is enhanced by a factor $M + 1$ over the SNR at the input; that is, show that

$$(\mathrm{SNR})_{\mathrm{out}} = \frac{P_1|\mathbf{h}^{\dagger}\mathbf{s}_{\omega_1}|^2}{\sigma_v^2 \mathbf{h}^{\dagger}\mathbf{h}} = \frac{P_1}{\sigma_v^2}(M + 1) = (M + 1)\,(\mathrm{SNR})_{\mathrm{in}}$$

(d) Derive an expression for the eigenvalue spread $\lambda_{\max}/\lambda_{\min}$ in terms of the parameters σ_v^2, P_1, and M.

(e) Show that if the delay Δ is removed; that is, $\Delta = 0$, then the optimal weight vector becomes equal to the unit vector

$$\mathbf{h} = [1,0,0, \ldots ,0]^T$$

and that this choice corresponds to complete cancellation of the input signal $x(n)$ from the output $e(n)$.

Problem 7.14: Computer Experiment

Consider the autoregressive process y_n generated by the difference equation

$$y_n = -a_1 y_{n-1} - a_2 y_{n-2} + \epsilon_n$$

where $a_1 = -1.6$, $a_2 = 0.8$, and ϵ_n is zero-mean, unit-variance, white noise. Generate a realization of y_n and process it through the LMS adaptive predictor of order 2, as discussed in Section 7.11. Use a value for the adaptation parameter μ of your own choice. Plot the adaptive prediction coefficients $a_1(n)$ and $a_2(n)$ versus n, and compare their converged values with the theoretical values given above.

Problem 7.15:

The adaptive predictor may be considered as the linearly constrained minimization problem $\mathcal{E} = E[e_n^2] = min$ subject to the constraint that the first element of $\mathbf{a} = [1,a_1, \ldots ,a_M]^T$ be unity. This constraint may be written compactly $\mathbf{u}^T\mathbf{a} = 1$, where $\mathbf{u} = [1,0, \ldots ,0]^T$. Rederive the adaptation equations of Section 7.11 using the formalism and results of Problem 7.2.

Problem 7.16: Computer Experiment

A complex-valued version of the LMS adaptive predictor of Section 7.11 is defined by

$$e_n = y_n + a_1(n)y_{n-1} + a_2(n)y_{n-2} + \cdots + a_M(n)y_{n-M}$$

$$a_m(n + 1) = a_m(n) - 2\mu e_n y_{n-m}^*, \quad m = 1,2, \ldots ,M$$

Let y_n consist of two complex sinusoids in zero-mean white noise

$$y_n = A_1 e^{j\omega_1 n} + A_2 e^{j\omega_2 n} + v_n$$

where the frequencies and the SNRs are

$$\omega_1 = 0.3\pi, \ \omega_2 = 0.7\pi \text{ [rads/sample]}$$

$$10 \log_{10}[|A_1|^2/\sigma_v^2] = 10 \log_{10}[|A_2|^2/\sigma_v^2] = 20 \text{ dB}$$

(a) Generate a realization of y_n and process it through an Mth order LMS adaptive predictor using an adaptation constant μ. Experiment with several choices of M and μ. In each case, stop the algorithm after convergence has taken place and plot the AR spectrum $S(\omega) = 1/|A(\omega)|^2$ versus frequency ω. Discuss your results.

(b) Using the same realization of y_n, iterate the adaptive Pisarenko algorithm defined by Eqs. (7.12.5) and (7.12.6). After convergence of the Pisarenko weights, plot the Pisarenko spectrum estimate $S(\omega) = 1/|A(\omega)|^2$ versus frequency ω.

(c) Repeat (a) and (b) when the SNR of the sinewaves is lowered to 0 dB. Compare the adaptive AR and Pisarenko methods.

Problem 7.17: Computer Experiment
Reproduce the results of Figs. 7.19 and 7.20.

Problem 7.18:
Derive Eqs. (7.14.9) and (7.14.10) that describe the operation of the adaptive linear combiner in the decorrelated basis provided by the Gram–Schmidt preprocessor.

Problem 7.19: Computer Experiment
Reproduce the results of Figs. 7.22 and 7.23.

Problem 7.20:
What is the exact operational count of the conventional RLS algorithm listed in Section 7.15? Note that the inverse matrices P_0 and P_1 are symmetric and thus only half of them need be updated.

Problem 7.21:
Verify the solution (7.15.56) for the rank-one updating of the LU factors L_0 and L_1. Also verify that Eq. (7.15.58) is equivalent to Eq. (7.15.54).

Problem 7.22: Computer Experiment
Reproduce the results of Fig. 7.24. Carry out the same experiment (with the same input data) using the conventional RLS algorithm and compare with FAEST. Carry out both experiments with various values of λ, and comment on the results.

Problem 7.23: Computer Experiment
Reproduce the results of Fig. 7.25.

References

1. B. Widrow and M. Hoff, Adaptive Switching Circuits, *IRE Wescon Conv. Rec.*, pt. 4, 96–104 (1960).
2. B. Widrow, Adaptive Filters, in R. Kalman and N. DeClaris, Eds., *Aspects of Network and System Theory*, New York, Holt, Rinehart and Winston, 1971.
3. M. Honig and D. Messerschmitt, *Adaptive Filters: Structures, Algorithms, and Applications*, Boston, Kluwer Academic, 1984.
4. C. F. N. Cowan and P. M. Grant, *Adaptive Filters*, Englewood Cliffs, NJ, Prentice-Hall, 1985.
5. A. A. Giordano and F. M. Hsu, *Least Square Estimation with Applications to Digital Signal Processing*, New York, Wiley, 1985.
6. B. Widrow and S. D. Stearns, *Adaptive Signal Processing*, Englewood Cliffs, NJ, Prentice-Hall, 1985.
7. S. T. Alexander, *Adaptive Signal Processing*, New York, Springer-Verlag, 1986.
8. S. Haykin, *Adaptive Filter Theory*, Englewood Cliffs, NJ, Prentice-Hall, 1986.
9. J. R. Treichler, C. R. Johnson, and M. G. Larimore, *Theory and Design of Adaptive Filters*, New York, Wiley, 1987.
10. B. Widrow, et al., Adaptive Noise Cancelling—Principles and Applications, *Proc. IEEE*, **63**, 1692–1716 (1975).
11. B. Widrow, et al., Adaptive Antenna Systems, *Proc IEEE*, **55**, 2143–2159 (1967).
12. S. P. Applebaum, Adaptive Arrays, *IEEE Trans. Antennas Prop.*, **AP-24**, 585–598 (1976).
13. F. Gabriel, Adaptive Arrays—An Introduction, *Proc. IEEE*, **64**, 239–272 (1976).
14. A. M. Vural and M. T. Stark, A Summary and the Present Status of Adaptive Array Processing Techniques, *19th IEEE Conference on Decision and Control*, 931–938 (1980).
15. R. A. Monzingo and T. W. Miller, *Introduction to Adaptive Arrays*, New York, Wiley, 1980.
16. J. E. Hudson, *Adaptive Array Principles*, Stevenage, UK, Peter Peregrinus, 1981.
17. D. E. N. Davies, K. G. Corless, D. S. Hicks, and K. Milne, Array Signal Processing, in A. W. Rudge, K. Milne, A. D. Olver, and P. Knight, Eds., *The Handbook of Antenna Design*, vol. 2, London, Peter Peregrinus, 1983.
18. B. Widrow, et al., Stationary and Nonstationary Learning Characteristics of the LMS Adaptive Filter, *Proc. IEEE*, **64**, 1151–1162 (1976).
19. R. W. Lucky, J. Salz, and E. J. Weldon, Jr., *Principles of Data Communication*, New York, McGraw-Hill, 1968.
20. J. G. Proakis, *Digital Communications*, New York, McGraw-Hill, 1983.
21. A. P. Clark, *Equalizers for Digital Modems*, New York, Halsted Press, 1985.
22. N. A. M. Vierhoeckx, H. Elzen, F. Snijders, and P. Gerwen, Digital Echo Cancellation for Baseband Data Transmission, *IEEE Trans. Acoust., Speech, Signal Process.*, **ASSP-27**, 768–781 (1979).
23. M. M. Sondhi and D. A. Berkley, Silencing Echoes on the Telephone Network, *Proc. IEEE*, **66**, 948–963 (1980).

24. D. L. Duttweiler and Y. S. Chen, A Single Chip VLSI Echo Canceler, *Bell Syst. Tech. J.*, **59,** 149 (1980).

25. D. L. Duttweiler, Bell's Echo-Killer Chip, *IEEE Spectrum,* **17,** 34–37 (1980).

26. D. G. Messerschmitt, Echo Cancellation in Speech and Data Transmission, *IEEE J. Selected Areas in Commun.,* **SAC-2,** 283 (1984).

27. C. W. Gritton and D. W. Lin, Echo Cancellation Algorithms, *ASSP Magazine,* **1,** no.2, 30 (1984).

28. W. A. Harrison, J. S. Lim, and E. Singer, A New Application of Adaptive Noise Cancellation, *IEEE Trans. Acoust., Speech, Signal Process.,* **ASSP-34,** 21 (1986).

29. G. S. Müller and C. K. Pauw, Acoustic Noise Cancellation, *Proc. 1986 Int. Conf. Acoust., Speech, Signal Process.,* Tokyo, p. 913.

30. J. J. Rodriguez, J. S. Lim, and E. Singer, Adaptive Noise Reduction in Aircraft Communication Systems, *Proc. 1987 Int. Conf. Acoust., Speech, Signal Process.,* Dallas, p. 169.

31. G. A. Powell, P. Darlington, and P. D. Wheeler, Practical Adaptive Noise Reduction in the Aircraft Cockpit Environment, *Proc. 1987 Int. Conf. Acoust., Speech, Signal Process.,* Dallas, p. 173.

32. J. Dunlop, M. Al-Kindi, and L. Virr, Application of Adaptive Noise Cancelling to Diver Voice Communications, *Proc. 1987 Int. Conf. Acoust., Speech, Signal Process.,* Dallas, p. 1708.

33. J. V. Candy, T. Casper, and R. Kane, Plasma Estimation: A Noise Cancelling Application, *Automatica,* **22,** 223 (1986).

34. W. Ciciora, G. Sgrignoli, and W. Thomas, A Tutorial on Ghost Cancelling in Television Systems, *IEEE Trans. Consum. Electron.,* **CE-25,** 9 (1979).

35. J. Glover, Adaptive Noise Cancelling Applied to Sinusoidal Interferences, *IEEE Trans. Acoust., Speech, Signal Process.,* **ASSP-25,** 484–491 (1977).

36. B. Widrow, J. McCool, and M. Ball, The Complex LMS Algorithm, *Proc. IEEE,* **63,** pp. 719–720 (1975).

37. B. Widrow, K. Duvall, R. Gooch, and W. Newman, Signal Cancellation Phenomena in Adaptive Antennas: Causes and Cures, *IEEE Trans. Antennas Prop.,* **AP-30,** 469–478 (1982).

38. M. J. Shensa, Non-Wiener Solutions of Adaptive Noise Canceller with a Noisy Reference, *IEEE Trans. Acoust., Speech, Signal Process.,* **ASSP-28,** 468–473 (1980).

39. S. J. Elliot and P. Darlington, Adaptive Cancellation of Periodic, Synchronously Sampled Interference, *IEEE Trans. Acoust., Speech, Signal Process.,* **ASSP-33,** 715 (1985).

40. S. J. Orfanidis, F. Aafif, and E. Micheli-Tzanakou, Visual Evoked Potential Extraction by Adaptive Filtering, *Proc. 9th IEEE EMBS Conf.,* Boston, November 1987.

41. J. R. Treichler, Transient and Convergent Behavior of the Adaptive Line Enhancer, *IEEE Trans. Acoust., Speech, Signal Process.,* **ASSP-27,** 53–62 (1979).

42. D. W. Tufts, L. J. Griffiths, B. Widrow, J. Glover, J. McCool, and J. Treichler, Adaptive Line Enhancement and Spectrum Analysis, *Proc. IEEE,* **65,** 169 (1977).

43. J. R. Zeidler, et al., Adaptive Enhancement of Multiple Sinusoids in Uncorrelated Noise, *IEEE Trans. Acoust., Speech, Signal Process.,* **ASSP-26,** 240–254 (1978).

44. L. J. Griffiths, Rapid Measurement of Digital Instantaneous Frequency, *IEEE Trans. Acoust., Speech, Signal Process.,* **ASSP-23,** 207–222 (1975).

45. D. Morgan and S. Craig, Real-Time Linear Prediction Using the Least Mean Square Gradient Algorithm, *IEEE Trans. Acoust., Speech, Signal Process.*, **ASSP-24,** 494–507 (1976).

46. P. Eykhoff, *System Identification: Parameter and State Estimation,* New York, Wiley, 1974.

47. K. J. Astrom and P. Eykhoff, System Identification—A Survey, *Automatica,* **7,** 123–162 (1971).

48. G. C. Goodwin and R. L. Payne, *Dynamic System Identification, Experimental Design and Data Analysis,* New York, Academic, 1977.

49. L. Ljung and T. Söderström, *Theory and Practice of Recursive Identification,* Cambridge, MA, MIT Press, 1983.

50. L. Ljung, *System Identification: Theory for the User,* Englewood Cliffs, NJ, Prentice-Hall, 1987.

51. K. J. Ästrom and B. Wittenmark, *Computer Controlled Systems,* Englewood Cliffs, NJ, Prentice-Hall, 1984.

52. K. J. Ästrom, Adaptive Feedback Control, *Proc. IEEE,* **75,** 185 (1987).

53. N. Sundararajan and R. C. Montgomery, Identification of Structural Dynamics Systems Using Least-Squares Lattice Filters, *J. Guidance and Control,* **6,** 374 (1983).

54. N. Sundararajan, J. P. Williams, and R. C. Montgomery, Adaptive Modal Control of Structural Dynamic Systems Using Recursive Lattice Filters, *J. Guidance and Control,* **8,** 223 (1985).

55. W. S. Hodgkiss and J. A. Presley, Jr., Adaptive Tracking of Multiple Sinusoids whose Power Levels are Widely Separated, *IEEE Trans. Acoust., Speech, Signal Process.*, **ASSP-29,** 710–721 (1981).

56. A. Isaksson, A. Wennberg, and L. H. Zetterberg, Computer Analysis of EEG Signals with Parametric Models, *Proc. IEEE,* **69,** 451–461 (1981).

57. T. Bohlin, Analysis of EEG Signals with Changing Spectra using a Short-Word Kalman Estimator, *Math. Biosci.*, **35,** 221–259 (1977).

58. W. F. Gabriel, Spectral Analysis and Adaptive Array Superresolution Techniques, *Proc. IEEE,* **68,** 654–666 (June 1980).

59. W. F. Gabriel, Using Spectral Estimation Techniques in Adaptive Processing Antenna Systems, *IEEE Trans. Antennas Propag.*, **AP-34,** 291 (1986).

60. F. M. Hsu and A. A. Giordano, Digital Whitening Techniques for Improving Spread Spectrum Communications Performance in the Presence of Narrowband Jamming and Interference, *IEEE Trans. Commun.*, **COM-26,** 209 (1978).

61. J. W. Ketchum and J. G. Proakis, Adaptive Algorithms for Estimating and Suppressing Narrow-Band Interference in PN Spread-Spectrum Systems, *IEEE Trans. Commun.*, **COM-30,** part I, 913 (1982).

62. L. M. Li and L. B. Milstein, Rejection of Narrow-Band Interference in PN Spread-Spectrum Systems Using Transversal Filters, *IEEE Trans. Commun.*, **COM-30,** 925 (1982).

63. R. A. Iltis and L. B. Milstein. Performance Analysis of Narrow-Band Interference Rejection Techniques in DS Spread-Spectrum Systems, *IEEE Trans. Commun.*, **COM-32,** 1169 (1984).

64. E. Masry, Closed-Form Analytical Results for the Rejection of Narrow-Band Interference in PN Spread-Spectrum Systems—Part I: Linear Prediction Filters, *IEEE Trans. Commun.*, **COM-32,** 888 (1984).
65. E. Masry, Closed-Form Analytical Results for the Rejection of Narrow-Band Interference in PN Spread-Spectrum Systems—Part II: Linear Interpolation Filters, *IEEE Trans. Commun.*, **COM-33,** 10 (1985).
66. A. Reichman and R. A. Scholtz, Adaptive Spread-Spectrum Systems Using Least-Squares Lattice Filters, *IEEE J. Selected Areas in Commun.*, **SAC-3,** 652 (1985).
67. P. A. Thompson, An Adaptive Spectral Analysis Technique for Unbiased Frequency Estimation in the Presence of White Noise, *Proc. 13th Asilomar Conf. Circuits, Systems, and Computers,* 529 (Nov. 1979).
68. M. G. Larimore and R. J. Calvert, Convergence Studies of Thompson's Unbiased Adaptive Spectral Estimator, *Proc. 14th Asilomar Conf. Circuits, Systems, and Computers,* 258 (Nov. 1980).
69. V. U. Reddy, B. Egard, and T. Kailath, Least Squares Type Algorithm for Adaptive Implementation of Pisarenko's Harmonic Retrieval Method, *IEEE Trans. Acoust., Speech, Signal Process.*, **ASSP-30,** 399–405 (June 1982).
70. F. K. Soong and A. M. Petersen, On the High Resolution and Unbiased Frequency Estimates of Sinusoids in White Noise—A New Adaptive Approach, *Proc. IEEE Int. Conf. Acoust., Speech, Signal Process.*, 1362 (April 1982).
71. A. Cantoni and L. Godara, Resolving the Directions of Sources in a Correlated Field Incident on an Array, *J. Acoust., Soc. Am.*, **67,** 1247–1255 (1980).
72. S. J. Orfanidis and L. M. Vail, Zero-Tracking Adaptation Algorithms, *Proc. ASSP Spectrum Estimation Workshop, II,* Tampa, FL (November 1983).
73. S. J. Orfanidis and L. M. Vail, Zero Tracking Adaptive Filters, *IEEE Trans. Acoust., Speech, Signal Process.*, **ASSP-34,** 1566 (1986).
74. Z. Rogowski, I. Gath, and E. Bental, On the Prediction of Epileptic Seizures, *Biol. Cybernetics,* **42,** 9–15 (1981).
75. A. V. Oppenheim and R. W. Schafer, *Digital Signal Processing,* Englewood Cliffs, NJ, Prentice-Hall, 1975.
76. L. J. Griffiths, A Continuously-Adaptive Filter Implemented as a Lattice Structure, *Int. Conf. Acoust., Speech, Signal Processing,* Hartford CT, 87–90 (1977).
77. J. Makhoul, A Class of All-Zero Lattice Digital Filters: Properties and Applications, *IEEE Trans. Acoust., Speech, Signal Process.*, **ASSP-26,** 304–314 (1978).
78. E. H. Satorius and S. T. Alexander, Channel Equalization Using Adaptive Lattice Algorithms, *IEEE Trans. Commun.*, **COM-27,** 899–905 (1979).
79. C. J. Gibson and S. Haykin, Learning Characteristics of Adaptive Lattice Filtering Algorithms, *IEEE Trans. Acoust., Speech, Signal Process.*, **ASSP-28,** 681–691 (1980).
80. M. L. Honig and D. G. Messerschmidt, Convergence Properties of the Adaptive Digital Lattice Filter, *IEEE Trans. Acoust., Speech, Signal Process.*, **ASSP-29,** 642–653 (1981).
81. R. S. Medaugh and L. J. Griffiths, A Comparison of Two Fast Linear Predictors, *Proc. IEEE Int. Conf. Acoust., Speech, Signal Processing,* Atlanta, GA (March 1981), 293–296.

82. C. Giraudon, Results on Active Sonar Optimum Array Processing, in J. W. R. Griffiths, et al., Eds., *Signal Processing,* New York, Academic, 1973.

83. W. D. White, Cascade Preprocessors for Adaptive Antennas, *IEEE Trans. Antennas Propag.,* **AP-24,** 670 (1976).

84. D. H. Brandwood and C. J. Tarran, Adaptive Arrays for Communications, *IEEE Proc.,* **129,** Pt. F, 223 (1982).

85. J. G. McWhirter and T. J. Shepherd, Adaptive Algorithms in the Space and Time Domains, *IEE Proc.,* **130,** Pts. F and H, 17 (1983).

86. F. Ling, D. Manolakis, and J. G. Proakis, A Recursive Modified Gram-Schmidt Algorithm for Least-Squares Estimation, *IEEE Trans. Acoust., Speech, Signal Process.,* **ASSP-34,** 829 (1986).

87. G. H. Golub and C. F. Van Loan, *Matrix Computations,* Baltimore, Johns Hopkins University Press, 1983.

88. D. D. Falconer and L. Ljung, Application of Fast Kalman Estimation to Adaptive Equalization, *IEEE Trans. Commun.,* **COM-26,** 1439–1446 (1976).

89. L. Ljung, M. Morf, and D. Falconer, Fast Calculations of Gain Matrices for Recursive Estimation Schemes, *Int. J. Control,* **27,** 1–19 (1978).

90. G. C. Carayannis, D. Manolakis, and N. Kalouptsidis, A Fast Sequential Algorithm for Least-Squares Filtering and Prediction, *IEEE Trans. Acoust., Speech, Signal Process.,* **ASSP-31,** 1394 (1983).

91. J. Cioffi and T. Kailath, Fast, Recursive Least-Squares, Transversal Filters for Adaptive Processing, *IEEE Trans. Acoust., Speech, Signal Process.,* **ASSP-34,** 304 (1984).

92. L. S. DeJong, Numerical Aspects of Recursive Realization Algorithms, *SIAM J. Control Optimiz.,* **16,** 646 (1978).

93. M. S. Mueller, On the Rapid Initial Convergence of Least-Squares Equalizer Adjustment Algorithms, *Bell Syst. Tech. J.,* **60,** 2345 (1981).

94. D. W. Lin, On the Digital Implementation of the Fast Kalman Algorithm, *IEEE Trans. Acoust., Speech, Signal Process.,* **ASSP-32,** 998 (1984).

95. F. Ling and J. G. Proakis, Numerical Accuracy and Stability: Two Problems of Adaptive Estimation Algorithms Caused by Round-Off Error, *Proc. 1984 IEEE Int. Conf. Acoust., Speech, Signal Process.,* San Diego, CA, p. 30.3.1.

96. C. G. Samson and V. U. Reddy, Fixed Point Error Analysis of the Normalized Ladder Algorithm, *IEEE Trans. Acoust., Speech, Signal Process.,* **ASSP-31,** 1177 (1983).

97. S. Ljung and L. Ljung, Error Propagation Properties of Recursive Least-Squares Adaptation Algorithms, *Automatica,* **21,** 157 (1985).

98. D. Manolakis, G. Carayannis, and V. Zervas, Fast RLS Algorithms for Adaptive Filtering: Some Engineering Problems, *Proc. 1987 IEEE Int. Conf. Circuits and Systems,* Philadelphia, PA, p. 985.

99. S. H. Ardalan and S. T. Alexander, Fixed-Point Roundoff Error Analysis of the Exponentially Windowed RLS Algorithm for Time-Varying Systems, *IEEE Trans. Acoust., Speech, Signal Process.,* **ASSP-35,** 770 (1987).

100. C. Caraiscos and B. Liu, A Roundoff Error Analysis of the LMS Adaptive Algorithm, *IEEE Trans. Acoust., Speech, Signal Process.,* **ASSP-32,** 34 (1984).

101. J. M. Cioffi, Limited-Precision Effects in Adaptive Filtering, *IEEE Trans. Circ. Syst.*, **CAS-34,** 821 (1987).
102. M. Morf and D. T. L. Lee, Recursive Least-Squares Ladder Forms for Fast Parameter Tracking, *Proc. 17th IEEE Conf. Decision Contr.*, 1326 (1979)
103. E. H. Satorius and M. J. Shensa, Recursive Lattice Filters—A Brief Overview, *Proc. 19th IEEE Conf. Decision Contr.*, 955–959 (1980).
104. D. Lee, M. Morf, and B. Friedlander, Recursive Square-Root Ladder Estimation Algorithms, *IEEE Trans. Acoust., Speech, Signal Process.*, **ASSP-29,** 627–641 (1981).
105. M. J. Shensa, Recursive Least-Squares Lattice Algorithms: A Geometrical Approach, *IEEE Trans. Autom. Control,* **AC-26,** 695–702 (1981).
106. E. H. Satorius and J. D. Pack, Application of Least-Squares Lattice Algorithms to Channel Equalization, *IEEE Trans. Commun.*, **COM-29,** 136–142 (1981).
107. E. Schichor, Fast Recursive Estimation Using the Lattice Structure, *Bell Syst. Tech. J.*, **61,** 97–115 (1981).
108. M. S. Mueller, Least-Squares Algorithms for Adaptive Equalizers, *Bell Syst. Tech. J.*, **60,** 1905–1925 (1981).
109. B. Friedlander, Lattice Filters for Adaptive Processing, *Proc. IEEE,* **70,** 829–867 (1982).
110. G. C. Carayannis, D. Manolakis, and N. Kalouptsidis, A Unified View of Parametric Processing Algorithms for Prewindowed Signals, *Signal Processing,* **10,** 335 (1986).
111. F. Ling, D. Manolakis, and J. G. Proakis, Numerically Robust Least-Squares Lattice-Ladder Algorithms with Direct Updating of the Reflection Coefficients, *IEEE Trans. Acoust., Speech, Signal Process.*, **ASSP-34,** 837 (1986).
112. P. E. Gill, G. H. Golub, W. Murray, and M. A. Saunders, Methods of Modifying Matrix Factorizations, *Math. Comp.*, **28,** 505 (1974).
113. P. E. Gill, W. Murray, and M. A. Saunders, Methods for Computing and Modifying the LVD Factors of a Matrix, *Math. Comp.*, **29,** 1051 (1975).
114. G. J. Bierman, *Factorization Methods for Discrete Sequential Estimation,* New York, Academic, 1977.
115. D. Godard, Channel Equalization Using a Kalman Filter for Fast Data Transmission, *IBM J. Res. Dev.*, **18,** 267–273, 1974.
116. R. D. Gitlin and F. R. Magee, Self-Orthogonalizing Adaptive Equalization Algorithms, *IEEE Trans. Commun.*, **COM-25,** 666 (1977).
117. R. W. Chang, A New Equalizer Structure for Fast Start-up Digital Communication, *Bell Syst. Tech. J.*, **50,** 1969–2014 (1971).
118. J. G. McWhirter and T. J. Shepherd, Least-Squares Lattice Algorithm for Adaptive Channel Equalization—A Simplified Derivation, *IEE Proc.*, **130,** Pt.F, 532 (1983).
119. J. Mendel, *Discrete Techniques of Parameter Estimation,* New York, Marcel Dekker, 1973.
120. L. E. Brennan, J. D. Mallet, and I. S. Reed, Adaptive Arrays in Airborne MTI Radar, *IEEE Trans. Antenn. Propag.*, **AP-24,** 607 (1976).
121. L. E. Brennan and I. S. Reed, Theory of Adaptive Radar, *IEEE Trans. Aerosp. Electron. Syst.*, **AES-9,** 237 (1973).

122. L. E. Brennan, J. D. Mallet, and I. S. Reed, Rapid Convergence Rate in Adaptive Arrays, *IEEE Trans. Aerosp. Electron. Syst.*, **AES-10,** 853 (1974).

123. J. Cioffi, When Do I Use an RLS Adaptive Filter? *Proc. 19th IEEE Asilomar Conf. Circ., Syst., Computers,* 1986, p. 636.

124. E. Eleftheriou and D. D. Falconer, Tracking Properties and Steady-State Performance of RLS Adaptive Filter Algorithms, *IEEE Trans. Acoust., Speech, Signal Process.,* **ASSP-34,** 1097 (1986).

125. G. H. Golub, Some Modified Matrix Eigenvalue Problems, *SIAM Rev.,* **15,** 318 (1973).

126. J. R. Bunch, C. P. Nielsen, and D. C. Sorensen, Rank-One Modification of the Symmetric Eigenproblem, *Numer. Math.,* **31,** 31 (1978).

127. K. J. Bathe and E. L. Wilson, *Numerical Methods in Finite Element Analysis,* Englewood Cliffs, NJ, Prentice-Hall, 1976.

128. B. N. Parlett, *The Symmetric Eigenvalue Problem,* Englewood Cliffs, NJ, Prentice-Hall, 1980.

129. W. Bühring, Adaptive Orthogonal Projection for Rapid Converging Interference Suppression, *Electron. Lett.,* **14,** 515 (1978).

130. N. L. Owsley, Adaptive Data Orthogonalization, *Proc. 1978 Int. Conf. Acoust., Speech, Signal Process.,* Tulsa, p. 109.

131. J. Karhunen, Adaptive Algorithms for Estimating Eigenvectors of Correlation Type Matrices, *Proc. 1984 Int. Conf. Acoust., Speech, Signal Process.,* San Diego, CA, p. 14.6.1.

132. Y. H. Hu, Adaptive Methods for Real Time Pisarenko Spectrum Estimate, *Proc. 1985 Int. Conf. Acoust., Speech, Signal Process.,* Tampa, FL, p. 105.

133. K. C. Sharman, T. S. Durranni and L. Vergara-Dominguez, Adaptive Algorithms for Eigenstructure Based Spectral Estimation and Filtering, *Proc. 1986 IEEE Int. Conf. Decision and Control,* Athens, p. 2224.

134. K. C. Sharman and T. S. Durrani, Eigenfilter Approaches to Adaptive Array Processing, *Proc. IEE, part F,* **130,** 22 (1983).

135. J. F. Yang and M. Kaveh, Adaptive Signal-Subspace Algorithms for Frequency Estimation and Tracking, *Proc. 1987 Int. Conf. Acoust., Speech, Signal Process.,* Dallas, p. 1593.

136. C. Samson, A Unified Treatment of Fast Algorithms for Identification, *Int. J. Control,* **35,** 909 (1982).

137. M. Honig, Recursive, Fixed-Order Covariance Least-Squares Algorithms, *Bell Syst. Tech. J.,* **62,** 2961 (1983).

138. H. Lev-Ari and T. Kailath, Least-Squares Adaptive Lattice and Transversal Filters: A Unified Geometric Theory, *IEEE Trans. Inform. Th.,* **IT-30,** 222 (1984).

139. N. Kalouptsidis, G. Carayannis, and D. Manolakis, Fast Design of FIR Least-Squares Filters with Optimum Lag, *IEEE Trans. Acoust., Speech, Signal Process.,* **ASSP-32,** 48 (1984).

140. N. Kalouptsidis, G. Carayannis, and D. Manolakis, Efficient Recursive-in-Order Least Squares FIR Filtering and Prediction, *IEEE Trans. Acoust., Speech, Signal Process.,* **ASSP-33,** 1175 (1985).

141. A. Nehorai and M. Morf, A Unified Derivation for Fast Estimation Algorithms by the Conjugate Direction Method, *Lin. Alg. Appl.,* **72,** 119 (1985).

142. J. D. Wang and H. J. Trussell, A Unified Derivation of the Fast RLS Algorithms, *Proc. 1986 Int. Conf. Acoust., Speech, Signal Process.*, Tokyo, p. 261.

143. S. T. Alexander, Fast Adaptive Filters: A Geometrical Approach, *ASSP Magazine*, **3,** no. 4, 18 (1986).

144. N. Kalouptsidis and S. Theodoridis, Fast Adaptive Least Squares Algorithms for Power Spectral Estimation, *IEEE Trans. Acoust., Speech, Signal Process.*, **ASSP-35,** 661 (1987).

145. D. Manolakis, F. Ling, and J. G. Proakis, Efficient Time-Recursive Least-Squares Algorithms for Finite-Memory Adaptive Filtering, *IEEE Trans. Circ. Syst.*, **CAS-34,** 400 (1987).

146. J. G. McWhirter, Recursive Least-Squares Minimization Using a Systolic Array, *Proc. SPIE, Real-Time Signal Processing IV*, **431,** 105 (1983).

147. F. Ling and J. G. Proakis, A Generalized Multichannel Least Squares Lattice Algorithm Based on Sequential Processing Stages, *IEEE Trans. Acoust., Speech, Signal Process.*, **ASSP-32,** 381 (1984).

148. C. R. Ward, A. J. Robson, P. J. Hargrave, and J. G. McWhirter, Application of a Systolic Array to Adaptive Beamforming, *IEE Proc.*, **131,** Pt. F, 638 (1984).

149. A. W. Bojanczyk, Systolic Implementation of the Lattice Algorithm for Least Squares Linear Prediction Problems, *Lin. Alg. Appl.*, **77,** 27 (1986).

150. H. Sakai, A Parallel Least-Squares Linear Prediction Method Based on the Circular Lattice Filter, *IEEE Trans. Acoust., Speech, Signal Process.*, **ASSP-34,** 640 (1986).

151. R. Schreiber, Implementation of Adaptive Array Algorithms, *IEEE Trans. Acoust., Speech, Signal Process.*, **ASSP-34,** 1038 (1986).

152. H. Kimura and T. Osada, Canonical Pipelining of Lattice Filters, *IEEE Trans. Acoust., Speech, Signal Process.*, **ASSP-35,** 878 (1987).

153. H. Lev-Ari, Modular Architectures for Adaptive Multichannel Lattice Algorithms, *IEEE Trans. Acoust., Speech, Signal Process.*, **ASSP-35,** 543 (1987).

154. T. H. Meng and D. G. Messerschmitt, Arbitrarily High Sampling Rate Adaptive Filters, *IEEE Trans. Acoust., Speech, Signal Process.*, **ASSP-35,** 455 (1987).

155. M. G. Bellanger, *Adaptive Digital Filters and Signal Analysis*, New York, Marcel Dekker, 1987.

156. S. J. Orfanidis, The Double/Direct RLS Lattice, *Proc. 1988 Int. Conf. Acoust., Speech, Signal Process.*, New York.

Appendix A
Random Number Generators

Uniform Random Number Generators

All computers have built-in routines for the generation of random numbers. They are implemented either as functions or subroutines, with typical names like **ran, rand, randu,** and **urand.** A call to such a routine generates a random number that is uniformly distributed in the range (0,1), with probability density shown below:

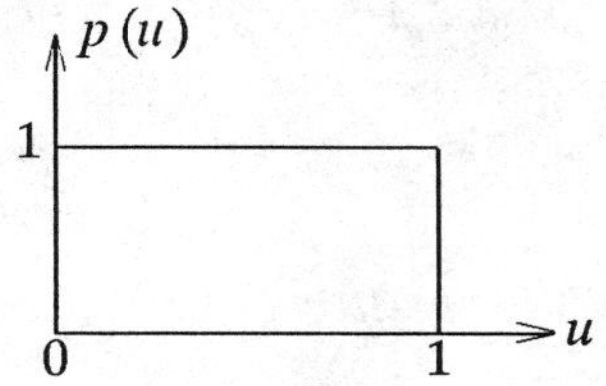

Typical subroutine inputs are:

1. An integer seed, *iseed*

Typical subroutine outputs are:

1. A uniform random number, u, in the range $0 < u < 1$
2. An updated value of *iseed*

In a typical call, *iseed* is used both as an input and an output, as follows:

$$u = ran(iseed)$$

Its effect is depicted below

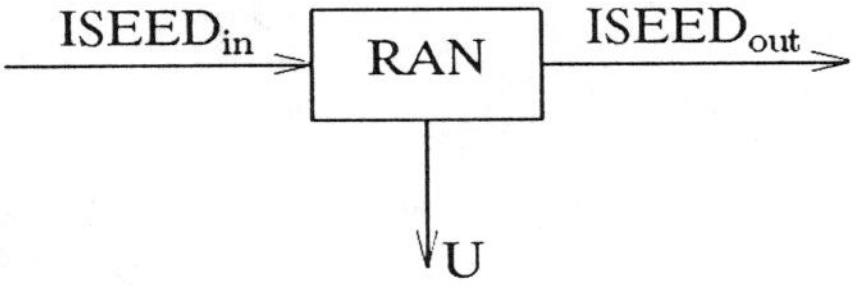

Starting with an initial value of *iseed,* subsequent calls of **ran** will produce a sequence of random numbers that are uniformly distributed in (0,1) and are mutually *independent,* as shown below

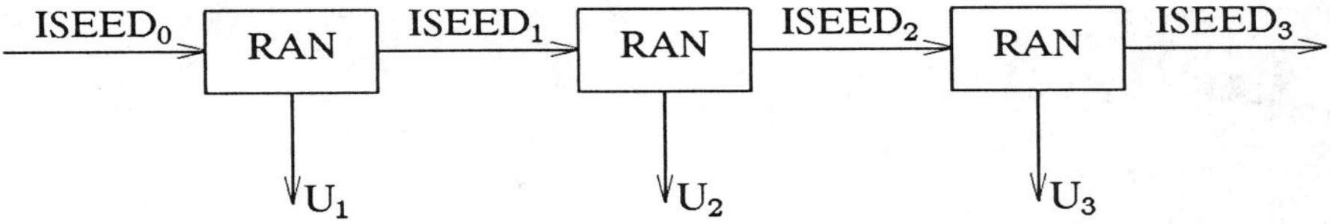

In some implementations, the seed is not explicitly available to the user but is updated internally; it is assigned static storage so that it is preserved across invocations of the routine. The maximal length of the generated sequence is algorithm dependent. There exist two basic types of algorithms for generating uniform random numbers:

1. Linear congruential generators
2. Shift-register sequence generators

The basic reference for both types is Knuth [1]; see also [2,3]. We will briefly discuss the first type that has been studied the most and is used in the built-in routines of computers. It should be mentioned, however, that for special purpose applications, such as very large simulations, there exist some very fast shift-register generators of extremely long lengths of the order of 2^{250} [4].

Linear Congruential Generators

Any sequence generated by a computer algorithm cannot possibly be truly random. But for all practical purposes it may behave as random, passing some standard tests of randomness. The linear congruential generator (LCG) algorithm is defined as follows:

1. Given integers a (the multiplier), c (the displacement), m (the modulus), and an initial integer seed I_0 in the range $0 \le I_0 \le m-1$, the algorithm computes the nth seed I_n and corresponding uniformly distributed random number u_n by the iteration:

2. $I_n = (aI_{n-1} + c)\,\mathrm{mod}(m)\,, \qquad u_n = \dfrac{I_n}{m}$

The modulo-m operation restricts the range of the seeds I_n to the interval $0 \le I_n \le m - 1$, and therefore, the resulting uniform random number is, strictly speaking, in the interval [0,1). The *maximum* possible length of such sequence is m. However, not every choice of $\{a,c,m\}$ will result in a maximal length sequence. There are certain guidelines for choosing $\{a,c,m\}$, discussed in [1], that will ensure maximal length sequences. Some examples are:

1. $I_n = (65539 I_{n-1}) \mathrm{mod}(2^{31})$. The routine RANDU in IBM's scientific subroutine package is based on this choice. Although it has been used widely for a long time, it has been found to possess undesirable nonrandom behavior. It is no longer recommended.
2. $I_n = (16807 I_{n-1}) \mathrm{mod}(2^{31} - 1)$. It is used widely, e.g., in the IMSL subroutine package.
3. $I_n = (69069 I_{n-1} + 1) \mathrm{mod}(2^{31})$. It is one of the best generators and is used in the CERN program library. See [5] for an assembly language IBM PC implementation that utilizes the 80-bit registers of the 8087 coprocessor.
4. $I_n = (25173 I_{n-1} + 13849) \mathrm{mod}(2^{16})$, is adequate for small simulations on 16-bit microcomputers.

The FORTRAN implementation of the last example is:

```
/* ran.for - uniform random number generator */

   function ran(iseed)

   integer a, c
   parameter (a = 25173, c = 13849, m = 65536)

   iseed = mod(a * iseed + c, m)
   ran = float(iseed) / float(m)

   return
   end
```

The implementation in C is:

```
/* ran.c - uniform random number generator */

#define a  25173
#define c  13849
#define m  65536

double ran(iseed)
long *iseed;
{
   *iseed = (a * *iseed + c) % m;
   return (double) *iseed / (double) m;
}
```

Note that *iseed* has been declared a pointer to long (4-byte) integer. In FORTRAN, this is the default length of integers; *iseed* is a pointer, because it must be passed in and out of the routine.

Gaussian Random Number Generators

It is remarkable that from uniform random numbers one can generate random numbers distributed according to *any* desired distribution. One method to do this is by *inversion.* Suppose we want to generate a random number x having probability density $p(x)$. The corresponding cumulative distribution function is

$$F(x) = \int_{-\infty}^{x} p(x')\,dx' = \text{Prob}[X \le x]$$

Given a uniform random number u, we can find x as the solution of

$$F(x) = u$$

that is, $x = F^{-1}(u)$. This method is convenient only if the inverse function $F^{-1}(x)$ is easy to compute. In particular, the method is not convenient for gaussian densities. There exist several methods for generating gaussian random numbers, such as the central limit theorem method, Box-Muller method, and others [1,2,6]. The first method is based on the *central limit theorem* which states that the sum of a large number of *independent* random numbers

$$u = u_1 + u_2 + u_3 + \cdots$$

is essentially gaussian, regardless of the distribution of the u_i. Actually, keeping only 12 terms in this sum gives a very good approximation to a gaussian random variable:

$$u = u_1 + u_2 + \cdots + u_{12}$$

If u_i is uniformly distributed over (0,1), then it has mean and variance $E[u_i] = 0.5$, and $\text{var}(u_i) = 1/12$. The mean and variance of u will be

$$E[u] = E[u_1] + E[u_2] + \cdots + E[u_{12}] = 0.5 + 0.5 + \cdots + 0.5 = 6$$

$$\text{var}(u) = \text{var}(u_1) + \text{var}(u_2) + \cdots + \text{var}(u_{12}) = \frac{1}{12} + \frac{1}{12} + \cdots + \frac{1}{12} = 1$$

Thus, u is approximately gaussian with variance 1. The range of values of u is $0 < u < 12$ with mean at 6. It is an adequate approximation to a gaussian because there are $\pm 6\sigma$ on either side of the mean, and we know that for gaussian random variables more than 99.99% of the values fall within $\pm 4\sigma$. By shifting and scaling,

$$x = \sigma(u - 6) + m$$

we obtain a gaussian random number x of mean m and variance σ^2. The following FORTRAN function, **gran,** is an implementation of this method. It uses the uniform random number generator **ran.** Starting with an integer seed, it produces a gaussian-distributed random number of prescribed mean and variance, and updates the seed:

```
/* gran.for - gaussian random number generator */

      function gran(mean, sigma, iseed)
      real mean

      u = 0

      do 1 i=1, 12
1        u = u + ran(iseed)                    any version of ran may be used here

      gran = sigma * (u - 6) + mean

      return
      end
```

The corresponding C version is:

```
/* gran.c - gaussian random number generator */

double ran();

double gran(mean, sigma, iseed)
double mean, sigma;
long *iseed;
{
      double u = 0;
      int i;

      for (i=0; i<12; i++)
            u += ran(iseed);

      return sigma * (u - 6) + mean;
}
```

Often, one must generate a block of N independent and gaussian-distributed numbers of prescribed mean and variance. The following routine, **gauss,** does that by starting at an initial seed and making N successive calls to **gran:**

```
/* gauss.for - generates an array of gaussian random numbers */

      subroutine gauss(N, x, mean, sigma, iseed)
      real x(0:N-1), mean

      do 1 i=0, N-1
1        x(i) = gran(mean, sigma, iseed)

      return
      end
```

The C version of **gauss** is:

```
/* gauss.c - generates an array of gaussian random numbers */

double gran();

void gauss(N, x, mean, sigma, iseed)
double x[], mean, sigma;
int N;
long *iseed;
{
       int i;

       for (i=0; i<N; i++)
              x[i] = gran(mean, sigma, iseed);
}
```

Note that in both versions, upon exit from the routine the input seed, *iseed,* is updated. This is a convenient feature allowing one to generate two or more blocks that are mutually independent. The following program example generates two independent length-100 blocks of zero-mean, unit-variance, gaussian random numbers.

```
/* example.c - generating two non-overlapping blocks */

#define N   100

void gauss();

main()
{
       long iseed = 21;                         initial seed is arbitrary
       double x1[N], x2[N];

       gauss(N, x1, 0.0, 1.0, &iseed);          the seed is passed by address
       gauss(N, x2, 0.0, 1.0, &iseed);
}
```

Improving Generators by Shuffling

The quality of a random number generator can be improved by shuffling, which is a process of making the generator *more* random than it actually is. Three popular methods of improving a generator are:

1. Using a generator to shuffle itself
2. Using one generator to shuffle another
3. Using three generators in combination

The first method [1,7,8] works in conjunction with an LCG of the type $I_n = (aI_{n-1} + c)\text{mod}(m)$ and uses an auxiliary array of integer seeds $v(0)$, $v(1)$, . . . ,$v(k-1)$, where k is typically of the order of 100; it also uses a temporary seed y. Initially, the v-array and y are filled with the first $k + 1$ seeds from the LCG. At each subsequent call, the random integer in y is used to get a pointer to the v-array by computing $i = \lfloor ky/m \rfloor$; by construction, $0 \leq i \leq k - 1$. The random integer in the ith slot of the v-array, $v(i)$, is the output of the routine. The call is completed by placing $v(i)$ in y and refilling $v(i)$ by another call of the LCG. This method is illustrated by the following FORTRAN function, **ran1**, which shuffles the previous routine **ran:**

```
/* ran1.for - shuffling of a given linear congruential generator */

      function ran1(iseed, init)

      integer a, c
      parameter (a = 25173, c = 13849, m = 65536, k = 100)
      integer v(0:k-1), y
      save v, y                       v and y must be saved across invocations of ran1

      if ( init .eq. 0) then          the first call of ran1 requires init =0 to
          do 1 i=0, k-1               initialize the v-array
              iseed = mod(a * iseed + c, m)
              v(i) = iseed
1         continue
          iseed = mod(a * iseed + c, m)
          y = iseed                   initialize y
          init = 1                    set init =1 for all subsequent calls
      endif

      i = k * y / m                   get pointer to v-array; i is in the range [0, k-1]
      y = v(i)                        place v(i) into y

      iseed = mod(a * iseed + c, m)
      v(i) = iseed                    refill v(i) with the next seed from LCG
      ran1 = float(y) / float(m)      output of ran1

      return
      end
```

The usage is $u = ran1(iseed,init)$. Note that one must set initially $init = 0$ to initialize the v-array and y. After the first call, the value of *init* is changed to 1. In FORTRAN 77 one must explicitly request the assignment of static storage by the *save* statement. However, in many FORTRAN compilers that still use the old convention, the *save* statement may be omitted. The corresponding C version is given below. Again, the v-array and y must be defined as *static* to preserve them across invocations.

```
/* ran1.c - shuffling of a given LCG */

#define a  25173
#define c  13849
#define m   65536
#define k  100

double ran1(iseed, init)
long *iseed;
int *init;
{
    static long v[k], y;
    int i;

    if (*init == 0) {
        for (i=0; i<k; i++) {
            *iseed = (a * *iseed + c) % m;
            v[i] = *iseed;
            }
        *iseed = (a * *iseed + c) % m;
        y = *iseed;
        *init = 1;
        }

    i = k * y / m;
    y = v[i];

    *iseed = (a * *iseed + c) % m;
    v[i] = *iseed;

    return (double) y / (double) m;
}
```

If one has an available system supplied routine, *ran(iseed),* but does not exactly know how it is implemented, one may improve it by the following variation of the routine **ran1**. In this case, the *v*-array and *y* are not integers but rather previous outputs from **ran**; that is, uniform random numbers in the range (0,1). The FORTRAN version is:

```
/* ran2.for - shuffling a given generator ran(iseed) */

    function ran2(iseed, init)

    parameter (k = 100)
    real v(0:k-1)
    save v, y
```

```
      if (init .eq. 0) then                          initialize v and y
          do 1 i=0, k-1
1             v(i) = ran(iseed)
          y = ran(iseed)
          init = 1                                   set init = 1 for subsequent calls
      endif

      i = k * y                                      y is in (0,1); thus, i is in [0, k-1]
      y = v(i)                                       update y

      v(i) = ran(iseed)                              refill v(i)

      ran2 = y                                       output

      return
      end
```

And, the C version:

```
/* ran2.c - shuffling a given generator ran(iseed) */

#define k   100

double ran();

double ran2(iseed, init)
long *iseed;
int *init;
{
       static double v[k], y;
       int i;

       if (*init == 0) {
              for (i=0; i<k; i++)
                     v[i] = ran(iseed);
              y = ran(iseed);
              *init = 1;
              }

       i = k * y;
       y = v[i];
       v[i] = ran(iseed);

       return y;
}
```

Using the shuffled versions of **ran,** one can easily write shuffled versions of the gaussian routines **gran** and **gauss.** For example, using **ran2** as the basic uniform random number routine, the corresponding shuffled version of **gran** will be:

```
/* gran2.for - shuffled version of gran */

      function gran2(mean, sigma, iseed, init)
      real mean

      u = 0

      do 1 i=1, 12
1           u = u + ran2(iseed, init)

      gran2 = sigma * (u - 6) + mean

      return
      end
```

with usage *u = gran2(mean, sigma, iseed, init)*. Again, one must set *init = 0* for the first call of **gran2.** The C version is:

```
/* gran2.c - shuffled version of gran */

double ran2();

double gran2(mean, sigma, iseed, init)
double mean, sigma;
long *iseed;
int *init;
{
      double u = 0.0;
      int i;

      for (i=0; i<12; i++)
            u += ran2(iseed, init);

      return sigma * (u - 6) + mean;
}
```

Similarly, the shuffled version of **gauss** is, in FORTRAN:

```
/* gauss2.for - shuffled version of gauss */

      subroutine gauss2(N, x, mean, sigma, iseed)
      real x(0:N-1), mean

      init = 0                                         init =0 for the first call

      do 1 i=0, N-1
1           x(i) = gran2(mean, sigma, iseed, init)

      return
      end
```

And, in C:

```
/* gauss2.c - shuffled version of gauss */

double gran2();

void gauss2(N, x, mean, sigma, iseed)
double x[ ], mean, sigma;

int N;
long *iseed;
{
     int i, init = 0;

     for (i=0; i<N; i++)
          x[i] = gran2(mean, sigma, iseed, &init);
}
```

Next, we discuss the second method of shuffling. It uses two different generators, neither of which may be good. One generator is used to shuffle the other. The shuffling algorithm [1,7] uses two LCGs of the type $I_n = (a_1 I_{n-1} + c_1)\text{mod}(m_1)$ and $J_n = (a_2 J_{n-1} + c_2)\text{mod}(m_2)$. It uses an auxiliary array of seeds $v(0)$, $v(1), \ldots, v(k-1)$ filled from the first LCG. Initially, the v-array is filled by the first k calls of the first LCG. Subsequently, the next seed of the second LCG is used to get a random index i into the v-array. The value of $v(i)$ is normalized by the modulus m_1 and serves as the output. The next seed of the first LCG is used to fill the slot $v(i)$ of the v-array. The algorithm is illustrated by the FORTRAN function **ran3.** The choice of LCG parameters is from Whitney [10], who used a slightly different procedure of refilling the v-array.

```
/* ran3.for - shuffling using two LCGs */

      function ran3(iseed1, iseed2, init)

      integer a1, a2, c1, c2
      parameter (a1 = 111, c1 = 11, m1 = 151)
      parameter (a2 = 113, c2 = 13, m2 = 137)
      parameter (k = 121)
      integer v(0:k-1)
      save v                                  v must be saved for subsequent
                                              invocations
      if ( init .eq. 0) then                  initialize v-array by setting init =0
         do 1 i=0, k-1
            iseed1 = mod(a1 * iseed1 + c1, m1)
            v(i) = iseed1
1        continue
         init = 1                             set init =1 for subsequent calls
      endif
```

```
iseed1 = mod(a1 * iseed1 + c1, m1)          next seed of 1st LCG
iseed2 = mod(a2 * iseed2 + c2, m2)          next seed of 2nd LCG

i = k * iseed2 / m2                         i is in the range [0, k-1]

ran3 = float(v(i)) / float(m1)              function output

v(i) = iseed1                               refill v(i)

return
end
```

The corresponding C version is:

```
/* ran3.c - shuffling using two LCGs */

#define a1 111
#define c1 11
#define m1 151
#define a2 113
#define c2 13
#define m2 137
#define k 121

double ran3(iseed1, iseed2, init)
long *iseed1, *iseed2;
int *init;
{
    double u;
    static long v[k];                        v-array must be preserved
    int i;                                   across invocations

    if (*init == 0) {
        for (i=0; i<k; i++) {
            *iseed1 = (a1 * *iseed1 + c1) % m1;
            v[i] = *iseed1;
            }
        *init = 1;
        }

    *iseed1 = (a1 * *iseed1 + c1) % m1;
    *iseed2 = (a2 * *iseed2 + c2) % m2;

    i = k * *iseed2 / m2;
    u = (double) v[i] / (double) m1;         output
    v[i] = *iseed1;

    return u;
}
```

The third method of improving random number generators is to combine more than one generator. For example, the method of [11,12] combines three generators as follows. From the three updated seeds,

$$I_n = (a_1 I_{n-1} + c_1)\text{mod}(m_1)$$

$$J_n = (a_2 J_{n-1} + c_2)\text{mod}(m_2)$$

$$K_n = (a_3 K_{n-1} + c_3)\text{mod}(m_3)$$

compute the corresponding three uniform random numbers, and take the output of the algorithm to be the fractional part of the sum, i.e.,

$$u_n = \text{mod}(\frac{I_n}{m_1} + \frac{J_n}{m_2} + \frac{K_n}{m_3}, 1.0)$$

The FORTRAN implementation of this method is:

```
/* ran4.for - shuffling using three LCGs */

      function ran4(iseed1, iseed2, iseed3)

      integer a1, a2, a3, c1, c2, c3
      parameter (a1 = 171, c1 = 0, m1 = 30269)
      parameter (a2 = 172, c2 = 0, m2 = 30307)
      parameter (a3 = 170, c3 = 0, m3 = 30323)

      iseed1 = mod(a1 * iseed1 + c1, m1)
      iseed2 = mod(a2 * iseed2 + c2, m2)
      iseed3 = mod(a3 * iseed3 + c3, m3)

      r1 = float(iseed1) / float(m1)
      r2 = float(iseed2) / float(m2)
      r3 = float(iseed3) / float(m3)

      ran4 = amod(r1 + r2 + r3, 1.0)

      return
      end
```

The parameters of the three LCGs are from [11]. The C version is:

```
/* ran4.c - shuffling using three LCGs */

#include <math.h>                    declares the function fmod()

#define a1 171
#define c1 0
#define m1 30269
```

```
#define a2  172
#define c2  0
#define m2  30307
#define a3  170
#define c3  0
#define m3  30323

double ran4(iseed1, iseed2, iseed3)
long *iseed1, *iseed2, *iseed3;
{
    double r1, r2, r3;

    *iseed1 = (a1 * *iseed1 + c1) % m1;
    *iseed2 = (a2 * *iseed2 + c2) % m2;
    *iseed3 = (a3 * *iseed3 + c3) % m3;

    r1 = (double) *iseed1 / (double) m1;
    r2 = (double) *iseed2 / (double) m2;
    r3 = (double) *iseed3 / (double) m3;

    return fmod(r1 + r2 + r3, 1.0);
}
```

References

1. D. E. Knuth, *The Art of Computer Programming,* vol. 2, (2nd ed.), Reading, MA, Addison-Wesley, 1981.
2. P. Bratley, B. L. Fox, and L. F. Schrage, *A Guide to Simulation,* New York, Springer-Verlag, 1983.
3. B. D. Ripley, Computer Generation of Random Variables: A Tutorial, *Int. Stat. Rev.,* **51,** 301 (1983).
4. S. Kirkpatrick and E. Stoll, A Very Fast Shift-Register Sequence Random Number Generator, *J. Comput. Phys.,* **40,** 517 (1981).
5. Y. K. Lee, Random Number Generation, *BYTE,* December 1985, p.426.
6. D. J. Best, Some Easily Programmed Pseudo-Random Normal Generators, *Austr. Comput. J.,* **11,** 60 (1979).
7. C. Bays and S. D. Durham, Improving a Poor Random Number Generator, *ACM Trans. Math. Soft.,* **2,** 59 (1976).
8. W. H. Press, B. P. Flannery, S. A. Teukolsky, and W. T. Vetterling, *Numerical Recipes,* New York, Cambridge Univ. Press, 1986.
9. G. Marsaglia and T. A. Bray, On-Line Random Number Generators and Their Use in Combinations, *Comm. ACM,* **11,** 757 (1968).
10. C. A. Whitney, Generating and Testing Pseudorandom Numbers, *BYTE,* October 1984, p. 128.

11. B. A. Wichmann and I. D. Hill, An Efficient and Portable Pseudo-Random Number Generator, *Appl. Stat.,* **31**, 188 (1982).
12. B. Wichmann and D. Hill, Building a Random Number Generator, *BYTE,* March 1987, p. 127.

Appendix B Subroutines in FORTRAN 77

This appendix contains a number of FORTRAN 77 subroutines designed to be used together as a pool of subroutines. The routines may be compiled separately and placed in an object library to be linked with the main programs. Tests for error conditions, such as divisions by zero, were not included in the routines; such tests can be incorporated easily. The routines, listed in order of appearance in the text, are:

1. sampcov	7. rlev	13. lwf	19. spike	25. abs2db	31. lmsap
2. corr	8. lattice	14. dwf	20. aicmdl	26. db2abs	32. glwf
3. sigav	9. schur	15. yw	21. snap	27. select	33. mgs
4. lev	10. schur1	16. burg	22. norm	28. music	34. rls
5. frwlev	11. schur2	17. scatter	23. fresp	29. minorm	35. faest
6. bkwlev	12. firw	18. dpd	24. invresp	30. lms	36. rlsl

1. *sampcov.for—recursive updating of sample covariance matrix*

It performs the recursive computation of the sample covariance matrix of Eq. (1.5.21) using the recursion (1.5.24). The subroutine inputs are M,R,y,N, and its output is R. The old matrix R is overwritten by the new one. The matrix R and *snapshot* vector $\mathbf{y}$ have dimension $M+1$, for example, $\mathbf{y} = [y_0, y_1, \ldots, y_M]^T$. Before the first call, the matrix R must be initialized to zero.

```
      subroutine sampcov(M, R, y, N)
      real R(0:M, 0:M), y(0:M)

      do 1 i=0, M
         do 1 j=0, i
            R(i, j) = R(i, j) + (y(i) * y(j) - R(i, j)) / N     update lower triangular
                                                                 part of R
            R(j, i) = R(i, j)                                    R is symmetric
 1    continue

      return
      end
```

2. *corr.for—sample cross correlation*

It computes the first $M+1$ lags of the sample cross correlation $\hat{R}_{yx}(k)$, $k = 0, 1, \ldots, M$, based on two length-N data blocks x_n, y_n, $n = 0, 1, \ldots, N-1$; that is,

$$\hat{R}_{yx}(k) = \frac{1}{N} \sum_{n=0}^{N-1-k} y_{n+k} x_n \,, \qquad k = 0, 1, \cdots, M$$

```
      subroutine corr(N, y, x, M, R)
      real x(0:N-1), y(0:N-1)                length-N data blocks
      real R(0:M)                            only M+1 lags are needed; M ≤ N-1

      do 1 k=0, M
         R(k) = 0
         do 1 i=0, N-1-k
            R(k) = R(k) + y(i+k) * x(i) / N
 1    continue

      return
      end
```

3. *sigav.for—signal averaging*

It performs signal averaging, discussed in Example 2.3.5. It reads M periods of length N from an input file and averages them. It assumes that the input data file has been opened and assigned to logical unit, *unit*. The input file must contain at least MN data points, one per line. The inputs to the routine are M, N, *unit*, and the output is the length-N averaged signal $x(i)$, $i = 0, 1, \ldots, N-1$.

```
      subroutine sigav(M, N, unit, x)
      integer unit
      real x(0:N-1)

      do 1 j=0, M-1                          for each period,
         do 1 i=0, N-1                        accumulate the samples
            read(unit, *) y
            x(i) = x(i) + y / M
1     continue

      return
      end
```

4. *lev.for—Levinson's algorithm*

It generates all the prediction-error filters and prediction errors up to a given order, from the autocorrelation lags. The subroutine inputs are M, R; its outputs are L, E (L must be declared real). R is the vector of autocorrelation lags $R(0), R(1), \ldots, R(M)$. L is the unit lower triangular matrix whose pth row holds the *reverse* of the pth prediction error filter; that is, $L(p,i) = a_{p,p-i}, i = 0,1, \ldots, p$. The first column of L holds the *negatives* of the reflection coefficients, $\gamma_p = -a_{pp} = -L(p,0)$, $p = 1,2, \ldots, M$. The vector $E(0), E(1), \ldots, E(M)$ holds the mean square prediction errors. The matrix L and the diagonal matrix $D = \text{diag}\{E(0), E(1), \ldots, E(M)\}$ define the UL factorization of the inverse of the autocorrelation matrix; that is, $R^{-1} = L^T D^{-1} L$.

```
      subroutine lev(M, R, L, E)
      real R(0:M), L(0:M, 0:M), E(0:M)

      integer p

      L(0, 0) = 1
      L(1, 1) = 1
      L(1, 0) = - R(1) / R(0)
      E(0) = R(0)
      E(1) = E(0) * (1 - L(1, 0) ** 2)

      do 1 p=2, M
         delta = 0
         do 2 i=0, p-1
2           delta = delta + R(i+1) * L(p-1, i)
         gamma = delta / E(p-1)                        Eq. (5.3.11)
         L(p, 0) = - gamma
         do 3 i=1, p-1
```

```
3            L(p, i) = L(p-1, i-1) - gamma * L(p-1, p-1-i)          Eq. (5.3.15)
        L(p, p) = 1
        E(p) = E(p-1) * (1 - gamma ** 2)                            Eq. (5.3.13)
1    continue

     return
     end
```

The following program, based on Example 5.3.1, illustrates the use of **lev**:

```
     parameter(M = 4)
     real L(0:M, 0:M), R(0:M), E(0:M)

     data R/128, -64, 80, -88, 89/

     call lev(M, R, L, E)

     do 1 i=0, M
1        write(*, '(10f9.4)') (L(i, j), j = 0, i)     lower triangular part of L

     write(*,'(10f9.4)') (E(i), i = 0, M)

     end
```

5. *frwlev.for—forward Levinson recursion*

The subroutine inputs are *M*, *gamma*; its output is *L*. Given the reflection coefficients *gamma* (*p*), *p* = 1,2, . . . ,*M*, it generates all the prediction-error filters up to order *M* by the forward recursion Eq. (5.3.18). The *reversed* filters are saved in the rows of *L*.

```
     subroutine frwlev(M, gamma, L)
     real gamma(M), L(0:M, 0:M)

     integer p

     L(0, 0) = 1
     L(1, 0) = - gamma(1)
     L(1, 1) = 1

     do 1 p=2, M                                    build the p-th row of L
         L(p, 0) = - gamma(p)
         L(p, p) = 1
         do 1 i=1, p-1
             L(p, i) = L(p-1, i-1) - gamma(p) * L(p-1, p-1-i)
1    continue

     return
     end
```

The following program, based on Example 5.3.1, illustrates the use of **frwlev**:

```
      parameter(M = 4)
      real gamma(M), L(0:M, 0:M)

      data gamma /-0.5, 0.5, -0.5, 0.5/

      call frwlev(M, gamma, L)

      do 1 i=0, M
1         write(*, '(10f9.4)') (L(i, j), j = 0, i)

      end
```

6. *bkwlev.for—backward Levinson recursion*

It generates all lower order prediction filters from a given polynomial. The subroutine inputs are M, a; its output is L. It determines the lattice realization of the Mth degree polynomial $\mathbf{a} = [1, a_1, a_2, \ldots, a_M]^T$ by the backward recursion Eq. (5.3.23). The rows of L are the lower order backward prediction filters; the reflection coefficients may be extracted from the first column of L. The routine may be used to test the minimum phase property of the polynomial **a**.

```
      subroutine bkwlev(M, a, L)
      real a(0:M), L(0:M, 0:M)

      integer p

      do 1 i=0, M
1         L(M, i) = a(M-i)                                  the M-th row of L

      do 2 p=M, 1, -1                                       the remaining rows of L
          gamma = - L(p, 0)
          F = 1 - gamma ** 2
          do 3 i=0, p-2
3             L(p-1, i) = ( L(p, i+1) + gamma * L(p, p-1-i) ) / F
          L(p-1, p-1) = 1
2     continue

      return
      end
```

The following program, based on Example 5.3.1, illustrates **bkwlev**:

```
      parameter(M = 4)
      real a(0:M), L(0:M, 0:M)

      data a/1, -0.25, -0.1875, 0.5, -0.5/

      call bkwlev(M, a, L)

      do 1 i=0, M
1         write(*, '(10f9.4)') (L(i, j), j = 0, i)

      end
```

7. *rlev.for—reverse of Levinson's algorithm*

The subroutine inputs are M, a, EM; the outputs are R, L. It generates the $M+1$ autocorrelation lags $R(0), R(1), \ldots, R(M)$ from the knowledge of the Mth prediction error $EM = E(M)$ and the order-M prediction filter $\mathbf{a} = [1, a_1, a_2, \ldots, a_M]^T$. It also generates all the lower order prediction filters arranged in the rows of L. It calls the routine **bkwlev** to get the lower order prediction filters and then reconstructs the autocorrelation function using Eqs. (5.3.24) and (5.3.25).

```
      subroutine rlev(M, a, EM, R, L)
      real a(0:M), R(0:M), L(0:M, 0:M)

      integer p

      call bkwlev(M, a, L)

      R(0) = EM
      do 1 p=1, M                                  Eq. (5.3.25)
1         R(0) = R(0) / (1 - L(p, 0) ** 2)

      do 2 p=1, M                                  Eq. (5.3.24)
          R(p) = 0
          do 2 i=0, p-1
              R(p) = R(p) - L(p, i) * R(i)
2     continue

      return
      end
```

The following program, based on Example 5.3.1, illustrates **rlev**:

```
      parameter(M = 4)
      real a(0:M), R(0:M), L(0:M, 0:M)

      data a/1, -0.25, -0.1875, 0.5, -0.5/EM/40.5/

      call rlev(M, a, EM, R, L)

      write(*,'(10f9.4)') (R(i), i = 0, M)
      write(*,*)

      do 1 i=0, M
1            write(*, '(10f9.4)') (L(i, j), j = 0, i)

      end
```

8. *lattice.for—lattice filter*

It realizes the cascade of M lattice sections. It transforms a pair of input samples $\{xa, xb\}$ at the forward/backward inputs of the *first* section into the pair of output samples $\{ya, yb\}$ from the *last* section. The array w holds the internal state of the filter; that is, the values held at the delay registers of the sections. The routine makes M successive calls to the routine **section,** which realizes a single lattice section. Each subcall to **section** also updates the internal state of that section.

```
      subroutine lattice(M, gamma, w, xa, xb, ya, yb)
      real gamma(M), w(M)

      do 1 i=1, M
           call section(gamma(i), w(i), xa, xb, ya, yb)     ith lattice section
           xa = ya                                          outputs from ith section,
           xb = yb                                          become inputs to the next
1     continue                                              section

      return
      end


      subroutine section(gamma, w, xa, xb, ya, yb)

      ya = xa - gamma * w
      yb =  w - gamma * xa

      w = xb                                                update internal state

      return
      end
```

9. *schur.for—Schur algorithm*

It generates the reflection coefficients and final prediction error from the autocorrelation lags. The subroutine inputs are M and the autocorrelation lags $R(0), R(1), \ldots, R(M)$; its outputs are the reflection coefficients $\gamma_1, \gamma_2, \ldots, \gamma_M$, and the order-$M$ prediction error $EM = E(M)$. The parameter MAX represents the maximum value of M; it may be changed to any desired value. The internal arrays *ga* and *gb* are the forward/backward gapped functions. They are updated in order from $p = 0$ to $p = M$.

```
      subroutine schur(M, R, gamma, EM)
      real R(0:M), gamma(M)

      parameter (MAX = 50)
      real ga(0:MAX), gb(0:MAX)
      integer p

      do 1 k=0, M                              order-0 gapped functions
         ga(k) = R(k)
         gb(k) = R(k)
 1    continue

      do 2 p=0, M-1
         c = ga(p+1) / gb(p)                   compute reflection coefficient
         do 3 k=M, p+1, -1                     count backward to avoid
            temp = ga(k)                       overwriting of gb
            ga(k) = temp - c * gb(k-1)         order-update gapped functions
            gb(k) = gb(k-1) - c * temp
 3       continue
         gamma(p+1) = c
 2    continue

      EM = gb(M)                               final order-M prediction error

      return
      end
```

10. *schur1.for—Schur algorithm for Cholesky factorization*

Same as **schur**, and in addition, it generates the Cholesky factors of the autocorrelation matrix, $R = GD^{-1}G^T$. The subroutine inputs are M and the autocorrelation lags $R(0), R(1), \ldots, R(M)$; its outputs are the reflection coefficients $\gamma_1, \gamma_2, \ldots, \gamma_M$, and the lower triangular Cholesky factor G. The mean square prediction errors may be extracted from the diagonal elements of G, i.e., $E_p = G(p,p), p = 0, 1, \ldots, M$. The pth column of G is the pth order backward-gapped function, $g_p^-(k) = G(k,p)$.

```
      subroutine schur1(M, R, gamma, G)
      real R(0:M), gamma(M), G(0:M, 0:M)

      parameter (MAX = 50)
      real ga(0:MAX)
      integer p

      do 1 k=0, M
           ga(k) = R(k)
           G(k, 0) = R(k)                         first column of G
1     continue

      do 2 p=0, M-1
           c = ga(p+1) / G(p, p)
           do 3 k=p+1, M
                temp = ga(k)
                ga(k) = temp - c * G(k-1, p)
                G(k, p+1) = G(k-1, p) - c * temp
3          continue
           gamma(p+1) = c
2     continue

      return
      end
```

11. *schur2.for—split Schur algorithm*

It generates the reflection coefficients and final prediction error from the autocorrelation lags. The subroutine inputs are M and $R(0), R(1), \ldots, R(M)$; its outputs are the reflection coefficients $\gamma_1, \gamma_2, \ldots, \gamma_M$, and the order-$M$ prediction error $EM = E(M)$. The internal array g is the symmetrized gapped function. It can be modified easily to output the coefficients *alpha* of the split lattice structure discussed in Section 5.7.

```
      subroutine schur2(M, R, gamma, EM)
      real R(0:M), gamma(M)

      parameter (MAX = 50)
      real g(0:MAX, 0:MAX)
      integer p

      g(0, 0) = R(0)

      do 1 k=1, M                              initialize
           g(0, k) = 2 * R(k)                  for order 0
           g(1, k) = R(k) + R(k-1)             and order 1
```

```
1     continue

      c = 0
      do 2 p=0, M-2
            alpha = g(p+1, p+1) / g(p, p)
            c = -1 + alpha / (1 - c)
            gamma(p+1) = c
            do 3 k=p+2, M
3                 g(p+2, k) = g(p+1, k) + g(p+1, k-1) - alpha * g(p, k-1)
2     continue

      alpha = g(M, M) / g(M-1, M-1)                      final order-M quantities
      gamma(M) = -1 + alpha / (1 - c)
      EM = g(M, M) * (1 - gamma(M))

      return
      end
```

12. *firw.for*—*FIR Wiener filter design*

The subroutine inputs are the order M, the cross-correlation lags $R_{xy}(0), R_{xy}(1), \ldots, R_{xy}(M)$, and the autocorrelation lags $R_{yy}(0), R_{yy}(1), \ldots, R_{yy}(M)$. The outputs are the filter weights $g(0), g(1), \ldots, g(M)$ of the lattice realization and the weights $h(0), h(1), \ldots, h(M)$ of the direct-form realization. It calls **lev** to produce the matrix L and vector E of prediction errors. The reflection coefficients may be extracted from the first column of L.

```
      subroutine firw(M, Rxy, Ryy, L, E, g, h)
      real Rxy(0:M), Ryy(0:M), L(0:M, 0:M), E(0:M), g(0:M), h(0:M)

      integer p

      call lev(M, Ryy, L, E)

      do 1 p=0, M                                        compute g = D^-1 L r_xy
            g(p) = 0
            do 2 i=0, p                                  L is lower triangular
2                 g(p) = g(p) + L(p, i) * Rxy(i)
            g(p) = g(p) / E(p)
1     continue

      do 3 p=0, M                                        compute h = L^T g
            h(p) = 0
            do 3 i=p, M                                  L is lower triangular
                  h(p) = h(p) + L(i, p) * g(i)
3     continue

      return
      end
```

13. *lwf.for—lattice Wiener filter*

It performs the filtering operations of the lattice Wiener filter. The subroutine inputs are the order M, the lattice filter weights $g(0), g(1), \ldots, g(M)$, the reflection coefficients $\gamma_1, \gamma_2, \ldots, \gamma_M$, the pair of input samples $\{x, y\}$, and the initialization variable *init*. The outputs are the filtered pair $\{xhat, e\}$. The internal arrays *ea* and *eb* are the forward and backward error signals, updated from one lattice section to the next. The array w is the internal state of the filter; namely, the signal values in the delay registers of the lattice sections, $w_p(n) = e^-_{p-1}(n-1), p = 1, \ldots, M$, so that $w_p(n+1) = e^-_{p-1}(n)$. Thus, the next state of the pth section is the present backward output of the previous order; this allows w to be updated at each call and saved for the next call. Entry with $init = 0$ will reset the internal state to zero and change the value of *init* to 1.

```
      subroutine lwf(M, g, gamma, x, y, xhat, e, init)
      real g(0:M), gamma(M)

      parameter (MAX = 50)                       maximum filter order; can be changed
      real ea(0:MAX), eb(0:MAX), w(MAX)          to any value
      integer p
      save w                                     save internal state for next call

      if (init .eq. 0) then                      set init =0 at the first call of lwf to
          do 1 p=1, M                            clear the internal state
1             w(p) = 0
          init = 1                               init =1 for subsequent calls
      endif

      ea(0) = y                                  overall inputs to first lattice section
      eb(0) = y
      xhat = g(0) * eb(0)                        estimate of x based on order-0 filter
      e = x - xhat                               estimation error based on order-0
                                                 filter
      do 2 p=1, M
          ea(p) = ea(p-1) - gamma(p) * w(p)      outputs from the pth lattice section
          eb(p) = w(p) - gamma(p) * ea(p-1)
          w(p) = eb(p-1)                         update internal state of pth section
          xhat = xhat + g(p) * eb(p)             estimate of x based on order-p filter
          e = e - g(p) * eb(p)                   estimation error based on order-p
2     continue                                   filter

      return
      end
```

The usage of this routine is illustrated by the following program segment. The file *x.dat* contains the signal samples $x_n, n = 0, 1, \ldots,$ one per line; the file *y.dat* contains y_n. The filtered samples $\hat{x}_n$, e_n are placed in the output files *xhat.dat, e.dat.*

```
        open(1, file='x.dat')
        open(2, file='y.dat')
        open(3, file='xhat.dat')
        open(4, file='e.dat')

        init = 0                          initialize filter's internal state to zero

10      continue
            read(1, *, END=20) x          keep reading x samples until
            read(2, *) y                  the end of file x.dat

            call lwf(M, g, gamma, x, y, xhat, e, init)

            write(3, *) xhat
            write(4, *) e
        goto 10

20      continue                          branch here when EOF of x.dat is reached
```

Note that because the internal state is initially zero, the initial transient behavior of the filter is correctly computed. However, the filtering operation stops as soon as the end-of-file of the input file *x.dat* is reached. To get the final transients after the input is turned off, one may pad M zeros at the end of the file *x.dat,* or alternatively, after branching to label-20, one may repeat the loop-10 M more times with $x = y = 0$.

14. *dwf.for—direct-form Wiener filter*

It performs the filtering operations of the direct-form Wiener filter. The subroutine inputs are M, the direct-form weights $h(0), h(1), \ldots, h(M)$, the input samples $\{x, y\}$, and *init.* The outputs are $\{xhat, e\}$. The array w is the internal state of the filter; namely, the signal values in the delay registers of the tapped delay line, $w_p(n) = y_{n-p}, p = 1, \ldots, M$, so that $w_p(n+1) = y_{n+1-p} = w_{p-1}(n)$. Thus, the next pth state is the current $(p-1)$st state; this allows w to be updated at each call and saved for the next call. Entry with $init = 0$ resets w to zero and changes *init* to 1. The same program segment illustrating the usage of **lwf** applies also to **dwf**.

```
        subroutine dwf(M, h, x, y, xhat, e, init)
        real h(0:M)

        parameter(MAX = 50)
        real w(0:MAX)
        integer p
        save w                            save for next call

        if (init .eq. 0) then             set init = 0 at the first call of dwf to
            do 1 p=1, M                   clear the internal state
1               w(p) = 0
            init = 1                      init =1 for subsequent calls
        endif
```

```
      w(0) = y                          current input to filter

      xhat = 0
      do 2 p=0, M                       compute filter output; estimate of x
2         xhat = xhat + h(p) * w(p)

      e = x - xhat                      estimation error

      do 3 p=M, 1, -1                   update internal state for next call
3         w(p) = w(p-1)

      return
      end
```

15. *yw.for—Yule–Walker method*

Yule–Walker or autocorrelation method of extracting the LP model parameters from a given data block. The subroutine inputs are the N data samples $y(0), y(1), \ldots, y(N-1)$, and the order M of the predictor; the outputs are the sample autocorrelation lags $R(0), R(1), \ldots, R(M)$, the matrix L, and the mean-square estimation errors $E(0), E(1), \ldots, E(M)$. It calls **corr** to compute R, and then it calls **lev** to compute L and E.

```
      subroutine yw(N, y, M, R, L, E)
      real y(0:N-1), R(0:M), L(0:M, 0:M), E(0:M)

      call corr(N, y, y, M, R)

      call lev(M, R, L, E)

      return
      end
```

16. *burg.for—Burg's method*

Burg's method of extracting the LP model parameters from a given data block. The subroutine inputs are the length-N block of data $y(0), y(1), \ldots, y(N-1)$ and the order M of the predictor; the outputs are the matrix L and the mean-square estimation errors $E(0), E(1), \ldots, E(M)$. The parameter $NMAX$ is the maximum value of N; it can be changed to any value. The internal arrays *ea* and *eb* are the forward/backward prediction error signals, updated from one order to the next.

```
      subroutine burg(N, y, M, L, E)
      real y(0:N-1), L(0:M, 0:M), E(0:M)

      parameter(NMAX = 500)
      real ea(0:NMAX-1), eb(0:NMAX-1), num
      integer p

      E(0) = 0                                           initialize in order
      do 1 i=0, N-1
         E(0)  =  E(0)  +  y(i) ** 2
         ea(i) = y(i)
         eb(i) = y(i)
1     continue

      E(0) = E(0) / N
      L(0, 0) = 1

      do 2 p=1, M                                        lattice stages p=1
         num = 0                                         to p=M
         den = 0
         do 3 i=p, N-1
            num = num + 2 * ea(i) * eb(i-1)
            den = den + ea(i) ** 2 + eb(i-1) ** 2
3        continue

         gamma = num / den                               Eq. (5.12.10)

         E(p) = E(p-1) * (1 - gamma ** 2)

         L(p, p) = 1                                     build pth row of L
         L(p, 0) = - gamma
         do 4 i=1, p-1
4           L(p, i) = L(p-1, i-1) - gamma * L(p-1, p-1-i)

         do 5 i=N-1, p, -1                               update prediction
            temp = ea(i)                                 error signals
            ea(i) = temp - gamma * eb(i-1)
            eb(i) = eb(i-1) - gamma * temp
5        continue

2     continue

      return
      end
```

The following program, based on Example 5.12.1, illustrates the use of **burg**:

```
      parameter (N = 6, M = 2)
      real y(0:N-1), L(0:M, 0:M), E(0:M)

      data y/4.684, 7.247, 8.423, 8.650, 8.640, 8.392/

      call burg(N, y, M, L, E)

      do 1 i=0, M
1           write(*,'(10f9.4)') (L(i,j), j = 0, i)

      end
```

17. *scatter.for—direct scattering problem*

From a given set of reflection coefficients, it generates all the lattice polynomials and a finite segment of the overall reflection response. The subroutine inputs are the number of layers M, the reflection coefficients $\rho_0, \rho_1, \ldots, \rho_M$, and the number N of reflection response samples to be computed. The outputs are the lower triangular matrices A and B whose rows are the coefficients of the polynomials $A_i(z)$ and $B_i(z)$, $i = 0, 1, \ldots, M$, and the N reflection response samples $R(0), R(1), \ldots, R(N-1)$ obtained as the first N terms in the inverse z-transform of $R(z) = B_M(z)/A_M(z)$.

```
      subroutine scatter(M, rho, A, B, N, R)
      real rho(0:M), A(0:M, 0:M), B(0:M, 0:M), R(0:N-1)
      A(0, 0) = 1
      B(0, 0) = rho(0)

      do 1 i=1, M                                   forward lattice recursion
         A(i, 0) = 1
         A(i, i) = rho(0) * rho(i)
         B(i, 0) = rho(i)
         B(i, i) = rho(0)
         do 2 j=1, i-1
            A(i, j) = A(i-1, j) + rho(i) * B(i-1, j-1)
            B(i, j) = B(i-1, j-1) + rho(i) * A(i-1, j)
2        continue
1     continue

      R(0) = B(M, 0)                                generate reflection response
      do 3 k=1, N-1                                 R(0), R(1), ···, R(N-1)
         S = 0
         do 4 i=1, min(k, M)
4           S = S - A(M, i) * R(k-i)
         if (k .le. M) then
            R(k) = B(M, k) + S
```

```
        else
             R(k) = S
        endif
3    continue

     return
     end
```

18. *dpd.for—dynamic predictive deconvolution*

From a finite segment of the observed reflection response, it generates all the lattice polynomials and reflection coefficients up to a given order. The subroutine inputs are N reflection response samples $R(0), R(1), \ldots, R(N-1)$ and the number of layers M. The outputs are the matrices A and B, and the auxiliary quantities PHI, L, E that facilitate the solution of normal equations via **lev**. The reflection coefficients may be extracted from the first column of B, $\rho_i = B(i,0)$, $i = 0, 1, \ldots, M$.

```
     subroutine dpd(N, R, M, A, B, PHI, L, E)
     real R(0:N-1), A(0:M, 0:M), B(0:M, 0:M)
     real PHI(0:M), L(0:M, 0:M), E(0:M)

     call corr(N, R, R, M, PHI)                autocorrelation of reflection response

     do 1 k=0, M                               autocorrelation of transmission response
1         PHI(k) = - N * PHI(k)                remove factor N introduced by corr
     PHI(0) = 1 + PHI(0)

     call lev(M, PHI, L, E)                    get A_M(z) by the Levinson recursion

     do 2 i=0, M
2         A(M, i) = L(M, M-i)

     do 3 i=0, M                               convolve A_M(z) with R(z) to get B_M(z)
          B(M, i) = 0
          do 3 j=0, i
               B(M, i) = B(M, i) + A(M, j) * R(i-j)
3    continue

     rho0 = B(M, M)                            begin the backward recursion
     do 4 i=M, 1, -1
          rho = B(i, 0)
          F = 1 - rho ** 2
          do 5 j=0, i-1
               A(i-1, j) = ( A(i, j) - rho * B(i, j) ) / F
               B(i-1, j) = ( B(i, j + 1) - rho * A(i, j + 1) ) / F
```

```
5          continue
           A(i-1, 0) = 1
           B(i-1, i-1) = rho0
4      continue

       return
       end
```

19. *spike.for — spiking filter design*

It generates all the spiking filters of a given order and their outputs that reshape a given waveform into a spike. The subroutine inputs are the $N+1$ samples of the waveform to be compressed into a spike, $y(0), y(1), \ldots, y(N)$, the order M of the spiking filter, and the Backus-Gilbert prewhitening parameter *eps*. Its outputs are R, L, E, P, H, where R is the vector of sample autocorrelation lags $R(0), R(1), \ldots, R(M)$ of the waveform $y(n)$, L and E are usual quantities outputted by **lev** and used to compute the matrix inverse $R^{-1} = L^T D^{-1} L$, P is the performance matrix (5.14.11) whose columns are the actual outputs of the spiking filters, and H, given by Eq. (5.14.15), holds the spiking filters in its columns.

```
      subroutine spike(N, y, M, R, L, E, P, H, eps)
      real y(0:N), R(0:M), L(0:M, 0:M), E(0:M)
      real P(0:N+M, 0:N+M), H(0:M, 0:N+M)

      integer s, t

      call corr(N+1, y, y, M, R)

      do 1 k=0, M                                       remove factor N+1 introduced
1           R(k) = (N+1) * R(k)                         by corr

      R(0) = (1 + eps) * R(0)                           prewhiten R(0)

      call lev(M, R, L, E)                              find the Cholesky factors of R^-1

      do 4 i=0, M                                       H = R^-1 Y^T = L^T D^-1 L Y^T
           do 4 j=0, N + M
                H(i, j) = 0
                do 4 s=i, M
                     do 4 t=max(0, j-N), min(j, s)      the limits ensure 0 <= j-t <= N
                          H(i, j) = H(i, j) + L(s, i) * L(s, t) * y(j-t) / E(s)
4     continue

      do 5 i=0, N + M                                   P = Y R^-1 Y^T = Y H
           do 5 j=0, N + M
```

```
          P(i, j) = 0
          do 5 t=max(0, i-N), min(i, M)          the limits ensure 0 ≤ i-t ≤ N
             P(i, j) = P(i, j) + y(i-t) * H(t, j)
5     continue

      return
      end
```

20. *aicmdl.for—AIC and MDL criteria*

It computes the AIC and MDL functions, $AIC(k)$, $MDL(k)$, for $k = 1, 2, \ldots, M+1$. Its inputs are the number of snapshots N and the $M+1$ empirical eigenvalues $\hat{\lambda}_0, \hat{\lambda}_1, \ldots, \hat{\lambda}_M$. Note that the log of the harmonic mean is computed as the arithmetic mean of the logs.

```
      subroutine aicmdl(M, lambda, N, AIC, MDL)
      real lambda(0:M), AIC(M+1), MDL(M+1)

      real L, logN

      avlog = 0
      av = 0
      logN = alog(float(N))

      do 1 k=1, M+1                                      averages are computed recursively
         av = av + (lambda(k-1) - av) / k                average of the first k eigenvalues
         avlog = avlog + (alog(lambda(k-1)) - avlog) / k    average of the logs
         L = (avlog - alog(av))                             of the eigenvalues
         AIC(k) = - 2 * N * k * L + 2 * (M + 1 - k) * (M + 1 + k)
         MDL(k) = - N * k * L + 0.5 * (M + 1 - k) * (M + 1 + k) * logN
1     continue

      return
      end
```

21. *snap.for—random snapshot generator*

Given an initial seed, it generates a snapshot vector $\mathbf{y}$ and updates the seed. Its inputs are the number of planewaves L, their wavenumbers and power levels $k_i, P_i, i = 1, 2, \ldots, L$, the number of array elements $M+1$, and the initial seed, *iseed*. Its outputs are the snapshot vector $\mathbf{y} = [y_0, y_1, \ldots, y_M]^T$ and an updated value of *iseed*. The wavenumbers k_i are in radians. The power levels P_i are in absolute units with respect to background gaussian noise of unit variance; they may be obtained by calling **db2abs** on the SNRs given in dB. The maximum number of sources *LMAX* may be changed to any value.

```
      subroutine snap(L, k, P, M, y, iseed)
      real k(L), P(L)
      complex y(0:M)

      parameter (LMAX = 20)                       maximum value of L
      complex A(LMAX)                             complex amplitudes of planewaves

      pi = 4 * atan(1.)
      sigma = 1 / sqrt(2.0)                       used for generating complex-valued
                                                  unit-variance noise
      do 1 i=1, L
         phi = 2 * pi * ran(iseed)                any version of ran may be used here
         A(i) = sqrt(P(i)) * cexp(cmplx(0., phi)) only the phase of A (i) is random
1     continue

      do 2 j=0, M
         v1 = gran(0., sigma, iseed)              gran is given in Appendix A
         v2 = gran(0., sigma, iseed)
         y(j) = cmplx(v1, v2)                     background noise of unit variance
         do 2 i=1, L
            y(j) = y(j) + A(i) * cexp(cmplx(0., -j * k(i)))
2     continue

      return
      end
```

22. *norm.for—normalization to unit norm*

It normalizes a vector $\mathbf{a} = [a_0, a_1, \ldots, a_M]^T$ to unit norm. The old vector is overwritten by the new one.

```
      subroutine norm(M, a)
      complex a(0:M)

      D = 0
      do 1 i=0, M
1        D = D + cabs(a(i)) ** 2

      D = sqrt(D)

      do 2 i=0, M
2        a(i) = a(i) / D

      return
      end
```

23. *fresp.for—frequency response*

It computes the magnitude response $|A(\omega)|^2$ of an M-order filter $\mathbf{a} = [a_0, a_1, \ldots, a_M]^T$ at a specified number of frequency points in the right-half of the Nyquist interval, $0 \leqslant \omega < \pi$. Its inputs are M, $\mathbf{a}$, and the number of desired frequency points, NF. Its output is the vector $AF(i) = |A(\omega_i)|^2$, $i = 0, 1, \ldots, NF - 1$, where $\omega_i = \pi i / NF$. The routine may be modified easily to include the entire Nyquist interval or any subinterval. It makes NF successive calls to the function **poly** that evaluates the polynomial z-transform $A(z)$ at a complex number z using Horner's rule.

```
      subroutine fresp(M, a, NF, AF)
      complex a(0:M)
      real AF(0:NF-1)

      complex z, poly

      pi = 4 * atan(1.)

      do 1 i=0, NF-1
         omega = pi * i / NF
         z = cexp(cmplx(0., -omega))          z inverse
         D = cabs(poly(M, a, z))
         AF(i) = D * D
 1    continue

      return
      end
```

```
      complex function poly(M, a, z)    computes A(z) = a0 + a1 z + a2 z^2 + ... + aM z^M
      complex a(0:M), z

      poly = a(M)

      do 1 i=M-1, 0, -1
 1       poly = a(i) + z * poly

      return
      end
```

24. *invresp.for—inverse frequency response*

It replaces the frequency response computed by **fresp** by its inverse; that is, $AF(i) \rightarrow 1/AF(i)$, $i = 0, \ldots, NF - 1$. It does not check for division by zero.

```
      subroutine invresp(NF, AF)
      real AF(0:NF-1)

      do 1 i=0, NF-1
1         AF(i) = 1 / AF(i)

      return
      end
```

25. *abs2db.for—absolute units to decibels*

```
      subroutine abs2db(NF, AF)          AF(i) must be strictly positive
      real AF(0:NF-1)

      do 1 i=0, NF-1
1         AF(i) = 10 * alog10(AF(i))

      return
      end
```

26. *db2abs.for—decibels to absolute units*

```
      subroutine db2abs(NF, AF)
      real AF(0:NF-1)

      do 1 i=0, NF-1
1         AF(i) = 10 ** (AF(i) / 10)

      return
      end
```

27. *select.for—select eigenvector*

This routine, and **music** and **minorm**, assume that the eigenvector matrix E is already available through some eigensystem package, such as EISPACK. The successive columns of E are the *orthonormal* eigenvectors of R belonging to the eigenvalues in *increasing* order. Given the eigenvector matrix E, this routine selects one of the eigenvectors, that is, one of the columns of E. Its inputs are M, E, and the column i to be extracted. Its output is the extracted eigenvector placed in the vector $\mathbf{a}$.

```
      subroutine select(M, E, i, a)
      complex E(0:M, 0:M), a(0:M)

      do 1 j=0, M
1        a(j) = E(j, i)

      return
      end
```

28. *music.for—MUSIC spectrum*

Given the eigenvector matrix E (in increasing eigenvalue order) and the dimension K of the noise subspace, it computes the MUSIC spectrum of Eq. (6.5.1) at a specified number of wavenumbers in the right half of the Nyquist interval, $0 \leq k < \pi$. Its inputs are M, E, and K. Its output is the vector $S(i)$, $i = 0, \ldots, NF - 1$ of computed spectral values; they may be processed by **abs2db** to convert them to decibels. The arrays AF and a are working arrays.

```
      subroutine music(M, E, K, NF, S, AF, a)
      complex E(0:M, 0:M), a(0:M)
      real S(0:NF-1), AF(0:NF-1)

      do 1 j=0, NF-1
1        S(j) = 0

      do 2 i=0, K-1
         call select(M, E, i, a)              extract ith eigenvector,
         call fresp(M, a, NF, AF)             compute its magnitude spectrum, and
         do 2 j=0, NF-1                       accumulate it
            S(j) = S(j) + AF(j) / K
2     continue

      call invresp(NF, S)

      return
      end
```

29. *minorm.for—minimum norm eigenvector*

Given the eigenvector matrix E and the dimension of the noise subspace K, it computes the minimum norm eigenvector $\mathbf{d}$ using Eq. (6.6.4). The vector $\mathbf{d}$ may be normalized to unit norm by calling **norm**.

```
      subroutine minorm(M, E, K, d)
      complex E(0:M, 0:M), d(0:M)

      do 1 j=0, M
         d(j)=0
         do 1 i=0, K-1
            d(j) = d(j) + conjg(E(0, i)) * E(j, i)      E_ji = (e_i)_j = jth component
1     continue                                          of ith eigenvector

      return
      end
```

30. *lms.for—LMS adaptive Wiener filter*

It implements the filtering and weight adaptation operations for the LMS adaptive Wiener filter. It is based on **dwf** with the LMS time-updates added to it. Its inputs are *M*, filter weights *h*, input samples $\{x,y\}$, LMS adaptation constant μ, and initialization variable *init*. Its outputs are the output samples $\{xhat, e\}$ and the new weights *h* to be used at the next call. Entry with $init = 0$ resets the internal state *w* and the filter weights *h* to zero, and changes *init* to 1. The program segment illustrating the usage of **lwf** applies equally well to **lms**.

```
      subroutine lms(M, h, x, y, xhat, e, mu, init)
      real h(0:M), mu

      parameter(MAX = 50)
      real w(0:MAX)
      integer p
      save w                                  save for next call

      if (init .eq. 0) then                   set init = 0 at the first call of lms to
         do 1 p=1, M                          zero the internal state and filter weights
            w(p) = 0
            h(p) = 0
1        continue
         h(0) = 0
         init = 1                             init =1 for subsequent calls
      endif

      w(0) = y                                current input to filter

      xhat = 0
      do 2 p=0, M                             compute filter output
2        xhat = xhat + h(p) * w(p)

      e = x - xhat                            estimation error
```

```
      do 3 p=0, M                                   LMS weight updates
3         h(p) = h(p) + 2 * mu * e * w(p)

      do 4 p=M, 1, -1                               update internal state for next call
4         w(p) = w(p-1)

      return
      end
```

31. *lmsap.for—LMS adaptive predictor*

It implements the LMS adaptive predictor discussed in Section 7.11. For simplicity, we use the entire prediction error filter $\mathbf{a} = [1, a_1, \ldots, a_M]^T$ with its zero-th coefficient set to unity, $a_0 = 1$. Its inputs are M, the filter weights $\mathbf{a}$, the input sample y, the LMS adaptation constant μ, and the initialization variable *init*. Its outputs are the prediction-error output e and the new weights $\mathbf{a}$ to be used at the next call. Entry with $init = 0$ resets the internal state w to zero and the filter weights to $\mathbf{a} = [1, 0, \ldots, 0]^T$, and changes *init* to 1.

```
      subroutine lmsap(M, a, y, e, mu, init)
      real a(0:M), mu

      parameter(MAX = 50)
      real w(0:MAX)
      integer p
      save w                                        save for next call

      if (init .eq. 0) then                         set init = 0 at the first call to
          do 1 p=1, M                               zero the internal state and filter weights
              w(p) = 0
              a(p) = 0
1         continue
          a(0) = 1                                  it remains unity at each iteration
          init = 1                                  init = 1 for subsequent calls
      endif

      w(0) = y                                      current input to filter

      e = 0
      do 2 p=0, M                                   compute filter output
2         e = e + a(p) * w(p)

      do 3 p=1, M                                   LMS weight updates
3         a(p) = a(p) - 2 * mu * e * w(p)

      do 4 p=M, 1, -1                               update internal state for next call
```

```
4         w(p) = w(p-1)

      return
      end
```

32. *glwf.for—gradient lattice Wiener filter*

It implements the gradient lattice algorithm discussed in Section 7.13. The lattice filtering part is the same as **lwf**. The additional inputs are the parameters λ and β. Entry with *init* = 0 will initialize to zero the internal state, lattice weights, reflection coefficients, and the auxiliary quantities *d* and *db*. In subsequent calls *init* is used as a counter that aids the updating of the lattice weights *g* during the startup period.

```
      subroutine glwf(M, g, gamma, x, y, xhat, e, lambda, beta, init)
      real g(0:M), gamma(M), lambda

      parameter (MAX = 50)
      real w(MAX), db(0:MAX), d(MAX)
      real ea(0:MAX), eb(0:MAX)
      integer p
      save w, db, d                                      save for next call

      if (init .eq. 0) then
          do 1 p=1, M
              w(p) = 0
              g(p) = 0
              gamma(p) = 0
              d(p) = 0
              db(p) = 0
1         continue
          g(0) = 0
          db(0) = 0
      endif

      ea(0) = y                                          overall inputs to first lattice section
      eb(0) = y
      xhat = g(0) * eb(0)                                estimate of x based on order-0 filter
      e = x - xhat                                       estimation error based on order-0
                                                         filter
      db(0) = lambda * db(0) + eb(0) * eb(0)

      g(0) = g(0) + beta * e * eb(0) / db(0)             time-update of g(0)

      do 2 p=1, M
          ea(p) = ea(p-1) - gamma(p) * w(p)              outputs from the pth lattice section
          eb(p) = w(p) - gamma(p) * ea(p-1)
```

```
        d(p) = lambda * d(p) + ea(p-1) * ea(p-1) + w(p) * w(p)
        gamma(p) = gamma(p) + beta * (ea(p) * w(p) + eb(p) * ea(p-1)) / d(p)
        xhat = xhat + g(p) * eb(p)                 estimate of x based on order-p filter
        e = e - g(p) * eb(p)                       estimation error based on order-p
                                                   filter
        db(p) = lambda * db(p) + eb(p) * eb(p)

        if (p .le. init) then                startup test; always true after the first M calls
            g(p) = g(p) + beta * e * eb(p) / db(p)   time-update of g(p)
        endif

        w(p) = eb(p-1)                             update internal state of pth section
  2   continue

      init = init + 1

      return
      end
```

33. *mgs.for—modified Gram–Schmidt adaptive preprocessor*

The inputs are M, the lower triangular matrix B, the current snapshot vector $\mathbf{y} = [y_0, y_1, \ldots, y_M]^T$, λ, and β. The outputs are the decorrelated vector $\boldsymbol{\epsilon} = [\epsilon_0, \epsilon_1, \ldots, \epsilon_M]^T$ and the updated matrix B. Only the strictly lower triangular part of the matrix B is used; it must be initialized to zero before the first call. The quantities $d(p)$ are estimates of the mean-square values $E[\epsilon_p^2]$, $p = 0, 1, \ldots, M$, and must also be initialized to zero. For complex signals, in the updating equation for $d(p)$ replace *eps* (*p*)**2 by *cabs* (*eps*(*p*))**2 and in the updating equation for *B*(*i*,*p*) replace *eps* (*p*) by *conjg* (*eps*(*p*)).

```
      subroutine mgs(M, B, y, eps, d, lambda, beta)
      real B(0:M, 0:M), y(0:M), eps(0:M), d(0:M), lambda

      integer p

      do 1 p=0, M
          eps(p) = y(p)
          d(p) = lambda * d(p) + eps(p) * eps(p)
          do 2 i=p+1, M
              y(i) = y(i) - B(i, p) * eps(p)                y is overwritten after
              B(i, p) = B(i, p) + beta * eps(p) * y(i) / d(p)   each column operation
  2       continue
  1   continue

      return
      end
```

34. *rls.for—conventional RLS algorithm*

The inputs are M, filter weights $\mathbf{h} = [h_0, h_1, \ldots, h_M]^T$, input x, input data vector $\mathbf{y} = [y_0, y_1, \ldots, y_M]^T$, parameter λ, and *init*. The outputs are the filtered estimate and estimation error, $\{xhat, e\}$. The inverse matrix P is saved for the next call. Entry with *init* = 0 resets the filter weights to zero, sets $P = \delta^{-1}I$, and changes *init* to 1. The entire data vector **y** must be supplied; thus, for time series problems the tapped-delay line updating of **y** must be done outside **rls** after each call.

```
      subroutine rls(M, h, x, y, xhat, e, lambda, init)
      real h(0:M), y(0:M), lambda

      parameter(MAX = 50, delta = 0.01)
      real k0(0:MAX), k1(0:MAX), P(0:MAX, 0:MAX)
      real mu, nu
      save P                                          save for next call

      if (init .eq. 0) then
         do 1 i=0, M
            h(i) = 0
            do 1 j=0, M
               if (j .eq. i) then
                  P(i, j) = 1 / delta
               else
                  P(i, j) = 0
               endif
 1       continue
         init = 1
      endif

      do 2 i=0, M                                     a priori Kalman gain
         k0(i) = 0
         do 2 j=0, M
            k0(i) = k0(i) + P(i, j) * y(j) / lambda
 2    continue

      nu = 0
      do 3 i=0, M                                     likelihood variable
 3       nu = nu + k0(i) * y(i)

      mu = 1 / (1 + nu)                               likelihood variable

      do 4 i=0, M                                     a posteriori Kalman gain
 4       k1(i) = mu * k0(i)

      do 5 i=0, M                                     matrix inverse update
```

```
        do 5 j=0, i                              only lower triangular part
             P(i, j) = P(i, j) / lambda - k1(i) * k0(j)   of P is updated
             P(j, i) = P(i, j)                   P is symmetric
5     continue

      xhat0 = 0
      do 6 i=0, M                                a priori estimate of x
6          xhat0 = xhat0 + h(i) * y(i)

      e0 = x - xhat0                             a priori estimation error
      e = mu * e0                                a posteriori estimation error
      xhat = x - e                               a posteriori estimate of x

      do 7 i=0, M                                update filter weights
7          h(i) = h(i) + e0 * k1(i)

      return
      end
```

35. *faest.for—FAEST algorithm*

It implements the FAEST fast RLS adaptive Wiener filtering algorithm. The filtering part and inputs/outputs of the routine are the same as **dwf**. It follows the notation and computational sequence listed in Section 7.15. The only change in notation is that E_{0a}, E_{0b} are denoted by D_{0a}, D_{0b} and E_{1a}, E_{1b} by D_{1a}, D_{1b}. Because the tilde and bar parts are the lower and upper parts of a vector, we have dimensioned the Kalman gain *ktilde* from 1 to M, and *kbar* from 0 to $M - 1$. The quantities *ktilde* and *nutilde* are updated at the end of the computational sequence using the shift-invariance property and saved for the next call. Entry with $init = 0$ resets to zero the internal state w, filter weights h, forward/backward predictors a, b (except for $a(0) = b(M) = 1$), and the gain vector *ktilde* and likelihood variable *nutilde*.

```
      subroutine faest(M, h, x, y, xhat, e, lambda, init)
      real h(0:M), lambda

      parameter(MAX = 50, delta = 0.01)
      real w(0:MAX)                              internal state of filter
      real a(0:MAX), b(0:MAX), k(0:MAX), ktilde(MAX), kbar(0:MAX-1)
      real nu, nutilde, nubar                    likelihood variables
      save w, a, b, D1a, D1b, ktilde, nutilde    save for next call

      if (init .eq. 0) then
          do 1 i=1, M
               h(i) = 0
               a(i) = 0
```

```
                b(i-1) = 0
                w(i) = 0
                ktilde(i) = 0
1           continue
            D1a = delta
            D1b = delta
            nutilde = 0
            h(0) = 0
            a(0) = 1
            b(M) = 1
            init = 1
        endif

        w(0) = y

        e0a = 0
        do 2 i=0, M                               a priori forward prediction error
2           e0a = e0a + a(i) * w(i)

        e1a = e0a / (1 + nutilde)                 a posteriori forward prediction error
        D0a = lambda * D1a                        rescale old D1a by λ
        k(0) = e0a / D0a                          first element of k
        D1a = D0a + e1a * e0a

        do 3 i=1, M
3           k(i) = ktilde(i) + k(0) * a(i)

        D0b = lambda * D1b                        rescale old D1b by λ
        e0b = k(M) * D0b                          k(M) = last element of k

        do 4 i=0, M-1
4           kbar(i) = k(i) - k(M) * b(i)

        nu = nutilde + e0a * k(0)
        nubar = nu - e0b * k(M)

        e1b = e0b / (1 + nubar)
        D1b = D0b + e1b * e0b

        do 5 i=1, M                               forward predictor update
5           a(i) = a(i) - e1a * ktilde(i)

        do 6 i=0, M-1                             backward predictor update
6           b(i) = b(i) - e1b * kbar(i)

        xhat0 = 0
        do 7 i=0, M                               a priori estimate of x
7           xhat0 = xhat0 + h(i) * w(i)

        e0 = x - xhat0                            a priori estimation error
```

```
      e = e0 / (1 + nu)                    a posteriori estimation error
      xhat = x - e                         a posteriori estimate of x

      do 8 i=0, M                          RLS weight update
8        h(i) = h(i) + e * k(i)

      do 9 i=1, M                          shift-invariance property
9        ktilde(i) = kbar(i-1)

      nutilde = nubar                      shift-invariance property

      do 10 i=M, 1, -1                     tapped delay line update
10       w(i) = w(i-1)

      return
      end
```

36. *rlsl.for—double/direct RLS lattice*

It implements the double/direct RLS lattice adaptive Wiener filtering algorithm. The filtering parts for both lattices are the same as **lwf**. It follows the notation and computational sequence listed in Section 7.15. Again, E_{1a}, E_{1b} are denoted by D_{1a}, D_{1b}. The reflection coefficients γ_a, γ_b are denoted by *gamma, gammb*. The quantity D is the delayed version of D_{1b}. The internal states of the two lattices are represented by the vectors $w0$, $w1$. Entry with $init = 0$ initializes to zero the internal states, reflection coefficients, lattice weights, and D_{1a}, D_{1b}. As in **glwf**, at subsequent calls *init* serves as a counter during the startup period.

```
      subroutine rlsl(M, g, gamma, gammb, x, y, xhat, e, lambda, init)
      real g(0:M), gamma(M), gammb(M), lambda

      parameter (MAX = 50)
      real w0(MAX), w1(MAX)                internal states of a priori/a posteriori lattices
      real e0a(0:MAX), e0b(0:MAX)          a priori forward/backward error signals
      real e1a(0:MAX), e1b(0:MAX)          a posteriori forward/backward error signals
      real D1a(0:MAX), D1b(0:MAX), D(0:MAX)
      integer p
      save w0, w1, D1a, D                  save for next call

      if (init .eq. 0) then
         do 1 p=1, M
            w0(p) = 0
            w1(p) = 0
            gamma(p) = 0
            gammb(p) = 0
            D1a(p) = 0
```

```
            D(p) = 0
            g(p) = 0
1       continue
        D1a(0) = 0
        D(0) = 0
        g(0) = 0
    endif

    e0a(0) = y                                   input to a priori lattice
    e0b(0) = y
    e1a(0) = y                                   input to a posteriori lattice
    e1b(0) = y

    D1a(0) = lambda * D1a(0) + e1a(0) * e0a(0)
    D1b(0) = lambda * D(0) + e1b(0) * e0b(0)

    e0 = x - g(0) * e0b(0)                       order-0 a priori estimation error
    g(0) = g(0) + e0 * e1b(0) / D1b(0)           time-update of g(0)
    xhat = g(0) * e1b(0)                         order-0 a posteriori estimate of x
    e = x - xhat                                 order-0 a posteriori estimation error

    do 2 p=1, M
        e0a(p) = e0a(p-1) - gammb(p) * w0(p)     a priori lattice recursions
        e0b(p) = w0(p) - gamma(p) * e0a(p-1)

        if (p .le. init) then                    reflection coefficient time-updates
            gamma(p) = gamma(p) + e0b(p) * e1a(p-1) / D1a(p-1)
            gammb(p) = gammb(p) + e0a(p) * w1(p) / D(p-1)
        endif

        e1a(p) = e1a(p-1) - gammb(p) * w1(p)     a posteriori lattice recursions
        e1b(p) = w1(p) - gamma(p) * e1a(p-1)

        D1a(p) = lambda * D1a(p) + e1a(p) * e0a(p)
        D1b(p) = lambda * D(p) + e1b(p) * e0b(p)

        w0(p) = e0b(p-1)                         update a priori lattice state
        w1(p) = e1b(p-1)                         update a posteriori lattice state
        D(p) = D1b(p)                            D is the delayed version of D1b

        e0 = e0 - g(p) * e0b(p)                  order-p a priori estimation error

        if (p .le. init) then                    startup test
            g(p) = g(p) + e0 * e1b(p) / D1b(p)   time-update of lattice weight g(p)
        endif

        e = e - g(p) * e1b(p)                    order-p a posteriori estimation error
        xhat = xhat + g(p) * e1b(p)              a posteriori estimate of x
```

```
2    continue
     D(0) = D1b(0)                    D is the delayed version of D1b
     init = init + 1
     return
     end
```

Appendix C
Subroutines in C

This appendix contains the C versions of the routines in Appendix B. They may be compiled separately and placed in a library to be linked with the main programs. The routines have the same usage and inputs/outputs as their FORTRAN counterparts and the same comments apply. Additional comments have been inserted only if they are specific to the C implementation. The routines have been developed using the Microsoft C compiler v4.0 and are quite portable.

For the routines that require the use of complex numbers, we have included a set of functions for complex arithmetic. A complex number is defined as a structure containing the real and imaginary parts. In Microsoft C v4.0, such a definition is already supplied in *math.h.* The data type *complex,* defined as a *typedef* equivalent to this structure, allows the declaration and usage of complex numbers just as in FORTRAN. Only C compilers that support structure assignment and passing may be used. The complex functions, named after their FORTRAN counterparts, are given below. We have placed them in a single file *complex.c.*

```
/* complex.c - complex arithmetic functions */

#include <math.h>

struct complex { double x, y };        omit for Microsoft C v4.0; already included in math.h

typedef struct complex complex;        use as in FORTRAN
```

```
complex cmplx(x, y)                              define complex number z = x + jy
double x, y;
{
    complex z;

    z.x = x;
    z.y = y;

    return z;
}

complex conjg(z)                                 complex conjugate
complex z;
{
    return cmplx(z.x, -z.y);
}

complex cadd(a, b)                               complex addition
complex a, b;
{
    return cmplx(a.x + b.x, a.y + b.y);
}

complex csub(a, b)                               complex subtraction
complex a, b;
{
    return cmplx(a.x - b.x, a.y - b.y);
}
complex cmul(a, b)                               complex multiplication
complex a, b;
{
    return cmplx(a.x * b.x - a.y * b.y, a.x * b.y + a.y * b.x);
}

complex rmul(a, z)                               multiplication by a real
double a;
complex z;
{
    return cmplx(a * z.x, a * z.y);
}

complex cdiv(a, b)                               complex division
complex a, b;
```

```
{
  double D = b.x * b.x + b.y * b.y;

  return cmplx((a.x * b.x + a.y * b.y) / D, (a.y * b.x - a.x * b.y) / D);
}

complex rdiv(z, a)                               division by a real
complex z;
double a;
{
     return cmplx(z.x/a, z.y/a);
}

double real(z)                                   real part
complex z;
{
     return z.x;
}

double aimag(z)                                  imaginary part
complex z;
{
     return z.y;
}

double cabs(z)                                   complex magnitude
complex z;                                       already supplied by Microsoft C v4.0
{
     return sqrt(z.x * z.x + z.y * z.y);
}

complex cexp(z)                                  complex exponential
complex z;
{
     double R = exp(z.x);

     return cmplx(R * cos(z.y), R * sin(z.y));
}
```

The following header file *complex.h* contains all the necessary declarations (with type checking). It may be included in the beginning of the main programs.

```
/* complex.h - complex function declarations */

struct complex { double x, y };        omit for Microsoft C v4.0; already included in math.h

typedef struct complex complex;

complex cmplx(double, double);
complex conjg(complex);
complex cadd(complex, complex);
complex csub(complex, complex);
complex cmul(complex, complex);
complex rmul(double, complex);
complex cdiv(complex, complex);
complex rdiv(complex, double);
double real(complex);
double aimag(complex);
double cabs(complex);                  omit for Microsoft C v4.0; already included in math.h
complex cexp(complex);
```

```
/* 1. sampcov.c - recursive updating of sample covariance matrix */

#define MAX 50                                 max value of M

void sampcov(M, R, y, N)
double R[][MAX+1], y[];                        max row dimension of R must be fixed
int M, N;
{
       int i, j;

       for (i=0; i<=M; i++)
              for (j=0; j<=i; j++) {
                     R[i][j] += (y[i] * y[j] - R[i][j]) / N;
                     R[j][i] = R[i][j];
              }
}
```

```
/* 2. corr.c - sample cross correlation */

void corr(N, y, x, M, R)
double y[], x[], R[];
int N, M;
{
       int k, i;
```

```
    for (k=0; k<=M; k++)
        for (R[k]=0, i=0; i<N-k; i++)
            R[k] += y[i+k] * y[i] / N;
}
```

```
/* 3. sigav.c - signal averaging */

#include <stdio.h>

void sigav(M, N, fp, x)
int M, N;
FILE *fp;                                   file pointer
double x[];
{
    int i, j;
    double y;

    for (j=0; j<M; j++)
        for (i=0; i<N; i++) {
            fscanf(fp, "%lf", &y);
            x[i] += y / M;
        }
}
```

```
/* 4. lev.c - Levinson's algorithm */

#define MAX 50

void lev(M, R, L, E)
double R[], L[][MAX+1], E[];     The row dimension of L is fixed. This routine, and
int M;                           frwlev, bkwlev, rlev, yw, burg, and spike,
{                                manipulate only the lower triangular part
    int i, p;                    of the (M+1)x(M+1) portion of L
    double delta, gamma;

    L[0][0] = 1;
    E[0] = R[0];

    for (p=1; p<=M; p++) {
        for (delta=0, i=0; i<p; i++)
            delta += R[i+1] * L[p-1][i];
        gamma = delta / E[p-1];
        L[p][0] = - gamma;
        for (i=1; i<p; i++)
            L[p][i] = L[p-1][i-1] - gamma * L[p-1][p-1-i];
```

```
        L[p][p] = 1;
        E[p] = E[p-1] * (1 - gamma * gamma);
        }
}
```

```
/* example of lev */

#include <stdio.h>

void lev();

#define MAX  50
#define M    4

main()
{
    double L[M+1][MAX+1], E[M+1];              MAX must be the same as in lev
    static double R[M+1] = {128, -64, 80, -88, 89};
    int i, j;

    lev(M, R, L, E);

    for (i=0; i<=M; i++)
        printf("%9.4lf", E[i]);

    for (i=0; i<=M; i++) {
        printf("\n");
        for (j=0; j<=i; j++)
            printf("%9.4lf", L[i][j]);
        }
}
```

```
/* 5. frwlev.c - forward Levinson recursion */

#define MAX 50

void frwlev(M, gamma, L)
double L[][MAX+1], gamma[];
int M;
{
    int i, p;

    L[0][0] = 1;

    for (p=1; p<=M; p++) {
```

```
        L[p][0] = -gamma[p-1];
        L[p][p] = 1;
        for (i=1; i<p; i++)
            L[p][i] = L[p-1][i-1] - gamma[p-1] * L[p-1][p-1-i];
        }
}
```

```
/* example of frwlev */

#include <stdio.h>

void frwlev();

#define MAX  50
#define M    4

main()
{
    double L[M+1][MAX+1];
    static double gamma[M] = {-0.5, 0.5, -0.5, 0.5};
    int i, j;

    frwlev(M, gamma, L);

    for (i=0; i<=M; i++) {
        printf("\n");
        for (j=0; j<=i; j++)
            printf("%9.4lf", L[i][j]);
        }
}
```

```
/* 6.bkwlev.c - backward Levinson recursion */

#define MAX  50

void bkwlev(M, a, L)
double a[], L[][MAX+1];
int M;
{
    int i, p;
    double gamma, F;

    for (i=0; i<=M; i++)
        L[M][i] = a[M-i];
```

```
    for (p=M; p>=1; p--) {
        gamma = - L[p][0];
        F = 1 - gamma * gamma;
        for (i=0; i<p-1; i++)
            L[p-1][i] = ( L[p][i+1] + gamma * L[p][p-1-i] ) / F;
        L[p-1][p-1] = 1;
        }
}


/* example of bkwlev */

#include <stdio.h>

void bkwlev();

#define MAX  50
#define M    4

main()
{
    double L[M+1][MAX+1];
    static double a[M+1] = {1, -0.25, -0.1875, 0.5, -0.5};
    int i, j;

    bkwlev(M, a, L);

    for (i=0; i<=M; i++) {
        printf("\n");
        for (j=0; j<=i; j++)
            printf("%9.4lf", L[i][j]);
        }
}


/* 7. rlev.c - reverse of Levinson's algorithm */

#define MAX  50

void bkwlev();
void rlev(M, a, EM, R, L)
double a[], EM, R[], L[][MAX+1];
int M;
{
    int i, p;

    bkwlev(M, a, L);
```

```
    for (R[0]=EM, p=1; p<=M; p++)
         R[0] /= 1 - L[p][0] * L[p][0];

    for (p=1; p<=M; p++)
         for (R[p]=0, i=0; i<p; i++)
              R[p] -= L[p][i] * R[i];
}
```

```
/* example of rlev */

#include <stdio.h>

void rlev();

#define MAX   50
#define M     4

main()
{
     double L[M+1][MAX+1], R[M+1], EM = 40.5;
     static double a[M+1] = {1, -0.25, -0.1875, 0.5, -0.5};
     int i, j;

     rlev(M, a, EM, R, L);

     for (i=0; i<=M; i++)
          printf("%9.4lf", R[i]);

     for (i=0; i<=M; i++) {
          printf("\n");
          for (j=0; j<=i; j++)
               printf("%9.4lf", L[i][j]);
          }
}
```

```
/* 8. lattice.c - lattice filter */

void section();

void lattice(M, gamma, w, xa, xb, ya, yb)
double gamma[], w[], xa, xb, *ya, *yb;          the outputs ya, yb are pointers
int M;
{
     int i;

     for (i=0; i<M; i++) {
```

```
            section(gamma[i], w+i, xa, xb, ya, yb);      w +i is the pointer to w[i]
            xa = *ya;
            xb = *yb;
            }
}
```

```
/* section.c - lattice section */

void section(gamma, w, xa, xb, ya, yb)
double gamma, *w, xa, xb, *ya, *yb;                     w is a pointer
{
      *ya = xa - gamma * (*w);
      *yb = (*w) - gamma * xa;

      *w = xb;
}
```

```
/* 9. schur.c - Schur algorithm */

#define MAX 50

void schur(M, R, gamma, EM)
double R[], gamma[], *EM;                               EM is a pointer
{
      int k, p;
      double ga[MAX+1], gb[MAX+1], c, temp;

      for (k=0; k<=M; k++) {
            ga[k] = R[k];
            gb[k] = R[k];
            }

      for (p=0; p<M; p++) {
            c = ga[p+1] / gb[p];
            for (k=M; k>=p+1; k--) {
                  temp = ga[k];
                  ga[k] = temp - c * gb[k-1];
                  gb[k] = gb[k-1] - c * temp;
                  }
            gamma[p] = c;
            }

      *EM = gb[M];
}
```

```
/* example of schur (not included in Appendix B) */

#include <stdio.h>

void schur();

#define MAX   50
#define M     4

main()
{
     double gamma[M], EM;
     static double R[M+1] = {128, -64, 80, -88, 89};
     int i, j;
     schur(M, R, gamma, &EM);                    EM is passed by address

     for (i=0; i<M; i++)
          printf("%9.4lf", gamma[i]);
     printf("\n\nEM = %9.4lf", EM);
}
```

```
/* 10. schur1.c - Schur algorithm for Cholesky factorization */

#define MAX   50

void schur1(M, R, gamma, G)
double R[ ], gamma[ ], G[ ][MAX+1];
int M;
{
     int k, p;
     double ga[MAX+1], c, temp;

     for (k=0; k<=M; k++) {
          ga[k] = R[k];
          G[k][0] = R[k];
          }

     for (p=0; p<M; p++) {                  only lower triangular part of G is affected
          c = ga[p+1] / G[p][p];
          for (k=p+1; k<=M; k++) {
               temp = ga[k];
               ga[k] = temp - c * G[k-1][p];
               G[k][p+1] = G[k-1][p] - c * temp;
               }
          gamma[p] = c;
          }
}
```

```
/* 11. schur2.c - split Schur algorithm */

#define MAX 50

void schur2(M, R, gamma, EM)
double R[ ], gamma[ ], *EM;
int M;
{
     int k, p;
     double g[MAX+1][MAX+1], alpha, c = 0;

     g[0][0] = R[0];

     for (k=1; k<=M; k++) {
          g[0][k] = 2 * R[k];
          g[1][k] = R[k] + R[k-1];
          }

     for (p=0; p<=M-2; p++) {
          alpha = g[p+1][p+1] / g[p][p];
          c = -1 + alpha / (1 - c);
          gamma[p] = c;
          for (k=p+2; k<=M; k++)
               g[p+2][k] = g[p+1][k] + g[p+1][k-1] - alpha * g[p][k-1];
          }

     alpha = g[M][M] / g[M-1][M-1];
     gamma[M-1] = -1 + alpha / (1 - c);
     *EM = g[M][M] * (1 - gamma[M-1]);
}
```

```
/* 12. firw.c - FIR Wiener filter design */

#define MAX 50

void lev();

void firw(M, Rxy, Ryy, L, E, g, h)
double Rxy[ ], Ryy[ ], L[ ][MAX+1], E[ ], g[ ], h[ ];
int M;
{
     int i, p;

     lev(M, Ryy, L, E);

     for (p=0; p<=M; p++) {
          for (g[p]=0, i=0; i<=p; i++)
               g[p] += L[p][i] * Rxy[i];
```

```
        g[p] /= E[p];
        }

    for (p=0; p<=M; p++)
        for (h[p]=0, i=p; i<=M; i++)
            h[p] += L[i][p] * g[i];
}
```

```
/* 13. lwf.c - lattice Wiener filter */

#define MAX 50

void lwf(M, g, gamma, x, y, xhat, e, init)
double g[ ], gamma[ ], x, y, *xhat, *e;             outputs xhat, e, and init are pointers
int M, *init;
{
    int p;
    double ea[MAX+1], eb[MAX+1];
    static double w[MAX];                           declared static to save it for next call

    if (*init == 0) {
        for (p=0; p<M; p++)
            w[p] = 0;
        *init = 1;
        }

    ea[0] = y;
    eb[0] = y;
    *xhat = g[0] * eb[0];
    *e = x - *xhat;
    for (p=1; p<=M; p++) {
        ea[p] = ea[p-1] - gamma[p-1] * w[p-1];      gamma and w are indexed
        eb[p] = w[p-1] - gamma[p-1] * ea[p-1];      from 0 to M-1
        w[p-1] = eb[p-1];
        *xhat += g[p] * eb[p];
        *e -= g[p] * eb[p];
        }
}
```

```
/* program segment - example of lwf */

    fpx = fopen("x.dat", "r");
    fpy = fopen("y.dat", "r");
    fpxhat = fopen("xhat.dat", "w");
    fpe = fopen("e.dat", "w");
```

```
    init = 0;

    while (fscanf(fpx, "%lf", &x) != EOF) {
          fscanf(fpy, "%lf", &y);

          lwf(M, g, gamma, x, y, &xhat, &e, &init);     xhat, e, init are passed by address

          fprintf(fpxhat, "%lf\n", xhat);
          fprintf(fpe, "%lf\n", e);
          }
```

```
/* 14. dwf.c - direct form Wiener filter */

#define MAX  50

void dwf(M, h, x, y, xhat, e, init)
double h[ ], x, y, *xhat, *e;
int M, *init;
{
      int p;
      static double w[MAX+1];                              save for next call

      if (*init == 0) {
            for (p=1; p<=M; p++)
                  w[p] = 0;
            *init = 1;
            }

      w[0] = y;

      for (*xhat=0, p=0; p<=M; p++)
            *xhat += h[p] * w[p];

      *e = x - *xhat;

      for (p=M; p>=1; p--)
            w[p] = w[p-1];
}
```

```
/* 15. yw.c - Yule-Walker method */

#define MAX  50

void corr(), lev();

void yw(N, y, M, R, L, E)
double y[ ], R[ ], L[ ][MAX+1], E[ ];
int N, M;
```

```
{
    corr(N, y, y, M, R);
    lev(M, R, L, E);
}


/* 16. burg.c - Burg's method */

#define MAX  50
#define NMAX  500

void burg(N, y, M, L, E)
double y[], L[][MAX+1], E[];
int N, M;
{
     int i, p;
     double ea[NMAX], eb[NMAX], num, den, gamma, temp;

     for (E[0]=0, i = 0; i < N; i++) {
          E[0] += y[i] * y[i];
          ea[i] = y[i];
          eb[i] = y[i];
          }
     E[0] /= N;
     L[0][0] = 1;

     for (p=1; p<=M; p++) {
          for (num=den=0, i=p; i<N; i++) {
               num += 2 * ea[i] * eb[i-1];
               den += ea[i] * ea[i] + eb[i-1] * eb[i-1];
               }

          gamma = num / den;

          E[p] = E[p-1] * (1 - gamma * gamma);

          L[p][p] = 1;
          L[p][0] = - gamma;
          for (i=1; i<p; i++)
               L[p][i] = L[p-1][i-1] - gamma * L[p-1][p-1-i];

          for (i=N-1; i>=p; i--) {
               temp = ea[i];
               ea[i] = temp - gamma * eb[i-1];
               eb[i] = eb[i-1] - gamma * temp;
               }
          }
}
```

```
/* example of burg */

#include <stdio.h>

void burg();

#define MAX 50
#define N   6
#define M   4

main()
{
    static double y[N] = {4.684, 7.247, 8.423, 8.650, 8.640, 8.392};
    double L[M+1][MAX+1], E[M+1];
    int i, p;

    burg(N, y, M, L, E);

    for (p=0; p<=M; p++) {
        printf("\n");
        for (i=0; i<=p; i++)
            printf("%9.4lf", L[p][i]);
        }
}


/* 17. scatter.c - direct scattering problem */

#define MAX 50

#define min(a, b)   (((a) <= (b)) ? (a) : (b))

void scatter(M, rho, A, B, N, R)
double rho[], A[][MAX+1], B[][MAX+1], R[];
int M, N;
{
    int i, j, k;
    double S;

    A[0][0] = 1;
    B[0][0] = rho[0];

    for (i=1; i<=M; i++) {
        A[i][0] = 1;
        A[i][i] = rho[0] * rho[i];
        B[i][0] = rho[i];
        B[i][i] = rho[0];
        for (j=1; j<i; j++) {
            A[i][j] = A[i-1][j] + rho[i] * B[i-1][j-1];
            B[i][j] = B[i-1][j-1] + rho[i] * A[i-1][j];
```

```
                }
            }
        R[0] = B[M][0];
        for (k=1; k<N; k++) {
            for (S=0, i=1; i<=min(k, M); i++)
                S -= A[M][i] * R[k-i];
            if (k <= M)
                R[k] = B[M][k] + S;
            else
                R[k] = S;
            }
}
```

```
/* 18. dpd.c - dynamic predictive deconvolution */

#define MAX 50

void corr(), lev();

void dpd(N, R, M, A, B, PHI, L, E)
double R[], A[][MAX+1], B[][MAX+1], PHI[], L[][MAX+1], E[];
int N, M;
{
    int i, j, k;
    double rho0, rho, F;

    corr(N, R, R, M, PHI);

    for (k=0 ; k<=M; k++)
        PHI[k] *= -N;
    PHI[0] += 1;

    lev(M, PHI, L, E);

    for (i=0; i<=M; i++)
        A[M][i] = L[M][M-i];

    for (i=0; i<=M; i++)
        for (B[M][i]=0, j=0; j<=i; j++)
            B[M][i] += A[M][j] * R[i-j];

    rho0 = B[M][M];
    for (i=M; i>=1; i--) {
        rho = B[i][0];
        F = 1 - rho * rho;
        for (j=0; j<i; j++) {
```

```
            A[i-1][j] = (A[i][j] - rho * B[i][j]) / F;
            B[i-1][j] = (B[i][j+1] - rho * A[i][j+1]) / F;
            }
        A[i-1][0] = 1;
        B[i-1][i-1] = rho0;
        }
}
```

```
/* 19. spike.c - spiking filter design */

#define MAX 50
#define NMAX 50

#define max(a, b)   (((a) >= (b)) ? (a) : (b))
#define min(a, b)   (((a) <= (b)) ? (a) : (b))

void lev(), corr();

void spike(N, y, M, R, L, E, P, H, eps)
double y[], R[], L[][MAX+1], E[], P[][NMAX+MAX+1],
                                        H[][NMAX+MAX+1], eps;
int N, M;
{
    int i, j, k, s, t;

    corr(N+1, y, y, M, R);

    for (k=0; k<=M; k++)
        R[k] *= N+1;

    R[0] *= 1 + eps;

    lev(M, R, L, E);

    for (i=0; i<=M; i++)
        for (j=0; j<=N+M; j++)
            for (H[i][j]=0, s=i; s<=M; s++)
                for (t=max(0, j-N); t<=min(j, s); t++)
                    H[i][j] += L[s][i] * L[s][t] * y[j-t] / E[s];

    for (i=0; i<=N+M; i++)
        for (j=0; j<=N+M; j++)
            for (P[i][j]=0, t=max(0, i-N); t<=min(i, M); t++)
                P[i][j] += y[i-t] * H[t][j];
}
```

```
/* 20. aicmdl.c - AIC and MDL criteria */

#include <math.h>

void aicmdl(M, lambda, N, AIC, MDL)
double lambda[], AIC[], MDL[];
int M, N;
{
    int k;
    double L, avlog = 0, av = 0, logN = log((double) N);

    for (k=1; k<=M+1; k++) {
        av += (lambda[k-1] - av) / k;
        avlog += (log(lambda[k-1]) - avlog) / k;
        L = avlog - log(av);
        AIC[k-1] = - 2 * N * k * L + 2 * (M + 1 - k) * (M + 1 + k);
        MDL[k-1] = - N * k * L + 0.5 * (M + 1 - k) * (M + 1 + k) * logN;
        }
}
```

```
/* 21. snap.c - random snapshot generator */

#include <math.h>
#include <complex.h>

double ran(), gran();

#define LMAX 20

void snap(L, k, P, M, y, iseed)
double k[], P[];
complex y[];
int L, M;
long *iseed;
{
    int i, j;
    complex A[LMAX];
    double phi, v1, v2, sigma = 1 / sqrt(2.0), pi = 4 * atan(1.0);

    for (i=0; i<L; i++) {
        phi = 2 * pi * ran(iseed);
        A[i] = rmul(sqrt(P[i]), cexp(cmplx(0., phi)));
        }

    for (j=0; j<=M; j++) {
        v1 = gran(0., sigma, iseed);
        v2 = gran(0., sigma, iseed);
```

```
        y[j] = cmplx(v1, v2);
        for (i=0; i<L; i++)
            y[j] = cadd(y[j], cmul(A[i], cexp(cmplx(0., -j * k[i]))));
        }
}
```

```
/* 22. norm.c - normalization to unit norm */

#include <math.h>
#include <complex.h>

void norm(M, a)
complex a[];
int M;
{
    int i;
    double D = 0;

    for (i=0; i<=M; i++)
        D += cabs(a[i]) * cabs(a[i]);

    D = sqrt(D);

    for (i=0; i<=M; i++)
        a[i] = rdiv(a[i], D);
}
```

```
/* 23. fresp.c - frequency response */

#include <math.h>
#include <complex.h>

complex poly();

void fresp(M, a, NF, AF)
complex a[];
double AF[];
int M, NF;
{
    int i;
    complex z;
    double omega, D, pi = 4 * atan(1.);
    for (i=0; i<NF; i++) {
        omega = pi * i / NF;
        z = cexp(cmplx(0., -omega));
```

```
        D = cabs(poly(M, a, z));
        AF[i] = D * D;
        }
}
```

```
/* poly.c - polynomial evaluation */

#include <complex.h>

complex poly(M, a, z)
complex a[ ], z;
int M;
{
    int i;
    complex p;

    for (p=a[M], i=M-1; i>=0; i--)
        p = cadd(a[i], cmul(z, p));

    return p;
}
```

```
/* 24. invresp.c - inverse frequency response */

void invresp(NF, AF)
double AF[ ];
int NF;
{
    int i;

    for (i=0; i<NF; i++)
        AF[i] = 1 / AF[i];
}
```

```
/* 25. abs2db.c - absolute units to decibels */

#include <math.h>

void abs2db(NF, AF)
double AF[ ];
int NF;
{
    int i;
```

```
    for (i=0; i<NF; i++)
        AF[i] = 10 * log10(AF[i]);
}
```

```
/* 26. db2abs.c - decibels to absolute units */

#include <math.h>

void db2abs(NF, AF)
double AF[];
int NF;
{
    int i;

    for (i=0; i<NF; i++)
        AF[i] = pow(10., AF[i] / 10);
}
```

```
/* 27. select.c - select eigenvector */

#include <complex.h>

#define MAX 50

void select(M, E, i, a)
complex E[][MAX+1], a[];
int M, i;
{
    int j;

    for (j=0; j<=M; j++)
        a[j] = E[j][i];
}
```

```
/* 28. music.c - MUSIC spectrum */

#include <complex.h>

#define MAX 50

void music(M, E, K, NF, S, AF, a)
complex E[][MAX+1], a[];
double S[], AF[];
int M, K, NF;
```

```
{
    int i, j;

    for (j=0; j<NF; j++)
        S[j] = 0;

    for (i=0; i<K; i++) {
        select(M, E, i, a);
        fresp(M, a, NF, AF);
        for (j=0; j<NF; j++)
            S[j] += AF[j] / K;
        }

    invresp(NF, S);
}
```

```
/* 29. minorm.c - minimum norm eigenvector */

#include <complex.h>

#define MAX  50

void minorm(M, E, K, d)
complex E[][MAX+1], d[];
int M, K;
{
    int i, j;

    for (j=0; j<=M; j++)
        for (d[j]=cmplx(0., 0.), i=0; i<K; i++)
            d[j] = cadd(d[j], cmul(conjg(E[0][i]), E[j][i]));
}
```

```
/* 30. lms.c - LMS adaptive Wiener filter */

#define MAX  50

void lms(M, h, x, y, xhat, e, mu, init)
double h[], x, y, *xhat, *e, mu;
int M, *init;
{
    int p;
    static double w[MAX+1];

    if (*init == 0) {
        for (p=1; p<=M; p++) {
```

```
            w[p] = 0;
            h[p] = 0;
            }
        h[0] = 0;
        *init = 1;
        }

    w[0] = y;

    for (*xhat=0, p=0; p<=M; p++)
        *xhat += h[p] * w[p];

    *e = x - *xhat;

    for (p=0; p<=M; p++)
        h[p] += 2 * mu * (*e) * w[p];

    for (p=M; p>=1; p--)
        w[p] = w[p-1];
}
```

```
/* 31. lmsap.c - LMS adaptive predictor */

#define MAX 50

void lmsap(M, a, y, e, mu, init)
double a[], y, *e, mu;
int M, *init;
{
    int p;
    static double w[MAX+1];

    if (*init == 0) {
        for (p=1; p<=M; p++) {
            w[p] = 0;
            a[p] = 0;
            }
        a[0] = 1;
        *init = 1;
        }

    w[0] = y;

    for (*e=0, p=0; p<=M; p++)
        *e += a[p] * w[p];
```

```
    for (p=1; p<=M; p++)
        a[p] -= 2 * mu * (*e) * w[p];

    for (p=M; p>=1; p--)
        w[p] = w[p-1];
}


/* 32. glwf.c - gradient Lattice Wiener filter */

#define MAX 50

void glwf(M, g, gamma, x, y, xhat, e, lambda, beta, init)
double g[ ], gamma[ ], x, y, *xhat, *e, lambda, beta;
int M, *init;
{
    int p;
    static double w[MAX], db[MAX+1], d[MAX];
    double ea[MAX+1], eb[MAX+1];

    if (*init == 0) {
        for (p=1; p<=M; p++) {
            w[p-1] = 0;                         w, gamma, d are indexed from 0 to M-1
            g[p] = 0;
            gamma[p-1] = 0;
            d[p-1] = 0;
            db[p] = 0;
            }
        g[0] = 0;
        db[0] = 0;
        }

    ea[0] = y;
    eb[0] = y;
    *xhat = g[0] * eb[0];
    *e = x - *xhat;

    db[0] = lambda * db[0] + eb[0] * eb[0];
    g[0] += beta * (*e) * eb[0] / db[0];

    for (p=1; p<=M; p++) {
        ea[p] = ea[p-1] - gamma[p-1] * w[p-1];
        eb[p] = w[p-1] - gamma[p-1] * ea[p-1];

        d[p-1] = lambda * d[p-1] + ea[p-1] * ea[p-1] + w[p-1] * w[p-1];

        gamma[p-1] += beta * (ea[p] * w[p-1] + eb[p] * ea[p-1]) / d[p-1];
```

```
        *xhat += g[p] * eb[p];
        *e -= g[p] * eb[p];

        db[p] = lambda * db[p] + eb[p] * eb[p];

        if (p <= *init)
            g[p] += beta * (*e) * eb[p] / db[p];

        w[p-1] = eb[p-1];
        }

    (*init)++;
}
```

```
/* 33. mgs.c - modified Gram-Schmidt adaptive preprocessor */

#define MAX 50

void mgs(M, B, y, eps, d, lambda, beta)
double B[][MAX+1], y[], eps[], d[], lambda, beta;
int M;
{
    int i, p;

    for (p=0; p<=M; p++) {
        eps[p] = y[p];
        d[p] = lambda * d[p] + eps[p] * eps[p];
        for (i=p+1; i<=M; i++) {
            y[i] -= B[i][p] * eps[p];
            B[i][p] += beta * eps[p] * y[i] / d[p];
            }
        }
}
```

```
/* 34. rls.c - conventional RLS algorithm */

#define MAX 50
#define delta 0.01

void rls(M, h, x, y, xhat, e, lambda, init)
double h[], x, y[], *xhat, *e, lambda;
int M, *init;
{
    double k0[MAX+1], k1[MAX+1], mu, nu, xhat0, e0;
    static double P[MAX+1][MAX+1];
    int i, j;
```

```
    if (*init == 0) {
        for (i=0; i<=M; i++)
            for (h[i]=0, j=0; j<=M; j++)
                if (j == i)
                    P[i][j] = 1 / delta;
                else
                    P[i][j] = 0;
        *init = 1;
        }

    for (i=0; i<=M; i++)
        for (k0[i]=0, j=0; j<=M; j++)
            k0[i] += P[i][j] * y[j] / lambda;

    for (nu=0, i=0; i<=M; i++)
        nu += k0[i] * y[i];

    mu = 1 / (1 + nu);

    for (i=0; i<=M; i++)
        k1[i] = mu * k0[i];

    for (i=0; i<=M; i++)
        for (j=0; j<=i; j++) {
            P[i][j] = P[i][j] / lambda - k1[i] * k0[j];
            P[j][i] = P[i][j];
            }

    for (xhat0=0, i=0; i<=M; i++)
        xhat0 += h[i] * y[i];

    e0 = x - xhat0;
    *e = mu * e0;
    *xhat = x - *e;

    for (i=0; i<=M; i++)
        h[i] += e0 * k1[i];
}
```

```
/* 35. faest.c - FAEST algorithm */

#define MAX 50
#define delta 0.01

void faest(M, h, x, y, xhat, e, lambda, init)
double h[], x, y, *xhat, *e, lambda;
int M, *init;
```

```
{
    static double w[MAX+1], a[MAX+1], b[MAX+1], ktilde[MAX];
    static double D1a, D1b, nutilde;
    double k[MAX+1], kbar[MAX], nu, nubar;
    double e0a, e0b, e1a, e1b, D0a, D0b, e0, xhat0;
    int i;

    if (*init == 0) {
        for (i=1; i<=M; i++) {
            h[i] = 0;
            a[i] = 0;
            b[i-1] = 0;
            w[i] = 0;
            ktilde[i-1] = 0;                    ktilde is indexed from 0 to M-1
            }
        D1a = delta;
        D1b = delta;
        nutilde = 0;
        h[0] = 0;
        a[0] = 1;
        b[M] = 1;
        *init = 1;
        }

    w[0] = y;

    for (e0a=0, i=0; i<=M; i++)
        e0a += a[i] * w[i];

    e1a = e0a / (1 + nutilde);
    D0a = lambda * D1a;
    k[0] = e0a / D0a;
    D1a = D0a + e1a * e0a;

    for (i=1; i<=M; i++)
        k[i] = ktilde[i-1] + k[0] * a[i];

    D0b = lambda * D1b;
    e0b = k[M] * D0b;

    for (i=0; i<M; i++)
        kbar[i] = k[i] - k[M] * b[i];

    nu = nutilde + e0a * k[0];
    nubar = nu - e0b * k[M];

    e1b = e0b / (1 + nubar);
    D1b = D0b + e1b * e0b;
```

```
    for (i=1; i<=M; i++)
        a[i] -= e1a * ktilde[i-1];

    for (i=0; i<M; i++)
        b[i] -= e1b * kbar[i];

    for (xhat0=0, i=0; i<=M; i++)
        xhat0 += h[i] * w[i];

    e0 = x - xhat0;
    *e = e0 / (1 + nu);
    *xhat = x - *e;

    for (i=0; i<=M; i++)
        h[i] += (*e) * k[i];

    for (i=1; i<=M; i++)
        ktilde[i-1] = kbar[i-1];

    nutilde = nubar;

    for (i=M; i>=1; i--)
        w[i] = w[i-1];
}


/* 36. rlsl.c - double/direct RLS lattice */

#define MAX  50

void rlsl(M, g, gamma, gammb, x, y, xhat, e, lambda, init)
double g[], gamma[], gammb[], x, y, *xhat, *e, lambda;
int M, *init;
{
    double e0a[MAX+1], e0b[MAX+1], e1a[MAX+1], e1b[MAX+1],
                                                  D1b[MAX+1], e0;
    static double w0[MAX], w1[MAX], D1a[MAX+1], D[MAX+1];
    int p;

    if (*init == 0) {
        for (p=1; p<=M; p++) {
            w0[p-1] = 0;            w0, w1, gamma, gammb, D indexed from 0 to M-1
            w1[p-1] = 0;
            gamma[p-1] = 0;
            gammb[p-1] = 0;
            D1a[p] = 0;
            D[p] = 0;
            g[p] = 0;
            }
```

```
        D1a[0] = 0;
        D[0] = 0;
        g[0] = 0;
        }

    e0b[0] = y;
    e0a[0] = y;
    e1b[0] = y;
    e1a[0] = y;

    D1a[0] = lambda * D1a[0] + e1a[0] * e0a[0];
    D1b[0] = lambda * D[0] + e1b[0] * e0b[0];

    e0 = x - g[0] * e0b[0];
    g[0] += e0 * e1b[0] / D1b[0];
    *xhat = g[0] * e1b[0];
    *e = x - *xhat;

    for (p=1; p<=M; p++) {
        e0a[p] = e0a[p-1] - gammb[p-1] * w0[p-1];
        e0b[p] = w0[p-1] - gamma[p-1] * e0a[p-1];

        if (p <= *init) {
            gamma[p-1] += e0b[p] * e1a[p-1] / D1a[p-1];
            gammb[p-1] += e0a[p] * w1[p-1] / D[p-1];
            }

        e1a[p] = e1a[p-1] - gammb[p-1] * w1[p-1];
        e1b[p] = w1[p-1] - gamma[p-1] * e1a[p-1];

        D1a[p] = lambda * D1a[p] + e1a[p] * e0a[p];
        D1b[p] = lambda * D[p] + e1b[p] * e0b[p];

        w0[p-1] = e0b[p-1];
        w1[p-1] = e1b[p-1];
        D[p] = D1b[p];

        e0 -= g[p] * e0b[p];

        if (p <= *init)
            g[p] += e0 * e1b[p] / D1b[p];

        *e -= g[p] * e1b[p];
        *xhat += g[p] * e1b[p];
        }

    D[0] = D1b[0];

    (*init)++;
}
```

Index